Animal Diversity

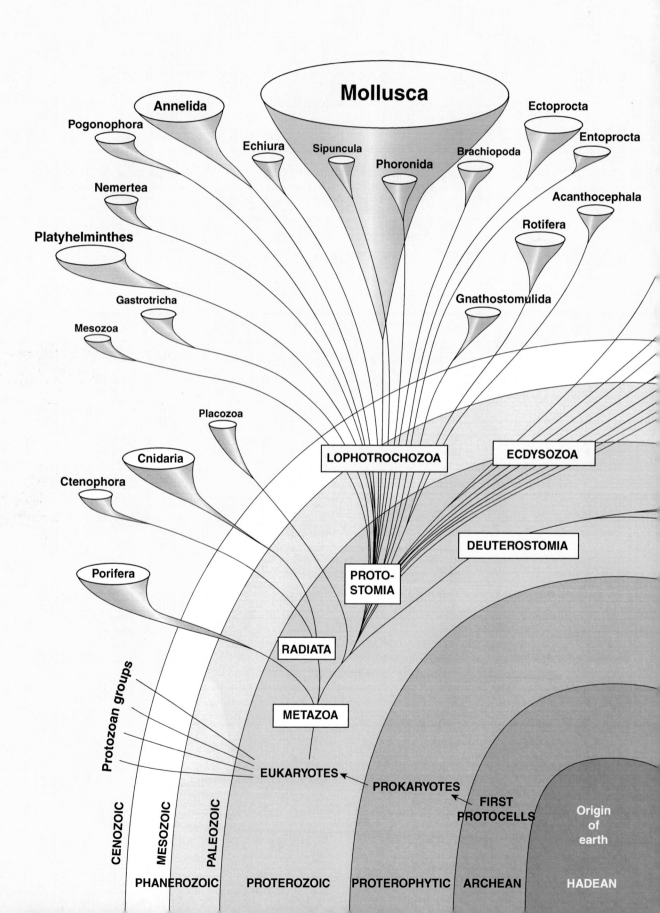

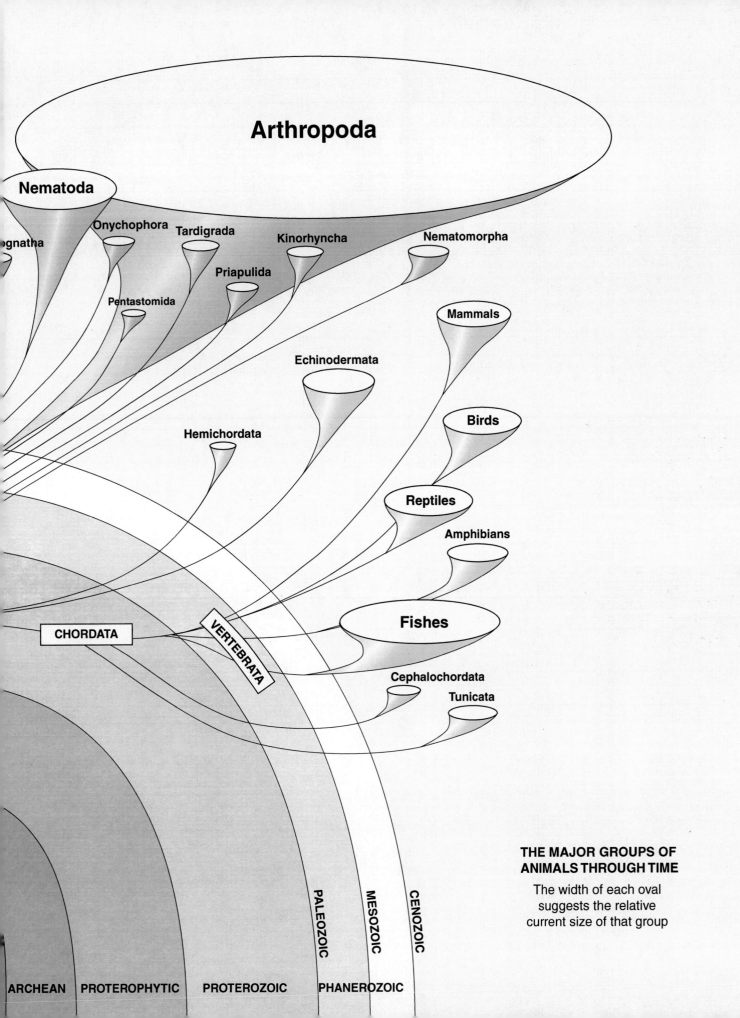

Arthropoda

Nematoda

ognatha

Onychophora

Tardigrada

Kinorhyncha

Nematomorpha

Pentastomida

Priapulida

Mammals

Echinodermata

Birds

Hemichordata

Reptiles

Amphibians

CHORDATA

VERTEBRATA

Fishes

Cephalochordata

Tunicata

PALEOZOIC

MESOZOIC

CENOZOIC

ARCHEAN   PROTEROPHYTIC   PROTEROZOIC   PHANEROZOIC

**THE MAJOR GROUPS OF
ANIMALS THROUGH TIME**

The width of each oval
suggests the relative
current size of that group

BIOLOGY 110

LIFE ON EARTH

 **Learning Solutions**

Boston   Burr Ridge, IL   Dubuque, IA   New York   San Francisco   St. Louis
Bangkok   Bogotá   Caracas   Lisbon   London   Madrid
Mexico City   Milan   New Delhi   Seoul   Singapore   Sydney   Taipei   Toronto

Biology 110
Life on Earth

This book is a McGraw-Hill Learning Solutions textbook and contains select material from the following sources:
The Living World, Sixth Edition by George B. Johnson and Jonathan B. Losos. Copyright © 2010 by The McGraw-Hill Companies, Inc.
Animal Diversity, Fifth Edition by Cleveland P. Hickman, Jr., Larry S. Roberts, Susan L. Keen, Allan Larson and David J. Eisenhour. Copyright © 2009 by The McGraw-Hill Companies, Inc.
Both are reprinted with permission of the publisher. Many custom published texts are modified versions or adaptations of our best-selling textbooks. Some adaptations are printed in black and white to keep prices at a minimum, while others are in color.

3 4 5 6 7 8 9 0 QSR QSR 0

ISBN-13: 978-0-07-736522-6
ISBN-10: 0-07-736522-4

Learning Solutions Representative: Ann Hayes
Production Editor: Jennifer Pickel
Printer/Binder: Quebecor World

Brief Contents

Contents

1

The Science of Biology

These Antarctic Adelie Penguins share many properties with you and all living things. Their bodies are made up of cells, just as yours is. They have families, with children that resemble their parents, just as your parents did. They grow by eating, as you do, although their diet is limited to fishes and krill they catch in the cold Antarctic waters. The sky above them shields them from the sun's harmful UV radiation, just as the sky above you shields you. Not in the summer, however. In the Antarctic summer an "ozone hole" appears, depleting the ozone above these penguins and exposing them to the danger of UV radiation. Scientists are analyzing this situation by a process of observation and experimentation, rejecting ideas that do not match their data. Proceeding in this way they are learning more and more about what is going on. The study of biology is a matter of observing carefully, and asking the right questions. When a possible answer—what a scientist calls a hypothesis—was proposed, that destruction of Antarctic ozone is the result of leakage of industrial chemicals containing chlorine into the world's atmosphere, scientists carried out experiments and further observations in an attempt to prove this hypothesis wrong. Nothing they have learned so far leads them to reject the hypothesis. It appears human activities far to the north are having a serious impact on the environment of these penguins. This chapter begins your study of biology, the science of life, of penguins, and people. Its study helps us to better understand ourselves, our world, and our impact on it.

1.1 The Diversity of Life

In its broadest sense, biology is the study of living things—the science of life. The living world teems with a breathtaking variety of creatures—whales, butterflies, mushrooms, and mosquitoes—all of which can be categorized into six groups, or **kingdoms,** of organisms. Representatives from each kingdom can be seen in figure 1.1. All organisms that are placed into a kingdom possess similar characteristics with all other organisms in that same kingdom and are very different from organisms in the other kingdoms.

Biologists study the diversity of life in many different ways. They live with gorillas, collect fossils, and listen to whales. They isolate bacteria, grow mushrooms, and examine the structure of fruit flies. They read the messages encoded in the long molecules of heredity and count how many times a hummingbird's wings beat each second. In the midst of all this diversity, it is easy to lose sight of the key lesson of biology, which is that all living things have much in common.

1.1 The living world is very diverse, but all things share many key properties.

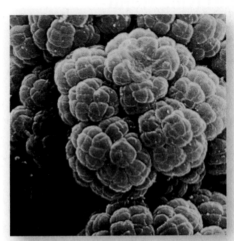

Archaea. This kingdom of prokaryotes (the simplest of cells that do not have nuclei) includes this methanogen, which manufactures methane as a result of its metabolic activity.

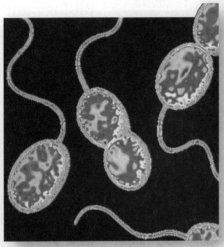

Bacteria. This group is the second of the two prokaryotic kingdoms. Shown here are purple sulfur bacteria, which are able to convert light energy into chemical energy.

Protista. Most of the unicellular eukaryotes (those whose cells contain a nucleus) are grouped into this kingdom, and so are the multicellular algae pictured here.

Fungi. This kingdom contains nonphotosynthetic organisms, mostly multicellular, that digest their food externally, such as these mushrooms.

Plantae. This kingdom contains photosynthetic multicellular organisms that are terrestrial, such as the flowering plant pictured here.

Animalia. Organisms in this kingdom are nonphotosynthetic multicellular organisms that digest their food internally, such as this ram.

Figure 1.1 The six kingdoms of life.
Biologists categorize all living things into six major categories called *kingdoms*. Each kingdom is profoundly different from the others.

1.2 Properties of Life

Biology is the study of life—but what does it mean to be alive? What are the properties that define a living organism? This is not as simple a question as it seems because some of the most obvious properties of living organisms are also properties of many non-living things—for example, *complexity* (a computer is complex), *movement* (clouds move in the sky), and *response to stimulation* (a soap bubble pops if you touch it). To appreciate why these three properties, so common among living things, do not help us to define life, imagine a mushroom standing next to a television: The television seems more complex than the mushroom, the picture on the television screen is moving while the mushroom just stands there, and the television responds to a remote control device while the mushroom continues to just stand there—yet it is the mushroom that is alive.

All living things share five basic properties, passed down over millions of years from the first organisms to evolve on earth: *Cellular organization, metabolism, homeostasis, growth and reproduction,* and *heredity.*

1. **Cellular organization.** All living things are composed of one or more cells. A cell is a tiny compartment with a thin covering called a *membrane.* Some cells have simple interiors, while others are complexly organized, but all are able to grow and reproduce. Many organisms possess only a single cell, like the paramecia in figure 1.2; your body contains about 10–100 trillion cells (depending on how big you are)—that's how many centimeters long a string would be wrapped around the world 1,600 times!

2. **Metabolism.** All living things use energy. Moving, growing, thinking—everything you do requires energy. Where does all this energy come from? It is captured from sunlight by plants and algae through photosynthesis. To get the energy that powers our lives, we extract it from plants or from plant-eating animals. That's what the kingfisher is doing in figure 1.3, eating a fish that ate algae. The transfer of energy from one form to another in cells is an example of *metabolism.* All organisms require energy to grow,

Figure 1.3   Metabolism.
This kingfisher obtains the energy it needs to move, grow, and carry out its body processes by eating fish. It metabolizes this food using chemical processes that occur within cells.

and all organisms transfer this energy from one place to another within cells using special energy-carrying molecules called ATP molecules.

3. **Homeostasis.** All living things maintain stable internal conditions so that their complex processes can be better coordinated. While the environment often varies a lot, organisms act to keep their interior conditions relatively constant; a process called *homeostasis.* Your body acts to maintain an internal temperature of 37°C (98.6°F), however hot or cold the weather might be.

4. **Growth and reproduction.** All living things grow and reproduce. Bacteria increase in size and simply split in two, as often as every 15 minutes, while more complex organisms grow by increasing the number of cells and reproduce sexually (some, like the bristlecone pine of California, have reproduced after 4,600 years).

5. **Heredity.** All organisms possess a genetic system that is based on the replication and duplication of a long molecule called *DNA (deoxyribonucleic acid).* The information that determines what an individual organism will be like is contained in a code that is dictated by the order of the subunits making up the DNA molecule, just as the order of letters on this page determines the sense of what you are reading. Each set of instructions within the DNA is called a *gene.* Together, the genes determine what the organism will be like. Because DNA is faithfully copied from one generation to the next, any change in a gene is also preserved and passed on to future generations. The transmission of characteristics from parent to offspring is a process called *heredity.*

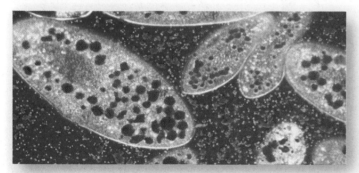

Figure 1.2   Cellular organization.
These paramecia are complex single-celled protists that have just ingested several yeast cells. Like these paramecia, many organisms consist of just a single cell, while others are composed of trillions of cells.

1.2   All living things possess cells that carry out metabolism, maintain stable internal conditions, reproduce themselves, and use DNA to transmit hereditary information to offspring.

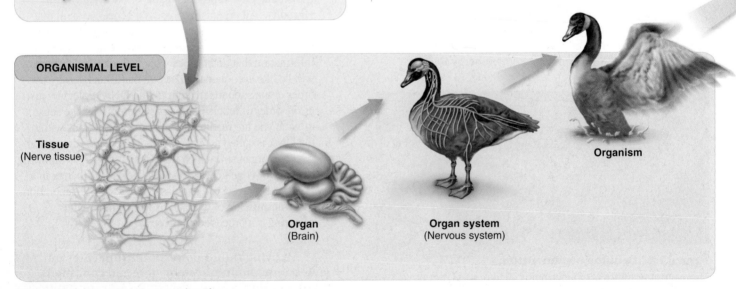

Atoms
(Hydrogen, carbon, nitrogen)

Molecule
(Adenine)

Macromolecule
(DNA)

Organelle
(Nucleus)

Cell
(Nerve cell)

ORGANISMAL LEVEL

Tissue
(Nerve tissue)

Organ
(Brain)

Organ system
(Nervous system)

Organism

1.3 The Organization of Life

The organisms of the living world function and interact with each other at many levels, from the very small and simple to the large and complex.

A Hierarchy of Increasing Complexity

A key factor in organizing these interactions is the degree of complexity. We will examine the complexity of life at three levels: Cellular, organismal, and populational.

Cellular Level Following down the first section of figure 1.4, you can see that structures get more and more complex—that there is a *hierarchy* of increasing complexity within cells.

1. **Atoms.** The fundamental elements of matter are atoms.
2. **Molecules.** Atoms are joined together into complex clusters called molecules.
3. **Macromolecules.** Large complex molecules are called macromolecules. DNA, which stores the hereditary information in all living organisms, is a macromolecule.
4. **Organelles.** Complex biological molecules are assembled into tiny compartments within cells called organelles, within which cellular activities are organized. The nucleus is an organelle within which the cell's DNA is stored.
5. **Cells.** Organelles and other elements are assembled in the membrane-bounded units we call cells. Cells are the smallest level of organization that can be considered alive.

Organismal Level At the organismal level, in the second section of figure 1.4, cells are organized into three levels of complexity.

6. **Tissues.** The most basic level is that of tissues, which are groups of similar cells that act as a functional unit.

Figure 1.4 Levels of organization.

A traditional and very useful way to sort through the many ways in which the organisms of the living world interact is to organize them in terms of levels of organization, proceeding from the very small and simple to the very large and complex. Here we examine organization within the cellular, organismal, and populational levels.

Nerve tissue is one kind of tissue, composed of cells called neurons that are specialized to carry electrical signals from one place to another in the body.

7. **Organs.** Tissues, in turn, are grouped into organs, which are body structures composed of several different tissues grouped together in a structural and functional unit. Your brain is an organ composed of nerve cells and a variety of connective tissues that form protective coverings and distribute blood.

8. **Organ Systems.** At the third level of organization, organs are grouped into organ systems. The nervous system, for example, consists of sensory organs, the brain and spinal cord, and neurons that convey signals to and from them and supporting cells.

9. **Organism.** Separate organ systems function together to form an organism.

Populational Level Organisms are further organized into several hierarchical levels within the living world, as you can see in the third section of figure 1.4.

10. **Population.** The most basic of these is the population, which is a group of organisms of the same species living in the same place. A flock of geese living together on a pond is a population.

11. **Species.** All the populations of a particular kind of organism together form a species, its members similar in appearance and able to interbreed. All Canada geese, whether found in Canada, Minnesota, or Missouri, are basically the same, members of the species *Branta canadensis*. Sandhill cranes are a different species.

12. **Community.** At a higher level of biological organization, a community consists of all the populations of different species living together in one place. Geese, for example, may share their pond with ducks, fish, grasses, and many kinds of insects. All interact in a single pond community.

13. **Ecosystem.** At the highest tier of biological organization, a biological community and the soil and water within which it lives together constitute an ecological system, or ecosystem.

Emergent Properties

At each higher level in the living hierarchy, novel properties emerge, properties that were not present at the simpler level of organization. These **emergent properties** result from the way in which components interact, and often cannot be guessed just by looking at the parts themselves. You have the same array of cell types as a giraffe, for example. Yet, examining a collection of its individual cells gives little clue of what your body is like.

The emergent properties of life are not magical or supernatural. They are the natural consequence of the hierarchy or structural organization which is the hallmark of life. Water, which makes up 50–75% of your body's weight, and ice are both made of H_2O molecules, but one is liquid and the other solid because the H_2O molecules in ice are more organized.

Functional properties emerge from more complex organization. Metabolism is an emergent property of life. The chemical reactions within a cell arise from interactions between molecules that are orchestrated by the orderly environment of the cell's interior. Consciousness is an emergent property of the brain that results from the interactions of many neurons in different parts of the brain.

POPULATIONAL LEVEL

Population

Species

> **1.3** Cells, multicellular organisms, and ecological systems each are organized in a hierarchy of increased complexity. Life's hierarchical organization is responsible for the emergent properties that characterize so many aspects of the living world.

Community

Ecosystem

Biological Themes

Just as every house is organized into thematic areas such as bedroom, kitchen, and bathroom, so the living world is organized by major *themes,* such as how energy flows within the living world from one part to another. As you study biology in this text, five general themes will emerge repeatedly, themes that serve to both unify and explain biology as a science (table 1.1):

1. evolution;
2. the flow of energy;
3. cooperation;
4. structure determines function;
5. homeostasis.

Evolution

Evolution is genetic change in a species over time. Charles Darwin was an English naturalist who, in 1859, proposed the idea that this change is a result of a process called **natural selection.** Simply stated, those organisms whose characteristics make them better able to survive the challenges of their environment live to reproduce, passing their favorable characteristics on to their offspring. Darwin was thoroughly familiar with variation in domesticated animals (in addition to many nondomesticated organisms), and he knew that varieties of pigeons could be selected by breeders to exhibit exaggerated characteristics, a process called **artificial selection.** You can see some of these extreme-looking pigeons pictured in table 1.1 under the heading "evolution." We now know that the characteristics selected are passed on through generations because DNA is transmitted from parent to offspring. Darwin visualized how selection in nature could be similar to that which had produced the different varieties of pigeons. Thus, the many forms of life we see about us on earth today, and the way we ourselves are constructed and function, reflect a long history of natural selection. Evolution will be explored in more detail in chapters 2 and 17.

The Flow of Energy

All organisms require energy to carry out the activities of living—to build bodies and do work and think thoughts. All of the energy used by most organisms comes from the sun and is passed in one direction through ecosystems. The simplest way to understand the flow of energy through the living world is to look at who uses it. The first stage of energy's journey is its capture by green plants, algae, and some bacteria by the process of photosynthesis. This process uses energy from the sun to synthesize sugars that photosynthetic organisms like plants store in their bodies. Plants then serve as a source of life-driving energy for animals that eat them. Other animals, like the eagle in table 1.1, may then eat the plant eaters. At each stage, some energy is used for the processes of living, some is transferred, and much is lost, primarily as heat. The flow of energy is a key factor in shaping ecosystems, affecting how many and what kinds of animals live in a community.

Cooperation

The ants cooperating in the upper right photo in table 1.1 protect the plant on which they live from predators and shading by other plants, while this plant returns the favor by providing the ants with nutrients (the yellow structures at the tips of the leaves). This type of cooperation between different kinds of organisms has played a critical role in the evolution of life on earth. For example, organisms of two different species that live in direct contact, like the ants and the plant on which they live, form a type of relationship called **symbiosis.** Animal cells possess organelles that are the descendants of symbiotic bacteria, and symbiotic fungi helped plants first invade land from the sea. The coevolution of flowering plants and insects—where changes in flowers influenced insect evolution and in turn, changes in insects influenced flower evolution—has been responsible for much of life's great diversity.

Structure Determines Function

One of the most obvious lessons of biology is that biological structures are very well suited to their functions. You will see this at every level of organization: Within cells, the shape of the proteins called enzymes that cells use to carry out chemical reactions are precisely suited to match the chemicals the enzymes must manipulate. Within the many kinds of organisms in the living world, body structures seem carefully designed to carry out their functions—the long tongue with which the moth in table 1.1 sucks nectar from a deep flower is one example. The superb fit of structure to function in the living world is no accident. Life has existed on earth for over 2 billion years, a long time for evolution to favor changes that better suit organisms to meet the challenges of living. It should come as no surprise to you that after all this honing and adjustment, biological structures carry out their functions well.

Homeostasis

The high degree of specialization we see among complex organisms is only possible because these organisms act to maintain a relatively stable internal environment, a process introduced earlier called homeostasis. Without this constancy, many of the complex interactions that need to take place within organisms would be impossible, just as a city cannot function without rules to maintain order. Maintaining homeostasis in a body as complex as yours or the hippo's in table 1.1 requires a great deal of signaling back-and-forth between cells.

As already stated, you will encounter these biological themes repeatedly in this text. But just as a budding architect must learn more than the parts of buildings, so your study of biology should teach you more than a list of themes, concepts, and parts of organisms. Biology is a dynamic science that will affect your life in many ways, and that lesson is one of the most important you will learn. It is also an awful lot of fun.

> **1.4 The five general themes of biology are (1) evolution, (2) the flow of energy, (3) cooperation, (4) structure determines function, and (5) homeostasis.**

TABLE 1.1   BIOLOGICAL THEMES

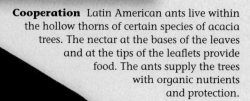

Cooperation Latin American ants live within the hollow thorns of certain species of acacia trees. The nectar at the bases of the leaves and at the tips of the leaflets provide food. The ants supply the trees with organic nutrients and protection.

Evolution Charles Darwin's studies of artificial selection in pigeons provided key evidence that selection could produce the sorts of changes predicted by his theory of evolution. The differences that have been obtained by artificial selection of the wild European rock pigeon (*top*) and such domestic races as the red fantail (*middle*) and the fairy swallow (*bottom*), with its fantastic tufts of feathers around its feet, are indeed so great that the birds probably would, if wild, be classified in different major groups.

The Flow of Energy Energy passes from the sun to plants to plant-eating animals to animal-eating animals, such as this eagle.

Homeostasis Homeostasis often involves water balance to maintain proper blood chemistry. All complex organisms need water—some, like this hippo, luxuriate in it. Others, like the kangaroo rat that lives in arid conditions where water is scarce, obtain water from food and never actually drink.

Structure Determines Function With its long tongue, this moth is able to reach the nectar deep within these flowers.

1.5 How Scientists Think

Deductive Reasoning

Science is a process of investigation, using observation, experimentation, and reasoning. Not all investigations are scientific. For example, when you want to know how to get to Chicago from St. Louis, you do not conduct a scientific investigation—instead, you look at a map to determine a route. In other investigations, you make individual decisions by applying a "guide" of accepted general principles. This is called **deductive reasoning.** Deductive reasoning, using general principles to explain specific observations, is the reasoning of mathematics, philosophy, politics, and ethics; deductive reasoning is also the way a computer works. All of us rely on deductive reasoning to make everyday decisions—like whether you need to slow down while driving along a city street in figure 1.5. We use general principles as the basis for examining and evaluating these decisions.

Inductive Reasoning

Where do general principles come from? Religious and ethical principles often have a religious foundation; political principles reflect social systems. Some general principles, however, are not derived from religion or politics but from observation of the physical world around us. If you drop an apple, it will fall, whether or not you wish it to and despite any laws you may pass forbidding it to do so. Science is devoted to discovering the general principles that govern the operation of the physical world.

How do scientists discover such general principles? Scientists are, above all, observers: They look at the world to understand how it works. It is from observations that scientists determine the principles that govern our physical world.

This way of discovering general principles by careful examination of specific cases is called **inductive reasoning.** Inductive reasoning first became popular about 400 years ago, when Isaac Newton, Francis Bacon, and others began to conduct experiments and from the results infer general principles about how the world operates. The experiments were sometimes quite simple. Newton's consisted simply of releasing an apple from his hand and watching it fall to the ground. This simple observation is the stuff of science. From a host of particular observations, each no more complicated than the falling of an apple, Newton inferred a general principle—that all objects fall toward the center of the earth. This principle was a possible explanation, or **hypothesis,** about how the world works. You also make observations and formulate general principles based on your observations, like forming a general principle about the timing of traffic lights in figure 1.5. Like Newton, scientists work by forming and testing hypotheses, and observations are the materials on which they build them.

> **1.5** Science uses inductive reasoning to infer general principles from detailed observation.

DEDUCTIVE REASONING

An Accepted General Principle

When traffic lights along city streets are "timed" to change at the time interval it takes traffic to pass between them, the result will be a smooth flow of traffic.

DEDUCTIVE REASONING

Using a General Principle to Make Everyday Decisions

Traveling at the speed limit, you approach each intersection anticipating that the red light will turn green as you reach the intersection.

INDUCTIVE REASONING

Observations of Specific Events

Driving down the street at the speed limit, you observe that the red traffic light turns green just as you approach the intersection.

Maintaining the same speed, you observe the same event at the next several intersections: the traffic lights turn green just as you approach the intersections. When you speed up, however, the light doesn't change until after you reach the intersection.

INDUCTIVE REASONING

Formation of a General Principle

You conclude that the traffic lights along this street are "timed" to change in the time it takes your car, traveling at the speed limit, to traverse the distance between them.

Figure 1.5 Deductive and inductive reasoning.
A deduction is a conclusion drawn from general principles. An inference is a conclusion drawn from specific observations. In this hypothetical example, a driver who assumes that the traffic signals are timed can use deductive reasoning to expect that the traffic lights will change predictably at intersections. In contrast, a driver who is not aware of the general control and programming of traffic signals can use inductive reasoning to determine that the traffic lights are timed as the driver encounters similar timing of signals at several intersections.

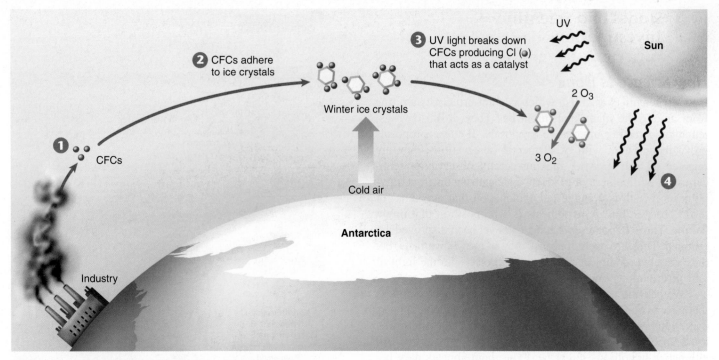

Figure 1.6 How CFCs attack and destroy ozone.
CFCs are stable chemicals that accumulate in the atmosphere as a by-product of industrial society ❶. In the intense cold of the Antarctic, these CFCs adhere to tiny ice crystals in the upper atmosphere ❷. UV light causes the breakdown of CFCs, producing chlorine (Cl). Cl acts as a catalyst, converting O_3 into O_2 ❸. As a result, more harmful UV radiation reaches the earth's surface ❹.

1.6 Science in Action: A Case Study

In 1985 Joseph Farman, a British earth scientist working in Antarctica, made an unexpected discovery. Analyzing the Antarctic sky, he found far less ozone (O_3, a form of oxygen gas) than should be there—a 30% drop from a reading recorded five years earlier in the Antarctic!

At first it was argued that this thinning of the ozone (soon dubbed the "ozone hole") was an as-yet-unexplained weather phenomenon. Evidence soon mounted, however, implicating synthetic chemicals as the culprit. Detailed analysis of chemicals in the Antarctic atmosphere revealed a surprisingly high concentration of chlorine, a chemical known to destroy ozone. The source of the chlorine was a class of chemicals called **chlorofluorocarbons (CFCs).** CFCs (the purple balls ❶ in figure 1.6) have been manufactured in large amounts since they were invented in the 1920s, largely for use as coolants in air conditioners, propellants in aerosols, and foaming agents in making Styrofoam. CFCs were widely regarded as harmless because they are chemically unreactive under normal conditions. But in the atmosphere over Antarctica, CFCs condense onto tiny ice crystals ❷; in the spring, the CFCs break down and produce chlorine, which acts as a catalyst, attacking and destroying ozone, turning it into oxygen gas without the chlorine being used up ❸.

The thinning of the ozone layer in the upper atmosphere 25 to 40 kilometers above the surface of the earth is a serious matter. The ozone layer protects life from the harmful ultraviolet (UV) rays from the sun that bombard the earth continuously. Like invisible sunglasses, the ozone layer filters out these dangerous rays. So when ozone is converted to oxygen gas, the UV rays are able to pass through to the earth ❹. When UV rays damage the DNA in skin cells, it can lead to skin cancer. It is estimated that every 1% drop in the atmospheric ozone concentration leads to a 6% increase in skin cancers.

The world currently produces less than 200,000 tons of CFCs annually, down from 1986 levels of 1.1 million tons. As scientific observations have become widely known, governments have rushed to correct the situation. By 1990, worldwide agreements to phase out production of CFCs by the end of the century had been signed. Production of CFCs declined by 86% in the following 10 years.

Nonetheless, most of the CFCs manufactured since they were invented are still in use in air conditioners and aerosols and have not yet reached the atmosphere. As these CFCs move slowly upward through the atmosphere, the problem can be expected to continue. Ozone depletion is still producing major ozone holes over the Antarctic.

But the worldwide reduction in CFC production is having a major impact. The period of maximum ozone depletion will peak in the next few years, and researchers' models predict that after that the situation should gradually improve, and that the ozone layer will recover by the middle of the 21st century. Clearly, global environmental problems can be solved by concerted action.

1.6 Industrially produced CFCs catalytically destroy ozone in the upper atmosphere.

Stages of a Scientific Investigation

How Science Is Done

How do scientists establish which general principles are true from among the many that might be? They do this by systematically testing alternative proposals. If these proposals prove inconsistent with experimental observations, they are rejected as untrue. After making careful observations concerning a particular area of science, scientists construct a hypothesis, which is a suggested explanation that accounts for those observations. A hypothesis is a proposition that might be true. Those hypotheses that have not yet been disproved are retained. They are useful because they fit the known facts, but they are always subject to future rejection if—in the light of new information—they are found to be incorrect.

We call the test of a hypothesis an experiment. Suppose that a room appears dark to you. To understand why it appears dark, you propose several hypotheses. The first might be, "The room appears dark because the light switch is turned off." An alternative hypothesis might be, "The room appears dark because the light bulb is burned out." And yet another alternative hypothesis might be, "I am going blind." To evaluate these hypotheses, you would conduct an experiment designed to eliminate one or more of the hypotheses. For example, you might reverse the position of the light switch. If you do so and the light does not come on, you have disproved the first hypothesis. Something other than the setting of the light switch must be the reason for the darkness. Note that a test such as this does not prove that any of the other hypotheses are true; it merely demonstrates that one of them is not. A successful experiment is one in which one or more of the alternative hypotheses is demonstrated to be inconsistent with the results and is thus rejected.

As you proceed through this text, you will encounter a great deal of information, often accompanied by explanations. These explanations are hypotheses that have withstood the test of experiment. Many will continue to do so; others will be revised as new observations are made. Biology, like all science, is in a constant state of change, with new ideas appearing and replacing old ones.

The Scientific Process

Joseph Farman, who first reported the ozone hole, is a practicing scientist, and what he was doing in Antarctica was science. Science is a particular way of investigating the world, of forming general rules about why things happen by observing particular situations. A scientist like Farman is an observer, someone who looks at the world in order to understand how it works.

Scientific investigations can be said to have six stages as illustrated in figure 1.7: ❶ observing what is going on; ❷ forming a set of hypotheses; ❸ making predictions; ❹ testing them and ❺ carrying out controls, until one or more of the hypotheses have been eliminated; and ❻ forming conclusions based on the remaining hypothesis.

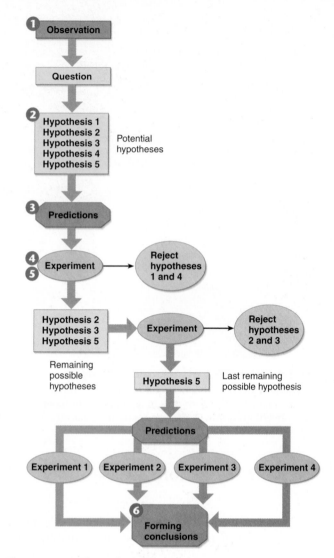

Figure 1.7   The scientific process.
This diagram illustrates the stages of a scientific investigation. First, observations are made that raise a particular question. Then a number of potential explanations (hypotheses) are suggested to answer the question. Next, predictions are made based on the hypotheses, and several rounds of experiments (including control experiments) are carried out in an attempt to eliminate one or more of the hypotheses. Finally, any hypothesis that is not eliminated is retained. Further predictions can be made based on the accepted hypothesis and tested with experiments. If it is validated by numerous experiments and stands the test of time, a hypothesis may eventually become a theory.

1. **Observation.** The key to any successful scientific investigation is careful **observation.** Farman and other scientists had studied the skies over the Antarctic for many years, noting a thousand details about temperature, light, and levels of chemicals. You can see an example in figure 1.8, where the purple colors represent the lowest levels of ozone that the scientists recorded. Had these scientists not kept careful records of what they observed, Farman might not have noticed that ozone levels were dropping. Observations usually generate questions, such as: Why were ozone levels dropping?

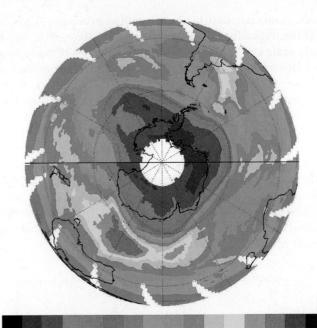

Figure 1.8 The ozone hole.
The swirling colors represent different concentrations of ozone over the South Pole as viewed from a satellite on September 15, 2001. As you can easily see, there is an "ozone hole" (the *purple* areas) over Antarctica covering an area about the size of the United States. (The color *white* indicates areas where no data were available.)

Dobson Units

2. **Hypothesis.** When the unexpected drop in ozone was reported and questioned, environmental scientists made a guess to answer their questions—perhaps something was destroying the ozone; maybe the culprit was CFCs. Of course, this was not a guess in the true sense; scientists had some working knowledge of CFC and what it might be doing in the upper atmosphere. We call such a guess a hypothesis. A hypothesis is a guess that might be true. What the scientists guessed was that chlorine from CFCs was reacting chemically with ozone over the Antarctic, converting ozone (O_3) into oxygen gas (O_2) and in the process removing the ozone shield from our earth's atmosphere. Often, scientists will form **alternative hypotheses** if they have more than one guess about what they observe. In this case, there were several other hypotheses advanced to explain the ozone hole. One suggestion explained it as the result of convection. A hypothesis was proposed that the seeming depletion of ozone was in fact a normal consequence of the spinning of the earth; the ozone spun away from the polar regions much as water spins away from the center as a clothes washer moves through its spin cycle. Another hypothesis was that the ozone hole was a transient phenomenon, due perhaps to sunspots, and would soon disappear.

3. **Predictions.** If the CFC hypothesis is correct, then several consequences can reasonably be expected.

We call these expected consequences **predictions.** A prediction is what you expect to happen if a hypothesis is true. The CFC hypothesis predicts that if CFCs are responsible for producing the ozone hole, then it should be possible to detect CFCs in the upper Antarctic atmosphere as well as the chlorine released from CFCs that attack the ozone.

4. **Testing.** Scientists set out to test the CFC hypothesis by attempting to verify some of its predictions. We call the test of a hypothesis an **experiment.** To test the hypothesis, atmospheric samples were collected from the stratosphere over 6 miles up by a high-altitude balloon. Analysis of the samples revealed CFCs, as predicted. Were the CFCs interacting with the ozone? The samples contained free chlorine and fluorine, confirming the breakdown of CFC molecules. The results of the experiment thus support the hypothesis.

5. **Controls.** Events in the upper atmosphere can be influenced by many factors. We call each factor that might influence a process a **variable.** To evaluate alternative hypotheses about one variable, all the other variables must be kept constant so that we do not get misled or confused by these other influences. This is done by carrying out two experiments in parallel: In the first experimental test, we alter one variable in a known way to test a particular hypothesis; in the second, called a **control experiment,** we do *not* alter that variable. In all other respects, the two experiments are the same. To further test the CFC hypothesis, scientists carried out control experiments in which the key variable was the amount of CFCs in the atmosphere. Working in laboratories, scientists reconstructed the atmospheric conditions, solar bombardment, and extreme temperatures found in the sky far above the Antarctic. If the ozone levels fell without addition of CFCs to the chamber, then CFCs could not be what was attacking the ozone, and the CFC hypothesis must be wrong. Carefully monitoring the chamber, however, scientists detected no drop in ozone levels in the absence of CFCs. The result of the control was thus consistent with the predictions of the hypothesis.

6. **Conclusion.** A hypothesis that has been tested and not rejected is tentatively accepted. The hypothesis that CFCs released into the atmosphere are destroying the earth's protective ozone shield is now supported by a great deal of experimental evidence and is widely accepted. While other factors have also been implicated in ozone depletion, destruction by CFCs is clearly the dominant phenomenon. A collection of related hypotheses that have been tested many times and not rejected is called a **theory.** A theory indicates a higher degree of certainty; however, in science, nothing is "certain." The theory of the ozone shield—that ozone in the upper atmosphere shields the earth's surface from harmful UV rays by absorbing them—is supported by a wealth of observation and experimentation and is widely accepted. The explanation for the destruction of this shield is still at the hypothesis stage.

How Scientists Analyze and Present Experimental Results

After a scientist conducts research, he or she must then analyze and present the results so that others can interpret them. To do this, the scientist focuses carefully on what is measured in an experiment, and on how the data are evaluated.

Variables Variables are the tools of research. They are manipulated and measured in an experiment as a means of answering questions and testing hypotheses. There are two types of variables in any experiment. An **independent variable** is one that a researcher is able to control—for example, the concentration of a chemical in a solution or the timing of when a measurement is taken. The independent variable is selected by the investigator based on the question he or she is trying to answer. A **dependent variable,** by contrast, is not predetermined by the investigator; it is the response that is measured by the investigator in the experiment.

Some research involves examining correlations between sets of variables, rather than the deliberate manipulation of a variable. For example, a researcher who measures both blood pressure and cholesterol level is actually comparing two dependent variables. While such a comparison can reveal correlations and so suggest potential relationships, **correlation does not prove causation**. What is happening to one variable may actually have nothing to do with what happens to the other variable. Only by manipulating a variable (making it an independent variable) can you test for causality. Just because people with high blood pressure might also have high cholesterol does not establish that high blood pressure *causes* high cholesterol. The "Visual Understanding" question 1 at the end of this chapter shows how an erroneous conclusion can be reached when comparing two dependent variables.

How to Present the Results as a Graph

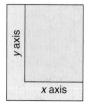

You will encounter a lot of graphs in this text and to interpret them, it is important to realize that all graphs are presented in a consistent way. The independent variable is always presented and labeled across the bottom, called the *x axis*. The dependent variable is always presented and labeled along the side (usually the left side), called the *y axis*.

In some situations, two sets of data may be presented in the same graph using the same independent variable—for example, a control experiment and a testing experiment. In this case, the two sets of data are presented as two different lines on the graph. Or a graph might show the results from two different experiments (two different dependent variables) with the same independent variable. In this situation, a graph might have two *y* axes, one on the left and one on the right, plotted against the same *x* axis.

Using the Appropriate Scale and Units to Present Data

A key aspect of presenting data in a graph is the selection of proper scale. Data presented in a table can utilize many scales, from seconds to centuries, with no problems. A graph, however, typically has a single scale on the *x* axis and a single scale on the *y* axis, which might consist of molecular units (for example, nanometers, microliters, micrograms) or macroscopic units (for example, feet, inches, liters, days, milligrams). In each instance, a scale must be chosen that fits what is being measured. Changes in centimeters would not be obvious in a graph scaled in miles. If a variable changes a great deal over the course of the experiment, it is often useful to use an expanding scale. A **log** or **logarithmic scale** is a series of numbers plotted as powers of 10 (1, 10, 100, 1,000, . . .) rather than in the linear progression seen on most graphs (2,000, 4,000, 6,000 . . .). Consider the two graphs below, where the *y* axis is plotted on a linear scale on the left and on a log scale on the right.

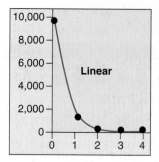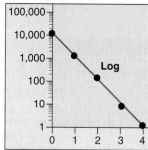

You can see that the log scale more clearly displays changes in the dependent variable (the *y* axis) for the upper values of the independent variable (the *x* axis, values 2, 3, and 4). Notice that the interval *between* each *y* axis number is not linear either—the interval between each number is itself subdivided on a log scale. Thus, 50 (the fourth tick mark between 10 and 100) is plotted much closer to 100 than to 10.

Individual graphs use different units of measurement, each chosen to best display the experimental data. By international convention, scientific data are presented in **metric units,** a system of units expressed as powers of 10. For example, weight is expressed in units called *grams*. Ten grams make up a decagram, and 1,000 grams is a kilogram. Smaller weights are expressed as a portion of a gram—for example, a centigram is a hundredth of a gram, and a milligram is a thousandth of a gram. The metric system was chosen over the English system used in the United States because the metric decimal-based system simplifies calculations and is very straightforward. The units of measurement employed in a graph are by convention indicated in parentheses next to the independent variable label on the *x* axis and the dependent variable label on the *y* axis.

Drawing a Line Most of the graphs that you will find in this text are **line graphs,** which are graphs composed of data points and one or more lines. Line graphs are typically used to present *continuous data*—that is, data that are discrete samples of a continuous process. An example might be data measuring how quickly the ozone hole develops over Antarctica in August and September each year. You could in principle measure the area of the ozone hole every day, but to make the project manageable in time and resources, you might actually take a measurement only every week. The ozone hole increases in area rapidly for about six weeks before shrinking, yielding six data points during its expansion. These six data points are like individual frames from a movie, frozen moments in time. The six data points might indicate a very consistent pattern, or they might not.

Consider the data in these graphs:

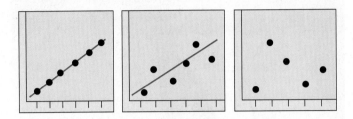

The data points on the left are changing in a very consistent way, with little variation from what a straight line (drawn in red) would predict. The graph in the middle shows more experimental variation, but a straight line still does a good job of revealing the overall pattern of how the data are changing. Such a straight "best-fit line" is called a **regression line** and is calculated by estimating the distance of each point to possible lines, adding the values, and selecting the line with the lowest sum. The data points in the graph on the right, unlike the other two, are randomly distributed and show no overall pattern, indicating that there is no relationship between the dependent and the independent variables.

Other Graphical Presentations of Data Sometimes the independent variable for a data set is not continuous but rather represents discrete sets of data. A line graph, with its assumption of continuity, cannot accurately represent the variation occurring in discrete sets of data, where the data sets are being compared with one another. The preferred presentation is that of a **histogram,** a kind of bar graph. For example, if you were surveying the heights of pine trees in a park, you might group their heights (the independent variable) into discrete

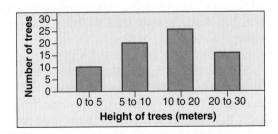

"categories" such as 0 to 5 meters tall, 5 to 10 meters, and so on. These categories are placed on the *x* axis. You would then count the number of trees in each category and present that dependent variable on the *y* axis.

Other types of data represent proportions of a whole data set, for example, the different types of trees in the park as a percentage of all the trees. This type of data is often presented in a **pie chart,** as shown here.

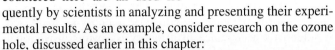

Putting Graphs to Work: The Ozone Hole

The sorts of graphs we have encountered here are all used frequently by scientists in analyzing and presenting their experimental results. As an example, consider research on the ozone hole, discussed earlier in this chapter:

A *line graph* can be used to present data on how the size of the ozone hole changes over the course of one year. In this case, the regression line is not a straight line, but rather a curve:

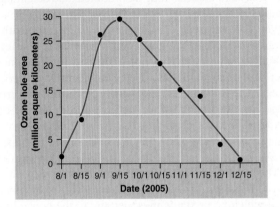

A *histogram* can be used to present data on how the peak size of the ozone hole has changed in two-year intervals over the past 26 years:

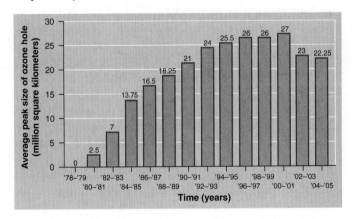

Inquiry & Analysis

The best way to learn how scientists ask questions and analyze data is to do it yourself. At the end of most chapters in this text you will find an *Inquiry & Analysis* feature that allows you to analyze a real experimental data set yourself.

1.7 Science progresses by systematically eliminating potential hypotheses that are not consistent with observation.

Theory and Certainty

A theory is a unifying explanation for a broad range of observations. Thus we speak of the theory of gravity, the theory of evolution, and the theory of the atom. Theories are the solid ground of science, that of which we are the most certain. There is no absolute truth in science, however, only varying degrees of uncertainty. The possibility always remains that future evidence will cause a theory to be revised. A scientist's acceptance of a theory is always provisional. For example, in another scientist's experiment, evidence that is inconsistent with a theory may be revealed. As information is shared throughout the scientific community, previous hypotheses and theories may be modified, and scientists may formulate new ideas.

Very active areas of science are often alive with controversy, as scientists grope with new and challenging ideas. This uncertainty is not a sign of poor science but rather of the push and pull that is the heart of the scientific process. The hypothesis that the world's climate is growing warmer due to humanity's excessive production of carbon dioxide (CO_2), for example, has been quite controversial, although the weight of evidence has increasingly supported the hypothesis.

The word theory is thus used very differently by scientists than by the general public. To a scientist, a theory represents that of which he or she is most certain; to the general public, the word theory implies a *lack* of knowledge or a guess. How often have you heard someone say, "It's only a theory!"? As you can imagine, confusion often results. In this text the word theory will always be used in its scientific sense, in reference to a generally accepted scientific principle.

The Scientific "Method"

It was once fashionable to claim that scientific progress is the result of applying a series of steps called the **scientific method;** that is, a series of logical "either/or" predictions tested by experiments to reject one alternative. The assumption was that trial-and-error testing would inevitably lead one through the maze of uncertainty that always slows scientific progress. If this were indeed true, a computer would make a good scientist—but science is not done this way! If you ask successful scientists like Farman how they do their work, you will discover that without exception they design their experiments with a pretty fair idea of how they will come out. Environmental scientists understood the chemistry of chlorine and ozone when they formulated the CFC hypothesis, and they could imagine how the chlorine in CFCs would attack ozone molecules. A hypothesis that a successful scientist tests is not just any hypothesis. Rather, it is a "hunch" or educated guess in which the scientist integrates all that he or she knows. The scientist also allows his or her imagination full play, in an attempt to get a sense of what *might* be true. It is because insight and imagination play such a large role in scientific progress that some scientists are so much better at science

Figure 1.9 Nobel Prize winner.
Sherwood Rowland, along with Mario Molina and Paul Crutzen, won the 1995 Nobel Prize in Chemistry for discovering how CFCs act to catalytically break down atmospheric ozone in the stratosphere, the chemistry responsible for the "ozone hole" over the Antarctic.

than others (figure 1.9)—just as Beethoven and Mozart stand out among composers.

The Limitations of Science

Scientific study is limited to organisms and processes that we are able to observe and measure. Supernatural and religious phenomena are beyond the realm of scientific analysis because they cannot be scientifically studied, analyzed, or explained. Supernatural explanations can be used to explain any result, and cannot be disproven by experiment or observation. Scientists in their work are limited to objective interpretations of observable phenomena.

It is also important to recognize that there are practical limits to what science can accomplish. While scientific study has revolutionized our world, it cannot be relied upon to solve all problems. For example, we cannot pollute the environment and squander its resources today, in the blind hope that somehow science will make it all right sometime in the future. Nor can science restore an extinct species. Science identifies solutions to problems when solutions exist, but it cannot invent solutions when they don't.

> **1.8 A scientist does not follow a fixed method to form hypotheses but relies also on judgment and intuition.**

Author's Corner

Where Are All My Socks Going?

All my life, for as far back as I can remember, I have been losing socks. Not pairs of socks, mind you, but single socks. I first became aware of this peculiar phenomenon when as a young man I went away to college. When Thanksgiving rolled around that first year, I brought an enormous duffle bag of laundry home. My mother, instead of braining me, dumped the lot into the washer and dryer, and so discovered what I had not noticed—that few of my socks matched anymore.

That was over 40 years ago, but it might as well have been yesterday. All my life, I have continued to lose socks. This last Christmas I threw out a sock drawer full of socks that didn't match, and took advantage of sales to buy a dozen pairs of brand-new ones. Last week, when I did a body count, three of the new pairs had lost a sock!

Enough. I set out to solve the mystery of the missing socks. How? The way Sherlock Holmes would have, scientifically. Holmes worked by eliminating those possibilities that he found not to be true. A scientist calls possibilities "hypotheses" and, like Sherlock, rejects those that do not fit the facts. Sherlock tells us that when only one possibility remains unrejected, then—however unlikely—it must be true.

Hypothesis 1: It's the socks. I have four pairs of socks bought as Christmas gifts but forgotten until recently. Deep in my sock drawer, they have remained undisturbed for five months. If socks disappear because of some intrinsic property (say the manufacturer has somehow designed them to disappear to generate new sales), then I could expect at least one of these undisturbed ones to have left the scene by now. However, when I looked, all four pairs were complete. Undisturbed socks don't disappear. Thus I reject the hypothesis that the problem is caused by the socks themselves.

Hypothesis 2: Transformation, a fanciful suggestion by science fiction writer Avram Davidson in his 1958 story "Or All the Seas with Oysters" that I cannot get out of the quirky corner of my mind. I discard the socks I have worn each evening in a laundry basket in my closet. Over many years, I have noticed a tendency for socks I have placed in the closet to disappear. Over that same long period, as my socks are disappearing, there is something in my closet that seems to multiply—COAT HANGERS! Socks are larval coat hangers! To test this outlandish hypothesis, I had only to move the laundry basket out of the closet. Several months later, I was still losing socks, so this hypothesis is rejected.

Hypothesis 3: Static cling. The missing single socks may have been hiding within the sleeves of sweat shirts or jackets, inside trouser legs, or curled up within seldom-worn garments. Rubbing around in the dryer, socks can garner quite a bit of static electricity, easily enough to cause them to cling to other garments. Socks adhering to the outside of a shirt or pant leg are soon dislodged, but ones that find themselves within a sleeve, leg, or fold may simply stay there, not "lost" so much as misplaced. However, after a diligent search, I did not run across any previously lost socks hiding in the sleeves of my winter garments or other seldom-worn items, so I reject this hypothesis.

Hypothesis 4: I lose my socks going to or from the laundry. Perhaps in handling the socks from laundry basket to the washer/dryer and back to my sock drawer, a sock is occasionally lost. To test this hypothesis, I have pawed through the laundry coming into the washer. No single socks. Perhaps the socks are lost after doing the laundry, during folding or transport from laundry to sock drawer. If so, there should be no single socks coming out of the dryer. But there are! The singletons are first detected among the dry laundry, before folding. Thus I eliminate the hypothesis that the problem arises from mishandling the laundry. It seems the problem is in the laundry room.

Hypothesis 5: I lose them during washing. Perhaps the washing machine is somehow "eating" my socks. I looked in the washing machine to see if a sock could get trapped inside, or chewed up by the machine, but I can see no possibility. The clothes slosh around in a closed metal container with water passing in and out through little holes no wider than a pencil. No sock could slip through such a hole. There is a thin gap between the rotating cylinder and the top of the washer through which an errant sock might escape, but my socks are too bulky for this route. So I eliminate the hypothesis that the washing machine is the culprit.

Hypothesis 6: I lose them during drying. Perhaps somewhere in the drying process socks are being lost. I stuck my head in our clothes dryer to see if I could see any socks, and I couldn't. However, as I look, I can see a place a sock could go—behind the drying wheel! A clothes dryer is basically a great big turning cylinder with dry air blowing through the middle. The edges of the turning cylinder don't push hard against the side of the machine. Just maybe, every once in a while, a sock might get pulled through, sucked into the back of the machine.

To test this hypothesis, I should take the back of the dryer off and look inside to see if it is stuffed with my missing socks. My wife, knowing my mechanical abilities, is not in favor of this test. Thus, until our dryer dies and I can take it apart, I shall not be able to reject hypothesis 6. Lacking any other likely hypothesis, I take Sherlock Holmes' advice and tentatively conclude that the dryer is the culprit.

1.9 Four Theories Unify Biology as a Science

The Cell Theory: Organization of Life

As was stated at the beginning of this chapter, all organisms are composed of cells, life's basic units. Cells were discovered by Robert Hooke in England in 1665. Hooke was using one of the first microscopes, one that magnified 30 times. Looking through a thin slice of cork, he observed many tiny chambers, which reminded him of monks' cells in a monastery. Not long after that, the Dutch scientist Anton van Leeuwenhoek used microscopes capable of magnifying 300 times, and discovered an amazing world of single-celled life in a drop of pond water like you see in figure 1.10. He called the bacterial and protist cells he saw "wee animalcules." However, it took almost two centuries before biologists fully understood their significance. In 1839, the German biologists Matthias Schleiden and Theodor Schwann, summarizing a large number of observations by themselves and others, concluded that all living organisms consist of cells. Their conclusion forms the basis of what has come to be known as the **cell theory.** Later, biologists added the idea that all cells come from other cells. The cell theory, one of the basic ideas in biology, is the foundation for understanding the reproduction and growth of all organisms. The nature of cells and how they function is discussed in detail in chapter 5.

Figure 1.10 Life in a drop of pond water.

All organisms are composed of cells. Some organisms, including these protists, are single-celled, while others, such as plants, animals, and fungi, consist of many cells.

The Gene Theory: Molecular Basis of Inheritance

Even the simplest cell is incredibly complex, more intricate than a computer. The information that specifies what a cell is like—its detailed plan—is encoded in a long cablelike molecule called **DNA (deoxyribonucleic acid).** Researchers James Watson and Francis Crick discovered in 1953 that each DNA molecule is formed from two long chains of building blocks, called nucleotides, wound around each other. You can see in figure 1.11 that the two chains face each other, like two lines of people holding hands. The chains contain information in the same way this sentence does—as a sequence of letters. There are four different nucleotides in DNA (symbolized as A, T, C, and G in the figure), and the sequence in which they occur encodes the information. Specific sequences of several hundred to many thousand nucleotides make up a *gene,* a discrete unit of hereditary information. A gene might encode a particular protein, or a different kind of unique molecule called RNA, or a gene might act to regulate other genes. All organisms on earth encode their genes in strands of DNA. This prevalence of DNA lead to the development of the **gene theory.** Illustrated in figure 1.12, the gene theory states that the

proteins and RNA molecules encoded by an organism's genes determine what it will be like. The entire set of DNA instructions that specifies a cell is called its **genome.** The sequence of the human genome, 3 billion nucleotides long, was decoded in 2001, a triumph of scientific investigation. How genes function is the subject of chapter 13. In chapters 14 and 15 we explore how detailed knowledge of genes is revolutionizing biology and having an impact on the lives of all of us.

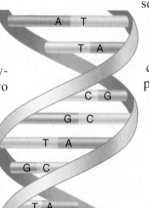

Figure 1.11 Genes are made of DNA.

Winding around each other like the rails of a spiral staircase, the two strands of a DNA molecule make a double helix. Because of its size and shape, the nucleotide represented by the letter A can only pair with the nucleotide represented by the letter T, and likewise G can only pair with C.

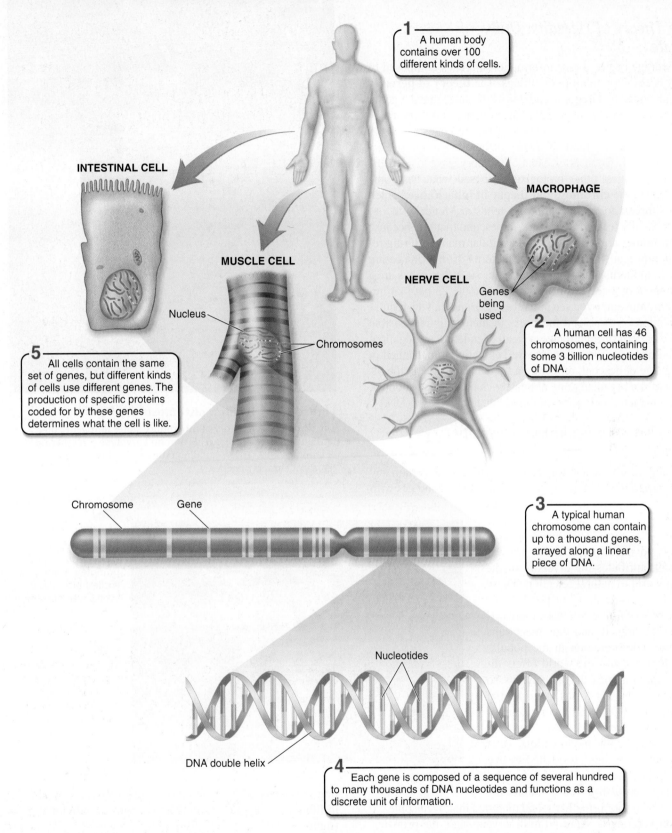

1 A human body contains over 100 different kinds of cells.

INTESTINAL CELL

MACROPHAGE

MUSCLE CELL

NERVE CELL

Genes being used

Nucleus

Chromosomes

2 A human cell has 46 chromosomes, containing some 3 billion nucleotides of DNA.

5 All cells contain the same set of genes, but different kinds of cells use different genes. The production of specific proteins coded for by these genes determines what the cell is like.

Chromosome   Gene

3 A typical human chromosome can contain up to a thousand genes, arrayed along a linear piece of DNA.

Nucleotides

DNA double helix

4 Each gene is composed of a sequence of several hundred to many thousands of DNA nucleotides and functions as a discrete unit of information.

Figure 1.12 The gene theory.

The gene theory states that what an organism is like is determined in large measure by its genes. Here you see how the many kinds of cells in the body of each of us are determined by which genes are used in making each particular kind of cell.

The Theory of Heredity: Unity of Life

The storage of hereditary information in genes composed of DNA is common to all living things. The **theory of heredity** first advanced by Gregor Mendel in 1865 states that the genes of an organism are inherited as discrete units. A triumph of experimental science developed long before genes and DNA were understood, Mendel's theory of heredity is the subject of chapter 11. Soon after Mendel's theory gave rise to the field of genetics, other biologists proposed what has come to be called the **chromosomal theory of inheritance,** which in its simplest form states that the genes of Mendel's theory are physically located on chromosomes, and that it is because chromosomes are parceled out in a regular manner during reproduction that Mendel's regular patterns of inheritance are seen. In modern terms, the two theories state that genes are a component of a cell's chromosomes (like the 23 pairs of human chromosomes you see in figure 1.13), and that the regular duplication of these chromosomes in meiosis is responsible for the pattern of inheritance we call Mendelian segregation. Sometimes a character is conserved essentially unchanged in a long line of descent, reflecting a fundamental role in the biology of the organism, one not easily changed once adopted. Other characters might be modified due to changes in DNA.

The Theory of Evolution: Diversity of Life

The unity of life, which we see in the retention of certain key characteristics among many related life-forms, contrasts with the incredible diversity of living things that have evolved to fill the varied environments of earth. The **theory of evolution,** advanced by Charles Darwin in 1859, attributes the diversity of the living world to natural selection. Those organisms best able to respond to the challenges of living will leave more offspring, he argued, and thus their traits become more common in the population. It is because the world offers diverse opportunities that it contains so many different life-forms. An essential component of Darwin's theory is, in his own words, that evolution is a process of "descent with modification," that all living organisms are related to one another in a common tree of descent, a family tree of life. For example, the first primate was a small arboreal mammal that lived some 65 million years ago. About 40 million years ago, the primates split into two groups: One group, prosimians (figure 1.14), has changed little since then, while the other, monkeys, apes, and our family line, has continued to evolve.

Today scientists can decipher many of the thousands of genes (the genome) of an organism. One of the great triumphs of science in the century and a half since Darwin is the detailed understanding of how Darwin's theory of evolution is related to the gene theory—of precisely how changes in life's diversity can result from changes in individual genes (figure 1.15).

The amount of diversity and variation in organisms that have evolved to inhabit the earth can be overwhelming to contemplate. As you learned in section 1.1, biologists divide all living organisms into six kingdoms, based on similar overall characteristics. In recent years, biologists have added a classification level above kingdoms, based on fundamental differences in cell structure. The six kingdoms are each

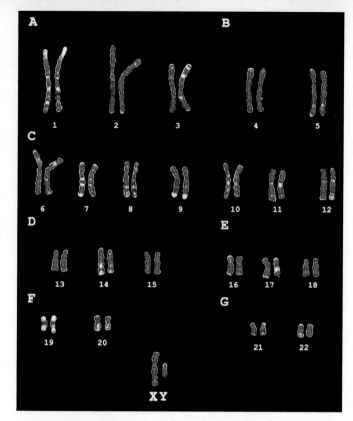

Figure 1.13 Human chromosomes.

The chromosomal theory of inheritance states that genes are located on chromosomes. This human karyotype (an ordering of chromosomes) shows banding patterns on chromosomes that represent clusters of genes.

Figure 1.14 Prosimians.

Humans and apes are primates. Among the earliest primates to evolve were prosimians, small nocturnal (night-active) insect eaters. These lemurs, prosimians native to Madagascar, show the features characteristic of all primates: grasping fingers and toes and binocular vision.

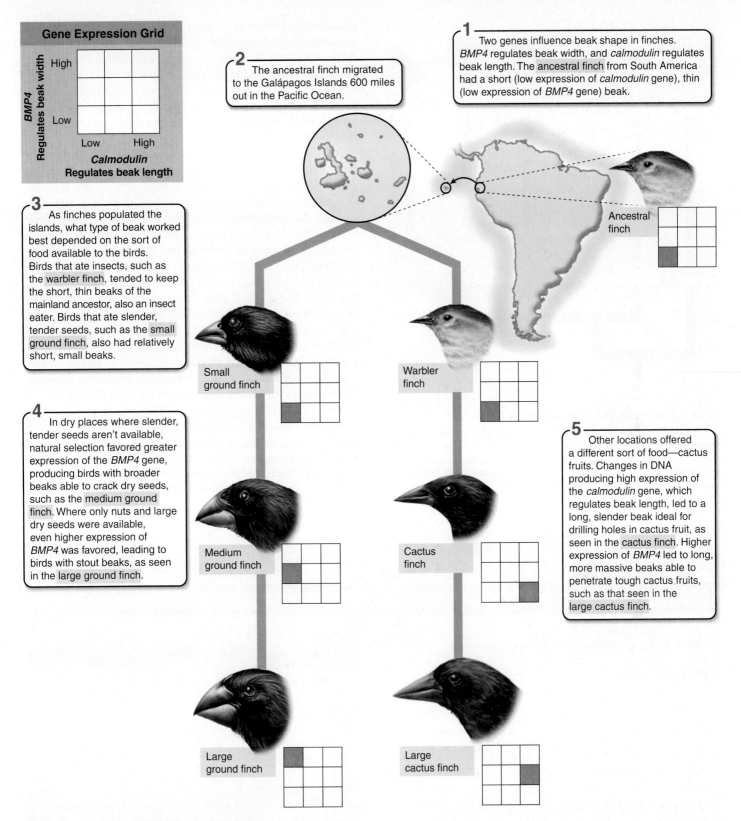

Gene Expression Grid

BMP4 Regulates beak width — High / Low
Calmodulin Regulates beak length — Low / High

1 Two genes influence beak shape in finches. *BMP4* regulates beak width, and *calmodulin* regulates beak length. The ancestral finch from South America had a short (low expression of *calmodulin* gene), thin (low expression of *BMP4* gene) beak.

2 The ancestral finch migrated to the Galápagos Islands 600 miles out in the Pacific Ocean.

3 As finches populated the islands, what type of beak worked best depended on the sort of food available to the birds. Birds that ate insects, such as the warbler finch, tended to keep the short, thin beaks of the mainland ancestor, also an insect eater. Birds that ate slender, tender seeds, such as the small ground finch, also had relatively short, small beaks.

4 In dry places where slender, tender seeds aren't available, natural selection favored greater expression of the *BMP4* gene, producing birds with broader beaks able to crack dry seeds, such as the medium ground finch. Where only nuts and large dry seeds were available, even higher expression of *BMP4* was favored, leading to birds with stout beaks, as seen in the large ground finch.

5 Other locations offered a different sort of food—cactus fruits. Changes in DNA producing high expression of the *calmodulin* gene, which regulates beak length, led to a long, slender beak ideal for drilling holes in cactus fruit, as seen in the cactus finch. Higher expression of *BMP4* led to long, more massive beaks able to penetrate tough cactus fruits, such as that seen in the large cactus finch.

Ancestral finch

Small ground finch

Warbler finch

Medium ground finch

Cactus finch

Large ground finch

Large cactus finch

Figure 1.15 The theory of evolution.
Darwin's theory of evolution proposes that many forms of a gene may exist among members of a population, and that those members with a form better suited to their particular habitat will tend to reproduce more successfully and so become more common in the population, a process Darwin dubbed "natural selection." Here you see how this process is thought to have worked on two pivotal genes that helped generate the diversity of finches on the Galápagos Islands, visited by Darwin in 1831 on his round-the-world voyage on HMS *Beagle*.

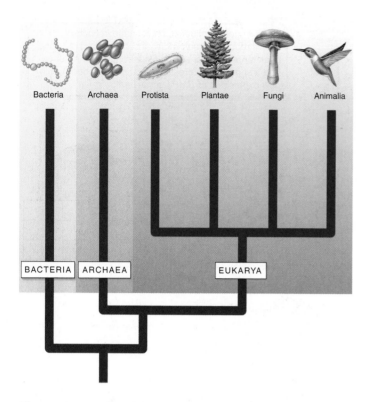

Figure 1.16 The three domains of life.
Biologists categorize all living things into three overarching groups called domains: Bacteria, Archaea, and Eukarya. Domain Bacteria contains the kingdom Bacteria, and domain Archaea contains the kingdom Archaea. Domain Eukarya is composed of four more kingdoms: Protista, Plantae, Fungi, and Animalia.

now assigned into one of three great groups called *domains:* Bacteria, Archaea, and Eukarya. Bacteria (the yellow zone in figure 1.16) and Archaea (the pink zone in figure 1.16) each consist of one kingdom of prokaryotes (single-celled organisms with little internal structure). Four more kingdoms composed of organisms with more complexly organized cells are placed within the domain Eukarya, the eukaryotes (the purple zone in figure 1.16).

The simplest and most ancient of the Eukarya is the Kingdom Protista, mostly composed of tiny unicellular organisms. The protists are the most diverse of the four eukaryotic kingdoms, and gave rise to the other three. Kingdom Plantae, the land plants, arose from a kind of photosynthetic protist called a green algae. Kingdom Fungi, the mushrooms and yeasts, arose from a protist that has not yet been clearly identified. Kingdom Animalia, of which we are a member, is thought to have arisen from a kind of protist called a choanoflagellate. The simplest animals, sponges, have special flagellated cells called choanocytes that line the body interior. By waving the choanocyte flagella, the sponge draws water into its interior through pores, filtering out food particles from the water as it passes. Each choanocyte cell of a sponge closely resembles a choanoflagellate protist, its presumed ancestor. The kingdoms of life are discussed in detail in chapter 18.

1.9 The theories uniting biology state that cellular organisms store hereditary information in DNA. Sometimes DNA alterations occur, which when preserved result in evolutionary change. Today's biological diversity is the product of a long evolutionary journey.

INQUIRY & ANALYSIS

Is the Size of the Ozone Hole Increasing?

Since 1980 scientists have measured the size of the ozone hole centered over Antarctica. The peak size each year is presented on the graph to the right.

1. **Applying Concepts** In the graph, what is the dependent variable? Explain.

2. **Making Inferences** Is the size of the ozone hole increasing from 1980 to 1990? from 1995 to 2005?

3. **Drawing Conclusions** Does the graph support the conclusion that the size of the ozone hole over Antarctica is increasing? Explain. What might account for the difference you observe between 1980–90 and 1995–2005?

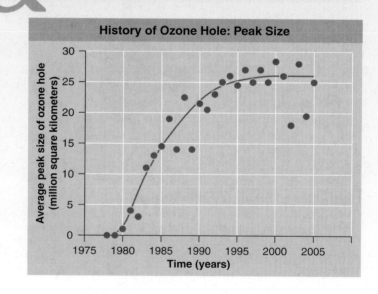

Biology and the Living World

1.1 The Diversity of Life

- Biology is the study of life. All living organisms share common characteristics, but they are also diverse and are categorized into six groups called kingdoms. The six kingdoms are Bacteria, Archaea, Protista, Fungi, Plantae, and Animalia (**figure 1.1**).

1.2 Properties of Life

- All living organisms share five basic properties: cellular organization, metabolism, homeostasis, growth and reproduction, and heredity. Cellular organization indicates that all living organisms are composed of cells. Metabolism means that all living organisms, like the kingfisher shown here from **figure 1.3**, use energy. Homeostasis is the process whereby

all living organisms maintain stable internal conditions. The properties of growth and reproduction indicate that all living organisms grow in size and reproduce. The property of heredity describes how all living organisms possess genetic information in DNA that determines how each organism looks and functions, and this information is passed on to future generations.

1.3 The Organization of Life

- Living organisms exhibit increasing levels of complexity within their cells (cellular level), within their bodies (organismal level), and within ecosystems (population level) (**figure 1.4**).

- Novel properties that appear in each level of the hierarchy of life are called emergent properties.

1.4 Biological Themes

- Five themes emerge from the study of biology: evolution, the flow of energy, cooperation, structure determines function, and homeostasis. These themes are used to examine the similarities and differences among organisms (**table 1.1**).

The Scientific Process

1.5 How Scientists Think

- Scientists use reasoning. Deductive reasoning is the process of using general principles to explain individual observations. Inductive reasoning is the process of using specific observations to formulate general principles (**figure 1.5**).

1.6 Science in Action: A Case Study

- Scientists observed a thinning of the ozone layer over Antarctica. Their scientific investigation of the "ozone hole" revealed that industrially produced CFCs were responsible for the thinning of the ozone layer in the earth's atmosphere (**figure 1.6**).

Winter ice crystals

Cold air

Antarctica

1.7 Stages of a Scientific Investigation

- Scientists use observations to formulate hypotheses. Hypotheses are possible explanations that are used to form predictions. These predictions are tested experimentally. Some hypotheses are rejected based on experimental results, while others are tentatively accepted.

- Scientific investigations often use a series of stages, called the scientific process, to study a scientific question. These stages are observations, forming hypotheses, making predictions, testing, establishing controls, and drawing conclusions (**figure 1.7**).

- After analyzing their data, scientists present it to others for interpretation and verification. Scientists use various methods of presenting data including line graphs, histograms, and charts. Deciding which type of visual presentation to use is based on the data set being presented.

1.8 Theory and Certainty

- Hypotheses that hold up to testing over time are combined into statements called theories. Theories carry a higher degree of certainty, although no theory in science is absolute.

- Science can only study what can be tested experimentally. A hypothesis can only be established through science if it can be tested and potentially disproven.

Core Ideas of Biology

1.9 Four Theories Unify Biology as a Science

- There are four unifying theories in biology: cell theory, gene theory, the theory of heredity, and the theory of evolution.

- The cell theory states that all living organisms are composed of cells, which grow and reproduce to form other cells (**figure 1.10**).

- The gene theory states that long molecules of DNA carry instructions for producing cellular components. These instructions are encoded in the nucleotide sequences in the strands of DNA, like this section of DNA from **figure 1.11**. The nucleotides are organized into discrete units called genes, and the genes determine how an organism looks and functions (**figure 1.12**).

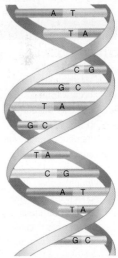

- The theory of heredity states that the genes of an organism are passed as discrete units from parent to offspring (**figure 1.13**).

- The theory of evolution states that modifications in genes that are passed from parent to offspring result in changes in future generations. These changes lead to greater diversity among organisms over time (**figure 1.15**).

- Organisms are organized into kingdoms based on similar characteristics. The kingdoms are further organized into three major groups called domains based on their cellular characteristics. The three domains are Bacteria, Archaea, and Eukarya (**figure 1.16**).

1. Biologists categorize all living things based on related characteristics into large groups, called
   a. kingdoms.   c. courses.
   b. planets.   d. territories.

2. Living things can be distinguished from nonliving things because they have
   a. complexity.   c. cellular organization.
   b. movement.   d. response to a stimulus.

3. Living things are organized. Choose the answer that illustrates this complexity, and is arranged from smallest to largest.
   a. cell, atom, molecule, tissue, organelle, organ, organ system, organism, population, species, community, ecosystem
   b. atom, molecule, organelle, cell, tissue, organ, organ system, organism, population, species, community, ecosystem
   c. atom, molecule, organelle, cell, tissue, organ, organ system, organism, community, population, species, ecosystem
   d. atom, molecule, cell wall, cell, organ, organelle, organism, species, population, community, ecosystem

4. At each higher level in the hierarchy of living things, properties occur that were not present at the simpler levels. These properties are referred to as
   a. novelistic properties.   c. incremental properties.
   b. complex properties.   d. emergent properties.

5. The five general biological themes include
   a. evolution, energy flow, competition, structure determines function, and homeostasis.
   b. evolution, energy flow, cooperation, structure determines function, and homeostasis.
   c. evolution, growth, competition, structure determines function, and homeostasis.
   d. evolution, growth, cooperation, structure determines function, and homeostasis.

6. When you are trying to understand something new, you begin by observation, and then put the observations together in a logical fashion to form a general principle. This method is called

   a. inductive reasoning.   c. theory production.
   b. rule enhancement.   d. deductive reasoning.

7. When trying to figure out explanations for observations, you usually construct a series of possible hypotheses. Then you make predictions of what will happen if each hypothesis is true, and
   a. test each hypothesis, using appropriate controls, to determine which hypothesis is true.
   b. test each hypothesis, using appropriate controls, to rule out as many as possible.
   c. use logic to determine which hypothesis is most likely true.
   d. use logic to determine which hypotheses are most likely false.

8. Which of the following statements is correct regarding a hypothesis?
   a. After sufficient testing, you can conclude that it is true.
   b. If it explains the observations, it doesn't need to be tested.
   c. After sufficient testing, you can accept it as probable, being aware that it may be revised or rejected in the future.
   d. You never have any degree of certainty that it is true; there are too many variables.

9. Cell theory states that
   a. all organisms have cell walls and all cell walls come from other cells.
   b. all cellular organisms undergo sexual reproduction.
   c. all living organisms use cells for energy, either their own or they ingest cells of other organisms.
   d. all living organisms consist of cells, and all cells come from other cells.

10. The gene theory states that all the information that specifies what a cell is and what it does
    a. is different for each cell type in the organism.
    b. is passed down, unchanged, from parents to offspring.
    c. is contained in a long molecule called DNA.
    d. is contained in the body's nucleus.

1. For over two centuries global temperatures have been warming, and over this same period of time the number of pirate ship attacks has steadily decreased. Does this graph support the conclusion that the number of pirate attacks has decreased because of warmer temperatures? Explain.

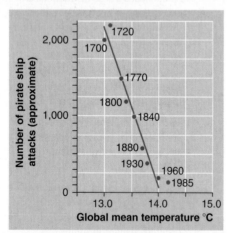

2. **Figure 1.5** You notice that on cloudy days people often carry umbrellas, folded or in a case. You also note that when umbrellas are open there are many car accidents. You conclude that open umbrellas cause car accidents. Referring back to figure 1.5, explain the type of reasoning used to reach this conclusion, and why it can sometimes be a problem.

1. You are the biologist in a group of scientists who have traveled to a distant star system and landed on a planet. You see an astounding array of shapes and forms. You have three days to take samples of living things before returning to earth. How do you decide what is alive?

2. St. John's wort is an herb that has been used for hundreds of years as a remedy for mild depression. How might a modern-day scientist research its effectiveness?

2

Evolution and Ecology

These four finches live on the Galápagos Islands, a cluster of volcanic islands far out to sea off the coast of South America. All descendants of a single ancestral migrant, blown to the islands from the mainland long ago, the Galápagos finches gave Darwin valuable clues about how natural selection shapes the evolution of species. The two upper finches are ground finches, their different beaks adapting them to eat different-sized seeds. The finch on the left consumes smaller, slender seeds. The stouter beak of the finch on the right enables it to crack open larger, drier seeds. On the lower left is a woodpecker finch, a kind of tree finch that carries around a cactus spine, which it uses to probe for insects in deep crevices. On the lower right is a warbler finch, which like its namesake eats crawling insects. Each of these species utilizes food resources differently. Evolution and ecology tell us different but related things about the diversity of the living world: Ecological interactions generate the selective pressures that shape the evolution of groups like Darwin's finches.

The great diversity of life on earth—ranging from bacteria to elephants and roses—is the result of a long process of **evolution,** the change that occurs in organisms' characteristics through time. In 1859, the English naturalist Charles Darwin (1809–82; figure 2.1) first suggested an explanation for why evolution occurs, a process he called **natural selection.** Biologists soon became convinced Darwin was right and now consider evolution one of the central concepts of the science of biology. A second key concept, and one that closely relates to evolution, is that of **ecology,** how organisms live in their environment. It has been said that evolution is the consequence of ecology over time. Ecology is of increasing concern to all of us, as a growing human population places ever-greater stress on our planet. In this chapter, we introduce these two key related concepts, evolution and ecology, to provide a foundation as you begin to explore the living world. While these concepts are presented here with broad strokes, highlighting only the key ideas, both will be revisited in much more detail later in the text (evolution in chapters 17–27 and ecology in chapters 37–40).

2.1 Darwin's Voyage on HMS *Beagle*

The theory of evolution proposes that a population can change over time, sometimes forming a new species, which is a population or group of populations that possess similar characteristics and can interbreed and produce fertile offspring. This famous theory provides a good example of how a scientist develops a hypothesis—in this case, a hypothesis of how evolution occurs—and how, after much testing, the hypothesis is eventually accepted as a theory.

Charles Robert Darwin was an English naturalist who, after 30 years of study and observation, wrote one of the most famous and influential books of all time. This book, *On the Origin of Species by Means of Natural Selection, or The Preservation of Favoured Races in the Struggle for Life,* created a sensation when it was published, and the ideas Darwin expressed in it have played a central role in the development of human thought ever since.

In Darwin's time, most people believed that the various kinds of organisms and their individual structures resulted from direct actions of the Creator. Species were thought to be specially created and unchangeable over the course of time. In contrast to these views, a number of earlier philosophers had presented the view that living things must have changed during the history of life on earth. Darwin proposed a concept he called natural selection as a coherent, logical explanation for this process. Darwin's book, as its title indicates, presented a conclusion that differed sharply from conventional wisdom. Although his theory did not challenge the existence of a Divine Creator, Darwin argued that this Creator did not simply create things and then leave them forever unchanged. Instead, Darwin's God expressed Himself through the operation of natural laws that produced change over time—evolution.

Figure 2.1   The theory of evolution by natural selection was proposed by Charles Darwin.
This rediscovered photograph appears to be the last ever taken of the great biologist. It was taken in 1881, the year before Darwin died.

The story of Darwin and his theory begins in 1831, when he was 22 years old. The small British naval vessel HMS *Beagle* that you see in figure 2.2 was about to set sail on a five-year navigational mapping expedition around the coasts of South America. The red arrows in figure 2.3 indicates the route taken by the HMS *Beagle.* The young (26-year-old) captain of HMS *Beagle,* unable by British naval tradition to have social contact with his crew, and anticipating a voyage that would last many years, wanted a gentleman companion, someone to talk to. Indeed, the *Beagle*'s previous skipper had broken down and shot himself to death after three solitary years away from home.

On the recommendation of one of his professors at Cambridge University, Darwin, son of a wealthy doctor and very much a gentleman, was selected to serve as the captain's companion, primarily to share his table at mealtime during every shipboard dinner of the long voyage. Darwin paid his own expenses, and even brought along a manservant.

Darwin took on the role of ship's naturalist (the official naturalist, a man named Robert McKormick, left the ship before the first year was out). During this long voyage, Darwin had the chance to study a wide variety of plants and animals on continents and islands and in distant seas. He was able to

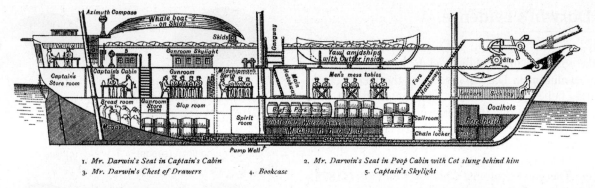

Figure 2.2 Cross section of HMS *Beagle*.
HMS *Beagle*, a 10-gun brig of 242 tons, only 90 feet in length, had a crew of 74 people! After he first saw the ship, Darwin wrote to his college professor Henslow: "The absolute want of room is an evil that nothing can surmount."

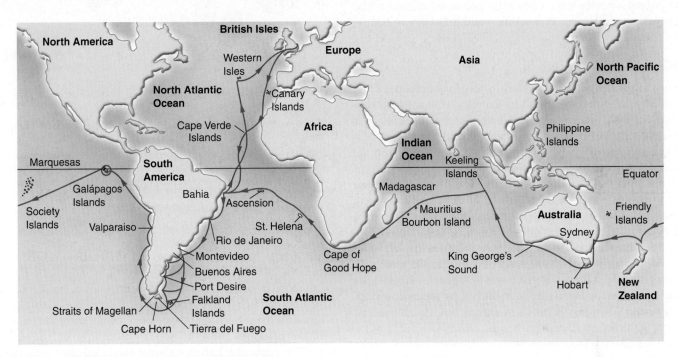

Figure 2.3 The five-year voyage of HMS *Beagle*.
Although the ship sailed around the world, most of the time was spent exploring the coasts and coastal islands of South America, such as the Galápagos Islands. Darwin's studies of the animals of these islands played a key role in the eventual development of his theory of evolution by means of natural selection.

explore the biological richness of the tropical forests, examine the extraordinary fossils of huge extinct mammals in Patagonia at the southern tip of South America, and observe the remarkable series of related but distinct forms of life on the **Galápagos Islands.** Such an opportunity clearly played an important role in the development of his thoughts about the nature of life on earth.

When Darwin returned from the voyage at the age of 27, he began a long period of study and contemplation. During the next 10 years, he published important books on several different subjects, including the formation of oceanic islands from coral reefs and the geology of South America. He also devoted eight years of study to barnacles, a group of small marine animals with shells that inhabit rocks and pilings, eventually writing a four-volume work on their classification and natural history. In 1842, Darwin and his family moved out of London to a country home at Down, in the county of Kent. In these pleasant surroundings, Darwin lived, studied, and wrote for the next 40 years.

2.1 Darwin was the first to propose natural selection as the mechanism of evolution that produced the diversity of life on earth.

Darwin's Evidence

One of the obstacles that had blocked the acceptance of any theory of evolution in Darwin's day was the incorrect notion, widely believed at that time, that the earth was only a few thousand years old. The discovery of thick layers of rocks, evidences of extensive and prolonged erosion, and the increasing numbers of diverse and unfamiliar fossils discovered during Darwin's time made this assertion seem less and less likely. The great geologist Charles Lyell (1797–1875), whose *Principles of Geology* (1830) Darwin read eagerly as he sailed on HMS *Beagle,* outlined for the first time the story of an ancient world of plants and animals in flux. In this world, species were constantly becoming extinct while others were emerging. It was this world that Darwin sought to explain.

What Darwin Saw

When HMS *Beagle* set sail, Darwin was fully convinced that species were immutable, meaning that they were not subject to being changed. Indeed, it was not until two or three years after his return that he began to seriously consider the possibility that they could change. Nevertheless, during his five years on the ship, Darwin observed a number of phenomena that were of central importance to him in reaching his ultimate conclusion. For example, in the rich fossil beds of southern South America, he observed fossils of the extinct armadillo shown on the right in figure 2.4. They were surprisingly similar in form to the armadillos that still lived in the same area, shown on the left. Why would similar living and fossil organisms be in the same area unless the earlier form had given rise to the other? Later, Darwin's observations would be strengthened by the discovery of other examples of fossils that show intermediate characteristics, pointing to successive change.

Repeatedly, Darwin saw that the characteristics of similar species varied somewhat from place to place. These geographical patterns suggested to him that organismal lineages change gradually as individuals move into new habitats. On the

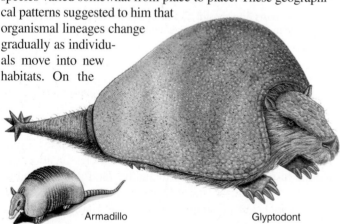

Armadillo   Glyptodont

Figure 2.4 Fossil evidence of evolution.
The now-extinct glyptodont was a large 2,000-kilogram South American armadillo (about the size of a small car), much larger than the modern armadillo, which weighs an average of about 4.5 kilograms and is about the size of a house cat. The similarity of fossils such as the glyptodonts to living organisms found in the same regions suggested to Darwin that evolution had taken place.

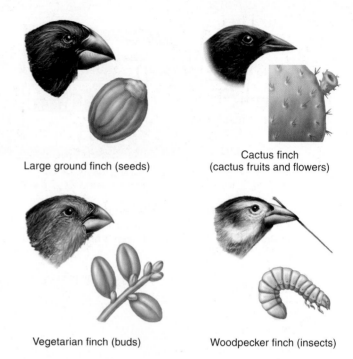

Large ground finch (seeds)

Cactus finch (cactus fruits and flowers)

Vegetarian finch (buds)

Woodpecker finch (insects)

Figure 2.5 Four Galápagos finches and what they eat.
Darwin observed 14 different species of finches on the Galápagos Islands, differing mainly in their beaks and feeding habits. These four finches eat very different food items, and Darwin surmised that the very different shapes of their beaks represented evolutionary adaptations improving their ability to do so.

Galápagos Islands, 900 kilometers (540 miles) off the coast of Ecuador, Darwin encountered a variety of different finches on the islands. The 14 species, although related, differed slightly in appearance. Darwin felt it most reasonable to assume all these birds had descended from a common ancestor blown by winds from the South American mainland several million years ago. Eating different foods, on different islands, the species had changed in different ways, most notably in the size of their beaks. The larger beak of the ground finch in the upper left of figure 2.5 is better suited to crack open the large seeds it eats. As the generations descended from the common ancestor, these ground finches changed and adapted, what Darwin referred to as "descent with modification"— evolution.

In a more general sense, Darwin was struck by the fact that the plants and animals on these relatively young volcanic islands resembled those on the nearby coast of South America. If each one of these plants and animals had been created independently and simply placed on the Galápagos Islands, why didn't they resemble the plants and animals of islands with similar climates, such as those off the coast of Africa, for example? Why did they resemble those of the adjacent South American coast instead?

2.2 The fossils and patterns of life that Darwin observed on the voyage of HMS *Beagle* eventually convinced him that evolution had taken place.

2.3 The Theory of Natural Selection

It is one thing to observe the results of evolution but quite another to understand how it happens. Darwin's great achievement lies in his formulation of the hypothesis that evolution occurs because of natural selection.

Darwin and Malthus

Of key importance to the development of Darwin's insight was his study of Thomas Malthus's *Essay on the Principle of Population* (1798). In his book, Malthus pointed out that populations of plants and animals (including human beings) tend to increase geometrically, while the ability of humans to increase their food supply increases only arithmetically. A geometric progression is one in which the elements increase by a constant factor; the blue line in figure 2.6 shows the progression 2, 6, 18, 54, . . . and each number is three times the preceding one. An arithmetic progression, in contrast, is one in which the elements increase by a constant difference; the red line shows the progression 2, 4, 6, 8, . . . and each number is two greater than the preceding one.

Because populations increase geometrically, virtually any kind of animal or plant, if it could reproduce unchecked, would cover the entire surface of the world within a surprisingly short time. Instead, population sizes of species remain fairly constant year after year, because death limits population numbers. Malthus's conclusion provided the key ingredient that was necessary for Darwin to develop the hypothesis that evolution occurs by natural selection.

Natural Selection

Sparked by Malthus's ideas, Darwin saw that although every organism has the potential to produce more offspring than can survive, only a limited number actually do survive and produce further offspring. Many examples appear in nature. Sea turtles, for instance, will return to the beaches where they hatched to lay their eggs. Each female will lay about 100 eggs. The beach could be covered with thousands of hatchlings, like in figure 2.7, trying to make it to water's edge. Less than 10% will actually reach adulthood and return to this beach to reproduce. Darwin combined his observation with what he had seen on the voyage of HMS *Beagle,* as well as with his own experiences in breeding domestic animals, and made an important association: Those individuals that possess physical, behavioral, or other attributes that help them live in their environment are more likely to survive than those that do not have these characteristics. By surviving, they gain the opportunity to pass on their favorable characteristics to their offspring. As the frequency of these characteristics increases in the population, the nature of the population as a whole will gradually change. Darwin called this process *selection.* The driving force he identified has often been referred to as survival of the fittest. However, this is not to say the biggest or the strongest always survive. These characteristics may be favorable in one environment but less favorable in another. The organisms that are "best suited" to their particular environment survive more often, and therefore produce more offspring than others

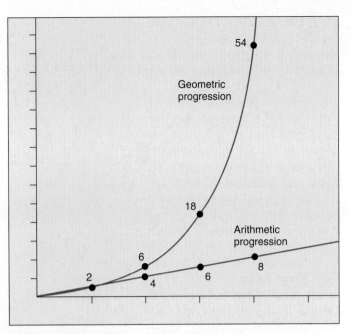

Figure 2.6 Geometric and arithmetic progressions.
An arithmetic progression increases by a constant difference (for example, units of 1 or 2 or 3), while a geometric progression increases by a constant factor (for example, by 2 or by 3 or by 4). Malthus contended that the human growth curve was geometric, but the human food production curve was only arithmetic. Can you see the problems this difference would cause?

Figure 2.7 Sea turtle hatchlings.
These newly-hatched sea turtles make their way to the ocean from their nests on the beach. Thousands of eggs may be laid on a beach during a spawning, but less then 10% will survive to adulthood. Natural predators, human egg poachers, and environmental challenges prevent the majority of offspring from surviving. As Darwin observed, sea turtles produce more offspring than will actually survive to reproduce.

in the population, and in this sense are the "fittest." The main points of Darwin's concept of evolution are discussed further in chapter 17, section 17.1.

Darwin was thoroughly familiar with variation in domesticated animals and began *On the Origin of Species* with a detailed discussion of pigeon breeding. He knew that breeders selected certain varieties of pigeons and other animals, such as dogs, to produce certain characteristics, a process Darwin called **artificial selection**. Once this had been done, the animals would breed true for the characteristics that had been selected. Darwin had also observed that the differences purposely developed between domesticated races or breeds were often greater than those that separated wild species. Domestic pigeon breeds, for example, show much greater variety than all of the hundreds of wild species of pigeons found throughout the world. Such relationships suggested to Darwin that evolutionary change could occur in nature too. Surely if pigeon breeders could foster such variation by "artificial selection," nature through environmental pressures could do the same, playing the breeder's role in selecting the next generation—a process Darwin called **natural selection.**

Darwin's theory provides a simple and direct explanation of biological diversity, or why animals are different in different places—because habitats differ in their requirements and opportunities, the organisms with characteristics favored locally by natural selection will tend to vary in different places. As we will discuss in chapter 17, section 17.5, there are five evolutionary forces that can affect biological diversity, although natural selection is the only evolutionary force that produces *adaptive* changes.

Darwin Drafts His Argument

Darwin drafted the overall argument for evolution by natural selection in a preliminary manuscript in 1842. After showing the manuscript to a few of his closest scientific friends, however, Darwin put it in a drawer and for 16 years turned to other research. No one knows for sure why Darwin did not publish his initial manuscript—it is very thorough and outlines his ideas in detail. Some historians have suggested that Darwin was wary of igniting public, and even private, criticism of his evolutionary ideas—there could have been little doubt in his mind that his theory of evolution by natural selection would spark controversy. Others have proposed that Darwin

Figure 2.8 Darwin greets his monkey ancestor.

In his time, Darwin was often portrayed unsympathetically, as in this drawing from an 1874 publication.

was simply refining his theory, although there is little evidence he altered his initial manuscript in all that time.

Wallace Has the Same Idea

The stimulus that finally brought Darwin's theory into print was an essay he received in 1858. A young English naturalist named Alfred Russel Wallace (1823–1913) sent the essay to Darwin from Malaysia; it concisely set forth the theory of evolution by means of natural selection, a theory Wallace had developed independently of Darwin. Like Darwin, Wallace had been greatly influenced by Malthus's 1798 book. Colleagues of Wallace, knowing of Darwin's work, encouraged him to communicate with Darwin. After receiving Wallace's essay, Darwin arranged for a joint presentation of their ideas at a seminar in London. Darwin then completed his own book, expanding the 1842 manuscript that he had written so long ago, and submitted it for publication.

Publication of Darwin's Theory

Darwin's book appeared in November 1859 and caused an immediate sensation. Although people had long accepted that humans closely resembled apes in many characteristics, the possibility that there might be a direct evolutionary relationship was unacceptable to many. Darwin did not actually discuss this idea in his book, but it followed directly from the principles he outlined. In a subsequent book, *The Descent of Man,* Darwin presented the argument directly, building a powerful case that humans and living apes have common ancestors. Many people were deeply disturbed with the suggestion that human beings were descended from the same ancestor as apes, and Darwin's book on evolution caused him to become a victim of the satirists of his day—the cartoon in figure 2.8 is a vivid example. Darwin's arguments for the theory of evolution by natural selection were so compelling, however, that his views were almost completely accepted within the intellectual community of Great Britain after the 1860s. Examination of the theory of evolution continues today, and the main points of this discussion are explored in more detail in chapter 17.

2.3 The fact that populations do not really expand geometrically implies that nature acts to limit population numbers. The traits of organisms that survive to produce more offspring will be more common in future generations—a process Darwin called natural selection.

2.4 The Beaks of Darwin's Finches

Darwin's Galápagos finches played a key role in his argument for evolution by natural selection. He collected 31 specimens of finch from three islands when he visited the Galápagos Islands in 1835. Darwin, not an expert on birds, had trouble identifying the specimens. He believed by examining their beaks that his collection contained wrens, "gross-beaks," and blackbirds.

The Importance of the Beak

Upon Darwin's return to England, ornithologist John Gould examined the finches. Gould recognized that Darwin's collection was in fact a closely related group of distinct species, all similar to one another except for their beaks. In all, 14 species are now recognized, 13 from the Galápagos and one from far-distant Cocos Island. The ground finches with the larger beaks in figure 2.9 feed on seeds that they crush in their beaks, whereas those with narrower beaks eat insects, including the warbler finch (named for its resemblance to a mainland bird). Other species include fruit and bud eaters, and species that feed on cactus fruits and the insects they attract; some populations of the sharp-beaked ground finch even include "vampires" that creep up on seabirds and use their sharp beaks to drink their blood. Perhaps most remarkable are the tool users, like the woodpecker finch you see in the upper left of the figure, that picks up a twig, cactus spine, or leaf stalk, trims it

Figure 2.10 A gene shapes the beaks of Darwin's finches.

A cell signalling molecule called "bone morphogenic protein 4" (BMP4) has been shown by DNA researchers to tailor the shape of the beak in Darwin's finches.

into shape with its beak, and then pokes it into dead branches to pry out grubs.

The differences in the beaks of Darwin's finches are due to differences in the genes of the birds. When biologists compare the DNA of large ground finches (with stout beaks for large cracking seeds) to the DNA of small ground finches (with more slender beaks), the only growth factor gene that is different in the DNA of the two species is *BMP4* (figure 2.10 and figure 1.15). The difference is in how the gene is used. The large ground finches, with larger beaks, make more BMP4 protein than do the small ground finches.

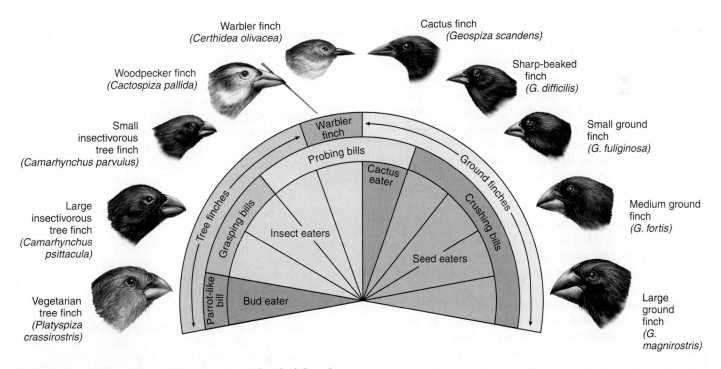

Figure 2.9 A diversity of finches on a single island.

Ten species of Darwin's finches from Isla Santa Cruz, one of the Galápagos Islands. The ten species show differences in beaks and feeding habits. These differences presumably arose when the finches arrived and encountered habitats lacking small birds. Scientists concluded that all of these birds derived from a single common ancestor.

The correspondence between the beaks of the 14 finch species and their food source immediately suggested to Darwin that evolution had shaped them:

"Seeing this gradation and diversity of structure in one small, intimately related group of birds, one might really fancy that from an original paucity of birds in this archipelago, one species has been taken and modified for different ends."

Was Darwin Wrong?

If Darwin's suggestion that the beak of an ancestral finch had been "modified for different ends" is correct, then it ought to be possible to see the different species of finches acting out their evolutionary roles, each using its beak to acquire its particular food specialty. The four species that crush seeds within their beaks, for example, should feed on different seeds, with those with stouter beaks specializing on harder-to-crush seeds.

Many biologists visited the Galápagos after Darwin, but it was 100 years before any tried this key test of his hypothesis. When the great naturalist David Lack finally set out to do this in 1938, observing the birds closely for a full five months, his observations seemed to contradict Darwin's proposal! Lack often observed many different species of finch feeding together on the same seeds. His data indicated that the stout-beaked species and the slender-beaked species were feeding on the very same array of seeds.

We now know that it was Lack's misfortune to study the birds during a wet year, when food was plentiful. The size of the finch's beak is of little importance in such flush times; slender and stout beaks work equally well to gather the abundant tender small seeds. Later work revealed a very different picture during dry years, when few seeds are available.

A Closer Look

Starting in 1973, Peter and Rosemary Grant of Princeton University and generations of their students have studied the medium ground finch, *Geospiza fortis,* on a tiny island in the center of the Galápagos called Daphne Major. These finches feed preferentially on small tender seeds, abundantly available in wet years. The birds resort to larger, drier seeds that are harder to crush when small seeds are hard to find. Such lean times come during periods of dry weather, when plants produce few seeds, large or small.

By carefully measuring the beak shape of many birds every year, the Grants were able to assemble for the first time a detailed portrait of evolution in action. The Grants found that beak depth changed from one year to the next in a predictable fashion. During droughts, plants produced few seeds, and all available small seeds quickly were eaten, leaving large seeds as the major remaining source of food. As a result, birds with large beaks survived better, because they were better able to break open these large seeds. Consequently, the average beak depth of birds in the population increased the next year because this next generation included offspring of the large-beaked birds that survived. The offspring of the surviving "dry year" birds had larger beaks, an evolutionary response which

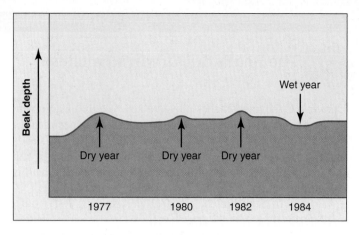

Figure 2.11   Evidence that natural selection alters beak size in *Geospiza fortis*.
In dry years, when only large, tough seeds were available, the mean beak size increased. In wet years, when many small seeds were available, smaller beaks became more common.

led to the peaks you see in the graph in figure 2.11. The reason they are peaks and not plateaus is that the average beak size decreased again when wet seasons returned because the larger beak size was no longer more favorable when seeds were plentiful and so smaller-beaked birds survived to reproduce.

Could these changes in beak dimension reflect the action of natural selection? An alternative possibility might be that the changes in beak depth do not reflect changes in gene frequencies but rather are simply a response to diet, with poorly fed birds having stouter beaks. To rule out this possibility, the Grants measured the relation of parent beak size to offspring beak size, examining many broods over several years. The depth of the beak was passed down faithfully from one generation to the next, suggesting the differences in beak size indeed reflected gene differences.

Support for Darwin

If the year-to-year changes in beak depth can be predicted by the pattern of dry years, then Darwin was right after all—natural selection influences beak size based on available food supply. In the study discussed here, birds with stout beaks have an advantage during dry periods, for they can break the large, dry seeds that are the only food available. When small seeds become plentiful once again with the return of wet weather, a smaller beak proves a more efficient tool for harvesting smaller seeds. Interestingly, 2003 and 2004 data showed a reverse trend toward smaller beaks during droughts, but the trend was still a response to natural selection; see the discussion of this study in the boxed reading *The Scientific Process: Character Displacement Among Darwin's Finches* in chapter 37.

2.4   In Darwin's finches, natural selection adjusts the shape of the beak in response to the nature of the food supply, adjustments that are occurring even today.

Evolution Repeats Itself in Caribbean Lizards

Darwin would have been puzzled at the average American's reluctance to accept his theory of evolution. The evidence supporting Darwin's theory is clear, and every year more supporting evidence accumulates.

There is a sticky point in Darwin's argument, however. If evolution is indeed guided by natural selection, as Darwin claims, then two environments that are similar should select in the same way—similar habitats should select for the same sorts of critters, all else being equal.

Is Darwin right? Do two communities of animals living in similar habitats evolve to be the same? Does evolution repeat itself at the community level?

This is not an easy question to answer, simply because it's difficult to find an array of similar but independent habitats to compare.

But not impossible. A team of researchers led by biology professor Jonathan Losos of Harvard University (an author of this text) has spent the last several years studying lizards of the genus *Anolis* (commonly called "anoles"), which live on large Caribbean islands. He has focused on Puerto Rico, Cuba, Haiti, and Jamaica. All four islands are inhabited by a diverse array of anole lizards (there are 57 species on Cuba alone), and all four islands have quite similar habitats and vegetation.

Unlike rats and cockroaches, which are generalists and much the same wherever you find them, anole lizards are specialists. In Puerto Rico, for example, one slender anole species with a long tail lives only in the grass. On narrow twigs at the base of trees you find a different species, also slender, but with stubby legs. On the higher branches of the tree a third species is found, of stocky build and long legs. High up in the leafy canopy of the tree lives a fourth giant green species.

Do the four Caribbean islands have similar lizard communities? Yes. If you go to Cuba, to Haiti, or to Jamaica, you can find on each island a species that looks nearly identical to each of the specialists on Puerto Rico, living in the same type of habitat and behaving in much the same manner.

Does this striking similarity of anole communities on the four islands indicate that the "Darwin experiment" has given the same result four times running?

The striking similarity of anole communities living on the four islands might be explained two different ways:

Hypothesis A Lizards migrated between the islands. A specialist anole like the one that lives in grass may have evolved only once, but then traveled to the other islands, perhaps on floating driftwood. If this is true, the similarity of communities is not the result of evolution repeating itself, but just a matter of specialists finding their way to the habitats they prefer.

Hypothesis B Lizards evolved in parallel on the four islands. The anole communities on the four islands may have evolved their similarity independently, evolution taking the same course again and again.

Working with Allan Larson of Washington University and Todd Jackman (now at Villanova University), Losos was able to choose between these two hypotheses by looking at the DNA of the lizards. The team compared several genes from more than 50 anole species. Points of similarity allowed them to construct a "phylogenetic tree," a family tree that showed who was related to who.

If hypothesis A is correct, then all the leaf specialists should be closely related to one another, whatever island they live on. The same would be expected for the four twig species, and also for the branch and canopy species.

On the other hand, if hypothesis B is correct, then a leaf specialist on one island should be more closely related to the other lizards on the same island, regardless of their specialty, than to a leaf specialist on another island.

Has evolution repeated itself? Yes. The DNA data are clear-cut: Specialist species on one island are not closely related to the same specialists elsewhere, and are closely related to other anoles inhabiting the same island. Hypothesis B is supported by the data. The four lizard communities evolved independently to be similar to one another.

The Losos research team has gone on to examine the functional consequences of Caribbean anole specializations, to see if natural selection can reasonably explain how each species has evolved. Why do some anole species have long legs, for example, while others have short stubby ones? These studies, involving both field and laboratory experiments, are science at its very best, insightful and fun. The rich picture of lizard evolution that is emerging would have delighted Darwin.

2.5 How Natural Selection Produces Diversity

Darwin believed that each Galápagos finch species had adapted to the particular foods and other conditions on the particular island it inhabited. Because the islands presented different opportunities, a cluster of species resulted. Presumably, the ancestor of Darwin's finches reached these newly formed islands before other land birds, so that when it arrived, all of the niches where birds occur on the mainland were unoccupied. A *niche* is what a biologist calls the way a species makes a living—the biological (that is, other organisms) and physical (climate, food, shelter, etc.) conditions with which an organism interacts as it attempts to survive and reproduce. As the new arrivals to the Galápagos moved into vacant niches and adopted new lifestyles, they were subjected to diverse sets of selective pressures. Under these circumstances, the ancestral finches rapidly split into a series of populations, some of which evolved into separate species.

The phenomenon by which a cluster of species change, as they occupy a series of different habitats within a region, is called *adaptive radiation*. Figure 2.12 shows how the 14 species of Darwin's finches on the Galápagos Islands and Cocos Island are thought to have evolved. The ancestral population, indicated by the base of the brackets, migrated to the islands about 2 million years ago and underwent adaptive radiation giving rise to the 14 different species. Such species clusters are often particularly impressive on island groups, in series of lakes, or in other sharply discontinuous habitats.

The descendants of the original finches that reached the Galápagos Islands now occupy many different kinds of habitats on the islands. The 14 species that inhabit the Galápagos Islands and Cocos Island occupy four types of niches:

1. **Ground finches.** There are six species of *Geospiza* ground finches. Most of the ground finches feed on seeds. The size of their beaks is related to the size of the seeds they eat. Some of the ground finches feed primarily on cactus flowers and fruits and have longer, larger, more pointed beaks.
2. **Tree finches.** There are five species of insect-eating tree finches. Four species have beaks that are suitable for feeding on insects. The woodpecker finch has a chisel-like beak. This unique bird carries around a twig or a cactus spine, which it uses to probe for insects in deep crevices.
3. **Vegetarian finch.** The very heavy beak of this bud-eating bird is used to wrench buds from branches.
4. **Warbler finches.** These unusual birds play the same ecological role in the Galápagos woods that warblers play on the mainland, searching continually over the leaves and branches for insects. They have a slender, warblerlike beak.

2.5 Darwin's finches, all derived from one similar mainland species, have radiated widely on the Galápagos Islands, filling unoccupied niches in a variety of ways.

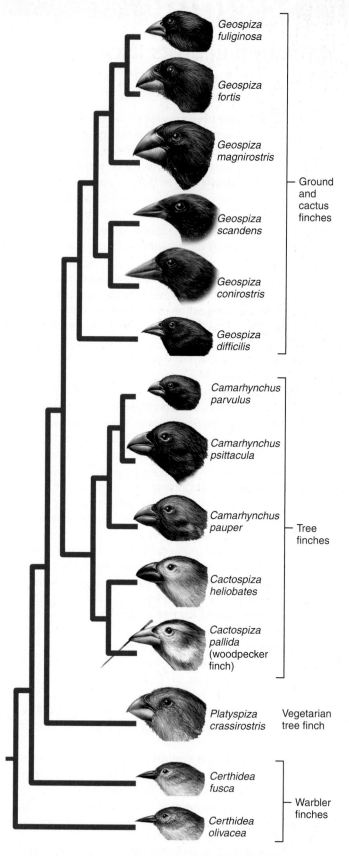

Figure 2.12 An evolutionary tree of Darwin's finches.

This family tree was constructed by comparing DNA of the 14 species. Their position at the base of the finch tree suggests that warbler finches were among the first adaptive types to evolve in the Galápagos.

2.6   What Is Ecology?

Darwin's finches teach us an important lesson about evolution, which is that understanding how natural selection occurs is really a matter of understanding how species adapt to particular niches. As we saw on the preceding pages, the diversity of finches Darwin found on the Galápagos Islands arose as a consequence of the availability of a variety of niches on the islands, each fostering the evolution of a new finch species. In a very real sense, the nature of the habitats the finches invaded, and the ways in which different populations of finches came to utilize these habitats, determined the course of the evolutionary radiation that followed. Biologists who study the nature of niches, and how the species that occupy them interact, are called *ecologists.*

The word **ecology** was coined in 1866 by the great German biologist Ernst Haeckel to describe the study of how organisms interact with each other and with their environment. It comes from the Greek words *oikos* (house, place where one lives) and *logos* (study of). Ecology also encompasses the study of the distribution and abundance of organisms, which includes population growth and the limits and influences on population growth. Our study of ecology, then, is a study of the house in which we live. Do not forget this simple analogy built into the word ecology—most of our environmental problems could be avoided if we treated the world in which we live the same way we treat our own homes. Would you pollute your own house?

Figure 2.13   A Galápagos Island ecosystem.
The Galápagos Islands are named after the giant tortoise, seen here climbing through the scrub vegetation of Isabela, the largest of the islands. Although this scene may at first glance seem barren, the island ecosystem is rich with plant and animal species. Sharing common resources, the giant tortoises, Darwin's finches, and other species possess many adaptations that promote their mutual survival.

Levels of Ecological Organization

Ecologists consider groups of organisms at six progressively more encompassing levels of organization. As mentioned in chapter 1, new characteristics called *emergent properties* arise at each higher level, resulting from the way components of each level interact.

1. **Populations.** Individuals of the same species that live together are members of a population. They potentially interbreed with one another, share the same habitat, and use the same pool of resources the habitat provides.
2. **Species.** All populations of a particular kind of organism form a species. Populations of the species can interact and affect the ecological characteristics of the species as a whole.
3. **Communities.** Populations of different species that live together in the same place are called communities. Different species typically use different resources within the habitat they share.
4. **Ecosystems.** A community and the nonliving factors with which it interacts is called an **ecosystem**. An ecosystem is affected by the flow of energy, ultimately derived from the sun, and the cycling of the essential elements on which the lives of its constituent organisms depend. The Galápagos Island pictured in figure 2.13 is an ecosystem, where the giant tortoise and other organisms interact with each other and with their biological and physical surroundings.
5. **Biomes.** Biomes are major terrestrial assemblages of plants, animals, and microorganisms that occur over wide geographical areas that have distinct physical characteristics. Examples include deserts, tropical forests, and grasslands. Similar groupings occur in marine and freshwater habitats.
6. **The biosphere.** All the world's biomes, along with its marine and freshwater assemblages, together constitute an interactive system we call the biosphere. Changes in one biome can have profound consequences for others.

Some ecologists, called *population ecologists,* focus on a particular species and how its populations grow. Other ecologists, called *community ecologists,* study how the different species living in a place interact with one another. Still other ecologists, called *systems ecologists,* are interested in how biological communities interact with their physical environment.

2.6   Ecology is the study of how the organisms that live in a place interact with each other and with their physical habitat.

A Closer Look at Ecosystems

In a sense, evolutionary biologists and ecologists study the same things from different perspectives. An evolutionary biologist focuses on the changes that occur in a species, while an ecologist focuses on how that species is interacting with other species and its physical environment. The one occurs as a result of the other.

Just as the population is the fundamental unit of evolution, so ecological systems, or ecosystems, are the fundamental units of ecology. An *ecosystem* is basically a biological community and the physical environment in which it lives. It is the most complex biological system that a biologist can study.

Energy Flows Through Ecosystems

All of the organisms within a community require energy to grow, reproduce, and carry out all of the many other activities of living. Almost all of this energy comes, ultimately, from the sun, captured through photosynthesis by organisms called *producers,* shown in the green box in figure 2.14. The plants, algae, and microbes that capture this energy are in turn consumed by plant-eating animals called *herbivores* (in the orange box), and some of the energy captured from sunlight is passed on to the herbivore. The herbivore may then be eaten by a meat-eating animal called a *carnivore* (in the blue box), which captures some of the energy of the herbivore. Energy thus flows through the ecosystem, from producer to herbivore to carnivore, a system called a **food chain.**

Unfortunately, much of the energy is used to drive the activities of life or lost as heat at each step of the food chain. Thus, because only so much energy is captured from the sun, food chains can be only so long—typically three or four steps. Can you see why there is no lion-eating top carnivore on the African savanna? It would need to consume so many lions to sustain itself that the available lions would be quickly depleted. Food chains and the loss of energy along the steps of a food chain will be discussed in greater detail in chapter 38.

Materials Cycle Within Ecosystems

The raw materials that make up organisms—the carbon, nitrogen, phosphorus, and other atoms—are not used up when the organisms die. Instead, as the organisms decompose, the materials of their bodies pass back into the ecosystem, where they can be used to make other organisms. The cycle you see in figure 2.15 shows how carbon cycles within the ecosystem: From carbon dioxide in the atmosphere (the blue box), to organisms (the green box) through photosynthesis, back into the atmosphere by respiration and into the soil through decomposition by bacteria and fungi (the brown box), finally making its way back to the atmosphere through diffusion and combustion of fossil fuels. As you can see, the carbon atoms become part of different substances and cycle between organisms and the physical environment. The carbon cycle is examined in more detail in chapter 38, in addition to the cycles of other materials, such as water.

Major Ecosystems

While many aspects of the environment act to limit the distribution of particular species, the two most important are rainfall and temperature. Particular organisms are adapted to particular combinations of rainfall and temperature, and every place with that combination of rainfall and temperature will tend to have organisms with similar adaptations living there. On land, these physical conditions with their similar sets of plants and animals are referred to as *biomes.* For example, a desert is a biome; no matter where on earth a desert appears, its plants and animals have similar adaptation to a dry, arid environment. Biomes will be discussed in detail in chapter 38.

> **2.7 An ecosystem is a dynamic ecological system that consumes energy and cycles materials.**

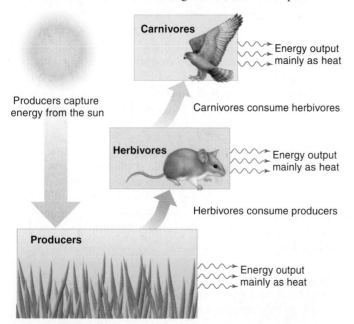

Figure 2.14 The flow of energy in an ecosystem.

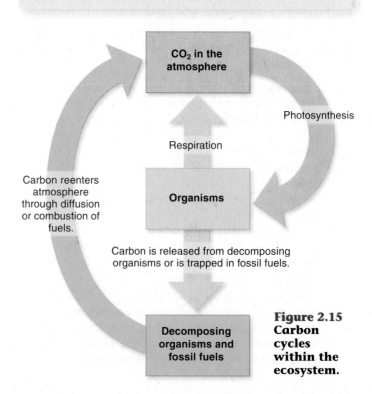

Figure 2.15 Carbon cycles within the ecosystem.

2.8 Communities

That part of an ecosystem that is living, all the animals and plants and other organisms that live together in an area, is called a **community.** The countless number of species that inhabit a rain forest or the sparse number of species that live in the boiling waters of a hot spring make up a community. Indeed, every inhabited place on earth supports its own particular array of organisms. Over time, the different species have made many complex adjustments to community living, evolving together and forging relationships that give the community character and stability. Both competition and cooperation have played key roles in molding these communities.

The magnificent redwood forest, shown in figure 2.16*a*, that extends along the coast of central and northern California and into the southwestern corner of Oregon is an example of a community. Within it, the most obvious organisms are the redwood trees, *Sequoia sempervirens.* These trees are the sole survivors of a genus that was once distributed throughout much of the Northern Hemisphere. A number of other plants, like the redwood sorrel flower shown in figure 2.16*b* and the sword fern in figure 2.16*c*, and animals, like the ground beetle feeding on a slug in figure 2.16*d*, are regularly associated with redwood trees. Their coexistence is in part made possible by the special conditions the redwood trees themselves create, providing shade, water (dripping from the branches), and relatively cool temperatures. This particular distinctive assemblage of organisms is called the redwood community. The organisms characteristic of this community have each had a complex and unique evolutionary history. They evolved at different times in the past and then came to be associated with the redwoods.

We recognize this community mainly because of the redwood trees, and its boundaries are determined by the redwood's distribution. The distributions of the other organisms in the redwood community may differ a good deal. Some organisms may not be distributed as widely as the redwoods, and some may be distributed over a broader range. In the redwood community or any other community, the ranges of the different organisms overlap; that is why they occur together.

Many communities are very similar in species composition and appearance over wide areas. For example, the open savanna that stretches across much of Africa includes many plant and animal species that coexist over thousands of square kilometers. Interactions between these organisms occur in a similar manner throughout these grassland communities, and some interactions have evolved over millions of years.

> **2.8** We recognize a community largely because of the presence of its dominant species, but many other kinds of organisms are also characteristic of each community. A community exists in a place because the ranges of its species overlap there.

Figure 2.16 The redwood community.

(*a*) The redwood forest of coastal California and southwestern Oregon is dominated by the redwoods (*Sequoia sempervirens*) themselves. Other organisms in the redwood community include (*b*) redwood sorrel (*Oxalis oregana*), (*c*) sword ferns (*Polystichum munitum*), and (*d*) ground beetles (*Scaphinotus velutinus*), this one feeding on a slug on a sword fern leaf. The ecological requirements of each of these organisms differ, but they overlap enough that the organisms occur together in the redwood community.

2.9 The Niche and Competition

The Niche Concept

Within a community, each organism occupies a particular biological role, or **niche.** The niche an organism occupies is the sum total of all the ways it uses the resources of its environment, including space, food, and many other factors of the environment. A niche is a pattern of living. The zebras you see in the African savanna community of figure 2.17 occupy a complex niche featuring open grassland and seasonal migration when food and water become scarce in dry seasons.

Sometimes organisms are not able to occupy their entire niche because some other organism is using it. We call such situations, when two organisms attempt to use the same resource, **competition**. Competition is the struggle of two organisms to use the same resource when there is not enough of the resource to satisfy both. However, just because two species occur in the same community and appear to use similar resources does not necessarily mean that they compete. Wildebeests also graze in the savanna alongside zebras, eating the same grass and drinking the same water, but for migrating herds these resources are not scarce. The lives of these two species differ in many other ways important to their survival so that they are not in competition.

Interspecific Competition

Interspecific competition refers to the interactions between individuals of different species when both require the same scarce resource. Interspecific competition is often greatest between organisms that obtain their food in similar ways; thus, green plants compete mainly with other green plants, herbivores with other herbivores, and carnivores with other carnivores. In general, competition is more acute between similar organisms than between those that are less similar. When you examine interspecific competition in detail in chapter 37, you will learn that interspecific competition can prevent a species from occupying all of its niche—what is possible becomes limited by the realities of sharing a community with other species using the same resources. The white-colored barnacles you see in figure 2.18 would have no trouble covering the entire surface of this ocean rock, but don't in fact do so, because the species of mussel competes with them for space, a very important limiting resource.

Intraspecific Competition

It is important to distinguish interspecific competition, which occurs between members of different species, from **intraspecific competition,** which occurs between individuals of a single species. The two seedlings in figure 2.19 are competing for the same resource, sunlight. The taller one, by growing faster, may ultimately shade out the shorter one.

Figure 2.17   The zebras fill a niche in this African savanna community.

Figure 2.18   Animals of two different species, barnacles (*white*) and mussels (*blue*), compete for limited space.

Figure 2.19 Two germinating seedlings, possibly siblings, compete with each other for resources.

2.9   A niche is the way in which an organism uses its environment. Two species sometimes compete for the same limiting resource and sometimes the competition is between two individuals of the same species.

Figure 2.20 Resource partitioning among lizard species.
Species of *Anolis* lizards in the Caribbean partition their tree habitats in a variety of ways. Some species of anoles occupy the canopy of trees (*a*), others use twigs on the periphery (*b*), and still others are found at the base of the trunk (*c*). In addition, some use grassy areas in the open (*d*). This same pattern of resource partitioning has evolved independently on different Caribbean islands.

2.10 How Species Evolve to Occupy Different Niches Within an Ecosystem

Each organism in an ecosystem confronts the challenge of survival in a different way. As we have just discussed, the niche an organism occupies is the sum total of all the ways it uses the resources of its environment, and may be described in terms of space utilization, food consumption, temperature range, appropriate conditions for mating, requirements for moisture, and other factors. *Niche* is not synonymous with **habitat,** the place where an organism lives. *Habitat* is a place, and *niche* is a pattern of living. Many species can share a habitat, but as we shall see, no two species can long occupy exactly the same niche.

Resource Partitioning

Competition is the struggle of two organisms to use the same resource when there is not enough of the resource to satisfy both. When two species compete for the same resource, the species that utilizes the resource more efficiently will eventually outcompete the other in that location and drive it to extinction there. Ecologists call this *the principle of competitive exclusion:* No two species with the same niche can coexist. Persistent competition between two species is rare in nature. Either one species drives the other to extinction, or natural selection favors changes that reduce the competition between them. In resource partitioning, species that live in the same geographical area avoid competition by living in different portions of the habitat or by using different food or other resources. A clear example of this is the *Anolis* lizards you see in figure 2.20. The rather exotic blue species in the upper left of the figure lives high in the tree, where it doesn't need to compete for food and space with the dark brown species in the upper right that lives on the tree's trunk.

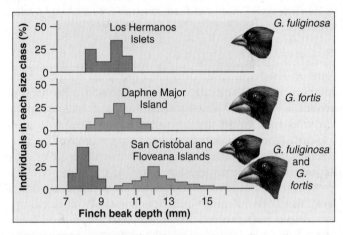

Figure 2.21 Character displacement.
These two species of Galápagos finches (genus *Geospiza*) have beaks of similar sizes when living apart, but different sizes when living together.

The changes that evolve in two species to reduce niche overlap—that is, to lessen the degree to which they compete for the same resources—are called **character displacements.** Character displacement can be seen clearly among Darwin's finches. The two Galápagos finches in figure 2.21 have beaks of similar size when each is living on an island where the other does not occur. On islands where they are found living together, the two species have evolved beaks of different sizes, one adapted to larger seeds, the other to smaller ones. In essence, the two finches have subdivided the food niche, creating two new smaller niches. By partitioning the available food resources, the two species have avoided direct competition with each other, and so are able to live together in the same habitat.

> **2.10 Species that live together partition available resources, reducing competition between them.**

Predation

Species that live together in a community interact in many ways, one of which is to eat one another. **Predation** is the consuming of one organism by another. The organism doing the eating is called the *predator*, while the organism being eaten is the *prey*. Predation includes everything from a leopard capturing and eating an antelope, a whale grazing on millions of microscopic ocean plankton, to locusts eating the leaves of plants.

Predator/Prey Cycles

Why doesn't a predator simply exterminate its prey, and then become extinct itself, having nothing left to eat. This is just what happens in laboratory experiments. However, if refuges are provided for the prey, its population drops to low levels but not to extinction. Low prey population levels then provide inadequate food for the predators, causing the predator population to decrease. When this occurs, the prey population can recover. In this way, predator and prey populations cycle in their abundance. Many small mammals like the lemming in figure 2.22 undergo population cycles. Some of them are true predator-prey cycles, while others are the result of cyclic climatic factors.

Defense Mechanisms

Animals defend themselves against predators with chemical defenses, warning coloration, and camouflage. The green frog you see in figure 2.23 is a poison dart frog from Latin America. The mucus that covers its skin contains a very toxic poison—a few micrograms will kill a person, a very effective chemical defense. Its bright green color is another defense, advertising its toxicity and so warning any potential predator not to attempt eating it. How does a predator know not to eat bright green frogs? By learning. One attempt is rarely repeated.

Plants have evolved many mechanisms to defend themselves from their predators, called herbivores. The most obvious are thorns, spines, and prickles. Chemical defenses are even more crucial, and are widespread in plants. Mustard oils, which give the sharp pungent taste to mustard, capers, cabbage, and horseradish, are toxic to many groups of insects.

Coevolution

Sometimes, predators and prey undergo long-term reciprocal evolutionary adjustments, a process termed **coevolution**. For example, some plants, like the mustard plant, produce oils that are toxic to many caterpillars. The cabbage butterfly caterpillar has evolved the ability to break down mustard oils and can feed on these plants. Like having the only key to a grocery store, the cabbage butterfly in figure 2.24 is able to use a new resource without competing with other herbivores for it. Responding with another evolutionary adjustment, the butterfly sense organs have evolved to detect mustard oils.

> **2.11** Members of a community often consume one another. As a result, prey species often evolve defensive adaptations.

Figure 2.22 Lemmings are rodents, eaten by predatory mammals and birds.

The populations of lemmings and their predators decrease and increase in a cyclic manner as both populations are affected by the population sizes of each other.

Figure 2.23 Warning coloration serves as a defense mechanism in Dendrobatidae.

The skin coloration of this poison dart frog warns potential predators of the toxic mucus covering the skin, and predators keep their distance.

Figure 2.24 Coevolution between mustard plant and white cabbage butterfly (Pieris rapae).

The mustard plant evolved a defense mechanism of toxic oils that deter predators. The caterpillar of this white cabbage butterfly coevolved a mechanism to break down the mustard oil, allowing it to feed on the plants.

2.12 Symbiosis

Not all interactions among the organisms of a community involve winners and losers, as both competition and predation do. Other relationships are more cooperative. **Symbiosis** is an interaction in which two or more kinds of organisms interact in cooperative, more-or-less permanent relationships. The major kinds of symbiotic relationships include (1) **commensalism,** in which one species benefits from the relationship while the other neither benefits nor is harmed; (2) **mutualism,** in which both participating species benefit; and (3) **parasitism,** in which one species benefits but the other is harmed.

Commensalism

Commensalism is a symbiotic relationship that benefits one species and neither hurts nor helps the other. The birds you see in figure 2.25 are oxpeckers, busily pecking ticks and other insects off of an impala for their dinner. In this symbiotic relationship, the oxpeckers receive a clear benefit in the form of nutrition. If the removal of the ticks benefits the impala, then the relationship is mutually beneficial and the relationship would be considered a form of mutualism. However, there is no evidence that this is so. In this instance, as in most examples of commensalism, it is difficult to be certain whether the partner receives a benefit or not.

Mutualism

Mutualism is a symbiotic relationship in which both species benefit. The pistol shrimp patrolling the surface of the coral in figure 2.26 is defending its homestead from sea stars, which prey on coral. When it encounters a sea star on the coral, the shrimp attacks, pinching the sea star's spines and tube feet and making loud snapping sounds with its enlarged pincers. The loud popping sounds, which have given the shrimp its name, are so intense they stun small fish. Protection from being eaten by sea stars certainly provides a benefit to the coral. The shrimp also clearly benefit, obtaining food and shelter from the coral. Because both parties benefit, their relationship is an example of mutualism.

Parasitism

Parasitism is a symbiotic relationship which benefits one species at the expense of the other. Typically the parasite is much smaller than its host, and remains closely associated with it. Parasitism is sometimes considered a special kind of predator-prey relationship in which the predator is much smaller than the prey, but unlike a predator the parasite typically does not kill its host. Parasites are very common among animals. The head louse you see in figure 2.27, for example, is one of two sucking lice that parasitize humans. Eggs like the one you see in the photograph are cemented to hair follicles.

2.12 In symbiosis, two species interact closely, with at least one species benefiting.

Figure 2.25 The oxpeckers and impala relationship is an example of commensalism.

Figure 2.26 The pistol shrimp defends the coral, which he calls home—an example of mutualism.

Figure 2.27 The head louse, shown here with its egg, feeds on its host and is an example of parasitism.

Does the Presence of One Species Limit the Population Size of Others?

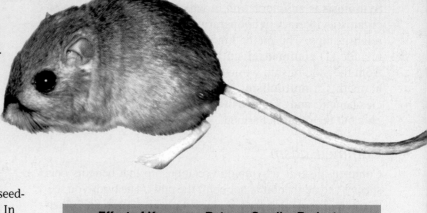

Implicit in Darwin's theory of evolution is the idea that species in nature compete for limiting resources. Does this really happen? Some of the best evidence of competition between species comes from experimental field studies, studies conducted not in the laboratory but out in natural populations. By setting up experiments in which two species occur either alone or together, scientists can determine whether the presence of one species has a negative impact on the size of the population of the other species. This experiment concerns a variety of seed-eating rodents that occur in North American deserts. In 1988, researchers set up a series of 50-meter × 50-meter enclosures to investigate the effect of kangaroo rats on smaller seed-eating rodents. Kangaroo rats were removed from half of the enclosures, but not from the other enclosures. The walls of all the enclosures had holes that allowed rodents to come and go, but in plots without kangaroo rats the holes were too small to allow the kangaroo rats to enter.

The graph to the right displays data collected over the course of the next three years as researchers monitored the number of the smaller rodents present in the enclosures. To estimate the population sizes, researchers determined how many small rodents could be captured in a fixed interval. Data were collected for each enclosure immediately after the kangaroo rats were removed in 1988, and at three-month intervals thereafter. The graph presents the relative population size—that is, the total number of captures averaged over the number of enclosures (an **average** is the numerical mean value, calculated by adding a list of values and then dividing this sum by the number of items in the list. For example, if a total of 30 rats were captured from 3 enclosures, the average would be 10 rats). As you can see, the two kinds of enclosures do not contain the same number of small rodents.

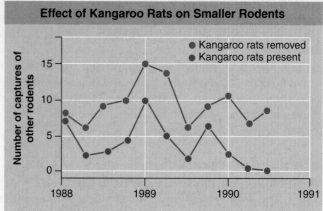

Effect of Kangaroo Rats on Smaller Rodents

- ● Kangaroo rats removed
- ● Kangaroo rats present

y-axis: Number of captures of other rodents (0, 5, 10, 15)
x-axis: 1988, 1989, 1990, 1991

1. **Applying Concepts**
   a. Variable. In the graph, what is the dependent variable?
   b. Relative Magnitude. Which of the two kinds of enclosures maintains the highest population of small rodents? Does it have kangaroo rats or have they been removed?
2. **Interpreting Data**
   a. What is the average number of small rodents in each of the two plots immediately after kangaroo rats were removed? after one year? after two?
   b. At what point is the difference between the two kinds of enclosures the greatest?
3. **Making Inferences**
   a. What precisely is the observed impact of kangaroo rats on the population size of small rodents?
   b. Examine the magnitude of the difference between the number of small rodents in the two plots. Is there a trend?
4. **Drawing Conclusions**
   Do these results support the hypothesis that kangaroo rats compete with other small rodents to limit their population sizes?
5. **Further Analysis**
   a. Can you think of any cause other than competition that would explain these results? Suggest an experiment that could potentially eliminate or confirm this alternative.
   b. Do the populations of the two kinds of enclosures change in synchrony (that is, grow and shrink at the same times) over the course of a year? If so, why might this happen? How would you test this hypothesis?

Evolution

2.1 Darwin's Voyage on the HMS *Beagle*

* Darwin's voyage on the HMS *Beagle* allowed him the opportunity to study a large variety of animal and plant species across the globe. Years after his voyage, he published the book *On the Origin of Species,* in which he proposed natural selection as the mechanism that underlies the process of evolution.

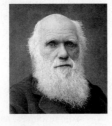

* The theory of evolution through natural selection is overwhelmingly accepted by scientists and is considered to be the backbone of the science of biology, but is viewed as controversial by some in the general public.

2.2 Darwin's Evidence

* Darwin observed fossils in South America of extinct species that resembled living species (**figure 2.4**). On the Galápagos Islands, Darwin observed finches that differed slightly in appearance between islands but resembled finches found on the South American mainland. These observations laid the groundwork for his proposal of evolution through natural selection (**figure 2.5**).

2.3 The Theory of Natural Selection

* Key to Darwin's hypothesis of evolution by natural selection was the observation by Malthus that the food supply limits population growth. A population, be it plants, animals, etc., has the potential to produce many offspring, but grows only as large as that which can live off of the available food which limits geometric growth of a population (**figure 2.6**).

* Using Malthus's observations and his own observations, Darwin proposed that individuals that are better suited to their environments survive to produce offspring, gaining the opportunity to pass their characteristics on to future generations, what Darwin called natural selection. As a result, future generations may be different from ancestral populations. Spurred by a similar proposal put forth years later by Alfred Wallace, Darwin published his book in 1859.

Darwin's Finches: Evolution in Action

2.4 The Beaks of Darwin's Finches

* By observing the different sizes and shapes of beaks in the closely related finches of the Galápagos Islands (**figure 2.9**), and correlating the beaks with the types of food consumed, Darwin concluded that the birds' beaks were modified from an ancestral species based on the food available, each suited to its food supply. Scientists have identified a gene, *BMP4,* that is expressed differently in birds with different shaped beaks.

* Research has since supported Darwin's hypothesis that natural selection influences beak size in island finches based on the available food supply (**figure 2.11**).

2.5 How Natural Selection Produces Diversity

* The 14 species of finches found on the islands off the coast of South America descended from a mainland species that adapted to different niches, a process called adaptive radiation (**figure 2.12**).

Ecology

2.6 What Is Ecology?

* Ecology is the study of how organisms, like this tortoise from **figure 2.13**, interact with each other and with their physical environment. There are six levels of ecological organization: populations, species, communities, ecosystems, biomes, and the biosphere.

2.7 A Closer Look at Ecosystems

* An ecosystem is a physical environment and the community of various organisms that live there. These organisms interact with each other and with their physical environment, extracting energy and raw materials from it (**figures 2.14** and **2.15**). Ecosystems found throughout the world that contain similar physical conditions and organisms are called biomes.

2.8 Communities

* The array of organisms that live together in an area is called a community. Different species in a community compete and cooperate with each other to make the community stable. Communities are often identified by the dominant species (**figure 2.16**).

2.9 The Niche and Competition

* A habitat is the place where an organism lives and its niche is the way it uses resources such as food and space. Limited resources lead to competition between organisms of different species, called interspecific competition, and between organisms of the same species, called intraspecific competition (**figures 2.17 — 2.19**).

2.10 How Species Evolve to Occupy Different Niches Within an Ecosystem

* Resource partitioning is the process whereby two competitive species coexist by utilizing different portions of the habitat or different resources such as food (**figure 2.20**). Physical changes, called character displacements, are adaptations in response to competition. The varying beak sizes seen in Darwin's finches, like the ones shown here from **figure 2.21**, suggest that the bird species evolved in part due to resource partitioning.

2.11 Predation

* Interactions where one organism consumes another is called predatory/prey relationships. The hunted is called the prey and the hunter is the predator. The population sizes of predator and prey often oscillate in response to each other (**figure 2.22**).

* Species of prey may evolved defense mechanisms to protect themselves and this in turn can lead to coevolution in the characteristics of the predator species (**figures 2.23** and **2.24**).

2.12 Symbiosis

* In symbiosis, two or more species live together in closely linked relationships. Commensalism is where one organism benefits and the other neither benefits nor is harmed (**figure 2.25**). Mutualism involves cooperation between species where they both benefit (**figure 2.26**). In parasitism, one organism serves as a host to another parasitic organism such that the host is harmed and the parasite benefits (**figure 2.27**).

1. The theory of evolution states that
   a. once a species is formed, it remains stable over time, and populations do not change.
   b. populations always change over time, forming new species.
   c. populations can change over time, sometimes forming new species.
   d. populations that change over time usually go extinct, such as the dinosaurs.

2. A key observation made by Darwin was
   a. a species always looked almost exactly the same wherever he saw it; traits were preserved.
   b. the characteristics of a species varied in different places; there were geographic patterns.
   c. the characteristics of a species varied in different places; it was unpredictable.
   d. everywhere he went there were wildly different and unrelated organisms.

3. Darwin was greatly influenced by Thomas Malthus, who pointed out that
   a. populations increase geometrically.
   b. populations increase arithmetically.
   c. populations are capable of geometric increase, yet remain at constant levels.
   d. the food supply usually increases faster than the population that depends on it.

4. Darwin proposed that individuals with traits that help them live in their immediate environment are more likely to survive and reproduce than individuals without those traits. He called this
   a. natural selection.
   b. the principle of population growth.
   c. the theory of evolution.
   d. Malthusian growth.

5. A great deal of research has been done on Darwin's finches over the last 70 years. The research
   a. seems to often contradict Darwin's original ideas.
   b. seems to agree with Darwin's original ideas.
   c. does not show any clear patterns that support or refute Darwin's original ideas.
   d. sometimes supports his ideas and sometimes does not.

6. The way a species makes its living—that is, the biological and physical conditions in which it exists—is called its
   a. population.   c. community.
   b. territory.   d. niche.

7. In the levels of ecological organization, the lowest level, composed of individuals of a single species who live near each other, share the same resources, and can potentially interbreed is called a (an)
   a. population.   c. ecosystem.
   b. community.   d. biome.

8. Within an ecosystem
   a. materials flow through once and are lost, while energy cycles and recycles.
   b. materials and energy both flow through once and are lost.
   c. materials and energy both cycle and recycle.
   d. energy flows through once and is lost, while materials cycle and recycle.

9. A major principle of ecology states that no two species can occupy exactly the same niche. One will utilize resources more efficiently than the other and will drive the second species to extinction. This is the principle of
   a. competition.
   b. natural selection.
   c. community organization.
   d. competitive exclusion.

10. The following are examples of symbiosis except
    a. mutualism.
    b. predation.
    c. parasitism.
    d. commensalism.

1. **Figure 2.15** Carbon cycles through the ecosystem among the atmosphere, organisms (such as producers, herbivores, and carnivores), and decomposers. This natural cycle maintains a somewhat constant level of carbon in the atmosphere. The burning of fossil fuels releases carbon into the cycle that has been trapped inside the earth. How does this affect the cycle and what problems can this cause?

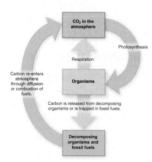

2. **Figure 2.20** Using Darwin's reasoning, explain how these four species of lizards, all closely related, came to be separate species on a Caribbean island.

1. The evolutionary pathways of some groups of related organisms seem to have moved from larger to smaller organisms over time, such as the glyptodont to the armadillo, the mammoth to the elephant. Yet other groups of related organisms have exhibited a trend of increased sizes of species over time, such as the tiny eohippus to the horse. Explain how this can occur.

2. *Chthamalus* is a small barnacle that lives on rocky shores. It can survive on rocks that are underwater, or on rocks that are exposed during low tide. *Balanus* is a larger barnacle that can outcompete *Chthamalus* if they both want the same spot. *Balanus* can only live on rocks that are seldom exposed to air. Explain what could happen when they are both present.

17
Evolution and Natural Selection

This photograph shows color variants of the peppered moth, *Biston betularia,* glued to the trunk of a soot-polluted tree. Historically, the dark form of the moth was rare, but with the onset of the Industrial Revolution the dark "melanic" forms became more common. To test the hypothesis that natural selection was favoring the dark form because of industrial pollution, biologists released equal numbers of the two variants in both polluted and nonpolluted areas. In polluted areas, twice as many dark individuals survived as light ones; in unpolluted areas, the reverse occurred, with more light-colored individuals surviving. This experiment clearly demonstrated that natural selection was favoring the dark form in polluted environments. How? The most likely hypothesis was that birds were eating the moths, selecting more often those that were most visible on tree trunks. As you can see in the photo, white moths are more visible on polluted tree trunks. As a test, moths were glued to dark tree trunks to see which the birds would eat. As you might expect, they ate the most visible ones. So is camouflage the reason natural selection favored the dark moths? Probably not. Further work showed these moths don't spend their days on tree trunks. Some other effect of the pollution seems to be at work. This peppered moth story has long been held to be a classic example of evolution in action, mentioned in all texts. The evidence for natural selection is exceptionally clear, and the recent reevaluation removing predation as a potential agent of selection in this case provides an excellent example of how science works, its conclusions always subject to revision as we learn more. However, a decade ago, critics of teaching evolution in the classroom began to criticize the teaching of the peppered moth story, suggesting its investigators cheated by gluing moths to trees. Although the evidence for natural selection is very strong and does not in any way depend on these studies, the spotted moth story has disappeared from most texts. In this chapter, we will look closely at the action of natural selection, at the evidence for evolution, and at the controversy surrounding its presentation in the nation's classrooms.

17.1 Evolution: Getting from There to Here

Since the publication of *On The Origin of Species* by Charles Darwin in 1859, the idea of evolution by natural selection has played a central role in the science of biology. Although the modern concept of biological evolution has been developed considerably since Darwin, his phrase "descent with modification" still captures the essence of his proposal.

Darwin's general concept of evolution was introduced in chapter 2, but it is important—before launching into a detailed discussion of evolution and natural selection—that we first review Darwin's proposal of how natural selection, the process that leads to evolution, works. The process of natural selection can be conveniently visualized as occurring in a series of steps:

1. There is gene variation among individuals of a population.
2. This variation is often passed on to offspring, so that offspring have a tendency to have traits more like their parents than like other members of the population.
3. All populations overproduce young—only some of the offspring will survive to reproduce.
4. The likelihood that a particular individual will survive and reproduce is not random. The traits it inherits make it more or less likely that it will be able to respond to environmental challenges and survive to reproduce.
5. Those individuals with traits that aid in responding to the environment, so that they are able to reproduce, will have a better chance of adding individuals to the next generation.
6. Over time, the population changes such that the traits of the more successful reproducers become more prevalent in the population.

Microevolution Leads to Macroevolution

When the word *evolution* is mentioned, it is difficult not to conjure up images of dinosaurs roaming the earth, woolly mammoths frozen in blocks of ice, or Darwin observing a monkey. Traces of ancient life-forms, now extinct, survive as fossils that help us piece together the evolutionary story. With such a background, we usually think of evolution in terms of changes that take place over long periods of time, changes in the kinds of animals and plants on earth as new forms arise from existing ones. This kind of evolution, called **macroevolution,** is evolutionary change on a grand scale. Macroevolution is larger, more complex changes that result in the creation of new species and higher taxonomic groups.

Much of the focus of Darwin's theory of natural selection, however, is directed not at the way in which new species form, but rather at the way that changes occur *within* a species to make that species different from its immediate ancestor. Natural selection is the process whereby some individuals in a population, those that possess certain inherited characteristics or *adaptations,* produce more surviving off-

The long, curved beak of this honeycreeper is an adaptation that allows the bird to reach nectar deep inside long, slender flowers.

spring than individuals lacking these characteristics. As a result, the population will gradually come to include more and more individuals with the advantageous characteristics—in other words, adaptation is the outcome of natural selection, and in this way the population evolves. Changes of this sort within populations are called **microevolution.** In essence, Darwin's explanation of evolution is that adaptation by natural selection is responsible for evolutionary changes *within* a species (microevolution), and that the accumulation of these changes results in the development of new species and higher taxonomic groups (macroevolution).

The Key Is the Source of the Variation

Darwin did not invent the idea of evolution. Rather, he agreed with many earlier philosophers and naturalists who deduced that the many kinds of organisms around us were produced by a process of evolution (see chapter 2, pages 26–28). The question that had not been answered was *how* organisms evolved. What mechanism caused it?

Until Darwin, there was no consensus among biologists about the mechanism causing evolution among the earth's organisms. An idea championed by a predecessor of Darwin, the prominent biologist Jean-Baptiste Lamarck, was that evolution occurred by the inheritance of acquired characteristics. According to Lamarck, individuals passed on to offspring body and behavior changes acquired during their lives. Figure 17.1a illustrates Lamarck's theory. Lamarck proposed that ancestral giraffes with short necks (the left-hand side of the figure) tended to stretch their necks to feed on tree leaves, and this extension of the neck was passed on to subsequent generations, leading to the long-necked giraffe.

In Darwin's theory, by contrast, the variation is not created by experience but already exists when selection acts on it, an idea illustrated in figure 17.1b. Populations of ancestral giraffes contained variation—you can see individuals on the left-hand side of the figure with longer necks. Able to feed higher up on the trees, these individuals had more food and so were better able to survive and reproduce than their shorter-necked relatives. When these longer-necked animals did reproduce, they passed their long-neck trait on to their offspring. Over time, the long-neck trait became more prevalent in the population, resulting in a change in the physical characteristics of the species—evolution. Rather than individuals acquiring characteristics during their lifetimes, Darwin proposed natural selection over generations as the mechanism.

It is important to remember that natural selection can only act on the variation already present in a population. New gene variations are constantly being introduced into populations through random mutations. Of course, for the variation to be passed on to offspring, the mutation must occur in the germ cells. Mutations that only affect somatic cells (for example, mutations in lung cells that result from tobacco use and lead to lung cancer) cannot be passed on to offspring.

The Rate of Evolution

For more than a century after the publication of *On the Origin of Species* in 1859, the standard view was that evolutionary change occurred extremely slowly. Such change would be nearly imperceptible from generation to generation, but would accumulate such that, over the course of millions of years, major changes could occur. This view is termed *gradualism*.

An alternative view, presented in 1972 by Niles Eldredge and Stephen Jay Gould, is that species experience long periods of little or no evolutionary change (termed *stasis*), punctuated by bursts of evolutionary change occurring over geologically short time intervals. This view, termed *punctuated equilibrium,* is contrasted with gradualism in figure 17.2. In some species, evolution appears to proceed in the spurts you see on the left in figure 17.2*a*. In times of environmental upheaval, evolutionary innovations give rise to new lines (the branch points in the figure); these lines then persist unchanged for a long time (the vertical bars), in "equilibrium," until a new spurt of evolution creates a "punctuation" in the fossil record. Some marine organisms seem to show the irregular pattern of evolutionary change the punctuated equilibrium model predicts. On the other hand, some other well-documented groups such as African mammals clearly have evolved gradually, and not in spurts, more like the pattern you see on the right in figure 17.2*b*. It appears, in fact, that gradualism and punctuated equilibrium are two ends of a continuum. Although some groups appear to have evolved solely in a gradual manner and others only in a punctuated mode, many other groups, such as planktonic protists, show evidence of both gradual and punctuated episodes at different times in their evolutionary history.

17.1 Darwin proposed that natural selection on variants within populations leads to evolution. Viewed over long time periods, some groups evolve at a uniform rate, others in fits and starts.

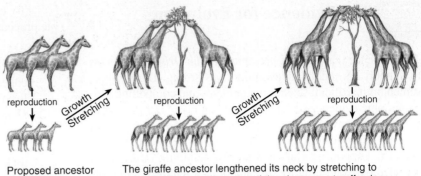

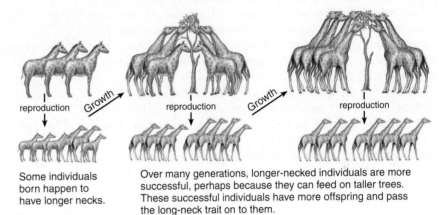

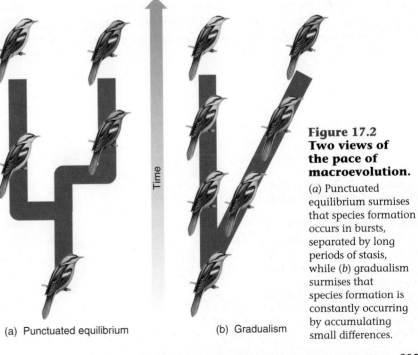

(a) Lamarck's theory: variation is acquired.

Proposed ancestor of giraffes has characteristics of modern-day okapi.

The giraffe ancestor lengthened its neck by stretching to reach tree leaves, then passed the change on to offspring.

(b) Darwin's theory: variation is inherited.

Some individuals born happen to have longer necks.

Over many generations, longer-necked individuals are more successful, perhaps because they can feed on taller trees. These successful individuals have more offspring and pass the long-neck trait on to them.

Figure 17.1 How did long necks evolve in giraffes?

(*a*) Lamarck proposed that the trait for a longer neck was acquired and then passed on to offspring. (*b*) Darwin proposed that there existed some variation in the length of the neck in the population, and over time longer necks became more prevalent in the population.

Figure 17.2 Two views of the pace of macroevolution.

(*a*) Punctuated equilibrium surmises that species formation occurs in bursts, separated by long periods of stasis, while (*b*) gradualism surmises that species formation is constantly occurring by accumulating small differences.

(a) Punctuated equilibrium   (b) Gradualism

Time

The Evidence for Evolution

The evidence that Darwin presented in *The Origin of Species* to support his theory of evolution was strong. Darwin presented both artificial selection arguments and compelling biogeographic evidence he had collected on his round-the-world voyage. You have already reviewed some of this evidence in chapter 2, section 2.2. We will now examine other lines of evidence supporting Darwin's theory, including information revealed by examining fossils, anatomical features, and molecules such as DNA and proteins.

The Fossil Record

The most direct evidence of macroevolution is found in the fossil record. **Fossils** are the preserved remains, tracks, or traces of once-living organisms. Fossils are created when organisms become buried in sediment. The calcium in bone or other hard tissue mineralizes, and the surrounding sediment eventually hardens to form rock. Most fossils are, in effect, skeletons. In the rare cases when fossils form in very fine sediment, feathers may also be preserved. When remains are frozen or become suspended in amber (fossilized plant resin), however, the entire body may be preserved. The fossils contained in layers of sedimentary rock reveal a history of life on earth.

By dating the rocks in which fossils occur, we can get an accurate idea of how old the fossils are. Rocks are dated by measuring the degree of decay of certain radioisotopes contained in the rock, a procedure you encountered in chapter 3.

Using Fossils to Test the Theory of Evolution

If the theory of evolution is correct, then the fossils we see preserved in rock should represent a history of evolutionary change. The theory makes the clear prediction that a parade of successive changes should be seen, as first one change occurs and then another. If the theory of evolution is not correct, on the other hand, then such orderly change is not expected.

To test this prediction, biologists follow a very simple procedure:

1. *Assemble a collection of fossils of a particular group of organisms.* You might for example gather together a collection of fossil titanotheres, a hoofed mammal that lived between about 50 million and 35 million years ago.
2. *Date each of the fossils.* In dating the fossils, it is important to make no reference to what the fossil is like. Imagine it as being concealed in a black box of rock, with only the box being dated.
3. *Order the fossils by their age.* Without looking in the "black boxes," place them in a series, beginning with the oldest and proceeding to the youngest.
4. *Now examine the fossils.* Do the differences between the fossils appear jumbled, or is there evidence of successive change as evolution predicts? You can judge for yourself in figure 17.3. During the 15 million years spanned by this collection of titanothere fossils, the small, bony protuberance located above the nose 50 million years ago evolved in a series of continuous changes into relatively large blunt horns.

The Fossil Record Confirms Evolution's Key Prediction

It is important not to miss the key point of the result you see illustrated in figure 17.3: Evolution is an observation, not a conclusion. Because the dating of the samples is independent of what the samples are like, *successive change through time is a data statement.* While the statement that evolution is the result of natural selection is a theory advanced by Darwin, the statement that macroevolution has occurred is a factual observation.

Many other examples illustrate this clear confirmation of the key prediction of Darwin's theory. The evolution of today's large, single-hoof horse with complex molar teeth from a much smaller four-toed ancestor with much simpler molar teeth is a familiar and clearly documented instance.

Fossils have been found linking all the major vertebrate groups. The forms linking mammals to reptiles are particularly well known. New fossils more completely revealing our evolution from primate ancestors are found practically every year.

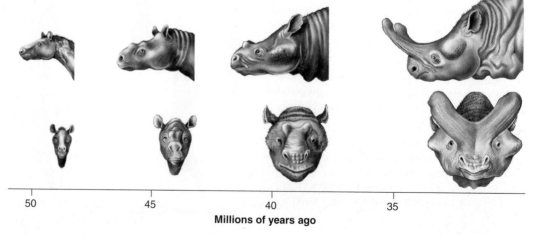

Figure 17.3 Testing the theory of evolution with fossil titanotheres.
Here you see illustrated changes in a group of hoofed mammals known as titanotheres between about 50 million and 35 million years ago. During this time, the small, bony protuberance located above the nose 50 million years ago evolved into relatively large, blunt horns.

50   45   40   35
Millions of years ago

Today's *Biology*

Darwin and Moby Dick

Moby Dick, the white whale hunted by Captain Ahab in Melville's novel, was a sperm whale. One of the ocean's great predators, a large sperm whale is a voracious meat-eater that may span over 60 feet and weigh 50 tons. A sperm whale is not a fish, though. Unlike the great white shark in *Jaws*, a whale has hairs (not many), and a female whale has milk-producing mammary glands with which it feeds its young. A sperm whale is a mammal, just as you are! This raises an interesting question. If Darwin is right about the fossil record reflecting life's evolutionary past, then fossils tell us mammals evolved from reptiles on land at about the time of the dinosaurs. How did they end up back in the water?

The evolutionary history of whales has long fascinated biologists, but only in recent years have fossils been discovered that reveal the answer to this intriguing question. A series of discoveries now allows biologists to trace the evolutionary history of the most colossal animals ever to live on earth back to their beginnings at the dawn of the Age of Mammals. Whales, it turns out, are the descendants of four-legged land mammals that reinvaded the sea some 50 million years ago, much as seals and walruses are doing today. It's pretty startling to realize that Moby Dick's evolutionary ancestor lived on the steppes of Asia and looked like a modest-sized pig a few feet long and weighing perhaps 50 pounds, with four toes on each foot.

From what land mammal did whales arise? Researchers had long speculated that it might be a hoofed meat-eater with three toes known as a mesonychid, related to rhinoceroses. Subtle clues suggested this—the arrangement of ridges on the molar teeth, the positioning of the ear bones in the skull. But findings announced in 2001 reveal these subtle clues to have been misleading. Ankle bones from two newly described 50 million-year-old whale species discovered by Philip Gingerich of the University of Michigan are those of an artiodactyl, a four-toed mammal related to hippos, cattle, and pigs. Even more recently, Japanese researchers studying DNA have discovered unique genetic markers shared today only by whales and hippos.

Biologists now conclude that whales, like hippos, are descended from a group of early four-hoofed mammals called anthracotheres, modest-sized grazing animals with a piggish appearance abundant in Europe and Asia 50 million years ago.

In Pakistan in 1994, biologists discovered its descendant, the oldest known whale. The fossil was 49 million years old, had four legs, each with four-toed feet and a little hoof at the tip of each toe. Dubbed *Ambulocetus* (walking whale), it was sharp-toothed and about the size of a large sea lion. Analysis of the minerals in its teeth reveal it drank fresh water, so like a seal it was not yet completely a marine animal. Its nostrils were on the end of the snout, like a dog's.

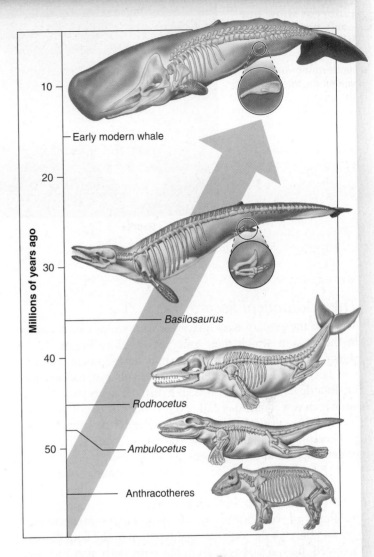

Appearing in the fossil record a few million years later is *Rodhocetus,* also seal-like but with smaller hind limbs and the teeth of an ocean water drinker. Its nostrils are shifted higher on the skull, halfway towards the top of the head.

Almost 10 million years later, about 37 million years ago, we see the first representatives of *Basilosaurus,* a giant 60-foot-long serpentlike whale with shrunken hind legs still complete down to jointed knees and toes.

The earliest modern whales appear in the fossil record 15 million years ago. The nostrils are now in the top of the head, a "blowhole" that allows it to break the surface, inhale, and resubmerge without having to stop or tilt the head up. The hind legs are gone, with vestigial tiny bones remaining that are unattached to the pelvis. Still, today's whales retain all the genes used to code for legs—occasionally a whale is born having sprouted a leg or two.

So it seems to have taken 35 million years to evolve a whale from the piglike ancestor of a hippopotamus—intermediate steps preserved in the fossil record for us to see. Darwin, who always believed that gaps in the vertebrate fossil record would eventually be filled in, would have been delighted.

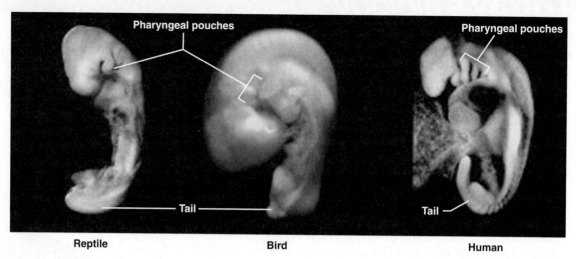

Figure 17.4 Embryos show our early evolutionary history.

These embryos, representing various vertebrate animals, show the primitive features that all vertebrates share early in their development, such as pharyngeal pouches and a tail.

Pharyngeal pouches

Pharyngeal pouches

Tail

Tail

Reptile   Bird   Human

The Anatomical Record

Much of the evolutionary history of vertebrates can be seen in the way in which their embryos develop. Figure 17.4 shows three different embryos early in development, and as you can see, all vertebrate embryos have pharyngeal pouches (that develop into gill slits in fish); and every vertebrate embryo has a long bony tail, even if the tail is not present in the fully developed animal. These relict developmental forms strongly suggest that all vertebrates share a basic set of developmental instructions.

As vertebrates have evolved, the same bones are sometimes still there but put to different uses, their presence betraying their evolutionary past. For example, the forelimbs of vertebrates are all **homologous structures;** that is, although the structure and function of the bones have diverged, they are derived from the same body part present in a common ancestor. You can see in figure 17.5 how the bones of the forelimb have been modified for different functions. The yellow- and purple-colored bones, which correspond in humans to the bones of the forearm and wrist and fingers, respectively, are modified to make up the wings in the bat, the full leg of the horse, and the paddle in the fin of the porpoise.

Not all similar features are homologous. Sometimes features found in different lineages come to resemble each other as a result of parallel evolutionary adaptations to similar environments. This form of evolutionary change is referred to as *convergent evolution,* and these similar-looking features are called **analogous structures.** For example, figure 17.6 shows that the wings of birds, pterosaurs, and bats are analogous structures, modified through natural selection to serve the same function and therefore look the same. Similarly, in the lower portion of the figure, the marsupial mammals of Australia evolved in isolation from placental mammals, but similar selective pressures have generated very similar kinds of animals.

Sometimes structures are put to no use at all! In living whales, which evolved from hoofed mammals, the bones of the pelvis that formerly anchored the two hind limbs are all

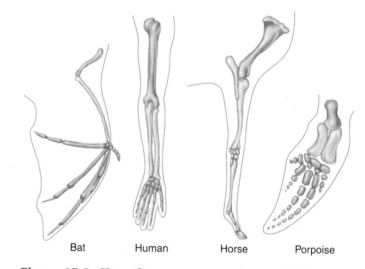

Bat   Human   Horse   Porpoise

Figure 17.5 Homology among vertebrate limbs.
Homologies among the forelimbs of four mammals show the ways in which the proportions of the bones have changed in relation to the particular way of life of each organism. Although considerable differences can be seen in form and function, the same basic bones are present in each forelimb.

that remain of the rear legs, unattached to any other bones and serving no apparent purpose (the reduced pelvic bone can be seen in the figure in the "Today's Biology" reading on the previous page). Another example of what are called *vestigial organs* is the human appendix. In the great apes, our closest relatives, we find an appendix much larger than ours attached to the gut tube, which functions in digestion, holding bacteria used in digesting the cellulose cell walls of the plants eaten by these primates. The human appendix is a vestigial version of this structure that now serves no function in digestion (although it may have acquired an alternate function in the lymphatic system).

Taking Flight
To take to the air, three very different vertebrates lightened bones and transformed hands into wings.

Samoan flying fox (fruitbat)

Pterosaur (extinct)

Eastern bluebird

Mouse

Marsupial mouse

Wolf

Two Worlds
Marsupials evolved the same sort of adaptations in isolation in Australia that placental mammals did elsewhere.

Tasmanian wolf

Flying phalanger

Flying squirrel

Figure 17.6 Convergent evolution: many paths to one goal.

Over the course of evolution, form often follows function. Members of very different animal groups often adapt in similar fashions when challenged by similar opportunities. These are but a few of many examples of such convergent evolution. The flying vertebrates represent mammals (bat), reptiles (pterosaur), and birds (bluebird). The three pairs of terrestrial vertebrates each contrast a North American placental mammal with an Australian marsupial one.

Source: *"Taking Flight" image from* **The New York Times, *December 15, 1988.* The New York Times. *Reprinted with permission.***

The Molecular Record

Traces of our evolutionary past are also evident at the molecular level. We possess the same set of color vision genes as our ancestors, only more complex, and we employ pattern formation genes during early development that all animals share. Indeed, if you think about it, the fact that organisms have evolved from a series of simpler ancestors implies that a record of evolutionary change is present in the cells of each of us, in our DNA. According to evolutionary theory, new alleles arise from older ones by mutation and come to predominance through favorable selection. A series of evolutionary changes thus implies a continual accumulation of genetic changes in the DNA. From this you can see that evolutionary theory makes a clear prediction: Organisms that are more distantly related should have accumulated a greater number of evolutionary differences than two species that are more closely related.

This prediction is now subject to direct test. Recent DNA research, referred to in section 15.3, allows us to directly compare the genomes of different organisms. The result is clear: For a broad array of vertebrates, the more distantly related two organisms are, the greater their genomic difference. This research is described later in this chapter in "A Closer Look" on pages 314 and 315.

This same pattern of divergence can be clearly seen at the protein level. Comparing the hemoglobin amino acid sequence of different species with the human sequence in figure 17.7, you can see that species more closely related to humans have fewer differences in the amino acid structure of their hemoglobin. Macaques, primates closely related to humans, have fewer differences from humans (only 8 different amino acids) than do more distantly related mammals like dogs (which have 32 different amino acids). Nonmammalian terrestrial vertebrates differ even more, and marine vertebrates are the most different of all. Again, the prediction of evolutionary theory is strongly confirmed.

Molecular Clocks This same pattern is seen when the DNA sequence of an individual gene is compared over a much broader array of organisms. One well-studied case is the mammalian *cytochrome c* gene (cytochrome *c* is a protein that plays a key role in oxidative metabolism). Figure 17.8 compares the time when two species diverged on the *x* axis to the number of differences in their cytochrome *c* gene on the *y* axis. To practice using this data set, go back about 75 million years ago to find a common ancestor for humans and rodents—in that time there have been about 60 base substitutions in cytochrome *c*. This graph reveals a very important finding: Evolutionary changes appear to accumulate in cytochrome *c* at a constant rate, as indicated by the straightness of the blue line connecting the points. This constancy is sometimes referred to as a **molecular clock.** Most proteins for which data are available appear to accumulate changes over time in this fashion, although different proteins can evolve at very different rates.

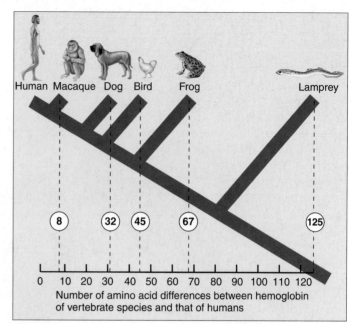

Figure 17.7   Molecules reflect evolutionary divergence.

The greater the evolutionary distance from humans (as revealed by the *blue* evolutionary tree based on the fossil record), the greater the number of amino acid differences in the vertebrate hemoglobin polypeptide.

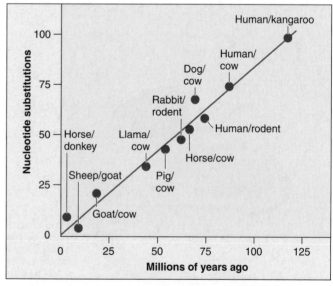

Figure 17.8   The molecular clock of cytochrome c.

When the time since each pair of organisms presumably diverged is plotted against the number of nucleotide differences in cytochrome *c*, the result is a straight line, suggesting that the *cytochrome c* gene is evolving at a constant rate.

17.2 The fossil record provides a clear record of successive evolutionary change. Comparative anatomy also offers evidence that evolution has occurred. Finally, the genetic record exhibits successive evolution, the DNA of organisms accumulating increasing numbers of changes over time.

Evolution's Critics

Of all the major ideas of biology, evolution is perhaps the best known to the general public, because many people mistakenly believe that evolution represents a challenge to their religious beliefs. As discussed in chapter 19 (page 352), a person can have a spiritual faith in God and still be an excellent scientist—and evolutionist. Because Darwin's theory of evolution is the subject of often-bitter public controversy, we will examine the objections of evolution's critics in detail, to see why there is such a disconnect between science and public opinion.

History of the Controversy

An Old Conflict Immediately after publication of *The Origin of Species,* English clergymen attacked Darwin's book as heretical; Gladstone, England's prime minister and a famous statesman, condemned it. The book was defended by Thomas Huxley and other scientists, who gradually won over the scientific establishment, and by the turn of the century evolution was generally accepted by the world's scientific community.

The Fundamentalist Movement By the 1920s the teaching of evolution had become frequent enough in American public schools to alarm conservative critics of evolution who saw Darwinism as a threat to their Christian beliefs. Between 1921 and 1929, fundamentalists introduced bills outlawing the teaching of evolution in 37 state legislatures. Four passed: Tennessee, Mississippi, Arkansas, and Texas.

Civil rights groups used the case of high school teacher John Scopes to challenge the Tennessee law within months of its being passed in 1925. The trial attracted national attention— you might have seen it portrayed in the film *Inherit the Wind.* Scopes, who had indeed violated the new law, lost.

After the 1920s, there were few other attempts to pass state laws preventing the teaching of evolution. Only one bill was introduced between 1930 and 1963. Why? Because Darwin's fundamentalist critics had succeeded quietly in winning their way. Textbooks published throughout the 1930s ignored evolution, new editions of texts removing the words *evolution* and *Darwin* from their indices. In the 1920–29 period, for example, the average number of words about the evolution of humans in 93 secondary school texts was 1,339; in the 1930–39 period it had dropped to 439. As late as 1950–59 it was 614. To quote biologist Ernst Mayr, "The word EVOLUTION simply disappeared from American schoolbooks."

These antievolution laws remained on the books for many years. Then in 1965 teacher Susan Epperson was convicted of teaching evolution under the 1928 Arkansas law. In 1968 the United States Supreme Court found the Arkansas antievolution law to be unconstitutional; the 1920s laws were soon repealed.

Russian advances in space in the early 1960s created a public outcry for better American science education. New biology textbooks reintroduced evolution, and gave it renewed emphasis. The average number of words per text devoted to the evolution of man, for example, rose from 614 in the period 1950–59 to 8,977 in the period 1960–69. By the 1970s, evolution again formed the core of most biology schoolbooks.

The Scientific Creationism Movement Again alarmed by the prevalence of evolution in public school biology classes, Darwin's critics took a new approach. It began with a proposal by the Institute for Creationism Research in 1964, which said, "Creationism is just as much a science as is evolution, and evolution is just as much a religion as is creation." This proposal has become known as *creationism science.* It was soon followed by the introduction of legislation in state legislatures mandating that "all theories of origins be accorded equal time." Creationism was represented as being as much a scientific theory as evolution, to which students had a right to be exposed.

In 1981 the state legislatures of Arkansas and Louisiana passed "equal-time" bills into law. The Louisiana equal-time law requiring "balanced treatment of creation-science and evolution-science in public schools" was struck down by the Supreme Court in 1987, which judged that creation science is not, in fact, science but rather a religious view that has no place in public science classrooms.

Local Action In the following decades, Darwin's critics began to substitute the school board for the legislature. Unlike most European countries, which set their school curricula through a central education ministry, U.S. education is highly decentralized, with elected education boards setting science standards at the state and local level. These standards determine the content of state-wide assessment tests, and have a major impact on what is taught in classrooms.

Critics of Darwin have run successfully for seats on local and state education boards across the United States, and from these positions have begun to alter standards to lessen the impact of evolution in the classroom. Great publicity followed the removal of evolution from the Kansas state standards in 1999 and again in 2005, but in many other states the same effect has been achieved more quietly. Only 22 states today mandate the teaching of natural selection, for example. Four states fail to mention evolution at all.

Intelligent Design In recent years, critics of Darwin have begun new attempts to combat the teaching of evolution in the classroom, arguing before state and local school boards that life is too complex for natural selection and so must reflect intelligent design. They go on to argue that this "theory of intelligent design" (ID) should be presented in the science classroom as an alternative to the theory of evolution.

Scientists object strongly to dubbing ID a scientific theory. The essence of science is seeking explanations in what can be observed, tested, replicated by others, and possibly falsified. Explanations that cannot be tested and potentially rejected simply aren't science. If someone invokes a nonnatural cause—a supernatural force—in their research, and you decide to test it, can you think of any way to do such that it could be falsified? Supernatural causation is not science.

The source of sharp public controversy, intelligent design has been overwhelmingly rejected by the scientific community, which does not regard intelligent design to be science at all, but rather thinly disguised creationism, a religious view that has no place in the science classroom.

Arguments Advanced by Darwin's Critics

Critics of evolution have raised a variety of objections to Darwin's theory of evolution by natural selection:

1. **Evolution is not solidly demonstrated.** *"Evolution is just a theory,"* critics point out, as if theory meant lack of knowledge, some kind of guess. Scientists, however, use the word theory in a very different sense than the general public does (see section 1.8). Theories are the solid ground of science, supported with much experimental evidence and that of which we are most certain. Few of us doubt the theory of gravity because it is "just a theory."

2. **There are no fossil intermediates.** *"No one ever saw a fin on the way to becoming a leg,"* critics claim, pointing to the many gaps in the fossil record in Darwin's day. Since then, however, most fossil intermediates in vertebrate evolution have indeed been found. A clear line of fossils now traces the transition between whales and hoofed mammals, between reptiles and mammals, and between apes and humans. The fossil evidence of evolution between major forms is compelling.

3. **The intelligent design argument.** *"The organs of living creatures are too complex for a random process to have produced."* This classic "argument from design" was first proposed nearly 200 years ago by William Paley in his book *Natural Theology*—the existence of a clock is evidence of the existence of a clockmaker, Paley argues. Similarly, Darwin's critics argue that organs like the mammalian ear are too complex to be due to blind evolution. There must have been a designer. Biologists do not agree. The intermediates in the evolution of the mammalian ear are well documented in the fossil record. Its three tiny bones originated from the reptile lower jaw, gradually reducing in size as more advanced mammals evolved. Eventually the bones migrated into the inner ear where we now find them in present-day mammals, helping amplify sound vibrations as they pass across the middle ear. These intermediate forms were each favored by natural selection because they each had value—being able to amplify sound a little is better than not being able to amplify it at all. Complex structures like the mammalian ear evolved as a progression of slight improvements. Nor is the solution always optimal, as your own eyes attest. As you can see in the blown-up image in figure 17.9, the receptor cells in the human eye are actually facing backward to the stimulus (light). No intelligent designer would design an eye backwards!

4. **Evolution violates the second law of thermodynamics.** *"A jumble of soda cans doesn't by itself jump neatly into a stack—things become more disorganized due to random events, not more organized."* Biologists point out that this argument ignores what the second law really says: Disorder increases in a closed system, which the earth most certainly is not. Energy enters the biosphere from the sun, fueling life and all the processes that organize it.

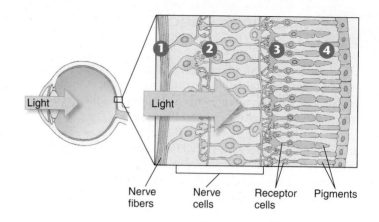

Figure 17.9 The vertebrate eye is poorly designed.
The visual pigments in a vertebrate eye that are stimulated by light are embedded in the retinal tissue, facing backward to the direction of the light. The light has to pass through nerve fibers ❶, nerve cells ❷, and receptor cells ❸, before reaching the pigments ❹.

Nerve fibers   Nerve cells   Receptor cells   Pigments

5. **Proteins are too improbable.** *"Hemoglobin has 141 amino acids. The probability that the first one would be leucine is 1/20, and that all 141 would be the ones they are by chance is $(1/20)^{141}$, an impossibly rare event."* You cannot use probability to argue backward. The probability that a student in a classroom has a particular birthday is 1/365; arguing this way, the probability that everyone in a class of 50 would have the birthdays they do is $(1/365)^{50}$, and yet there the class sits.

6. **Natural selection does not imply evolution.** *"No scientist has come up with an experiment where fish evolve into frogs and leap away from predators."* Is microevolution (evolution within a species) the mechanism that has produced macroevolution (evolution among species)? Most biologists that have studied the problem think so. The differences between breeds produced by artificial selection—such as Chihuahuas, dachshunds, and greyhounds—are more distinctive than differences between wild canine species. Laboratory selection experiments with insects easily create forms that cannot interbreed and thus would in nature be considered different species. Thus, production of radically different forms has indeed been observed, repeatedly.

7. **Life could not have evolved in water.** *"Because the peptide bond does not form spontaneously in water, amino acids could never have spontaneously linked together to form proteins; nor is there any chemical reason why biological proteins contain only the L-isomer and not the D-isomer."* Both of these contentions are valid, but do not require rejecting evolution. Rather, they suggest that the early evolution of life took place on a surface rather than in solution. Amino acids link up spontaneously on the surface of clays, for example, which can have a shape that selects the L-isomer. Several hypotheses about the origin of life are discussed in more detail in chapter 19.

The Irreducible Complexity Fallacy

The century-and-a-half-old "intelligent design" argument of William Paley has been recently articulated in a new molecular guise by Lehigh University biochemistry professor Michael Behe. In his 1996 book *Darwin's Black Box: The Biochemical Challenge to Evolution,* Behe argues that the intricate molecular machinery of our cells is so elaborate, our body processes so interconnected, that they cannot be explained by evolution from simpler stages in the way that Darwinists explain the evolution of the mammalian ear. The molecular machinery of the cell is "irreducibly complex." Behe defines an irreducibly complex system as "a single system composed of several well-matched, interacting parts that contribute to the basic function, wherein the removal of any one of the parts causes the system to effectively cease functioning." Each part plays a vital role. Remove just one, Behe emphasizes, and cell molecular machinery cannot function.

As an example of such an irreducibly complex system, Behe describes the series of more than a dozen blood clotting proteins that act in our body to cause blood to clot around a wound. Take out any step in the complex cascade of reactions that leads to coagulation of blood, says Behe, and your body's blood would leak out from a cut like water from a ruptured pipe. Remove a single enzyme from the complementary system that confines the clotting process to the immediate vicinity of the wound, and all your lifeblood would harden. Either condition would be fatal. The need for *all* the parts of such complex systems to work leads directly to Behe's criticism of Darwin's theory of evolution by natural selection. Behe writes that "irreducibly complex systems cannot evolve in a Darwinian fashion." If dozens of different proteins all must work correctly to clot blood, how could natural selection act to fashion any one of the individual proteins? No one protein does anything on its own, just as a portion of a watch doesn't tell time. Behe argues that, like Paley's watch, the blood clotting system must have been designed all at once, as a single functioning machine.

What's wrong with Behe's argument, as evolutionary scientists have been quick to point out, is that each part of a complex molecular machine does not evolve by itself, despite Behe's claim that it must. The several parts evolve together, in concert, precisely because evolution acts on the system, not its parts. That's the fundamental fallacy in Behe's argument. Natural selection can act on a complex system because at every stage of its evolution, the system functions. Parts that improve function are added, and, because of later changes, eventually become essential, in the same way that the second rung of a ladder becomes essential once you have added a third.

The mammalian blood clotting system, for example, has evolved in stages from much simpler systems. By comparing the amino acid sequences of the many proteins, biochemist Russell Doolittle has estimated how long it has been since each protein evolved. You can see what he has learned in figure 17.10. The core of the vertebrate clotting system, called the "common pathway" (highlighted in blue), evolved at the dawn of the vertebrates approximately 600 million years ago,

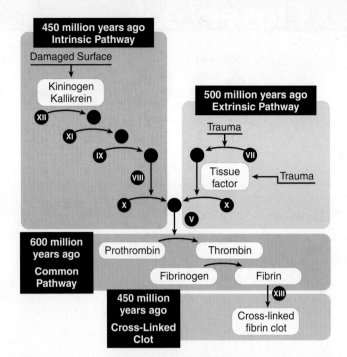

Figure 17.10   How blood clotting evolved.
The blood clotting system evolved in steps, with new proteins adding on to the preceding step.

and is found today in lampreys, the most primitive fish. As vertebrates evolved, proteins were added to the clotting system, improving its efficiency. The so-called extrinsic pathway (highlighted in pink), triggered by substances released from damaged tissues, was added 500 million years ago. Each step in the pathway amplifies what goes before, so adding the extrinsic pathways greatly increases the amplification and thus the sensitivity of the system. Fifty million years later, a third component was added, the so-called intrinsic pathway (highlighted in tan). It is triggered by contact with the jagged surfaces produced by injury. Again, amplification and sensitivity were increased to ultimately end up with blood clots formed by the cross linking of fibrin (highlighted in green). At each stage as the clotting system evolved to become more complex, its overall performance came to depend on the added elements. Mammalian clotting, which utilizes all three pathways, no longer functions if any one of them is disabled. Blood clotting has become "irreducibly complex"—as the result of Darwinian evolution. Behe's claim that complex cellular and molecular processes can't be explained by Darwinism is wrong. Indeed, examination of the human genome reveals that the cluster of blood clotting genes arose through duplication of genes, with increasing amounts of change. The evolution of the blood clotting system is an observation, not a surmise. Its irreducible complexity is a fallacy.

17.3   Darwin's theory of evolution has not been accepted by religious conservatives in the United States, who object to its being taught in public school. Their criticisms are without scientific merit, but have considerable public support.

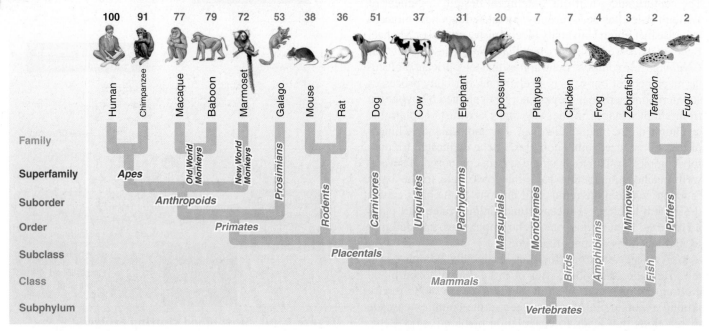

100	91	77	79	72	53	38	36	51	37	31	20	7	7	4	3	2	2
Human	Chimpanzee	Macaque	Baboon	Marmoset	Galago	Mouse	Rat	Dog	Cow	Elephant	Opossum	Platypus	Chicken	Frog	Zebrafish	Tetradon	Fugu

Family
Superfamily — *Apes* — *Old World Monkeys* — *New World Monkeys* — *Prosimians* — *Rodents* — *Carnivores* — *Ungulates* — *Pachyderms* — *Marsupials* — *Monotremes* — *Minnows* — *Puffers*
Suborder — *Anthropoids*
Order — *Primates*
Subclass — *Placentals*
Class — *Mammals* — *Birds* — *Amphibians* — *Fish*
Subphylum — *Vertebrates*

Putting Darwin (and Intelligent Design) to the Test

In the spring of 2006 the South Carolina Board of Education rejected a state panel's proposal to change high school standards by calling on students to critically analyze evolution. The Board stated it felt the proposal was a ploy to promote the avoidance of teaching evolution. Similar proposals to add a requirement that students critically analyze evolution had been rejected earlier in the year by the Utah and Ohio Boards of Education, and are currently under consideration in several other states.

What are we to make of this? Surely no scientist can object to critically analyzing any theory. That is what science is all about, seeking explanations for what can be observed, tested, replicated, and possibly falsified. Indeed, biologists claim that Darwin's theory of evolution has been subjected to as much critical analysis as any theory in the history of science.

So why the objection to this change in high school standards? Because many scientists and teachers, apparently including the South Carolina Board of Education, feel the change is simply intended to promote the teaching of a non-scientific alternative to evolution in classrooms.

This distinction between an assertion that can be tested and one that cannot goes to the very nature of science. Actually, nothing makes this difference more clear cut than the critical analysis so sought after by South Carolina's critics of evolution. So let's do it. Let's put Darwin to the test.

As explained earlier in the chapter, if Darwin's assertion is correct, that organisms evolved from ancestral species, then we should be able to track evolutionary changes in our DNA. The variation that we see between species reflects adaptations to environmental challenges, adaptations that result from changes in DNA. Therefore, a series of evolutionary changes should be reflected in an accumulation of genetic changes in the DNA. This hypothesis, that evolutionary changes reflect accumulated changes in DNA, leads to the following prediction: Two species that are more distantly related (for example, humans and mice) should have accumulated a greater number of evolutionary differences than two species that are more closely related (say, humans and chimpanzees).

So have they? Let's compare vertebrate species to see. The "family tree" above shows how biologists believe 18 different vertebrate species are related. Apes and monkeys, because they are in the same order (primates), are considered more closely related to each other than either are to members of another order, such as mice and rats (rodents).

The wealth of genomes (a genome is all the DNA that an organism possesses) that have been sequenced since completion of the human genome project allows us to directly compare the DNA of these 18 vertebrates. To reduce the size of the task, investigators at the National Human Genome Research Institute working at the University of California, Santa Cruz, focused on 44 so-called ENCODE regions scattered around the vertebrate genomes. These regions, corresponding to 30 Mb (megabase, or million bases) or roughly 1% of the total human genome, were selected to be representative of the genome as a whole, containing protein-encoding genes as well as non-coding DNA.

For each vertebrate species, the investigators determined the similarity of its DNA to that of humans—that is, the percent of the nucleotides in that organism's 44 ENCODE regions which match those of the human genome.

You can see the result in each instance presented as a number above the picture of each organism on the vertebrate family tree. As Darwin's theory predicts, the closer the relatives, the less the genomic difference we see. The chimpanzee genome is more like the human genome (91%) than the monkey genomes are (72 to 79%). Furthermore, these five genomes, all in the same order, are more like each other than any are to those of another order, such as rodents (mouse and rat).

In general, as you proceed through the taxonomic categories of the vertebrate family tree from very distant relatives on the right (some in the same class as humans) to very close ones on the left (in the same family), you can see clearly that genomic similarity increases as taxonomic distance decreases—just as Darwin's theory predicts. The prediction of evolutionary theory is solidly confirmed.

The analysis does not have to stop here. The evolutionary history of the vertebrates is quite well known from fossils, and because many of these fossils have been independently dated using tools such as radioisotope dating, it is possible to recast the analysis in terms of concrete intervals of time, and assess directly whether or not vertebrate genomes accumulate more differences over longer periods of time as Darwin's theory predicts.

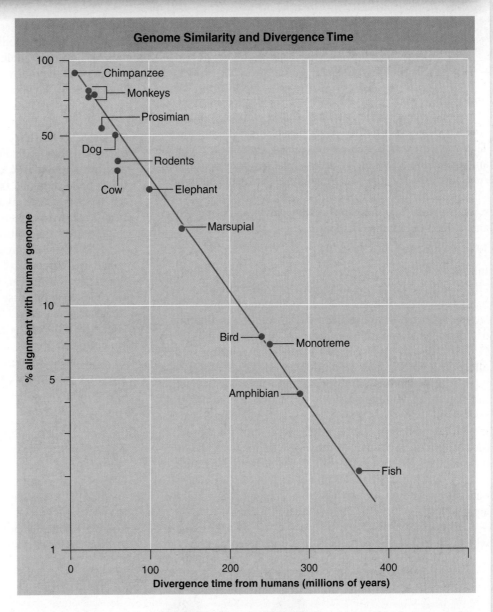

For each of the 18 vertebrates being analyzed, the graph above plots genomic similarity—how alike the DNA sequence of the vertebrate's ENCODE regions are to those of the human genome—against divergence time (that is, how many millions of years have elapsed since that vertebrate and humans shared a common ancestor in the fossil record). Thus the last common ancestor shared by chickens and humans was an early reptile called a dicynodont that lived some 250 million years ago; since then the genomes of the two species have changed so much that only 7% of their ENCODE sequences are still the same.

The result seen in the graph is striking and very clear: Over their more than 300 million year history, vertebrates have accumulated more and more genetic change in their DNA. "Descent with modification" was Darwin's definition of evolution, and that is exactly what we see in the graph. The evolution of the vertebrate genome is not a theory, but an observation.

The wealth of data made available by the human genome project has allowed a powerful test of Darwin's prediction. The conclusion to which the test leads us is that evolution is an observed fact, clearly revealed in the DNA of vertebrates.

This is the sort of critical analysis that science requires, and that the theory of evolution has again passed. Anyone suggesting that a nonscientific alternative to evolution, such as Intelligent Design, offers an alternative scientific explanation to evolution is welcome to subject it to the same sort of critical analysis you have seen employed here. Can you think of a way to do so? It is precisely because the assertion of intelligent design cannot be critically analyzed—it does not make any testable prediction—that it is not science and has no place in science classrooms.

17.4 | Genetic Change Within Populations: The Hardy-Weinberg Rule

Population genetics is the study of the properties of genes in populations. Genetic variation within natural populations could not be explained by Darwin and his contemporaries. The way in which meiosis produces genetic segregation among the progeny of a hybrid had not yet been discovered. And, although Mendel performed his experiments during this same time period, his work was largely unknown. Selection, scientists then thought, should always favor an optimal form, and so tend to eliminate variation.

Hardy-Weinberg Equilibrium

Indeed, variation within populations puzzled many scientists; **alleles** (alternative forms of a gene) that were dominant were believed to drive recessive alleles out of populations, with selection favoring an optimal form. The solution to the puzzle of why genetic variation persists was developed in 1908 by G. H. Hardy and W. Weinberg. Hardy and Weinberg studied **allele frequencies** (the proportion of alleles of a particular type in a population) in a population's *gene pool*, which is the sum of all of the genes in a population, including all alleles in all individuals. Hardy and Weinberg pointed out that in a large population in which there is random mating, and in the absence of forces that change allele frequencies, the original genotype proportions remain constant from generation to generation. Dominant alleles do not, in fact, replace recessive ones. Because their proportions do not change, the genotypes are said to be in **Hardy-Weinberg equilibrium.**

The Hardy-Weinberg rule is viewed as a baseline to which the frequencies of alleles in a population can be compared. If the allele frequencies are not changing (they are in Hardy-Weinberg equilibrium), the population is not evolving. If, however, allele frequencies are sampled at one point in time and they differ greatly from what would be expected under Hardy-Weinberg equilibrium, then the population is undergoing evolutionary change.

Hardy and Weinberg came to their conclusion by analyzing the frequencies of alleles in successive generations. The **frequency** of something is defined as the proportion of individuals with a certain characteristic, compared to the entire population. Thus, in the population of 1,000 cats shown in figure 17.11, there are 840 black cats and 160 white cats. To determine the frequency of black cats, divide 840 by 1,000 (840/1,000), which is 0.84. The frequency of white cats is 160/1,000 = 0.16.

Knowing the frequency of the phenotype, one can calculate the frequency of the genotypes and alleles in the population. By convention, the frequency of the more common of two alleles (in this case B for the black allele) is designated by the letter *p* and that of the less common allele (*b* for the white allele) by the letter *q*. Because there are only two alleles, the sum of *p* and *q* must always equal 1 ($p + q = 1$).

In algebraic terms, the Hardy-Weinberg equilibrium is written as an equation. For a gene with two alternative alleles *B* (frequency *p*) and *b* (frequency *q*), the equation looks like this:

$$p^2 + 2pq + q^2 = 1$$

p^2	$2pq$	q^2
Individuals homozygous for allele *B*	**Individuals heterozygous for alleles *B* and *b***	**Individuals homozygous for allele *b***

You will notice that not only does the sum of the alleles add up to 1 but so does the sum of the frequencies of genotypes.

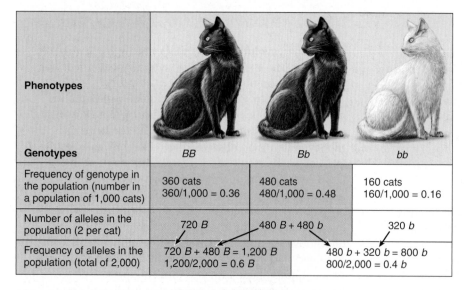

Phenotypes			
Genotypes	*BB*	*Bb*	*bb*
Frequency of genotype in the population (number in a population of 1,000 cats)	360 cats 360/1,000 = 0.36	480 cats 480/1,000 = 0.48	160 cats 160/1,000 = 0.16
Number of alleles in the population (2 per cat)	720 *B*	480 *B* + 480 *b*	320 *b*
Frequency of alleles in the population (total of 2,000)	720 *B* + 480 *B* = 1,200 *B* 1,200/2,000 = 0.6 *B*	480 *b* + 320 *b* = 800 *b* 800/2,000 = 0.4 *b*	

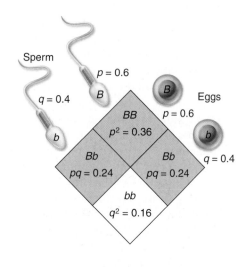

Figure 17.11 Hardy-Weinberg equilibrium.

In the absence of factors that alter them, the frequencies of gametes, genotypes, and phenotypes remain constant generation after generation. The example shown here involves a population of 1,000 cats, in which 160 are white and 840 are black. White cats are *bb*, and black cats are *BB* or *Bb*. The potential crosses in this cat population can be determined using a Punnett square analysis.

Knowing the frequencies of the alleles in a population doesn't reveal whether the population is evolving or not. We need to look at future generations to determine this. Using the allele frequencies calculated for our population of cats, we can predict what the genotypic and phenotypic frequencies will be in future generations. The Punnett square shown in figure 17.11 is constructed with allele frequencies of 0.6 for the *B* allele and 0.4 for the *b* allele, taken from the bottom row of the chart. It might help you to consider these frequencies as percentages, with a 0.6 representing 60% of the population and 0.4 representing 40% of the population. According to the Hardy-Weinberg rule, 60% of the sperm in the population will carry the *B* allele (indicated as $p = 0.6$ in the Punnett square) and 40% of the sperm will carry the *b* allele ($q = 0.4$). When these are crossed with eggs carrying the same allele frequencies (60% or $p = 0.6$ *B* allele and 40% or $q = 0.4$ *b* allele), the predicted genotypic frequencies can be simply calculated. The genotypic ratio for *BB*, in the upper quadrant, equals the frequency of *B* (0.6) multiplied by the frequency of *B* (0.6) or (0.6 x 0.6 = 0.36). So, if the population is not evolving, the genotypic ratio for *BB* would stay the same, and 0.36 or 36% of the cats in future generations would be homozygous dominant (*BB*) for coat color. Likewise, 0.48 or 48% of the cats would be heterozygous *Bb* (0.24 + 0.24 = 0.48), and 0.16 or 16% of the cats would be homozygous recessive *bb*.

Hardy-Weinberg Assumptions

The Hardy-Weinberg rule is based on certain assumptions. The equation on page 316 is true only if the following five assumptions are met:

1. The size of the population is very large or effectively infinite.
2. Individuals mate with one another at random.
3. There is no mutation.
4. There is no input of new copies of any allele from any extraneous source (such as migration from a nearby population) or losses of copies of alleles through emigration (individuals leaving the population).
5. All alleles are replaced equally from generation to generation (natural selection is not occurring).

Hardy-Weinberg: A Null Hypothesis

Many populations, and most human populations, are large and randomly mating with respect to most traits (a few traits affecting appearance undergo strong sexual selection in humans). Thus, many populations are similar to the ideal population envisioned by Hardy and Weinberg. For some genes, however, the observed proportion of heterozygotes does not match the value calculated from the allele frequencies. When this occurs, it indicates that something is acting on the population to alter one or more of the genotypic frequencies, whether it is selection, nonrandom mating, migration, or some other factor. Viewed in this light, Hardy-Weinberg can be viewed as a *null hypothesis*. A null hypothesis is a prediction that is made stating there will be no differences in the parameters being measured. If over several generations, the genotypic

frequencies in the population do not match those predicted by the Hardy-Weinberg equation, the null hypothesis would be rejected and the assumption made that some force is acting on the population to change the frequencies of alleles. The factors that can affect the frequencies of alleles in a population are discussed in detail later in this chapter.

Case-Study: Cystic Fibrosis in Humans

How valid are the predictions made by the Hardy-Weinberg equation? For many genes, they prove to be very accurate. As an example, consider the recessive allele responsible for the serious human disease cystic fibrosis. This allele (q) is present in Caucasians in North America at a frequency of 0.022. What proportion of Caucasian North Americans, therefore, is expected to express this trait? The frequency of double-recessive individuals (q^2) is expected to be

$$q^2 = 0.022 \times 0.022 = 0.00048$$

which equals 0.48 in every 1,000 individuals or about 1 in every 2,000 individuals, very close to real estimates.

What proportion is expected to be heterozygous carriers? If the frequency of the recessive allele q is 0.022, then the frequency of the dominant allele p must be $p = 1 - q$ or:

$$p = 1 - 0.022 = 0.978$$

The frequency of heterozygous individuals ($2pq$) is thus expected to be:

$$2 \times 0.978 \times 0.022 = 0.043$$

It is estimated that 12 million individuals in the United States are carriers of the cystic fibrosis allele. In a population of 292 million people, that is a frequency of 0.041, very close to projections using the Hardy-Weinberg equation. However, if the frequency of the cystic fibrosis allele in the United States were to change, this would suggest that the population is no longer following the assumptions of the Hardy-Weinberg rule. For example, if prospective parents who were carriers of the allele chose not to have children, the frequency of the allele would decrease in future generations. Mating would no longer be random, because those carrying the allele would not mate. Consider another scenario. If gene therapies were developed that were able to cure the symptoms of cystic fibrosis, patients would survive longer and would have more of an opportunity to reproduce. This would increase the frequency of the allele in future generations. An increase could also result from an influx of the allele into the population by migration, if the allele were more frequent among individuals migrating into the country.

17.4 In a large, randomly-mating population that fulfills the other Hardy-Weinberg assumptions, allele frequencies can be expected to be in Hardy-Weinberg equilibrium. If they are not, then the population is undergoing evolutionary change.

17.5 Agents of Evolution

Many factors can alter allele frequencies. But only five alter the proportions of homozygotes and heterozygotes enough to produce significant deviations from the proportions predicted by the Hardy-Weinberg rule (table 17.1):

1. Mutation
2. Migration
3. Genetic drift
4. Nonrandom mating
5. Selection

Mutation

A **mutation** is a change in a nucleotide sequence in DNA. For example, a T nucleotide could undergo a mutation and be replaced with an A nucleotide. Mutation from one allele to another obviously can change the proportions of particular alleles in a population. But mutation rates are generally too low to significantly alter Hardy-Weinberg proportions of common alleles. Many genes mutate 1 to 10 times per 100,000 cell divisions. Some of these mutations are harmful, while others are neutral or, even rarer, beneficial. Also, the mutations must affect the DNA of the germ cells (egg and sperm), or the mutation will not be passed on to offspring. The mutation rate is so slow that few populations are around long enough to accumulate significant numbers of mutations. However, no matter how rare, mutation is the ultimate source of genetic variation in a population.

Migration

Migration is defined in genetic terms as the movement of individuals between populations. It can be a powerful force, upsetting the genetic stability of natural populations. Migration includes movement of individuals into a population, called *immigration,* or the movement of individuals out of a population, called *emigration.* If the characteristics of the newly arrived individuals differ from those already there, and if the newly arrived individuals adapt to survive in the new area and mate successfully, then the genetic composition of the receiving population may be altered.

Sometimes migration is not obvious. Subtle movements include the drifting of gametes of plants, or of the immature stages of marine organisms, from one place to another. For example, a bee can carry pollen from a flower in one population to a flower in another population. By doing this, the bee may be introducing new alleles into a population. However it occurs, migration can alter the genetic characteristics of populations and cause a population to be out of Hardy-Weinberg equilibrium. Thus, migration can cause evolutionary change. The magnitude of effects of migration is based on two factors: (1) the proportion of migrants in the population, and (2) the difference in allele frequencies between the migrants and the original population. The actual evolutionary impact of migration is difficult to assess, and depends heavily on the selective forces prevailing at the different places where the populations occur.

TABLE 17.1	AGENTS OF EVOLUTION	
Factor		**Description**
Mutation	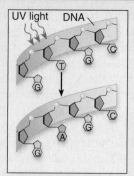	The ultimate source of genetic variation. Individual mutations occur so rarely that mutation alone does not change allele frequency much.
Migration		A very potent agent of change. Migration acts to promote evolutionary change by enabling populations that exchange members to converge toward one another. This bee carries pollen from one population of flowers to another.
Genetic drift		Chance events may result in the loss of individuals and therefore the loss of alleles in a population. Usually occurs only in very small populations. A small number of alleles can also impact a newly formed population, such as the founder effect on an island.
Nonrandom mating	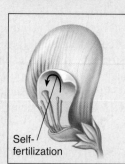	Inbreeding is the most common form of nonrandom mating. It does not alter allele frequency but decreases the proportion of heterozygotes ($2pq$). See text for explanation.
Selection	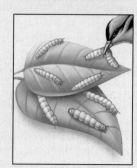	The only form that produces *adaptive* evolutionary changes. Only rapid for allele frequency greater than .01.

Genetic Drift

In small populations, the frequencies of particular alleles may be changed drastically by chance alone. In an extreme case, individual alleles of a given gene may all be represented in few individuals, and some of the alleles may be accidentally lost if those individuals fail to reproduce or die. This loss of individuals and their alleles is due to random events rather than the fitness of the individuals carrying those alleles. This is not to say that alleles are always lost with genetic drift, but allele frequencies appear to change randomly, as if the frequencies were drifting; thus, random changes in allele frequencies is known as **genetic drift.** A series of small populations that are isolated from one another may come to differ strongly as a result of genetic drift.

When one or a few individuals migrate and become the founders of a new, isolated population at some distance from their place of origin, the alleles that they carry are of special significance in the new population. Even if these alleles are rare in the source population, they will become a significant fraction of the new population's genetic endowment. In the example illustrated in table 17.1, about half the mainland population of birds exhibit the red coloring of the migrating bird, but the red coloring became much more common in the island population that arose from this bird. This is called the **founder effect.** As a result of the founder effect, rare alleles and combinations often become more common in new, isolated populations. The founder effect is particularly important in the evolution of organisms that occur on oceanic islands, such as the Galápagos Islands, which Darwin visited. Most of the kinds of organisms that occur in such areas were probably derived from one or a few initial founders. In a similar way, isolated human populations are often dominated by the genetic features that were characteristic of their founders, particularly if only a few individuals were involved initially (figure 17.12).

Even if organisms do not move from place to place, occasionally their populations may be drastically reduced in size. This may result from flooding, drought, earthquakes, and other natural forces or from progressive changes in the environment. The surviving individuals constitute a random genetic sample of the original population. Such a restriction in genetic variability has been termed the **bottleneck effect.** The very low levels of genetic variability seen in African cheetahs today is thought to reflect a near-extinction event in the past.

Nonrandom Mating

Individuals with certain genotypes sometimes mate with one another either more or less commonly than would be expected on a random basis, a phenomenon known as **nonrandom mating.** One type of nonrandom mating is **sexual selection,** choosing a mate often based on certain physical characteristics. Another type of nonrandom mating is inbreeding, or mating with relatives, such as in the self-fertilization of a flower. Inbreeding increases the proportions of individuals that are homozygous because no individuals mate with any genotype but their own. As a result, inbred populations contain more homozygous individuals than predicted by the Hardy-Weinberg rule. For this reason, populations of self-fertilizing plants consist primarily of homozygous

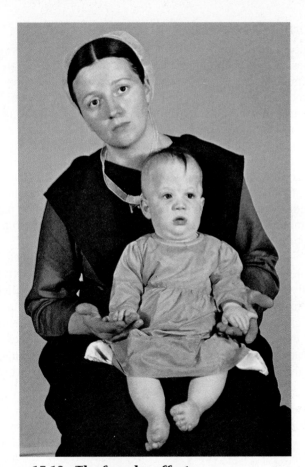

Figure 17.12   The founder effect.
This Amish woman is holding her child, who has Ellis-van Creveld syndrome. The characteristic symptoms are short limbs, dwarfed stature, and extra fingers. This disorder was introduced in the Amish community by one of its founders in the eighteenth century and persists to this day because of reproductive isolation.

individuals, whereas outcrossing plants, which interbreed with individuals different from themselves, have a higher proportion of heterozygous individuals. Nonrandom mating alters genotype frequencies but not allele frequencies. The allele frequencies remain the same—the alleles are just distributed differently among the offspring.

Selection

As Darwin pointed out, some individuals leave behind more progeny than others, and the likelihood they will do so is affected by their inherited characteristics. The result of this process is called **selection** and was familiar even in Darwin's day to breeders of horses and farm animals. In so-called **artificial selection,** the breeder selects for the desired characteristics. For example, mating larger animals with each other produces offspring that are larger. In **natural selection,** Darwin suggested the environment plays this role, with conditions in nature determining which kinds of individuals in a population are the most fit (meaning individuals that are best suited to their environment, see section 2.3) and so affecting the proportions of genes among individuals of future populations. The environment imposes the conditions that determine the results of selection and, thus, the direction of evolution.

Forms of Selection

Selection operates in natural populations of a species as skill does in a football game. In any individual game, it can be difficult to predict the winner, because chance can play an important role in the outcome. But over a long season, the teams with the most skillful players usually win the most games. In nature, those individuals best suited to their environments tend to win the evolutionary game by leaving the most offspring, although chance can play a major role in the life of any one individual. While you cannot predict the fate of any one individual, or any one coin toss, it is possible to predict which kind of individual will tend to become more common in populations of a species, as it is possible to predict the proportion of heads after many coin tosses.

In nature, many traits, perhaps most, are affected by more than one gene. The interactions between genes are typically complex, as you saw in chapter 11. For example, alleles of many different genes play a role in determining human height (see figure 11.12). In such cases, selection operates on all the genes, influencing most strongly those that make the greatest contribution to the phenotype. How selection changes the population depends on which genotypes are favored.

Three types of natural selection have been identified: stabilizing selection, disruptive selection, and directional selection. Figure 17.13 shows the results of these three types of selection on body size.

Stabilizing Selection

When selection acts to eliminate both extremes from an array of phenotypes—for example, eliminating the larger and smaller body sizes (the red-shaded areas under the curve in figure 17.13a)—the result is an increase in the frequency of the already common intermediate phenotype (a midsized body). This is called **stabilizing selection.** In effect, selection is operating to prevent change away from the middle range of values. In a classic study carried out after an "uncommonly severe storm of snow, rain, and sleet" on February 1, 1898, 136 starving English sparrows were collected and brought to the laboratory of H. C. Bumpus at Brown University in Providence, Rhode Island. Of these, 64 died and 72 survived. Bumpus took standard measurements on all the birds. He found that among males, the surviving birds tended to be bigger, as one might expect from the action of directional selection (discussed later). However, among females,

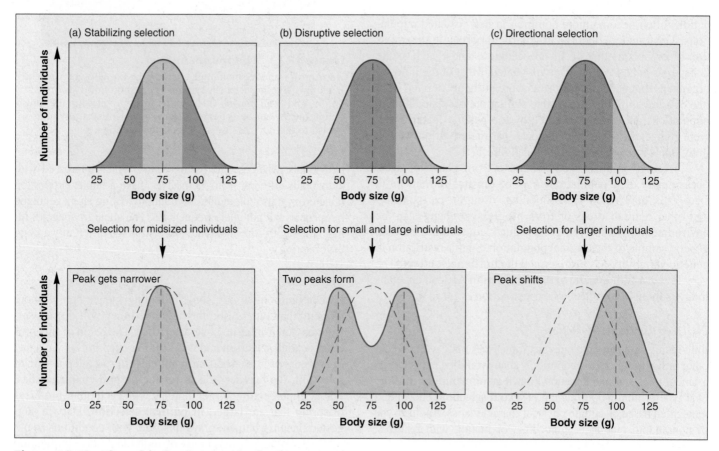

Figure 17.13 Three kinds of natural selection.

In the top panels, the *blue* areas indicate the phenotypes that are being selected for and the *red* areas are the phenotypes that are not being preferentially selected for. The bottom panels show the phenotypic results of the selection. (*a*) In *stabilizing selection*, individuals with midrange phenotypes are favored, with selection acting against both ends of the range of phenotypes. (*b*) In *disruptive selection*, individuals in the middle of the range of phenotypes of a certain trait are selected against, and the extreme forms of the trait are favored. (*c*) In *directional selection*, individuals concentrated toward one extreme of the array of phenotypes are favored.

Selection on Color in Guppies

evolution, biologists have traditionally investigated
happened in the past, sometimes many millions of
. To learn about dinosaurs, a paleontologist looks at
fossils. To study human evolution, an anthropologist
human fossils and, increasingly, examines the "fam-
of mutations that have accumulated in human DNA
ions of years. For the biologists taking this tradi-
roach, evolutionary biology is similar to astronomy
ry, relying on observation rather than experiment to
ideas about past events.

netheless, evolutionary biology is not entirely an obser-
cience. Darwin was right about many things, but one
hich he was mistaken concerns the pace at which evo-
urs. Darwin thought that evolution occurred at a very
ost imperceptible, pace. However, in recent years many
ies have demonstrated that in some circumstances evo-
change can occur rapidly. Consequently, it is possible
sh experimental studies to test evolutionary hypotheses.
laboratory studies on fruit flies and other organisms
common for more than 50 years, it has only been in
ars that scientists have started conducting experimen-
s of evolution in nature. One excellent example of how
ions of the natural world can be combined with rigorous
nts in the lab and in the field concerns research on the
ecilia reticulata.

es Live in Different Environments

py is a popular aquarium fish because of its bright col-
nd prolific reproduction. In nature, guppies are found
streams in northeastern South America and the near-
d of Trinidad. In Trinidad, guppies are found in many
n streams. One interesting feature of several streams is
have waterfalls. Amazingly, guppies and some other
apable of colonizing portions of the stream above the
. The killifish, *Rivulus hartii*, is a particularly good
r; apparently on rainy nights, it will wriggle out of the
nd move through the damp leaf litter. Guppies are not
ient, but they are good at swimming upstream. During
sons, rivers sometimes overflow their banks, creating
y channels that move through the forest. During these
s, guppies may be able to move upstream and invade
ove waterfalls. By contrast, not all species are capable
ispersal and thus are only found in these streams below
waterfall. One species whose distribution is restricted
falls is the pike cichlid, *Crenicichla alta,* a voracious
that feeds on other fish, including guppies.

cause of these barriers to dispersal, guppies can be
two very different environments. The guppies you
g in pools just below the waterfalls in figure 17.18
d with predation by the pike cichlid. This substan-
keeps rates of survival relatively low. By contrast,
r pools just above the waterfall, the only predator

present is the killifish, which only rarely preys on guppies.
Guppy populations above and below waterfalls exhibit many
differences. In the high-predation pools, male guppies exhibit the drab coloration you see in the guppies below the
waterfall in figure 17.18. Moreover, they tend to reproduce
at a younger age and attain relatively smaller adult sizes. By
contrast, male fish above the waterfall in the figure display
gaudy colors that they use to court females. Adults mature
later and grow to larger sizes.

These differences suggest the function of natural selection. In the low-predation environment, males display gaudy
colors and spots that help in mating. Moreover, larger males
are most successful at holding territories and mating with
females, and larger females lay more eggs. Thus, in the absence of predators, larger and more colorful fish may have
produced more offspring, leading to the evolution of those
traits. In pools below the waterfall, however, natural selection would favor different traits. Colorful males are likely to
attract the attention of the pike cichlid, and high predation
rates mean that most fish live short lives; thus, individuals
that are more drab and shunt energy into early reproduction,
rather than into growth to a larger size, are likely to be favored by natural selection.

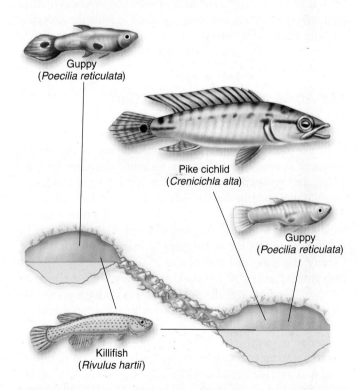

**Figure 17.18 The evolution of protective coloration
in guppies.**

In pools below waterfalls where predation is high, male guppies
(*Poecilia reticulata*) are drab colored. In the absence of the highly
predatory pike cichlid (*Crenicichla alta*), male guppies in pools
above waterfalls are much more colorful and attractive to females.
The killifish (*Rivulus hartii*) is also a predator but only rarely eats
guppies. The evolution of these differences in guppies can be
experimentally tested.

---

the birds that survived were those that were more average in
size. Among the female birds that perished were many more
individuals that had extreme measurements, either very large
or very small. Selection had acted most strongly against
these "extreme-sized" female birds. Stabilizing selection
does not change which phenotype is the most common of
the population—the average-sized birds were already the
most common phenotype—but rather makes it even more
common by eliminating extremes. Many examples similar
to Bumpus's female sparrows are known. In humans, infants
with intermediate weight at birth (the blue-screened area in
figure 17.14a) have the highest survival rate, with the red
line indicating that infant mortality is at its lowest for babies
of intermediate weight. In chickens, eggs of intermediate
weight have the highest hatching success.

Disruptive Selection

In some situations, selection acts to eliminate the intermediate type, the red area under the curve in figure 17.13b, resulting in the two more extreme phenotypes becoming more
common in the population. This type of selection is called
disruptive selection. A clear example is the different beak
sizes of the African black-bellied seedcracker finch *Pyren-
estes ostrinus* (figure 17.14b). Populations of these birds
contain individuals with large and small beaks, but very few
individuals with intermediate-sized beaks. As their name implies, these birds feed on seeds, and the available seeds fall
into two size categories: large and small. Only large-beaked
birds, like the one on the left in the figure, can open the tough
shells of large seeds, whereas birds with the smallest beaks,
like the one on the right, are more adept at handling small
seeds. Birds with intermediate-sized beaks are at a disadvantage with both seed types: unable to open large seeds and
too clumsy to efficiently process small seeds. Consequently,
selection acts to eliminate the intermediate phenotypes, in
effect partitioning the population into two phenotypically
distinct groups.

Directional Selection

When selection acts to eliminate one extreme from an array of
phenotypes—for example, the smaller body sizes indicated by
the red area under the curve in figure 17.13c—the genes determining this extreme become less frequent in the population.
This form of selection is called **directional selection.** In the
Drosophila population illustrated in figure 17.14c, flies that
flew toward light, a behavior called phototropism, were eliminated from the population. The remaining flies were mated
and the experiment repeated. After 20 generations of selected
mating, flies exhibiting phototropism were far less frequent in
the population.

> **17.5** Five evolutionary forces have the potential
> to significantly alter allele and genotype
> frequencies in populations: mutation, migration,
> genetic drift, nonrandom mating, and selection.
> Selection on traits affected by many genes can
> favor intermediate values, or one or both extremes.

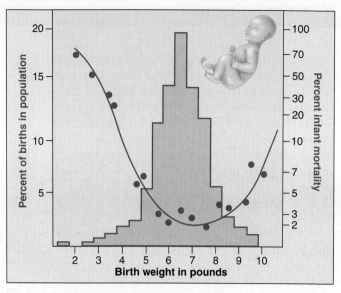

(a) Stabilizing selection for birth weight. The death rate
among human babies is lowest at an intermediate birth weight
between 7 and 8 pounds indicated by the *red* line. The intermediate
weights are also the most common in the population, indicated by
the *blue* area. Larger and smaller babies both occur less frequently
and have a greater tendency to die at or near birth.

(b) Disruptive selection for large and small beaks. Differences
in beak size in the black-bellied seedcracker finch of West Africa are
the result of disruptive selection for two distinct food sources.

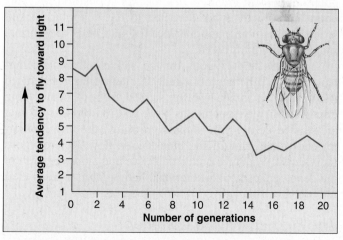

**(c) Directional selection for negative phototropism in
Drosophila.** Individuals of the fly *Drosophila* were selectively bred.
Flies that moved toward light were discarded, and only flies that
moved away from light were used as parents for the next generation. After 20 generations, the offspring of parents that tended not
to fly toward light had an ever greater tendency to avoid light.

Figure 17.14 Examples of selection.

In the time since Darwin suggested the pivotal role of natural selection in evolution, many examples have been found in which natural selection is clearly acting to change the genetic makeup of species, just as Darwin predicted. Here we will examine two examples: sickle-cell anemia (a defect in human hemoglobin proteins) and color selection in South American guppy populations.

17.6 Sickle-Cell Anemia

Sickle-cell anemia is a hereditary disease affecting hemoglobin molecules in the blood. It was first detected in 1904 in Chicago in a blood examination of an individual complaining of tiredness. You can see the original doctor's report in figure 17.15. The disorder arises as a result of a single nucleotide change in the gene encoding β-hemoglobin, one of the key proteins used by red blood cells to transport oxygen. The sickle-cell mutation changes the sixth amino acid in the β-hemoglobin chain (position B6) from glutamic acid (very polar) to valine (nonpolar). The unhappy result of this change is that the nonpolar *valine* at position B6, protruding from a corner of the hemoglobin molecule, fits nicely into a nonpolar pocket on the opposite side of another hemoglobin molecule; the nonpolar regions associate with each other. As the two-molecule unit that forms still has both a B6 valine and an opposite nonpolar pocket, other hemoglobins clump on, and long chains form as in figure 17.16a. The result is the deformed "sickle-shaped" red blood cell you see in figure 17.16b. In normal everyday hemoglobin, by contrast, the polar amino acid *glutamic acid* occurs at position B6. This polar amino acid is not attracted to the nonpolar pocket, so no hemoglobin clumping occurs, and cells are normal shaped as in figure 17.16c.

Persons homozygous for the sickle-cell genetic mutation in the β-hemoglobin gene frequently have a reduced life span. This is because the sickled form of hemoglobin does not carry oxygen atoms well, and red blood cells that are sickled do not flow smoothly through the tiny capillaries but instead jam up and block blood flow. Heterozygous individuals, who have both a defective and a normal form of the gene, make enough functional hemoglobin to keep their red blood cells healthy.

The Puzzle: Why So Common?

The disorder is now known to have originated in Central Africa, where the frequency of the sickle-cell allele is about 0.12. One in 100 people is homozygous for the defective allele and develops the fatal disorder. Sickle-cell anemia affects roughly two African Americans out of every thousand but is almost unknown among other racial groups.

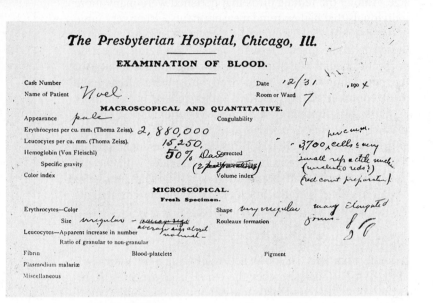

Figure 17.15 The first known sickle-cell anemia patient.
Dr. Ernest Irons's blood examination report on his patient Walter Clement Noel, December 31, 1904, described his oddly shaped red blood cells.

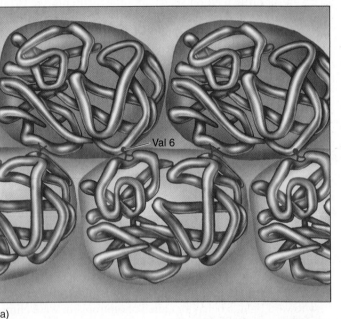

(a)

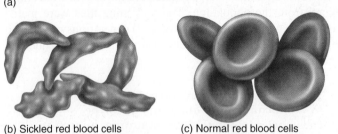

(b) Sickled red blood cells   (c) Normal red blood cells

Figure 17.16 Why the sickle-cell mutation causes hemoglobin to clump.

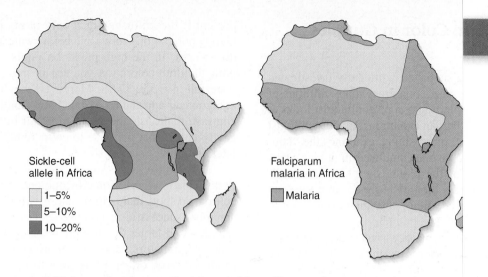

Sickle-cell
allele in Africa

1–5%
5–10%
10–20%

Falciparum
malaria in Africa

Malaria

Figure 17.17 How stabilizing selection maintains sickle-cell anemia.
The diagrams show the frequency of the sickle-cell allele (*left*) and the distribution of falciparum malaria (*right*). Fal the most devastating forms of the often fatal disease. As you can see, its distribution in Africa is closely correlated w sickle-cell characteristic.

If Darwin is right, and natural selection drives evolution, then why has natural selection not acted against the defective allele in Africa and eliminated it from the human population there? Why is this potentially fatal allele instead very common there?

The Answer: Stabilizing Selection

The defective allele has not been eliminated from Central Africa because people who are heterozygous for the sickle-cell allele are much less susceptible to malaria, one of the leading causes of death in Central Africa. Examine the maps in figure 17.17, and you will see the relationship between sickle-cell anemia and malaria clearly. The map on the left shows the frequency of the sickle-cell allele, the darker green areas indicating a 10% to 20% frequency of the allele. The map on the right indicates the distribution of malaria in dark orange. Clearly, the areas that are colored in darker green on the left map overlap many of the dark orange areas in the map on the right. Even though the population pays a high price—the many individuals in each generation who are homozygous for the sickle-cell allele die—the deaths are far fewer than would occur due to malaria if the heterozygous individuals were not malaria resistant. One in 5 individuals (20%) are heterozygous and survive malaria, while only 1 in 100 (1%) are homozygous and die of sickle-cell anemia. Similar inheritance patterns of the sickle-cell allele are found in other countries frequently exposed to malaria, such as areas around the Mediterranean, India, and Indonesia. Natural selection has favored the sickle-cell allele in Central Africa and other areas hit by malaria because the payoff in survival of heterozygotes more than makes up for the price in death of homozygotes. This phenomenon is an example of **heterozygote advantage.**

Stabilizing selection (also called *balancing selection*) is thus acting on the sickle-cell allele: (1) Selection tends to elimi-

nate the sickle-cell allele because of it gous individuals, and (2) selection te allele because it protects heterozygo manager balancing a store's inventory the frequency of an allele in a specie thing to be gained by it, until the cost

Stabilizing selection occurs be counterbalances lethal anemia. Malar has essentially been eradicated in the ly 1950s, and stabilizing selection has allele here. Africans brought to Ame have not gained any evolutionary adva being heterozygous for the sickle-ce efit to being resistant to malaria if th malaria anyway. As a result, the selec allele in America is not counterbalan the allele has become far less comm cans than among native Africans in C

Stabilizing selection is though other human genes in a similar fashi causing cystic fibrosis is unusually Europeans. Apparently, the bacteriu uses the healthy version of the CF to enter the cells it infects, but it can version of the protein. As with sick gotes are protected.

17.6 The prevalence of sickle African populations is though action of natural selection. Na favors individuals carrying on cell allele, because they are re common in Africa.

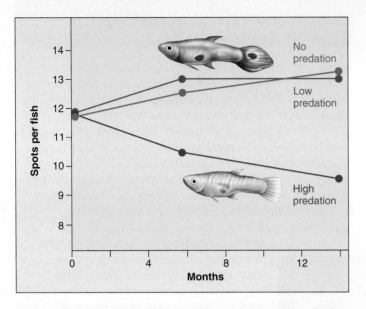

Figure 17.19 Evolutionary change in spot number.
Guppies raised in low-predation or no predation environments in laboratory greenhouses had a greater number of spots, whereas selection in more dangerous environments, like the pools with the highly predatory pike cichlid, led to less conspicuous fish. The same results are seen in field experiments conducted in pools above and below waterfalls (photo).

The Experiments

Although the differences between guppies living above and below the waterfalls suggest that they represent evolutionary responses to differences in the strength of predation, alternative explanations are possible. Perhaps, for example, only very large fish are capable of swimming upstream past the waterfall to colonize pools. If this were the case, then a founder effect would occur in which the new population was established solely by individuals with genes for large size.

Laboratory Experiment The only way to rule out such alternative possibilities is to conduct a controlled experiment. John Endler, now of the University of California, Santa Barbara, conducted the first experiments in large pools in laboratory greenhouses. At the start of the experiment, a group of 2,000 guppies was divided equally among 10 large pools. Six months later, pike cichlids were added to four of the pools and killifish to another four, with the remaining two pools left to serve as "no predator" controls. Fourteen months later (which corresponds to 10 guppy generations), the scientists compared the populations. You can see their results in figure 17.19. The guppies in the killifish pool (the blue line) and control pools (the green line) were notably large, brightly colored fish with about 13 colorful spots per individual. In contrast, the guppies in the pike cichlid pools (the red line) were smaller and drab in coloration, with a reduced number of spots (about 9 per fish). These results clearly suggest that predation can lead to rapid evolutionary change, but do these laboratory experiments reflect what occurs in nature?

Field Experiment To find out, Endler and colleagues—including David Reznick, now at the University of California, Riverside—located two streams that had guppies in pools below a waterfall, but not above it (see photograph in figure 17.19). As in other Trinidadian streams, the pike cichlid was present in the lower pools, but only the killifish was found above the waterfalls. The scientists then transplanted guppies to the upper pools and returned at several-year intervals to monitor the populations. Despite originating from populations in which predation levels were high, the transplanted populations rapidly evolved the traits characteristic of low-predation guppies: They matured late, attained greater size and had brighter colors. Control populations in the lower pools, by contrast, continued to be drab and matured early and at smaller sizes. Laboratory studies confirmed that the differences between the populations were the result of genetic differences. These results demonstrate that substantial evolutionary change can occur in less than 12 years. More generally, these studies indicate how scientists can formulate hypotheses about how evolution occurs and then test these hypotheses in natural conditions. The results give strong support to the theory of evolution by natural selection.

> **17.7 Experiments can be conducted in nature to test hypotheses about how evolution occurs. Such studies reveal that natural selection can lead to rapid evolutionary change.**

Are Bird-Killing Cats Nature's Way of Making Better Birds?

Death is not pretty, early in the morning on the doorstep. A small dead bird was left at our front door one morning, lying by the newspaper as if it might at any moment fly away. I knew it would not. Like other birds before it, it was a gift to our household by Feisty, a cat who lives with us. Feisty is a killer of birds, and every so often he leaves one for us, like rent.

We have four cats, and the other three, true housecats, would not know what to do with a bird. Feisty is different, a long-haired gray Persian with the soul of a hunter. While the other three cats sleep safely in the house with us, Feisty spends most nights outside, prowling.

Feisty's nocturnal donations are not well received by my family. More than once it has been suggested, as we donate the bird to the trashman, that perhaps Feisty would be happier living in the country.

As a biologist I try to take a more scientific view. I tell my girls that getting rid of Feisty is unwarranted, because hunting cats like Feisty actually help birds, in a Darwinian sort of way. Like an evolutionary quality control check, I explain, predators ensure that only those individuals of a population that are better-suited to their environment contribute to the next generation, by the simple expedient of removing the lesser-suited. By taking the birds who are least able to escape predation—the sick and the old—Feisty culls the local bird population, leaving it on average a little better off.

That's what I tell my girls. It all makes sense, from a biological point of view, and it is a story they have heard before, in movies like *Never Cry Wolf*, and *The Lion King*. So Feisty is given a reprieve, and survives to hunt another night.

What I haven't told my girls is how little evidence actually backs up this pretty defense of Feisty's behavior. My explanation may be couched in scientific language, but without proof this "predator-as-purifier" tale is no more than a hypothesis. It might be true, and then again it might not. By such thin string has Feisty's future with our family hung.

Recently the string became a strong cable. Two French biologists put the hypothesis I had been using to defend Feisty to the test. To my great relief, it was supported.

Drs. Anders Møller and Johannes Erritzoe of the Université Pierre et Marie Curie in Paris devised a simple way to test the hypothesis. They compared the health of birds killed by domestic cats like Feisty with that of birds killed in accidents such as flying into glass windows or moving cars. Glass windows do not select for the weak or infirm—a healthy bird flies into a glass window and breaks its neck just as easily as a sickly bird. If cats are actually selecting the less-healthy birds, then their prey should include a larger proportion of sickly individuals than those felled by flying into glass windows.

How can we know what birds are sickly? Drs. Møller and Erritzoe examined the size of the dead bird's spleens. The size of its spleen is a good indicator of how healthy a bird is. Birds experiencing a lot of infections, or harboring a lot of parasites, have smaller spleens than healthy birds.

They examined 18 species of birds, more than 500 individuals. In all but two species (robins and goldcrests) they found that the spleens of birds killed by cats were significantly smaller than those killed accidently. We're not splitting hairs here, talking about some minor statistical difference. Spleens were on average a third smaller in cat-killed birds. In five bird species (blackcaps, house sparrows, lesser whitethroats, skylarks, and spotted flycatchers), the spleens of birds pounced on by cats were less than half the size of those killed by flying at speed into glass windows or moving cars.

As a control to be sure that additional factors were not operating, the Paris biologists checked for other differences between birds killed by cats and birds killed accidentally. Weight, sex, and wing length, all of which you could imagine might be important, were not significant. Cat-killed birds had, on average, the same weight, proportion of females, and wing length as accident-killed birds.

One other factor did make a difference: age. About 50% of the birds killed accidently were young, while fully 70% of the birds killed by cats were. Apparently it's not quite so easy to catch an experienced old codger as it is a callow youth.

So Feisty was just doing Darwin's duty, I pleaded, informing my girls that the birds he catches would soon have died anyway. But a dead bird on a doorstep argues louder than any science, and they remained unconvinced.

They are my daughters, and thus not ones to give in without a fight. Scouring the Internet, they assembled this counter-argument: Predatory house cats not unlike Feisty, as well as feral cats (domesticated cats that have been abandoned to the wild), are causing major problems for native bird populations of England, New Zealand, and Australia, as well as here in the United States. Although house cats like Feisty have the predatory instincts of their ancestors, they seem to lack the restraint that their wild relatives have. Most wild cats hunt only when hungry, but pet and feral cats seem to "love the kill," not killing for food but for sport.

So Darwin and I lost this argument. It seems I must restrict Feisty's hunting expeditions after all. While a little pruning may benefit a bird population, wholesale slaughter only devastates it. I will always see a lion whenever I look at Feisty on the prowl, but it will be a lion restricted to indoor hunting.

17.8 The Biological Species Concept

A key aspect of Darwin's theory of evolution is his proposal that adaptation (microevolution) leads ultimately to large-scale changes leading to species formation and higher taxonomic groups (macroevolution). The way natural selection leads to the formation of new species has been thoroughly documented by biologists, who have observed the stages of the species-forming process, or **speciation,** in many different plants, animals, and microorganisms. Speciation usually involves successive change: First, local populations become increasingly specialized; then, if they become different enough, natural selection may act to keep them that way.

Before we can discuss how one species gives rise to another, we need to understand exactly what a species is. The evolutionary biologist Ernst Mayr coined the **biological species concept,** which defines species as "groups of actually or potentially interbreeding natural populations which are reproductively isolated from other such groups."

In other words, the biological species concept says that a species is composed of populations whose members mate with each other and produce fertile offspring—or would do so if they came into contact. Conversely, populations whose members do not mate with each other or who cannot produce fertile offspring are said to be **reproductively isolated** and, thus, members of different species.

What causes reproductive isolation? If organisms cannot interbreed or cannot produce fertile offspring, they clearly belong to different species. However, some populations that are considered to be separate species can interbreed and produce fertile offspring, but they ordinarily do not do so under natural conditions. They are still considered to be reproductively isolated in that genes from one species generally will not be able to enter the gene pool of the other species. Table 17.2 summarizes the steps at which barriers to successful reproduction may occur. Examine this table carefully. We will return to it throughout our discussion of species formation. Such barriers are termed **reproductive isolating mechanisms** because they prevent genetic exchange between species. We will first discuss **prezygotic isolating mechanisms,** those that prevent the formation of zygotes. Then we will examine **postzygotic isolating mechanisms,** those that prevent the proper functioning of zygotes after they have formed.

Even though the definition of what constitutes a species is of fundamental importance to evolutionary biology, this issue has still not been completely settled and is currently the subject of considerable research and debate.

17.8 A species is generally defined as a group of similar organisms that does not exchange genes extensively with other groups in nature.

TABLE 17.2 ISOLATING MECHANISMS

Mechanism		Description
Prezygotic Isolating Mechanisms		
Geographic isolation		Species occur in different areas, which are often separated by a physical barrier such as a river or mountain range.
Ecological isolation		Species occur in the same area, but they occupy different habitats. Survival of hybrids is low because they are not adapted to either environment of their parents.
Temporal isolation		Species reproduce in different seasons or at different times of the day.
Behavioral isolation		Species differ in their mating rituals.
Mechanical isolation		Structural differences between species prevent mating.
Prevention of gamete fusion		Gametes of one species function poorly with the gametes of another species or within the reproductive tract of another species.
Postzygotic Isolating Mechanisms		
Hybrid inviability or infertility		Hybrid embryos do not develop properly, hybrid adults do not survive in nature, or hybrid adults are sterile or have reduced fertility.

Prezygotic Isolating Mechanisms

Geographical Isolation This mechanism is perhaps the easiest to understand; species that exist in different areas are not able to interbreed. The two populations of flowers in the first panel of table 17.2 are separated by a mountain range and so would not be capable of interbreeding.

Ecological Isolation Even if two species occur in the same area, they may utilize different portions of the environment and thus not hybridize because they do not encounter each other, like the lizards in the second panel of table 17.2. One lives on the ground and the other in the trees. Another example in nature is the ranges of lions and tigers in India. Their ranges overlapped until about 150 years ago. Even when they did overlap, however, there were no records of natural hybrids. Lions stayed mainly in the open grassland and hunted in groups called prides; tigers tended to be solitary creatures of the forest. Because of their ecological and behavioral differences, lions and tigers rarely came into direct contact with each other, even though their ranges overlapped thousands of square kilometers. Figure 17.20 shows that hybrids are possible; the tigon shown in figure 17.20c is a hybrid of a lion and tiger. These matings do not occur in the wild but can happen in artificial environments such as zoos.

Temporal Isolation *Lactuca graminifolia* and *L. canadensis*, two species of wild lettuce, grow together along roadsides throughout the southeastern United States. Hybrids between these two species are easily made experimentally and are completely fertile. But such hybrids are rare in nature because *L. graminifolia* flowers in early spring and *L. canadensis* flowers in summer. This is called temporal isolation and is shown in the third panel in table 17.2. When the blooming periods of these two species overlap, as they do occasionally, the two species do form hybrids, which may become locally abundant.

Behavioral Isolation In chapter 39, we will consider the often elaborate courtship and mating rituals of some groups of animals, which tend to keep these species distinct in nature even if they inhabit the same places. This behavioral isolation is discussed in the fourth panel of table 17.2. For example, mallard and pintail ducks are perhaps the two most common freshwater ducks in North America. In captivity, they produce completely fertile offspring, but in nature they nest side-by-side and rarely hybridize.

Mechanical Isolation Structural differences that prevent mating between related species of animals and plants is called mechanical isolation and is shown in panel five of table 17.2. Flowers of related species of plants often differ significantly in their proportions and structures. Some of these differences limit the transfer of pollen from one plant species to another. For example, bees may pick up the pollen of one species on a

(a)

(b)

(c)

Figure 17.20 Lions and tigers are ecologically isolated.

The ranges of lions and tigers used to overlap in India. However, lions and tigers do not hybridize in the wild because they utilize different portions of the habitat. (a) Tigers are solitary animals that live in the forest, whereas (b) lions live in open grassland. (c) Hybrids, such as this tigon, have been successfully produced in captivity, but hybridization does not occur in the wild.

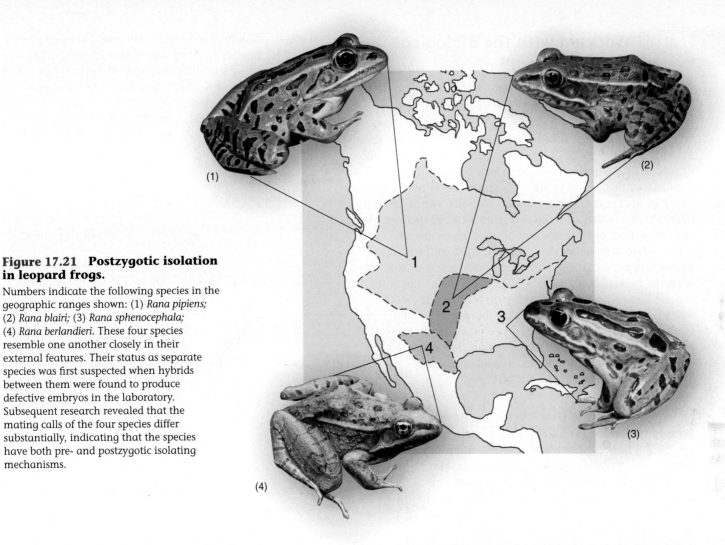

Figure 17.21 Postzygotic isolation in leopard frogs.
Numbers indicate the following species in the geographic ranges shown: (1) *Rana pipiens;* (2) *Rana blairi;* (3) *Rana sphenocephala;* (4) *Rana berlandieri*. These four species resemble one another closely in their external features. Their status as separate species was first suspected when hybrids between them were found to produce defective embryos in the laboratory. Subsequent research revealed that the mating calls of the four species differ substantially, indicating that the species have both pre- and postzygotic isolating mechanisms.

certain place on their bodies; if this area does not come into contact with the receptive structures of the flowers of another plant species, the pollen is not transferred.

Prevention of Gamete Fusion In animals that shed their gametes directly into water, eggs and sperm derived from different species may not attract one another. Many land animals may not hybridize successfully because the sperm of one species may function so poorly within the reproductive tract of another that fertilization never takes place. In plants, the growth of pollen tubes may be impeded in hybrids between different species. In both plants and animals, the operation of such isolating mechanisms prevents the union of gametes even following successful mating. The sixth panel in table 17.2 discusses this isolating mechanism.

Postzygotic Isolating Mechanisms

All of the factors we have discussed up to this point tend to prevent hybridization. If hybrid matings do occur, and zygotes are produced, many factors may still prevent those zygotes from developing into normally functioning, fertile individuals. Development in any species is a complex process. In hybrids, the genetic complements of two species may be so different that they cannot function together normally in embryonic development. For example, hybridization between sheep and goats usually produces embryos that die in the earliest developmental stages.

Figure 17.21 shows four species of leopard frogs (genus *Rana*) and their ranges throughout North America. It was assumed for a long time that they constituted a single species. However, careful examination revealed that although the frogs appear similar, successful mating between them is rare because of problems that occur as the fertilized eggs develop. Many of the hybrid combinations cannot be produced even in the laboratory. Examples of this kind, in which similar species have been recognized only as a result of hybridization experiments, are common in plants.

Even if hybrids survive the embryo stage, however, they may not develop normally. If the hybrids are weaker than their parents, they will almost certainly be eliminated in nature. Even if they are vigorous and strong, as in the case of the mule, a hybrid between a female horse and a male donkey, they may still be sterile and thus incapable of contributing to succeeding generations. Sterility may result in hybrids because the development of sex organs may be abnormal, because the chromosomes derived from the respective parents may not pair properly, or from a variety of other causes.

> **17.9** Prezygotic isolating mechanisms lead to reproductive isolation by preventing the formation of hybrid zygotes. Postzygotic mechanisms lead to the failure of hybrid zygotes to develop normally, or prevent hybrids from becoming established in nature.

17.10 Working with the Biological Species Concept

Speciation is a two-part process. First, initially identical populations must diverge. Second, reproductive isolation must evolve to maintain these differences, overcoming the homogenizing effect of gene flow between populations, which acts to erase any differences that may arise, either by genetic drift or natural selection. However, gene flow occurs only between populations that are in contact, so speciation is much more likely in geographically isolated populations, which become isolated for a variety of reasons. Figure 17.22 gives three examples of how populations can become geographically isolated. A bird or population of birds flying from the mainland and colonizing an island is geographically isolated from the birds on the mainland (figure 17.22a). The population in figure 17.22b splits into two different populations when a volcano reduces movement between the two populations. In figure 17.22c, two populations are linked by an intermediate population. The extinction of the intermediate population prevents gene flow and isolates the far populations.

Allopatric Divergence

Ernst Mayr was the first biologist to strongly make the case for **allopatric speciation.** Marshalling data from a wide variety of organisms and localities, Mayr was clearly able to demonstrate that geographically separated, or *allopatric,* populations appear much more likely to have evolved substantial differences leading to speciation. For example, the Papuan kingfisher, *Tanysiptera hydrocharis,* varies little throughout its wide range in New Guinea despite the great variation in the island's topography and climate. By contrast, isolated populations on nearby islands are strikingly different from each other.

Sympatric Speciation

Sympatric speciation is one species splitting into two at a single locality, without the new species ever having been geographically separated. Instantaneous sympatric speciation occurs when an individual is reproductively isolated from all other members of its species through the process of **polyploidy,** the condition describing an individual who has more than two sets of chromosomes. Polyploids can self-fertilize or mate with other similar polyploids but *not* with the parent diploid species (hence reproductive isolation and speciation). Polyploidy occurs commonly in plants but is more rare in animals.

Polyploids can arise in two ways. In **autopolyploidy,** all sets of the chromosomes are from the same species. Typically, the chromosomes in a gamete of a diploid species fail to separate in meiosis. The gamete thus possesses two sets of chromosomes rather than one. This gamete cannot produce fertile offspring with a normal gamete because such offspring are triploid (three sets of chromosomes) and so are sterile. Occasionally, however, the chromosomes of such a gamete spontaneously double, forming a viable zygote. Such individuals, termed tetraploids, can fertilize themselves or mate with other tetraploids. A new species has formed.

A more common type of polyploid speciation is **allopolyploidy,** which occurs sometimes when two species hybridize. The resulting offspring, with one copy of the chromosomes of each species, is usually infertile because the chromosomes have no pairing partners in meiosis. However, such individuals are often otherwise healthy and can reproduce asexually, and if the chromosomes of such an individual spontaneously double, as just described, the resulting tetraploid would have

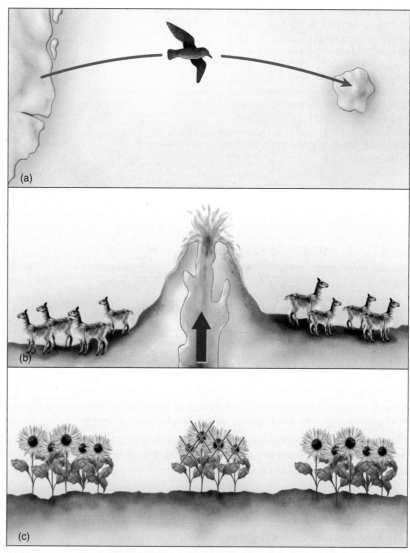

Figure 17.22 Populations can become geographically isolated for a variety of reasons.

(a) Colonization of distant areas by one or a few individuals can establish populations in a distant place. (b) Barriers to movement can split an ancestral population into two isolated populations. (c) Extinction of intermediate populations can leave the remaining populations isolated from each other.

two copies of each set of chromosomes. Consequently, pairing would no longer be a problem in meiosis because each chromosome could pair with its double. As a result, such tetraploids would be able to intermate, and a new species would have been created.

It is estimated that about half of the approximately 260,000 species of plants have a polyploid episode in their history, including many of great commercial importance, such as bread wheat, cotton, tobacco, sugarcane, bananas, and potatoes. Although much rarer than in plants, speciation by polyploidy is also known from a variety of animals, including insects, fish, and salamanders.

Problems with the Biological Species Concept

The biological species concept has proven to be an effective way of understanding the existence of species in nature. Nonetheless, it has a number of problems that have led some scientists to propose alternative species concepts.

Reproductive Isolation in Plants One criticism concerns the extent to which all species truly are reproductively isolated. By definition, under the biological species concept, species should not interbreed and produce fertile offspring. Nonetheless, in recent years, biologists have detected much greater amounts of hybridization than previously realized between populations that seem to coexist as distinct biological entities. Botanists have always been aware that species can often experience substantial amounts of hybridization. For example, more than 50% of California plant species included in one study were not well defined by genetic isolation. Such coexistence without genetic isolation can be long-lasting. Fossil data show that balsam poplars and cottonwoods have been phenotypically distinct for 12 million years but have routinely produced hybrids throughout this time. Consequently, many botanists have long felt that the biological species concept only applies to animals, mainly vertebrates.

Reproductive Isolation in Animals What is becoming increasingly evident, however, is that hybridization is not all that uncommon in animals, either. One recent survey indicated that almost 10% of the world's 9,500 bird species are known to have hybridized in nature. Recent years have seen the documentation of many cases of substantial hybridization between animal species. Galápagos finches provide a particularly well-studied example. Three species on the island of Daphne Major—the medium ground finch, the cactus finch, and the small ground finch—are clearly distinct morphologically and occupy different ecological niches. Studies over the past 20 years by Peter and Rosemary Grant found that, on average, 2% of the medium ground finches and 1% of the cactus finches mated with other species every year. Furthermore, hybrid offspring appeared to be at no disadvantage in terms of survival or subsequent reproduction. This is not a trivial amount of genetic exchange, and one might expect to see the species coalesce into one genetically variable population, but the species are maintaining their distinctiveness.

This is not to say hybridization is rampant throughout the animal world. Most bird species do not hybridize, and even fewer probably experience significant amounts of hybridization. Still, it is common enough to cast doubt about whether reproductive isolation is the only force maintaining the integrity of species.

Other Problems with the Biological Species Concept The biological species concept has been criticized for other reasons as well. For example, it can be difficult to apply the concept to populations that do not occur together in nature or together in time, such as extinct species. Because individuals of these populations do not encounter each other, it is not possible to observe whether they would interbreed naturally. Although experiments can determine whether fertile hybrids can be produced, this information is not enough because many species that will coexist without interbreeding in nature will readily hybridize in the artificial settings of the laboratory or zoo. Consequently, evaluating whether such populations constitute different species is ultimately a judgment call. In addition, the concept is more limited than its name would imply. The vast majority of organisms on this earth are asexual and reproduce without mating; reproductive isolation has no meaning for such organisms.

Natural Selection and the Ecological Species Concept

An alternative hypothesis is that the distinctions among species are maintained by natural selection. The idea is that each species has adapted to its own specific part of the environment. Stabilizing selection then maintains the species' adaptations; hybridization has little effect because alleles introduced into the gene pool from other species are quickly eliminated by natural selection.

This and a variety of other ideas put forward to establish criteria for defining species are specific to a particular type of organism, and none has universal applicability. In truth, it may be that there is no single explanation for what maintains the identity of species. Given the incredible variation evident in plants, animals, and microorganisms in all aspects of their biology, it is perhaps not surprising that different processes are operating in different organisms. In addition, some scientists have turned from emphasizing the processes that maintain species distinctions to examining the history of populations. These genealogical species concepts are currently a topic of great debate. The study of species concepts is thus an area of active research that demonstrates the dynamic nature of the field of evolutionary biology.

17.10 Speciation occurs much more readily in the absence of gene flow among populations. However, speciation can occur in sympatry by means of polyploidy. Because of the diversity of living organisms, no single definition of what constitutes a species may be universally applicable.

Does Natural Selection Act on Enzyme Polymorphism?

The essence of Darwin's theory of evolution is that, in nature, selection favors some gene alternatives over others. Many studies of natural selection have focused on genes encoding enzymes because populations in nature tend to possess many alternative alleles of their enzymes (a phenomenon called *enzyme polymorphism*). Often investigators have looked to see if weather influences which alleles are more common in natural populations. A particularly nice example of such a study was carried out on a fish, the mummichog (*Fundulus heteroclitus*), which ranges along the East Coast of North America. Researchers studied allele frequencies of the gene encoding the enzyme lactate dehydrogenase, which catalyzes the conversion of pyruvate to lactate. As you learned in chapter 8, this reaction is a key step in energy metabolism, particularly when oxygen is in short supply. There are two common alleles of lactate dehydrogenase in these fish populations, with allele *a* being a better catalyst at lower temperatures than allele *b*.

In an experiment, investigators sampled the frequency of allele *a* in 41 fish populations located over 14 degrees of latitude, from Jacksonville, Florida (31° North), to Bar Harbor, Maine (44° North). Annual mean water temperatures change 1° C per degree change in latitude. The survey is designed to test a prediction of the hypothesis that natural selection acts on this enzyme polymorphism. If it does, then you would expect that allele *a*, producing a better "low-temperature" enzyme, would be more common in the colder waters of the more northern latitudes. The graph on the right presents the results of this survey. The points on the graph are derived from pie chart data such as shown for 20 populations in the map (a **pie chart diagram** assigns a slice of the pie to each variable; the size of the slice is proportional to the contribution made by that variable to the total). The blue line on the graph is the line that best fits the data (a **"best-fit" line,** also called a **regression line,** is determined statistically by a process called *regression analysis*).

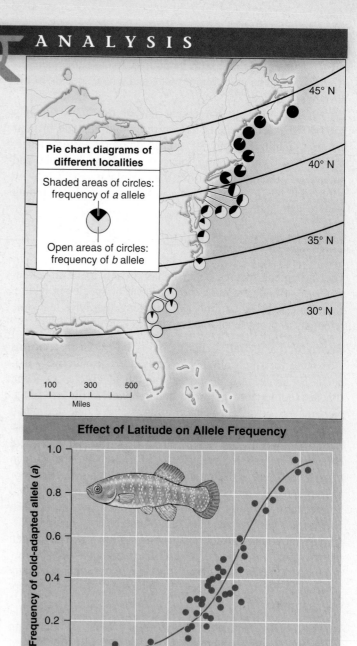

1. **Applying Concepts**
   a. Variable. In the graph, what is the dependent variable?
   b. Reading pie charts. In the fish population located at 35° N latitude, what is the frequency of the *a* allele? Locate this point on the graph.
   c. Analyzing a continuous variable. Compare the frequency of allele *a* among fish captured in waters at 44° N latitude with the frequency among fish captured at 31° N latitude. Is there a pattern? Describe it.
2. **Interpreting Data** At what latitude do fish populations exhibit the greatest variability in allele *a* frequency?
3. **Making Inferences**
   a. Are fish populations in cold waters at 44° N latitude

more or less likely to contain heterozygous individuals than fish populations in warm waters at 31° N latitude? Why this difference, or lack of it?
   b. Where along this latitudinal gradient in the frequency of allele *a* would you expect to find the highest frequency of heterozygous individuals? Why?
4. **Drawing Conclusions** Are the differences in population frequencies of allele *a* consistent with the hypothesis that natural selection is acting on the alleles encoding this enzyme? Explain.
5. **Further Analysis** If you were to release fish captured at 32° N into populations located at 44° N, so that the local population now had equal frequencies of the two alleles, what would you expect to happen in future generations? How might you test this prediction?

The Theory of Evolution

17.1 Evolution: Getting from There to Here

- The process of evolution through natural selection involves several elements: Genetic variation is passed down from parents to offspring. Inherited traits may help certain offspring survive to reproduce, contributing more individuals to the next generation. Over time the population changes to reflect the traits of the more successful reproducers.

- Darwin's proposal of evolution by natural selection focuses primarily on microevolution. Microevolution occurs as changes in allele frequencies in a population. Over time, microevolution can lead to macroevolution, large-scale changes that lead to the formation of new species (**figure 17.1**).

- The rate of evolution is not the same in all populations. Some evolve at a uniform rate, gradualism, while others evolve in spurts, punctuated equilibrium (**figure 17.2**).

17.2 The Evidence for Evolution

- The evidence for evolution includes the fossil record. The titanothere and its ancestors are known only from the fossil record (**figure 17.3**). The fossil record reveals organisms that are intermediate in form between the ancestral species and the present-day species.

- The evidence for evolution includes the anatomical record, which reveals similarities in structures between species (**figure 17.4**). Homologous structures are similar in structure but differ in their functions (**figure 17.5**). Analogous structures are similar in function but differ in their underlying structure. Analogous structures arise from convergent evolution (**figure 17.6**).

- The evidence for evolution includes the molecular record, which traces changes in the genomes of populations and taxonomic groups over time (**figures 17.7** and **17.8**).

17.3 Evolution's Critics

- Darwin's theory of evolution through natural selection has always had its critics. Their criticisms of evolution however are without scientific merit (**figures 17.9** and **17.10**).

How Populations Evolve

17.4 Genetic Change Within Populations: The Hardy-Weinberg Rule

- If a population follows the five assumptions of Hardy-Weinberg, the frequencies of alleles within the population will not change (**figure 17.11**). However, if a population is small, has selective mating, experiences mutations, migration, or is under the influence of natural selection, the allele frequencies will be different from those predicted by the Hardy-Weinberg Rule.

17.5 Agents of Evolution

- Five factors act on populations to change their allele and genotype frequencies (**table 17.1**). Mutations are changes in DNA. Migrations are the movements of individuals or alleles into or out of a population. Genetic drift is the random loss of alleles in a population due to chance occurrences, not due to fitness. In the founder effect, a small group of individuals establishes a new population such that their alleles, whether common or rare in the parent population, become common in the newly established population. Nonrandom mating occurs when individuals seek out mates based on certain traits. Selection occurs when individuals with certain traits leave more offspring because their traits allow them to better respond to the challenges of their environment.

- Selection can change allele frequencies. When a trait is controlled by more than one gene, selection can act on the genes in that population in several different ways (**figure 17.13**). Stabilizing selection tends to reduce extreme phenotypes, making the intermediate phenotype more common (**figure 17.14a**). Disruptive selection tends to reduce intermediate phenotypes, leaving extreme phenotypes in the population (**figure 17.14b**). Directional selection tends to reduce one extreme phenotype from the population (**figure 17.14c**).

Adaptation Within Populations

17.6 Sickle-Cell Anemia

- Sickle-cell anemia is an example of heterozygote advantage, where individuals who are heterozygous for a trait tend to survive better under certain conditions than individuals who are homozygous dominant or homozygous recessive. In areas with malaria, people who are heterozygous for the sickle-cell trait survive better than individuals with either of the two homozygous phenotypes (**figures 17.16** and **17.17**).

17.7 Selection on Color in Guppies

- Experimentation, both in the laboratory and in the field, have shown evolutionary change in guppy populations due to natural selection (**figures 17.18** and **17.19**).

How Species Form

17.8 The Biological Species Concept

- The biological species concept states that a species is a group of organisms that mate with each other and produce fertile offspring, or would do so if in contact with each other. If they cannot mate, or mate but cannot produce fertile offspring, they are said to be reproductively isolated. Many barriers to successful reproduction lead to reproductive isolation, such as temporal isolation shown here from **table 17.2**, which is when species mate at different times of the day or year.

17.9 Isolating Mechanisms

- There are two types of isolating mechanisms, prezygotic and postzygotic (**table 17.2**). Prezygotic isolating mechanisms prevent the formation of a hybrid zygote. Postzygotic isolating mechanisms prevent normal development of a hybrid zygote or result in sterile offspring (**figure 17.21**).

17.10 Working with the Biological Species Concept

- Speciation is more likely to occur between populations that are geographically isolated from each other, called allopatric speciation (**figure 17.22**). The biological species concept doesn't explain all situations of speciation, and so other concepts have been proposed, but no single concept is adequate.

1. Change in organisms over time that results in the formation of new species is known as
    a. natural selection.
    c. macroevolution.
    b. microevolution.
    d. punctuated equilibrium.

2. One of the major sources of evidence for evolution is in the comparative anatomy of organisms. Features that have a similar look but different structural origin are called
    a. homologous structures.
    c. vestigial structures.
    b. analogous structures.
    d. equivalent structures.

3. Homologous structures in organisms are the result of
    a. divergence.
    c. stasis.
    b convergent evolution.
    d. polyploidy.

4. A factor that doesn't affect Hardy-Weinberg equilibrium is
    a. natural selection.
    c. migration.
    b. large population size.
    d. mutation.

5. A large group of organisms lives in a large, stable ecosystem. There is no competition for resources. Individuals mate at random. All organisms appear to be identical except for a few individuals in the most recent generation of offspring that exhibit a different fur coat color and pattern. The ecosystem and population are geographically isolated from other populations of the same organism. Which Hardy-Weinberg assumption has been violated?
    a. large population size
    b. random mating within the population
    c. no mutation within the population
    d. no input of new alleles from outside or loss of alleles

6. A population of 1,000 individuals has 200 individuals who show a homozygous recessive phenotype and 800 individuals who express the dominant phenotype. What is the frequency of homozygous recessive individuals in this population?
    a. 0.20
    c. 0.45
    b. 0.30
    d. 0.55

7. A chance event occurs that causes a population to lose some individuals (they died)—hence, a loss of alleles in the population results from
    a. mutation.
    c. selection.
    b. migration.
    d. genetic drift.

8. Selection that causes one extreme phenotype to be more frequent in a population is an example of
    a. disruptive selection.
    c. directional selection.
    b. stabilizing selection.
    d. equivalent selection.

9. A key element of Ernst Mayr's biological species concept is
    a. homologous isolation.
    c. convergent isolation.
    b. divergent isolation.
    d. reproductive isolation.

10. Sympatric species are populations of species that live in the same habitat. Sympatric species of deer mice (*Peromyscus* sp.) are externally identical. However, the males of different species have a differently shaped baculum, or bone found in the penis. This is an example of which type of reproductive isolation?
    a. temporal
    c. behavioral
    b. mechanical
    d. ecological

1. **Figure 17.13** Because of prolonged drought, the trees on an island are producing nuts that are much smaller with thicker and harder shells. What will happen to the birds that depend on the nuts for food? What type of selection will result?

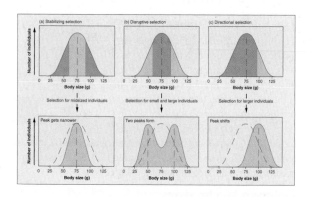

2. **Table 17.2** A very heavy rainstorm floods a mountain river, changing its course and digging a deep canyon through the soft soils of the meadow in the valley below. How could mice populations on either side of the valley be affected?

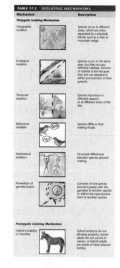

1. How does microevolution differ from macroevolution?

2. How likely is it that any naturally occurring population on a continent (not on an island) will meet all the assumptions of the Hardy-Weinberg rule? Explain your reasoning.

3. Use Hardy-Weinberg and the tenets of natural selection to explain why there are colorful, large guppies in pools without pike cichlids, and drab, small guppies when pike cichlids are present.

4. In a courtroom in 2005, biologist Ken Miller criticized the claims of intelligent design. After noting that 99.9% of the organisms that have ever lived on earth are now extinct, he said that "an intelligent designer who designed things, 99.9% of which didn't last, certainly wouldn't be very intelligent." Evaluate Miller's criticism.

19

Prokaryotes: The First Single-Celled Creatures

These two children wait in May 1995 outside the hospital in the Congo (formerly Zaire) town of Kikwit, where their parents and others infected with Ebola virus are being isolated. Seventy-eight percent of the infected died. Although viruses are not organisms—just fragments of DNA or RNA encased in protein—they can have a deadly impact on living organisms. Even the simplest living creatures, prokaryotes, are subject to viral infection; multiplying within infected cells, the viruses eventually burst forth, killing the cell. A person infected with Ebola virus suffers a similar fate, the virus invading connective tissue and fatally rupturing blood vessels. It used to be popular to talk of viruses as somehow transitional between living and nonliving, but biologists no longer hold this view. Rather, viruses are viewed as renegade segments of genomes, bits of DNA or RNA that have broken away from chromosomes but, using a host cell's machinery, are still able to produce copies of themselves. In this chapter, we will examine the simplest cellular organisms, the prokaryotes, and the viruses that infect them. We begin with a discussion on the origins of life and an examination of bacteria and archaea. We finish by taking a closer look at the viruses that infect animals and plants. Many of them have a major impact on human health; for example, influenza has been responsible for millions of human deaths.

19.1   Origin of Life

All living organisms are constructed of the same four kinds of macromolecules, discussed in chapter 4, the bricks and mortar of cells. Where the first macromolecules came from and how they came to be assembled together into cells are among the least understood questions in biology—questions that address the very origin of life itself.

No one knows for sure where the first organisms (thought to be like today's bacteria) came from. It is not possible to go back in time and watch how life originated, nor are there any witnesses. Nevertheless, it is difficult to avoid being curious about the origin of life, about what, or who, is responsible for the appearance of the first living organisms on earth. There are, in principle, at least three possibilities:

1. **Extraterrestrial origin.** Life may not have originated on earth at all but instead may have been carried to it, perhaps as an extraterrestrial infection of spores originating on a planet of a distant star. How life came to exist on that planet is a question we cannot hope to answer soon.
2. **Special creation.** Life-forms may have been put on earth by supernatural or divine forces. This viewpoint, called *creationism* or *intelligent design,* is common to most Western religions. However, almost all scientists reject creationism and intelligent design because to accept its supernatural explanation requires abandoning the scientific approach.
3. **Evolution.** Life may have evolved from inanimate matter, with associations among molecules becoming more and more complex. In this view, the force leading to life was selection; changes in molecules that increased their stability caused the molecules to persist longer.

In this text, we focus on the third possibility and attempt to understand whether the forces of evolution could have led to the origin of life and, if so, how the process might have occurred. This is not to say that the third possibility, evolution, is definitely the correct one. Any one of the three possibilities might be true. Nor does the third possibility preclude religion: A divine agency might have acted via evolution. Rather, we are limiting the scope of our inquiry to scientific matters. Of the three possibilities, only the third permits testable hypotheses to be constructed and so provides the only scientific explanation—that is, one that could potentially be disproved by experiment.

Forming Life's Building Blocks

How can we learn about the origin of the first cells? One way is to try to reconstruct what the earth was like when life originated 2.5 billion years ago. We know from rocks that there was little or no oxygen in the earth's atmosphere then and more of the hydrogen-rich gases hydrogen sulfide (SH_2), ammonia (NH_3), and methane (CH_4). Electrons in these gases would have been frequently pushed to higher energy levels by photons crashing into them from the sun or by electrical energy in lightning (figure 19.1). Today, high-energy electrons are quickly soaked up by the oxygen in earth's atmosphere (air is 21% oxygen, all of it contributed by photosynthesis) because oxygen atoms have a great "thirst" for such electrons. But in the absence of oxygen, high-energy electrons would have been free to help form biological molecules.

When the scientists Stanley Miller and Harold Urey reconstructed the oxygen-free atmosphere of the early earth in their laboratory and subjected it to the lightning and UV radiation it would have experienced then, they found that many of the building blocks of organisms, such as amino acids and nucleotides, formed spontaneously. They concluded that life may have evolved in a "primordial soup" of biological molecules formed in the ancient earth's oceans.

Figure 19.1   Lightning provides energy to form molecules.

Before life evolved, the simple molecules in the earth's atmosphere combined to form more complex molecules. The energy that drove these chemical reactions is thought to have come from UV radiation, lightning, and other forms of geothermal energy.

Figure 19.2   A chemical process involving bubbles may have preceded the origin of life.
In 1986, geophysicist Louis Lerman proposed that the chemical processes leading to the evolution of life took place within bubbles on the ocean's surface.

Recently, concerns have been raised regarding the "primordial soup" hypothesis as the origin of life on earth. If the earth's atmosphere had no oxygen soon after it was formed, as Miller and Urey assumed (and most evidence supports this assumption), then there would have been no protective layer of ozone to shield the earth's surface from the sun's damaging UV radiation. Without an ozone layer, scientists think UV radiation would have destroyed any ammonia and methane present in the atmosphere. When these gases are missing, the **Miller-Urey experiment** does not produce key biological molecules such as amino acids. If the necessary ammonia and methane were not in the atmosphere, where were they?

In the last two decades, support has grown among scientists for what has been called the **bubble model.** This model, proposed by geophysicist Louis Lerman in 1986, suggests that the problems with the primordial soup hypothesis disappear if the model is "stirred up" a bit. The bubble model, shown in figure 19.2, proposes that the key chemical processes generating the building blocks of life took place not in a primordial soup but rather within bubbles on the ocean's surface. Bubbles produced by erupting volcanoes under the sea ❶ contain various gases. Because water molecules are polar, water bubbles

tend to attract other polar molecules, in effect concentrating them within the bubbles ❷. Chemical reactions would proceed much faster in bubbles, where polar reactants would be concentrated. The bubble model solves a key problem with the primordial soup hypothesis. Inside the bubbles, the methane and ammonia required to produce amino acids would have been protected from destruction by UV radiation, with the surface of the bubble reflecting the UV rays. The bubbles pop when they reach the surface ❸ and release their chemical contents into the atmosphere ❹. Eventually the molecules reenter the oceans packaged in raindrops ❺.

If you have ever watched the ocean surge upon the shore, you may have noticed the foamy froth created by the agitated water. The edges of the primitive oceans were more than likely very frothy places bombarded by ultraviolet and other ionizing radiation, and exposed to an atmosphere that may have contained methane and other simple organic molecules.

19.1 Life appeared on earth 2.5 billion years ago. It may have arisen spontaneously, although the nature of the process is not clearly understood.

How Cells Arose

It is one thing to make amino acids spontaneously and quite another to link them together into proteins. Recall from figure 4.6 that making a peptide bond involves producing a molecule of water as one of the products of the reaction. Because this chemical reaction is freely reversible, it should not occur spontaneously in water (an excess of water would push it in the opposite direction). Scientists now suspect that the first macromolecules to form were not proteins but RNA molecules. When "primed" with high-energy phosphate groups (available in many minerals), RNA nucleotides spontaneously form polynucleotide chains that might, folded up, have been capable of catalyzing the formation of the first proteins.

The First Cells

We don't know how the first cells formed, but most scientists suspect they aggregated spontaneously. When complex carbon-containing macromolecules are present in water, they tend to gather together, sometimes forming aggregations big enough to see without a microscope. Try vigorously shaking a bottle of oil-and-vinegar salad dressing—tiny bubbles called **microspheres** form spontaneously, suspended in the vinegar. Similar microspheres might have represented the first step in the evolution of cellular organization. A bubble, such as those produced by soap solutions, is a hollow spherical structure. Certain molecules, particularly those with hydrophobic regions, will spontaneously form bubbles in water. The structure of the bubble shields the hydrophobic regions of the molecules from contact with water. Such microspheres have many cell-like properties—their outer boundary resembles the membranes of a cell in that it has two layers (see figure 5.5), and the microspheres can increase in size and divide. Bubble models, such as the Lerman model discussed on the previous page, propose that over millions of years, those microspheres better able to incorporate molecules and energy would have tended to persist longer than others. Although it is true that lipid microspheres will form readily in water, there appears to be no hereditary mechanism to transfer these improvements from parent microsphere to offspring.

As we learned earlier, scientists suspect that the first macromolecules to form were RNA molecules, and with the recent discovery that RNA molecules can behave as enzymes, catalyzing their own assembly, this provides a possible early mechanism of inheritance. Perhaps the first cellular components were RNA molecules, and initial steps on the evolutionary journey led to increasingly complex and stable RNA molecules. Later, the stability of RNA might have improved even more when surrounded by a microsphere. Eventually DNA may have taken the place of RNA as the storage molecule for genetic information because the double-stranded DNA would have been more stable than single-stranded RNA.

When we speak of it having taken millions of years for a cell to develop, it is hard to believe there would be enough time for an organism as complicated as a human to develop. But in the scheme of things, human beings are recent additions. If we look

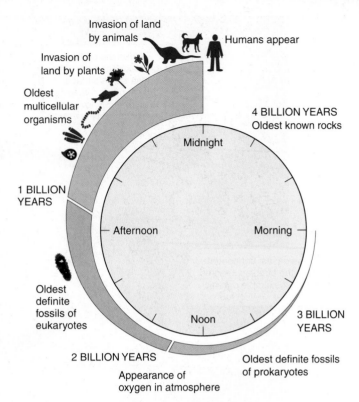

Figure 19.3 A clock of biological time.
A billion seconds ago, most students using this text had not yet been born. A billion minutes ago, Jesus was alive and walking in Galilee. A billion hours ago, the first modern humans were beginning to appear. A billion days ago, the ancestors of humans were beginning to use tools. A billion months ago, the last dinosaurs had not yet been hatched. A billion years ago, no creature had ever walked on the surface of the earth.

at the development of living organisms as a 24-hour clock of biological time shown in figure 19.3, with the formation of the earth 4.5 billion years ago being midnight, humans do not appear until the day is almost all over, only minutes before its end.

As you can see, the scientific vision of life's origin is at best a hazy outline. Although scientists have not disproven the hypothesis that life originated naturally and spontaneously, little is known about what actually happened. Many different scenarios seem possible, and some have solid support from experiments. Deep-sea hydrothermal vents are an interesting possibility; the prokaryotes populating these vents are among the most primitive of living organisms. Other researchers have proposed that life originated deep in the earth's crust.

Because we know so little about how DNA, RNA, and hereditary mechanisms first developed, science is currently unable to resolve disputes concerning the origin of life. How life might have originated naturally and spontaneously remains a subject of intense interest, research, and discussion among scientists.

19.2 Little is known about how the first cells originated. Current hypotheses involve chemical evolution within bubbles, but this is an area of intense interest in research.

Today's *Biology*

Has Life Evolved Elsewhere?

We should not overlook the possibility that life processes might have evolved in different ways on other planets. A functional genetic system, capable of accumulating and replicating changes and thus of adaptation and evolution, could theoretically evolve from molecules other than carbon, hydrogen, nitrogen, and oxygen in a different environment. Silicon, like carbon, needs four electrons to fill its outer energy level, and ammonia is even more polar than water. Perhaps under radically different temperatures and pressures, these elements might form molecules as diverse and flexible as those carbon has formed on earth.

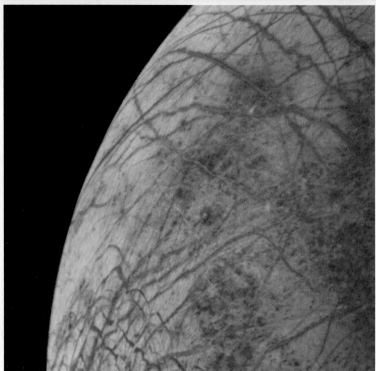

The universe has 10^{20} (100,000,000,000,000,000,000) stars similar to our sun. We don't know how many of these stars have planets, but it seems increasingly likely that many do. Since 1996, astronomers have been detecting planets orbiting distant stars. At least 10% of stars are thought to have planetary systems. If only 1 in 10,000 of these planets is the right size, and at the right distance from its star to duplicate the conditions in which life originated on earth, the "life experiment" will have been repeated 10^{15} times (that is, a million billion times). It does not seem likely that we are alone.

A dull gray chunk of rock collected in 1984 in Antarctica ignited an uproar about ancient life on Mars with the report that the rock contains evidence of possible life. Analysis of gases trapped within small pockets of the rock indicate it is a meteorite from Mars. It is, in fact, the oldest rock known to science—fully 4.5 billion years old. Evidence collected by the 2004 NASA Mars mission (the photo below of the Martian surface was taken by the rover Spirit) suggests that the surface, now cold and arid, was much warmer when the Antarctic meteorite formed 4.5 billion years ago, that water flowed over its surface, and that it had a carbon dioxide atmosphere—conditions not too different from those that spawned life on earth.

When examined with powerful electron microscopes, carbonate patches within the meteorite exhibit what look like microfossils, some 20 to 100 nanometers in length. One hundred times smaller than any known bacteria, it is not clear they actually are fossils, but the resemblance to bacteria is striking.

Viewed as a whole, the evidence of bacterial life associated with the Mars meteorite is not compelling. Clearly, more painstaking research remains to be done before the discovery can claim a scientific consensus. However, while there is no conclusive evidence of bacterial life associated with this meteorite, it seems very possible that life has evolved on other worlds in addition to our own.

There are planets other than ancient Mars with conditions not unlike those on earth. Europa, a large moon of Jupiter, is a promising candidate (photo above). Europa is covered with ice, and photos taken in close orbit in the winter of 1998 reveal seas of liquid water beneath a thin skin of ice. Additional satellite photos taken in 1999 suggest that a few miles under the ice lies a liquid ocean of water larger than earth's, warmed by the push and pull of the gravitational attraction of Jupiter's many large satellite moons. The conditions on Europa now are far less hostile to life than the conditions that existed in the oceans of the primitive earth. In coming decades, satellite missions are scheduled to explore this ocean for life.

19.3 The Simplest Organisms

Judging from fossils in ancient rocks, prokaryotes have been plentiful on earth for over 2.5 billion years. From the diverse array of early living forms, a few became the ancestors of the great majority of organisms alive today. Several ancient forms including cyanobacteria have survived; others gave rise to different members of the diverse prokaryotic group Bacteria, and still others to the second great group of prokaryotes, the Archaea. The fossil record indicates that eukaryotic cells, being much larger than prokaryotes and exhibiting elaborate shapes in some cases, did not appear until about 1.5 billion years ago. Therefore, for at least 1 billion years prokaryotes were the only organisms that existed.

Today, prokaryotes are the simplest and most abundant form of life on earth. In a spoonful of farmland soil, 2.5 billion bacteria may be present. In 1 hectare (about 2.5 acres) of wheat land in England, the weight of bacteria in the soil is approximately equal to that of 100 sheep!

It is not surprising, then, that prokaryotes occupy a very important place in the web of life on earth. They play a key role in cycling minerals within the earth's ecosystems. Bacteria are responsible for some of the most deadly animal and plant diseases, including many humans diseases. Bacteria and archaea are our constant companions, present in everything we eat and on everything we touch. Our bodies contain some 10 to 100 trillion human cells—and 100 trillion bacteria (mostly in our intestines)!

The Structure of a Prokaryote

The essential character of prokaryotes can be conveyed in a simple sentence: **Prokaryotes** are small, simply organized, single cells that lack an organized nucleus. Therefore, bacteria and archaea are prokaryotes; their single circle of DNA is not confined by a nuclear membrane in a nucleus, as in the cells of eukaryotes. Too tiny to see with the naked eye, bacterial cells are simple in form, either rod-shaped (bacilli), spherical (cocci), or spirally coiled (spirilla). A few kinds of bacteria aggregate into stalked structures or filaments.

The prokaryotic cell's plasma membrane is encased within a cell wall. The cell wall of bacteria is made of peptidoglycan, a network of polysaccharide molecules linked together by peptide interbridges. The cell walls of archaea lack peptidoglycan and are made of proteins or polysaccharides or both.

Many species of bacteria have a cell wall composed of layers of peptidoglycan. Other species have an outer membrane composed of large molecules of lipopolysaccharide (figure 19.4). This outer layer covers a thinner peptidoglycan

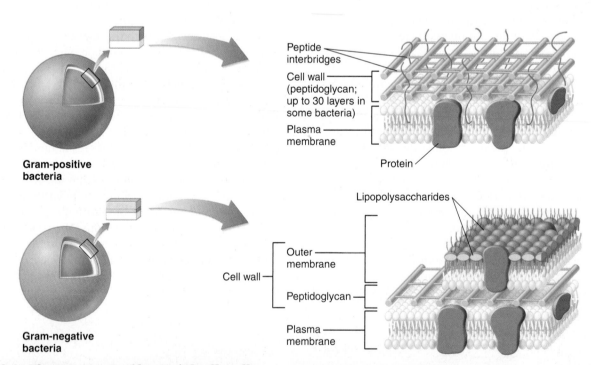

Figure 19.4 The structures of bacterial cell walls.

The thick peptidoglycan layer encasing gram-positive bacteria traps crystal violet dye, so the bacteria appear *purple* under the microscope in a Gram-stained smear (named after Hans Christian Gram, who developed the technique). Because gram-negative bacteria have much less peptidoglycan (located between the plasma membrane and an outer membrane), they do not retain the crystal violet dye and so exhibit the *red* counterstain color (usually a safranin dye). Gram-negative bacteria appear *red* in Gram-stained smears.

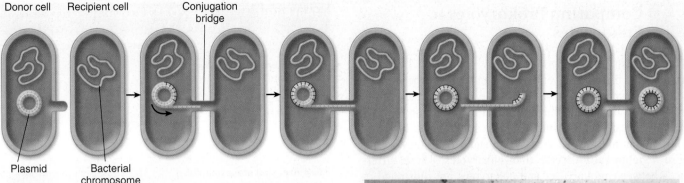

Donor cell   Recipient cell   Conjugation
                                     bridge

Plasmid   Bacterial
               chromosome

Figure 19.5   Bacterial conjugation.
Donor cells contain a plasmid that recipient cells lack. The pilus of
a donor cell contacts a recipient cell and draws the cells closer. The
plasmid replicates itself and transfers the copy across a conjugation
bridge. The remaining strand of the plasmid serves as a template
to build a replacement. When the single strand enters the recipient
cell, it serves as a template to assemble a double-stranded plasmid.
When the process is complete, both cells contain a complete copy of
the plasmid.

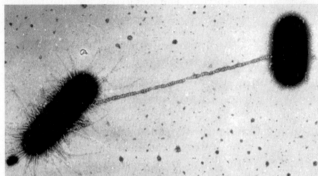

A pilus connects two bacterial cells.

cell wall. Bacteria are commonly classified by the presence
or absence of this membrane. **Gram-positive** bacteria have
no outer membrane (as in the upper panel of figure 19.4), and
gram-negative bacteria possess an outer membrane (as in the
lower panel). The name refers to the Danish microbiologist
Hans Gram, who developed a staining process that stains the
cell types differently. A purple dye is retained in the thicker
peptidoglycan layer in the cell walls of gram-positive bacteria,
and they stain purple. In bacteria with an outer membrane, the
peptidoglycan layer is thinner and does not retain the purple
dye, which is washed away easily. A counterstain with a red
dye is retained and so the cells stain red, not purple. The outer
membranes of gram-negative bacteria make them resistant to
antibiotics that attack the bacterial cell wall. That is why peni-
cillin, which targets the protein cross-links of the bacterial cell
wall, is effective only against gram-positive bacteria. Outside
the cell wall and membrane, many bacteria have a gelatinous
layer called a **capsule.**

Many kinds of bacteria possess threadlike **flagella,**
long strands of protein that may extend out several times
the length of the cell body. Bacteria swim by twisting these
flagella in a corkscrew motion. Some bacteria also possess
shorter outgrowths called **pili** (singular, **pilus**), which act
as docking cables, helping the cell to attach to surfaces or
other cells.

When exposed to harsh conditions (dryness or high temperature), some bacteria form thick-walled **endospores** around
their DNA and a small bit of cytoplasm. These endospores are
highly resistant to environmental stress and may germinate to
form new active bacteria even after centuries. The formation
of endospores is the reason that the bacterium responsible for
botulism, *Clostridium botulinum,* sometimes persists in cans
and bottles if the containers have not been heated at a high
enough temperature to kill the spores.

How Prokaryotes Reproduce

Prokaryotes, like all other living cells, grow and divide.
Prokaryotes reproduce using a process called **binary fission**
(see figure 9.1), in which an individual cell simply increases in
size and divides in two. Following replication of the prokaryote DNA, the plasma membrane and cell wall grow inward
and eventually divide the cell by forming a new wall from the
outside toward the center of the old cell.

Some bacteria can exchange genetic information by
passing plasmids from one cell to another in a process called
conjugation. Recall from section 14.3 that a plasmid is a small,
circular fragment of DNA that replicates outside the main bacterial chromosome. In bacterial conjugation, seen in figure 19.5,
the pilus of a donor cell contacts a recipient cell; the pilus draws
the two cells close together. A passageway called a *conjugation
bridge* forms between the two cells. The plasmid in the donor
cell begins to replicate its DNA, passing the replicated copy
out across the bridge and into the recipient cell, where a complementary strand is synthesized. The remaining strand in the
donor cell serves as a template for the synthesis of its complement. Both the recipient cell and the donor cell now contain a
complete copy of the genetic material found in the donor cell.
Genes that produce antibiotic resistance in bacteria are often
transferred from one bacterial cell to another through conjugation. In addition to conjugation, bacteria can also obtain genetic information by taking up DNA from the environment
(transformation; see figure 12.1) or from bacterial viruses
(discussed later in this chapter; see figure 19.11).

> **19.3   Prokaryotes are the smallest and simplest
> organisms, a single cell with no internal
> compartments or organelles. They divide by
> binary fission.**

19.4 Comparing Prokaryotes to Eukaryotes

Prokaryotes differ from eukaryotes in many respects: The cytoplasm of prokaryotes has very little internal organization, prokaryotes are unicellular and much smaller than eukaryotes, the prokaryotic chromosome is a single circle of DNA, cell division and flagella are simple, and prokaryotes are far more metabolically diverse than eukaryotes. These differences between prokaryotes and eukaryotes are illustrated in table 19.1.

Prokaryotic Metabolism

Prokaryotes have evolved many more ways than eukaryotes to acquire the carbon atoms and energy necessary for growth and reproduction. Many are **autotrophs,** organisms that obtain their carbon from inorganic CO_2. Autotrophs that obtain their energy from sunlight are called *photoautotrophs*, whereas those that harvest energy from inorganic chemicals are called *chemoautotrophs*. Other prokaryotes are **heterotrophs,** organisms that obtain at least some of their carbon from organic molecules like glucose. Heterotrophs that obtain their energy from sunlight are called *photoheterotrophs*, whereas those that harvest energy from organic molecules are called *chemoheterotrophs*.

Photoautotrophs   Many prokaryotes carry out photosynthesis, using the energy of sunlight to build organic molecules from carbon dioxide. The cyanobacteria use chlorophyll *a* as the key light-capturing pigment and use H_2O as an electron donor, leaving oxygen gas as a by-product. Other prokaryotes use bacteriochlorophyll as their pigment and H_2S as an electron donor, leaving elemental sulfur as the by-product.

Chemoautotrophs   Some prokaryotes obtain their energy by oxidizing inorganic substances. Nitrifiers, for example, oxidize ammonia or nitrite to form the nitrate that is taken up by plants. Other prokaryotes oxidize sulfur, hydrogen gas, and other inorganic molecules. On the dark ocean floor at depths of 2,500 meters, entire ecosystems subsist on prokaryotes that oxidize hydrogen sulfide as it escapes from volcanic vents.

Photoheterotrophs   The so-called purple nonsulfur bacteria use light as their source of energy but obtain carbon from organic molecules such as carbohydrates or alcohols that have been produced by other organisms.

Chemoheterotrophs   Most prokaryotes obtain both carbon atoms and energy from organic molecules. These include decomposers and most pathogens (disease-causing bacteria).

> **19.4** Prokaryotes differ from eukaryotes in having no nucleus or other interior compartments, in being far more metabolically diverse, and in many other fundamental respects.

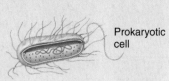

TABLE 19.1   PROKARYOTES COMPARED TO EUKARYOTES

Feature	Example

Internal compartmentalization. Unlike eukaryotic cells, prokaryotic cells contain no internal compartments, no internal membrane system, and no cell nucleus.

Prokaryotic cell

Cell size. Most prokaryotic cells are only about 1 micrometer in diameter, whereas most eukaryotic cells are well over 10 times that size.

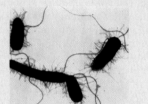

Prokaryotic cell   Eukaryotic cell

Unicellularity. All prokaryotes are fundamentally single-celled. Even though some may adhere together in a matrix or form filaments, their cytoplasms are not directly interconnected, and their activities are not integrated and coordinated, as is the case in multicellular eukaryotes.

Unicellular bacteria

Chromosomes. Prokaryotes do not possess chromosomes in which proteins are complexed with the DNA, as eukaryotes do. Instead, their DNA exists as a single circle in the cytoplasm.

Prokaryotic chromosome

Eukaryotic chromosomes

Cell division. Cell division in prokaryotes takes place by binary fission (see chapter 9). The cells simply pinch in two. In eukaryotes, microtubules pull chromosomes to opposite poles during the cell division process, called mitosis.

Binary fission in prokaryotes

Mitosis in eukaryotes

Flagella. Prokaryotic flagella are simple, composed of a single fiber of protein that is spun like a propeller. Eukaryotic flagella are more complex structures, with a 9 + 2 arrangement of microtubules, that whip back and forth rather than rotate.

Simple bacterial flagellum

Metabolic diversity. Prokaryotes possess many metabolic abilities that eukaryotes do not: Prokaryotes perform several different kinds of anaerobic and aerobic photosynthesis; prokaryotes can obtain their energy from oxidizing inorganic compounds (so-called chemoautotrophs); and prokaryotes can fix atmospheric nitrogen.

Chemoautotrophs

Importance of Prokaryotes

Prokaryotes, the first organisms to evolve on earth, affect our lives in many important ways.

Prokaryotes and the Environment

Prokaryotes were largely responsible for creating the properties of the atmosphere and the soil for over 2 billion years. They are metabolically much more diverse than eukaryotes, which is why they are able to exist in such a wide range of habitats. The many autotrophic bacteria—either photoautotrophic or chemoautotrophic—make major contributions to the world carbon balance in terrestrial, freshwater, and marine habitats. Other heterotrophic bacteria play a key role in world ecology by breaking down organic compounds. The carbon, nitrogen, phosphorus, sulfur, and other atoms that make up living organisms come from the environment, and when organisms die and decay, they all return to the environment. The prokaryotes, and other organisms such as fungi, that carry out the breakdown portion of this cycle are called *decomposers.* Another key role of prokaryotes in the world ecosystem relates to the fact that only a few genera of bacteria—and no other organisms—have the ability to fix atmospheric nitrogen and thus make it available for use by other organisms.

Bacteria and Genetic Engineering

Applying genetic engineering methods to produce improved strains of bacteria for commercial use holds enormous promise for the future. Bacteria are under intense investigation, for example, as nonpolluting insect control agents. *Bacillus thuringiensis* produces a protein that is toxic when ingested by certain insects, and improved, highly specific strains of B. *thuringiensis* have greatly increased its usefulness as a biological control agent. Genetically modified bacteria have also been extraordinarily useful in producing insulin and other therapeutic proteins. Gene modified bacteria are also playing a part in removing environmental pollutants. Oil-degrading bacteria were used to clean up the *Exxon Valdez* oil spill off the coast of Alaska. The rocks on the left in figure 19.6 below show the oil contamination, while the rocks on the right shows an area that was cleaned up using bacteria.

Bacteria, Disease, and Bioterrorism

Some bacteria cause major diseases in plants and animals, including humans. Among important human bacterial diseases that can be lethal are anthrax, cholera, plague, pneumonia, tuberculosis (TB), and typhus. Many pathogenic (disease-causing) bacteria like cholera are dispersed in food and water. Some like typhus and plague, spread among rodents and humans by fleas. Others, like TB, are spread through the air in water droplets (from a cough or sneeze), infecting those who inhale the droplets. Among these inhalation pathogens is anthrax, a disease associated with livestock that rarely kills humans. Most human infections are cutaneous, infecting a cut in the skin, but if a significant number of anthrax endospores are inhaled, the pulmonary (lung) infection is often fatal. Biological warfare programs in the United States and the former Soviet Union focused on anthrax as a near-ideal biological weapon, although it has never been used in war. Bioterrorists struck at the United States with anthrax endospores in 2001.

> **19.5 Prokaryotes make many important contributions to the world ecosystem, including occupying key roles in cycling carbon and nitrogen.**

Figure 19.6 Using bacteria to clean up oil spills.
Bacteria can often be used to remove environmental pollutants, such as petroleum hydrocarbons and chlorinated compounds. In areas contaminated by the *Exxon Valdez* oil spill (*rocks on the left*), oil-degrading bacteria produced dramatic results (*rocks on the right*).

Prokaryotic Lifestyles

Archaea

Many of the archaea that survive today are **methanogens,** prokaryotes that use hydrogen (H_2) gas to reduce carbon dioxide (CO_2) to methane (CH_4). Methanogens are strict anaerobes, poisoned by oxygen gas. They live in swamps and marshes, where other microbes have consumed all the oxygen. The methane that they produce bubbles up as "marsh gas." Methanogens also live in the guts of cows and other herbivores that live on a diet of cellulose, converting the CO_2 produced by its digestion to methane gas. The best understood archaea are extremophiles, which live in unusually harsh environments, such as the very salty Dead Sea and the Great Salt Lake (over 10 times saltier than seawater). **Thermoacidophiles** favor hot, acidic springs such as the sulfur springs of Yellowstone National Park (figure 19.7), where the water is nearly 80°C, with an acidic pH of 2 or 3.

Bacteria

Almost all prokaryotes that have been described by scientists are members of the kingdom Bacteria. Many are heterotrophs that power their lives by consuming organic molecules, whereas others are photosynthetic, gaining their energy from the sun. **Cyanobacteria** are among the most prominent of the photosynthetic bacteria. We have already mentioned the critical role that the members of this ancient phylum played in the history of the earth by generating the oxygen in our atmosphere. Cyanobacteria are filamentous bacteria like the *Anabaena* pictured in figure 19.8. They usually have a mucilaginous sheath, which is often deeply pigmented. Nitrogen fixation occurs in almost all cyanobacteria, within specialized cells called **heterocysts** (the enlarged cells that appear along the filament of *Anabaena* and in many of the other filamentous members of this phylum). These cells begin to form when available nitrogen falls below a certain threshold; when nitrogen is abundant, their formation is inhibited. In **nitrogen fixation,** atmospheric nitrogen is converted to a form that can be used by living organisms.

There are numerous phyla of nonphotosynthetic bacteria. Some are chemoautotrophs, but most are heterotrophs. Some of these heterotrophs are decomposers, breaking down organic material. Bacteria and fungi play the leading role in breaking down organic molecules formed by biological processes, thereby making the nutrients in these molecules available once more for recycling. Decomposition is just as indispensable to the continuation of life on earth as is photosynthesis.

Although bacteria are unicellular organisms, they sometimes form associations, as in *Anabaena;* also layers of bacterial cells, called **biofilms,** can form on the surface of a substrate. By forming biofilms, the bacteria create a microenvironment that facilitates their growth. Biofilms are found in nature but also impact humans because they can form on teeth and on medical equipment such as catheters and contact lenses. Biofilms can protect the bacteria from disinfectants.

Figure 19.7 Thermoacidophiles live in hot springs.
These archaea growing in Sulfide Spring, Yellowstone National Park, Wyoming, are able to tolerate high acid levels and very hot temperatures.

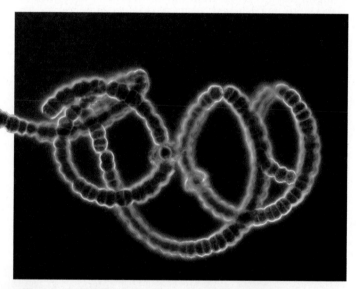

Figure 19.8 The cyanobacterium *Anabaena.*
Individual cells adhere in filaments. The larger cells (areas on the filament that seem to be bulging) are heterocysts, specialized cells in which nitrogen fixation occurs. These organisms exhibit one of the closest approaches to multicellularity among the bacteria.

Bacteria cause many diseases in humans (table 19.2), including cholera, diphtheria, and leprosy. Among the most serious of bacterial diseases is **tuberculosis (TB),** a disease of the respiratory tract caused by the bacterium *Mycobacterium tuberculosis.* TB is a leading cause of death throughout the world. Spread through the air, tuberculosis is quite infectious. TB was a major health risk in the United States until the discovery of effective drugs to suppress it in the 1950s. The appearance of drug-resistant strains in the 1990s has raised serious concern within the medical community, and the search is on for new types of anti-TB drugs.

> **19.6 Most commonly encountered prokaryotes are bacteria; some cause significant diseases in humans.**

TABLE 19.2   IMPORTANT HUMAN BACTERIAL DISEASES

Disease	Pathogen	Vector/ Reservoir	Symptoms and Mode of Transmission
Anthrax	*Bacillus anthracis*	Farm animals	Bacterial infection that can be transmitted through inhaled endospores, by contact, or ingestion. Rare except in sporadic outbreaks. Pulmonary (inhaled) anthrax is often fatal, while cutaneous anthrax (infection through cuts) is readily treated with antibiotics. Anthrax endospores have been used as a biological weapon.
Botulism	*Clostridium botulinum*	Improperly prepared food	Contracted through ingestion of contaminated food. Produces acutely toxic poison; can be fatal.
Chlamydia	*Chlamydia trachomatis*	Humans (STD)	Urogenital infections with possible spread to eyes and respiratory tract. Occurs worldwide; increasingly common over past 20 years.
Cholera	*Vibrio cholerae*	Humans (feces), plankton	Causes severe diarrhea that can lead to death by dehydration; 50% peak mortality if the disease goes untreated. A major killer in times of crowding and poor sanitation; over 100,000 died in Rwanda in 1994 during a cholera outbreak.
Dental caries	*Streptococcus*	Humans	A dense collection of this bacteria on the surface of teeth leads to secretion of acids that destroy minerals in tooth enamel—sugar will not cause caries but bacteria feeding on it will.
Diphtheria	*Corynebacterium diphtheriae*	Humans	Acute inflammation and lesions of mucous membranes. Spread through contact with infected individual. Vaccine available.
Gonorrhea	*Neisseria gonorrhoeae*	Humans only	STD, on the increase worldwide. Usually not fatal.
Hansen's disease (leprosy)	*Mycobacterium leprae*	Humans, feral armadillos	Chronic infection of the skin; worldwide incidence about 10 to 12 million, especially in Southeast Asia. Spread through contact with infected individuals.
Lyme disease	*Borrelia burgdorferi*	Ticks, deer, small rodents	Spread through bite of infected tick. Lesion followed by malaise, fever, fatigue, pain, stiff neck, and headache.
Peptic ulcers	*Helicobacter pylori*	Humans	Originally thought to be caused by stress or diet, most peptic ulcers now appear to be caused by this bacterium; good news for ulcer sufferers as it can be treated with antibiotics.
Plague	*Yersinia pestis*	Fleas of wild rodents: rats and squirrels	Killed one-fourth of the population of Europe in the fourteenth century; endemic in wild rodent populations of the western United States in the 1990s.
Pneumonia	*Streptococcus, Mycoplasma, Chlamydia, Klebsiella*	Humans	Acute infection of the lungs, often fatal if not treated.
Tuberculosis	*Mycobacterium tuberculosis*	Humans	An acute bacterial infection of the lungs, lymph, and meninges. Its incidence is on the rise, complicated by the emergence of new strains of the bacteria that are resistant to antibiotics.
Typhoid fever	*Salmonella typhi*	Humans	A systemic bacterial disease of worldwide incidence. Less than 500 cases a year are reported in the United States. The disease is spread through contaminated water or foods (such as improperly washed fruits and vegetables). Vaccines are available for travelers.
Typhus	*Rickettsia*	Lice, rat fleas, humans	Historically, a major killer in times of crowding and poor sanitation; transmitted from human to human through the bite of infected lice and fleas. Typhus has a peak untreated mortality rate of 70%.

19.7 The Structure of Viruses

The border between the living and the nonliving is very clear to a biologist. Living organisms are cellular and able to grow and reproduce independently, guided by information encoded within DNA. As discussed earlier in this chapter, the simplest creatures living on earth today that satisfy these criteria are prokaryotes. Viruses, on the other hand, do not satisfy the criteria for "living" because they possess only a portion of the properties of organisms. **Viruses** are literally "parasitic" chemicals, segments of DNA (or sometimes RNA) wrapped in a protein coat. They cannot reproduce on their own, and for this reason they are not considered alive by biologists. They can, however, reproduce within cells, often with disastrous results to the host organism. For this reason, viruses have a major impact on the living world.

Viruses are very small. The smallest viruses are only about 17 nanometers in diameter; the largest ones are long filamentous viruses that measure up to 1,000 nanometers in length. Viruses are so small that they are smaller than many of the molecules in a cell. Most viruses can be detected only by using the higher resolution of an electron microscope.

The true nature of viruses was discovered in 1935, when the biologist Wendell Stanley prepared an extract of a plant virus called *tobacco mosaic virus (TMV)* and attempted to purify it. To his great surprise, the purified TMV preparation precipitated (that is, separated from solution) in the form of crystals. This was surprising because precipitation is something that only chemicals do—the TMV virus was acting like a chemical rather than an organism. Stanley concluded that TMV is best regarded as just that—a chemical matter rather than a living organism.

Each particle of TMV virus is in fact a mixture of two chemicals: RNA and protein. The TMV virus, pictured in figure 19.9*b*, has the structure of a Twinkie, a tube made of an RNA core (the green springlike structure) surrounded by a coat of protein (the purple structures that encircle the RNA). Later workers were able to separate the RNA from the protein and purify and store each chemical. Then, when they reassembled the two components, the reconstructed TMV particles were fully able to infect healthy tobacco plants and so clearly *were* the virus itself, not merely chemicals derived from it.

Viruses occur in all organisms, from bacteria to humans, and in every case the basic structure of the virus is the same, a core of nucleic acid surrounded by protein. There is considerable difference, however, in the details. In figure 19.9 you can compare the structure of bacterial, plant, and animal viruses—they are clearly quite different from one another and there is even a wide variety of shapes and structures within each group of viruses. Bacterial viruses, called *bacteriophages,* can have elaborate structures like the bacteriophage in figure 19.9*a*, that looks more like a lunar module than a virus. Many plant viruses like TMV have a core of RNA, and some animal viruses like HIV (figure 19.9*c*) do too. Several different segments of DNA or RNA may be present in animal virus particles, along with many different kinds of protein. Like TMV, most viruses form a protein sheath, or **capsid,** around their nucleic acid core. In addition, many viruses (like HIV) form a membranelike **envelope,** rich in proteins, lipids, and glycoprotein molecules, around the capsid.

> **19.7** Viruses are genomes of DNA or RNA, encased in a protein shell, that can infect cells and replicate within them. They are chemical assemblies, not cells, and are not alive.

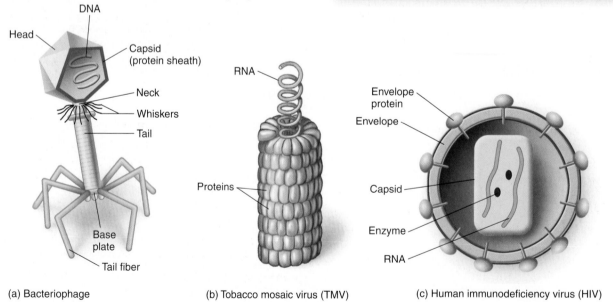

(a) Bacteriophage   (b) Tobacco mosaic virus (TMV)   (c) Human immunodeficiency virus (HIV)

Figure 19.9   The structure of bacterial, plant, and animal viruses.

(*a*) Bacterial viruses, called bacteriophages, often have a complex structure. (*b*) TMV infects plants and consists of 2,130 identical protein molecules (*purple*) that form a cylindrical coat around the single strand of RNA (*green*). The RNA backbone determines the shape of the virus and is protected by the identical protein molecules packed tightly around it. (*c*) In the human immunodeficiency virus (HIV), the RNA core is held within a capsid that is encased by a protein envelope.

How Bacteriophages Enter Prokaryotic Cells

Bacteriophages are viruses that infect bacteria. They are diverse both structurally and functionally and are united solely by their occurrence in bacterial hosts. Bacteriophages with double-stranded DNA have played a key role in molecular biology. Many of these bacteriophages are large and complex, with relatively large amounts of DNA and proteins. Some of them have been named as members of a "T" series (T1, T2, and so forth); others have been given different kinds of names. To illustrate the diversity of these viruses, T3 and T7 bacteriophages are icosahedral and have short tails. In contrast, the so-called T-even bacteriophages (T2, T4, and T6) are more complex, as shown by the T4 bacteriophage in figure 19.9a. T-even phages have an icosahedral head that holds the DNA (shown in the cutaway view), a capsid that consists primarily of three proteins, a connecting neck with a collar and "whiskers," a long tail, and a complex base plate. Many of these structures are also visible in the photo of T4 bacteriophage in figure 19.10a.

The Lytic Cycle

During the process of bacterial infection by a T4 bacteriophage, at least one of the tail fibers contacts the lipopolysaccarides of the host bacterial cell wall. The other tail fibers set the bacteriophage perpendicular to the surface of the bacterium and bring the base plate into contact with the cell surface, as seen on the left side in figure 19.10b. After the bacteriophage is in place, the tail contracts, and the tail tube passes through an opening that appears in the base plate, piercing the bacterial cell wall (as shown on the right side of figure 19.10b). The contents of the head, mostly DNA, are then injected into the host cytoplasm.

The T-series bacteriophages and other phages such as lambda (λ) are all virulent viruses, multiplying within infected cells and eventually lysing (rupturing) them. When a virus kills the infected host cell in which it is replicating, the reproductive cycle is referred to as a *lytic cycle* (see figure 19.11). The viral DNA that is injected in the cell is transcribed and translated by the host cell into viral components that are assembled in the host cell. Eventually, the host cell ruptures and the new lambda phages are released, ready to infect more cells.

The Lysogenic Cycle

Many bacteriophages do not immediately kill the cells they infect, instead integrating their nucleic acid into the genome of the infected host cell (see the lower cycle shown in figure 19.11). While residing there, it is called a **prophage.** Among the bacteriophages that do this is the lambda phage of *Escherichia coli,* which is also a lytic phage as described above. We know as much about this bacteriophage as we do about virtually any other biological particle; the complete sequence of its 48,502 bases has been determined. At least 23 proteins are associated with the development and maturation of lambda phage, and many other enzymes are involved in the integration of these viruses into the host genome.

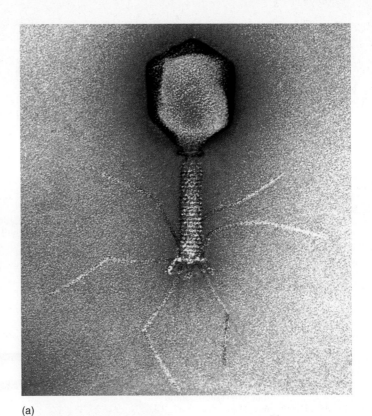

(a)

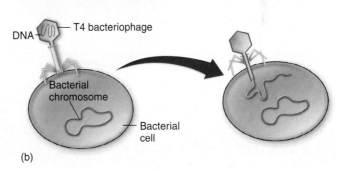

(b)

Figure 19.10   A T4 bacteriophage.
(a) Electron micrograph of T4 and (b) diagram of a T4 bacteriophage infecting a bacterial cell.

The integration of a virus into a cellular genome is called lysogeny. At a later time, the prophage may exit the genome and initiate virus replication. This sort of reproductive cycle, involving a period of genome integration, is called a *lysogenic cycle.* Viruses that become stably integrated within the genome of their host cells are called lysogenic viruses or temperate viruses.

Lysogenic Conversion

During the integrated portion of a lysogenic reproductive cycle, virus genes are often expressed. RNA polymerase reads them just as if they were host genes, and sometimes expression of these genes has an important effect on the host cell, a process called *lysogenic conversion.* In a more general sense, the genetic alteration of a cell's genome by the introduction of naked DNA is called transformation.

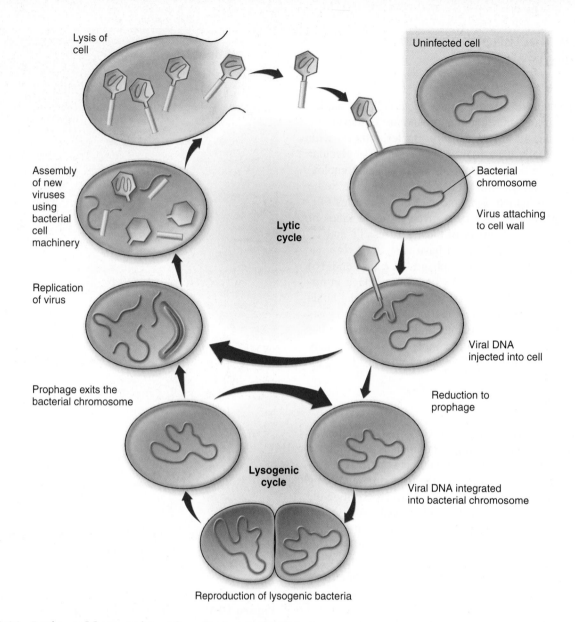

Figure 19.11 Lytic and lysogenic cycles of a bacteriophage.
In the lytic cycle, the bacteriophage exists as viral DNA, free in the bacterial host cell's cytoplasm. The viral DNA directs the production of new viral particles by the host cell until the virus kills the cell by lysis. In the lysogenic cycle, the bacteriophage DNA is integrated into the large, circular DNA molecule of the host bacterium and reproduces. It may continue to replicate and produce lysogenic bacteria or enter the lytic cycle and kill the cell. Bacteriophages are much smaller relative to their hosts than illustrated in this diagram.

Converting the Cholera-Causing Bacterium

An important example of this sort of cell conversion directed by viral genes is provided by the bacterium responsible for an often-fatal human disease. The bacteria *Vibrio cholerae* usually exist in a harmless form, but a second disease-causing, virulent form also occurs. In this latter form, the bacterium causes the deadly disease cholera. Research now shows that a bacteriophage that infects *V. cholerae* introduces into the host bacterial cell a gene that codes for the cholera toxin. This gene becomes incorporated into the bacterial DNA, where it is translated along with the other host genes, thereby transforming the benign bacterium to a disease-causing agent.

Lysogenic conversion is also responsible for the presence of toxin genes in (and much of the virulence of) other pathogens like *Corynebacterium diphtheriae*, which causes diphtheria, *Streptococcus pyogenes*, which causes scarlet fever, and *Clostridium botulinum*, which causes botulism.

> **19.8 Bacteriophages are a diverse group of viruses that attack bacteria. Some kill their host in a lytic cycle; others integrate into the host's genome, initiating a lysogenic cycle. Bacteriophages transform *Vibrio cholerae* and other bacteria into disease-causing agents.**

Prions and Mad Cow Disease

For decades scientists have been fascinated by a peculiar group of fatal brain diseases. These diseases have the unusual property that they are transmissible from one individual to another, but it is years and often decades before the disease is detected in infected individuals. The brains of these individuals develop numerous small cavities as neurons die, producing a marked spongy appearance as shown here in the photo. Called **transmissible spongiform encephalopathies (TSEs),** these diseases include scrapie in sheep, "mad cow" disease in cattle, and kuru and Creutzfeldt-Jakob disease in humans.

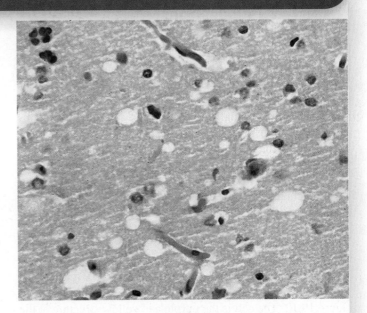

TSEs can be transmitted between individuals of a species by injecting infected brain tissue into a recipient animal's brain. TSEs can also spread via tissue transplants and, apparently, food. Kuru was common in the Fore people of Papua New Guinea when they practiced ritual cannibalism, literally eating the brains of infected individuals. Mad cow disease spread widely among the cattle herds of England in the 1990s because cows were fed bone meal prepared from sheep carcasses to increase the protein content of their diet. Like the Fore, the British cattle were literally eating the tissue of sheep that had died of scrapie.

In the 1960s, British researchers T. Alper and J. Griffith noted that infectious TSE preparations remained infectious even after exposure to radiation that would destroy DNA or RNA. They suggested that the infectious agent was a protein. Perhaps, they speculated, the protein usually preferred one folding pattern but could sometimes misfold and then catalyze other proteins to do the same, the misfolding spreading like a chain reaction. This heretical suggestion was not accepted by the scientific community, as it violates a key tenet of molecular biology: Only DNA or RNA act as hereditary material, transmitting information from one generation to the next.

In the early 1970s, physician Stanley Prusiner, moved by the death of a patient from Creutzfeldt-Jakob disease, began to study TSEs. Prusiner became fascinated with Alper and Griffith's hypothesis. Try as he might, Prusiner could find no evidence of nucleic acids, bacteria, or viruses in the infectious TSE preparation. He concluded, as Alper and Griffith had, that the infectious agent was a *protein,* which he named a **prion,** for "proteinaceous infectious particle."

Prusiner went on to isolate a distinctive prion protein, and for two decades he continued to amass evidence that prions play a key role in triggering TSEs. The scientific community resisted Prusiner's renegade conclusions, but eventually experiments done in Prusiner's and other laboratories began to convince many. For example, when Prusiner injected prions of different abnormal conformations into several different hosts, these hosts developed prions with the same abnormal conformations

as the parent prions. In another important experiment, Charles Weissmann showed that mice genetically engineered to lack Prusiner's prion protein are immune to TSE infection. However, if brain tissue with the prion protein is grafted into the mice, the grafted tissue—but not the rest of the brain—can then be infected with TSE. In 1997, Prusiner was awarded the Nobel Prize in Physiology or Medicine for his work on prions.

Can Humans Catch Mad Cow Disease by Eating Infected Meat?

Many scientists are becoming worried that prions may be transmitting such diseases to humans. Specifically, they worry that prion-caused bovine spongiform encephalopathy (BSE), a brain disease in cows commonly known as **mad cow disease,** may infect humans and produce a similar fatal disorder called variant Creutzfeldt-Jakob disease (vCJD). In March 1996, an outbreak of mad cow disease in Britain, with over 80,000 cows infected, created widespread concern. BSE, a degeneration of the brain caused by prions, appears to have entered the British cattle herds from sheep! Sheep are subject to a prion disease called *scrapie,* and the disease is thought to have passed from sheep to cows through protein-supplemented feed pellets containing ground-up sheep brains. The passage of prions from one species to another has a scary consequence: Prions can also pass from cows to people! At least 148 British consumers of BSE-infected beef have subsequently died of vCJD. Tissue from the brains of the dead Britons and from BSE cows induce the same brain lesions in mice, while classic CJD produces quite different lesions—clearly the form of vCJD that killed them was caused by the same agent that caused BSE.

The appearance of BSE-infected cows in Canadian and United States herds in 2003 has led to increased scrutiny of commercial beef in the United States in an attempt to eliminate any possibility of BSE contamination.

How Animal Viruses Enter Cells

As we just discussed, bacterial viruses punch a hole in the bacterial cell wall and inject their DNA inside. Plant viruses like TMV enter plant cells through tiny rips in the cell wall at points of injury. Animal viruses typically enter their host cells by membrane fusion, or sometimes by endocytosis, a process described in chapter 5 in which the cell's plasma membrane dimples inward, surrounding and engulfing the virus particle.

A diverse array of viruses occur among animals. A good way to gain a general idea of how they enter cells is to look at one animal virus in detail. Here we will look at the virus responsible for a comparatively new and fatal disease, acquired immunodeficiency syndrome (AIDS). AIDS was first reported in the United States in 1981. It was not long before the infectious agent, human immunodeficiency virus (HIV), was identified by laboratories. HIV is shown budding off of a cell in figure 19.12. The cell is the purple and yellow structure at the bottom, and the HIVs are the circular structures suspended above the surface of the cell. HIV's genes are closely related to those of a chimpanzee virus, suggesting that HIV first entered humans in Africa from chimpanzees.

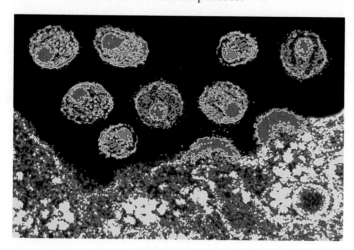

Figure 19.12 The AIDS virus.
HIV particles exit a cell, to spread and infect neighboring cells.

One of the cruelest aspects of AIDS is that clinical symptoms typically do not begin to develop until long after infection by the HIV virus, generally 8 to 10 years after the initial exposure to HIV. During this long interval, carriers of HIV have no clinical symptoms but are typically fully infectious, making the spread of HIV very difficult to control.

Attachment

When HIV is introduced into the human bloodstream, the virus particle circulates throughout the entire body but will only infect certain cells, ones called *macrophages* (Latin, big eaters). Macrophages are the garbage collectors of the body, taking up and recycling fragments of ruptured cells and other bits of organic debris. It is not surprising that HIV specializes in infecting this one kind of cell—many other animal viruses are similarly narrow in their requirements. For example, poliovirus has an affinity for motor nerve cells, and hepatitis virus infects primarily liver cells.

How does a virus such as HIV recognize a specific kind of target cell such as a macrophage? Every kind of cell in the human body has a specific array of cell surface marker proteins, molecules that serve to identify the cells. HIV viruses are able to recognize the macrophage cell surface markers. Studding the surface of each HIV virus are spikes that bang into any cell the virus encounters. Look back to figure 19.9c, a drawing of HIV, that shows these spikes (the lollipop-looking structures embedded in the envelope). Each spike is composed of a protein called *gp120*. Only when gp120 happens onto a cell surface marker that matches its shape does the HIV virus adhere to an animal cell and infect it. It turns out that gp120 precisely fits a cell surface marker called **CD4,** and that CD4 occurs on the surfaces of macrophages. Panel 1 in figure 19.13 shows the gp120 protein of HIV docking onto the CD4 surface marker on the macrophage.

Entry into Macrophages

Certain cells of the immune system, called T lymphocytes, or *T cells,* also possess CD4 markers. Why are they not infected right away, as macrophages are? This is the key question underlying the mystery of the long AIDS latent period. When T lymphocytes become infected and killed, AIDS commences. So what holds off T cell infection so long?

Researchers have learned that after docking onto the CD4 receptor of a macrophage, the HIV virus requires a second receptor protein, called **CCR5,** to pull itself across the plasma membrane. After gp120 binds to CD4, its shape becomes twisted (a chemist would say it goes through a conformational change) into a new form that fits the CCR5 coreceptor molecule. Investigators speculate that after the conformational change, the coreceptor CCR5 passes the gp120-CD4 complex through the plasma membrane by triggering membrane fusion. Macrophages have the CCR5 coreceptor, as shown in panel 1, but T lymphocytes do not.

Replication

Panel 1 also shows that once inside the macrophage cell, the HIV virus particle sheds its protective coat. This leaves the virus nucleic acid (RNA in this case) floating in the cell's cytoplasm, along with a viral enzyme that was also within the virus shell. This enzyme, called **reverse transcriptase,** binds to the tip of the virus RNA and slides down it, synthesizing DNA that matches the information contained in the virus RNA, shown in panel 2. Importantly, the HIV reverse transcriptase enzyme doesn't do its job very accurately. It often makes mistakes in reading the HIV RNA, and so creates many new mutations. The mistake-ridden double-stranded DNA that it produces may integrate itself into the host cell's DNA as in panel 2; it can then direct the host cell's machinery to produce many copies of the virus, shown in panel 3.

In all of this process, no lasting damage is done to the host cell. HIV does not rupture and kill the macrophage cells it infects. Instead, the new viruses are released from the cell by budding (shown in the upper right of panel 4), a process much like exocytosis, in which the new viruses fold out

The Life Cycle of HIV

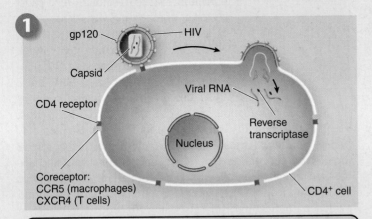

1 The gp120 glycoprotein on the surface of HIV attaches to CD4 and one of two coreceptors on the surface of a CD4+ cell. The viral contents enter the cell by membrane fusion.

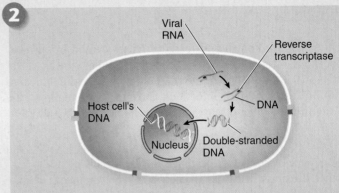

2 Reverse transcriptase catalyzes, first, the synthesis of a DNA copy of the viral RNA, and, second, the synthesis of a second DNA strand complementary to the first one. The double-stranded DNA is then incorporated into the host cell's DNA.

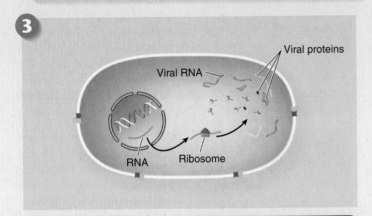

3 Transcription of the DNA results in the production of RNA. This RNA can serve as the genome for new viruses and can be translated to produce viral proteins.

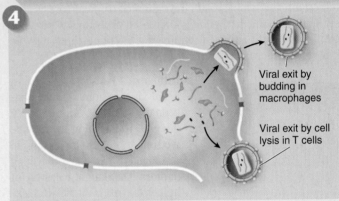

4 Complete HIV particles are assembled. In macrophages, HIV buds out of the cell without rupturing the cell. In T cells, HIV exits the cell by rupturing it, effectively killing the cell.

Figure 19.13 How the HIV infection cycle works.

opposite to the way that HIV initially gained entry into the cell at the start of the infection.

This, then, is the basis of the long latency period characteristic of AIDS. The HIV virus cycles through macrophages over a period of years, multiplying powerfully but doing little apparent damage to the body.

Starting AIDS: Entry into T Cells

During this long latent period, HIV is constantly replicating and mutating as it cycles through successive generations of macrophages. Eventually, by chance, HIV alters the gene for gp120 in a way that causes the gp120 protein to change its coreceptor allegiance. This new form of gp120 protein prefers to bind instead to a different coreceptor, **CXCR4,** a receptor that occurs on the surface of T cells that have the CD4 cell surface marker. Soon the body's T cells become infected with HIV.

This has deadly consequences, as new viruses exit T cells by bursting through the plasma membrane. This rupturing destroys the T cell's physical integrity and kills it (as shown at the lower right in panel 4). Therefore, HIV can either bud off the cell as in macrophages or it can cause cell lysis in T cells. In the case of T cells, as the released viruses infect nearby CD4+ T cells, they in turn are ruptured, in a widening circle of cell death. It is this destruction of the body's T cells, which fight other infections in the body, that blocks the body's immune response and leads directly to the onset of AIDS. Cancers and opportunistic infections are free to invade the defenseless body.

19.9 Animal viruses enter cells using specific receptor proteins to cross the plasma membrane.

Humans have known and feared diseases caused by viruses for thousands of years. Among the diseases that viruses cause (table 19.3) are AIDS, influenza, yellow fever, polio, chicken pox, measles, herpes, infectious hepatitis, and smallpox, as well as many other diseases not as well known.

The Origin of Viral Diseases

Sometimes viruses that originate in one organism pass to another, causing a disease in the new host. Thus, influenza is fundamentally a bird virus, and smallpox is thought to have passed from cattle to humans when cows were first domesticated.

New pathogens arising in this way, called *emerging viruses,* represent a greater threat today than in the past, as air travel and world trade in animals allows infected individuals and animals to move about the world quickly, spreading an infection. The widespread conversion of tropical forests into agricultural land has greatly increased the contact between people and wild animals, amplifying the opportunity for the introduction into people of novel viruses.

Influenza Perhaps the most lethal virus in human history has been the influenza virus. Between 40 and 100 million worldwide died of flu within 19 months in 1918 and 1919—an astonishing number. The natural reservoir of influenza virus is in ducks, chickens, and pigs in central Asia. Major flu pandemics (that is, worldwide epidemics) have arisen in Asian ducks through recombination within multiple infected individuals, putting together novel combinations of virus surface proteins unrecognizable by human immune defenses. The Asian flu of 1957 killed over 100,000 Americans. The Hong Kong flu of 1968 infected 50 million people in the United States alone, of which 70,000 died.

AIDS (HIV, human immunodeficieny virus) The virus that causes AIDS first entered humans from chimpanzees somewhere in Central Africa, probably between 1910 and 1950. The chimpanzee virus, called simian immunodeficiency virus, or SIV, mutates rapidly, at a rate of 1% a year, and in humans it continued to do so, soon becoming what we now know as HIV and spreading widely, mostly through sexual contact with an infected person. Where did chimpanzees acquire SIV? SIV viruses are rampant in African monkeys, and chimpanzees eat monkeys. Study of the nucleotide sequences of monkey SIVs revealed in 2001 that one end of the chimp virus RNA closely resembles the SIV found in red-capped mangabey monkeys, while the other end resembles the virus from the greater spot-nosed monkey. It thus seems certain that chimpanzees acquired SIV from monkeys they ate.

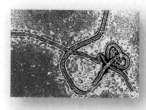

Ebola virus Among the most lethal of emerging viruses are a collection of filamentous viruses arising in Central Africa that attack human connective tissue. With lethality rates in excess of 50%, these so-called filoviruses cause some of the most lethal infectious diseases known. One, Ebola virus, has exhibited lethality rates in excess of 90% in isolated outbreaks in Central Africa. Luckily, victims die too fast to spread the disease very far. Extensive searches among wild and domestic animals have failed to reveal for certain the identity of the natural host of Ebola virus. Researchers in 2005 reported evidence implicating fruit bats, eaten for food everywhere in Central Africa that outbreaks have occurred.

Hantavirus A sudden outbreak of a highly fatal hemorrhagic infection in the southwestern United States in 1993 was soon attributed to a species of hantavirus, an RNA virus associated with rodents. This species was eventually traced to deer mice. The deer mouse hantavirus is transmitted to humans through fecal contamination in areas of human habitation. Control of deer mouse populations has limited the disease.

SARS A recently emerged strain of coronavirus was responsible for a worldwide outbreak in 2003 of *severe acute respiratory syndrome* (SARS), a respiratory infection with pneumonia-like symptoms that in over 8% of cases is fatal. When the 29,751-nucleotide RNA genome of the SARS virus was sequenced, it proved to be a completely new form of coronavirus, not closely related to any of the three previously described forms. Virologists in 2005 identified the Chinese horseshoe bat as the natural host of the SARS virus. Because these bats are healthy carriers not sickened by the virus, and occur commonly throughout Asia, it will be difficult to prevent future outbreaks.

West Nile Virus A mosquito-borne virus, West Nile virus, first infected people in North America in 1999, killing four people in Queens, New York. Carried by infected crows and other birds, the virus proceeded to spread across the country, with 4,156 cases at its peak in 2002, 284 of whom died. Fewer cases were reported in 2004, and by 2005 the wave of infection had greatly lessened. First detected in humans in Uganda, Africa, in 1937, the virus is common among birds, and is thought to have been transmitted to humans by mosquitoes that had previously bitten infected birds, much as it is being transmitted now. Earlier spread of the virus through Europe also abated after several years.

TABLE 19.3   IMPORTANT HUMAN VIRAL DISEASES

Disease	Pathogen	Vector/Reservoir	Symptoms and Mode of Transmission
AIDS	HIV	Humans	Destroys immune defenses, resulting in death by infection or cancer. About 33 million are infected with HIV worldwide.
Chicken pox	Human herpes-virus 3 (HHV-3 or varicella-zoster)	Humans	Spread through contact with infected individuals. No cure. Rarely fatal. Vaccine approved in United States in early 1995.
Ebola hemorrhagic fever	Filoviruses (such as Ebola virus)	Unknown	Acute hemorrhagic fever; virus attacks connective tissue, leading to massive hemorrhaging and death. Peak mortality is 50% to 90% if the disease goes untreated. Outbreaks confined to local regions of Central Africa.
Hepatitis B (viral)	Hepatitis B virus (HBV)	Humans	Highly infectious through contact with infected body fluids. Approximately 1% of U.S. population infected. Vaccine available, no cure. Can be fatal.
Herpes	Herpes simplex virus (HSV or HHV-1/2)	Humans	Fever blisters; spread primarily through contact with infected saliva. Very prevalent worldwide. No cure. Exhibits latency—the disease can be dormant for several years.
Influenza	Influenza viruses	Humans, ducks, pigs	Historically a major killer (between 40 and 100 million died in 1918–19); wild Asian ducks, chickens, and pigs are major reservoirs. The ducks are not affected by the flu virus, which shuffles its antigen genes while multiplying within them, leading to new flu strains.
Measles	Paramyxoviruses	Humans	Extremely contagious through contact with infected individuals. Vaccine available. Usually contracted in childhood, when it is not serious; more dangerous to adults.
Polio	Poliovirus	Humans	Acute viral infection of the central nervous system that can lead to paralysis and is often fatal. Prior to the development of Salk's vaccine in 1954, 60,000 people a year contracted the disease in the United States alone.
Rabies	Rhabdovirus	Wild and domestic Canidae (dogs, foxes, wolves, coyotes, etc.)	An acute viral encephalomyelitis transmitted by the bite of an infected animal. Fatal if untreated.
SARS	Coronavirus	Small mammals	Acute respiratory infection; can be fatal, but as with any emerging disease, this can change rapidly.
Smallpox	Variola virus	Formerly humans, now thought to exist only in government labs	Historically a major killer, the last recorded case of smallpox was in 1977. A worldwide vaccination campaign wiped out the disease completely. There is current debate as to whether the virus has been removed from government labs of the former Soviet Union and could now be made available to terrorists.
Yellow fever	Flavivirus	Humans, mosquitoes	Spread from individual to individual by mosquito bites; a notable cause of death during the construction of the Panama Canal. If untreated, this disease has a peak mortality rate of 60%.

The Continuing Threat of Influenza: Bird Flu

As mentioned on page 368, the influenza virus has been one of the most lethal viruses in human history. Flu viruses are animal RNA viruses containing eleven genes. An individual flu virus resembles a sphere studded with spikes composed of two kinds of protein. Different strains of flu virus, called subtypes, differ in their protein spikes. One of these proteins, hemagglutinin (H), aids the virus in gaining access to the cell interior. The other, neuraminidase (N), helps the daughter virus break free of the host cell once virus replication has been completed. Flu viruses are currently classified into 13 distinct H subtypes and 9 distinct N subtypes, each of which requires a different vaccine to protect against infection. Thus, the virus that caused the Hong Kong flu epidemic of 1968 has type 3 H molecules and type 2 N molecules, and is called H3N2.

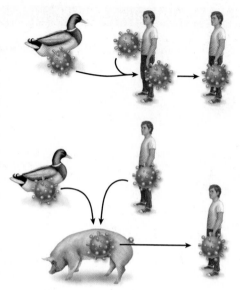

Recombination within humans
A person infected with a flu virus can become infected with another type of flu virus by direct contact with birds. The two viruses can undergo genetic recombination to produce a third type of virus, which can spread from human to human.

Recombination within pigs
Pigs can contract flu viruses from both birds and humans. The flu viruses can undergo genetic recombination in the pig, to produce a new kind of flu virus, which can spread from pigs to humans.

Figure 19.14   How a new strain of bird flu might arise.

How New Flu Strains Arise   Indeed, worldwide epidemics of the flu in the last century have been caused by shifts in flu virus H-N combinations. The "killer flu" of 1918, H1N1, thought to have passed directly from birds to humans, killed between 40 and 100 million people worldwide. The Asian flu of 1957, H2N2, killed over 100,000 Americans, and the Hong Kong flu of 1968, H3N2, killed 70,000 Americans.

It is no accident that new strains of flu usually originate in the Far East. The most common hosts of influenza virus are ducks, chickens, and pigs, which in Asia often live in close proximity to each other and to humans. Pigs are subject to infection by both bird and human strains of the virus, and individual animals are often simultaneously infected with multiple strains. This creates conditions favoring genetic recombination between strains, as illustrated in figure 19.14, sometimes putting together novel combinations of H and N spikes unrecognizable by human immune defenses specific for the old configuration. The Hong Kong flu, for example, arose from recombination between H3N8 from ducks and H2N2 from humans. The new strain of influenza, in this case H3N2, then passed back to humans, creating an epidemic because the human population has never experienced that H-N combination before.

Conditions for a Pandemic   Not every new strain of influenza creates a worldwide flu epidemic. Three conditions are necessary: (1) The new strain must contain a novel combination of H and N spikes, so that the human population has no significant immunity from infection; (2) the new strain must be able to replicate in humans and cause death—many bird influenza viruses are harmless to people because they cannot multiply in human cells; (3) the new strain must be efficiently transmitted between humans. The H1N1 killer flu of 1918 spread in water droplets exhaled from infected individuals and subsequently inhaled into the lower respiratory tract of nearby people.

The new strain need not be deadly to every infected person in order to produce a pandemic—the H1N1 flu of 1918 had an overall mortality rate of only 2%, and yet killed 50 million people. Why did so many die? Because the H1N1 virus was very infectious, spreading rapidly anywhere people came together.

Bird Flu   A potentially deadly new strain of flu virus emerged in Hong Kong in 1997, H5N1. Like the 1918 pandemic strain, H5N1 passes to humans directly from infected birds, usually chickens or ducks, and for this reason has been dubbed "bird flu." Bird flu has gotten an unusual amount of public attention, because it satisfies the first two conditions of a pandemic. Bird flu is a novel combination of H and N spikes for which humans have little immunity, and the resulting strain is particularly deadly. Of 256 individuals infected by handling birds by the end of 2006, 151 died of the infection, a mortality of 59% (for comparison, the mortality of the 1918 strain was 2%). Fortunately, the third condition for a pandemic is not yet met: The H5N1 strain of flu virus does not spread easily from person to person, and the number of human infections remains small.

Prudent Preparations   Public health officials remain concerned that the genes of H5N1 could yet mix with those of a human strain to create a virus able to spread from person to person. Vaccines are being developed directed against the existing H5N1 strain, in the hope they will add some protection against a more transmissible strain that might emerge. A worldwide surveillance network seems very effective at detecting new cases, so sites of potential human-to-human transmission can be flooded with antiviral drugs, putting out the fire before it spreads.

19.10   Viruses are responsible for some of the most lethal diseases of humans. Some of the most serious examples are viruses that have transferred to humans from some other host. Influenza virus is a bird virus that causes major epidemics when strains arise that are able to pass between people.

Origin of the First Cells

19.1 Origin of Life

- Life on earth may have originated from an extraterrestrial source, may have been put on this earth by a divine being, or may have evolved from inanimate matter. Only the third explanation is scientifically testable at this point.

- In experiments, reconstructing the conditions of early earth led to the hypothesis that life evolved spontaneously in a "primordial soup" of biological molecules. This hypothesis is in question, but the "bubble model" suggests that biological molecules were captured in bubbles, as shown here from **figure 19.2**, where they underwent chemical reactions, leading to the origin of life.

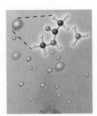

19.2 How Cells Arose

- We don't know how the first cells formed, but current hypotheses suggest that they may have formed spontaneously, from bubble-enclosed molecules such as RNA.

- Bubbles, called microspheres, form spontaneously, and scientists proposed that if organic molecules, such as RNA that has enzymatic capabilities, was trapped inside a microsphere, the structure would have the ability to carry hereditary information and to make copies of itself.

Prokaryotes

19.3 The Simplest Organisms

- Bacteria are the most ancient form of life, existing more than 2.5 billion years ago. These early prokaryotes gave rise to the present-day bacteria and archaea.

- Prokaryotes have very simple internal structures, lacking nuclei and other membrane-bound compartments.

- The plasma membrane of prokaryotes is encased in a cell wall. The cell wall of bacteria is made of peptidoglycan, and the cell wall of archaea lacks peptidoglycan, being made of protein and/ or polysaccharides. Bacteria are divided into two groups, gram-positive and gram-negative, based on the construction of their cell walls (**figure 19.4**).

- Bacteria may have flagella or pili and may form endospores. They reproduce by splitting in two, called binary fission, and may exchange genetic information through conjugation.

- Conjugation occurs when two bacterial cells are brought into contact, and the pilus of one cell, the donor, contacts another cell, called a recipient. A conjugation bridge forms between the two cells. The plasmid in the donor cell is copied, and a single strand of the DNA is transferred to the recipient cell across the conjugation bridge. Once inside the recipient cell, a complementary strand is synthesized, completing the plasmid. Now, the recipient cell contains the same genetic information found on the plasmid of the donor cell (**figure 19.5**).

19.4 Comparing Prokaryotes to Eukaryotes

- Prokaryotes, like the one shown here from **table 19.1**, are different from eukaryotes in many ways, including that they lack interior compartments, including nuclei, and are more metabolically diverse.

19.5 Importance of Prokaryotes

- Bacteria were instrumental in creating the properties of the atmosphere and soil found on earth. They are major participants in the carbon and nitrogen cycles. They were key to the development of genetic engineering; however, they are responsible for many diseases.

19.6 Prokaryotic Lifestyles

- Although archaea live in many different environments, the best understood are the extremophiles, which live in unusually harsh environments.

- Bacteria are the most abundant organisms on the planet. They are a very diverse group: Some are photosynthetic, some are able to fix nitrogen, and some are decomposers. Some bacteria are also pathogenic, causing human diseases (**table 19.2**).

Viruses

19.7 The Structure of Viruses

- Viruses are not living organisms, but rather are parasitic chemicals that enter and replicate inside cells. They contain a nucleic acid core surrounded by a protein coat called a capsid, and some have an outer membranelike envelope. Viruses infect bacteria, plants, and animals, and while all viruses have the same general structure, they vary greatly in shape and size (**figure 19.9**).

19.8 How Bacteriophages Enter Prokaryotic Cells

- Viruses that infect bacteria are called bacteriophages. They do not enter the host cell but instead inject their nucleic acid into the host as shown here from **figure 19.10**. The virus then enters either a lytic cycle or a lysogenic cycle. In the lytic cycle, the viral DNA directs the production of multiple copies of the virus in the host cell, which eventually ruptures, releasing the viruses to infect other cells. In the lysogenic cycle, the viral DNA becomes incorporated into the host DNA. Viral DNA is replicated with the host DNA and is passed on to offspring. At some point, the viral DNA enters the lytic cycle (**figure 19.11**).

19.9 How Animal Viruses Enter Cells

- Animal viruses enter host cells through endocytosis or membrane fusion. The HIV virus attaches to surface receptors on the host where it is engulfed. Once inside the cell, HIV produces DNA from its viral RNA using the enzyme reverse transcriptase. The viral DNA enters the host DNA and directs the formation of new viruses that bud off the host cell (**figure 19.13**). At some point, HIV is altered so that it binds to receptors on CD4+ T cells. The CD4+ infection ends in lysis of the cells, rapidly killing T cells needed to fight other infections.

19.10 Disease Viruses

- Viruses, like the influenza virus shown here from **table 19.3**, cause many diseases, often spreading from animals to humans. Influenza, a deadly virus that killed millions in 1918, poses a continuing threat.

1. Which is *not* an assumption used in the Miller and Urey experiment?
   a. The primordial atmosphere of the earth contained methane.
   b. The primordial atmosphere of the earth contained the same amount of oxygen as today.
   c. Lightning provided energy for chemical reactions.
   d. Small inorganic chemicals used to make larger organic molecules were present in the atmosphere and the water.

2. While it is still unknown how the first cells formed, scientists suspect that the first active biological macromolecule was
   a. protein.   c. RNA.
   b. DNA.   d. carbohydrates.

3. Bacteria
   a. are prokaryotic.
   b. have been on the earth for at least 2.5 billion years.
   c. are the most abundant life-form on earth.
   d. All answers are correct.

4. Some species of prokaryotes are able to obtain carbon from CO_2 and energy by oxidizing inorganic chemicals. These species are also called
   a. photoautotrophs.   c. photoheterotrophs.
   b. chemoautotrophs.   d. chemoheterotrophs.

5. Which of the following can be attributed to bacteria?
   a. decomposition of dead organic matter
   b. increasing oxygen levels in the atmosphere
   c. insect resistance in plants
   d. All of the above

6. Cyanobacteria are thought to have been very prominent in earth's history by
   a. making nucleic acids.
   b. making proteins.
   c. producing the carbon dioxide that is in the atmosphere.
   d. producing the oxygen that is in the atmosphere.

7. Viruses are
   a. protein coats that contain DNA or RNA.
   b. simple eukaryotic cells.
   c. simple prokaryotic cells.
   d. alive.

8. The virus reproductive cycle where the virus enters the cell, uses the cell structures to make more viruses, then breaks open the cell to release the new viruses is called the
   a. lysogenic cycle.
   b. lambda cycle.
   c. lytic cycle.
   d. prophage cycle.

9. Animal viruses enter animal cells by
   a. exocytosis.
   b. matching a marker on the surface of the virus to a complementary marker on the surface of a cell.
   c. contacting the host cell with protein tail fibers.
   d. contacting any place on the cell's membrane with the virus's protein coat.

10. HIV is a virus that contains RNA. To insert its genetic material into the cell's genome, HIV must
   a. use the cell's ribosomes and enzymes to read the RNA backward to produce DNA.
   b. do nothing; the virus RNA will insert itself into the cell DNA without changing.
   c. use an enzyme called reverse transcriptase to convert the virus RNA to DNA, which is then integrated into the cell's chromosome.
   d. No answer is correct.

Visual Understanding

1. **Figure 19.2** What provides the energy to form the molecules shown in this figure?

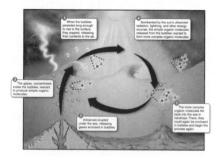

2. **Figure 19.9** Viruses have dramatically different forms and shapes. What are the consistent features of all the viruses shown?

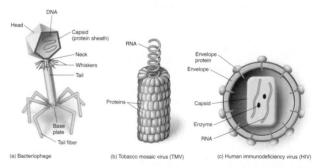

(a) Bacteriophage   (b) Tobacco mosaic virus (TMV)   (c) Human immunodeficiency virus (HIV)

Challenge Questions

1. Why can't we prove how life began on earth?
2. How do prokaryotes obtain the energy for life?

3. Why are some diseases, such as AIDS, so difficult to track and to defend against infection?

20

Protists: Advent of the Eukaryotes

Y ou are a eukaryote, an organism composed of cells that contain a nucleus. All the organisms you see around you are eukaryotes, too, as prokaryote organisms are too small for you to see without a microscope to magnify them. Biologists sort the eukaryotes of the living world into four great groups, called kingdoms: animals, plants, fungi, and everything else. This chapter concerns the fourth catch-all group, the protists (kingdom Protista). The beautiful flowerlike creature you see here is a protist, the green algae *Acetabularia*. It is photosynthetic and grows as long slender stalks as long as your thumb. In the last century some biologists considered it to be a very simple sort of plant. Today, however, most biologists consider *Acetabularia* to be a protist, restricting the plant kingdom to multicellular terrestrial photosynthetic organisms (and a few marine and aquatic species like water lilies clearly derived from terrestrial ancestors). *Acetabularia* is marine, not terrestrial, and it is unicellular, with a single nucleus found in the base of its stalk. In this chapter, we will explore how protists are thought to have evolved, and the sorts of creatures found among this most diverse of biological kingdoms. Multicellularity evolved many times within the protists, producing the ancestors of the animal, plant, and fungi kingdoms, as well as several kinds of multicellular algae, some as large as trees.

20.1 The Origin of Eukaryotic Cells

The First Eukaryotic Cells

All fossils more than 1.7 billion years old are small, simple cells, similar to the bacteria of today. In rocks about 1.7 billion years old, we begin to see the first microfossils, which are noticeably larger than bacteria and have internal membranes and thicker walls. A new kind of organism had appeared, called a **eukaryote** (Greek *eu*, "true," and *karyon*, "nut"). One of the main features of a eukaryotic cell is the presence of an internal structure called a nucleus (see section 5.5). As discussed in chapter 18, animals, plants, fungi, and protists are all eukaryotes. In this chapter, we will explore the protists, from which all other eukaryotes evolved. But first we will examine some of the unifying characteristics of eukaryotes, and how they might have originated.

To begin, how might a nucleus have arisen? Many bacteria have infoldings of their outer membranes extending into the interior that serve as passageways between the surface and the cell's interior. The network of internal membranes in eukaryotes, called the endoplasmic reticulum (ER), is thought to have evolved from such infoldings, as did the nuclear envelope (figure 20.1). The prokaryotic cell shown on the far left has infoldings of the plasma membrane with its DNA in the center of the cell. In ancestral eukaryotic cells, these internal membrane extensions evolved to project farther into the cell, continuing their function as passageways between the interior and exterior of the cell. Eventually, these membranes came to form an enclosure surrounding the DNA, on the right, which became the nuclear envelope.

What was the first eukaryote like? We cannot be sure, but a good model is *Pelomyxa palustris,* a single-celled, nonphotosynthetic organism that appears to represent an early stage in the evolution of eukaryotic cells. The cells of *Pelomyxa* are much larger than bacterial cells and contain a complex system of internal membranes. Although they resemble some of the largest early fossil eukaryotes, these cells are unlike those of any other eukaryote: *Pelomyxa* lacks mitochondria and does not undergo mitosis as in eukaryotes. This primitive eukaryote is so distinctive that it is assigned a phylum all its own, Caryoblastea.

Biologists know very little of the origin of *Pelomyxa,* except that in many fundamental ways it resembles the archaea far more than the bacteria. Because of similarities in their DNA, it is widely assumed that the first eukaryotic cells were nonphotosynthetic descendants of archaea.

Endosymbiosis

In addition to an internal system of membranes and a nucleus, eukaryotic cells contain several other distinctive organelles. These organelles were discussed in chapter 5. Two of these organelles, mitochondria and chloroplasts, are especially unique because they resemble bacterial cells and even contain their own DNA. As discussed in section 5.7 and section 18.9, mitochondria and chloroplasts are thought to have arisen by endosymbiosis, where one organism comes to live inside another. The **endosymbiotic theory,** now widely accepted, suggests that at a critical stage in the evolution of eukaryotic cells, energy-producing aerobic bacteria came to reside symbiotically (that is, cooperatively) within larger early eukaryotic cells, eventually evolving into the cell organelles we now know as mitochondria. Similarly, photosynthetic bacteria came to live within some of these early eukaryotic cells, leading to the evolution of chloroplasts (figure 20.2), the photosynthetic organelles of plants and algae. Now, let's examine the evidence supporting the endosymbiotic theory a little more closely.

Mitochondria Mitochondria, the energy-generating organelles in eukaryotic cells, are sausage-shaped organelles about 1 to 3 micrometers long, about the same size as most bacteria. Mitochondria are bounded by *two* membranes. The outer membrane is smooth and was apparently derived from the host cell as it wrapped around the bacterium. The inner membrane is folded into numerous layers, embedded within which are the proteins of oxidative metabolism.

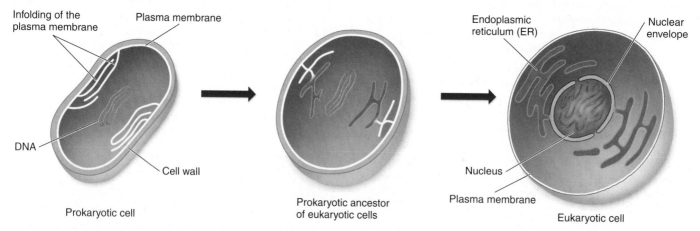

Infolding of the plasma membrane · Plasma membrane · DNA · Cell wall · Prokaryotic cell · Prokaryotic ancestor of eukaryotic cells · Endoplasmic reticulum (ER) · Nuclear envelope · Nucleus · Plasma membrane · Eukaryotic cell

Figure 20.1   Origin of the nucleus and endoplasmic reticulum.
Many bacteria today have infoldings of the plasma membrane. The eukaryotic internal membrane system called the endoplasmic reticulum (ER) and the nuclear envelope may have evolved from such infoldings of the plasma membrane of prokaryotic cells that gave rise to eukaryotic cells.

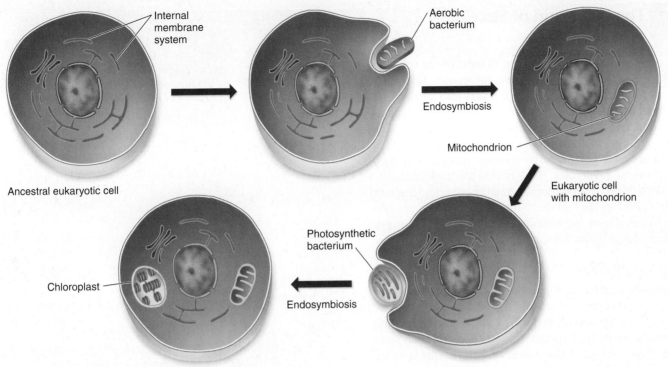

Figure 20.2 The theory of endosymbiosis.
Scientists propose that ancestral eukaryotic cells engulfed aerobic bacteria, which then became mitochondria in the eukaryotic cell. Chloroplasts may also have originated in this way, with eukaryotic cells engulfing photosynthetic bacteria that became chloroplasts.

During the billion-and-a-half years in which mitochondria have existed as endosymbionts within eukaryotic cells, most of their genes have been transferred to the chromosomes of the host cells—but not all. Each mitochondrion still has its own genome, a circular, closed molecule of DNA similar to that found in bacteria, on which is located genes encoding some of the essential proteins of oxidative metabolism. These genes are transcribed within the mitochondrion, using mitochondrial ribosomes that are smaller than those of eukaryotic cells, very much like bacterial ribosomes in size and structure. Mitochondria divide by simple fission, just as bacteria do, and can divide on their own without the cell nucleus dividing. Mitochondria also replicate and sort their DNA much as bacteria do. However, the cell's nuclear genes direct the process, and mitochondria cannot be grown outside of the eukaryotic cell, in cell-free culture.

Chloroplasts   Many eukaryotic cells contain other endosymbiotic bacteria in addition to mitochondria. Plants and algae contain chloroplasts, bacteria-like organelles that were apparently derived from symbiotic photosynthetic bacteria. Chloroplasts have a complex system of inner membranes and a circle of DNA. While all mitochondria are thought to have arisen from a single symbiotic event, it is difficult to be sure with chloroplasts. Three biochemically distinct classes of chloroplasts exist, but all appear to have their origin in the cyanobacteria.

Red algae and green algae seem to have acquired cyanobacteria directly as endosymbionts, and may be sister groups. Other algae have chloroplasts of secondary origin, having taken up one of these algae in their past. The chloroplasts of euglenoids are thought to be green algal in origin, while those of brown algae and diatoms are likely of red algal origin. The chloroplasts of dinoflagellates seem to be of complex origins, which might include diatoms.

Mitosis

As mentioned earlier, the primitive eukaryote *Pelomyxa* does not exhibit mitosis, the eukaryotic process of cell division. How did mitosis evolve? The mechanism of mitosis, now so common among eukaryotes, did not evolve all at once. Traces of very different, and possibly intermediate, mechanisms survive today in some of the eukaryotes. In fungi and some groups of protists, for example, the nuclear membrane does not dissolve, and mitosis is confined to the nucleus. When mitosis is complete in these organisms, the nucleus divides into two daughter nuclei, and only then does the rest of the cell divide. This separate nuclear division phase of mitosis does not occur in most protists, or in plants or animals. We do not know if it represents an intermediate step on the evolutionary journey to the form of mitosis that is characteristic of most eukaryotes today, or if it is simply a different way of solving the same problem. There are no fossils in which we can see the interiors of dividing cells well enough to be able to trace the history of mitosis.

20.1 The theory of endosymbiosis proposes that mitochondria originated as symbiotic aerobic bacteria and chloroplasts originated from a second endosymbiotic event with photosynthetic bacteria.

The Evolution of Sex

In the previous section, we mentioned some of the structural differences between prokaryotes and eukaryotes. But one of the most profoundly important characteristics of eukaryotes is the capacity for sexual reproduction. Indeed, many types of protists undergo sexual reproduction. In **sexual reproduction,** two different parents contribute gametes to form the offspring. Gametes are usually formed by meiosis, discussed in chapter 10. In most eukaryotes, the gametes are haploid (have a single copy of each chromosome), and the offspring produced by their fusion are diploid (have two copies of each chromosome). In this section, we examine sexual reproduction among the eukaryotes and how it evolved.

Life Without Sex

To fully understand sexual reproduction, we must first examine asexual reproduction among the eukaryotes. Consider, for example, a sponge. A sponge can reproduce by simply fragmenting its body, a process called *budding.* Each small portion grows and gives rise to a new sponge. This is an example of **asexual reproduction,** reproduction without forming gametes. In asexual reproduction, the offspring are genetically identical to the parent, barring mutation. The majority of protists reproduce asexually most of the time. Some protists such as the green algae exhibit a true sexual cycle, but only transiently. Asexual reproduction in a protist called *Paramecium* is shown in figure 20.3a. The single cell duplicates its DNA, grows larger, and then splits in two. The fusion of two haploid cells to create a diploid zygote, the essential act of sexual reproduction, occurs only under stress. *Paramecium* is again shown in figure 20.3b but now undergoing sexual reproduction. In this case, the cell is not splitting in half; rather two cells are coming into close contact. In a process called *conjugation,* they exchange genetic information in their haploid nuclei.

The development of an adult from an unfertilized egg is a form of asexual reproduction called **parthenogenesis.** Parthenogenesis is a common form of reproduction among insects. In bees, for example, fertilized eggs develop into females, while unfertilized eggs become males. Some lizards, fishes, and amphibians reproduce by parthenogenesis; an unfertilized egg undergoes mitosis without cytokinesis to produce a diploid cell, which then undergoes development as if it had been produced by sexual union of two gametes.

Many plants and marine fishes undergo a form of sexual reproduction that does not involve partners. In **self-fertilization,** one individual provides both male and female gametes. Mendel's peas discussed in chapter 11 produced their F_2 generations by "selfing." Why isn't this asexual reproduction (after all, there is only one parent)? This is considered to be sexual rather than asexual reproduction because the offspring are not genetically identical to the parent. During the production of the gametes by meiosis, considerable genetic reassortment occurs—that is why Mendel's F_2 plants were not all the same!

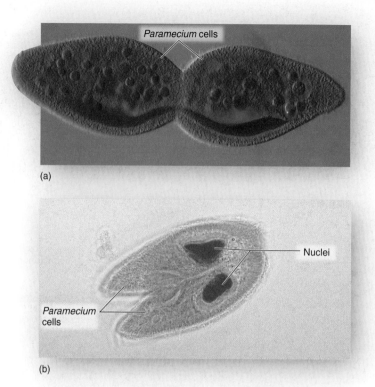

Figure 20.3 Reproduction among paramecia.
(a) When *Paramecium* reproduces asexually, a mature individual divides, and two genetically identical individuals result. (b) In sexual reproduction, two mature cells fuse in a process called conjugation (×100) and exchange haploid nuclei.

Why Sex?

If reproduction without sex is so common among eukaryotes today, it is a fair question to ask why sex occurs at all. Evolution is the result of changes that occur at the level of *individual* survival and reproduction, and it is not immediately obvious what advantage is gained by the progeny of an individual that engages in sexual reproduction. Indeed, the segregation of chromosomes that occurs in meiosis tends to disrupt advantageous combinations of genes more often than it assembles new, better-adapted ones. Because all the progeny could maintain a parent's successful gene combinations if the parent employed asexual reproduction, the widespread use of sexual reproduction among eukaryotes raises a puzzle: Where is the benefit from sex that promoted the evolution of sexual reproduction?

How Sex Evolved

In attempting to answer this question, biologists have looked more carefully at where sex first evolved—among the protists. Why do many protists form a diploid cell in response to stress? Biologists think this occurs because only in a diploid cell can certain kinds of chromosome damage be repaired effectively, particularly double-strand breaks in DNA. Such breaks are induced, for example, by desiccation—drying out. The early stages of meiosis, in which the two copies of

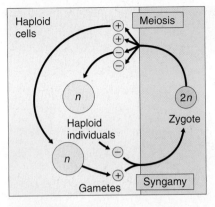

(a) Zygotic meiosis

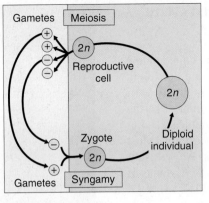

(b) Gametic meiosis

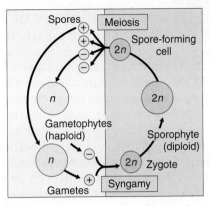

(c) Sporic meiosis

Figure 20.4 Three types of eukaryotic life cycles.
(*a*) Zygotic meiosis, a life cycle found in most protists. (*b*) Gametic meiosis, a life cycle typical of animals. (*c*) Sporic meiosis, a life cycle found in plants.

each chromosome line up and pair with each other, seems to have evolved originally as a mechanism for repairing double-strand damage to DNA by using the undamaged version of the chromosome as a template to guide the fixing of the damaged one. In yeasts, mutations that inactivate the system that repairs double-strand breaks of the chromosomes also prevent crossing over. Thus, it seems likely that sexual reproduction and the close association between pairs of chromosomes that occurs during meiosis first evolved as mechanisms to repair chromosomal damage by using the second copy of the chromosome as a template.

Why Sex Is Important

One of the most important evolutionary innovations of eukaryotes was the invention of sex. Sexual reproduction provides a powerful means of shuffling genes, quickly generating different combinations of genes among individuals. Genetic diversity is the raw material for evolution. In many cases the pace of evolution appears to be geared to the level of genetic variation available for selection to act upon—the greater the genetic diversity, the more rapid the evolutionary pace. Programs for selecting larger domestic cattle and sheep, for example, proceed rapidly at first but then slow as all of the existing genetic combinations are exhausted; further progress must then await the generation of new gene combinations. The genetic recombination produced by sexual reproduction has had an enormous evolutionary impact because of its ability to rapidly generate extensive genetic diversity.

Sexual Life Cycles

Many protists are haploid all their lives, but with few exceptions, animals and plants are diploid at some stage of their lives. That is, the body cells of most animals and plants have two sets of chromosomes, one from the male and one from the female parent. The production of haploid gametes by meiosis, followed by the union of two gametes in sexual reproduction, is called the **sexual life cycle.**

Eukaryotes are characterized by three major types of sexual life cycles (figure 20.4):

1. In the simplest of these, found in many algae, the zygote formed by the fusion of gametes is the only diploid cell. This sort of life cycle, which you can see in figure 20.4*a*, is said to represent **zygotic meiosis,** because in algae the zygote undergoes meiosis. Haploid cells occupy the major portion of the life cycle, as indicated by the larger yellow box; the diploid zygote undergoes meiosis immediately after it is formed.

2. In most animals, the gametes are the only haploid cells. They exhibit **gametic meiosis,** because in animals meiosis produces the gametes. Here the diploid cells occupy the major portion of the life cycle, as indicated by the larger blue box in figure 20.4*b*.

3. Plants exhibit **sporic meiosis,** because in plants the spore-forming cells undergo meiosis. In plants there is a regular **alternation of generations** between a haploid phase (the yellow boxed area in figure 20.4*c*) and a diploid phase (the blue boxed area in figure 20.4*c*). The diploid phase produces spores that give rise to the haploid phase, and the haploid phase produces gametes that fuse to give rise to the diploid phase.

The genesis of sex, then, involved meiosis and fertilization with the participation of two parents. We have previously said that bacteria lack true sexual reproduction, although in some groups, two bacteria do pair up in conjugation and exchange parts of their genome. The evolution of true sexual reproduction among the protists has no doubt contributed importantly to their tremendous diversification and adaptation to an extraordinary range of ways of life, as we shall see in section 20.3.

> **20.2** Sex evolved among eukaryotes as a mechanism to repair chromosomal damage, but its importance is as a means of generating diversity.

20.3 General Biology of Protists, the Most Ancient Eukaryotes

Protists are the most ancient eukaryotes and are united on the basis of a single negative characteristic: They are not fungi, plants, or animals. In all other respects, they are highly variable with no uniting features. Many are unicellular, like the *Vorticella* you see in figure 20.5 with its contractible stalk, but there are numerous colonial and multicellular groups. Most are microscopic, but some are as large as trees. We will start our discussion of the protists with an overview of some of their important features, and then in section 20.4, we begin our examination of the principle kinds of protists.

The Cell Surface

Protists possess varied types of cell surfaces. All protists have plasma membranes. But some protists, like algae and molds, are additionally encased within strong cell walls. Still others, like diatoms and radiolarians, secrete glassy shells of silica.

Locomotor Organelles

Movement in protists is also accomplished by diverse mechanisms. Protists move by cilia, flagella, pseudopods, or gliding mechanisms. Many protists wave one or more flagella to propel themselves through the water, whereas others use banks of short, flagella-like structures called cilia to create water currents for their feeding or propulsion. Pseudopodia are the chief means of locomotion among amoebas, whose pseudopods are large, blunt extensions of the cell body called lobopodia. Other related protists extend thin, branching protrusions called filopodia. Still other protists extend long, thin pseudopodia called axopodia supported by axial rods of microtubules. Axopodia can be extended or retracted. Because the tips can adhere to adjacent surfaces, the cell can move by a rolling motion, shortening the axopodia in front and extending those in the rear.

Cyst Formation

Many protists with delicate surfaces are successful in quite harsh habitats. How do they manage to survive so well? They survive inhospitable conditions by forming **cysts.** A cyst is a dormant form of a cell with a resistant outer covering in which cell metabolism is more or less completely shut down. Amoebic parasites in vertebrates, for example, form cysts that are quite resistant to gastric acidity (although they will not tolerate desiccation or high temperature).

Nutrition

Protists employ every form of nutritional acquisition except chemoautotrophy, which has so far been observed only in prokaryotes. Some protists are photosynthetic autotrophs and are called **phototrophs.** Others are heterotrophs that obtain energy from organic molecules synthesized by other organisms. Among heterotrophic protists, those that ingest visible particles of food are called **phagotrophs,** or **holozoic feeders.**

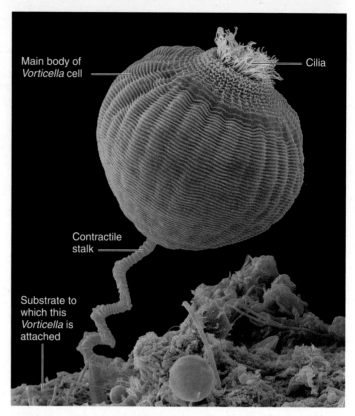

Figure 20.5 A unicellular protist.
The protist kingdom is a catch-all kingdom for many different groups of unicellular organisms, such as this *Vorticella* (phylum Ciliophora), which is heterotrophic, feeds on bacteria, and has a contractile stalk.

Those ingesting food in soluble form are called **osmotrophs,** or **saprozoic feeders.**

Phagotrophs ingest food particles into intracellular vesicles called **food vacuoles,** or **phagosomes.** Lysosomes fuse with the food vacuoles, introducing enzymes that digest the food particles within. As the digested molecules are absorbed across the vacuolar membrane, the food vacuole becomes progressively smaller.

Reproduction

Protists typically reproduce asexually, most reproducing sexually only in times of stress. Asexual reproduction involves mitosis, but the process is often somewhat different from the mitosis that occurs in multicellular animals. The nuclear membrane, for example, often persists throughout mitosis, with the microtubular spindle forming within it. In some groups, asexual reproduction involves spore formation, in others fission. The most common type of fission is **binary,** in which a cell simply splits into nearly equal halves. When the progeny cell is considerably smaller than its parent, and then grows to adult size, the fission is called **budding.** In multiple fission, or **schizogony,** common among some protists, fission is preceded by several nuclear divisions, so that fission produces several individuals almost simultaneously.

Sexual reproduction also takes place in many forms among the protists. In ciliates, **gametic meiosis** occurs just before gamete formation, as it does in most animals. In the sporozoans, **zygotic meiosis** occurs directly *after* fertilization, and all the individuals that are produced are haploid until the next zygote is formed. In algae, there is **sporic meiosis,** producing an alternation of generations similar to that seen in plants, with significant portions of the life cycle spent as haploid as well as diploid.

Multicellularity

A single cell has limits. It can only be so big without encountering serious surface-to-volume problems. Said simply, as a cell becomes larger, there is too little surface area for so much volume. The evolution of multicellular individuals composed of many cells solved this problem. **Multicellularity** is a condition in which an organism is composed of many cells, permanently associated with one another, that integrate their activities. The key advantage of multicellularity is that it allows specialization—distinct types of cells, tissues, and organs can be differentiated within an individual's body, each with a different function. With such functional "division of labor" within its body, a multicellular organism can possess cells devoted specifically to protecting the body, others to moving it about, still others to seeking mates and prey, and yet others to carry on a host of other activities. This allows the organism to function on a scale and with a complexity that would have been impossible for its unicellular ancestors. In just this way, a small city of 50,000 inhabitants is vastly more complex and capable than a crowd of 50,000 people in a football stadium— each city dweller is specialized in a particular activity that is interrelated to everyone else's, rather than just being another body in a crowd.

Colonies A **colonial organism** is a collection of cells that are permanently associated but in which little or no integration of cell activities occurs. Many protists form colonial assemblies, consisting of many cells with little differentiation or integration. In some protists, the distinction between colonial and multicellular is blurred. For example, in the green algae *Volvox* shown in figure 20.6, individual motile cells aggregate into a hollow ball of cells that moves by a coordinated beating of the flagella of the individual cells—like scores of rowers all pulling their oars in concert. A few cells near the rear of the moving colony are reproductive cells, but most are relatively undifferentiated.

Aggregates An **aggregation** is a more transient collection of cells that come together for a period of time and then separate. Cellular slime molds, for example, are unicellular organisms that spend most of their lives moving about and feeding as single-celled amoebas. They are common in damp soil and on rotting logs, where they move about, ingesting bacteria and other small organisms. When the individual amoebas exhaust the supply of bacteria in a given area and are near starvation, all of the individual organisms in that immediate area aggregate into a large moving mass of cells called a slug. By moving to a different location, the aggregation increases the chance that food will be found.

Multicellular Individuals True multicellularity, in which the activities of the individual cells are coordinated and the cells themselves are in contact, occurs only in eukaryotes and is one of their major characteristics. Three groups of protists have independently attained true but simple multicellularity—the brown algae (phylum Phaeophyta), green algae (phylum Chlorophyta), and red algae (phylum Rhodophyta). In **multicellular organisms,** individuals are composed of many cells that interact with one another and coordinate their activities.

Simple multicellularity does not imply small size or limited adaptability. Some marine algae grow to be enormous. An individual kelp, one of the brown algae, may grow to tens of meters in length—some taller than a redwood! Red algae grow at great depths in the sea, far below where kelp or other algae are found. Not all algae are multicellular. Green algae, for example, include many kinds of multicellular organisms but an even larger number of unicellular ones.

> **20.3** Protists exhibit a wide range of forms, locomotion, nutrition, and reproduction. Their cells form clusters with varying degrees of specialization, from transient aggregations to more persistent colonies to permanently multicellular organisms.

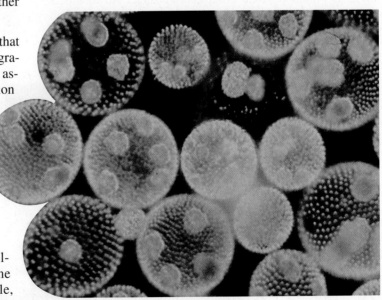

Figure 20.6 A colonial protist.
Individual, motile, unicellular green algae are united in the protist *Volvox* as a hollow colony of cells that moves by the beating of the flagella of its individual cells. Some species of *Volvox* have cytoplasmic connections between the cells that help coordinate colony activities. The *Volvox* colony is a highly complex form that has many of the properties of multicellular life.

20.4 Classifying the Protists

Protists are the most diverse of the four kingdoms in the domain Eukarya. The 200,000 different forms in the kingdom Protista include many unicellular, colonial, and multicellular groups. Protists were the first cells to contain a nucleus, as described in section 20.1—indeed, an organized internal membrane system that creates organelle compartments is the key feature that distinguished protists and other eukaryotes from archaea and bacteria. The evolution of early protists, like the fossil algae seen in figure 20.7, was one of the most important steps in life's evolutionary journey.

Probably the most important statement we can make about classifying the Kingdom Protista is that it is an artificial group; as a matter of convenience, single-celled eukaryotic organisms have typically been grouped together into this kingdom. This lumps many very different and only distantly related forms together. A taxonomist would say that the kingdom Protista is not monophyletic—that it contains many groups that do not share a common ancestor.

Traditionally, biologists have grouped protists artificially into functionally-related categories, much as was done in the nineteenth century. Protists were typically grouped into photosynthesizers (algae), heterotrophs (protozoa), and absorbers (funguslike protists).

New applications of a wide variety of molecular methods are providing important new insights into the evolutionary relationships among the different groups of protists. For the first time, we can begin to see how many are related. Molecular taxonomists have assigned 12 of the 17 major protist phyla to 7 monophyletic groups, or "clades." All members within each clade share the same common ancestor. The seven

Figure 20.7 Early eukaryotic fossil.
Fossil algae that lived in Siberia 1 billion years ago.

groups can be tentatively arrayed on the protist phylogenetic tree as pictured in figure 20.8, although much remains uncertain. The lineages connecting the seven groups may change as we learn more.

Five major protist phyla cannot yet be placed on this tree with any confidence, but they are described in table 20.1, along with the other protist phyla. These five phyla include some of the more familiar protists such as amoebas. As researchers carry out more detailed DNA-level comparisons, our understanding of these five groups will increase.

It seems likely that over the next few years, the traditional "matter of convenience" kingdom Protista will be replaced by a more illuminating arrangement that expresses the evolutionary relationships among the members of this very diverse kingdom.

20.4 12 of the 17 protist phyla can be assigned positions on the protist phylogenetic tree; the relationship of five others is still being worked out.

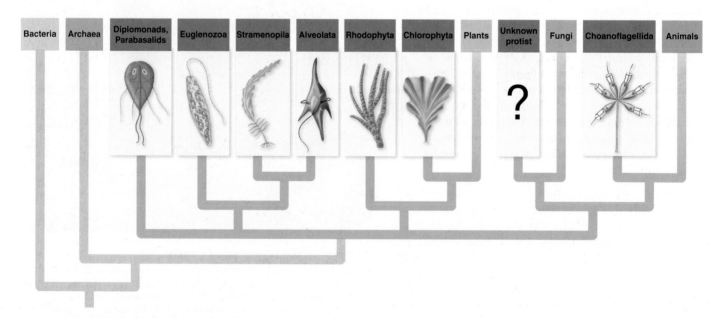

Figure 20.8 The major protist clades.

TABLE 20.1   KINDS OF PROTISTS

Group	Phylum	Typical Examples		Key Characteristics
DIPLOMONADS				
Diplomonads	Diplomonadida	*Giardia intestinalis*		Move by flagella; have two nuclei
PARABASALIDS				
Parabasalids	Parabasalida	*Trichomonas vaginalis*		Undulating membrane; some are pathogens, others digest cellulose in gut of termites
EUGLENOZOA				
Euglenoids	Euglenozoa	*Euglena*		Unicellular; some photosynthetic; others heterotrophic; contain chlorophylls *a* and *b* or none
Trypanosomes	Euglenozoa	Trypanosomes		Heterotrophic; unicellular
STRAMENOPILA				
Brown algae	Phaeophyta	Kelp		Multicellular; contain chlorophylls *a* and *c*
Diatoms	Chrysophyta	*Diatoma*		Unicellular; manufacture the carbohydrate chrysolaminarin; unique double shells of silica; contain chlorophylls *a* and *c*
Water molds	Oomycota	*Phytophthora infestans*		Terrestrial and freshwater
ALVEOLATA				
Ciliates	Ciliophora	*Paramecium*		Heterotrophic unicellular protists with cells of fixed shape possessing two nuclei and many cilia; many contain highly complex and specialized organelles
Dinoflagellates	Pyrrhophyta	Red tides		Unicellular; two flagella; contain chlorophylls *a* and *b*
Sporozoans	Apicomplexa	*Plasmodium*		Nonmotile; unicellular; the apical end of the spores contains a complex mass of organelles
RHODOPHYTA				
Red algae	Rhodophyta	Coralline algae		Most multicellular; contain chlorophyll *a* and a red pigment
CHLOROPHYTA				
Green algae	Chlorophyta	*Chlamydomonas, Ulva*		Unicellular or multicellular; contain chlorophylls *a* and *b*; ancestor of plants
CHOANOFLAGELLIDA				
Choanoflagellates	Choanozoa	Choanoflagellates		Flagellated feeding funnel; ancestor of animals
PHYLOGENY NOT YET DETERMINED				
Amoebas	Rhizopoda	*Amoeba*		Move by pseudopodia
Forams	Foraminifera	Forams		Rigid shells; move by protoplasmic streaming
Radiolarians	Actinopoda	Radiolarians		Glassy skeletons; needlelike pseudopods
Cellular slime molds	Acrasiomycota	*Dictyostelium*		Colonial aggregations of individual cells; most closely related to amoebas
Plasmodial slime molds	Myxomycota	*Fuligo*		Stream along as a multinucleate mass of cytoplasm

20.5 The Base of the Protist Tree

As discussed in section 20.1, we don't know a great deal about what the first eukaryotes were like, but among the 17 phyla of living protists, two unicellular groups seem more closely linked to these early eukaryotes. Indeed, molecular comparisons place these two groups at the very base of the protist phylogenetic tree. Both groups possess flagella, but lack mitochondria. Because mitochondrial genes are found in their nuclei, it seems that these two groups lost their mitochondria, rather than never having had them.

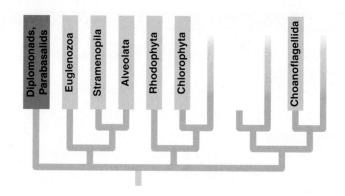

Diplomonads Have Two Nuclei

Diplomonads propel themselves through the water with flagella, and are unusual in that each single-celled individual has two nuclei. The diplomonad *Giardia intestinalis,* a common parasite, passes from one human to another via feces-contaminated water, causing diarrhea.

Parabasalids Swim with Undulating Membranes

Parabasalids propel themselves through the water with undulating membranes as well as flagella. The *Trichomonas vagi-*

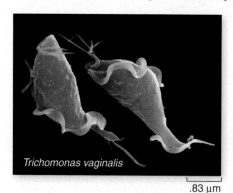

Trichomonas vaginalis

.83 µm

nalis seen in this photograph is a parasite that causes vaginitis, a sexually transmitted disease in humans. Other species of parabasalids play key roles in forest ecosystems. They live in the guts of termites and digest cellulose, something the termites themselves cannot do; this symbiosis aids forests in recycling the carbon tied up in fallen trees.

20.5 Molecular evidence suggests that diplomonads and parabasalids are the closest living protists to now-extinct early eukaryotes.

20.6 A Diverse Kingdom

Molecular comparisons allow us to place 12 of the 17 protist phyla with some confidence on the protist phylogenetic tree (we will get to the other five later). The largest branch of the protist phylogenetic tree contains seven phyla clustered within three monophyletic groups.

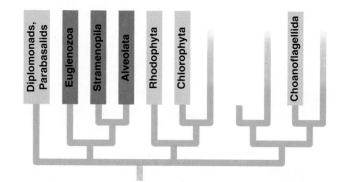

Euglenozoa Are Free-living Protists with Anterior Flagella

Euglenozoa are freshwater protists with the majority having two flagella. There are two major groups in the phylum Euglenozoa, the euglenoids and the trypanosomes.

Euglenoids like *Euglena* are euglenozoans with two flagella. As shown in figure 20.9, the flagella are attached at the base of a flask-shaped opening called the reservoir located at the anterior end of the cell. One of the flagella is long and has a row of very fine, short, hairlike projections along one side. A second, shorter flagellum is located within the reservoir but does not emerge from it. Contractile vacuoles collect excess water from all parts of the organism and empty it into the reservoir, which apparently helps regulate the osmotic pressure within the organism. The stigma is light-sensitive and helps these photosynthetic organisms move toward light. Reproduction is by mitotic cell division; no sexual reproduction is known in this group.

Figure 20.9 *Euglena.* In euglenoids such as *Euglena,* starch forms around pyrenoids; other food reserves are stored in paramylon granules.

Euglenoids clearly illustrate the folly of attempting to classify protists as tiny animals or plants. About one-third of the 1,000 known species have chloroplasts and are photosynthetic; the others lack chloroplasts, ingest their food, and are heterotrophic. In the dark, many photosynthetic euglenoids reduce the size of their chloroplasts (they may appear to disappear!) and become heterotrophs until they return to the light.

Trypanosomes are euglenozoans with a unique single mitochondrion, which contains two circles of DNA. Trypanosomes are important pathogens of human beings, responsible for many serious diseases. Perhaps the most devastating is African sleeping sickness, in which infected individuals experience extreme lethargy and fatigue. The trypanosomes spend some of their life cycle in the blood and saliva of a carrier, such as the tsetse fly shown in figure 20.10a When the fly feeds on a human, the trypanosomes are spread to the human host, where they circulate in its blood. You can see a trypanosome in figure 20.10b, the worm-like shape among the circular red blood cells.

Leishmaniasis is a trypanosome infection transmitted by sand flies that causes severe skin sores. If the protists reach internal organs, death can result. About 1.5 million new cases are reported each year.

Stramenopila Are Protists with Fine Hairs

Another major group of phyla on the protist phylogenetic tree contains three phyla which possess fine hairs on their flagella. These flagellated cells may only appear at certain times in the life cycle, or may have been lost completely, as in the diatoms.

Brown algae, members of the phylum Phaeophyta, contain the longest, fastest-growing, and most photosynthetically productive living organisms, the giant kelp. Kelp form underwater forests with individuals over 100 meters long. The 1,500 species of brown algae are all multicellular and almost all marine. They are the most conspicuous seaweeds in the ocean. The larger brown algae, like the one in figure 20.11a, have flattened blades, stalks, and anchoring bases and often contain complex internal plumbing like that of plants. The life cycle has alternating generations, the large individuals being the sporophyte (diploid) generation.

Diatoms, members of the phylum Chrysophyta, are photosynthetic unicellular protists with a unique double shell of silica. Like tiny oysters, the shells resemble small boxes with lids, one fitting inside the other.

Diatoms are abundant in both oceans and lakes. There are over 11,500 species, of two sorts: some with radial symmetry that look like tiny wheels and others with bilateral (two-sided) symmetry (figure 20.11b). The shells of fossil diatoms form thick deposits that are mined commercially as "diatomaceous earth," used as an abrasive or to make paint sparkle. Diatoms move in a complex manner that is still being inves-

Figure 20.10 Trypanosomes cause sleeping sickness.

(a) A tsetse fly is sucking blood from a human arm in Tanzania, East Africa. The fly's saliva can transmit the trypanosomes that cause sleeping sickness to the human it bites. (b) In this photograph, the undulating, changeable shape of *Trypanosoma* is visible among human red blood cells.

(a)

(b)

(a)

(b)

Figure 20.11 Two of the more common stramenopila.

(a) Massive "groves" of giant kelp, a kind of brown algae, contain some of the largest organisms on earth. (b) These diatoms have unique silica, two-part shells.

tigated. Their movement involves protoplasmic streaming along grooves in their shell and the waving of tiny vibrating fibrils within the grooves.

Water molds, phylum Oomycota, are the downy mildews that are often seen in moist environments. There are 580 named species, all of which either parasitize living organisms or feed on dead organic matter. Many oomycetes are important plant pathogens, including *Phytophthora infestans,* which causes late blight in potatoes. This mold was responsible for the Irish potato famine of 1845–47, during which about 400,000 Irish people starved.

Alveolata Are Protists with Submembrane Vesicles

The third main "branch" on the protist phylogenetic tree contains three phyla all of which have a layer of flattened vesicles called alveoli beneath their plasma membrane. The alveoli are thought to function in the transport of materials out of the cell, similar to Golgi bodies.

Ciliates, members of the phylum Ciliophora, are very complex and unusual unicellular heterotrophs with large numbers of cilia (tiny beating hairs) covering the outside of the body, and two nuclei per cell (the micronucleus and macronucleus). Ciliates are so different from other eukaryotes (they even use the genetic code differently!) that many taxonomists argue they should be placed in a separate kingdom of their own. About 8,000 species have been named.

Ciliates have a pellicle, a protein scaffold inside the plasma membrane that can change shape, which makes the body wall tough but flexible. The body interior is extremely complex, inspiring some biologists to consider ciliates multicellular organisms without cell boundaries rather than unicellular. The *Paramecium* in figure 20.12 is a typical ciliate. It has a complex digestive process, with a gullet ("mouth") that serves as an intake channel for bacteria and food particles. Once ingested, they are then enclosed in membrane bubbles called food vacuoles and digested by enzymes. Reproduction is usually by fission, with the body splitting in half, but ciliates also undergo a form of sexual reproduction called *conjugation* (see page 376, figure 20.3*b*), in which haploid nuclei that have arisen by meiosis are exchanged.

Dinoflagellates, members of the phylum Pyrrhophyta, are photosynthetic unicellular protists, most with two flagella of unequal length. There are about 1,000 species. Some occur in freshwater, but most are marine. Bioluminescent dinoflagellates produce the twinkling light sometimes seen in marine waters at night. Most dinoflagellates have a stiff coat of cellulose, often encrusted with silica, giving them unusual shapes. The four genera of dinoflagellates in figure 20.13 show how their flagella are unique, unlike those of any other phylum: One beats in a groove circling the body like a belt, the other in a groove perpendicular to it. Their beating rotates the body like a top.

A few dinoflagellates produce powerful toxins such as the poisonous "red tides," which are population explosions of such dinoflagellates. You can see in figure 20.14 why they are called red tides, coloring the water a reddish color. The toxins can affect humans when they eat seafood taken from red tide contaminated waters. Dinoflagellates reproduce by splitting in half.

Sporozoans are spore-forming unicellular parasites of animals, all members of the phylum Apicomplexa. They are named after a unique arrangement of microtubules and other cell organelles at one end of the cell called an apical complex. This complex is used to facilitate invading a host cell.

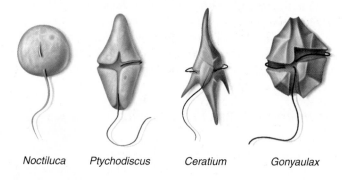

Noctiluca Ptychodiscus Ceratium Gonyaulax

Figure 20.13 Dinoflagellates.
Noctiluca, which lacks the heavy cellulosic armor characteristic of most dinoflagellates, is one of the bioluminescent organisms that causes the waves to sparkle in warm seas at certain times of the year. In the other three genera, the shorter encircling flagellum may be seen in its groove, and the longer one projects away.

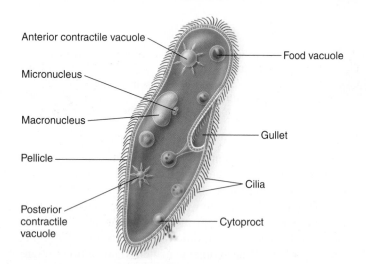

Figure 20.12 A ciliate.
The main features of the familiar ciliate *Paramecium* are shown.

- Anterior contractile vacuole
- Food vacuole
- Micronucleus
- Macronucleus
- Gullet
- Pellicle
- Cilia
- Posterior contractile vacuole
- Cytoproct

Figure 20.14 Red tide.
Red tides are caused by population explosions of dinoflagellates. The pigments in the dinoflagellates, or in some cases other organisms, color the water.

Sporozoans are responsible for many diseases in humans and domestic animals. Sporozoans infect animals with small spores that are transmitted from host to host.

Sporozoans have complex life cycles that involve both asexual and sexual phases, as illustrated in figure 20.15. Sporozoans of the genus *Plasmodium* are spread among humans by mosquitoes of the genus *Anopheles*. When a mosquito inserts its proboscis into a human, it injects about a thousand sporozoites into the blood ❶. They travel to the liver within a few minutes. If even one sporozoite reaches the liver, it will multiply rapidly there and still cause malaria ❷. The sporozoites transform inside the liver and spread to the blood where they progress through several more stages ❸, some of which develop into gametocytes ❹. The gametocytes are ingested by a mosquito ❺, where fertilization takes place forming sporozoites ❻, and the cycle begins anew.

Malaria is one of the most serious diseases in the world. About 500 million people are affected by it at any one time, and approximately 2 million of them, mostly children, die each year.

> **20.6** Seven phyla clustered in the largest branch of the protist phylogenetic tree exhibit an amazing diversity of form and function.

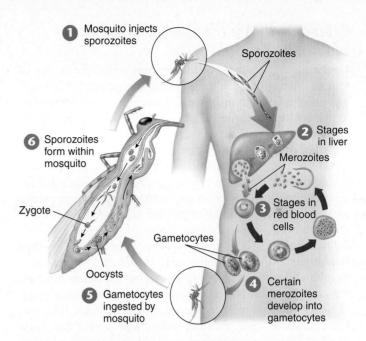

Figure 20.15 A sporozoan life cycle.

Plasmodium is the sporozoan that causes malaria. *Plasmodium* has a complex life cycle that alternates between mosquitoes and mammals.

20.7 The Road to Plants

Another key lineage on the protist phylogenetic tree, the red and green algae, marks the path that had led to the evolution of plants. Both red and green algae contain similar chloroplasts, and molecular analysis indicates a single endosymbiotic origin for both, confirming a common ancestry. The red algae appear to have arisen before the evolutionary lineage that led from green algae to plants.

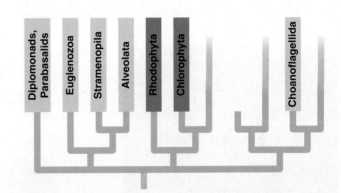

Rhodophyta Are Ancient Photosynthesizers

Red algae, members of the phylum Rhodophyta, possess red pigments called phycobilins that give them their characteristic color, as shown in figure 20.16. Almost all of the 4,000 species of red algae are multicellular and live in the sea, where they grow more deeply than any other photosynthetic organism. Red algae have complex bodies made of interwoven filaments of cells. The laboratory media agar is made from the cell walls of red algae. The life cycle of red algae is complex, usually involving alternation of generations, like in plants. None of the red algae have flagella or centrioles, suggesting that red algae may be one of the more ancient groups of eukaryotes.

Figure 20.16 Red algae.

These red algae have their cellulose cell walls heavily impregnated with calcium carbonate, the same material of which oyster shells are made. Because they are hard and occur on coral reefs, they are called coralline algae.

Chlorophyta Are the Direct Ancestors of Plants

Green algae, members of the phylum Chlorophyta, are of special interest because the ancestor of terrestrial plants was a member of this group. Green algae chloroplasts are similar to plant chloroplasts, and like them, they contain chlorophylls *a* and *b*.

Green algae are an extremely varied group of more than 7,000 species, mostly mobile and aquatic like *Chlamydomonas,* shown in figure 20.17*a*, but a few (like *Chlorella*) are immobile in moist soil or on tree trunks. Although most green algae are microscopic and unicellular, some are intermediate, colonial, or truly multicellular. Some of the most elaborate colonies are seen in *Volvox*, a species which forms a hollow sphere made of 500 or more cells (figure 20.17*b*). The two flagella of each cell beat in time with all the others to rotate the colony, which has reproductive cells at one end. While *Volvox* borders on multicellularity, the green algae, *Ulva* (sea lettuce), shows true multicellularity. The sexual life cycle in *Ulva* alternates between a multicellular haploid structure called a gametophyte, and a multicellular diploid structure called a sporophyte (figure 20.18). The sporophyte is similar in appearance to the gametophyte.

> **20.7   The red and green algae share a common ancestor, but the green algae gave rise to terrestrial plants.**

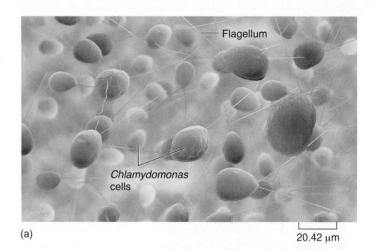

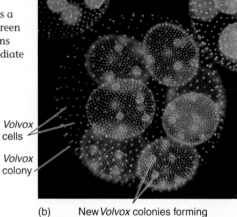

Figure 20.17 Green algae.

(*a*) *Chlamydomonas* is a unicellular mobile green algae. (*b*) *Volvox* forms colonies, an intermediate stage on the way to multicellularity.

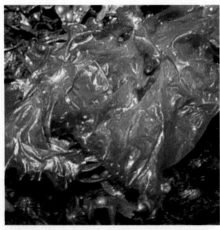

Figure 20.18   A green algae life cycle: *Ulva.*

Individuals of this green algae exhibit a life cycle that is somewhat unique among algae in that they alternate between a haploid form called the gametophyte and a diploid form called the sporophyte, which are identical in appearance and consist of flattened sheets two cells thick. In the haploid (*n*) gametophyte, gametangia give rise to haploid gametes, which fuse to form a diploid (2*n*) zygote. The zygote germinates to form the diploid sporophyte. Sporangia within the sporophyte give rise to haploid spores by meiosis. The haploid spores develop into haploid gametophytes.

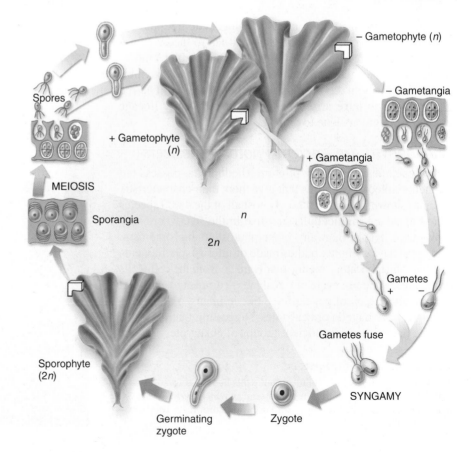

20.8 The Road to Animals

Just as plants (and undoubtedly fungi) had protist ancestors, so too did animals, in this case an unusual single-celled heterotroph called a choanoflagellate.

Choanoflagellida Are the Direct Ancestors of Animals

Choanoflagellates are unicellular, heterotrophic protists with a single, long flagellum. The flagellum is surrounded by a funnel-shaped contractible collar of closely placed filaments, not unlike the woven strands of a basket. The whipping motion of the flagellum draws water into the funnel, forcing it past the filaments, which strain bacteria from the water. The choanoflagellate protist feeds on these bacteria. Precisely this same type of filtering cell is found in sponges, the most primitive of animals (discussed in chapter 25).

While no choanoflagellate is multicellular, some are colonial, forming spherical assemblies (figure 20.19) that look very much like freshwater sponges. This close relationship between choanoflagellates and animals is also seen when molecular comparisons are made. A cell surface receptor used to initiate an intercellular signal pathway is the same in both choanoflagellates and sponges. Detailed genomic comparisons are not yet available, but can be expected to further confirm this relationship.

> **20.8** **Choanoflagellates have a unique cell structure also found in sponges, and are believed to be the direct ancestors of animals.**

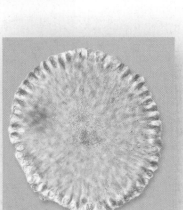

Figure 20.19 Colonial choanoflagellates.

Colonial choanoflagellates resemble their close animal relatives, the sponges.

25 μm

20.9 "Not Yet Located on the Protist Phylogenetic Tree"

Five major phyla of protists cannot yet be located on the protist phylogenetic tree. Amoebas, forams, radiolarians, and both cellular and plasmodial slime molds have no permanent locomotor apparatus, and instead use their cytoplasm to aid movement. Molecular information about these less understood phyla can be expected to provide a clearer picture of their relationship to the other protists.

Amoebas

Amoebas, members of the phylum Rhizopoda, lack flagella and cell walls. There are several hundred species. They move from place to place by **pseudopodia** (Greek, *pseudo,* false, and *podium,* foot), flowing projections of cytoplasm that extend outward. In figure 20.20*a,* you can see an amoeba putting a pseudopod forward and then flowing into it. Amoebas are abundant in soil, and many are parasites of animals. Reproduction in amoebas occurs by simple fission into two daughter cells of equal volume (figure 20.20*b*). They do undergo mitosis but lack meiosis and any form of sexual reproduction.

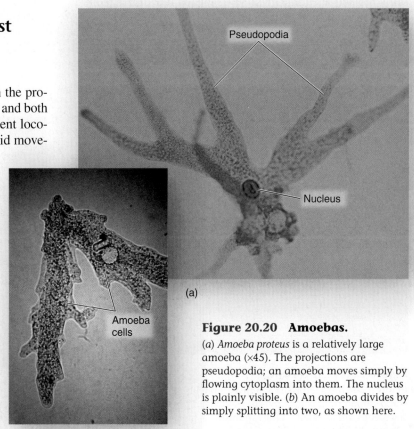

Figure 20.20 Amoebas.

(*a*) *Amoeba proteus* is a relatively large amoeba (×45). The projections are pseudopodia; an amoeba moves simply by flowing cytoplasm into them. The nucleus is plainly visible. (*b*) An amoeba divides by simply splitting into two, as shown here.

Forams

Forams, members of the phylum Foraminifera, possess rigid shells and move by *cytoplasmic streaming.* They are marine protists with pore-studded shells called *tests* that may be as big as several centimeters in diameter. There are several hundred species of forams. Their shells, built largely of calcium carbonate, are often brilliantly colored—vivid yellow, bright red, or salmon pink—and may have many chambers arrayed in a spiral shape resembling a tiny snail. Their multichambered body can be seen in figure 20.21.

Most forams live in sand, but a few are free-floating organisms, part of the ocean's plankton community. Long, thin cytoplasmic projections called *podia* radiate out through the pores in the shells of these protists and are used for swimming and capturing prey. The life cycle of forams is complex, involving alternation between haploid and diploid generations. Forams have deposited massive accumulations of their shells for more than 200 million years. Limestone is often rich in forams's remains—the White Cliffs of Dover, the famous landmark on the southern England seacoast shown in figure 20.22, is made almost entirely of foram shells.

Radiolarians

Radiolarians are unusual amoeboid protists that belong to another phylum, Actinopoda. While most amoeboid cells have an amorphous shape, radiolarians secrete a glassy exoskeleton made of silica that gives their body a distinctive shape. Either radially or bilaterally symmetrical, the shells of different species form elaborate shapes. The pseudopods of *Actinosphaerium,* seen in figure 20.23, extrude outward along spiky projections of the glassy exoskeleton like thorns radiating out from the cell body.

Figure 20.22 White cliffs of Dover.

The limestone that forms these cliffs is composed almost entirely of fossil shells of protists, including foraminifera.

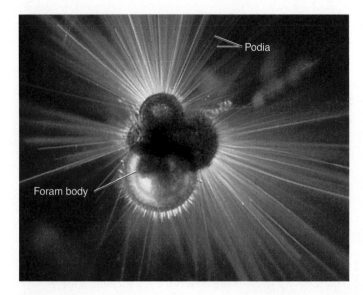

Figure 20.21 A foram.

In this living foram, a representative of phylum Foraminifera, the podia—thin cytoplasmic projections—extend through pores in the calcareous test, or shell, of the organism.

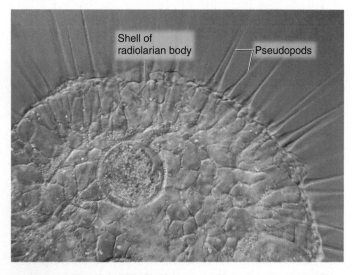

Figure 20.23 A radiolarian.

This amoeba-like radiolarian *Actinosphaerium* (×300), of the phylum Actinopoda, has striking needlelike pseudopods.

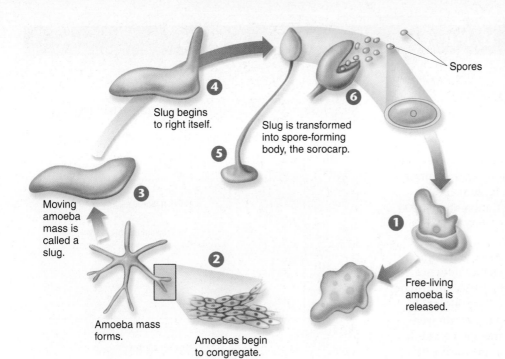

Figure 20.24 Slime mold.
The life cycle of the cellular slime mold *Dictyostelium discoideum* (phylum Acrasiomycota). ❶ Germinating spores form amoebas. ❷ The amoebas aggregate and move toward a fixed center. ❸ They form a multicellular slug 2 to 3 millimeters long that migrates toward light. ❹ The slug stops moving and begins to differentiate into a spore-forming body, called a sorocarp ❺. Within the heads of the sorocarps, the amoebas become encysted as spores ❻.

Slug begins to right itself.

Slug is transformed into spore-forming body, the sorocarp.

Moving amoeba mass is called a slug.

Spores

Amoeba mass forms.

Amoebas begin to congregate.

Free-living amoeba is released.

Cellular Slime Molds

Slime molds are heterotrophic protists that are sometimes confused with fungi, although they do not resemble them in any significant respect. For example, slime molds have cell walls made of cellulose, whereas fungal walls are made of chitin. Also, slime molds carry out normal mitosis, while fungal mitosis is unusual and will be discussed in chapter 21.

The two major kinds of slime molds that originated at different times are only distantly related. In the **cellular slime molds,** phylum Acrasiomycota, individual cells aggregate and differentiate into complex associations called *slugs.* Slugs are mobile and while not truly multicellular, they are far along that evolutionary path.

Cellular slime molds are more closely related to amoebas than any other phylum. There are 70 named species, the best known of which is *Dictyostelium discoideum. Dictyostelium* is basically a unicellular scavenger with the interesting life cycle shown in figure 20.24. When deprived of food, thousands of individual *Dictyostelium* amoebas ❶ come together forming a slug (❷ through ❹) that moves to a new habitat. There, the colony differentiates into a base, a stalk, and a swollen tip ❺ that develops **spores.** Each of these spores, when released ❻, becomes a new amoeba, which begins to feed and so restarts the life cycle.

Plasmodial Slime Molds

Plasmodial slime molds, phylum Myxomycota, comprise a group of about 500 species that stream along as a **plasmodium,** a nonwalled multinucleate mass of cytoplasm. The yellow mass you see in figure 20.25 is composed of a group of cells without cell walls separating the individual cells. They move together as a single unit. Plasmodia can flow around obstacles and even pass through a mesh cloth. Extending

Figure 20.25 Plasmodial slime mold.
This multinucleate plasmodium (phylum Myxomycota) moves about in search of the bacteria and other organic particles that it ingests.

pseudopodia as they move, they engulf and digest bacteria and other organic material. If the plasmodium begins to dry or starve, it migrates away rapidly and then stops and often divides into many small mounds, each of which produces a spore-laden structure. Spores germinate when favorable conditions return.

> **20.9 Amoebas, forams, radiolarians, and molds are heterotrophs with restricted mobility, many of which form aggregates. Their position on the protist phylogenetic free is not yet firmly established.**

Defining a Treatment Window for Malaria

While malaria kills more people each year than any other infectious disease, the combination of mosquito control and effective treatment has virtually eliminated this disease from the United States. In 1941, more than 4,000 Americans died of malaria; in the year 2006, by contrast, fewer than five people died of malaria.

The key to controlling malaria has come from understanding its life cycle. The first critical advance came in 1897 in a remote field hospital in Secunderabad, India, when English physician Ronald Ross observed that hospital patients who did not have malaria were more likely to develop the disease in the open wards (those without screens or netting) than in wards with closed windows or screens. Observing closely, he saw that patients in the open wards were being bitten by mosquitoes of the genus *Anopheles*. Dissecting mosquitoes who had bitten malaria patients, he found the plasmodium parasite. Newly-hatched mosquitoes who had not yet fed, when allowed to feed on malaria-free blood, did not acquire the parasite. Ross reached the conclusion that mosquitoes were spreading the disease from one person to another, passing along the parasite while feeding. In every country where it has been possible to eliminate the *Anopheles* mosquitoes, the incidence of the disease malaria has plummeted.

The second critical advance came with the development of drugs to treat malaria victims. The British had discovered in India in the mid-1800s that a bitter substance called quinine taken from the bark of cinchona trees was useful in suppressing attacks of malaria. The boys in the photograph are being treated with an intravenous solution of quinine. Quinine also reduces the fever during attacks, but does not cure the disease. Today physicians instead use the synthetic drugs chloroquine and primaquine, which are much more effective than quinine, with fewer side effects.

Unlike quinine these two drugs can cure patients completely, because they attack and destroy one of the phases of the plasmodium life cycle, the merozoites

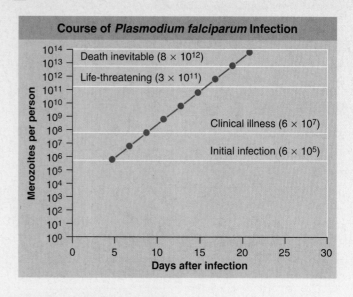

Course of *Plasmodium falciparum* Infection

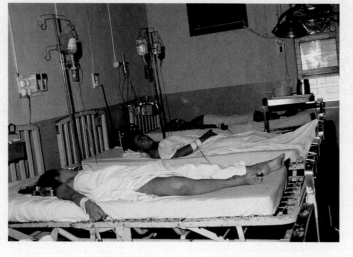

released into the bloodstream several days after infection—but only if the drugs are administered soon enough after the bite that starts the infection.

In order to determine the time frame for successful treatment, doctors have carefully studied the time course of a malarial infection. The graph above presents what they have found. Numbers of merozoites are presented on the y axis on a log scale—each step reflects a 10-fold increase in numbers. The infection becomes life-threatening if 1% of red blood cells become infected, and death is almost inevitable if 20% of red blood cells are infected.

1. **Applying Concepts** What is the dependent variable?
2. **Making Inferences**
   a. How long after infection is it before the liver releases merozoites into the blood stream (that is, initial infection by merozoites)? before the disease becomes life-threatening? before death is inevitable?
   b. How long does it take merozoites to multiply 10-fold?
3. **Drawing Conclusions** After the first appearance of clinical illness symptoms, how many days can the disease be treated before becoming life-threatening? before treatment has little or no chance of saving the patient's life?

The Evolution of Eukaryotes

20.1 The Origin of Eukaryotic Cells

- Eukaryotic cells, with internal organelles, first appear as microfossils about 1.7 billion years ago.

- Many bacteria have infoldings of their plasma membranes that extend toward the interior of the cell. It is thought that this type of membrane infolding gave rise to the endoplasmic reticulum and formed the nuclear envelope (**figure 20.1**).

- Some eukaryotic organelles may have arisen from endosymbiotic events when energy-producing bacteria became incorporated into the cells of early eukaryotic cells, giving rise to mitochondria (**figure 20.2**). Similarly, photosynthetic bacteria may have become incorporated into some eukaryotic cells, giving rise to chloroplasts.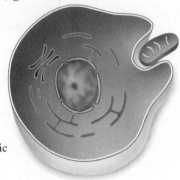

20.2 The Evolution of Sex

- A key characteristic of eukaryotes is the process of sexual reproduction, forming offspring from the fusion of two gametes. Many eukaryotes are capable of asexual reproduction through budding and parthenogenesis and reproduction that involves only one parent (self-fertilization). However, biologists think that sexual reproduction first evolved in eukaryotes not as a means of reproduction but rather as a mechanism for repairing damaged chromosomes during meiosis when homologues align.

- Sexual reproduction permits genetic recombination that leads to genetic diversity in future generations.

- There are three major types of sexual life cycles: (1) zygotic meiosis, where the haploid phase makes up the majority of the life cycle, (2) gametic meiosis, where the diploid phase is the dominant form, and (3) sporic meiosis, where the cycle alternates equally between the haploid and diploid phases (**figure 20.4**).

The Protists

20.3 General Biology of Protists, the Most Ancient Eukaryotes

- Protists were the earliest eukaryotic cells, but they are a very diverse kingdom of organisms.

- Protists have diverse cell surfaces. They exhibit diverse modes of locomotion. Some protists form cysts to protect themselves in harsh environmental conditions. Protists have diverse modes of acquiring nutrients. Most protists reproduce asexually except for times of stress, when they engage in sexual reproduction. Some protists exist as single cells (**figure 20.5**), whereas others form colonies (**figure 20.6**) or aggregates of cells. True multicellularity is present in the algae.

20.4 Classifying the Protists

- The classification of the organisms in the kingdom Protista is in a state of flux. Traditionally, they were grouped into three functionally-related categories: photosynthesizers (algae), heterotrophs (protozoa), and absorbers (funguslike protists). These artificial categories did not imply evolutionary relationships. Molecular methods of analyzing the various types of protists are providing insight into the evolutionary relationships among the protist groups, aiding in classification.

- 12 of the 17 major protist phyla have been assigned to one of seven monophyletic groups. The tentative protist phylogenetic tree will likely change (**figure 20.8** and **table 20.1**).

- Five major protist phyla have not yet been placed on the phylogenetic tree, but as researchers learn more the evolutionary relationships between these groups will become clearer.

20.5 The Base of the Protist Tree

- Two protists groups, Diplomonads and Parabasalids, are unicellular organisms that may be the closest living relatives to the ancestral eukaryote. Both groups have flagella but lack mitochondria. Molecular analysis reveals that mitochondrial genes are present in their nuclei, and so it seems they lost their mitochondria rather than never having had these organelles.

20.6 A Diverse Kingdom

- The largest branch of the protist phylogenetic tree contains the Euglenozoa, Stramenopila, and Alveolata. The Euglenozoa sub-branch and phylum contains two groups, the euglenoids and the trypanosomes. Both groups are freshwater protists that have two flagella (**figures 20.9** and **20.10**).

- The Stramenopila sub-branch contains three protist phyla (Phaeophyta, Chrysophyta, and Oomycota) that have fine hairs on their flagella. Brown algae (phylum Phaeophyta) include fast-growing giant kelp (**figure 20.11a**). Diatoms (phylum Chrysophyta) are unicellular photosynthetic protists with a unique double shell made of silica (**figure 20.11b**). The water molds (phylum Oomycota) feed on dead organisms.

- The Alveolata sub-branch contain the ciliates, the dinoflagellates, and the sporozoans. The ciliates (phylum Ciliophora) have large numbers of cilia covering their bodies (**figure 20.12**). The dinoflagellates (phylum Pyrrhophyta) are photosynthetic, unicellular protists with two flagella (**figure 20.13**). Some are bioluminescent, and a few produce powerful toxins, such as poisonous red tides (**figure 20.14**). The sporozoans, phylum Apicomplexa, are unicellular, nonmotile spore-forming protists (**figure 20.15**).

20.7 The Road to Plants

- Another branch on the protist phylogenetic tree contains the photosynthetic red algae (phylum Rhodophyta, **figure 20.16**) and green algae (phylum Chlorophyta, **figures 20.17** and **20.18**). Green algae are the direct ancestors of terrestrial plants.

20.8 The Road to Animals

- The branch on the protist phylogenetic tree that gave rise to animals contains a group called the choanoflagellates. Some choanoflagellates are colonial, forming spherical assemblies of cells (**figure 20.19**).

20.9 "Not Yet Located on the Protist Phylogenetic Tree"

- Five major phyla have not yet been placed on the protist phylogenetic tree: Amoebas, forams, radiolarians, and cellular and plasmodial slime molds (**figures 20.20–20.25**).

1. One piece of supporting evidence for the endosymbiotic theory for the origin of eukaryotic cells is that
   a. eukaryotic cells have internal membranes.
   b. mitochondria and chloroplasts have their own DNA.
   c. Golgi bodies and endoplasmic reticulum were present in ancestral cells.
   d. the nuclear membrane could only have come from another cell.

2. Many protists survive unfavorable environmental conditions by forming
   a. gametes.
   b. zygotes.
   c. cysts.
   d. aggregations.

3. Protists do *not* include
   a. algae.
   b. amoebas.
   c. slime molds.
   d. mushrooms.

4. Some members of the phylum Euglenozoa
   a. do not have chloroplasts.
   b. conduct photosynthesis.
   c. are human pathogens.
   d. All of the above.

5. Kelp, which sometimes forms large, underwater forests, are actually protists called
   a. diatoms.
   b. brown algae.
   c. dinoflagellates.
   d. red algae.

6. Sporozoans have life cycles that
   a. have both a sexual and an asexual phase.
   b. have only an asexual phase.
   c. have only a sexual phase.
   d. only require fragmentation to produce new individuals.

7. The ancestor of plants was a member of what group of protists?
   a. Brown algae
   b. Alveolata
   c. Green algae
   d. Both b and c.

8. Scientists believe that the ancestral animal cell comes from the protist group
   a. ciliates.
   b. choanoflagellates.
   c. dinoflagellates.
   d. euglenoids.

9. Amoebas, foraminifera, and radiolarians move using their
   a. cytoplasm.
   b. flagella.
   c. cilia.
   d. setae.

10. Protists that form aggregates, have cellulose cell walls, and are heterotrophic are probably
    a. ciliates.
    b. radiolarians.
    c. slime molds.
    d. euglenoids.

1. **Figure 20.18** What is the difference between the leaf-shaped structures in the yellow portion of the cycle and the leaf-shaped structures in the blue portion of the cycle?

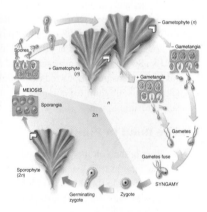

2. **Figure 20.24** Is the slime mold shown here a multicelled organism or numerous single-celled organisms working together?

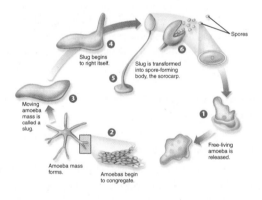

1. Your friend, Tomiko, complains that she doesn't understand how anyone can believe in the endosymbiotic theory. She asks you to explain what evidence there is for this theory. What do you tell her?

2. The cellular slime molds, the plasmodial slime molds, and the water molds all exhibit a similar means of restricted mobility. Can we conclude that they are closely related? Discuss.

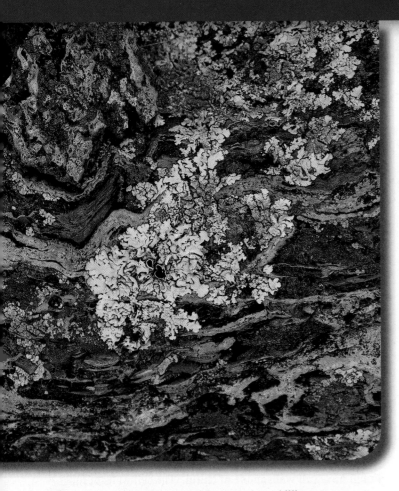

21

Fungi Invade the Land

L ife evolved in the sea, and for more than a billion years was confined to the oceans of the earth. On land, there was only bare rock. This bleak terrestrial picture changed over half a billion years ago, when the first fungi are thought to have invaded the land. The difficulty of the challenge this first invasion posed cannot be overstated. Animals could not be the first to invade. Animals are heterotrophs—what would they eat? Fungi, also heterotrophs, faced the same problem. Algae are photosynthetic, and so food did not present such a challenge for their invasion of land. Sunlight would be able to provide all the energy they might need. But how would they obtain nutrients? Phosphorus, nitrogen, iron, and many other chemical elements critical to life cannot be obtained by algae from bare rock. The solution to this dilemma was a sort of "You scratch my back, I'll scratch yours" cooperation. Fungi called ascomycetes formed associations with photosynthetic algae, forming a two-member partnership called a lichen. The lichen you see in this photo is growing on bare rock. The algae within it harvest energy from sunlight, while the fungal cells derive minerals from the rock. In this chapter you will become better acquainted with fungi and then explore their partnerships with algae and plants.

21.1 Complex Multicellularity

The algae are structurally simple multicellular organisms that fill the evolutionary gap between unicellular protists and more complex multicellular organisms (fungi, plants, and animals). In **complex multicellular organisms,** individuals are composed of many highly specialized kinds of cells that coordinate their activities. There are three kingdoms that exhibit complex multicellularity:

1. **Plants.** Multicellular green algae were almost certainly the direct ancestors of the plants (see chapter 20) and were themselves considered plants in the nineteenth century. However, green algae are basically aquatic and much simpler in structure than plants and are considered protists in the six-kingdom system used widely today.

2. **Animals.** Animals arose from a unicellular protist ancestor. Several groups of animal-like protists have been considered to be tiny animals in the past ("protozoa"), including flagellates, ciliates, and amoebas. The simplest (and seemingly most primitive) animals today, the sponges, seem clearly to have evolved from a kind of flagellate.

3. **Fungi.** Fungi also arose from a unicellular protist ancestor, one different from the ancestor of animals. Certain protists, including slime molds and water molds, have been considered fungi ("molds"), although they are usually classified as protists and are not thought to resemble ancestors of fungi. The true protist ancestor of fungi is as yet unknown. This is one of the great unsolved problems of taxonomy.

Perhaps the most important characteristic of complex multicellular organisms is *cell specialization.* If you think about it, having a variety of different sorts of cells within the same individual implies something very important about the genes of the individual: *Different cells are using different genes!* The process whereby a single cell (in humans, a fertilized egg) becomes a multicellular individual with many different kinds of cells is called **development.** The cell specialization that is the hallmark of complex multicellular life is the direct result of cells developing in different ways by activating different genes.

A second key characteristic of complex multicellular organisms is *intercellular coordination,* the adjustment of a cell's activity in response to what other cells are doing. The cells of all complex multicellular organisms communicate with one another with chemical signals called hormones. In some organisms like sponges, there is relatively little coordination between the cells; in other organisms like humans, almost every cell is under complex coordination.

> **21.1** Fungi, plants, and animals are complexly multicellular, with specialized cell types and coordination between cells.

21.2 A Fungus Is Not a Plant

The fungi are a distinct kingdom of organisms, comprising about 74,000 named species. **Mycologists,** scientists who study fungi, believe there may be many more species in existence. Although fungi were at one time included in the plant kingdom, they lack chlorophyll and resemble plants only in their general appearance and lack of mobility. Significant differences between fungi and plants include the following:

Fungi are heterotrophs. Perhaps most obviously, a mushroom is not green because it does not contain chlorophyll. Virtually all plants are photosynthesizers, whereas no fungi carry out photosynthesis. Instead, fungi obtain their food by secreting digestive enzymes onto whatever they are attached to and then absorbing into their bodies the organic molecules that are released by the enzymes.

Fungi have filamentous bodies. A plant is built of groups of functionally different cells called tissues, with different parts typically made of several different tissues. Fungi by contrast are basically filamentous in their growth form (that is, their bodies consist entirely of cells organized into long, slender filaments called *hyphae*), even though these filaments may be packed together to form a mass, called a *mycelium* (figure 21.1).

Fungi have nonmotile sperm. Some plants have motile sperm with flagella. The majority of fungi do not.

Fungi have cell walls made of chitin. The cell walls of fungi contain chitin, the same tough material that a crab shell is made of. The cell walls of plants are made of cellulose, also a strong building material. Chitin, however, is far more resistant to microbial degradation than is cellulose.

Figure 21.1 Masses of hyphae form mycelia.
The body of a fungus is composed of strings of cells called hyphae (too small to be seen with the naked eye). Hyphae pack together to form a mycelium. The dense, interwoven mat you see here growing through leaves on a forest floor in Maryland is a mycelium made up of microscopic hyphae. Most of the body of a fungus is occupied by its mycelium.

Fungi have nuclear mitosis. Mitosis in fungi is different from plants and most other eukaryotes in one key respect: The nuclear envelope does not break down and re-form; instead, all of mitosis takes place *within* the nucleus. A spindle apparatus forms there, dragging chromosomes to opposite poles of the *nucleus* (not the cell, as in all other eukaryotes).

You could build a much longer list, but already the take-home lesson is clear: Fungi are not like plants at all! Their many unique features are strong evidence that fungi are not closely related to any other group of organisms.

The Body of a Fungus

Fungi exist mainly in the form of slender filaments, barely visible with the naked eye, called **hyphae** (singular, **hypha**). A hypha is basically a long string of cells. Different hyphae then associate with each other to form much larger structures, like the shelf fungus you see growing on a tree in figure 21.2.

The main body of a fungus is not the mushroom, which is a temporary reproductive structure, but rather the extensive network of fine hyphae that penetrate the soil, wood, or flesh in which the fungus is growing. A mass of hyphae is called a **mycelium** (plural, **mycelia**) and may contain many meters of individual hyphae.

Fungal cells are able to exhibit a high degree of communication within such structures, because although most cells of fungal hyphae are separated by cross-walls called *septa* (singular, *septum*), these septa rarely form a complete barrier, and as a consequence cytoplasm is able to flow from one cell to another throughout the hyphae. The photo in figure 21.3 shows a junction between two fungal cells and the septum that partially separates them. From one fungal cell to the next, cytoplasm flows, streaming freely down the hypha through openings in the septa. Keep in mind the differences in scale between the hyphae and mycelia; the hypha in figure 21.3 is about 3.4 μm across whereas the mycelia in figure 21.1 is visible with the naked eye.

Because of such cytoplasmic streaming, proteins synthesized throughout the hyphae can be carried to the hyphal tips. This novel body plan is perhaps the most important innovation of the fungal kingdom. As a result of it, fungi can respond quickly to environmental changes, growing very rapidly when food and water are plentiful and the temperature is optimal. This body organization creates a unique relationship between the fungus and its environment. All parts of the fungal body are metabolically active, secreting digestive enzymes and actively attempting to digest and absorb any organic material with which the fungus comes in contact.

Also due to cytoplasmic streaming, many nuclei may be connected by the shared cytoplasm of a fungal mycelium. None of them (except for reproductive cells) are isolated in any one cell; all of them are linked cytoplasmically with every

Figure 21.2 A shelf fungus, *Trametes versicolor*.

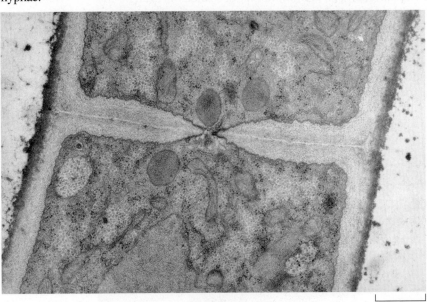

.54 μm

Figure 21.3 Septum and pore between cells in a hypha.
This photomicrograph clearly shows cytoplasmic streaming through a pore in the septum between two adjacent cells of a fungal hypha.

cell of the mycelium. Indeed, the entire concept of multicellularity takes on a new meaning among the fungi, the ultimate communal sharers among the multicellular organisms.

> **21.2 Fungi are not at all like plants. The fungal body is basically long strings of cells, often interconnected.**

21.3 Reproduction and Nutrition of Fungi

How Fungi Reproduce

Fungi reproduce both asexually and sexually. All fungal nuclei except for the zygote are haploid. Often in the sexual reproduction of fungi, individuals of different "mating types" must participate, much as two sexes are required for human reproduction. Sexual reproduction is initiated when two hyphae of genetically different mating types come in contact, and the hyphae fuse. What happens next? In animals and plants, when the two haploid gametes fuse, the two haploid nuclei immediately fuse to form the diploid nucleus of the zygote. As you might by now expect, fungi handle things differently. In most fungi, the two nuclei do not fuse immediately. Instead, they remain unmarried inhabitants of the same house, coexisting in a common cytoplasm for most of the life of the fungus! A fungal hypha that has two nuclei is called **dikaryotic.** If the nuclei are derived from two genetically different individuals, it is called a **heterokaryon** (Greek, *heteros*, other, and *karyon*, kernel or nucleus). A fungal hypha in which all the nuclei are genetically similar is said to be a **homokaryon** (Greek, *homo*, one).

When reproductive structures are formed in fungi, complete septa form between cells, the only exception to the free flow of cytoplasm between cells of the fungal body. There are three kinds of reproductive structures: (1) **gametangia** form haploid gametes, which fuse to give rise to a zygote that undergoes meiosis; (2) **sporangia** produce haploid spores that can be dispersed; and (3) **conidiophores** produce asexual spores called **conidia** that can be produced quickly and allow for the rapid colonization of a new food source.

Spores are a common means of reproduction among the fungi. The puffball fungus in figure 21.4 is releasing spores in a somewhat explosive manner. Spores are well suited to

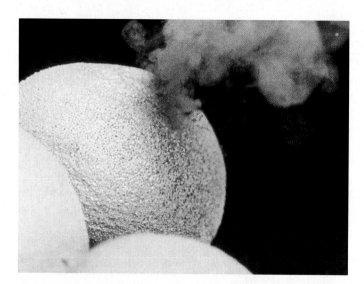

Figure 21.4 Many fungi produce spores.
Spores explode from the surface of a puffball fungus.

Figure 21.5 The oyster mushroom.
This species, *Pleurotus ostreatus,* immobilizes nematodes, which the fungus uses as a source of food.

the needs of an organism anchored to one place. They are so small and light that they may remain suspended in the air for long periods of time and may be carried great distances. When a spore lands in a suitable place, it germinates and begins to divide, soon giving rise to a new fungal hypha.

How Fungi Obtain Nutrients

All fungi obtain their food by secreting digestive enzymes into their surroundings and then absorbing back into the fungus the organic molecules produced by this **external digestion.** Many fungi are able to break down the cellulose in wood, cleaving the linkages between glucose subunits and then absorbing the glucose molecules as food. That is why fungi are so often seen growing on trees.

Just as some plants like the Venus's-flytrap are active carnivores, so some fungi are active predators. For example, the edible oyster fungus *Pleurotus ostreatus,* shown growing on a tree in figure 21.5, attracts tiny roundworms known as nematodes that feed on it—and secretes a substance that anesthetizes the nematodes. When the worms become sluggish and inactive, the fungal hyphae envelop and penetrate their bodies and absorb their contents, a rich source of nitrogen (always in short supply in natural ecosystems). Other fungi are even more active predators, snaring or trapping prey or firing projectiles into nematodes, rotifers, and other small animals that come near.

> **21.3 Fungi reproduce both asexually and sexually. They obtain their nutrients by secreting digestive enzymes into their surroundings and then absorbing the digested molecules back into the fungal body.**

21.4 Kinds of Fungi

Fungi are an ancient group of organisms at least 400 million years old. There are nearly 74,000 described species, in five groups (described in table 21.1), and many more awaiting discovery. Many fungi are harmful because they decay, rot, and spoil many different materials as they obtain food and because they cause serious diseases in animals and particularly in plants. Other fungi, however, are extremely useful. The manufacturing of both bread and beer depends on the biochemical activities of yeasts, single-celled fungi that produce abundant quantities of carbon dioxide and ethanol. Fungi are used on a major scale in industry to convert one complex organic molecule into another; many commercially important steroids are synthesized in this way.

The four major fungal phyla, distinguished from one another primarily by their mode of sexual reproduction, are the zygomycetes, the ascomycetes, the basidiomycetes, and the chytridiomycetes. A fifth group, the imperfect fungi, is an artificial grouping of fungi in which sexual reproduction has not been observed; these organisms are assigned to an appropriate group once their mode of sexual reproduction is identified. Molecular data is contributing to our understanding of the fungal phylogeny and as additional molecular evidence is acquired, a new fungal phylogeny is likely to appear. However, it already seems clear that fungi are more closely related to animals than to plants.

> **21.4 The fungal phyla are distinguished primarily by their modes of sexual reproduction. However, molecular sequence data will undoubtedly result in changes to the fungal phylogeny in the future.**

TABLE 21.1 FUNGI

Phylum	Typical Examples	Key Characteristics	Approximate Number of Living Species
Zygomycota	*Rhizopus* (black bread mold)	Reproduce sexually and asexually; multinucleate hyphae lack septa except for reproductive structures; fusion of hyphae leads directly to formation of a zygote, in which meiosis occurs just before it germinates	1,050
Ascomycota	Yeasts, truffles, morels	Reproduce by sexual means; ascospores are formed inside a sac called an ascus; asexual reproduction is also common	32,000
Basidiomycota	Mushrooms, toadstools, rusts	Reproduce by sexual means; basidiospores are borne on club-shaped structures called basidia; the terminal hyphal cell that produces spores is called a basidium; asexual reproduction occurs occasionally	22,000
Chytridiomycota	*Allomyces*	Produce flagellated gametes (zoospores); predominately aquatic, some freshwater and some marine; oldest group of fungi	1,500
Imperfect fungi (not a phylum)	*Aspergillus*, *Penicillium*	Sexual reproduction has not been observed; most are thought to be ascomycetes that have lost the ability to reproduce sexually	17,000

21.5 Zygomycetes

The **zygomycetes,** members of the phylum Zygomycota, are unique among the fungi in that the fusion of hyphae does not produce a heterokaryon (a cell with two haploid nuclei). Instead, the two nuclei fuse and form a single diploid nucleus. Just as the fusion of sperm and egg produces a zygote in plants and animals, so this fusion produces a zygote. The name *zygomycetes* means "fungi that make zygotes."

Zygomycetes are the exception to the rule among fungi, and there are not many different kinds of them—only about 1,050 named species (about 1% of the named fungi). Included among them are some of the most frequent bread molds (the so-called black molds) and many microscopic fungi found on decaying organic material including strawberries and other fruits. Another important group of zygomycetes is called the Glomales. These soil-borne fungi form symbiotic relationships with roots of terrestrial plants and may have aided in the evolution of terrestrial plants, enhancing the uptake of minerals and water from the soil.

Reproduction among the zygomycetes is typically asexual. A cell at the tip of a hypha becomes walled off by a complete septum, forming an erect stalk tipped by a sporangium within which haploid spores are produced. These are the lollipop-shaped structures you see in the life cycle illustrated in figure 21.6. Their spores are shed into the wind and blown to new locations, where the spores germinate and attempt to start new mycelia. Sexual reproduction is unusual but may occur in times of stress. It is shown in the lower part of the figure, where hyphae from two different mating strains (+ is green and − is red) fuse and their nuclei also fuse, forming a diploid zygote. At the point where the two hyphae fuse, a sturdy and resistant structure called a **zygosporangium** forms. The zygosporangium is a very effective survival mechanism, a resting structure that allows the organism to remain dormant for long periods of time when conditions are not favorable. When conditions improve, the zygosporangium forms a stalked structure topped with a sporangium. Meiosis occurs within the sporangia and haploid spores are released, just as in the asexual portion of the life cycle.

> **21.5 Zygomycetes are unusual fungi that typically reproduce asexually; when hyphae do fuse, a zygote (one *2n* nucleus), rather than a heterokaryon (two haploid nuclei), is produced.**

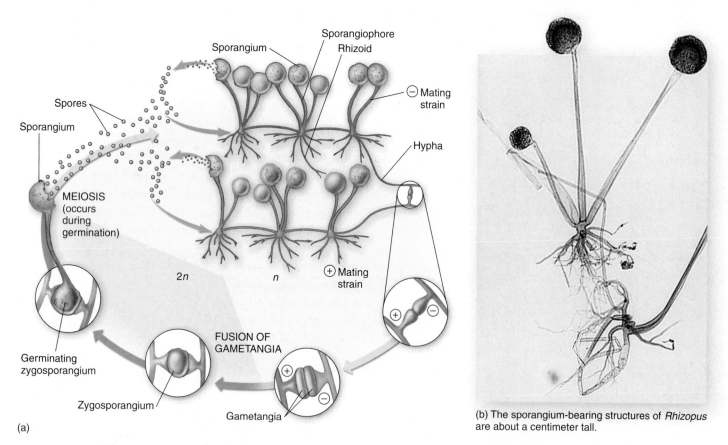

(b) The sporangium-bearing structures of *Rhizopus* are about a centimeter tall.

(a)

Figure 21.6 Life cycle of a zygomycete.

(*a*) In the life cycle of *Rhizopus*, a zygomycete that grows on moist bread and other similar substrates, the hyphae grow over the surface of the bread or other material on which the fungus feeds, producing erect, sporangium-bearing stalks in clumps, also shown in (*b*). If two hyphae grow together, their nuclei may fuse, producing a zygote. This zygote, which is the only diploid cell of the life cycle, acquires a thick, black coat (colored *purple* in the diagram above) and is then called a zygosporangium. Meiosis occurs during its germination, and normal, haploid hyphae grow from the haploid spores that result from this process.

Phylum Ascomycota, the **ascomycetes,** is the largest of the fungal phyla, with about 32,000 named species and many more being discovered each year. Among the ascomycetes are such familiar and economically important fungi as yeasts, morels, and truffles, as well as molds such as *Neurospora* (a historically important organism in genetic research) and many plant fungal pathogens, such as those that cause Dutch elm disease and chestnut blight.

Reproduction among the ascomycetes is usually asexual, just as it is among the zygomycetes. The hyphae of ascomycetes possess incomplete septa that separate the cells but have a large central pore in them, so that the flow of cytoplasm up and down the hypha is not impeded. Asexual reproduction occurs when the tips of hyphae become fully isolated from the rest of the mycelium by a complete septum, forming asexual spores called conidia (figure 21.7*a*, in the enlarged, circled area), each often containing several nuclei. When one of these conidia is released, air currents carry it to another place, where it may germinate to form a new mycelium.

It is important not to get confused by the number of nuclei in conidia. These multinucleate spores are *haploid*, not diploid, because there is only one version of the genome (one set of ascomycete chromosomes) present, whereas in a diploid cell there are two genetically different sets of chromosomes present. The actual number of nuclei is not what's important—it's the number of different genomes.

The ascomycetes are named for their sexual reproductive structure, the **ascus** (plural, **asci**), which differentiates within a larger structure called the ascocarp. The morel in figure 21.7*b* shows an ascocarp. The ascus is a microscopic cell that forms on the tips of the hyphae within the ascocarp, and it is where the zygote forms. The formation of the ascus is shown in the drawing where the tips of the hyphae appear swollen. The zygote is the only diploid nucleus of the ascomycete life cycle, indicated by the light blue section of the life cycle. The zygote undergoes meiosis, producing haploid spores called ascospores. When a mature ascus bursts, individual ascospores may be thrown as far as 30 centimeters. Considering how small the ascus is (only 10 micrometers long), this is truly an amazing distance. This would be like you hitting a baseball 1.25 kilometers, 10 times longer than Babe Ruth's longest home run!

> **21.6 Most fungi are ascomycetes, which form zygotes within reproductive structures called asci.**

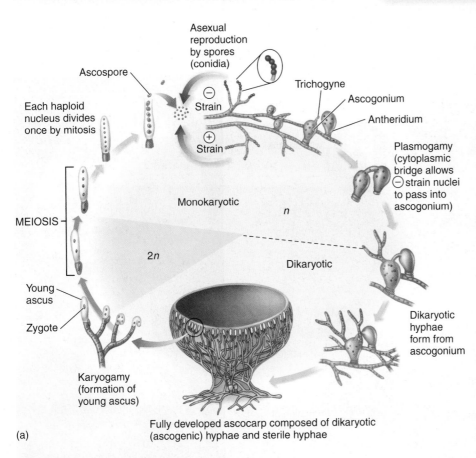

(b) This yellow morel is an ascomycete.

Figure 21.7 Life cycle of an ascomycete.
(*a*) Asexual reproduction takes place by means of conidia, spores cut off by septa at the ends of modified hyphae. Sexual reproduction occurs when the female gametangium, or *ascogonium*, fuses with the male gametangium, or *antheridium*, through a structure called the trichogyne. The ascocarp (*b*) develops from the dikaryotic hyphae and sterile hyphae. The nuclei fuse forming the diploid zygote inside the ascus. The zygote undergoes meiosis, leading to the formation of haploid ascospores.

Basidiomycetes

The phylum Basidiomycota contains the most familiar of the fungi among their 22,000 named species—the mushrooms, toadstools, puffballs, and shelf fungi. Many mushrooms are used as food, but others are deadly poisonous. Some species are cultivated as crops—the button mushroom *Agaricus campestris* is grown in more than 70 countries, producing a crop in 1998 with a value of over $15 billion. Also among the **basidiomycetes** are bread yeasts and plant pathogens including rusts and smuts. Rust infections resemble rusting metal, whereas smut infections appear black and powdery due to their spores.

The life cycle of a basidiomycete (figure 21.8*a*) starts with the production of a hypha from a germinating spore. These hyphae lack septa at first, just as in zygomycetes. Eventually, however, septa are formed between each of the nuclei—but as in ascomycetes, there are holes in these cell separations, allowing cytoplasm to flow freely between cells. These hyphae grow, forming complex mycelia, and when hyphae of two different mating types ($\oplus$ and $\ominus$) fuse, they form cells in which the nuclei remain separate—they do not fuse into one nucleus. Recall that if two distinct nuclei occur within each cell of the hypha, it is called

dikaryotic, indicated by the $n + n$ tan area of the cycle. The dikaryotic hypha that results goes on to form a dikaryotic mycelium. The mycelium forms a complex structure made of dikaryotic hyphae called the basidiocarp, or mushroom (figure 21.8*b*).

The two nuclei in each cell of a dikaryotic hypha can coexist together for a very long time without fusing. Unlike the other two fungal phyla, asexual reproduction is infrequent among the basidiomycetes, which typically reproduce sexually.

In sexual reproduction, zygotes (the only diploid cells of the life cycle) form when the two nuclei of dikaryotic cells fuse (on the right-hand side of the cycle). This occurs within a club-shaped reproductive structure called the **basidium** (plural, **basidia**). Meiosis occurs in each basidium, forming haploid spores called basidiospores. The basidia occur in a dense layer on the underside of the cap of the mushroom, where the surface is folded like an accordion. It has been estimated that a mushroom with an 8-centimeter cap produces as many as 40 million spores per hour!

> **21.7 Mushrooms are basidiomycetes, which form club-shaped reproductive structures called basidia.**

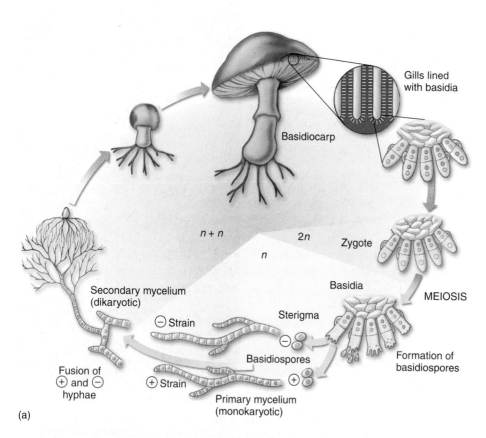

(a)

(b) An *Amanita* mushroom

Figure 21.8 Life cycle of a basidiomycete.

(*a*) Basidiomycetes usually reproduce sexually, with the fusion of nuclei in the basidia to produce a zygote. Meiosis follows syngamy and produces basidiospores that eventually form a basidiocarp (*b*).

Chytridiomycetes, Imperfect Fungi, and Yeasts

Chytridiomycetes

The phylum Chytridiomycota (chytrids) are mostly aquatic organisms, although some are found in soils and other terrestrial environments. Chytrids are the most primitive fungi retaining flagellated gametes (called zoospores) from their protist ancestors. The other fungal groups are thought to have lost their flagellated stage at some point early in their evolutionary history as fungi. Like other fungi, the cell wall of most chytrids contains chitin.

Several species of chytrids are plant pathogens that cause minor diseases. One species of chytrid, *Batrachochytrium dendrobatidis,* has been identified as a potential pathogen of frogs. *B. dendrobatidis* has been found in frogs that have died from a cutaneous chytridiomycosis (a skin disease caused apparently by the chytrid). The spores released by the fungi become embedded in the skin, where they seem to interfere with normal skin functions like respiration. A reddening of the skin on the legs and abdomen of the infected frog in figure 21.9 is a symptom of a *B. dendrobatidis* infection. This fatal disease appears to be a contributing cause to the recent sharp declines in amphibian populations seen worldwide.

Imperfect Fungi

In addition to the four phyla of fungi that differ primarily in their mode of sexual reproduction, there are some 17,000 described species of fungi in whom sexual reproduction has not been observed. These cannot be formally assigned to one of the four sexually reproducing phyla and so are grouped for convenience as the so-called **imperfect fungi** (figure 21.10). The imperfect fungi are fungi that have lost the ability to reproduce sexually. Most of them appear to be ascomycetes, although some basidiomycetes are also included—these can be distinguished by features of the hyphae and asexual reproduction. Most of the fungi that cause skin diseases, including athlete's foot and ringworm, are caused by imperfect fungi. Fungal diseases are often difficult to treat pharmaceutically because of the ancestral relationship between animals and fungi. Medicines that kill fungal cells may also adversely affect animal cells.

Figure 21.9 Chytrid infection.
The pathogenic chytrid, *Batrachochytrium dendrobatidis,* has infected this frog.

**Figure 21.10
Imperfect fungi.**
Imperfect fungi are fungi in which sexual reproduction is unknown. *Verticillium alboatrum,* an important pathogen of alfalfa, has whorled conidia. The single-celled conidia of this member of the imperfect fungi are borne at the ends of the conidiophores.

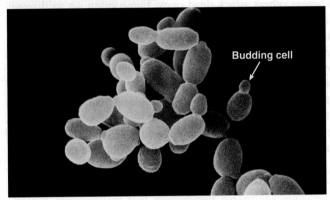

Figure 21.11 Budding in *Saccharomyces.*
These yeast cells tend to hang together in chains, a feature that calls to mind the derivation of single-celled yeast from multicellular ancestors.

Yeasts

Yeast is the generic (general) name given to any unicellular fungus. Although single-celled, yeasts appear almost certainly to have been derived from multicellular ancestors. There are about 250 named species of yeasts, including *Saccharomyces cerevisiae* (brewer's yeast), used for thousands of years in the production of bread, beer, and wine. Other yeasts are pathogens, including *Candida,* a common source of vaginal infection.

Just as in ascomycetes, most of yeast reproduction is asexual and takes place by cell fission or budding (the formation of a small cell from a portion of a larger one as you see happening at the arrow in figure 21.11). Sexual reproduction among yeasts occurs when two yeast cells fuse. The new cell containing two nuclei functions as an ascus. After the two nuclei fuse, meiosis produces four ascospores, which develop directly into new yeast cells.

> **21.8 Chytridiomycetes** are a group of fungi most closely related to ancestral fungi. Imperfect fungi may have lost the ability to reproduce sexually. Yeasts are unicellular fungi.

1. The most important characteristic of complex multicellular organisms is
   a. intercellular communication.
   b. cell development.
   c. cell specialization.
   d. cell reproduction.

2. Which of the following is *not* a characteristic of the fungi kingdom?
   a. heterotrophic
   b. cellulose cell walls
   c. nuclear mitosis
   d. nonmotile sperm

3. The main body of a fungus is the
   a. hyphae.
   b. septa.
   c. mushroom.
   d. mycelium.

4. Fungi reproduce
   a. both sexually and asexually.
   b. sexually only.
   c. asexually only.
   d. by fragmentation.

5. Morels and truffles belong to the fungus phylum
   a. Zygomycota.
   b. Ascomycota.
   c. Basidiomycota.
   d. Chytridiomycota.

6. Zygomycetes are different from other fungi because they do not produce
   a. mycelium.
   b. fruiting bodies.
   c. a heterokaryon.
   d. a sporangium.

7. Ascomycetes form reproductive spores in
   a. a special sac called the ascus.
   b. gills on the basidiocarp.
   c. sporangiophores.
   d. the mycelium.

8. Meiosis in basidiomycetes occurs in the
   a. hyphae.
   b. basidia.
   c. mycelium.
   d. basidiocarp.

9. Lichens are mutualistic associations between
   a. plants and fungi.
   b. algae and fungi.
   c. termites and fungi.
   d. coral and fungi.

10. Mycorrhizae help plants obtain
    a. water.
    b. oxygen.
    c. carbon dioxide.
    d. minerals.

Visual Understanding

1. **Figure 21.8a** Explain what part of the fungus life cycle is the familiar mushroom that you see in stores.

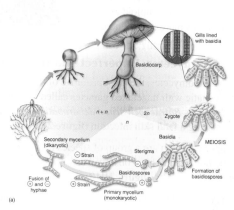

2. **Figure 21.15** What are two of the methods that mycorrhizae use to contact and live with plant roots?

Challenge Questions

1. What are the two key characteristics of multicellular organisms exhibited by fungi?

2. Describe some of the ways that fungi cooperate with other organisms.

3. Your friend, Michael, has athlete's foot and is unhappy with how long it is taking to get rid of it. Disgusted, he asks you what good are fungi, anyway? Is there anything useful we get from them? What do you tell him?

22
Evolution of Plants

Plants are thought to be descendants of green algae. Plants first invaded the land over 455 million years ago in partnership with fungi—the most ancient surviving plants have mycorrhizal associations. One of the many challenges posed by the terrestrial environment was the difficulty of finding a mate when anchored to one spot. The solution adopted by most early plants was for male individuals to cast their gametes—pollen—into the wind, and let air currents carry pollen grains to nearby female plants. This strategy works particularly well in dense stands, in which there are many nearby individuals of the same species. The massive redwood tree seen here, one of the largest individual organisms living on land, grows in dense stands and is wind pollinated. An alternative solution proved even better, however. Plants evolved flowers, devices to attract insects. When insects visit the flower to obtain nectar, they become coated with pollen. When they then visit another flower seeking more nectar, they deposit some of this pollen, pollinating that flower. It doesn't matter how far apart the two plants are from each other—the insect will seek them out. In this chapter, you will explore this and other evolutionary challenges met by plants as they colonized the land.

22.1 Adapting to Terrestrial Living

Plants are complex multicellular organisms that are terrestrial **auto-trophs**—that is, they occur almost exclusively on land and feed themselves by photosynthesis. The name *autotroph* comes from the Greek, *autos,* self, and *trophos,* feeder. Today, plants are the dominant organisms on the surface of the earth (figure 22.1). Nearly 300,000 species are now in existence, covering almost every part of the terrestrial landscape. In this chapter, we see how plants adapted to life on land.

The green algae that were probably the ancestors of today's plants are aquatic organisms that are not well adapted to living on land. Before their descendants could live on land, they had to overcome many environmental challenges. For example, they had to absorb minerals from the rocky surface. They had to find a means of conserving water. They had to develop a way to reproduce on land.

Absorbing Minerals

Plants require relatively large amounts of six inorganic minerals: nitrogen, potassium, calcium, phosphorus, magnesium, and sulfur. Each of these minerals constitutes 1% or more of a plant's dry weight. Algae absorb these minerals from water, but where is a plant on land to get them? From the soil. Soil is the weathered outer layer of the earth's crust. It is composed of a mixture of ingredients, which may include sand, rocks, clay, silt, humus (partly decayed organic material), and various other forms of mineral and organic matter. The soil is also rich in microorganisms that break down and recycle organic debris. Plants absorb these materials, along with water, through their *roots* (described in chapter 23). Most roots are found in topsoil, which is a mixture of mineral particles, living organisms, and humus. When topsoil is lost due to erosion, the soil loses its ability to hold water and nutrients.

The first plants seem to have developed a special relationship with fungi, which was a key factor in their ability to absorb minerals in terrestrial habitats. Within the roots or underground stems of many early fossil plants like *Cooksonia* (see figure 22.7) and *Rhynia,* fungi can be seen living intimately within and among the plant's cells. As you may recall from chapter 21, these kinds of

Figure 22.1 Plants dominate life on land.

Plants are astonishingly diverse and are key components in the biosphere. Photosynthesis conducted by plants and algae creates the majority of oxygen in the atmosphere. Also, through photosynthesis, plants convert energy from the sun into organic material that can be used by the many members of an ecosystem. Plants play key roles in the cycling of water and many nutrients. They are the main source of food for humans and many other organisms (directly and indirectly), and plants provide us with wood, cloth, paper, and many other nonfood products.

symbiotic associations are called **mycorrhizae.** In plants with mycorrhizae, the fungi enable the plant to take up phosphorus and other nutrients from rocky soil, while the plant supplies organic molecules to the fungus.

Conserving Water

One of the key challenges to living on land is to avoid drying out. To solve this problem, plants have a watertight outer covering called a **cuticle.** The covering is formed from a waxy substance that is impermeable to water. Like the wax on a shiny car, the cuticle prevents water from entering or leaving the stem or leaves. Water enters the plant only from the roots, while the cuticle prevents water loss to the air. Passages do exist through the cuticle, in the form of specialized pores called **stomata** (singular, **stoma**) in the leaves and sometimes the green portions of the stems. Figure 22.2 shows a stoma on the underside of a leaf. The cutaway view allows you to see the placement of the stoma in relation to other cells in the leaf. Stomata, which occur on at least some portions of all plants except liverworts, allow carbon dioxide to pass into the plant bodies (by diffusion) for photosynthesis and allow

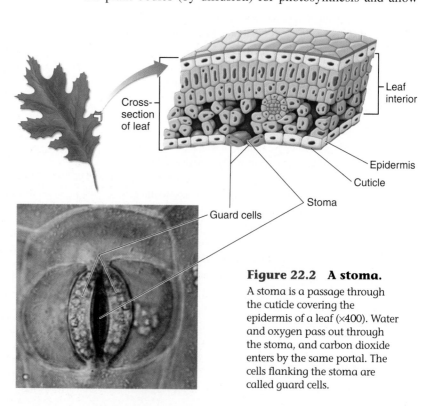

Cross-section of leaf

Leaf interior

Epidermis

Cuticle

Stoma

Guard cells

Figure 22.2 A stoma.

A stoma is a passage through the cuticle covering the epidermis of a leaf (×400). Water and oxygen pass out through the stoma, and carbon dioxide enters by the same portal. The cells flanking the stoma are called guard cells.

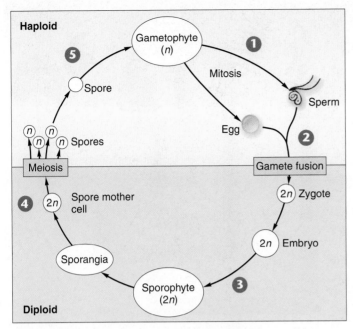

Figure 22.3 Generalized plant life cycle.
In a plant life cycle, a diploid generation alternates with a haploid one. Gametophytes, which are haploid (*n*), alternate with sporophytes, which are diploid (*2n*). ❶ Gametophytes give rise by mitosis to sperm and eggs. ❷ The sperm and egg ultimately come together to produce the first diploid cell of the sporophyte generation, the zygote. ❸ The zygote undergoes cell division, ultimately forming the sporophyte. ❹ Meiosis takes place within the sporangia, the spore-producing organs of the sporophyte, resulting in the production of the spores, which are haploid and are the first cells ❺ of gametophyte generations.

(a)

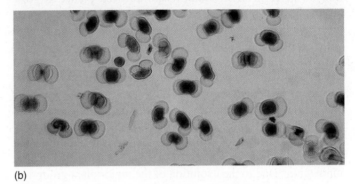
(b)

Figure 22.4 Two types of gametophytes.
(*a*) This gametophyte of a moss (a nonvascular plant) is green and free-living. (*b*) Male gametophytes (pollen) of a pine (a vascular plant) are barely large enough to be visible to the naked eye (×200).

water and oxygen gas to pass out of them. The two *guard cells* that border the stoma swell (opening the stoma) and shrink (closing the stoma) when water moves into and out of them by osmosis. This controls the loss of water from the leaf while allowing the entrance of carbon dioxide (see also figure 23.21). In most plants, water enters through the roots as a liquid and exits through the underside of the leaves as water vapor. Water movement within a plant is discussed in more detail in section 23.6.

Reproducing on Land

To reproduce sexually on land, it is necessary to pass gametes from one individual to another, which was a challenge because plants cannot move about. In the first plants, the eggs were surrounded by a jacket of cells, and a film of water was required for the sperm to swim to the egg and fertilize it. In other plants, pollen evolved, providing a means of transferring gametes without drying out. The pollen grain is protected from drying and allows plants to transfer gametes by wind or insects.

Changing the Life Cycle   Among many algae, haploid cells occupy the major portion of the life cycle (see section 20.2). The zygote formed by the fusion of gametes is the only diploid cell, and it immediately undergoes meiosis to form haploid cells again. In early plants, by contrast, meiosis was delayed

and the cells of the zygote divided to produce a multicellular diploid structure. Thus for a significant portion of the life cycle, the cells were diploid. This change resulted in an **alternation of generations,** in which a diploid generation alternates with a haploid one. The life cycle in figure 22.3 shows a life cycle that exhibits an alternation of generation. Botanists call the haploid generation (indicated by the yellow boxed area) the **gametophyte** because it forms haploid gametes by mitosis, in ❶. The diploid generation (indicated by the blue boxed area) is called the **sporophyte** because it forms haploid spores by meiosis, in ❹. When you look at primitive plants such as liverworts and mosses, you see mostly gametophyte tissue, the green leafy structures in figure 22.4*a*—the sporophytes are smaller brown structures (not visible in the photo) attached to or enclosed within the tissues of the larger gametophyte. When you look at plants that evolved later, such as a pine tree, you see mostly sporophyte tissue. The gametophytes of these plants are always much smaller than the sporophytes and are often enclosed within sporophyte tissues. Figure 22.4*b* shows the gametophyte (pollen grains) of a pine tree. They are not photosynthetic cells and are dependent upon the sporophyte tissue in which it is usually enclosed.

> **22.1   Plants are multicellular terrestrial photosynthesizers that evolved from green algae. Plants adapted to life on land by developing ways to absorb minerals in partnership with fungi, to conserve water with watertight coverings, and to reproduce on land.**

Plant Evolution

Once plants became established on land, they gradually developed many other features that aided their evolutionary success in this new, demanding habitat. For example, among the first plants there was no fundamental difference between the aboveground and the belowground parts. Later, roots and shoots with specialized structures evolved, each suited to its particular below- or aboveground environment. The evolution of specialized *vascular tissue* allowed plants to grow larger. For example, compare the size of a moss, a more primitive type of plant, to the more recently evolved tree on which it grows.

As we explore plant diversity, we will examine several key evolutionary innovations that have given rise to the wide variety of plants we see today. Table 22.1 provides you with an overview of the plant phyla and their characteristics. While other interesting and important changes also arose, four key innovations discussed in this chapter serve to highlight the evolutionary trends exhibited by the plant kingdom. These innovations lead to the evolution of the major plant groups, as shown in figure 22.5.

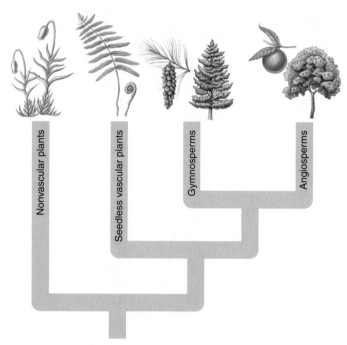

Figure 22.5 The evolution of plants.

TABLE 22.1	PLANT PHYLA		
Phylum	**Typical Examples**	**Key Characteristics**	**Approximate Number of Living Species**
Nonvascular Plants			
Hepaticophyta (liverworts)	*Marchantia*	Without true vascular tissues; lack true roots and leaves; live in moist habitats and obtain water and nutrients by osmosis and diffusion; require water for fertilization; gametophyte is dominant structure in the life cycle; the three phyla were once grouped together	15,600
Anthocerophyta (hornworts)	*Anthoceros*		
Bryophyta (mosses)	*Polytrichum, Sphagnum* (hairy cap and peat moss)		
Seedless Vascular Plants			
Lycophyta (lycopods)	*Lycopodium* (club mosses)	Seedless vascular plants, some are similar in appearance to mosses but diploid; require water for fertilization; sporophyte is dominant structure in life cycle; found in moist woodland habitats	1,150
Pterophyta (ferns)	*Azolla, Sphaeropteris* (water and tree ferns)	Seedless vascular plants; require water for fertilization; sporophytes diverse in form and dominate the life cycle	11,000
	Equisetum (horsetails)		
	Psilotum (whisk ferns)		

Four key evolutionary innovations serve to trace the evolution of the plant kingdom:

1. **Alternation of generations.** Although algae exhibit a haploid and diploid phase, the diploid phase is not a significant portion of their life cycle. By contrast, even in early plants (the nonvascular plants indicated by the first vertical bar in figure 22.5) the diploid sporophyte is a larger structure and offers protection for the egg and developing embryo. The dominance of the sporophyte, both in size and the proportion of time devoted to it in the life cycle, becomes greater throughout the evolutionary history of plants.

2. **Vascular tissue.** A second key innovation was the emergence of vascular tissue. Vascular tissue transports water and nutrients throughout the plant body and provides structural support. With the evolution of vascular tissue, plants were able to supply the upper portions of their bodies with water absorbed from the soil and had some rigidity, allowing the plants to grow larger and in drier conditions. The first vascular plants were the seedless vascular plants, the second vertical bar in figure 22.5.

3. **Seeds.** The evolution of *seeds* (see section 22.6) was a key innovation that allowed plants to dominate their terrestrial environments. Seeds provide nutrients and a tough, durable cover that protects the embryo until it encounters favorable growing conditions. The first plants with seeds were the gymnosperms, the third vertical bar in figure 22.5.

4. **Flowers and fruits.** The evolution of flowers and fruits were key innovations that improved the chances of successful mating in sedentary organisms and facilitated the dispersal of their seeds. Flowers both protected the egg and improved the odds of its fertilization, allowing plants that were located at considerable distances to mate successfully. Fruit, which surrounds the seed and aids in its dispersal, allows plant species to better invade new and possibly more favorable environments. The angiosperms, the fourth vertical bar in figure 22.5, are the only plants to produce flowers and fruits.

22.2 Plants evolved from freshwater green algae and eventually developed more dominant diploid phases of the life cycle, conducting systems of vascular tissue, seeds that protected the embryo, and flowers and fruits that aided in fertilization and distribution of the seeds.

TABLE 22.1	*(continued)*		
Phylum	**Typical Examples**	**Key Characteristics**	**Approximate Number of Living Species**
Seed Plants			
Coniferophyta (conifers)	Pines, spruce, fir, redwood, cedar	Gymnosperms; wind pollinated; ovules partially exposed at time of pollination; flowerless; seeds are dispersed by the wind; sperm lack flagella; sporophyte is dominant structure in life cycle; leaves are needlelike or scalelike; most species are evergreens and live in dense stands; among the most common trees on earth	601
Cycadophyta (cycads)	Cycads, sago palms	Gymnosperms; wind pollination or possibly insect-pollination; very slow growing, palmlike trees; sperm have flagella: trees are either male or female; sporophyte dominant in the life cycle	206
Gnetophyta (shrub teas)	Mormon tea, *Welwitschia*	Gymnosperms; nonmotile sperm; shrubs and vines; wind pollination and possibly insect pollination; plants are either male or female; sporophyte is dominant in the life cycle	65
Ginkgophyta (ginkgo)	Ginkgo trees	Gymnosperms; fanlike leaves that are dropped in winter (deciduous); seeds fleshy and ill-scented; motile sperm; trees are either male or female; sporophyte is dominant in the life cycle	1
Anthophyta (flowering plants, also called angiosperms)	Oak trees, corn, wheat, roses	Flowering; pollination by wind, animal, and water; characterized by ovules that are fully enclosed by the carpel; fertilization involves two sperm nuclei; one forms the embryo, the other fuses with the polar body to form endosperm for the seed; after fertilization, carpels and the fertilized ovules (now seeds) mature to become fruit; sporophyte is dominant in life cycle	250,000

22.3 Nonvascular Plants

Liverworts and Hornworts

The first successful land plants had no vascular system—no tubes or pipes to transport water and nutrients throughout the plant. This greatly limited the maximum size of the plant body because all materials had to be transported by osmosis and diffusion (see section 5.10). However, these simple plants are highly adapted to a diversity of terrestrial environments. Only two phyla of living plants, the **liverworts** (phylum Hepaticophyta) and the **hornworts** (phylum Anthocerophyta), completely lack a vascular system. The word *wort* meant *herb* in medieval Anglo-Saxon when these plants were named. Liverworts are the simplest of all living plants. About 6,000 species of liverworts and 100 species of hornworts survive today, usually growing in moist and shady places.

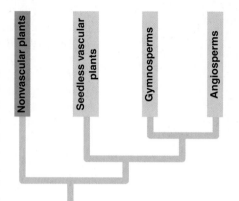

Primitive Conducting Systems: Mosses

Another phylum of plants, the **mosses** (phylum Bryophyta), were the first plants to evolve strands of specialized cells that conduct water and carbohydrates up the stem of the gametophyte. The conducting cells do not have specialized wall thickenings; instead they are like nonrigid pipes and cannot carry water very high. Because these conducting cells could at the most be considered a primitive vascular system, mosses are usually grouped by botanists with the liverworts and hornworts as "nonvascular" plants. Today about 9,500 species of mosses grow in moist places all over the world. In the Arctic and Antarctic, mosses are the most abundant plants. "Peat moss" (genus *Sphagnum*) can be used as a fuel or a soil conditioner. The moss *Physcomitrella patens,* whose genome was sequenced in 2006, has been the subject of many genetic studies. The life cycle of a moss is illustrated in figure 22.6. You can see that the majority of the life cycle consists of the haploid gametophyte generation (the green part of the plant), which exists as male or female plants. The diploid sporophyte (the brown stalk with the swollen head) grows out of the gametophyte of the female plant ❸, after the egg cell has been fertilized. Cells within the sporophyte undergo meiosis to produce haploid spores ❹ that grow into gametophytes ❺.

> **22.3** While liverworts and hornworts totally lack a vascular system, mosses have simple soft strands of conducting cells.

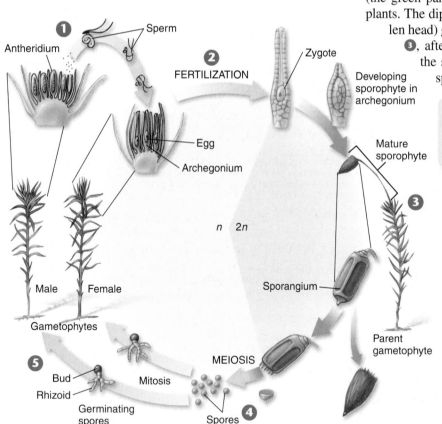

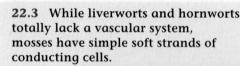

A hair-cup moss, *Polytrichum*

Figure 22.6   The life cycle of a moss.
On the haploid gametophytes, sperm are released from each antheridium (sperm-producing structure) ❶. They then swim through free water to an archegonium (egg-producing structure) and down its neck to the egg. Fertilization takes place there ❷; the resulting zygote develops into a diploid sporophyte. The sporophyte grows out of the archegonium, forming the sporangium at its apex ❸. The sporophyte grows on the gametophyte, as shown in the photo, and eventually produces spores as a result of meiosis. The spores are shed from the sporangium ❹. The spores germinate, giving rise to gametophytes ❺.

22.4 The Evolution of Vascular Tissue

The remaining seven phyla of plants, which have efficient vascular systems made of highly specialized cells, are called **vascular plants.** The first vascular plant appeared approximately 430 million years ago, but only incomplete fossils have been found. The first vascular plants for which we have relatively complete fossils, the extinct phylum Rhyniophyta, lived 410 million years ago. Among them is the oldest known vascular plant, *Cooksonia*. The fossil in figure 22.7 clearly shows that the plant had branched, leafless shoots that formed spores at the tips in structures called *sporangia*.

Cooksonia and the other early plants that followed became successful colonizers of the land through the development of efficient water- and food-conducting systems known as **vascular tissues** (Latin, *vasculum,* vessel or duct). These tissues, discussed in detail in chapter 23, consist of strands of specialized cylindrical or elongated cells that form a network of tubelike structures throughout a plant, extending from near the tips of the roots (when present), through the stems, and into the leaves (when present; figure 22.8). One type of vascular tissue, *xylem,* conducts water and dissolved minerals upward from the roots; another type of vascular tissue, *phloem,* conducts carbohydrates throughout the plant. The presence of a cuticle and stomata are also characteristic of vascular plants.

Most early vascular plants seem to have grown by cell division at the tips of the stem and roots. Imagine stacking dishes—the stack can get taller but not wider! This sort of growth is called **primary growth** and was quite successful. During the so-called Coal Age (between 350 and 290 million years ago), when much of the world's fossil fuel was formed, the lowland swamps that covered Europe and North America were dominated by an early form of seedless tree called a lycophyte. Lycophyte trees grew to heights of 10 to 35 meters (33 to 115 ft), and their trunks did not branch until they attained most of their total height. The pace of evolution was rapid during this period, for the world's climate was changing, growing dryer and colder. As the world's swamplands began to dry up, the lycophyte trees vanished, disappearing abruptly from the fossil record. They were replaced by tree-sized ferns, a form of vascular plant that will be described in detail in section 22.5. Tree ferns grew to heights of more than 20 meters (66 ft) with trunks 30 centimeters (12 in) thick. Like the lycophytes, the trunks of tree ferns were formed entirely by primary growth.

About 380 million years ago, vascular plants developed a new pattern of growth, in which a cylinder of cells beneath the bark divides, producing new cells in regions around the plant's periphery. This growth is called **secondary growth.** Secondary growth makes it possible for a plant stem to increase in diameter. Only after the evolution of secondary growth could vascular plants become thick-trunked and therefore tall. Redwood trees today reach heights of up to 117 meters (384 ft) and trunk diameters in excess of 11 meters (36 ft). This evolutionary advance made possible the dominance of the tall forests that today cover northern North America. You

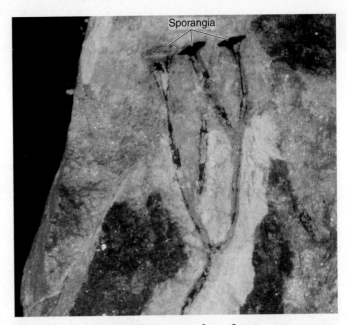

Figure 22.7 The earliest vascular plant.
The earliest vascular plant of which we have complete fossils is *Cooksonia.* This fossil shows a plant that lived some 410 million years ago; its upright branched stems terminated in spore-producing sporangia at the tips.

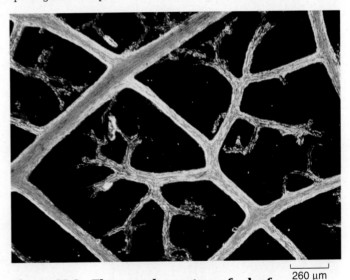

260 μm

Figure 22.8 The vascular system of a leaf.
The veins of a vascular plant contain strands of specialized cells for conducting food and water. The veins from a leaf are shown in this magnified view.

are familiar with the product of plant secondary growth as **wood.** The growth rings that are so visible in cross sections of trees are zones of secondary growth (spring–summer) spaced by zones of little growth (fall–winter).

> **22.4 Vascular plants have specialized vascular tissue composed of hollow tubes that conduct water from the roots to the leaves. Another type of vascular tissue forms cylinders that conduct food from the leaves to the rest of the plant.**

22.5 Seedless Vascular Plants

The earliest vascular plants lacked seeds, and two of the seven phyla of modern-day vascular plants do not have them. The two phyla of living seedless vascular plants include the ferns, phylum Pterophyta. This phylum includes the typical ferns seen growing on forests floors, like those shown in figure 22.9a, b. It also includes the whisk ferns (figure 22.9c) and the horsetails (figure 22.9d). The other phylum, Lycophyta, contains the club mosses (figure 22.9e). These phyla have free-swimming sperm that require the presence of free water for fertilization.

By far the most abundant of seedless vascular plants are the **ferns,** with about 11,000 living species. Ferns are found throughout the world, although they are much more abundant in the tropics than elsewhere. Many are small, only a few centimeters in diameter, but some of the largest plants that live today are also ferns. Descendants of ancient tree ferns, they can have trunks more than 24 meters (79 ft) tall and leaves up to 5 meters (16 ft) long!

Figure 22.9 Seedless vascular plants.

(a) A tree fern in the forests of Malaysia (phylum Pterophyta). The ferns are by far the largest group of spore-producing vascular plants.
(b) Ferns on the floor of a redwood forest. (c) A whisk fern. Whisk ferns have no roots or leaves. (d) A horsetail, *Equisetum telmateia.* This species forms two kinds of erect stems; one is green and photosynthetic, and the other, which terminates in a spore-producing "cone," is mostly light brown. (e) The club moss *Lycopodium lucidulum,* recently renamed *Huperzia lucidula* (phylum Lycophyta). Although superficially similar to the gametophytes of mosses, the conspicuous club moss plants shown here are sporophytes.

The Life of a Fern

In ferns, the life cycle of plants begins a revolutionary change that culminates later with seed plants. Nonvascular plants like mosses are made largely of gametophyte (haploid) tissue. Vascular seedless plants like ferns have both gametophyte and sporophyte individuals, each independent and self-sufficient. The gametophyte (the heart-shaped plant at the top of figure 22.10) produces eggs and sperm. After sperm swim through water and fertilize the egg, the zygote grows into a sporophyte. The sporophyte bears haploid spores on the underside of their leaves (in the brown clusters called sori (singular, sorus)). The spores are released from the sorus and float to the ground where they germinate, growing into haploid gametophytes. The fern gametophytes are small, thin, heart-shaped photosynthetic plants, usually no more than a centimeter in length, that live in moist places. The fern sporophytes are much larger and more complex, with long vertical leaves called **fronds.** When you see a fern, you are almost always looking at the sporophyte.

> **22.5 Ferns are among the vascular plants that lack seeds, reproducing with spores as nonvascular plants do.**

Figure 22.10 Fern life cycle.

The haploid gametophytes grow in moist places. Rhizoids (anchoring structures) project from their lower surface. Eggs develop in an archegonium, and sperm develop in an antheridium, both located on the gametophyte's lower surface. The sperm, when released, swim through free water to the mouth of the archegonium, entering and fertilizing the single egg. Following the fusion of egg and sperm to form a zygote—the first cell of the diploid sporophyte generation—the zygote starts to grow within the archegonium. Eventually, the sporophyte, the fern plant, becomes much larger than the gametophyte. Most ferns have more or less horizontal stems, called rhizomes, that creep along below ground. On the sporophyte's leaves, called fronds, occur clusters (called sori; singular, sorus) of sporangia, within which meiosis occurs and spores are formed. The release of these spores, which is explosive in many ferns, and their germination lead to the development of new gametophytes.

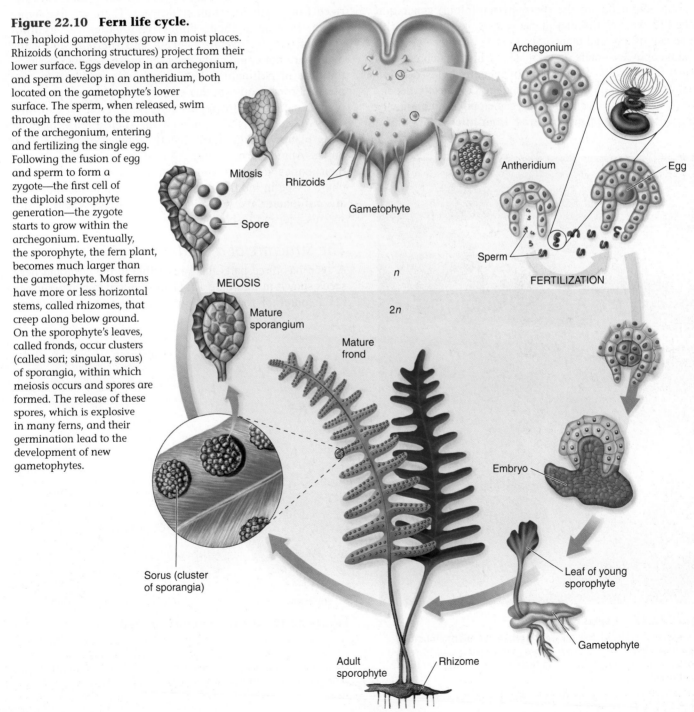

Mitosis

Rhizoids

Gametophyte

Spore

MEIOSIS

Mature sporangium

Mature frond

Sorus (cluster of sporangia)

Adult sporophyte

Rhizome

Archegonium

Antheridium

Egg

Sperm

n

FERTILIZATION

2*n*

Embryo

Leaf of young sporophyte

Gametophyte

22.6 Evolution of Seed Plants

A key evolutionary advance among the vascular plants was the development of a protective cover for the embryo called a **seed.** The seed is a crucial adaptation to life on land because it protects the embryonic plant when it is at its most vulnerable stage. The plant in figure 22.11 is a cycad and its seeds (the green balls in the photo) develop on the edges of the scales of the cone. The embryonic plants are inside the seeds where they are protected. The evolution of the seed was a critical step in allowing plants to dominate life on land.

The dominance of the sporophyte (diploid) generation in the life cycle of vascular plants reaches its full force with the advent of the seed plants. Seed plants produce two kinds of gametophytes—male and female, each of which consists of just a few cells. Both kinds of gametophytes develop separately within the sporophyte and are completely dependent on it for their nutrition. Male gametophytes, commonly referred to as **pollen grains,** arise from **microspores.** The

Figure 22.11 A seed plant.
The seeds of this cycad, like all seeds, consist of a plant embryo and a protective covering. A cycad is a gymnosperm (naked-seeded plant), and its seeds develop out in the open on the edges of the cone scales.

pollen grains become mature when sperm are produced. The sperm are carried to the egg in the female gametophyte without the need for free water in the environment. A female gametophyte contains the egg and develops from a **megaspore** produced within an **ovule.** The transfer of pollen to an ovule by insects, wind, or other agents is referred to as **pollination.** The pollen grain then cracks open and sprouts, or germinates, and the pollen tube, containing the sperm cells, grows out, transporting the sperm directly to the egg. Thus free water is not required in the pollination and fertilization process.

Botanists generally agree that all seed plants are derived from a single common ancestor. There are five living phyla. In four of them, collectively called the **gymnosperms** (Greek, *gymnos,* naked, and *sperma,* seed), the ovules are not completely enclosed by sporophyte tissue at the time of pollination. Gymnosperms were the first seed plants. From gymnosperms evolved the fifth group of seed plants, called **angiosperms** (Greek, *angion,* vessel, and *sperma,* seed), phylum Anthophyta. Angiosperms, or flowering plants, are the most recently evolved of all the plant phyla. Angiosperms differ from all gymnosperms in that their ovules are completely enclosed by a vessel of sporophyte tissue in the flower called the **carpel** at the time they are pollinated. We will discuss gymnosperms and angiosperms later in this chapter.

The Structure of a Seed

A seed has three parts that are visible in the corn and bean seeds shown in figure 22.12: (1) a sporophyte plant embryo, (2) a source of food for the developing embryo called **en-**

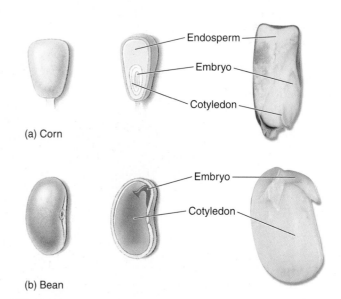

(a) Corn

(b) Bean

Figure 22.12 Basic structure of seeds.
A seed contains a sporophyte (diploid) embryo and a source of food, either endosperm (*a*) or food stored in the cotyledons (*b*). A seed coat, formed of sporophytic tissue from the parent, surrounds the seed and protects the embryo.

Figure 22.13 Seeds allow plants to bypass the dry season.
Seeds remain dormant until conditions are favorable for growth. When it does rain, seeds can germinate, and plants can grow rapidly to take advantage of the relatively short periods when water is available. This palo verde desert tree (*Cercidium floridum*) has tough seeds (*inset*) that germinate only after they are cracked. Rains leach out the chemicals in the seed coats that inhibit germination, and the hard coats of the seeds may be cracked when they are washed down gullies in temporary floods.

dosperm in flowering plants (the endosperm makes up most of the seed in corn and is the white part of popcorn), and (3) a drought-resistant protective cover. In some seeds, the endosperm is used up during the development of the embryo and is stored as food by the embryo in thick "leaflike" structures called **cotyledons.** The endosperm is replaced by the cotyledon, as in the bean seed. Seeds are one way in which plants, anchored by their roots to one place in the ground, are able to disperse their progeny to new locations. The hard cover of the seed (formed from the tissue of the parent plant) protects the seed while it travels to a new location. The seed travels by many means such as by air, water, and animals. Many airborne seeds have devices to aid in carrying them farther. Most species of pine, for example, have seeds with thin flat wings attached. These wings help catch air currents, which carry the seeds to new areas. Seed dispersal will be discussed further later in this chapter and in chapter 24.

Once a seed has fallen to the ground, it may lie there, dormant, for many years. When conditions are favorable, however, and particularly when moisture is present, the seed germinates and begins to grow into a young plant (figure 22.13). Most seeds have abundant food stored in them to provide a ready source of energy for the new plant as it starts its growth.

The advent of seeds had an enormous influence on the evolution of plants. Seeds are particularly adapted to life on land in at least four respects:

1. **Dispersal.** Most important, seeds facilitate the migration and dispersal of plant offspring into new habitats.
2. **Dormancy.** Seeds permit plants to postpone development when conditions are unfavorable, as during a drought, and to remain dormant until conditions improve.
3. **Germination.** By making the reinitiation of development dependent upon environmental factors such as temperature, seeds permit the course of embryonic development to be synchronized with critical aspects of the plant's habitat, such as the season of the year.
4. **Nourishment.** The seed offers the young plant nourishment during the critical period just after germination, when the seedling must establish itself.

22.6 A seed is a dormant diploid embryo encased with food reserves in a hard protective coat. Seeds play critical roles in improving a plant's chances of successfully reproducing in a varied environment.

22.7 Gymnosperms

Four phyla constitute the gymnosperms (figure 22.14): the conifers (Coniferophyta), the cycads (Cycadophyta), the gnetophytes (Gnetophyta), and the ginkgo (Ginkgophyta). The conifers are the most familiar of the four phyla of gymnosperms and include pine, spruce, hemlock, cedar, redwood, yew, cypress, and fir trees, such as the Douglas firs in figure 22.14a. Conifers are trees that produce their seeds in cones. The seeds (ovules) of conifers develop on scales within the cones and are exposed at the time of pollination. Most of the conifers have needlelike leaves, an evolutionary adaptation for retarding water loss. Conifers are often found growing in moderately dry regions of the world, including the vast taiga forests of the northern latitudes. Many are very important as sources of timber and pulp.

There are about 600 living species of conifers. The tallest living vascular plant, the coastal sequoia (*Sequoia sempervirens*), found in coastal California and Oregon, is a conifer and reaches over 100 meters (328 ft). The biggest redwood, however, is the mountain sequoia redwood species (*Sequoiadendron gigantea*) of the Sierra Nevadas. The largest individual tree is nicknamed after General Sherman of the Civil War, and it stands more than 83 meters (274 ft) tall while measuring 31 meters (102 ft) around its base. Another much smaller type of conifer, the bristlecone pines in Nevada, may be the oldest trees in the world—about 5,000 years old.

The other three gymnosperm phyla are much less widespread. Cycads (figure 22.14b), the predominant land

Nonvascular plants

Seedless vascular plants

Gymnosperms

Angiosperms

(a)

(b)

(c)

(d)

Figure 22.14 Gymnosperms.
(a) These Douglas fir trees, a type of conifer, often occur in vast forests. (b) An African cycad, *Encephalartos transvenosus*, phylum Cycadophyta. The cycads have fernlike leaves and seed-forming cones, like the ones shown here. (c) *Welwitschia mirabilis*, phylum Gnetophyta, is found in the extremely dry deserts of southwestern Africa. In *Welwitschia*, two enormous, beltlike leaves grow from a circular zone of cell division that surrounds the apex of the carrot-shaped root. (d) Maidenhair tree, *Ginkgo biloba*, the only living representative of the phylum Ginkgophyta, a group of plants that was abundant 200 million years ago. Among living seed plants, only the cycads and ginkgo have swimming sperm.

plant in the golden age of dinosaurs, the Jurassic period (213–144 million years ago), have short stems and palmlike leaves. They are still widespread throughout the tropics. The gnetophytes, phylum Gnetophyta, contains only three kinds of plants, all unusual. One of them is perhaps the most bizarre of all plants, *Welwitschia*, shown in figure 22.14c, which grows on the exposed sands of the harsh Namibian Desert of southwestern Africa. *Welwitschia* acts like a plant standing on its head! Its two beltlike, leathery leaves are generated continuously from their base, splitting as they grow out over the desert sands. There is only one living species of ginkgo, the maidenhair tree, which has fan-shaped leaves (shown in figure 22.14d) that are shed in the autumn. Because ginkgos are resistant to air pollution, they are commonly planted along city streets.

The fossil record indicates that members of the ginkgo phylum were once widely distributed, particularly in the Northern Hemisphere; today, only one living species, the maidenhair tree (*Ginkgo biloba*), remains. The reproductive structures of ginkgos are produced on separate trees. The fleshy outer coverings of the seeds of female ginkgo plants exude the foul smell of rancid butter caused by butyric and isobutyric acids. In many Asian countries, however, the seeds are considered a delicacy. In Western countries, because of the seed odor, male plants that are vegetatively propagated are preferred for cultivation.

The Life of a Gymnosperm

We will examine conifers as typical gymnosperms. The conifer life cycle is illustrated in figure 22.15. Conifer trees form two kinds of cones. Seed cones ❸ contain the female gametophytes, with their egg cells; pollen cones ❶ contain pollen grains. Conifer pollen grains ❷ are small and light and are carried by the wind to seed cones. Because it is very unlikely that any particular pollen grain will succeed in being carried to a seed cone (the wind can take it anywhere), a great many pollen grains are produced to be sure that at least a few succeed in pollinating seed cones. For this reason, pollen grains are shed from their cones in huge quantities, often appearing as a sticky yellow layer on the surfaces of ponds and lakes—and even on windshields.

When a grain of pollen settles down on a scale of a female cone, a slender tube grows out of the pollen cell up into the scale, delivering the male gamete (sperm cell in ❺) to the female gametophyte containing the egg, or ovum. Fertilization occurs when the sperm cell fuses with the egg, forming a zygote that develops into an embryo. This zygote is the beginning of the sporophyte generation. What happens next is the essential improvement in reproduction achieved by

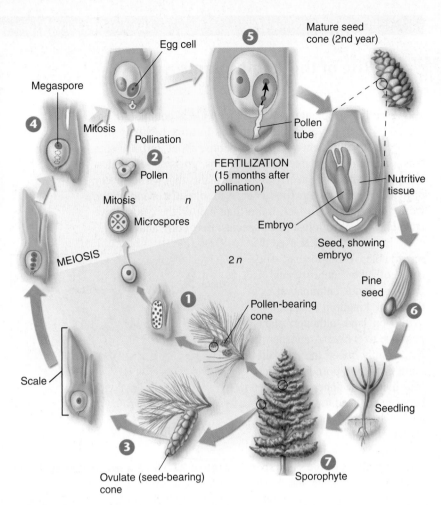

Figure 22.15 Life cycle of a conifer.
In all seed plants, the gametophyte generation is greatly reduced. In conifers such as pines, the relatively delicate pollen-bearing cones ❶ contain microspores, which give rise to pollen grains ❷, the male gametophytes. The familiar seed-bearing cones of pines ❸ are much heavier and more substantial structures than the pollen-bearing cones. Two ovules, and ultimately two seeds, are borne on the upper surface of each scale, which contains the megaspores that give rise to the female gametophytes ❹. After a pollen grain has reached a scale, it germinates, and a slender pollen tube grows toward the egg. When the pollen tube grows to the vicinity of the female gametophyte, sperm are released ❺, fertilizing the egg and producing a zygote there. The development of the zygote into an embryo takes place within the ovule, which matures into a seed ❻. Eventually, the seed falls from the cone and germinates, the embryo resuming growth and becoming a new pine tree ❼.

seed plants. Instead of the zygote growing immediately into an adult sporophyte—just as you grew directly into an adult from a fertilized zygote—the fertilized ovule forms a seed ❻. The pine seed contains a sail-like structure that helps the seed be carried by the wind. The seed can then be dispersed into new habitats. If conditions are favorable where the seed lands, it will germinate and begin to grow, forming a new sporophyte plant ❼.

> **22.7 Gymnosperms are seed plants in which the ovules are not completely enclosed by diploid tissue at pollination. Gymnosperms do not have flowers.**

22.8 Rise of the Angiosperms

Angiosperms are plants in which the ovule is completely enclosed by sporophyte tissue when it is fertilized. Ninety percent of all living plants are angiosperms, about 250,000 species, including many trees, shrubs, herbs, grasses, vegetables, and grains—in short, nearly all of the plants that we see every day. Virtually all of our food is derived, directly or indirectly, from angiosperms. In fact, more than half of the calories we consume come from just three species: rice, corn, and wheat.

In a very real sense, the remarkable evolutionary success of the angiosperms is the apparent culmination of the plant kingdom's adaptation to life on land, although plants continue to evolve. Angiosperms successfully meet the last difficult challenge posed by terrestrial living: the inherent conflict between the need to obtain nutrients (solved by roots, which anchor the plant to one place) and the need to find mates (solved by accessing plants of the same species). This challenge has never really been overcome by gymnosperms, whose pollen grains are carried passively by the wind on the chance that they might by luck encounter a female cone. Think about how inefficient this is! Angiosperms are also able to deliver their pollen directly, as if in an addressed envelope, from one individual of a species to another. How? *By inducing insects and other animals to carry it for them!* The tool that makes this animal-dictated pollination possible, the great advance of the angiosperms, is the flower. While some very successful later-evolving angiosperms like grasses have reverted to wind pollination, the directed pollination of flowering plants has led to phenomenal evolutionary success.

The Flower

Flowers are the reproductive organs of angiosperm plants. A flower is a sophisticated pollination machine. It employs bright colors to attract the attention of insects (or birds or small mammals), nectar to induce the insect to enter the flower, and structures that coat the insect with pollen grains while it is visiting. Then, when the insect visits another flower, it carries the pollen with it into that flower.

The basic structure of a flower consists of four concentric circles, or **whorls,** connected to a base called the **receptacle:**

1. The outermost whorl, called the **sepals** of the flower, typically serves to protect the flower from physical damage. These are the green leaflike structures in figure 22.16*a* and are in effect modified leaves that protect the flower while it is a bud. The sepals can be

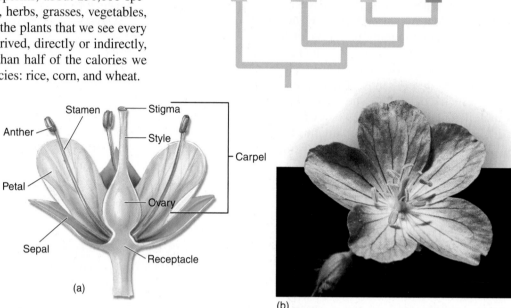

Figure 22.16 An angiosperm flower.

(a) The basic structure of a flower is a series of four concentric circles, or whorls: the sepals, petals, stamens, and the carpel (ovary, style, and stigma), also seen in (b) the wild woodland plant *Geranium*.

seen surrounding the flower bud to the lower left of the flower in figure 22.16*b*.

2. The second whorl, called the **petals** of the flower, serves to attract specific pollinators. Petals have particular pigments, often vividly colored like the light purple color in figure 22.16.
3. The third whorl, called the **stamens** of the flower, contains the "male" parts that produce the pollen grains. Stamens are the slender, threadlike filaments in figure 22.16 with a swollen **anther** at the tip containing pollen.
4. The fourth and innermost whorl, called the **carpel** of the flower, contains the "female" parts that produce eggs. The carpel is the vase-shaped structure in figure 22.16. The carpel is sporophyte tissue that completely encases the ovules within which the egg cell develops. The ovules occur in the bulging lower portion of the carpel, called the **ovary;** usually there is a slender stalk rising from the ovary called the **style,** with a sticky tip called a **stigma,** which receives pollen. When the flower is pollinated, a pollen tube grows down from the pollen grain on the stigma through the style to the ovary to fertilize the egg.

22.8 Angiosperms are seed plants in which the ovule is completely enclosed by diploid tissue at pollination.

22.9 Why Are There Different Kinds of Flowers?

If you were to watch insects visiting flowers, you would quickly discover that the visits are not random. Instead, certain insects are attracted by particular flowers. Insects recognize a particular color pattern and odor and search for flowers that are similar. Insects and plants have coevolved (see chapters 24 and 37) so that certain insects specialize in visiting particular kinds of flowers. As a result, a particular insect carries pollen from one individual flower to another *of the same species*. It is this keying to particular species that makes insect pollination so effective.

Of all insect pollinators, the most numerous are bees. Bees evolved soon after flowering plants, some 125 million years ago. Today there are over 20,000 species. Bees locate sources of nectar largely by odor at first (that is why flowers smell sweet) and then focus in on the flower's color and shape. Bee-pollinated flowers are usually yellow or blue, like the yellow flower in figure 22.17a. They frequently have guiding stripes or lines of dots to indicate the position in the flower of the nectar, usually in the throat of the flower, but these markings may not always be visible to the human eye. For example, the yellow flower in figure 22.17a looks very different through an ultraviolet filter in figure 22.17b. The UV rays show a dark area in the middle of the flower, where the nectar is located. Why have hidden signals? Because they are not hidden from bees that can detect UV rays. While inside the flower, the bee becomes coated with pollen, as in figure 22.17c. When the bee leaves this flower and visits another, it takes the pollen along for the ride, pollinating a neighboring flower.

Many other insects pollinate flowers. Butterflies tend to visit flowers of plants like phlox that have "landing platforms" on which they can perch. These flowers typically have long, slender floral tubes filled with nectar that a butterfly can reach by uncoiling its long proboscis (a hoselike tube extending out from the mouth). Moths, which visit flowers at night, are attracted to white or very pale-colored flowers, often heavily scented, that are easy to locate in dim light. Flowers pollinated by flies, such as members of the milkweed family, are usually brownish in color and foul smelling.

Red flowers, interestingly, are not typically visited by insects, most of which cannot "see" red as a distinct color. Who pollinates these flowers? Hummingbirds and sunbirds (figure 22.18)! To these birds, red is a very conspicuous color, just as it is to us. Birds do not have a well-developed sense of smell, and do not orient to odor, which is why red flowers often do not have a strong smell.

Some angiosperms have reverted to the wind pollination practiced by their ancestors, notably oaks, birches, and, most important, the grasses. The flowers of these plants are small, greenish, and odorless. Other angiosperm species are aquatic, and while some have developed specialized pollination systems where the pollen is transported underwater or floats from one plant to another, most aquatic angiosperms are either wind pollinated or insect pollinated like their terrestrial ancestors. Their flowers extend up above the surface of the water.

Figure 22.17 How a bee sees a flower.
(a) A yellow flower photographed in normal light and (b) with a filter that selectively transmits ultraviolet light. The outer sections of the petals reflect both yellow and ultraviolet, a mixture of colors called "bee's purple"; the inner portions of the petals reflect yellow only and therefore appear dark in the photograph that emphasizes ultraviolet reflection. To a bee, this flower appears as if it has a conspicuous central bull's-eye. (c) When inside the flower, the bee becomes covered in pollen, which it takes to a neighboring flower.

Figure 22.18 Red flowers are pollinated by hummingbirds.
This long-tailed hermit hummingbird is extracting nectar from the red flowers of *Heliconia imbricata* in the forests of Costa Rica. Note the pollen on the bird's beak.

22.9 Flowers can be viewed as pollinator-attracting devices, with different kinds of pollinators attracted to different kinds of flowers.

Improving Seeds: Double Fertilization

The seeds of gymnosperms often contain food to nourish the developing plant in the critical time immediately after germination, but the seeds of angiosperms have greatly improved on this aspect of seed function. Angiosperms produce a special, highly nutritious tissue called **endosperm** within their seeds. Here is how it happens. The angiosperm life cycle is presented in figure 22.19, but there are actually two parts to the cycle, a male and a female part, indicated by the two sets of arrows at the top of the cycle. We'll begin with the flower of the sporophyte on the left side of the cycle ❶. The development of the male gametophyte (the pollen grain) occurs in the anthers and is indicated in the upper set of arrows. The anthers are shown in cross section in ❷ so you can see the microspores mother cells that develop into pollen grains. The pollen grain contains two haploid sperm. Upon adhering to the stigma at the top of the carpel (the female organ in where the egg cell is produced), the pollen begins to form a pollen tube ❹. The yellow pollen tube grows down into the carpel until it reaches the ovule in the ovary ❺. The two sperm (the small purplish cells) travel down the pollen tube and into the ovary. The first sperm fuses with the egg (the green cell at the base of the ovary), as in all sexually reproducing organisms, forming the zygote that develops into the embryo. The other sperm cell fuses with two other products of meiosis, called polar nuclei, to form a triploid (three copies of the chromosomes, $3n$) endosperm cell. This cell divides much more rapidly than the zygote, giving rise to the nutritive endosperm tissue within the seed (the tan material surrounding the embryo ❻). This process of fertilization with two sperm to produce both a zygote and endosperm is called **double fertilization.** Double fertilization forming endosperm is exclusive to angiosperms.

In some angiosperms, such as the common pea or bean, the endosperm is fully used up by the time the seed is mature. Food reserves are stored by the embryo in swollen, fleshy leaves called cotyledons, or seed leaves. In other angiosperms, such as corn, the mature seed contains abundant endosperm, which is used after germination. It also contains a cotyledon, but its seed leaf is used to protect the plant during germination and not as a food source.

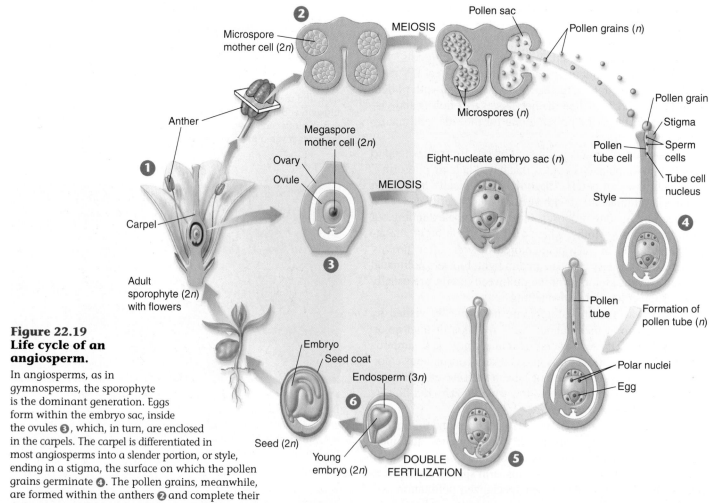

Figure 22.19
Life cycle of an angiosperm.

In angiosperms, as in gymnosperms, the sporophyte is the dominant generation. Eggs form within the embryo sac, inside the ovules ❸, which, in turn, are enclosed in the carpels. The carpel is differentiated in most angiosperms into a slender portion, or style, ending in a stigma, the surface on which the pollen grains germinate ❹. The pollen grains, meanwhile, are formed within the anthers ❷ and complete their differentiation to the mature, three-celled stage either before or after grains are shed. Fertilization is distinctive in angiosperms, being a double process ❺. A sperm and an egg come together, producing a zygote; at the same time, another sperm fuses with the two polar nuclei, producing the primary endosperm nucleus, which is triploid. The zygote and the primary endosperm nucleus divide mitotically, giving rise, respectively, to the embryo and the endosperm ❻. The endosperm is the tissue, almost exclusive to angiosperms, that nourishes the embryo and young plant.

Some angiosperm embryos have two cotyledons, and are called *dicotyledons,* or **dicots.** The first angiosperms were like this. Dicots typically have leaves with netlike branching of veins and flowers with four to five parts per whorl (figure 22.20, *top*). Oak and maple trees are dicots, as are many shrubs.

The embryos of other angiosperms, which evolved somewhat later, have a single cotyledon and are called *monocotyledons,* or **monocots.** Monocots typically have leaves with parallel veins and flowers with three parts per whorl (figure 22.20, *bottom*). Grasses, one of the most abundant of all plants, are wind-pollinated monocots. There are also differences in the organization of vascular tissue in the stems of monocots and dicots, which will be compared in more detail in chapter 23.

> **22.10** Two sperm fertilize each angiosperm ovule. One fuses with the egg to form the zygote, the other with two polar nuclei to form triploid (3*n*) nutritious endosperm.

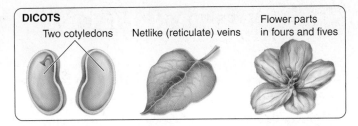

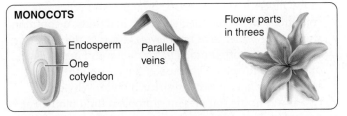

Figure 22.20 Dicots and monocots.
Dicots have two cotyledons and netlike (reticulate) veins. Their flower parts occur in fours and fives. Monocots are characterized by one cotyledon, parallel veins, and the occurrence of flower parts in threes (or multiples of three).

22.11 Improving Seed Dispersal: Fruits

Just as a mature ovule becomes a seed, so a mature ovary that surrounds the ovule becomes all or a part of the **fruit.** This is why fruit forms in angiosperm and not in gymnosperm. Compare the life cycles of the gymnosperm in figure 22.15 and that of the angiosperm in figure 22.19. Both types of plants have tissue that surrounds the egg, called the ovule. The ovule becomes the seed in both. But, in the angiosperm life cycle, you will notice that the ovule is surrounded by another layer of tissue, the ovary, which develops into the fruit. A fruit is a mature ripened ovary containing fertilized seeds. Fruits provide angiosperms with a second way of dispersing their progeny than simply sending their seeds off on the wind. Just as in pollination, they employ animals. By making fruits fleshy and tasty to animals, like the berries in figure 22.21*a,* angiosperms encourage animals to eat them. The seeds within the fruit are resistant to chewing and digestion. They pass out of the animal with the feces, undamaged and ready to germinate at a new location far from the parent plant.

Although many fruits are dispersed by animals, some fruits are dispersed by water, like the coconut in figure 22.21*b,* and many plant fruits are specialized for wind dispersal. The small, nonfleshy fruits of the dandelion, for example, have a plumelike structure that allows them to be carried long distances on wind currents. The fruits of many grasses are small particles, so light wind bears them easily. Maples have long wings attached to the fruit, as in figure 22.21*c,* that allows them to be carried by the wind before reaching the ground. In tumbleweeds, the whole plant breaks off and is blown across open country by the wind, scattering seeds as it rolls. Fruits will be discussed in more detail in chapter 24.

> **22.11** A fruit is a mature ovary containing fertilized seeds, often specialized to aid in seed dispersal.

(a)   (b)   (c)

Figure 22.21 Different ways of dispersing fruits.
(*a*) Berries are fruits that are dispersed by animals. (*b*) Coconuts are fruits dispersed by water, where they are carried off to new island habitats. (*c*) The fruits of maples are dry and winged, carried by the wind like small helicopters floating through the air.

How Does Arrowgrass Tolerate Salt?

Plants grow almost everywhere on earth, thriving in many places where exposure, drought, and other severe conditions challenge their survival. In deserts, a common stress is the presence of high levels of salt in the soils. Soil salinity is also a problem for millions of acres of abandoned farmland because of the accumulation of salt from irrigation water restricts growth. Why does excess salt in the soil present a problem for a plant? For one thing, high levels of sodium ion that are taken up by the roots are toxic. For another, a plant's roots cannot obtain water when growing in salty soil. Osmosis (the movement of water molecules to areas of higher solute concentrations, see page 99) causes water to move in the opposite direction, drawn out of the roots by the soil's high levels of salt. And yet plants do grow in these soils. How do they manage?

To investigate this, researchers have studied seaside arrowgrass (*Triglochin maritima*), the plant you see below. Arrowgrass plants are able to grow in very salty seashore soils, where few other plants survive. How are they able to survive? Researchers found that their roots do not take up salt, and so do not accumulate toxic levels of salt.

However, this still leaves the arrowgrass plant the challenge of preventing its root cells from losing water to the surrounding salty soil. How then do the roots achieve osmotic balance? In an attempt to find out, researchers grew arrowgrass plants in nonsalty soil for two weeks, then transferred them to one of several soils which differed in salt level. After ten days, shoots were harvested and analyzed for amino acids, because accumulating amino acids could be one way that the cells maintain osmotic balance. Results are presented in the graph.

1. **Applying Concepts**
   a. Variable. What is the dependent variable?
   b. Concentration. What do the abbreviations "mM" and "mmol/Kg" mean?

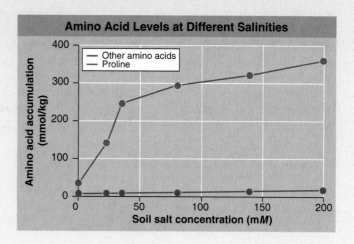

2. **Interpreting Data**
   a. In salt-free soil (that is, the mM soil salt concentration = 0), how much proline has accumulated in the roots after ten days? How much of other amino acids?

   b. In salty beach soils with salt levels of 35 mM, how much proline has accumulated in the roots after ten days? How much of other amino acids?

3. **Making Inferences**
   a. In general, what is the effect of soil salt concentration on arrowgrass plant's accumulation of the amino acid proline? of other amino acids?
   b. Is the effect of salt on proline accumulation the same at low salt (below 50 mM) as at high salt (above 50 mM)?

4. **Drawing Conclusions** Are these results consistent with the hypothesis that arrowgrass accumulates proline to achieve osmotic balance with salty soils?

5. **Further Analysis** What do you think might account for the different rates of proline accumulation in low-salt and high-salt soils? Can you think of a way to test this hypothesis?

Plants

22.1 Adapting to Terrestrial Living

- Plants are complex multicellular autotrophs, producing their own food through photosynthesis.

- Plants acquire water and minerals from the soil. They control water loss through a watertight layer called the cuticle. Openings, called stomata, allow for gas exchange with the air (**figure 22.2**).

- The adaptation of pollen allowed land plants to transfer gametes on land under dry conditions. The pollen grain protects the gamete from drying out. Plant life cycles involve an alternation of generations where a haploid gametophyte alternates with a diploid sporophyte, with the sporophyte dominating the life cycle more and more as plants evolved (**figure 22.3**).

22.2 Plant Evolution

- Plants evolved from green algae, helped by four innovations: an alternation of generations life cycle, vascular tissue, seeds, and flower and fruits (**figure 22.5** and **table 22.1**).

- In an alternation of generations, the plant spends a portion of its life in a multicellular haploid phase that produces gametes and another portion in a multicellular diploid phase. As plants evolved, the diploid sporophyte became a more dominant structure, both in size and in its duration of time in the life cycle.

- The evolution of vascular tissue allowed plants to transport water and minerals from the ground and up through their bodies, distributing food throughout the plant and allowing them to grow taller.

- Seeds provide protection and nutrients for the developing embryo. Flowers and fruits improve the chances of successful mating and the distribution of seeds.

Seedless Plants

22.3 Nonvascular Plants

- Liverworts and hornworts don't have vascular tissue. Mosses have specialized cells for conducting water and carbohydrates in the plant, but not rigid vascular tissue. These plants are grouped together as nonvascular plants. Their life cycles are dominated by the haploid gametophyte (**figure 22.6**).

22.4 The Evolution of Vascular Tissue

- Vascular tissue consists of specialized cylindrical or elongated cells that form a network throughout the plant. These cells conduct water from the roots and carbohydrates manufactured in the leaves throughout the plant (**figure 22.8**).

22.5 Seedless Vascular Plants

- Among the most primitive vascular plants are the Pterophyta (ferns) and Lycophyta (**figure 22.9**). These plants can grow very tall due to vascularization, but they lack seeds and require water for fertilization. The sporophyte, shown here from **figure 22.10**, is larger than its gametophyte.

The Advent of Seeds

22.6 Evolution of Seed Plants

- In seed plants, the sporophyte becomes the dominant structure in the life cycle. The plants contain separate male and female gametophytes. The male gametophyte, called a pollen grain, produces sperm which are carried to the egg, which is contained in the small female gametophyte. Pollination in seed plants doesn't require water.

- The seed was an evolutionary innovation that provided protection for the plant embryo. The seed contains the embryo and food inside a drought-resistant cover (**figure 22.12**). Seeds are a key adaptation to land-dwelling plants because they improve the dispersal of embryos, allow dormancy when needed, germinate when conditions are favorable, and provide nourishment during germination.

22.7 Gymnosperms

- Gymnosperms are nonflowering seed plants and include conifers, cycads, gnetophytes, and the ginkgo. The seeds are produced in cones where pollination occurs. Pollen, produced in smaller cones, travels by wind to the seed-bearing cones, where fertilization of the egg takes place. The ovules are not completely enclosed by diploid tissue, as is the case with flowering plants. The seed, like the one shown here from **figure 22.15**, disperses the embryo.

The Evolution of Flowers

22.8 Rise of the Angiosperms

- Angiosperms, flowering plants, are plants in which the ovule is completely enclosed by sporophyte tissue.

- The flowers are the reproductive structures. The basic structure of a flower includes four concentric whorls, shown here from **figure 22.16**. The outermost green sepals protect the flower. Next, the colorful petals attract pollinators. The third whorl contains the stalklike stamen with the pollen-bearing anthers. The innermost whorl is a vaselike structure called the carpel that contains the egg within the ovary. Flowers improved the efficiency of mating.

22.9 Why Are There Different Kinds of Flowers?

- Flowers vary greatly in size, shape, and color so that they are identifiable by a particular pollinator. This improves the likelihood that the pollen will be carried to the appropriate mate (**figures 22.17** and **22.18**).

22.10 Improving Seeds: Double Fertilization

- Double fertilization provides food for the germinating plant. The pollen grain produces two sperm cells that travel through the pollen tube, as shown here from **figure 22.19**. One fuses with the egg, and the other fuses with two polar nuclei, producing triploid endosperm. The angiosperms are divided into two groups: monocots and dicots (**figure 22.20**).

22.11 Improving Seed Dispersal: Fruits

- A further advancement in angiosperms was the development of the ovary into fruit tissue. Fruits aid in the dispersal of seeds to new habitats (**figure 22.21**).

1. A major consideration for the evolution of terrestrial plants is the problem of
   a. lack of nutrients.
   c. dehydration.
   b. predators.
   d. not enough carbon.

2. Which of the following structures or systems was *not* an emergent property in plant evolution?
   a. chloroplasts
   c. seeds
   b. vascular tissue
   d. flowers and fruits

3. Mosses, liverworts, and hornworts do not reach a large size because
   a. they lack chlorophyll.
   b. they do not have specialized vascular tissue to transport water very high.
   c. photosynthesis does not take place at a very fast rate.
   d. alternation of generations does not allow the plants to grow very tall before reproduction.

4. One characteristic that separates ferns from complex vascular plants is that ferns do not have
   a. a vascular system.
   b. chloroplasts.
   c. alternation of generations in their life cycle.
   d. seeds.

5. As seed plants evolved, the _____ form became more visible.
   a. gametophyte
   c. sporophyte
   b. gymnosperm
   d. angiosperm

6. In seeds, the seed coat aids in
   a. germination.
   c. nourishment.
   b. photosynthesis.
   d. dispersal.

7. What separates the gymnosperms from the rest of the vascular plants is/are
   a. a vascular system.
   b. ovules completely covered by the gametophyte.
   c. ovules not completely covered by the sporophyte.
   d. fruits and flowers.

8. What separates the angiosperms from the rest of the vascular plants is/are
   a. a vascular system.
   b. ovules completely covered by the gametophyte.
   c. fruits and flowers.
   d. ovules not completely covered by the sporophyte.

9. Flower shape and color can be linked to the process of
   a. pollination.
   c. seed dispersal.
   b. photosynthesis.
   d. secondary growth.

10. If the seeds of a plant are encased in a fleshy fruit, then the most likely form of dispersal is
    a. to attach to an animal's fur or skin.
    b. wind.
    c. an animal's digestive system and processes.
    d. water.

Visual Understanding

1. **Figure 22.5** Explain which key innovation leads to the evolution of each group and why the innovation was significant.

2. **Figure 22.12** When farmers harvest corn, soybeans, wheat, and rice, they collect the seeds and get rid of the rest of the plant. Why do we eat the seeds rather than the stems or roots of these plants? *Hint:* Think about the purpose of a seed in the life cycle of the plant.

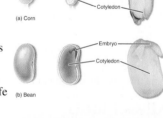

3. **Figure 22.13** These seeds fall from the tree and are scattered about on the ground nearby. What are the benefits or drawbacks to having:
   (*a*) chemicals in the seed to inhibit sprouting, and
   (*b*) hard seed coats?

Challenge Questions

1. Why do most plant pollinators have wings?
2. Why are mosses limited to moist places?
3. Why does a pine tree, which might live more than 100 years, produce hundreds of pine cones each year, each with 30 to 50 seeds?

4. Your friend, Jessica, is admiring the wildflowers one spring day, and wonders aloud why in the world plants evolved such beautiful colors and shapes and produce such wonderful scents. What do you tell her?

25

Evolution of the Animal Phyla

A nimals are the most diverse in appearance of all eukaryotes. *Polistes,* the common paper wasp you see here, is a member of the most diverse of all animal groups, the insects. It has been a major challenge for biologists to sort out the millions of kinds of animals. This wasp has a segmented external skeleton and jointed appendages, and so, based on these characteristics, is classified as an arthropod. But how are arthropods related to mollusks such as snails, and to segmented worms like earthworms? Until recently, biologists grouped all three kinds of animals together, as they all share a coelom body cavity, a character assumed to be so fundamental it could have evolved only once. Now, molecular analyses suggest this assumption may be wrong. Instead, mollusks and segmented worms are grouped together with other animals that grow the same way you do, by adding additional mass to an existing body, while arthropods are grouped with other molting animals. These animals increase in size by molting their external skeletons, an ability that seems to have evolved only once. Thus we learn that even in a long-established field like taxonomy, biology is constantly changing.

25.1 General Features of Animals

As best as biologists can determine, we and all other animals evolved from a kind of protist called a choanoflagellate, which as you may recall from chapter 20 is thought to have given rise to sponges. From these early animal ancestors, a great diversity of animals has since evolved. While the evolutionary relationships among the different types of animals are being debated (see section 25.2), all animals have several features in common (table 25.1): (1) Animals are heterotrophs and must ingest plants, algae, or other animals for nourishment. (2) All animals are multicellular, and unlike plants and protists, animal cells lack cell walls. (3) Animals are able to move from place to place. (4) Animals are very diverse in form and habitat. (5) Most animals reproduce sexually. (6) Animals have characteristic tissues and patterns of embryonic development.

> **25.1 Animals are complex, multicellular, heterotrophic organisms. Most animals also possess internal tissues.**

TABLE 25.1	**GENERAL FEATURES OF ANIMALS**

Heterotrophs. Unlike autotrophic plants and algae, animals cannot construct organic molecules from inorganic chemicals. All animals are heterotrophs—that is, they obtain energy and organic molecules by ingesting other organisms. Some animals (herbivores) consume autotrophs, other animals (carnivores) consume heterotrophs; others, like the bear to the right, are omnivores that eat both autotrophs and heterotrophs, and still others (detritivores) consume decomposing organisms.

Multicellular. All animals are multicellular, often with complex bodies like that of this brittlestar (*right*). The unicellular heterotrophic organisms called protozoa, which were at one time regarded as simple animals, are now considered members of the large and diverse kingdom Protista, discussed in chapter 20.

No Cell Walls. Animal cells are distinct among those of multicellular organisms because they lack rigid cell walls and are usually quite flexible, like these cancer cells. The many cells of animal bodies are held together by extracellular lattices of structural proteins such as collagen. Other proteins form a collection of unique intercellular junctions between animal cells.

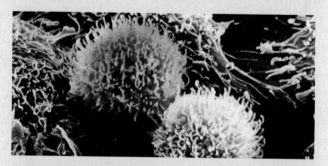

Active Movement. The ability of animals to move more rapidly and in more complex ways than members of other kingdoms is perhaps their most striking characteristic, one that is directly related to the flexibility of their cells and the evolution of nerve and muscle tissues. A remarkable form of movement unique to animals is flying, an ability that is well developed among vertebrates and insects like this butterfly. The only terrestrial vertebrate group never to have evolved flight is amphibians.

TABLE 25.1 *(continued)*

Diverse in Form. Almost all animals (99%) are **invertebrates,** which, like this millipede, lack a backbone. Of the estimated 10 million living animal species, only 42,500 have a backbone and are referred to as **vertebrates.** Animals are very diverse in form, ranging in size from organisms too small to see with the unaided eye to enormous whales and giant squids.

Diverse in Habitat. The animal kingdom includes about 35 phyla, most of which, like these jellyfish (phylum Cnidaria), occur in the sea. Far fewer phyla occur in freshwater and fewer still occur on land. Members of three successful marine phyla, Arthropoda (insects), Mollusca (snails), and Chordata (vertebrates), dominate animal life on land.

Sexual Reproduction. Most animals reproduce sexually, as these tortoises are doing. Animal eggs, which are nonmotile, are much larger than the small, usually flagellated sperm. In animals, cells formed in meiosis function directly as gametes. The haploid cells do not divide by mitosis first, as they do in plants and fungi, but rather fuse directly with each other to form the zygote. Consequently, with a few exceptions, there is no counterpart among animals to the alternation of haploid (gametophyte) and diploid (sporophyte) generations characteristic of plants.

Embryonic Development. Most animals have a similar pattern of embryonic development. The zygote first undergoes a series of mitotic divisions, called *cleavage,* and, like this dividing frog egg, becomes a solid ball of cells, the **morula,** then a hollow ball of cells, the **blastula.** In most animals, the blastula folds inward at one point to form a hollow sac with an opening at one end called the **blastopore.** An embryo at this stage is called a **gastrula.** The subsequent growth and movement of the cells of the gastrula differ widely from one phylum of animals to another.

Unique Tissues. The cells of all animals except sponges are organized into structural and functional units called **tissues,** collections of cells that have joined together and are specialized to perform a specific function. Animals are unique in having two tissues associated with movement: (1) muscle tissue, which powers animal movement, and (2) nervous tissue, which conducts signals among cells. Neuromuscular junctions, where nerves connect with muscle tissue, are shown here.

The Animal Family Tree

The features described in the previous section evolved over millions of years. And indeed the great diversity of animals today is the result of this long evolutionary journey. The multicellular animals, or metazoans, are traditionally divided into 35 distinct and very different phyla. How these phyla are related to each other has been the source of much discussion among biologists.

The Traditional Viewpoint

Taxonomists have traditionally attempted to create animal **phylogenies** (family trees; see section 18.5) by comparing anatomical features and aspects of embryological development. A broad consensus emerged over the last century about the main branches of the animal family tree.

The First Branch: Tissues The kingdom Animalia is traditionally divided by taxonomists into two main branches: **Parazoa** ("beside animals")—animals that for the most part lack a definite symmetry and possess neither tissues nor organs, mostly composed of the sponges, phylum Porifera, and **Eumetazoa** ("true animals")—animals that have a definite shape and symmetry and, in most cases, tissues organized into organs and organ systems (see section 1.3). In figure 25.1, all animals shown to the right of Parazoa are eumetazoans. Although very different in structure, the two subkingdoms are thought to be monophyletic, that is, to have evolved from a common ancestral form. All the branches in the animal family tree trace back to one ancestor at the base of the phylogeny. This shared ancestor was probably a choanoflagellate, a colo-

nial flagellated protist that lived in the Precambrian era over 700 million years ago.

The Second Branch: Symmetry The eumetazoan branch of the animal family tree itself has two principal branches, differing in the nature of the embryonic layers that form during development and go on to differentiate into the tissues of the adult animal. Eumetazoans of the subgroup **Radiata** (having radial symmetry) have two layers, an outer *ectoderm* and an inner *endoderm,* and thus are called diploblastic. All other eumetazoans are the **Bilateria** (having bilateral symmetry) and are triploblastic, producing a third layer, the *mesoderm,* between the ectoderm and endoderm.

Further Branches Further branches of the animal family tree were assigned by taxonomists by comparing traits that seemed profoundly important to the evolutionary history of phyla, key features of the body plan shared by all animals belonging to that branch. Thus, the bilaterally symmetrical animals were split into groups with a body cavity and those without (acoelomates); animals with a body cavity were split into those with a true coelom (body cavity enclosed by mesoderm) and those without (the pseudocoelomates); animals with a coelom were split into those whose coelom derived from the digestive tube and those that did not, and so on.

Because of the either-or nature of the categories set up by traditional taxonomists, this approach has produced a family tree like the one in figure 25.1, with a lot of paired branches. The arbitrary nature of the divisions has always been obvious to biologists, but in spite of that, most biologists feel that it faithfully represents the general nature of the evolutionary history of metazoans.

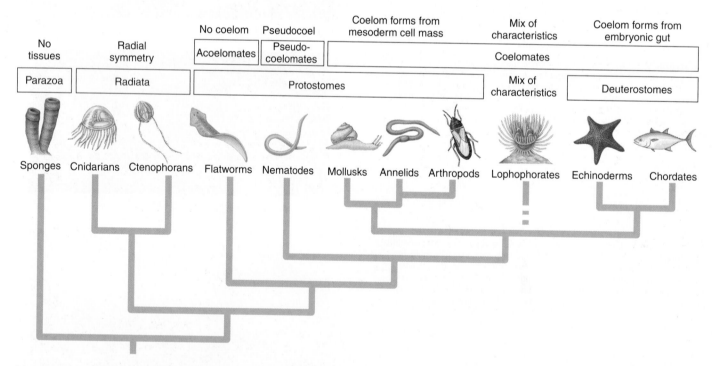

Figure 25.1 The animal family tree: The traditional viewpoint.
Biologists have traditionally divided the animals into 35 distinct phyla. The diagram above illustrates the relationships among some of the major animal phyla. The bilaterally symmetrical animals (those to the right of Radiata in the figure above) are sorted into three groups that differ with respect to their body cavity: acoelomates, pseudocoelomates, and coelomates.

A New Look at the Animal Family Tree

The traditional animal phylogeny, while accepted by a broad consensus of biologists for almost a century, is now being re-evaluated. Its simple either-or organization has always presented certain problems—puzzling minor groups do not fit well into the standard scheme. Results hint strongly that the key body-form characteristics that biologists have traditionally used to construct animal phylogenies—segmentation, coeloms, jointed appendages, and the like—are not the always preserved characters we had supposed. These features appear to have been gained and lost again during the course of the evolution of some unusual animals. If this pattern of change in what had been considered basic characters should prove general, our view of how the various animal phyla relate to one another is in need of major revision.

The last decade has seen a wealth of new molecular RNA and DNA sequence data on the various animal groups. The new field of **molecular systematics** uses unique sequences within certain genes to identify clusters of related groups. Using these sorts of molecular data, a variety of molecular phylogenies have been produced in the last decade. While differing from one another in many important respects, the new molecular phylogenies have the same deep branch structure as the traditional animal family tree (compare the lower branches in the "new" family tree in figure 25.2 with the lower branches in figure 25.1). However, most agree on one revolutionary difference from the traditional phylogeny used in this text and presented in figure 25.1: The protostomes (which have a different pattern of development than the deuterostomes—a topic that will be discussed later in this chapter) are broken into two distinct clades. Figure 25.2 is a consensus molecular phylogeny developed from DNA, ribosomal RNA, and protein studies. In it, the traditional protostome group is broken up into Lophotrochozoa and Ecdysozoa.

Lophotrochozoans are animals that grow by adding mass to an existing body. They are named for a distinctive feeding apparatus called a lophophore found in some phyla of the molecularly-defined group. These animals—which usually live in water, have ciliary locomotion, and trochophore larvae—include flatworms, mollusks, and annelids.

Ecdysozoans have exoskeletons that must be shed for the animal to grow. This sort of molting process is called ecdysis, which is why these animals are called ecdysozoans. They include the roundworms (nematodes) and arthropods. How an animal grows wasn't a key characteristic when classifying animals in the traditional approach, but proves to be an important characteristic when comparing animals molecularly.

This new view of the metazoan Tree of Life is only a rough outline—at present, molecular phylogenetic analysis of the animal kingdom is in its infancy. Phylogenies developed from different molecules sometimes suggest quite different evolutionary relationships. For this reason, in this text you will explore animal diversity guided by the traditional animal family tree. However, the childhood of the new molecular approach is likely to be short. Over the next few years, a mountain of additional molecular data can be anticipated. As more data are brought to bear, the confusion can be expected to lessen and the relationships within groupings more confidently resolved.

> **25.2** Major groups are related in very different ways in molecular phylogenies than in the more traditional approach based on form and structure.

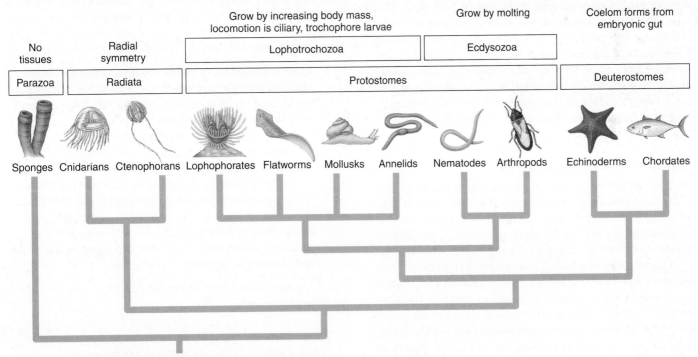

Figure 25.2 The animal family tree: A new look.
New phylogenies suggest that the protostomes might be better grouped according to whether they grow by adding mass to an existing body (Lophotrochozoa) or by molting (Ecdysozoa).

25.3 Five Key Transitions in Body Plan

In the traditional phylogeny, the evolution of animals is marked by five key transitions: the evolution of tissues, bilateral symmetry, a body cavity, deuterostome development, and segmentation. These five body transitions are indicated at the branchpoints of the animal evolutionary tree in figure 25.3.

1. Evolution of Tissues

The simplest animals, the Parazoa, lack both defined tissues and organs. Characterized by the sponges, these animals exist as aggregates of cells with minimal intercellular coordination. All other animals, the Eumetazoa, have distinct tissues with highly specialized cells. The evolution of tissues is the first key transition in the animal body plan.

2. Evolution of Bilateral Symmetry

Sponges also lack any definite symmetry, growing asymmetrically as irregular masses. Virtually all other animals have a definite shape and symmetry that can be defined along an imaginary axis drawn through the animal's body.

Radial Symmetry Symmetrical bodies first evolved in marine animals exhibiting **radial symmetry.** The parts of their bodies are arranged around a central axis in such a way that any plane passing through the central axis divides the organism into halves that are approximate mirror images.

Bilateral Symmetry The bodies of all other animals are marked by a fundamental **bilateral symmetry,** a body design in which the body has a right and a left half that are mirror images of each other. Bilateral symmetry constitutes the second major evolutionary advance in the animal body plan. This unique form of organization allows parts of the body to evolve in different ways, permitting different organs to be located in different parts of the body. Also, bilaterally symmetrical animals move from place to place more efficiently than radially symmetrical ones, which, in general, lead a sessile or passively floating existence. Due to their increased mobility, bilaterally symmetrical animals are efficient in seeking food, locating mates, and avoiding predators.

3. Evolution of a Body Cavity

A third key transition in the evolution of the animal body plan was the evolution of the body cavity. The evolution of efficient organ systems within the animal body was not possible until a body cavity evolved for supporting organs, distributing materials, and fostering complex developmental interactions.

The presence of a body cavity allows the digestive tract to be larger and longer. This longer passage allows for storage of undigested food and longer exposure to enzymes for more complete digestion. Such an arrangement allows an animal to eat a great deal when it is safe to do so and then to hide during the digestive process, thus limiting the animal's exposure to predators. The body cavity architecture is also more flexible, thus allowing the animal greater freedom to move.

An internal body cavity also provides space within which the gonads (ovaries and testes) can expand, allowing the accumulation of large numbers of eggs and sperm. Such storage capacity allows the diverse modifications of breeding strategy that characterize the more advanced phyla of animals. Furthermore, large numbers of gametes can be stored and released when the conditions are as favorable as possible for the survival of the young animals.

4. The Evolution of Deuterostome Development

Bilateral animals can be divided into two groups based on differences in the basic pattern of development. One group is called the **protostomes** (from the Greek words *protos,* first, and *stoma,* mouth) and includes the flatworms, nematodes, mollusks, annelids, and arthropods. Two outwardly dissimilar groups, the echinoderms and the chordates, together with a few other smaller related phyla, comprise the second group, the **deuterostomes** (Greek, *deuteros,* second, and *stoma,* mouth). Protostomes and deuterostomes differ in several aspects of embryo growth and will be discussed later in the chapter.

Deuterostomes evolved from protostomes more than 630 million years ago, and the consistency of deuterostome development, and its distinctiveness from that of the protostomes, suggests that it evolved once, in a common ancestor to all of the phyla that exhibit it.

5. The Evolution of Segmentation

The fifth key transition in the animal body plan involved the subdivision of the body into **segments.** Just as it is efficient for workers to construct a tunnel from a series of identical prefabricated parts, so segmented animals are assembled from a succession of identical segments. During the animal's early development, these segments become most obvious in the mesoderm but later are reflected in the ectoderm and endoderm as well. Two advantages result from early embryonic segmentation:

1. In annelids and other highly segmented animals, each segment may go on to develop a more or less complete set of adult organ systems. Damage to any one segment need not be fatal to the individual, since the other segments duplicate that segment's functions.
2. Locomotion is far more effective when individual segments can move independently because the animal as a whole has more flexibility of movement. Because the separations isolate each segment into an individual skeletal unit, each is able to contract or expand autonomously in response to changes in hydrostatic pressure. Therefore, a long body can move in ways that are often quite complex.

Characteristics of the major animal phyla are described in table 25.2.

25.3 Five key transitions in body design are responsible for most of the differences we see among the major animal phyla.

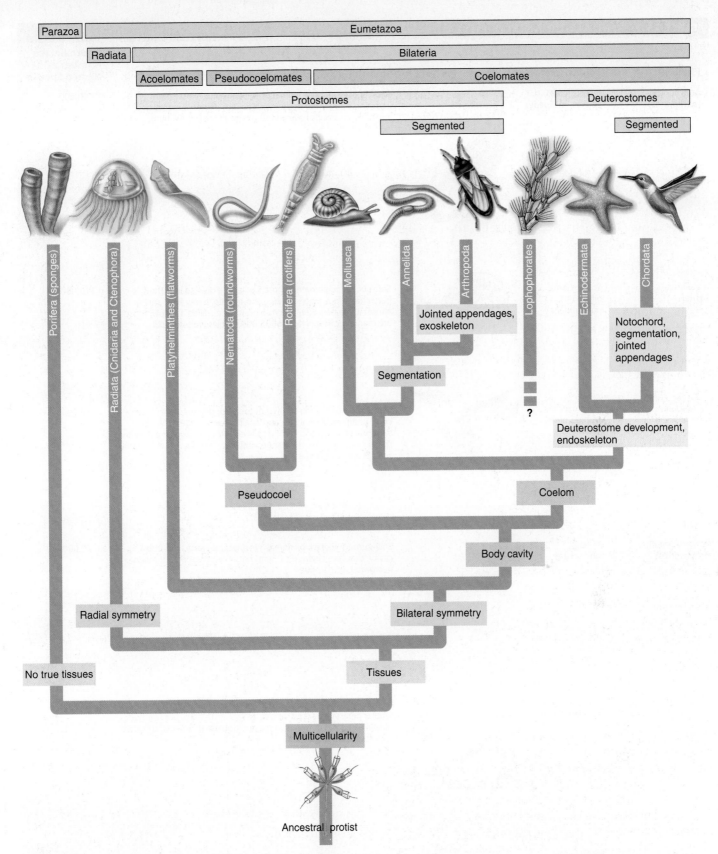

Figure 25.3 Evolutionary trends among the animals.

In this chapter, we examine a series of key evolutionary innovations in the animal body plan, shown here along the branches. Some of the major animal phyla are shown on this tree. Lophophorates is a group that contains two phyla that exhibit a mix of protostome and deuterostome characteristics.

TABLE 25.2   THE MAJOR ANIMAL PHYLA

Phylum	Typical Examples		Key Characteristics	Approximate Number of Named Species
Arthropoda (arthropods)	Insects, crabs, spiders, millipedes		Most successful of all animal phyla; chitinous exoskeleton covering segmented bodies with paired, jointed appendages; most insect groups have wings; nearly all are freshwater or terrestrial	1,000,000
Mollusca (mollusks)	Snails, clams, octopuses, nudibranchs		Soft-bodied coelomates whose bodies are divided into three parts: head-foot, visceral mass, and mantle; many have shells; almost all possess a unique rasping tongue called a radula; most are marine or freshwater but 35,000 species are terrestrial	110,000
Chordata (chordates)	Mammals, fish, reptiles, birds, amphibians		Segmented coelomates with a notochord; possess a dorsal nerve cord, pharyngeal pouches, and a tail at some stage of life; in vertebrates, the notochord is replaced during development by the spinal column; most are marine, many are freshwater, and 20,000 species are terrestrial	56,000
Platyhelminthes (flatworms)	*Planaria*, tapeworms, flukes		Solid, unsegmented, bilaterally symmetrical worms; no body cavity; digestive cavity, if present, has only one opening; marine, freshwater, or parasitic	20,000
Nematoda (roundworms)	*Ascaris*, pinworms, hookworms, *Filaria*		Pseudocoelomate, unsegmented, bilaterally symmetrical worms; tubular digestive tract passing from mouth to anus; tiny; without cilia; live in great numbers in soil and aquatic sediments; some are important animal parasites	20,000
Annelida (segmented worms)	Earthworms, marine worms, leeches		Coelomate, serially segmented, bilaterally symmetrical worms; complete digestive tract; most have bristles called setae on each segment that anchor them during crawling; marine, freshwater, and terrestrial	12,000

TABLE 25.2 *(continued)*

Phylum	Typical Examples	Key Characteristics	Approximate Number of Named Species
Cnidaria (cnidarians)	Jellyfish, hydra, corals, sea anemones	Soft, gelatinous, radially symmetrical bodies whose digestive cavity has a single opening; possess tentacles armed with stinging cells called cnidocytes that shoot sharp harpoons called nematocysts; almost entirely marine	10,000
Echinodermata (echinoderms)	Sea stars, sea urchins, sand dollars, sea cucumbers	Deuterostomes with radially symmetrical adult bodies; endoskeleton of calcium plates; pentamerous (five-part) body plan and unique water vascular system with tube feet; able to regenerate lost body parts; all are marine	6,000
Porifera (sponges)	Barrel sponges, boring sponges, basket sponges, vase sponges	Asymmetrical bodies without distinct tissues or organs; saclike body consists of two layers breached by many pores; internal cavity lined with food-filtering cells called choanocytes; most marine (150 species live in freshwater)	5,150
Lophophorates (Bryozoa, also called moss animals or Ectoprocta)	*Bowerbankia, Plumatella,* sea mats, sea moss	Microscopic, aquatic deuterostomes that form branching colonies, possess circular or U-shaped row of ciliated tentacles for feeding called a lophophore that usually protrudes through pores in a hard exoskeleton; Bryozoa are also called Ectoprocta because the anus, or proct, is external to the lophophore; marine or freshwater	4,000
Rotifera (wheel animals)	Rotifers	Small, aquatic pseudocoelomates with a crown of cilia around the mouth resembling a wheel; almost all live in freshwater	2,000

25.4 Sponges: Animals Without Tissues

The kingdom Animalia consists of two subkingdoms: (1) *Parazoa,* animals that lack a definite symmetry and possess neither tissues nor organs, and (2) *Eumetazoa,* animals that have a definite shape and symmetry, and in most cases tissues organized into organs. The subkingdom Parazoa consists primarily of the sponges, phylum Porifera. The other animals, comprising about 35 phyla, belong to the subkingdom Eumetazoa.

Sponges, members of the phylum Porifera, are the simplest animals. Most sponges completely lack symmetry, and although some of their cells are highly specialized, they are not organized into tissues. The bodies of sponges consist of little more than masses of specialized cells embedded in a gel-like matrix, like chopped fruit in Jell-O. However, sponge cells do possess a key property of animal cells: cell recognition. For example, when a sponge is passed through a fine silk mesh, individual cells separate and then reaggregate on the other side to re-form the sponge. Clumps of cells disassociated from a sponge can give rise to entirely new sponges.

About 5,000 species exist, almost all in the sea. Some are tiny, and others are more than 2 meters in diameter (the diver in figure 25.4*a* could almost crawl inside the sponge shown). The body of an adult sponge is anchored in place on the seafloor and is shaped like a vase (as you can see in figure 25.4*b*). The outside of the sponge is covered with a skin of flattened cells called epithelial cells that protect the sponge.

Figure 25.5 takes you on a tour through a sponge. The body of the sponge is perforated by tiny holes. The name of the phylum, Porifera, refers to this system of pores. Unique flagellated cells called **choanocytes,** or collar cells, line the body cavity of the sponge (see the enlarged drawing of the choanocyte). The beating of the flagella of the many choanocytes draws water in through the pores (indicated by the black arrows) and through the cavity. One cubic centimeter of sponge tissue can propel more than 20 liters of water a day in and out of the sponge body! Why all this moving of water? The sponge is a "filter-feeder." The beating of each choanocyte's flagellum draws water through its collar, made of small hairlike projections resembling a picket fence (you can see this in the enlarged view). Any food particles in the water, such as protists and tiny animals, are trapped in the fence and later ingested by the choanocyte or other cells of the sponge.

The choanocytes of sponges very closely resemble a kind of protist called choanoflagellates (see boxed insert in figure 25.5), which seem almost certain to have been the ancestors of sponges. Indeed, they may be the ancestors of *all* animals, although it is difficult to be certain that sponges are the direct ancestors of the other more complex phyla of animals.

> **25.4** Sponges have a multicellular body with specialized cells but lack definite symmetry and organized tissues.

(a)

(b)

Figure 25.4 Diversity in sponges.

These two marine sponges are barrel sponges. They are among the largest of sponges, with well-organized forms. Many are more than 2 meters in diameter (*a*), while others are smaller (*b*).

Phylum Porifera: Sponges

Key Evolutionary Innovation: MULTICELLULARITY

The body of a sponge (phylum Porifera) is **multicellular**—it contains many cells, of several distinctly different types, whose activities are coordinated with each other. The sponge body is not symmetrical and has no organized tissues.

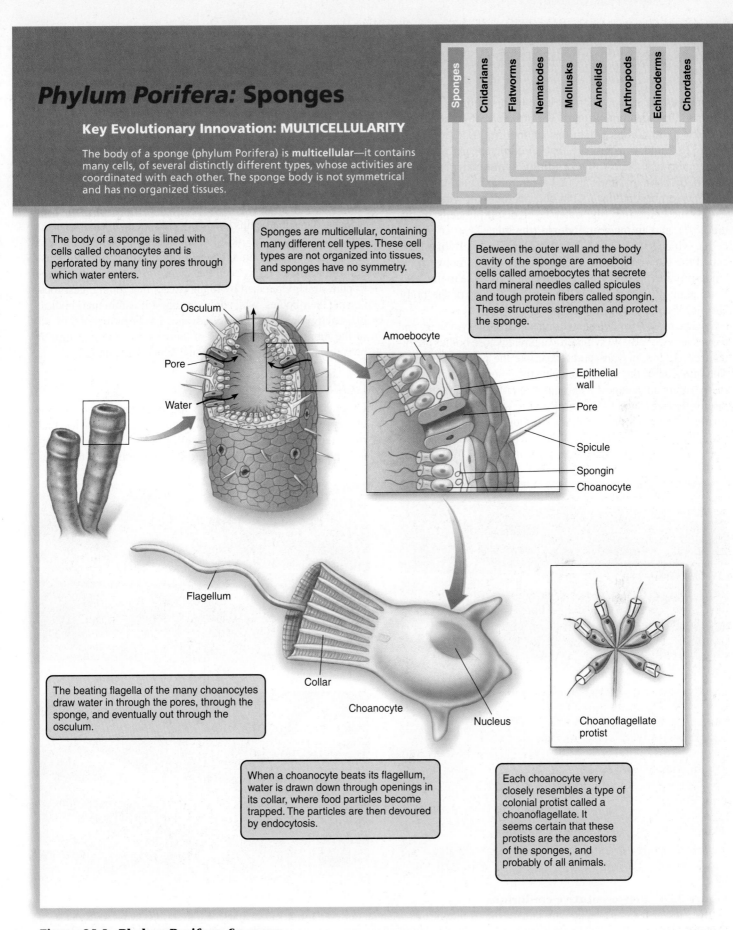

The body of a sponge is lined with cells called choanocytes and is perforated by many tiny pores through which water enters.

Sponges are multicellular, containing many different cell types. These cell types are not organized into tissues, and sponges have no symmetry.

Between the outer wall and the body cavity of the sponge are amoeboid cells called amoebocytes that secrete hard mineral needles called spicules and tough protein fibers called spongin. These structures strengthen and protect the sponge.

Osculum

Pore

Water

Amoebocyte

Epithelial wall

Pore

Spicule

Spongin

Choanocyte

Flagellum

Collar

Choanocyte

Nucleus

Choanoflagellate protist

The beating flagella of the many choanocytes draw water in through the pores, through the sponge, and eventually out through the osculum.

When a choanocyte beats its flagellum, water is drawn down through openings in its collar, where food particles become trapped. The particles are then devoured by endocytosis.

Each choanocyte very closely resembles a type of colonial protist called a choanoflagellate. It seems certain that these protists are the ancestors of the sponges, and probably of all animals.

Sponges | Cnidarians | Flatworms | Nematodes | Mollusks | Annelids | Arthropods | Echinoderms | Chordates

Figure 25.5 Phylum Porifera: Sponges.

25.5 Cnidarians: Tissues Lead to Greater Specialization

All animals other than sponges have both symmetry and tissues and thus are eumetazoans. The structure of eumetazoans is much more complex than that of sponges. Look ahead to figure 25.7 and you will see that all eumetazoans form distinct embryonic layers. The **radially symmetrical** (that is, with body parts arranged around a central axis) eumetazoans have two embryonic layers, an outer **ectoderm,** which gives rise to the epidermis (the outer layer of purple cells in figure 25.7), and an inner **endoderm** (the inner layer of yellow cells), which gives rise to the gastrodermis. A jellylike layer called the *mesoglea* (the red-colored area) forms between the epidermis and gastrodermis. These layers give rise to the basic body plan, differentiating into the many tissues of the body. No such tissues are present in sponges.

The most primitive eumetazoans to exhibit symmetry and tissues are two radially symmetrical phyla whose bodies are organized around an oral-aboral axis, like the petals of a daisy. The oral side of the animal contains the "mouth." Radial symmetry offers advantages to animals that either remain attached or closely associated to the surface or to animals that are freefloating. These animals don't pass through their environment, but rather they interact with their environment on all sides. These two phyla are Cnidaria (pronounced ni-DAH-ree-ah),

which includes hydra (figure 25.6*a*), jellyfish (figure 25.6*b*), corals (figure 25.6*c*), and sea anemones (figure 25.6*d*), and Ctenophora (pronounced tea-NO-fo-rah), a minor phylum that includes the comb jellies. These two phyla together are called the Radiata. The bodies of all other eumetazoans, the Bilateria, are marked by a fundamental bilateral symmetry (discussed in section 25.6). Even sea stars, which exhibit radial symmetry as adults, are bilaterally symmetrical when young.

A major evolutionary innovation among the radiates is the **extracellular digestion** of food. In sponges, food trapped by a choanocyte is taken directly by endocytosis into that cell, or into a circulating amoeboid cell, where the food is digested. In radiates, digestion begins *outside of cells,* in a gut cavity, called the *gastrovascular cavity.* After the food is broken down into smaller pieces, cells lining the gut cavity will complete digestion intracellularly. Extracellular digestion is the same heterotrophic strategy pursued by fungi, except that fungi digest food outside their bodies, while animals digest it within their bodies, in a cavity. This evolutionary advance has been retained by all of the more advanced groups of animals. For the first time it became possible to digest an animal larger than oneself.

Cnidarians

Cnidarians (phylum Cnidaria) are carnivores that capture their prey, such as fishes and shellfish, with tentacles that ring their mouths. Figure 25.7 walks through the key characteristics of cnidarians, including the spaghetti-like tentacles

(a)

(b)

(c)

(d)

Figure 25.6 Representative cnidarians.

(*a*) Hydroids are a group of cnidarians that are mostly marine and colonial. However, *Hydra,* shown above, is a freshwater genus whose members exist as solitary polyps. (*b*) Jellyfish are translucent, marine cnidarians. Together, (*c*) corals and (*d*) sea anemones comprise the largest group of cnidarians.

Phylum Cnidaria: Cnidarians

Sponges | Cnidarians | Flatworms | Nematodes | Mollusks | Annelids | Arthropods | Echinoderms | Chordates

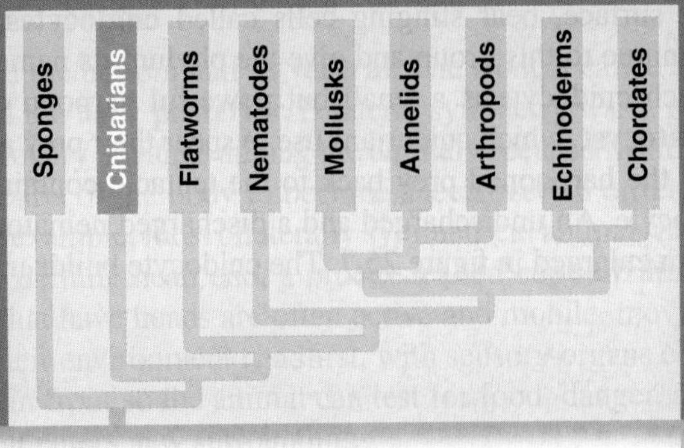

Key Evolutionary Innovations: SYMMETRY and TISSUES

The cells of a cnidarian like *Hydra* (phylum Cnidaria) are organized into specialized **tissues**. The interior gut cavity is specialized for **extracellular digestion**—that is, digestion within a gut cavity rather than within individual cells. Unlike sponges, cnidarians are **radially symmetrical**, with parts arranged around a central axis like the petals of a daisy.

Hydra and other cnidarians are radially symmetrical, and the cells of cnidarians are organized into tissues.

A major innovation of cnidarians is extracellular digestion of food—that is, digestion within a gut cavity.

Cnidarians are carnivores that capture their prey with tentacles that ring their mouth.

Tentacles and body have stinging cells (cnidocytes) that contain small but very powerful harpoons called nematocysts. Hydra use nematocysts to spear prey and then draw the wounded prey back to the hydra.

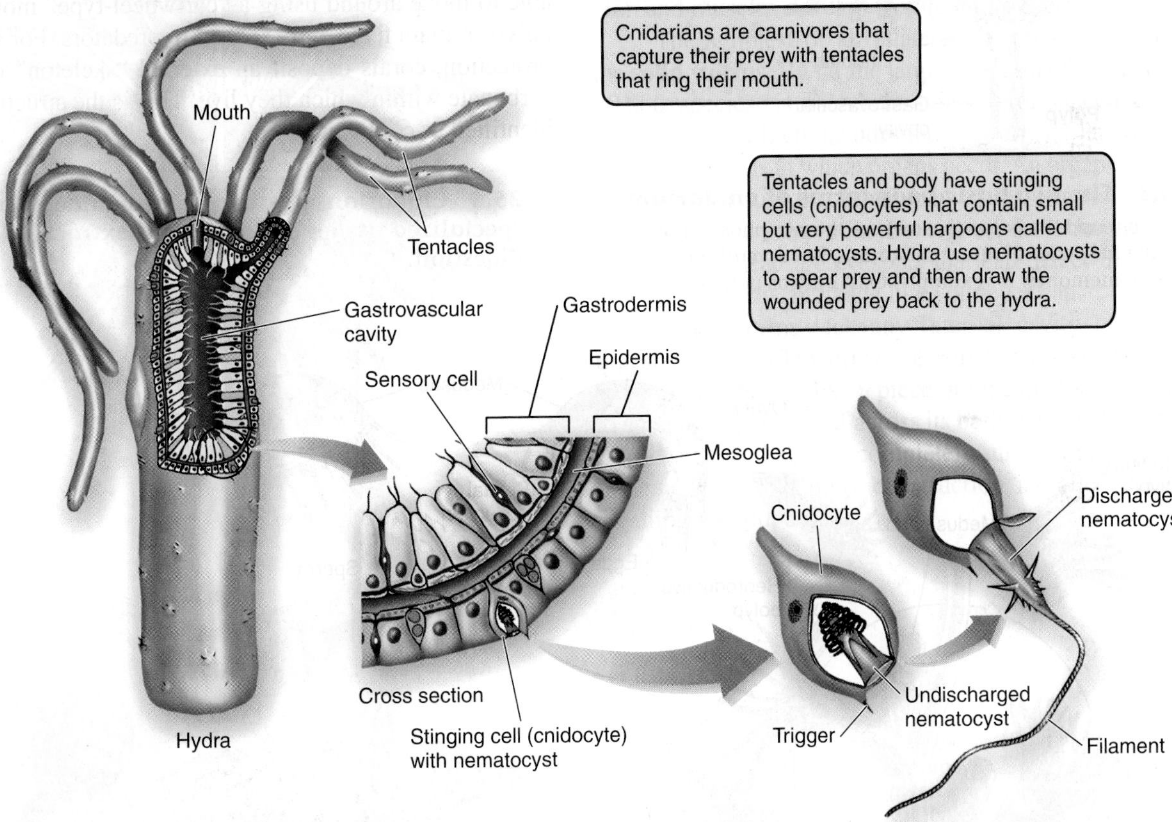

Mouth

Tentacles

Gastrovascular cavity

Gastrodermis

Epidermis

Sensory cell

Mesoglea

Cnidocyte

Discharged nematocyst

Cross section

Hydra

Stinging cell (cnidocyte) with nematocyst

Trigger

Undischarged nematocyst

Filament

A nematocyst explodes out of the stinging cell at a high velocity and can even penetrate the hard shell of a crustacean.

The harpoonlike nematocyst is propelled by osmotic pressure and is one of the fastest and most powerful processes in nature.

Figure 25.7 **Phylum Cnidaria: Cnidarians.**

Flatworms

Although flatworms have a simple body design, they do have a definite head at the anterior end and they do possess organs. Flatworms range in size from a millimeter or less to many meters long, as in some tapeworms. Most species of flatworms are parasitic, occurring within the bodies of many other kinds of animals. Other flatworms are free-living, occurring in a wide variety of marine and freshwater habitats, as well as moist places on land (figure 25.12). Free-living flatworms are carnivores and scavengers; they eat various small animals and bits of organic debris. They move from place to place by means of ciliated epithelial cells concentrated on their ventral surfaces.

There are two classes of parasitic flatworms, which live within the bodies of other animals: flukes and tapeworms. Both groups of worms have epithelial layers resistant to the digestive enzymes and immune defenses produced by their hosts—an important feature in their parasitic way of life. Some parasitic flatworms require only one host, but many flukes require two or more hosts to complete their life cycles. The liver fluke shown in figure 25.13 requires two hosts besides humans (or some other mammal). The eggs are released from the mammal ❶ and ingested by a snail where the fluke develops into a tadpolelike larva ❷ that is released into the water. The larvae bore into the muscle of a fish where they form cysts. Mammals become infected when they eat raw, infected fish ❸. The parasitic lifestyle has resulted in the eventual loss of features not used or needed by the parasite. Parasitic flatworms lack certain features of the free-living flatworms, such as cilia in the adult stage, eyespots, and other sensory organs that lack adaptive significance for an organism that lives within the body of another animal, a loss sometimes dubbed "degenerative evolution." The tapeworm described in figure 25.14 is a classic example of degenerative evolution. As you read through the characteristics in the blue boxes, notice that the tapeworm's body has been reduced to two functions, eating and reproducing.

Parasitic flatworms, like the human liver fluke *Clonorchis sinensis* in figure 25.13, have had a significant impact on humans. Other very important flukes are the blood flukes of the genus *Schistosoma*. They afflict more than 200 million people throughout tropical Asia, Africa, Latin America, and the Middle East, about 1 in 20 of the world's population. Three species of *Schistosoma* cause the disease called schistosomiasis, or bilharzia. Over 20,000 people die each year from this disease.

Figure 25.12   Flatworms.

(*a*) A common flatworm, *Planaria*. (*b*) A marine free-living flatworm.

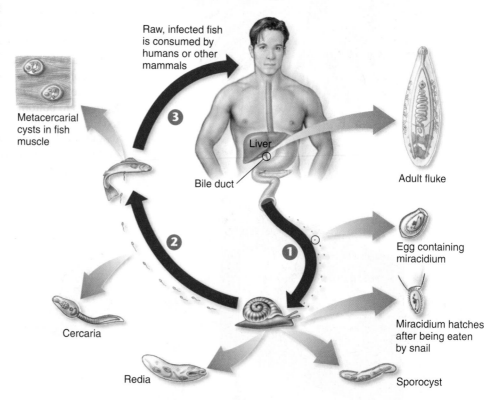

Figure 25.13   Life cycle of the human liver fluke, *Clonorchis sinensis*.

Adult flukes are 1–2 centimeters long and live in the bile passages of the liver. Eggs containing a complete, first-stage larva, or miracidium, are passed into water from feces and may be ingested by a snail ❶. Within the snail, the egg transforms into a sporocyst, which produces larvae called rediae. These grow into tadpolelike larvae called cercariae. Cercariae escape into the water ❷ where they bore into the muscles of certain fish (members of the goldfish and carp family) forming cysts. Mammals eating raw fish consume the cysts ❸. The flukes emerge from the cyst and travel to the bile duct where they mature and infest the liver, causing liver damage.

Phylum Platyhelminthes: Solid Worms

Key Evolutionary Innovation: BILATERAL SYMMETRY

Acoelomate solid worms such as the flatworms (phylum Platyhelminthes) were the first animals to be **bilaterally symmetrical** and to have a distinct **head**. The evolution of the mesoderm in solid worms allowed the formation of digestive and other organs.

Sponges / Cnidarians / Flatworms / Nematodes / Mollusks / Annelids / Arthropods / Echinoderms / Chordates

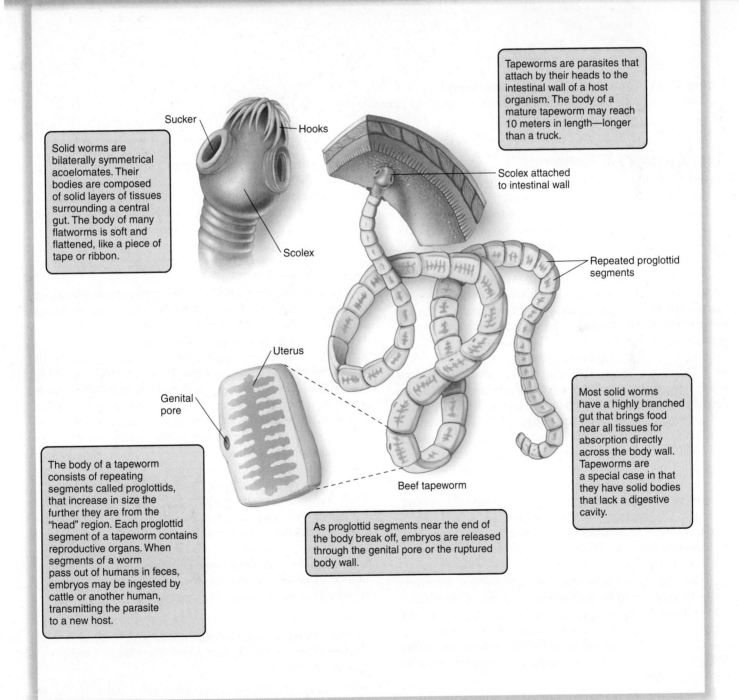

Tapeworms are parasites that attach by their heads to the intestinal wall of a host organism. The body of a mature tapeworm may reach 10 meters in length—longer than a truck.

Solid worms are bilaterally symmetrical acoelomates. Their bodies are composed of solid layers of tissues surrounding a central gut. The body of many flatworms is soft and flattened, like a piece of tape or ribbon.

Sucker

Hooks

Scolex attached to intestinal wall

Scolex

Repeated proglottid segments

Uterus

Genital pore

Most solid worms have a highly branched gut that brings food near all tissues for absorption directly across the body wall. Tapeworms are a special case in that they have solid bodies that lack a digestive cavity.

The body of a tapeworm consists of repeating segments called proglottids, that increase in size the further they are from the "head" region. Each proglottid segment of a tapeworm contains reproductive organs. When segments of a worm pass out of humans in feces, embryos may be ingested by cattle or another human, transmitting the parasite to a new host.

Beef tapeworm

As proglottid segments near the end of the body break off, embryos are released through the genital pore or the ruptured body wall.

Figure 25.14 Phylum Platyhelminthes: Solid worms.

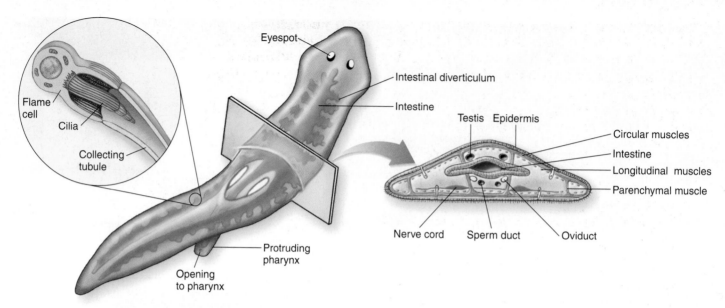

Figure 25.15 Diagram of flatworm anatomy.

The organism shown is *Dugesia,* the familiar freshwater "planaria" used in many biology laboratories.

Characteristics of Flatworms

Those flatworms that have a digestive cavity have an incomplete gut, one with only one opening. As a result, they cannot eat, digest, and eliminate undigested particles of food simultaneously. Thus, flatworms cannot feed continuously, as more advanced animals can. The gut is branched and extends throughout the body (the gut is the green structure in the *Planaria* in figure 25.15), functioning in both digestion and transport of food. Cells that line the gut engulf most of the food particles by phagocytosis and digest them; but, as in the cnidarians, some of these particles are partly digested extracellularly. Tapeworms, which are parasitic flatworms, lack digestive systems. They absorb their food directly through their body walls as described in figure 25.14.

Unlike cnidarians, flatworms have an excretory system, which consists of a network of fine tubules (little tubes) that runs throughout the body. Cilia line the hollow centers of bulblike **flame cells** (shown in the enlarged view in figure 25.15), which are located on the side branches of the tubules. Cilia in the flame cells move water and excretory substances into the tubules and then out through exit pores located between the epidermal cells. Flame cells were named because of the flickering movements of the tuft of cilia within them. They primarily regulate the water balance of the organism. The excretory function of flame cells appears to be a secondary one. A large proportion of the metabolic wastes excreted by flatworms probably diffuses directly into the gut and is eliminated through the mouth.

Like sponges, cnidarians, and ctenophorans, flatworms lack a **circulatory system,** which is a network of vessels that carries fluids, oxygen, and food molecules to parts of the body. Consequently, all flatworm cells must be within diffusion distance of oxygen and food. Flatworms have thin bodies and highly branched digestive cavities that make such a relationship possible.

The nervous system of flatworms is very simple. Some primitive flatworms have only a loosely organized nerve net. However, most members of this phylum have longitudinal nerve cords (blue structures on the ventral side in the cross section above) that constitute a simple central nervous system. Between the longitudinal cords are cross connections, so that the flatworm nervous system resembles a ladder extending the length of the body.

Free-living flatworms use sensory pits or tentacles along the sides of their heads to detect food, chemicals, or movements of the fluid in which they are living. Free-living members of this phylum also have eyespots on their heads. These are inverted, pigmented cups containing light-sensitive cells connected to the nervous system. These eyespots enable the worms to distinguish light from dark. Flatworms are far more active than cnidarians or ctenophores. Such activity is characteristic of bilaterally symmetrical animals. In flatworms, this activity seems to be related to the greater concentration of sensory organs and, to some degree, the nervous system elements in the heads of these animals.

The reproductive systems of flatworms are complex. Most flatworms are **hermaphroditic,** with each individual containing both male and female sexual structures. In some parasitic flatworms, there is a complex succession of distinct larval forms (as shown in figure 25.13). Some genera of flatworms are also capable of asexual regeneration; when a single individual is divided into two or more parts, each part can regenerate an entirely new flatworm.

> **25.6 Flatworms have internal organs, bilateral symmetry, and a distinct head. They do not have a body cavity.**

25.7 Roundworms: The Evolution of a Body Cavity

A key transition in the evolution of the animal body plan was the evolution of the body cavity. All bilaterally symmetrical animals other than solid worms have a cavity within their body. The evolution of an internal body cavity was an important improvement in animal body design for three reasons:

1. **Circulation.** Fluids that move within the body cavity can serve as a circulatory system, permitting the rapid passage of materials from one part of the body to another and opening the way to larger bodies.
2. **Movement.** Fluid in the cavity makes the animal's body rigid, permitting resistance to muscle contraction and thus opening the way to muscle-driven body movement.
3. **Organ function.** In a fluid-filled enclosure, body organs can function without being deformed by surrounding muscles. For example, food can pass freely through a gut suspended within a cavity, at a rate not controlled by when the animal moves.

Kinds of Body Cavities

There are three basic kinds of body plans found in bilaterally symmetrical animals. Acoelomates, such as solid worms that we discussed in the previous section and that are shown at the top of figure 25.16, have no body cavity. **Pseudocoelomates,** shown in the middle of the figure, have a body cavity called the **pseudocoel** located between the mesoderm (red layer) and endoderm (yellow layer). A third way of organizing the body is one in which the fluid-filled body cavity develops not between endoderm and mesoderm but rather entirely within the mesoderm. Such a body cavity is called a **coelom** (the two arch-shaped cavities in the worm at the bottom of the figure), and animals that possess such a cavity are called **coelomates.** In coelomates, the gut is suspended, along with other organ systems of the animal, within the coelom; the coelom, in turn, is surrounded by a layer of epithelial cells entirely derived from the mesoderm.

The development of a body cavity poses a problem—circulation—solved in pseudocoelomates by churning the fluid within the body cavity. In coelomates, the gut is again surrounded by tissue that presents a barrier to diffusion, just as it was in solid worms. This problem is solved among coelomates by the development of a circulatory system. The circulating fluid, or blood, carries nutrients and oxygen to the tissues and removes wastes and carbon dioxide. Blood is usually pushed through the circulatory system by contraction of one or more muscular hearts. In an open circulatory system, the blood passes from vessels into sinuses, mixes with body fluid, and then reenters the vessels later in another location. In a closed circulatory system, the blood remains separated from the body fluid in a network

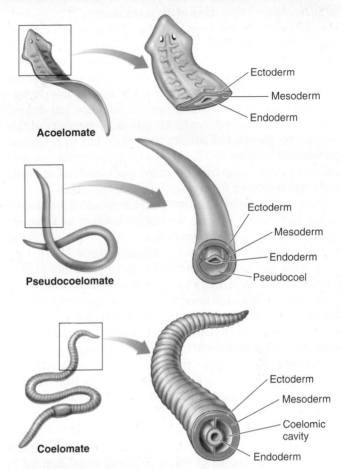

Figure 25.16 Three body plans for bilaterally symmetrical animals.

Acoelomates, such as flatworms, have no body cavity between the digestive tract (endoderm) and the outer body layer (ectoderm). Pseudocoelomates have a body cavity, the pseudocoel, between the endoderm and the mesoderm. Coelomates have a body cavity, the coelom, that develops entirely within the mesoderm, and so is lined on both sides by mesoderm tissue.

of vessels that can be separately controlled. Also, blood moves through a closed circulatory system faster and more efficiently than it does through an open system.

The evolutionary relationship among coelomates, pseudocoelomates, and acoelomates is not clear. Acoelomates, for example, could have given rise to coelomates, but scientists also cannot rule out the possibility that acoelomates were derived from coelomates. The two main phyla of pseudocoelomates do not appear to be closely related.

Roundworms: Pseudocoelomates

As we have noted, all bilaterally symmetrical animals except solid worms possess an internal body cavity. Among them, seven phyla are characterized by their possession of a pseudocoel. In all pseudocoelomates, the pseudocoel serves as a hydrostatic skeleton—one that gains its rigidity from being filled with fluid under pressure. The animal's muscles can work against this "skeleton," thus making the movements of pseudocoelomates far more efficient than those of the acoelomates.

Only one of the seven pseudocoelomate phyla includes a large number of species. This phylum, Nematoda, includes some 20,000 recognized species of **nematodes,** eelworms, and other roundworms. Scientists estimate that the actual number might approach 100 times that many. Members of this phylum are found everywhere. Nematodes are abundant and diverse in marine and freshwater habitats, and many members of this phylum are parasites of animals and plants, like the intestinal roundworm in figure 25.17a. Many nematodes are microscopic and live in soil. It has been estimated that a spadeful of fertile soil may contain, on the average, a million nematodes.

A second phylum consisting of animals with a pseudocoelomate body plan is Rotifera, the rotifers. **Rotifers** are common, small, basically aquatic animals that have a crown of cilia at their heads, which can just barely be seen in figure 25.17b; they range from 0.04 to 2 millimeters long. About 2,000 species exist throughout the world. Bilaterally symmetrical and covered with chitin, rotifers depend on their cilia for both locomotion and feeding, ingesting bacteria, protists, and small animals.

All pseudocoelomates lack a defined circulatory system; this role is performed by the fluids that move within the pseudocoel. Most pseudocoelomates have a complete, one-way digestive tract that acts like an assembly line. Food is broken down, absorbed, and then treated and stored.

Phylum Nematoda: The Roundworms

Nematodes are bilaterally symmetrical, cylindrical, unsegmented worms. Shown in longitudinal and cross sections in figure 25.18, they are covered by a flexible, thick cuticle, which is molted as they grow. Their muscles constitute a layer beneath the epidermis and extend along the length of the worm, rather than encircling its body. These longitudinal muscles, which can be seen in the cross section attaching to the outer layer of the body, pull both against the cuticle and the pseudocoel, which forms a hydrostatic skeleton. When nematodes move, their bodies whip about from side to side.

Near the mouth of a nematode, at its anterior end (toward the left side of the diagram), are usually 16 raised, hair-like sensory organs. The mouth is often equipped with piercing organs called **stylets.** Food passes through the mouth as a result of the sucking action of a muscular chamber called the **pharynx.** After passing through a short corridor into the pharynx, food continues through the other portions of the digestive tract, where it is broken down and then digested. Some of the water with which the food has been mixed is reabsorbed near the end of the digestive tract, and material that has not been digested is eliminated through the anus.

Nematodes completely lack flagella or cilia, even on sperm cells. Reproduction in nematodes is sexual, with sexes usually separate (a female with a uterus, ovary, and oviducts is shown in figure 25.18). Their development is simple, and the adults consist of very few cells. For this reason, nematodes have become extremely important subjects for genetic and developmental studies. The 1-millimeter-long *Caenorhabditis elegans* matures in only three days, its body is transparent,

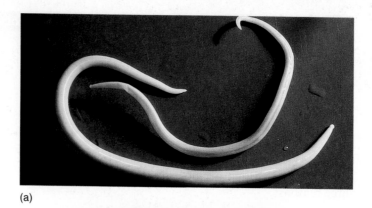
(a)

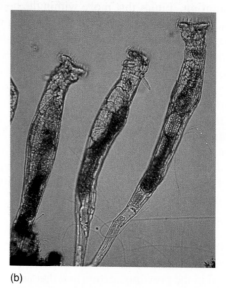
(b)

Figure 25.17 Pseudocoelomates.
(*a*) These nematodes (phylum Nematoda) are intestinal roundworms that infect humans and some other animals. Their fertilized eggs pass out with feces and can remain viable in soil for years.
(*b*) Rotifers (phylum Rotifera) are common aquatic animals that depend on their crown of cilia for feeding and locomotion.

and it has only 959 cells. It is the only animal whose complete developmental cellular anatomy is known, and the first animal whose genome (97 million DNA bases encoding over 21,000 different genes) was fully sequenced.

Some nematodes are parasitic in humans, cats, dogs, and animals of economic importance, such as cows and sheep. Heartworm infections in dogs and cats are caused by a parasitic nematode that infest the heart of the animal. About 50 species of nematodes, including several that are rather common in the United States, regularly parasitize human beings. Trichinosis, a nematode-caused disease in temperate regions, is caused by worms of the genus *Trichinella.* These worms live in the small intestine of pigs, where fertilized female worms burrow into the intestinal wall. Once it has penetrated these tissues, each female produces about 1,500 live young. The young enter the lymph channels and travel to muscle tissue throughout the body, where they mature and form cysts. Infection in human beings or other animals arises from eating undercooked or raw pork in which the cysts of *Trichinella* are present. If the worms are abundant, a fatal infection can result, but such infections are rare.

Phylum Nematoda: Roundworms

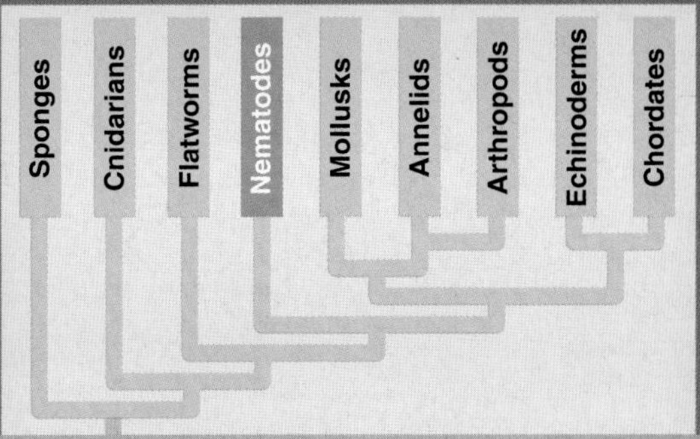
Sponges
Cnidarians
Flatworms
Nematodes
Mollusks
Annelids
Arthropods
Echinoderms
Chordates

Key Evolutionary Innovation: BODY CAVITY

The major innovation in body design in roundworms (phylum Nematoda) is a **body cavity** between the gut and the body wall. This cavity is the pseudocoel. It allows nutrients to circulate throughout the body and prevents organs from being deformed by muscle movements.

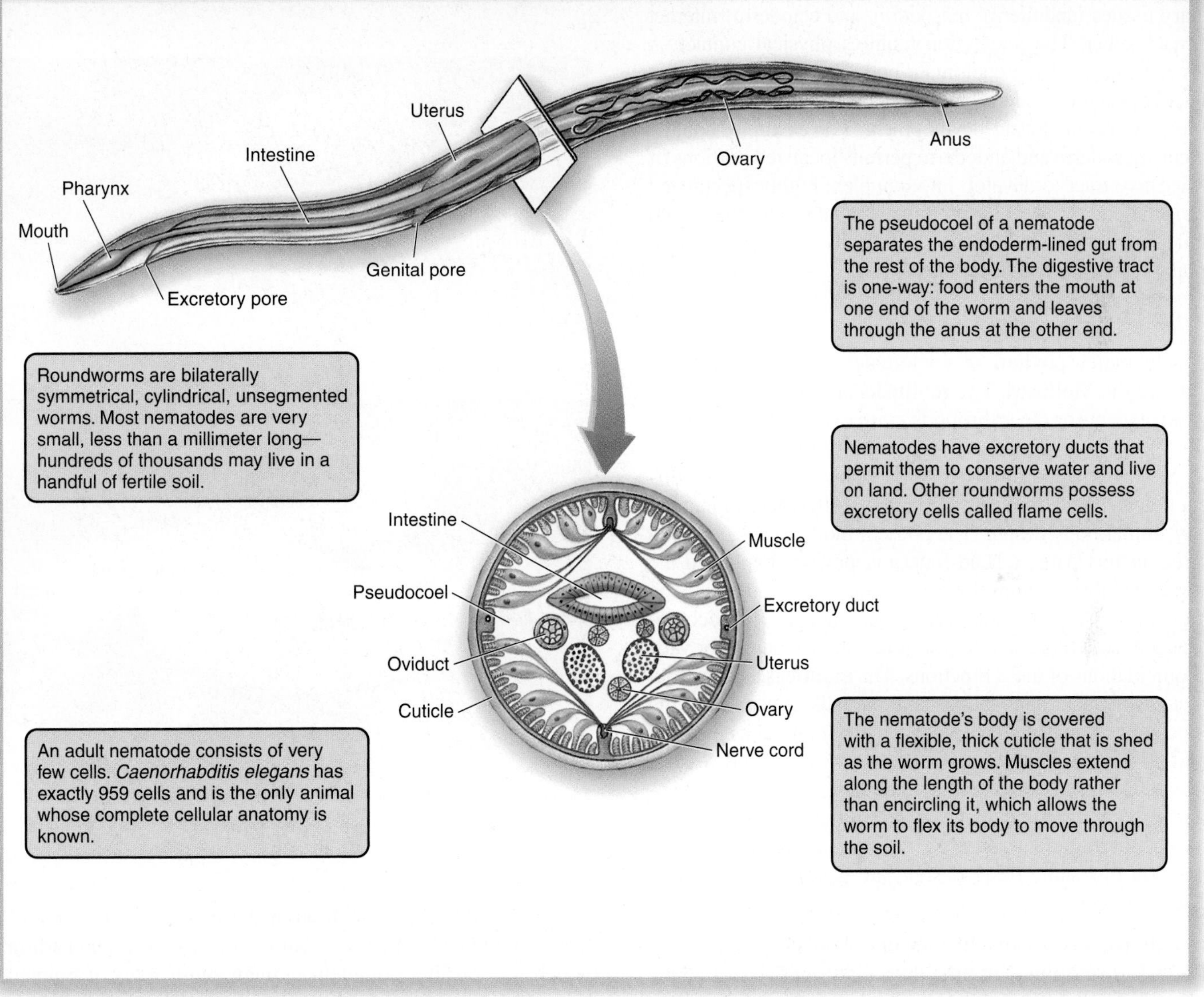
Uterus
Intestine
Pharynx
Mouth
Excretory pore
Genital pore
Ovary
Anus
The pseudocoel of a nematode separates the endoderm-lined gut from the rest of the body. The digestive tract is one-way: food enters the mouth at one end of the worm and leaves through the anus at the other end.
Roundworms are bilaterally symmetrical, cylindrical, unsegmented worms. Most nematodes are very small, less than a millimeter long—hundreds of thousands may live in a handful of fertile soil.
Nematodes have excretory ducts that permit them to conserve water and live on land. Other roundworms possess excretory cells called flame cells.
Intestine
Pseudocoel
Oviduct
Cuticle
Muscle
Excretory duct
Uterus
Ovary
Nerve cord
An adult nematode consists of very few cells. *Caenorhabditis elegans* has exactly 959 cells and is the only animal whose complete cellular anatomy is known.
The nematode's body is covered with a flexible, thick cuticle that is shed as the worm grows. Muscles extend along the length of the body rather than encircling it, which allows the worm to flex its body to move through the soil.

Figure 25.18 Phylum Nematoda: Roundworms.

A more prevalent human parasitic nematode is *Ascaris lumbricoides*. This intestinal worm infects approximately one of six people worldwide but is rare in areas with modern plumbing. These worms live in the intestines and spread their fertilized eggs in feces, which can remain viable in the soil for years. Adult females, which are up to 30 centimeters long, contain up to 30 million eggs, and can lay up to 20,000 of them each day.

25.7 Some body cavities develop between the endoderm and mesoderm (pseudocoelomates), others within the mesoderm (coelomates). Roundworms have a pseudocoel body cavity. Nematodes, a kind of roundworm, are very common in soil, and several are parasites.

Coelomates

Even though acoelomates and pseudocoelomates have proven very successful, the bulk of the animal kingdom consists of coelomates. Coelomates have a new body design that repositions the fluid. What is the functional difference between a pseudocoel and a coelom, and why has the latter kind of body cavity been so overwhelmingly successful? The answer has to do with the nature of animal embryonic development. In animals, development of specialized tissues involves a process called **primary induction,** in which the three primary tissues (endoderm, mesoderm, and ectoderm) interact with each other. The interaction requires physical contact. A major advantage of the coelomate body plan is that it allows contact between mesoderm and endoderm, so that primary induction can occur during development. For example, contact between mesoderm and endoderm permits localized portions of the digestive tract to develop into complex, highly specialized regions like the stomach. In pseudocoelomates, mesoderm and endoderm are separated by the body cavity, limiting developmental interactions between these tissues.

Mollusks

The only major phylum of coelomates without segmented bodies are the Mollusca. The **mollusks** are the largest animal phylum, except for the arthropods, with over 110,000 species. Mollusks are mostly marine, but occur almost everywhere.

Mollusks include three general groups with outwardly different body plans. However, the seeming differences hide a basically similar body design. The body of mollusks is composed of three distinct parts: a head-foot, a central section called the visceral mass that contains the body's organs, and a mantle. The foot of a mollusk is muscular and may be adapted for locomotion, attachment, food capture (in squids and octopuses), or various combinations of these functions. The **mantle** is a heavy fold of tissue wrapped around the visceral mass like a cape, with the gills positioned on its inner surface like the lining of a coat. The **gills** are filamentous projections of tissue, rich in blood vessels, that capture oxygen from the water circulating between the mantle and visceral mass and release carbon dioxide.

The three major groups of mollusks, all different variations upon this same basic design, are gastropods, bivalves, and cephalopods.

1. **Gastropods** (snails, like the one shown in figure 25.19*a*, and slugs) use the muscular foot to crawl, and their mantle often secretes a single, hard protective shell. All terrestrial mollusks are gastropods.
2. **Bivalves** (clams, oysters, and scallops) secrete a two-part shell with a hinge (figure 25.19*b*), as their name implies. They filter-feed by drawing water into their shell.
3. **Cephalopods** (octopuses, like the one shown in figure 25.19*c*, and squids) have modified the mantle cavity to create a jet propulsion system that can propel them rapidly through the water. In most groups, the shell is greatly reduced to an internal structure or is absent.

(a)

(b)

(c)

Figure 25.19 Three major groups of mollusks.
(*a*) A gastropod. (*b*) A bivalve. (*c*) A cephalopod.

Figure 25.20 walks you through the characteristics of mollusks including a unique feature of mollusks, the **radula,** which is a rasping, tonguelike organ. With rows of pointed, backward-curving teeth, the radula is used by some snails to scrape algae off rocks. The small holes often seen in oyster shells are produced by gastropods that have bored holes to kill the oyster and extract its body.

In most mollusks, as stated earlier, the outer surface of the mantle also secretes a protective shell, partially cut away in figure 25.20. The shell consists of a horny outer layer, rich in protein, which protects the two underlying calcium-rich layers from erosion. The inner layer is pearly and is used as mother-of-pearl. Pearls themselves are formed when a foreign

Phylum Mollusca: Mollusks

Key Evolutionary Innovation: COELOM

The body cavity of a mollusk like this snail (phylum Mollusca) is a **coelom**, completely enclosed within the mesoderm. This allows physical contact between the mesoderm and the endoderm, permitting interactions that lead to development of highly specialized organs such as a stomach.

Sponges | Cnidarians | Flatworms | Nematodes | Mollusks | Annelids | Arthropods | Echinoderms | Chordates

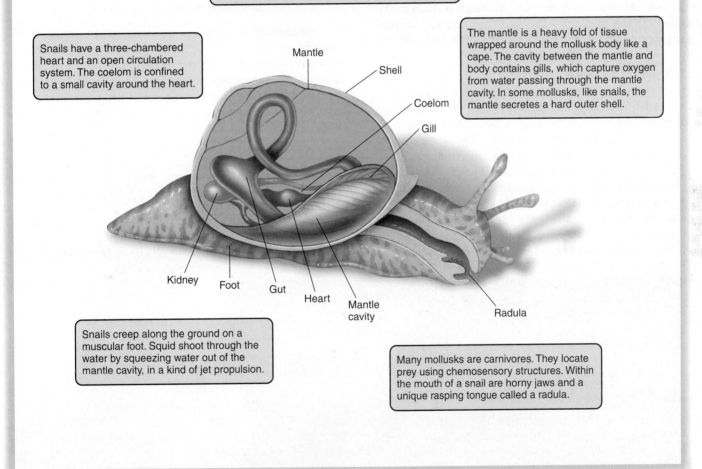

Mollusks were among the first animals to develop an efficient excretory system. Tubular structures called nephridia (a type of kidney) gather wastes from the coelom and discharge them into the mantle cavity.

Snails have a three-chambered heart and an open circulation system. The coelom is confined to a small cavity around the heart.

The mantle is a heavy fold of tissue wrapped around the mollusk body like a cape. The cavity between the mantle and body contains gills, which capture oxygen from water passing through the mantle cavity. In some mollusks, like snails, the mantle secretes a hard outer shell.

Mantle
Shell
Coelom
Gill
Kidney   Foot   Gut   Heart   Mantle cavity   Radula

Snails creep along the ground on a muscular foot. Squid shoot through the water by squeezing water out of the mantle cavity, in a kind of jet propulsion.

Many mollusks are carnivores. They locate prey using chemosensory structures. Within the mouth of a snail are horny jaws and a unique rasping tongue called a radula.

Figure 25.20   Phylum Mollusca: Mollusks.

object, such as a grain of sand, becomes lodged between the mantle and the inner shell layer of a bivalve, including clams and oysters. The mantle coats the foreign object with layer upon layer of shell material to reduce irritation. The shell serves primarily for protection with some mollusks withdrawing into their shell when threatened.

25.8   Mollusks have a coelom body cavity but are not segmented. Although diverse, their basic body plans include a foot, the visceral mass, and a mantle.

25.9 Annelids: The Rise of Segmentation

One of the early key innovations in body plan to arise among the coelomates was **segmentation,** the building of a body from a series of similar segments. The first segmented animals to evolve were the **annelid worms,** phylum Annelida. These advanced coelomates are assembled as a chain of nearly identical segments, like the boxcars of a train. The great advantage of such segmentation is the evolutionary flexibility it offers—a small change in an existing segment can produce a new kind of segment with a different function. Thus, some segments are modified for reproduction, some for feeding, and others for eliminating wastes.

Two-thirds of all annelids live in the sea (about 8,000 species, including the bristle worm in figure 25.21*b*), but some live in freshwater, and most of the rest—some 3,100 species—are earthworms (shown emerging from underground in figure 25.21*a*). The basic body plan of an annelid is a tube within a tube: The digestive tract, the light pink tube in figure 25.22, is suspended within the coelom, which is itself a tube running from mouth to anus. There are three characteristics of this organization discussed below and shown in figure 25.22:

1. **Repeated segments.** The body segments of an annelid are visible as a series of ringlike structures running the length of the body, looking like a stack of doughnuts (which can be seen externally in figure 25.22 as well as in the longitudinal section drawing). The segments are divided internally from one another by partitions, just as walls separate the rooms of a building. In each of the cylindrical segments, the excretory and locomotor organs are repeated. The body fluid within the coelom of each segment creates a hydrostatic (liquid-supported) skeleton that gives the segment rigidity, like an inflated balloon. Muscles within each segment pull against the fluid in the coelom. Because each segment is separate, each is able to expand or contract independently. This lets the worm's body move in ways that are quite complex. When an earthworm crawls on a flat surface, for example, it lengthens some parts of its body while shortening others.

2. **Specialized segments.** The anterior (front) segments of annelids contain the sensory organs of the worm. Elaborate eyes with lenses and retinas have evolved in some annelids. One anterior segment contains a well-developed cerebral ganglion, or brain (the yellow bulbed structures in figure 25.22).

3. **Connections.** Because partitions separate the segments, it is necessary to provide ways for materials and information to pass between segments. A circulatory system (the red vessels in figure 25.22) carries blood from one segment to another, while nerve cords (the yellow chainlike structure along the ventral wall in the figure) connect the nerve centers located in each segment with each other and the brain. The brain can then coordinate the worm's activities.

Segmentation underlies the body organization of all complex coelomate animals, not only annelids but also arthropods (crustaceans, spiders, and insects) and chordates (mostly vertebrates). For example, vertebrate muscles develop from repeated blocks of tissue called somites that occur in the embryo. Vertebrate segmentation is also seen in the vertebral column, which is a stack of very similar vertebrae.

> **25.9** Annelids are segmented worms. Most species are marine, but some—about one-third of the species—are terrestrial.

(a)

(b)

Figure 25.21 Representative annelids.
(a) Earthworms are the terrestrial annelids. This night crawler, *Lumbricus terrestris,* is in its burrow. (b) This bristle worm is an aquatic annelid, a polychaete.

Phylum Annelida: Annelids

Key Evolutionary Innovation: SEGMENTATION

Marine polychaetes and earthworms (phylum Annelida) were the first organisms to evolve a body plan based on **repeated body segments**. Most segments are identical and are separated from other segments by partitions.

Sponges | Cnidarians | Flatworms | Nematodes | Mollusks | Annelids | Arthropods | Echinoderms | Chordates

Each segment contains a set of excretory organs (nephridia) and a nerve center.

Earthworms crawl by anchoring bristles called setae to the ground and pulling against them. Polychaete annelids have a flattened body and swim or crawl by flexing it.

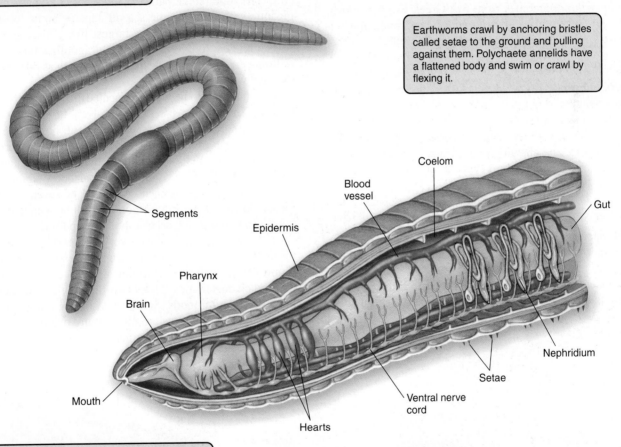

Segments

Coelom

Blood vessel

Gut

Epidermis

Pharynx

Brain

Nephridium

Setae

Mouth

Ventral nerve cord

Hearts

Segments are connected by the circulatory and nervous systems. A series of hearts at the anterior (front) end pump the blood. A well-developed brain located in an anterior segment coordinates the activities of all segments.

Each segment has a coelom. Muscles squeeze the fluid of the coelom, making each segment rigid, like an inflated balloon. Because each segment can contract independently, a worm can crawl by lengthening some segments while shortening others.

Figure 25.22   Phylum Annelida: Annelids.

25.10 Arthropods: Advent of Jointed Appendages

The evolution of segmentation among the annelids marked a major innovation in body structure among the coelomates. An even more profound innovation was to come. It marks the origin of the body plan characteristic of the most successful of all animal groups, the **arthropods,** phylum Arthropoda. This innovation was the development of jointed appendages. Jointed appendages lead to the evolution of insects, which make up nearly 80% of all arthropod species (represented by five of the eight areas in the pie chart in figure 25.23). Jointed appendages are also present in crustaceans (represented by the orange area), spiders (represented by the light grey area), and other types of arthropods (represented by the darker blue area).

Jointed Appendages

The name *arthropod* comes from two Greek words, *arthros,* jointed, and *podes,* feet. All arthropods have jointed appendages. Some are legs, and others may be modified for other uses. To gain some idea of the importance of jointed appendages, imagine yourself without them—no hips, knees, ankles, shoulders, elbows, wrists, or knuckles. Without jointed appendages, you could not walk or grasp an object. Arthropods use jointed appendages as legs and wings for moving, as antennae to sense their environment, and as mouthparts for sucking, ripping, and chewing prey. A scorpion, for example, seizes and tears apart its prey with mouthpart appendages modified as large pincers.

Rigid Exoskeleton

The arthropod body plan has a second great innovation: Arthropods have a rigid external skeleton, or **exoskeleton,** made of chitin. In any animal, a key function of the skeleton is to provide places for muscle attachment, and in arthropods the muscles attach to the interior surface of the hard chitin shell, which also protects the animal from predators and impedes water loss.

However, while chitin is hard and tough, it is also brittle and cannot support great weight. As a result, the exoskeleton must be much thicker to bear the pull of the muscles in large insects than in small ones, so there is a limit to how big an arthropod body can be. That is why you don't see beetles as big as birds or crabs the size of a cow—the exoskeleton would be so thick the animal couldn't move its great weight. Another limitation on size is the fact that in many arthropods, including insects, all parts of the body need to be near a respiratory passage to obtain oxygen. The reason for this is that the respiratory system (see figure 30.1c), not the circulatory system, carries oxygen to the tissues.

In fact, the great majority of arthropod species consist of small animals—mostly about a millimeter in length—but members of the phylum range in adult size from about 80 micrometers long (some parasitic mites) to 3.6 meters across (a gigantic crab found in the sea off Japan). Some lobsters are nearly a meter in length. The largest living insects are about 33 centimeters long, but the giant dragonflies that lived 300 million years ago had wingspans of as much as 60 centimeters (2 feet)!

Arthropod bodies are segmented like those of annelids, from which they almost certainly evolved. Individual segments often exist only during early development, however, and fuse into functional groups as adults. For example, a caterpillar (a larval stage) has many segments, while a butterfly (and other adult insects) has only three functional body regions—head, thorax, and abdomen—each composed of several fused segments. Some of the segmentation can still be seen in the grasshopper in figure 25.24, especially in the abdomen.

Arthropods have proven very successful due to the arthropod innovations of jointed appendages and exoskeletons. Figure 25.25 walks you through a succinct overview of arthropod characteristics. About two-thirds of all named species on earth are arthropods. Scientists estimate that a quintillion (a billion billion) insects are alive at any one time—200 million insects for each living human!

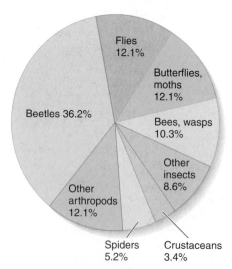

Figure 25.23 Arthropods are a successful group.
About two-thirds of all named species are arthropods. About 80% of all arthropods are insects, and about half of the named species of insects are beetles.

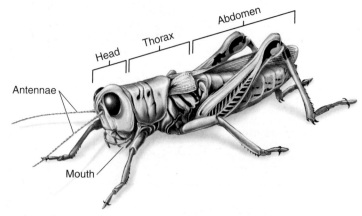

Figure 25.24 Segmentation in insects.
This grasshopper illustrates the body segmentation found in adult insects. The many segments found in most larval stages of insects become fused in the adult, giving rise to three adult body regions: the head, thorax, and abdomen. The appendages—legs, wings, mouthparts, antennae—are jointed.

Phylum Arthropoda: Arthropods

Key Evolutionary Innovations: JOINTED APPENDAGES and EXOSKELETON

Insects and other arthropods (phylum Arthropoda) have a coelom, segmented bodies, and **jointed appendages.** The three body regions of an insect (head, thorax, and abdomen) are each actually composed of a number of segments that fuse during development. All arthropods have a strong **exoskeleton** made of chitin. One class of arthropods, the insects, has evolved **wings,** which permit them to fly rapidly through the air.

Sponges | Cnidarians | Flatworms | Nematodes | Mollusks | Annelids | Arthropods | Echinoderms | Chordates

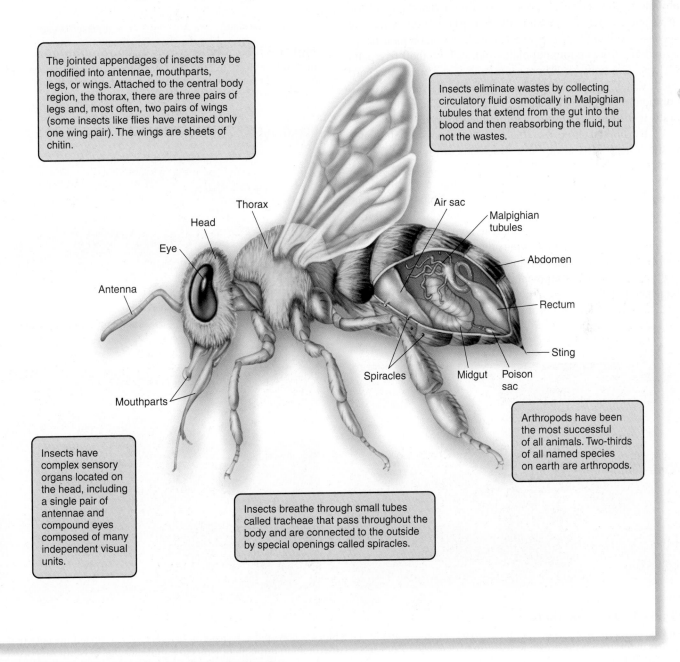

The jointed appendages of insects may be modified into antennae, mouthparts, legs, or wings. Attached to the central body region, the thorax, there are three pairs of legs and, most often, two pairs of wings (some insects like flies have retained only one wing pair). The wings are sheets of chitin.

Insects eliminate wastes by collecting circulatory fluid osmotically in Malpighian tubules that extend from the gut into the blood and then reabsorbing the fluid, but not the wastes.

Insects have complex sensory organs located on the head, including a single pair of antennae and compound eyes composed of many independent visual units.

Insects breathe through small tubes called tracheae that pass throughout the body and are connected to the outside by special openings called spiracles.

Arthropods have been the most successful of all animals. Two-thirds of all named species on earth are arthropods.

Thorax · Head · Eye · Antenna · Mouthparts · Air sac · Malpighian tubules · Abdomen · Rectum · Sting · Spiracles · Midgut · Poison sac

Figure 25.25 Phylum Arthropoda: Arthropods.

Chelicerates

Arthropods such as spiders, mites, scorpions, and a few others lack jaws, or **mandibles,** and are called **chelicerates.** Their mouthparts, known as **chelicerae,** evolved from the appendages nearest the animal's anterior end, as in the jumping spider pictured in figure 25.26a. The chelicerae are the foremost appendages located on the head. The remaining arthropods have mandibles, formed by the modification of one of the pairs of anterior appendages, not necessarily the foremost set of appendages. The foremost set of appendages in the bullfrog ant pictured in figure 25.26b is the antennae with the mandibles forming from the next set of appendages. These arthropods, called **mandibulates,** include the crustaceans, insects, centipedes, millipedes, and a few other groups.

The chelicerate fossil record goes back as far as that of any multicellular animal, about 630 million years. One of the most ancient groups contains the horseshoe crabs, with five species surviving today. Horseshoe crabs swim on their backs by moving their abdominal plates and walk on their five pairs of legs. The body of a horseshoe crab is covered by a hard shell, which has a long tailpiece (figure 25.27); there are two compound eyes and two simple eyes on the shell. Horseshoe crabs feed at night, primarily on mollusks and annelids.

By far the largest of the three classes of chelicerates is the largely terrestrial class Arachnida, with some 57,000 named species, including the spiders (two poisonous spiders found in North America are pictured in figure 25.28), ticks, mites, scorpions, and daddy longlegs. Arachnids have a pair of chelicerae, a pair of pedipalps (see figure 25.26a), and four pairs of walking legs. The chelicerae consist of a stout basal portion and a movable fang often connected to a poison gland. **Pedipalps,** the next pair of appendages, may resemble legs, but they have one less segment. In scorpions, the pedipalps are large and pinching. Most **arachnids** are carnivorous, although mites are largely herbivorous. Ticks are blood-feeding ecto-

parasites of vertebrates, and some ticks may carry diseases, such as Rocky Mountain spotted fever and Lyme disease.

Sea spiders are also chelicerates and are relatively common, especially in coastal waters, and more than 1,000 species are in the class.

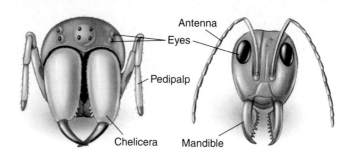

(a) Chelicerate　　　　　　(b) Mandibulate

Figure 25.26　Chelicerates and mandibulates.

In the chelicerates (a), the chelicerae are the foremost appendages of the body. In contrast, the foremost appendages in the mandibulates, (b), are the antennae, followed by the mandibles.

Figure 25.27　Horseshoe crabs.

These horseshoe crabs, *Limulus,* are emerging from the sea to mate.

(a)　　　　　　(b)

Figure 25.28　Arachnids.

(a) One of the poisonous spiders in the United States and Canada is the black widow spider, *Latrodectus mactans.* (b) Another of the poisonous spiders in this area is the brown recluse, *Loxosceles reclusa.* Both species are common throughout temperate and subtropical North America, but they rarely bite humans.

Mandibulates

Crustaceans The **crustaceans** (subphylum Crustacea) are a large, diverse group of primarily aquatic organisms, including some 35,000 species of crabs, shrimps, lobsters, crayfish, water fleas, pillbugs, sowbugs, barnacles, and related groups (figure 25.29). Often incredibly abundant in marine and freshwater habitats, and playing a role of critical importance in virtually all aquatic ecosystems, crustaceans have been called "the insects of the water." Most crustaceans have two pairs of antennae (the first pair are shorter and often referred to as antennules, as labeled in figure 25.30), three pairs of chewing appendages (one pair being the mandibles), and various numbers of pairs of legs. The nauplius larva stage through which all crustaceans pass provides evidence that all members of this diverse group are descended from a common ancestor. The nauplius hatches with three pairs of appendages and metamorphoses through several stages before reaching maturity. In many groups, this nauplius stage is passed in the egg, and development of the hatchling to the adult form is direct.

Crustaceans differ from the insects in that the head and thorax are fused together, forming the cephalothorax, and they have legs on their abdomen as well as on their thorax. Many crustaceans have compound eyes. In addition, they have delicate tactile hairs that project from the cuticle all over the body. Larger crustaceans have feathery gills near the bases of their legs. In smaller members of this class, gas exchange takes place directly through the thinner areas of the cuticle or the entire body. Most crustaceans have separate sexes. Many different kinds of specialized copulation occur among the crustaceans, and the members of some orders carry their eggs with them, either singly or in egg pouches, until they hatch.

Crustaceans include marine, freshwater, and terrestrial forms. Crustaceans such as shrimp, lobsters, crabs, and

(a)

(b)   (c)

Figure 25.29 Crustaceans.

(a) Dark-fingered coral crab. (b) Sowbugs, *Porcellio scaber*.
(c) Barnacles are sessile animals that permanently attach themselves to a hard substrate.

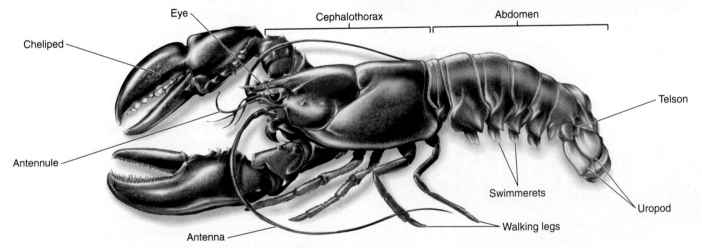

Figure 25.30 Body of a lobster, *Homarus americanus*.

Some of the specialized terms used to describe crustaceans are indicated. For example, the head and thorax are fused together into a cephalothorax. Appendages called swimmerets occur in lines along the sides of the abdomen and are used in reproduction and also for swimming. Flattened appendages known as uropods form a kind of compound "paddle" at the end of the abdomen. Lobsters may also have a telson, or tail spine.

crayfish are called decapods, meaning "ten-footed" like the lobster in figure 25.30. Pillbugs and sowbugs are terrestrial crustaceans but usually live in moist places. Barnacles are a group of crustaceans that are sessile as adults but have free-swimming larvae. The larvae attach their heads to rocks or other submerged objects and then stir food into their mouths with their feathery legs.

Millipedes and Centipedes Millipedes and centipedes have bodies that consist of a head region followed by numerous similar segments. Centipedes have one pair of legs on each body segment, and millipedes have two. This difference is apparent if you compare the leg arrangements in the centipede in figure 25.31*a* and the millipede in 25.31*b*. The centipedes are all carnivorous and feed mainly on insects. The appendages of the first trunk segment are modified into a pair of venomous fangs. In contrast, most millipedes are herbivores, feeding mostly on decaying vegetation. Millipedes live mainly in damp, protected places, such as under leaf litter, in rotting logs, under bark or stones, or in the soil. The first animal to have lived on land was a millipede; its 420-million-year-old fossil was reported in 2004.

Insects The **insects,** class Insecta, are by far the largest group of arthropods, whether measured in terms of numbers

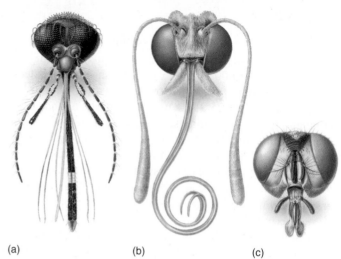

(a)   (b)   (c)

Figure 25.32 Modified mouthparts in three kinds of insects.

(*a*) Mosquito, *Culex;* (*b*) alfalfa butterfly, *Colias;* (*c*) housefly, *Musca domestica.*

(a)

(b)

Figure 25.31 Centipedes and millipedes.

Centipedes are active predators, whereas millipedes are sedentary herbivores. (*a*) Centipede, *Scolopendra.* (*b*) Millipede, *Sigmoria,* in North Carolina.

of species or numbers of individuals; as such, they are the most abundant group of eukaryotes on earth. Most insects are relatively small, ranging from 0.1 millimeters to about 30 centimeters in length. Insects have three body sections:

1. **Head.** The insect head is very elaborate, with a single pair of antennae and elaborate mouthparts that are well-suited to their diets. For example, the mouthparts in the mosquito in figure 25.32*a* are modified for piercing the skin; the long proboscis of the butterfly in figure 25.32*b* can uncoil to reach down into flowers; and the short mouthparts of the housefly in figure 25.32*c* are modified for sopping up liquids. Most insects have compound eyes, which are composed of independent visual units.
2. **Thorax.** The thorax consists of three segments, each of which has a pair of legs. Most insects also have two pairs of wings attached to the thorax. In some insects, such as beetles, grasshoppers, and crickets, the outer pair of wings is adapted for protection rather than flight.
3. **Abdomen.** The abdomen consists of up to 12 segments. Digestion takes place primarily in the stomach, and excretion takes place through organs called *Malpighian tubules,* which constitute an efficient mechanism for water conservation and were a key adaptation facilitating invasion of the land by arthropods.

Although primarily a terrestrial group, insects live in every conceivable habitat on land and in freshwater, and a few have even invaded the sea. About 1 million species have been identified with many others awaiting detection and classification (figure 25.33).

25.10 Arthropods, the most successful animal phylum, have jointed appendages, a rigid exoskeleton, and, in the case of insects, wings.

Figure 25.33 Insect diversity.

(*a*) Some insects have a tough exoskeleton, like this stag beetle (order Coleoptera). (*b*) Human flea, *Pulex irritans* (order Siphonaptera). Fleas are flattened laterally, slipping easily through hair. (*c*) The honeybee, *Apis mellifera* (order Hymenoptera), is a widely domesticated and efficient pollinator of flowering plants. (*d*) This pot dragonfly (order Odonata) has a fragile exoskeleton. (*e*) A true bug, *Edessa rufomarginata* (order Hemiptera), in Panama. (*f*) Copulating grasshoppers (order Orthoptera). (*g*) Luna moth, *Actias luna,* in Virginia. Luna moths and their relatives are among the most spectacular insects (order Lepidoptera).

25.11 Protostomes and Deuterostomes

There are two major kinds of coelomate animals representing two distinct evolutionary lines. All the coelomates we have met so far have essentially the same kind of embryonic development. Cell divisions of the fertilized egg produce a hollow ball of cells, a blastula, which indents to form a two-layer-thick ball with a blastopore opening to the outside. In mollusks, annelids, and arthropods, the mouth (stoma) develops from or near the blastopore. This same pattern of development, in a general sense, is seen in all noncoelomate animals. An animal whose mouth develops in this way is called a **protostome** (figure 25.34, *top*). If such an animal has a distinct anus or anal pore, it develops later in another region of the embryo.

A second distinct pattern of embryological development occurs in the echinoderms and the chordates. In these animals, the anus forms from or near the blastopore, and the mouth forms subsequently on another part of the blastula. This group of phyla consists of animals that are called the **deuterostomes** (figure 25.34, *bottom*).

Deuterostomes represent a revolution in embryonic development. In addition to the fate of the blastopore, deuterostomes differ from protostomes in three other features:

1. The progressive division of cells during embryonic growth is called *cleavage*. The cleavage pattern relative to the embryo's polar axis determines how the cells array. In nearly all protostomes, each new cell buds off at an angle oblique to the polar axis. As a result, a new cell nestles into the space between the older ones in a closely packed array (see the 16-cell stage in the upper row of cells). This pattern is called **spiral cleavage** because a line drawn through a sequence of dividing cells spirals outward from the polar axis, (indicated by the curving blue arrow at the 32-cell stage).

   In deuterostomes, the cells divide parallel to and at right angles to the polar axis. As a result, the pairs of cells from each division are positioned directly above and below one another (see the 16-cell stage in the lower row of cells); this process gives rise to a loosely packed array of cells. This pattern is called **radial cleavage** because a line drawn through a sequence of dividing cells describes a radius outward from the polar axis (indicated by the straight blue arrow at the 32-cell stage).

2. In protostomes, the developmental fate of each cell in the embryo is fixed when that cell first appears. Even at the four-celled stage, each cell is different, containing different chemical developmental signals and no one cell, if separated from the others, can develop into a complete animal. In deuterostomes, on the other hand, the first cleavage divisions of the fertilized embryo produce identical daughter cells, and any single cell, if separated, can develop into a complete organism.

3. In all coelomates, the coelom originates from mesoderm. In protostomes, this occurs simply and directly: The mesoderm cells simply move away from one another as the coelomic cavity expands within the mesoderm. However, in deuterostomes, the coelom is normally produced by an evagination of the **archenteron**—the main cavity within the gastrula, also called the primitive gut. This cavity, lined with endoderm, opens to the outside via the blastopore and eventually becomes the gut cavity. The evaginating cells give rise to the mesodermal cells, and the mesoderm expands to form the coelom.

> **25.11** In protostomes, the egg cleaves spirally, and the blastopore becomes the mouth. In deuterostomes, the egg cleaves radially, and the blastopore becomes the animal's anus.

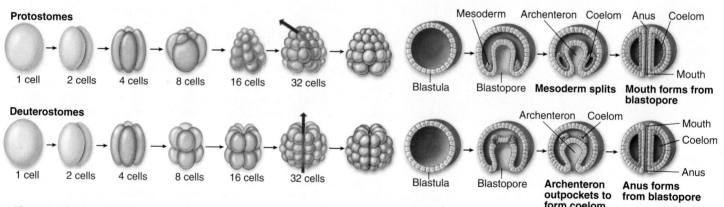

Figure 25.34 Embryonic development in protostomes and deuterostomes.
Cleavage of the egg produces a hollow ball of cells called the blastula. Invagination, or infolding, of the blastula produces the blastopore. In protostomes, embryonic cells cleave in a spiral pattern and become tightly packed. The blastopore becomes the animal's mouth, and the coelom originates from a mesodermal split. In deuterostomes, embryonic cells cleave radially and form a loosely packed array. The blastopore becomes the animal's anus, and the mouth develops at the other end. The coelom originates from an evagination, or outpouching, of the archenteron in deuterostomes.

A Closer Look

Diversity Is Only Skin Deep

Perhaps the most important lesson to emerge from the study of animal diversity is not the incredible variety of animal forms, from worms and spiders to sharks and antelopes, but rather their deep similarities. The body plans of all animals are assembled along a similar path, as if from the same basic blueprint. The same genes play critical roles throughout the animal kingdom, small changes in how they are activated leading to very different body forms.

The molecular mechanisms used to orchestrate development are thought to have evolved very early in the history of multicellular life. Animals utilize transcription factors like those discussed on page 244 to turn on or off particular sets of genes as they develop, determining just what developmental processes occur, where, and when. In many cases the same gene is found to control the same developmental process in many, if not all, animals. For example, a gene in mice called *Pax6* encodes a transcription factor that initiates development of the eye. Mice without a functional copy of this gene do not make the transcription factor and are eyeless. When a gene was discovered in fruit flies that caused the flies to lack eyes, this gene was found to have essentially the same DNA sequence as the mouse gene—the same *Pax6* master regulator gene was responsible for triggering eye development in both insects and vertebrates. Indeed, when Swiss biologist Walter Gehring inserted the mouse version of *Pax6* into the fruitfly genome, a compound eye (the multi-faceted kind that fly's have) was formed on the leg of the fly! It seems that although insects and vertebrates diverged from a common ancestor more than 500 million years ago, they still control their development with genes so similar that the vertebrate gene seems to function quite normally in the insect genome.

Pax6 plays this same role of releasing eye development in many other animals. Even marine ribbon worms use it to initiate development of their eye spots. The *Pax6* genes of all these animals have similar gene sequences, suggesting that Pax6 acquired its evolutionary role in eye development only a single time more than 500 million years ago, in the common ancestor of all animals that use *Pax6* today.

A more ancient master regulator gene called *Hox* determines basic body form. *Hox* genes appeared before the divergence of plants and animals; in plants they modulate shoot growth and leaf form, and in animals they establish the basic body plan.

All segmented animals appear to use organized clusters of *Hox* genes to control their development. After the sequential action of several "segmentation" genes, the body of these early embryos have a basically segmented body plan. This is true of the embryos of earthworms, fruit flies, mice—and human beings. The key to the further development of the animal body is to now give identity to

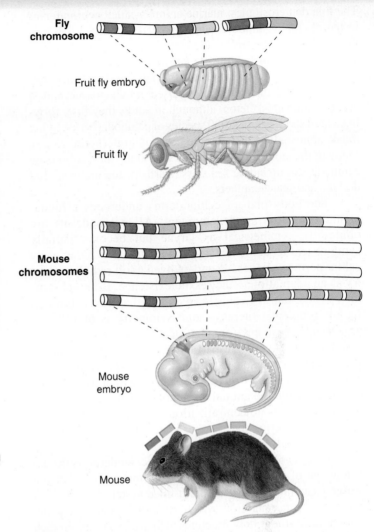

Fly chromosome

Fruit fly embryo

Fruit fly

Mouse chromosomes

Mouse embryo

Mouse

each of the segments—to determine whether a particular segment will become back, or neck, or head, for example. In fruit flies and mice, similar clusters of *Hox* genes control this process. Flies have a single set of *Hox* genes, located on the same chromosome, while mice have four sets, each on a different chromosome (it appears the vertebrate genome underwent two entire duplications early in vertebrate evolution). In the illustration here, the genes are color-coded to match the parts of the body in which they are expressed.

How does a cluster of *Hox* genes work together to control segment development? Each *Hox* gene produces a protein with an identical 60-amino acid segment that lets it bind to DNA as a transcription factor and, in so doing, activate the genes located where it binds. The differences between each *Hox* gene of a set determine where on DNA a Hox protein binds, and so which set of genes it activates.

Hox genes have also been found in clusters in radially symmetrical cnidarians such as hydra, suggesting that the ancestral *Hox* cluster preceded the divergence of radially and symmetrical animals in animal evolution.

25.12 Echinoderms: The First Deuterostomes

The first deuterostomes, marine animals called **echinoderms** in the phylum Echinodermata, appeared more than 650 million years ago. The term *echinoderm* means "spiny skin" and refers to an **endoskeleton** composed of hard, calcium-rich plates called ossicles just beneath the delicate skin. When they are first formed, the plates are enclosed in living tissue, and so are truly an endoskeleton, although in adults they fuse, forming a hard shell. About 6,000 species of echinoderms are living today, almost all of them on the ocean bottom (figure 25.35). Many of the most familiar animals seen along the seashore are echinoderms, including sea stars (starfish), sea urchins, sand dollars, and sea cucumbers.

The body plan of echinoderms undergoes a fundamental shift during development: All echinoderms are bilaterally symmetrical as larvae but become radially symmetrical as adults. Many biologists believe that early echinoderms were sessile and evolved adult radial symmetry as an adaptation to the sessile existence. Bilateral symmetry is of adaptive value to an animal that travels through its environment, whereas radial symmetry is of value to an animal whose environment meets it on all sides. Adult echinoderms have a five-part body plan, easily seen in the five arms of a sea star in figure 25.36. Its nervous system consists of a central ring of nerves from which five branches arise—while the animal is capable of complex response patterns, there is no centralization of function, no "brain." Some echinoderms like feather stars have 10 or 15 arms, but always multiples of five.

A key evolutionary innovation of echinoderms is the development of a hydraulic system to aid movement. Called a **water vascular system,** this fluid-filled system is composed of a central ring canal from which five radial canals extend out into the arms (the yellow structures in figure 25.36). From each radial canal, tiny vessels extend through short side branches into thousands of tiny, hollow **tube feet.** At the base of each tube foot is a fluid-filled muscular sac that acts as a valve (the yellow balls labeled "ampulla"). When a sac contracts, its fluid is prevented from reentering the radial canal and instead is forced into the tube foot, thus extending it. When extended, the tube foot attaches itself to the ocean bottom, often aided by suckers. The sea star can then pull against these tube feet and so haul itself over the seafloor.

Most echinoderms reproduce sexually, but they have the ability to regenerate lost parts, which can lead to asexual reproduction. In a few sea stars, asexual reproduction takes place by splitting, and the broken parts of the sea star can sometimes regenerate whole animals.

Key characteristics of the phylum Echinodermata are summarized in figure 25.36.

> **25.12** Echinoderms are deuterostomes with an endoskeleton of hard plates, often fused together. Adults are radially symmetrical.

Figure 25.35 Diversity in echinoderms.
(*a*) Warty sea cucumber, *Parastichopus parvimensis.* (*b*) Feather star (class Crinoidea) on the Great Barrier Reef in Australia. (*c*) Brittle star, *Ophiothrix* (class Ophiuroidea). (*d*) Sand dollar, *Echinarachnius parma.* (*e*) Giant red sea urchin, *Strongylocentrotus franciscanus.* (*f*) Sea star, *Oreaster occidentalis* (class Asteroidea), in the Gulf of California, Mexico.

Phylum Echinodermata: Echinoderms

Key Evolutionary Innovations: DEUTEROSTOME DEVELOPMENT and ENDOSKELETON

Echinoderms like sea stars (phylum Echinodermata) are coelomates with a **deuterostome** pattern of development. A delicate skin stretches over an **endoskeleton** made of calcium-rich plates, often fused into a continuous, tough spiny layer.

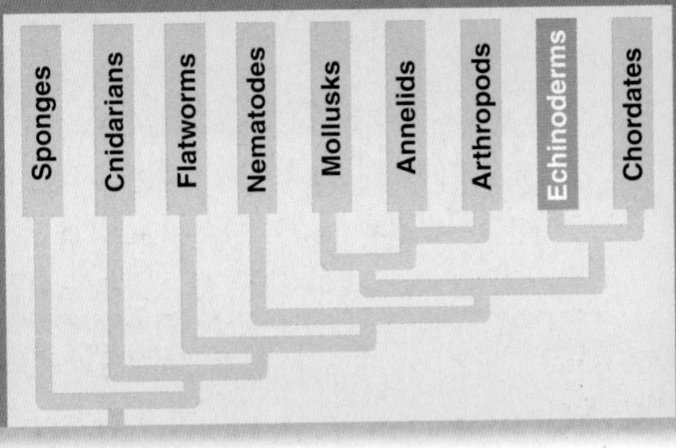

Sponges Cnidarians Flatworms Nematodes Mollusks Annelids Arthropods Echinoderms Chordates

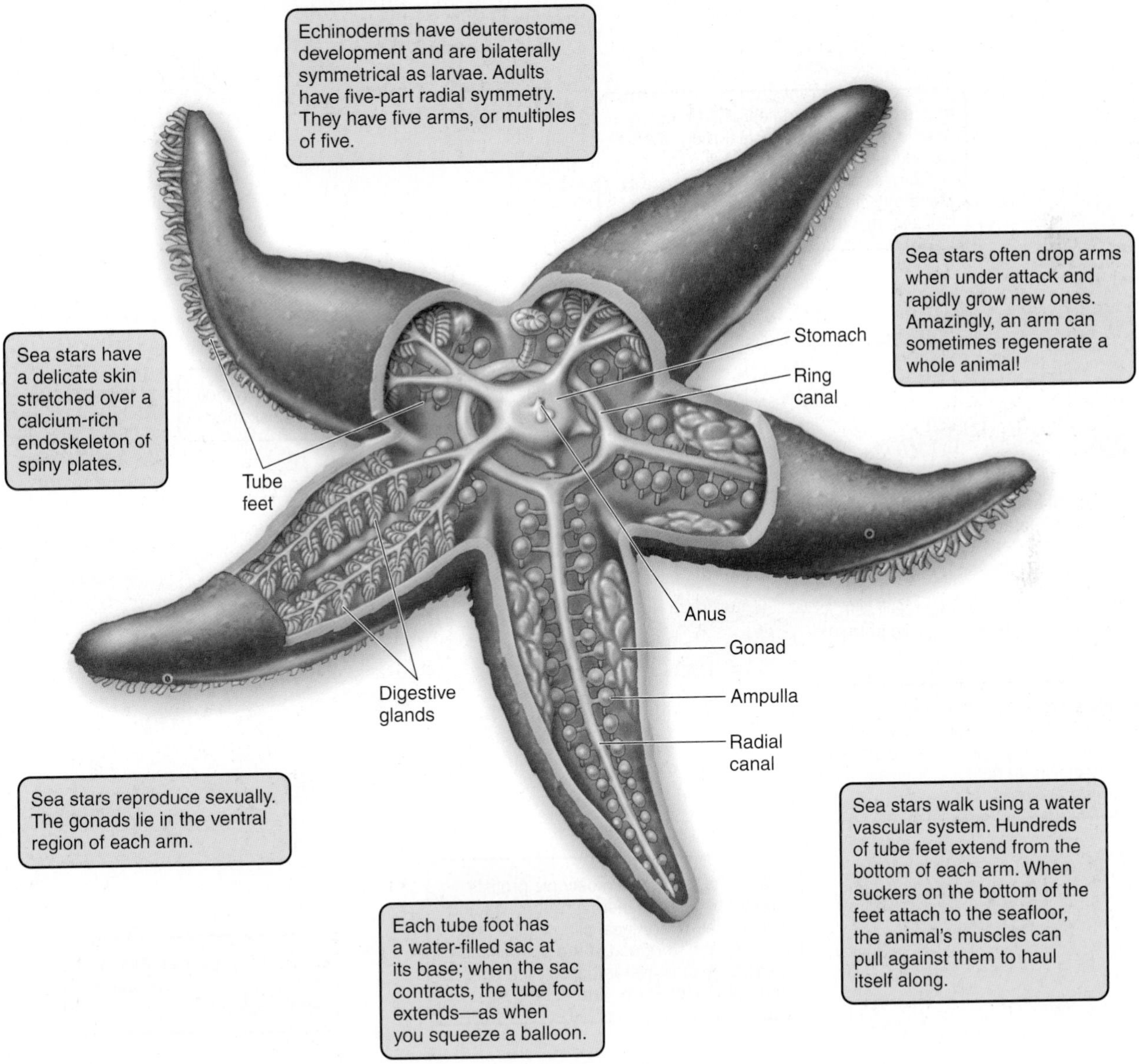

Echinoderms have deuterostome development and are bilaterally symmetrical as larvae. Adults have five-part radial symmetry. They have five arms, or multiples of five.

Sea stars often drop arms when under attack and rapidly grow new ones. Amazingly, an arm can sometimes regenerate a whole animal!

Sea stars have a delicate skin stretched over a calcium-rich endoskeleton of spiny plates.

Stomach

Ring canal

Tube feet

Anus

Gonad

Ampulla

Radial canal

Digestive glands

Sea stars reproduce sexually. The gonads lie in the ventral region of each arm.

Each tube foot has a water-filled sac at its base; when the sac contracts, the tube foot extends—as when you squeeze a balloon.

Sea stars walk using a water vascular system. Hundreds of tube feet extend from the bottom of each arm. When suckers on the bottom of the feet attach to the seafloor, the animal's muscles can pull against them to haul itself along.

Figure 25.36 Phylum Echinodermata: Echinoderms.

Phylum Chordata: Chordates

Key Evolutionary Innovation: NOTOCHORD

Vertebrates, tunicates, and lancelets are chordates (phylum Chordata), coelomate animals with a stiff, but flexible, rod, the **notochord**, that acts to anchor internal muscles, permitting rapid body movements. Chordates also possess **pharyngeal pouches** (relics of their aquatic ancestry) and a dorsal **hollow nerve cord**. In vertebrates, the notochord is replaced during embryonic development by the vertebral column.

Sponges | Cnidarians | Flatworms | Nematodes | Mollusks | Annelids | Arthropods | Echinoderms | Chordates

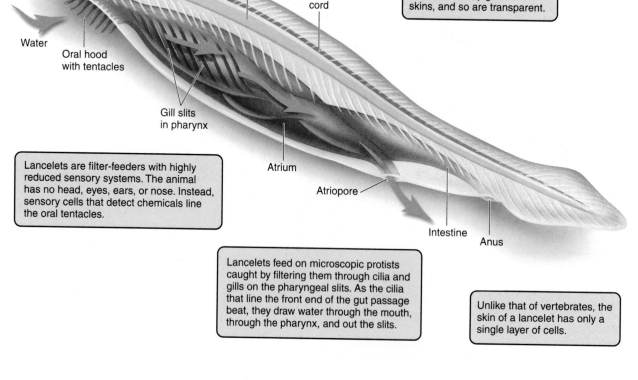

In a lancelet, the simplest chordate, the flexible notochord persists throughout life and aids swimming by giving muscles something to pull against. In the lancelet these muscles form a series of discrete blocks that can easily be seen.

Notochord

Dorsal nerve cord

Lancelets lack pigment in their skins, and so are transparent.

Water

Oral hood with tentacles

Gill slits in pharynx

Atrium

Lancelets are filter-feeders with highly reduced sensory systems. The animal has no head, eyes, ears, or nose. Instead, sensory cells that detect chemicals line the oral tentacles.

Atriopore

Intestine

Anus

Lancelets feed on microscopic protists caught by filtering them through cilia and gills on the pharyngeal slits. As the cilia that line the front end of the gut passage beat, they draw water through the mouth, through the pharynx, and out the slits.

Unlike that of vertebrates, the skin of a lancelet has only a single layer of cells.

Figure 25.37   Phylum Chordata: Chordates.

25.13 Chordates: Improving the Skeleton

General Characteristics of Chordates

Chordates (phylum Chordata) are deuterostome coelomates whose nearest relations in the animal kingdom are the echinoderms, also deuterostomes. Chordates exhibit great improvements in the endoskeleton over what is seen in echinoderms. The endoskeleton of echinoderms is functionally similar to the exoskeleton of arthropods, in that it is a hard shell that encases the body, with muscles attached to its inner surface. Chordates employ a very different kind of endoskeleton, one that is truly internal. Members of the phylum Chordata are characterized by a flexible rod called a **notochord** that develops along the back of the embryo. Muscles attached to this rod allowed early chordates to swing their bodies back and forth, swimming through the water. This key evolutionary innovation, attaching muscles to an internal element, started chordates along an evolutionary path that leads to the vertebrates and for the first time to truly large animals.

The approximately 56,000 species of chordates are distinguished by four principal features:

1. **Notochord.** A stiff, but flexible, rod that forms beneath the nerve cord in the early embryo (the yellow rod in figure 25.37).
2. **Nerve cord.** A single dorsal (along the back) hollow nerve cord (the blue rod in figure 25.37), to which the nerves that reach the different parts of the body are attached.
3. **Pharyngeal pouches.** A series of pouches behind the mouth that develop into slits in some animals. The slits open into the pharynx, which is a muscular tube that connects the mouth to the digestive tract and windpipe (the gill slits are labeled in figure 25.37).
4. **Postanal tail.** Chordates have a postanal tail, a tail that extends beyond the anus. A postanal tail is present at least during their embryonic development if not in the adult. Nearly all other animals have a terminal anus.

All chordates have all four of these characteristics at some time in their lives. For example, the tunicates in figure 25.38a look more like sponges than chordates, but their larval stage, which resembles a tadpole, has all four features listed above. Human embryos have pharyngeal pouches, a nerve cord, a notochord, and a postanal tail as embryos. The nerve cord remains in the adult, differentiating into the brain and spinal cord. The pharyngeal pouches and postanal tail disappear during human development, and the notochord is replaced with the vertebral column.

Vertebrates

In their body plan, chordates are segmented, and distinct blocks of muscles can be seen clearly in many forms (figure 25.39). With the exception of tunicates (figure 25.38a) and lancelets

(a)   (b)

Figure 25.38 Nonvertebrate chordates.

(a) Beautiful blue and gold tunicates. (b) Two lancelets, *Branchiostoma lanceolatum*, partly buried in shell gravel, with their anterior ends protruding. The muscle segments are clearly visible in this photograph.

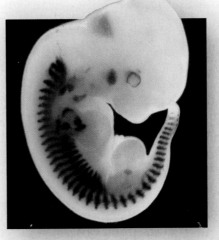

Figure 25.39 A mouse embryo.

At 11.5 days of development, the muscle is already divided into segments called somites (stained *dark* in this photo), reflecting the fundamentally segmented nature of all chordates.

(figure 25.38b), all chordates are **vertebrates.** Vertebrates differ from tunicates and lancelets in two important respects:

1. **Backbone.** The notochord becomes surrounded and then replaced during the course of the embryo's development by a bony vertebral column, a tube of hollow bones called *vertebrae* that encloses the dorsal nerve cord like a sleeve and protects it.
2. **Head.** All vertebrates except the earliest fishes have a distinct and well-differentiated head, with a skull and brain.

All vertebrates have an internal skeleton made of bone or cartilage against which the muscles work. This endoskeleton makes possible the great size and extraordinary powers of movement that characterize the vertebrates.

The evolution and characteristics of the major groups of vertebrates are discussed in detail in chapter 26.

> **25.13 Chordates have a notochord at some stage of their development. In adult vertebrates, the notochord is replaced by a backbone.**

Punctuated Equilibrium: Evaluating a Case History

Biologists have long argued over the rate at which evolution occurs. As you read in chapter 17 (section 17.1, under "The Rate of Evolution"), some organisms appear to have evolved gradually (gradualism), while in others evolution seems to have occurred in spurts (punctuated equilibrium). There is evidence of both patterns in the fossil record. Perhaps the most famous claim of punctuated equilibrium has been made by researchers studying the fossil record of marine bryozoans. Bryozoans are microscopic aquatic animals that form branching colonies. You encountered them earlier in this chapter as lophophorates. The fossil record is particularly well documented for Caribbean bryozoan species of the genus *Metrarabdotos,* whose fossil record extends back more than 15 million years without interruption (a **fossil** is the mineralized stonelike remains of a long-dead organism; a **fossil record** is the total collection of fossils of that particular kind of organism known to science).

The graph to the upper right displays an analysis of the *Metrarabdotos* fossil record. Researchers first formulated a comprehensive character index based upon a broad array of bryozoan traits. (A **character index** is a number assigned to a specimen based on its morphology. Different characteristics are measured and assigned quantitative values, and the character index is determined by adding together the individual character values that apply to the specimen. The closer the character indices are for two specimens, the more closely related they are.) Then each fossil is measured for all of the traits. They then calculated the index number for that fossil and plotted it on the graph as a black dot. Each cluster of dots within an oval represents a distinct species.

1. **Applying Concepts**
   a. Variable. In the diagram, is there a dependent variable? If so, what is it?
   b. Analyzing Diagrams. How many different species are included in the study illustrated by this diagram? How many of these are extinct?

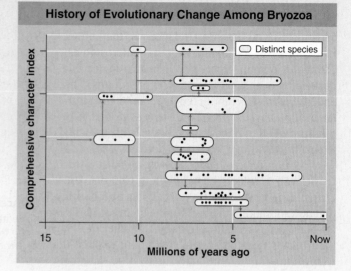

History of Evolutionary Change Among Bryozoa

Comprehensive character index

Distinct species

15 — 10 — 5 — Now

Millions of years ago

2. **Interpreting Data**
   a. For each species, estimate how long that species survives in the fossil record. For simplicity, a species found only once should be assigned a duration of 1 million years. What is the average evolutionary duration of a *Metrarabdotos* species?
   b. Create a histogram of your species-duration estimates (place the duration times on the *x* axis and the number of species on the *y* axis). What general statement can be made regarding the distribution of *Metrarabdotos* species durations?
3. **Making Inferences**
   a. How many of the species exhibit variation in the comprehensive character index?
   b. How does the magnitude of this variation *within* species compare with the variation seen *between* species?
4. **Drawing Conclusions** Does major evolutionary change, as measured by significant changes in this comprehensive character index, occur gradually or in occasional bursts?
5. **Further Analysis** Plot the number of *Metrarabdotos* species versus date (millions of years ago), in increments of 1 million years. Characterize the result. What do you suppose is responsible for this? How would you go about assessing this possibility?

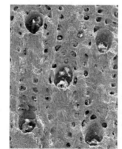
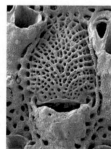
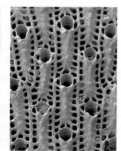
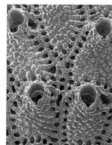

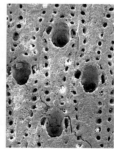

Six species of fossil *Metrarabdotos*

Introduction to the Animals

25.1 General Features of Animals

- Animals are complex multicellular heterotrophs. They are mobile and reproduce sexually. Animals cells do not have cell walls, and animal embryos have a similar pattern of development (**table 25.1**).

25.2 The Animal Family Tree

- Traditionally, animals have been classified based on morphological characteristics. Phylogeny was also determined using anatomical features and embryological development (**figure 25.1**). But, this traditional view of animal phylogeny is now being reevaluated. New molecular methods that compare RNA and DNA of animals are producing new phylogenies (**figure 25.2**). The classification of the protostomes has been reorganized based on how they grow.

25.3 Five Key Transitions in Body Plan

- The large diversity of animals can be traced to five key transitions in body plan—the evolution of tissues, bilateral symmetry, a body cavity, deuterostome pattern of development, and body segmentation. The beetle shown here from **figure 25.3** exhibits four of these five transitions, lacking only deuterostome development.

The Simplest Animals

25.4 Sponges: Animals Without Tissues

- Sponges, in the subkingdom Parazoa, are aquatic, have specialized cells, but lack tissues. The vase-shaped adult is anchored to a substrate (**figure 25.4**). Sponges are filter-feeders. Specialized cells called choanocytes trap food particles that are filtered from the water (**figure 25.5**).

25.5 Cnidarians: Tissues Lead to Greater Specialization

- Cnidarians have radially symmetrical bodies and two embryonic cell layers, an ectoderm and an endoderm (**figure 25.7**). Cnidarians are carnivores, capturing their prey and digesting it extracellularly in the gastrovascular cavity. Many cnidarians exist only as polyps or medusae (**figure 25.8**), but some cnidarians alternate forms during their life cycles (**figure 25.9**).

The Advent of Bilateral Symmetry

25.6 Solid Worms: Bilateral Symmetry

- All other animals exhibit bilateral symmetry (**figure 25.10**). In addition to the ectoderm and endoderm, the bilateral eumetazoans also have a mesoderm layer that forms between the other two.

- The simplest bilaterally symmetrical animals are the solid worms, including flatworms (**figure 25.11**), flukes (**figure 25.13**), and other parasitic worms (**figure 25.14**). They have three embryonic tissue layers and a digestive cavity but are acoelomates, lacking a body cavity. In many flatworms, the gut is branched, as shown here from **figure 25.15** and serves in both digestion and circulation. Flatworms have an excretory system to get rid of waste using specialized cells called flame cells.

The Advent of a Body Cavity

25.7 Roundworms: The Evolution of a Body Cavity

- The evolution of a body cavity improved circulation, movement, and organ function. The roundworms have a body cavity between the endoderm and mesoderm, which is not a true body cavity, so they are called pseudocoelomates (**figures 25.16** and **25.18**).

25.8 Mollusks: Coelomates

- Mollusks are coelomates, having a true body cavity that forms within the mesoderm. There are three major groups of mollusks: gastropods (snails and slugs), bivalves (clams and oysters), and cephalopods (octopuses and squids). The group is diverse, but all contain a head-foot, a visceral mass (that contains the body organs), and a mantle. Many mollusks also have a rasping tonguelike structure called a radula (**figure 25.20**).

25.9 Annelids: The Rise of Segmentation

- Segmentation first evolved in annelid worms, phylum Annelida, which provided evolutionary flexibility in that different segments could become specialized for different functions. The basic body plan of annelids is a tube-in-a-tube; the digestive tract and other organs are suspended in the coelom (**figure 25.22**).

25.10 Arthropods: Advent of Jointed Appendages

- Arthropods are the most successful animal phylum. About two-thirds of all named species are arthropods. Arthropods are segmented, with segments fusing to form three body parts: head, thorax, and abdomen (**figure 25.24**). Jointed appendages first evolved in this group, which allowed for improved mobility, grasping, biting, and chewing A rigid exoskeleton provides protection for the animal and serves as an anchor for muscles (**figure 25.25**). Arthropods include a wide variety of animals including spiders, mites, scorpions, crustaceans, insects, centipedes, and millipedes (**figures 25.27** through **25.33**).

Redesigning the Embryo

25.11 Protostomes and Deuterostomes

- There are two different developmental patterns in coelomates. In protostomes, the blastopore develops into the mouth. Mollusks, annelids, and arthropods are protostomes. In deuterostomes, the echinoderms and chordates, the blastopore develops into the anus. Other aspect of development differ between these two groups including spiral cleavage in protostomes and radial cleavage in deuterostomes, as shown here from **figure 25.34**.

25.12 Echinoderms: The First Deuterostomes

- Echinoderms have an endoskeleton made up of bony plates that lie under the skin. The adults are radially symmetrical, which appears to be an adaptation to their environment (**figure 25.36**).

25.13 Chordates: Improving the Skeleton

- The chordates have a truly internal endoskeleton and are distinguished by the presence of a notochord, a dorsal nerve cord, pharyngeal pouches, and a postanal tail (**figure 25.37**). The notochord is replaced with the backbone in vertebrates.

1. The traditional organization of the animal family tree of classification is based mostly on
   a. DNA sequences.
   b. protein structure.
   c. conserved anatomical characteristics.
   d. ribosome structure.

2. Sponges possess unique, collared flagellated cells called
   a. cnidocytes.
   b. choanocytes.
   c. choanoflagellates.
   d. epithelial cells.

3. A characteristic that animals in the phylum Cnidaria share with fungi is
   a. chitinous structural support.
   b. sporulation.
   c. extracellular digestion.
   d. cnidocytes.

4. Which of the following characteristics is *not* seen in the phylum Platyhelminthes?
   a. cephalization
   b. the presence of a mesoderm
   c. specialization of digestive tract
   d. bilateral symmetry

5. One difference between the pseudocoel found in the phylum Nematoda (roundworms) and the coelom found in the phylum Annelida (segmented worms) is the pseudocoel develops between the mesoderm and the _____ in roundworms and the coelom develops in the _____ in segmented worms.
   a. ectoderm; mesoderm
   b. endoderm; mesoderm
   c. ectoderm; endoderm
   d. endoderm; ectoderm

6. Unlike other coelomate animal phyla, mollusks lack
   a. segmentation.
   b. cephalization.
   c. three primary tissue layers.
   d. some type of body cavity.

7. Segmentation, first seen in annelids, allows evolutionary advantages by
   a. allowing more fluid movement for less energy expense.
   b. specialization of segments to carry out different functions.
   c. allowing coelom development.
   d. concentrating sensory and nervous tissues and organs in the direction of motion.

8. The main limiting factor of arthropod size is the
   a. inefficiency of open circulatory systems.
   b. weight of the muscles needed to move the organism.
   c. weight of the thick exoskeleton needed to support very large insects.
   d. entire weight of the organism that would crush the soft body of the arthropod during molting.

9. Echinoderms begin life as free-swimming larvae with bilateral symmetry and then become adults with radial symmetry. Some biologists explain this change in symmetry as a change in form appropriate for
   a. an animal traveling through the environment to a form more appropriate to a sessile lifestyle.
   b. an animal with a sessile lifestyle to a form more appropriate to traveling through the environment.
   c. a predator to a form more appropriate to a filter-feeder.
   d. an animal living in freshwater to a form more appropriate to an animal living in a marine environment.

10. Which of the following animals is *not* a chordate?
    a. dogs
    b. sea cucumbers
    c. tunicates
    d. lancelets

1. **Figure 25.23** About two-thirds of all the named species on our planet are arthropods. From the arthropod pie chart, estimate about what percentage of the named species on our planet are beetles.

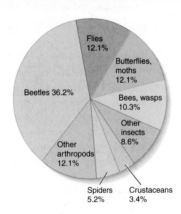

Flies 12.1%
Butterflies, moths 12.1%
Beetles 36.2%
Bees, wasps 10.3%
Other insects 8.6%
Other arthropods 12.1%
Spiders 5.2%
Crustaceans 3.4%

2. **Figures 25.24 and 25.30** What segment of the grasshopper, a typical insect, contains the legs? What segment of the lobster, a typical crustacean, contains the legs? Look at some of the other images in the chapter. Does this seem to be true of all arthropods?

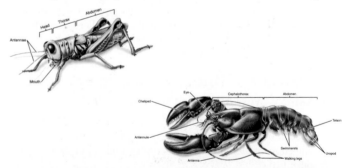

1. You have discovered a new organism deep in the jungle. You are trying to decide if it is a very slow-moving animal or a plant that responds to light and touch. What characteristics can you investigate to help you decide?

2. Compare sponges and cnidarians. How do food particles and waste products enter and leave the organism?

3. Is there some digestive advantage to being a planarian rather than an organism such as a cnidarian?

4. Why is the body cavity such a useful innovation in the animal kingdom?

5. Why is the internal skeleton of vertebrates so useful, compared to the external skeleton of many other animals?

Appendix A
Answers to Self-Test Questions

Chapter 1: The Science of Biology

1. a. kingdoms 2. c. cellular organization
3. b. atom, molecule, organelle, cell, tissue, organ, organ system, organism, population, species, community, ecosystem
4. d. emergent properties 5. b. evolution, energy flow, cooperation, structure determines function, and homeostasis
6. a. inductive reasoning 7. b. test each hypothesis, using appropriate controls, to rule out as many as possible 8. c. After sufficient testing, you can accept it as probable, being aware that it may be revised or rejected in the future 9. d. all living organisms consist of cells, and all cells come from other cells 10. c. is contained in a long molecule called DNA

Chapter 2: Evolution and Ecology

1. c. populations can change over time, sometimes forming new species 2. b. the characteristics of a species varied in different places; there were geographic patterns 3. c. populations are capable of geometric increase, yet remain at constant levels 4. a. natural selection 5. b. seems to agree with Darwin's original ideas 6. d. niche 7. a. population 8. d. energy flows through once and is lost, while materials cycle and recycle 9. d. competitive exclusion 10. b. predation

Chapter 3: The Chemistry of Life

1. b. an atom 2. c. an ion 3. d. ionic, covalent, and hydrogen 4. b. it can form four single covalent bonds 5. d. All of these are correct 6. a. hydrogen bonds between the individual water molecules 7. c. heat storage and heat of vaporization
8. a. cohesion 9. a. (1) acids and (2) bases
10. c. to keep pH from ever changing

Chapter 4: Molecules of Life

1. b. proteins, carbohydrates, lipids, and nucleic acids 2. c. polypeptides
3. c. structure, function 4. d. All of these
5. d. are information storage devices found in body cells 6. a. Adenine forms hydrogen bonds with thymine 7. a. structure and for energy 8. a. glycogen 9. d. All of these are

characteristics of fats. 10. c. energy storage and for some hormones

Chapter 5: Cells

1. a. cells are the smallest living things. Nothing smaller than a cell is considered alive 2. b. a double lipid layer with proteins inserted in it, which surrounds every cell individually 3. d. prokaryotes, eukaryotes
4. a. a nucleolus 5. c. endoplasmic reticulum and the Golgi complex
6. d. mitochondria and the chloroplasts
7. b. Eukaryotic cells in plants and fungi, and all prokaryotes, have a cell wall
8. d. slowly disperse throughout the water; this is because of diffusion 9. b. endocytosis and phagocytosis 10. c. energy and specialized pumps or channels

Chapter 6: Energy and Life

1. c. energy 2. d. says that energy can change forms, but cannot be made or destroyed 3. b. says that entropy, or disorder, continually increases in a closed system 4. a. exergonic and release energy
5. b. enzymes 6. c. temperature and pH
7. d. All of these are true 8. c. an inhibitor molecule competes with the substrate for the active site on the enzyme 9. a. ATP molecules 10. b. gained energy

Chapter 7: Photosynthesis: Acquiring Energy from the Sun

1. c. photosynthesis 2. b. with molecules called pigments that absorb photons and use their energy 3. c. a small portion in the middle of the spectrum 4. a. red, blue, and orange 5. d. All of these are true 6. c. only go through the system once; they are obtained by splitting a water molecule
7. b. chemiosmosis 8. a. electron transport system of photosystem I, Calvin cycle
9. c. build sugar molecules 10. b. use C_4 photosynthesis or CAM

Chapter 8: How Cells Harvest Energy from Food

1. a. breaking down the organic molecules that were consumed 2. b. fermentation
3. c. substrate-level phosphorylation
4. b. glycolysis 5. b. makes ATP by splitting glucose and capturing the energy

6. b. NAD^+, the electron transport chain
7. a. pyruvate 8. c. mitochondria of the cell and are broken down in the presence of O_2 to make more ATP 9. d. during the electron transport chain 10. c. each type of macromolecule is broken down into its subunits, which enter the oxidative respiration pathway

Chapter 9: Mitosis

1. a. copying DNA then undergoing binary fission 2. c. in the production of daughter cells 3. c. and most eukaryotes have between 10 and 50 pairs of chromosomes
4. c. carry information about the same traits located in the same places on the chromosomes 5. b. metaphase
6. c. cytokinesis 7. a. a series of checkpoints
8. b. cancer 9. c. an oncogene 10. d. All of the above

Chapter 10: Meiosis

1. d. the germ cells went through meiosis; the egg and sperm only have half the parental chromosomes 2. d. 23 3. a. $1n$ gametes (haploid), followed by $2n$ zygotes (diploid) 4. b. Homologous chromosomes randomly separate, called independent assortment 5. c. The duplicated sister chromatids separate 6. a. prophase I
7. c. homologous chromosomes become closely associated 8. a. make diploid cells / make haploid cells 9. c. has a lot of genetic reassortment due to processes in meiosis I
10. a. sexual reproduction

Chapter 11: Foundations of Genetics

1. d. All of these 2. a. all purple flowers
3. c. 3/4 purple and 1/4 white flowers
4. b. some factor, or information, about traits to their offspring and it may or may not be expressed 5. a. dihybrid cross
6. d. multiple genes 7. c. codominant traits
8. b. sex-linked eye color in fruit flies
9. d. All of the above 10. d. genetic screening and prenatal diagnosis is now available

Chapter 12: DNA: The Genetic Material

1. b. hereditary information can be added to cells from other cells 2. d. DNA

3. a. structure of DNA 4. c. the type of nitrogen base 5. d. adenine and guanine 6. b. TAACGTA 7. b. splits down the middle into two single strands, and each one then acts as a template to build its complement 8. a. a primer 9. c. by mutation or by recombination 10. a. germ-line tissues and be passed on to future generations

Chapter 13: How Genes Work

1. a. nRNA (nuclear RNA) 2. d. a codon 3. c. 64 4. c. transcription 5. a. promotor 6. d. translation 7. c. AUG 8. d. some genes are always off while a repressor is bound 9. c. Repressors block transcription by binding to the DNA. 10. c. chemically modifying the mRNA so it can't be translated

Chapter 14: Gene Technology

1. c. Genetic engineering can only transfer genes between two prokaryotic organisms or two eukaryotic organisms, but not between prokaryotic and eukaryotic organisms 2. c. restriction enzyme 3. b. cleaving DNA, producing recombinant DNA, cloning, and screening 4. b. transformation 5. d. All of these answers are correct 6. b. exposing the cytoplasmic mRNA of the desired gene to the enzyme reverse transcriptase 7. a. the drug to be produced in far larger amounts than in the past 8. c. prime killer T cells to attack specific viruses when they enter the body 9. a. increased yield 10. d. harm to the crop itself from mutations

Chapter 15: Genomics

1. c. genome 2. a. Frederick Sanger 3. d. All answers are correct 4. a. Genes are expressed at different times and in different ways 5. d. whole-genome duplication 6. c. segmental duplications 7. b. the exons used to make a specific mRNA can be rearranged to form different proteins 8. b. structural DNA 9. c. Barbara McClintock 10. a. diagnose cancer or a genetic disorder before it is expressed

Chapter 16: The Revolution in Cell Technology

1. a. combines an adult cell with an egg cell whose nucleus has been removed 2. d. synchronizing the egg and nucleus to the same stage of the cell cycle 3. b. the reprogramming of DNA that determines which genes are "readable" and at what time during the organism's life cycle they are read 4. d. methylation or demethylation of DNA 5. b. able to form any kind of body tissue 6. c. the inner cell mass of blastocysts 7. a. immunological rejection of the tissue by the patient 8. c. viruses 9. b. failed due to immunological response caused by the method of gene transmission 10. b. deciding on whether or not to use a genetic intervention means carefully examining risks and benefits

Chapter 17: Evolution and Natural Selection

1. c. macroevolution 2. b. analogous structures 3. a. divergence 4. b. large population size 5. c. no mutation within the population 6. a. 0.20 7. d. genetic drift 8. c. directional selection 9. d. reproductive isolation 10. b. mechanical

Chapter 18: How We Name Living Things

1. a. the red fox is in the same family, but different genus than dogs and wolves 2. b. phylogeny 3. a. physical, behavioral, and molecular characteristics 4. e. share a more recent common ancestor than those organisms that are farther apart 5. d. cell structure and DNA sequence 6. b. Archaea 7. d. do not have an internal membrane system 8. c. Protista 9. b. multicellular 10. d. endosymbiosis of bacteria

Chapter 19: Prokaryotes: The First Single-Celled Creatures

1. b. the primordial atmosphere of the earth contained the same amount of oxygen as today 2. c. RNA 3. d. All answers are correct 4. b. chemoautotrophs 5. d. All of the above 6. d. producing the oxygen that is in the atmosphere 7. a. protein coats that contain DNA or RNA 8. c. lytic cycle 9. b. matching a marker on the surface of the virus to a complementary marker on the surface of a cell 10. c. use an enzyme called reverse transcriptase to convert the viral RNA to DNA, which is then integrated into the cell's chromosome.

Chapter 20: Protists: Advent of the Eukaryotes

1. b. mitochondria and chloroplasts have their own DNA 2. c. cysts 3. d. mushrooms 4. d. All of the above 5. b. brown algae 6. a. have both a sexual and an asexual phase 7. c. green algae 8. b. choanoflagellates 9. a. cytoplasm 10. c. slime molds

Chapter 21: Fungi Invade the Land

1. c. cell specialization 2. b. cellulose cell walls 3. d. mycelium 4. a. both sexually and asexually 5. b. Ascomycota 6. c. a heterokaryon 7. a. a special sac called the ascus 8. b. basidia 9. b. algae and fungi 10. d. minerals

Chapter 22: Evolution of Plants

1. c. dehydration 2. a. chloroplasts 3. b. they do not have specialized vascular tissue to transport water very high 4. d. seeds 5. c. sporophyte 6. d. dispersal 7. c. ovules not completely covered by the sporophyte 8. c. fruits and flowers 9. a. pollination 10. c. an animal's digestive system and processes

Chapter 23: Plant Form and Function

1. c. meristematic tissue 2. b. transports carbohydrates 3. a. stomata 4. d. at the pericycle 5. c. cambium 6. b. organization of vascular tissue 7. c. spongy mesophyll 8. a. photosynthesis 9. b. translocation 10. d. osmosis

Chapter 24: Plant Reproduction and Growth

1. a. pollen 2. b. monoecious 3. b. animal pollinators 4. d. oxygen and water 5. a. ovary 6. c. hormones 7. c. cells in plant stems to elongate 8. b. fruit to ripen 9. c. photoperiod 10. a. thigmotropism

Chapter 25: Evolution of the Animal Phyla

1. c. conserved anatomical characteristics 2. b. choanocytes 3. c. extracellular digestion 4. c. specialization of digestive tract 5. b. endoderm; mesoderm 6. a. segmentation 7. b. specialization of segments to carry out different functions 8. c. weight of the thick exoskeleton needed to support very large insects 9. a. an animal traveling through the environment to a form more appropriate to a sessile lifestyle 10. b. sea cucumbers

Chapter 26: History of the Vertebrates

1. b. era, period, epoch, age 2. d. arthropods and the chordates 3. a. amphibians 4. d. All answers are correct 5. b. jaws 6. c. an internal skeleton made of cartilage 7. c. middle ear bones 8. d. thin, hollow bones in the skeleton 9. b. They have high

metabolic rates 10. c. a placenta and internal development of offspring

Chapter 27: How Humans Evolved

1. b. opposable digits on hands 2. a. Africa
3. c. lemurs 4. d. All of the above
5. d. bipedalism 6. a. brain size
7. b. *Australopithecus anamensis*
8. d. *Homo habilis* 9. d. *Homo erectus*
10. b. Africa

Chapter 28: The Animal Body and How It Moves

1. b. more flexible movement as individual segments can move independently of each other 2. a. cells, tissues, organs, organ systems, organism 3. c. move the body
4. d. red blood cells 5. c. osteoblasts; osteoclasts 6. b. neurotransmitters
7. a. skeletal 8. b. axial skeleton 9. a. a single muscle can only pull and not push
10. d. expose myosin attachment sites on actin

Chapter 29: Circulation

1. d. All of the above are functions of the circulatory system 2. c. by passing warm blood near cold blood in the extremities to warm the blood 3. a. capillaries 4. d. carry fluids 5. d. erythrocyte 6. c. A heart with separate chambers is first seen in fishes
7. b. better separation of oxygenated and deoxygenated blood 8. a. Only arteries carry oxygenated blood 9. d. endothermy
10. b. sphygmomanometer

Chapter 30: Respiration

1. c. the animal's blood to be continually exposed to water of higher oxygen concentration 2. b. increase the surface area available for gas exchange 3. a. energy need for different vertebrate classes increases
4. c. fish 5. c. It takes three cycles of breathing for air to pass through the bird's respiratory system 6. c. contracting the muscles in the thoracic cavity pushes your chest out 7. a. hemoglobin in red blood cells 8. b. the blood plasma as bicarbonate
9. a. bicarbonate 10. d. All of the above

Chapter 31: The Path of Food Through the Animal Body

1. b. specialization of different regions of the digestive system 2. a. herbivores
3. d. begin the physical digestion of food
4. c. soft palate 5. c. stomach 6. b. Only ruminants are able to digest cellulose
7. c. small intestine 8. d. increase the surface area of the small intestine for absorption of nutrients 9. c. the concentration of solid wastes 10. a. pancreas

Chapter 32: Maintaining the Internal Environment

1. b. homeostasis 2. d. negative feedback loop 3. a. pancreas 4. b. ants 5. b. glycogen to break down 6. b. no water and excrete large volumes of urine that are hypotonic to body fluids 7. b. freshwater fish 8. c. loop of Henle 9. d. osmosis 10. d. urea

Chapter 33: How the Animal Body Defends Itself

1. a. sweat and oil glands 2. b. do not have the proper cell surface proteins that identify the cell as the body's own 3. c. increase the number of immune system cells in an infected area 4. b. pathogenic bacteria do not grow well at high temperatures
5. a. T cells 6. c. B cells 7. d. destroy cells infected by pathogens 8. b. memory T and B cells 9. c. an autoimmune response
10. a. helper T cells

Chapter 34: The Nervous System

1. c. the amount of associative neurons, which eventually formed the "brain"
2. a. exchange of sodium and potassium ions 3. a. sodium ion gates in the postsynaptic cell 4. d. coordinates emotions
5. d. brain stem 6. b. relay messages to skeletal muscles 7. b. interoceptors
8. c. semicircular canals 9. c. The vertebrate eye adjusts the amount of light entering the eye by contracting the ciliary muscles
10. a. pressure waves

Chapter 35: Chemical Signaling Within the Animal Body

1. c. chemical signals stick around longer than nervous signals and can be used for slow processes 2. a. hypothalamus 3. a. all fit into receptors specifically shaped for them 4. b. steroid hormones must enter the cell to begin action, whereas peptide hormones must begin action on the external surface of the cell membrane 5. d. posterior pituitary gland 6. a. ACTH 7. a. pancreas 8. c. too much calcium in the blood 9. d. sympathetic nervous system 10. a. lack of iodine

Chapter 36: Reproduction and Development

1. b. sexual reproduction 2. d. internal fertilization 3. a. viviparity 4. d. scrotum 5. b. FSH and LH 6. a. embryo releasing hCG 7. d. gastrulation is complete
8. c. nervous 9. a. respiratory system is not fully formed 10. c. oxytocin

Chapter 37: Populations and Communities

1. c. carrying capacity 2. b. increased competition for food 3. a. short life span
4. b. will decrease, and the mortality will increase 5. d. community 6. c. resource partitioning 7. b. commensalism
8. b. decreasing competitive exclusion between prey species 9. a. aposematic coloration 10. c. secondary succession

Chapter 38: Ecosystems

1. c. producers 2. d. All answers are correct
3. d. amount of energy transferred to the top carnivores 4. a. from plants 5. b. light energy in photosynthesis 6. c. ATP
7. d. desert conditions on the downwind side of a mountain due to increased moisture-holding capacity of the winds as the air heats up 8. b. decreases, temperature increases 9. d. thermocline 10. c. tundra

Chapter 39: Behavior and the Environment

1. b. cannot be modified, as these behaviors seem built into the brain and nervous system 2. a. there is a clear link between presence or absence of a specific gene, a specific metabolic pathway, and a specific behavior 3. b. operant conditioning
4. c. reproductive fitness 5. d. foraging behavior 6. c. intersexual selection
7. b. polyandry 8. c. reciprocity 9. b. kin selection 10. d. ecological factors such as food type and predation

Chapter 40: How Humans Influence the Living World

1. d. sulfur oxides as a major air pollutant
2. b. coal-powered industry 3. a. ammonia
4. d. All answers are correct
5. c. chlorofluorocarbons
6. a. environmental costs are hardly ever recognized as part of the economy
7. a. needed to preserve possible direct value from species, such as new medicines
8. c. increasing amounts of open space as countries develop 9. d. captive propagation
10. a. keystone species

Glossary

Terms & Concepts

A

absorption (L. *absorbere*, to swallow down) The movement of water and substances dissolved in water into a cell, tissue, or organism.

acid Any substance that dissociates to form H^+ ions when dissolved in water. Having a pH value less than 7.

acoelomate (Gr. *a*, not + *koiloma*, cavity) A bilaterally symmetrical animal not possessing a body cavity, such as a flatworm.

actin (Gr. *actis*, ray) One of the two major proteins that make up myofilaments (the other is myosin). It provides the cell with mechanical support and plays major roles in determining cell shape and cell movement.

action potential A single nerve impulse. A transient all-or-none reversal of the electrical potential across a neuron membrane. Because it can activate nearby voltage-sensitive channels, an action potential propagates along a nerve cell.

activation energy The energy a molecule must acquire to undergo a specific chemical reaction.

active transport The transport of a solute across a membrane by protein carrier molecules to a region of higher concentration by the expenditure of chemical energy. One of the most important functions of any cell.

adaptation (L. *adaptare*, to fit) Any peculiarity of structure, physiology, or behavior that promotes the likelihood of an organism's survival and reproduction in a particular environment.

adenosine triphosphate (ATP) A molecule composed of ribose, adenine, and a triphosphate group. ATP is the chief energy currency of all cells. Cells focus all of their energy resources on the manufacture of ATP from ADP and phosphate, which requires the cell to supply 7 kilocalories of energy obtained from photosynthesis or from electrons stripped from foodstuffs to form 1 mole of ATP. Cells then use this ATP to drive endergonic reactions.

adhesion (L. *adhaerere*, to stick to) The molecular attraction exerted between the surfaces of unlike bodies in contact, as water molecules to the walls of the narrow tubes that occur in plants.

aerobic (Gr. *aer*, air + *bios*, life) Oxygen-requiring.

allele (Gr. *allelon*, of one another) One of two or more alternative forms of a gene.

allele frequency The relative proportion of a particular allele among individuals of a population. Not equivalent to gene frequency, although the two terms are sometimes confused.

allosteric interaction (Gr. *allos*, other + *stereos*, shape) The change in shape that occurs when an activator or repressor binds to an enzyme. These changes result when specific, small molecules bind to the enzyme, molecules that are not substrates of that enzyme.

alternation of generations A reproductive life cycle in which the multicellular diploid phase produces spores that give rise to the multicellular haploid phase and the multicellular haploid phase produces gametes that fuse to give rise to the zygote. The zygote is the first cell of the multicellular diploid phase.

alveolus, *pl.* alveoli (L. *alveus*, a small cavity) One of the many small, thin-walled air sacs within the lungs in which the bronchioles terminate.

amniotic egg An egg that is isolated and protected from the environment by a more or less impervious shell. The shell protects the embryo from drying out, nourishes it, and enables it to develop outside of water.

anaerobic (Gr. *an*, without + *aer*, air + *bios*, life) Any process that can occur without oxygen. Includes glycolysis and fermentation. Anaerobic organisms can live without free oxygen.

anaphase In mitosis and meiosis II, the stage initiated by the separation of sister chromatids, during which the daughter chromosomes move to opposite poles of the cell; in meiosis I, marked by separation of replicated homologous chromosomes.

angiosperms The flowering plants, one of five phyla of seed plants. In angiosperms, the ovules at the time of pollination are completely enclosed by tissues.

anterior (L. *ante*, before) Located before or toward the front. In animals, the head end of an organism.

anther (Gr. *anthos*, flower) The part of the stamen of a flower that bears the pollen.

antibody (Gr. *anti*, against) A protein substance produced by a B cell lymphocyte in response to a foreign substance (antigen) and released into the bloodstream. Binding to the antigen, antibodies mark them for destruction by other elements of the immune system.

anticodon The three-nucleotide sequence of a tRNA molecule that is complementary to, and base pairs with, an amino acid-specifying codon in mRNA.

antigen (Gr. *anti*, against + *genos*, origin) A foreign substance, usually a protein, that stimulates lymphocytes to proliferate and secrete specific antibodies that bind to the foreign substance, labeling it as foreign and destined for destruction.

apical meristem (L. *apex*, top + Gr. *meristos*, divided) In vascular plants, the growing point at the tip of the root or stem.

aposematic coloration An ecological strategy of some organisms that "advertise" their poisonous nature by the use of bright colors.

appendicular skeleton (L. *appendicula*, a small appendage) The skeleton of the limbs of the human body containing 126 bones.

archaea A group of prokaryotes that are among the most primitive still in existence, characterized by the absence of peptidoglycan in their cell walls, a feature that distinguishes them from bacteria.

asexual Reproducing without forming gametes. Asexual reproduction does not involve sex. Its outstanding characteristic is that an individual offspring is genetically identical to its parent.

association neuron A nerve cell found only in the CNS that acts as a functional link between sensory neurons and motor neurons. Also called interneuron.

atom (Gr. *atomos*, indivisible) A core (nucleus) of protons and neutrons surrounded by an orbiting cloud of electrons. The chemical behavior of an atom is largely determined by the distribution of its electrons, particularly the number of electrons in its outermost level.

atomic number The number of protons in the nucleus of an atom. In an atom that does not bear an electric charge (that is, one that is not an ion), the atomic number is also equal to the number of electrons.

autonomic nervous system (Gr. *autos*, self + *nomos*, law) The motor pathways that carry commands from the central nervous system to regulate the glands and nonskeletal muscles of the body. Also called the involuntary nervous system.

autosome (Gr. *autos*, self + *soma*, body) Any of the 22 pairs of human chromosomes that are similar in size and morphology in both males and females.

autotroph (Gr. *autos*, self + *trophos*, feeder) An organism that can harvest light energy from the sun or from the oxidation of inorganic compounds to make organic molecules.

axial skeleton The skeleton of the head and trunk of the human body containing 80 bones.

axon (Gr., axle) A process extending out from a neuron that conducts impulses away from the cell body.

B

bacterium, *pl.* **bacteria (Gr. *bakterion*, dim. of *baktron*, a staff)** The simplest cellular organism. Its cell is smaller and prokaryotic in structure, and it lacks internal organization.

basal body In eukaryotic cells that contain flagella or cilia, a form of centriole that anchors each flagellum.

base Any substance that combines with H^+ ions thereby reducing the H^+ ion concentration of a solution. Having a pH value above 7.

Batesian mimicry After Henry W. Bates, English naturalist. A situation in which a palatable or nontoxic organism resembles another kind of organism that is distasteful or toxic. Both species exhibit warning coloration.

B cell A lymphocyte that recognizes invading pathogens much as T cells do, but instead of attacking the pathogens directly, it marks them with antibodies for destruction by the nonspecific body defenses.

bilateral symmetry (L. *bi*, two + *lateris*, side; Gr. *symmetria*, symmetry) A body form in which the right and left halves of an organism are approximate mirror images of each other.

binary fission (L. *binarius*, consisting of two things or parts + *fissus*, split) Asexual reproduction of a cell by division into two equal, or nearly equal, parts. Bacteria divide by binary fission.

binomial system (L. *bi*, twice, two + Gr. *nomos*, usage, law) A system of nomenclature that uses two words. The first names the genus, and the second designates the species.

biomass (Gr. *bios*, life + *maza*, lump or mass) The total weight of all of the organisms living in an ecosystem.

biome (Gr. *bios*, life + *-oma*, mass, group) A major terrestrial assemblage of plants, animals, and microorganisms that occur over wide geographical areas and have distinct characteristics. The largest ecological unit.

C

calorie (L. *calor*, heat) The amount of energy in the form of heat required to raise the temperature of 1 gram of water 1 degree Celsius.

calyx (Gr. *kalyx*, a husk, cup) The sepals collectively. The outermost flower whorl.

cancer Unrestrained invasive cell growth. A tumor or cell mass resulting from uncontrollable cell division.

capillary (L. *capillaris*, hairlike) A blood vessel with a very small diameter. Blood exchanges gases and metabolites across capillary walls. Capillaries join the end of an arteriole to the beginning of a venule.

carbohydrate (L. *carbo*, charcoal + *hydro*, water) An organic compound consisting of a chain or ring of carbon atoms to which hydrogen and oxygen atoms are attached in a ratio of approximately 1:2:1. A compound of carbon, hydrogen, and oxygen having the generalized formula $(CH_2O)_n$, where n is the number of carbon atoms.

carcinogen (Gr. *karkinos*, cancer + -gen) Any cancer-causing agent.

cardiovascular system (Gr. *kardia*, heart + L. *vasculum*, vessel) The blood circulatory system and the heart that pumps it. Collectively, the blood, heart, and blood vessels.

carpel (Gr. *karpos*, fruit) A leaflike organ in angiosperms that encloses one or more ovules.

carrying capacity The maximum population size that a habitat can support.

catabolism (Gr. *katabole*, throwing down) A process in which complex molecules are broken down into simpler ones.

catalysis (Gr. *katalysis*, dissolution + *lyein*, to loosen) The enzyme-mediated process in which the subunits of polymers are positioned so that their bonds undergo chemical reactions.

catalyst (Gr. *kata*, down + *lysis*, a loosening) A general term for a substance that speeds up a specific chemical reaction by lowering the energy required to activate or start the reaction. An enzyme is a biological catalyst.

cell (L. *cella*, a chamber or small room) The smallest unit of life. The basic organizational unit of all organisms. Composed of a nuclear region containing the hereditary apparatus within a larger volume called the cytoplasm bounded by a lipid membrane.

cell cycle The repeating sequence of growth and division through which cells pass each generation.

cellular respiration The process in which the energy stored in a glucose molecule is released by oxidation. Hydrogen atoms are lost by glucose and gained by oxygen.

central nervous system The brain and spinal cord, the site of information processing and control within the nervous system.

centromere (Gr. *kentron*, center + *meros*, a part) A constricted region of the chromosome joining two sister chromatids, to which the kinetochore is attached.

chemical bond The force holding two atoms together. The force can result from the attraction of opposite charges (ionic bond) or from the sharing of one or more pairs of electrons (a covalent bond).

chemiosmosis The cellular process responsible for almost all of the adenosine triphosphate (ATP) harvested from food and for all the ATP produced by photosynthesis.

chemoautotroph An autotrophic bacterium that uses chemical energy released by specific inorganic reactions to power its life processes, including the synthesis of organic molecules.

chiasma, *pl.* **chiasmata (Gr. a cross)** In meiosis, the points of crossing over where portions of chromosomes have been exchanged during synapsis. A chiasma appears as an X-shaped structure under a light microscope.

chloroplast (Gr. *chloros*, green + *plastos*, molded) A cell-like organelle present in algae and plants that contains chlorophyll (and usually other pigments) and is the site of photosynthesis.

chromatid (Gr. *chroma*, color + L. *-id*, daughters of) One of two daughter strands of a duplicated chromosome that is joined by a single centromere.

chromatin (Gr. *chroma*, color) The complex of DNA and proteins of which eukaryotic chromosomes are composed.

chromosome (Gr. *chroma*, color + *soma*, body) The vehicle by which hereditary information is physically transmitted from one generation to the next. In a eukaryotic cell, long threads of DNA that are associated with protein and that contain hereditary information.

cilium, *pl.* **cilia (L. eyelash)** Refers to flagella, which are numerous and organized in dense rows. Cilia propel cells through water. In human tissue, they move water or mucus over the tissue surface.

cladistics A taxonomic technique used for creating hierarchies of organisms based on derived characters that represent true phylogenetic relationship and descent.

class A taxonomic category ranking below a phylum (division) and above an order.

clone (Gr. *klon*, twig) A line of cells, all of which have arisen from the same single cell by mitotic division. One of a population of individuals derived by asexual reproduction from a single ancestor. One of a population of genetically identical individuals.

codominance In genetics, a situation in which the effects of both alleles at a particular locus are apparent in the phenotype of the heterozygote.

codon (L. code) The basic unit of the genetic code. A sequence of three adjacent nucleotides in DNA or mRNA that codes for one amino acid or for polypeptide termination.

coelom (Gr. *koilos*, a hollow) A body cavity formed between layers of mesoderm and in which the digestive tract and other internal organs are suspended.

coenzyme A cofactor of an enzyme that is a nonprotein organic molecule.

coevolution (L. *co-*, together + *e-*, out + *volvere*, to fill) A term that describes the long-term evolutionary adjustment of one group of organisms to another.

commensalism (L. *cum*, together with + *mensa*, table) A symbiotic relationship in which one species benefits while the other neither benefits nor is harmed.

community (L. *communitas*, community, fellowship) The populations of different species that live together and interact in a particular place.

competition Interaction between individuals for the same scarce resources. Intraspecific competition is competition between individuals of a single species. Interspecific competition is competition between individuals of different species.

competitive exclusion The hypothesis that if two species are competing with one another for the same limited resource in the same place, one will be able to use that resource more efficiently than the other and eventually will drive that second species to extinction locally.

complement system The chemical defense of a vertebrate body that consists of a battery of proteins that insert in bacterial and fungal cells, causing holes that destroy the cells.

concentration gradient The concentration difference of a substance as a function of distance. In a cell, a greater concentration of its molecules in one region than in another.

condensation The coiling of the chromosomes into more and more tightly compacted bodies begun during the G_2 phase of the cell cycle.

conjugation (L. *conjugare*, to yoke together) An unusual mode of reproduction in unicellular organisms in which genetic material is exchanged between individuals through tubes connecting them during conjugation.

consumer In ecology, a heterotroph that derives its energy from living or freshly killed organisms or parts thereof. Primary consumers are herbivores; secondary consumers are carnivores or parasites.

cortex (L. bark) In vascular plants, the primary ground tissue of a stem or root, bounded externally by the epidermis and internally by the central cylinder of vascular tissue. In animals, the outer, as opposed to the inner, part of an organ, as in the adrenal, kidney, and cerebral cortexes.

cotyledon (Gr. *kotyledon*, a cup-shaped hollow) Seed leaf. Monocot embryos have one cotyledon, and dicots have two.

countercurrent flow In organisms, the passage of heat or of molecules (such as oxygen, water, or sodium ions) from one circulation path to another moving in the opposite direction. Because the flow of the two paths is in opposite directions, a concentration difference always exists between the two channels, facilitating transfer.

covalent bond (L. *co-*, together + *valare*, to be strong) A chemical bond formed by the sharing of one or more pairs of electrons.

crossing over An essential element of meiosis occurring during prophase when nonsister chromatids exchange portions of DNA strands.

cuticle (L. *cutis*, skin) A very thin film covering the outer skin of many plants.

cytokinesis (Gr. *kytos*, hollow vessel + *kinesis*, movement) The C phase of cell division in which the cell itself divides, creating two daughter cells.

cytoplasm (Gr. *kytos*, hollow vessel + *plasma*, anything molded) A semifluid matrix that occupies the volume between the nuclear region and the cell membrane. It contains the sugars, amino acids, proteins, and organelles (in eukaryotes) with which the cell carries out its everyday activities of growth and reproduction.

cytoskeleton (Gr. *kytos*, hollow vessel + *skeleton*, a dried body) In the cytoplasm of all eukaryotic cells, a network of protein fibers that supports the shape of the cell and anchors organelles, such as the nucleus, to fixed locations.

D

deciduous (L. *decidere*, to fall off) In vascular plants, shedding all the leaves at a certain season.

dehydration reaction Water-losing. The process in which a hydroxyl (OH) group is removed from one subunit of a polymer and a hydrogen (H) group is removed from the other subunit, linking the subunits together and forming a water molecule as a by-product.

demography (Gr. *demos*, people + *graphein*, to draw) The statistical study of population. The measurement of people or, by extension, of the characteristics of people.

density The number of individuals in a population in a given area.

deoxyribonucleic acid (DNA) The basic storage vehicle or central plan of heredity information. It is stored as a sequence of nucleotides in a linear nucleotide polymer. Two of the polymers wind around each other like the outside and inside rails of a circular staircase.

depolarization The movement of ions across a cell membrane that wipes out locally an electrical potential difference.

deuterostome (Gr. *deuteros*, second + *stoma*, mouth) An animal in whose embryonic development the anus forms from or near the blastopore, and the mouth forms later on another part of the blastula. Also characterized by radial cleavage.

dicot Short for dicotyledon; a class of flowering plants generally characterized by having two cotyledons, netlike veins, and flower parts in fours or fives.

diffusion (L. *diffundere*, to pour out) The net movement of molecules to regions of lower concentration as a result of random, spontaneous molecular motions. The process tends to distribute molecules uniformly.

dihybrid (Gr. *dis*, twice + L. *hibrida*, mixed offspring) An individual heterozygous for two genes.

dioecious (Gr. *di*, two + *eikos*, house) Having male and female flowers on separate plants of the same species.

diploid (Gr. *diploos*, double + *eidos*, form) A cell, tissue, or individual with a double set of chromosomes.

directional selection A form of selection in which selection acts to eliminate one extreme from an array of phenotypes. Thus, the genes promoting this extreme become less frequent in the population.

disaccharide (Gr. *dis*, twice + *sakcharon*, sugar) A sugar formed by linking two monosaccharide molecules together. Sucrose (table sugar) is a disaccharide formed by linking a molecule of glucose to a molecule of fructose.

disruptive selection A form of selection in which selection acts to eliminate rather than favor the intermediate type.

diurnal (L. *diurnalis*, day) Active during the day.

division Traditionally, a major taxonomic group of the plant kingdom comparable to a phylum of the animal kingdom. Today divisions are called phyla.

dominant allele An allele that dictates the appearance of heterozygotes. One allele is said to be dominant over another if an individual heterozygous for that allele has the same appearance as an individual homozygous for it.

dorsal (L. *dorsum*, the back) Toward the back, or upper surface. Opposite of ventral.

double fertilization A process unique to the angiosperms, in which one sperm nucleus fertilizes the egg and the second one fuses with the polar nuclei. These two events result in the formation of the zygote and the primary endosperm nucleus, respectively.

E

ecdysis (Gr. *ekdysis*, stripping off) The shedding of the outer covering or skin of certain animals. Especially the shedding of the exoskeleton by arthropods.

ecology (Gr. *oikos*, house + *logos*, word) The study of the relationships of organisms with one another and with their environment.

ecosystem (Gr. *oikos*, house + *systema*, that which is put together) A community, together with the nonliving factors with which it interacts.

ectoderm (Gr. *ecto*, outside + *derma*, skin) One of three embryonic germ layers that forms in the gastrula; giving rise to the outer epithelium and to nerve tissue.

ectothermic Referring to animals whose body temperature is regulated by their behavior or their surroundings.

electron A subatomic particle with a negative electrical charge. The negative charge of one electron exactly balances the positive charge of one proton. Electrons orbit the atom's positively charged nucleus and determine its chemical properties.

electron transport chain A collective term describing the series of membrane-associated electron carriers embedded in the inner mitochondrial membrane. It puts the electrons harvested from the oxidation of glucose to work driving proton-pumping channels.

electron transport system A collective term describing the series of membrane-associated electron carriers embedded in the thylakoid membrane of the chloroplast. It puts the electrons harvested from water molecules and energized by photons of light to work driving proton-pumping channels.

element A substance that cannot be separated into different substances by ordinary chemical methods.

endergonic (Gr. *endon*, within + *ergon*, work) Reactions in which the products contain more energy than the reactants and require an input of usable energy from an outside source before they can proceed. These reactions are not spontaneous.

endocrine gland (Gr. *endon*, **within +** *krinein*, **to separate**) A ductless gland producing hormonal secretions that pass directly into the bloodstream or lymph.

endocrine system The dozen or so major endocrine glands of a vertebrate.

endocytosis (Gr. *endon*, **within +** *kytos*, **cell**) The process by which the edges of plasma membranes fuse together and form an enclosed chamber called a vesicle. It involves the incorporation of a portion of an exterior medium into the cytoplasm of the cell by capturing it within the vesicle.

endoderm (Gr. *endon*, **outside +** *derma*, **skin**) One of three embryonic germ layers that forms in the gastrula; giving rise to the epithelium that lines internal organs and most of the digestive and respiratory tracts.

endoskeleton (Gr. *endon*, **within +** *skeletos*, **hard**) In vertebrates, an internal scaffold of bone or cartilage to which muscles are attached.

endosperm (Gr. *endon*, **within +** *sperma*, **seed**) A nutritive tissue characteristic of the seeds of angiosperms that develops from the union of a male nucleus and the polar nuclei of the embryo sac. The endosperm is either digested by the growing embryo or retained in the mature seed to nourish the germinating seedling.

endosymbiotic (Gr. *endon*, **within +** *bios*, **life**) **theory** A theory that proposes how eukaryotic cells arose from large prokaryotic cells that engulfed smaller ones of a different species. The smaller cells were not consumed but continued to live and function within the larger host cell. Organelles that are believed to have entered larger cells in this way are mitochondria and chloroplasts.

endothermic The ability of animals to maintain an elevated body temperature using their metabolism.

energy The capacity to bring about change, to do work.

enhancer A site of regulatory protein binding on the DNA molecule distant from the promoter and start site for a gene's transcription.

entropy (Gr. *en*, **in +** *tropos*, **change in manner**) A measure of the disorder of a system. A measure of energy that has become so randomized and uniform in a system that the energy is no longer available to do work.

enzyme (Gr. *enzymos*, **leavened; from** *en*, **in +** *zyme*, **leaven**) A molecule capable of speeding up specific chemical reactions by lowering the energy required to activate or start the reaction but that remains unaltered in the process.

epidermis (Gr. *epi*, **on or over +** *derma*, **skin**) The outermost layer of cells. In vertebrates, the nonvascular external layer of skin of ectodermal origin; in invertebrates, a single layer of ectodermal epithelium; in plants, the flattened, skinlike outer layer of cells.

epistasis (Gr. *epistasis*, **a standing still**) An interaction between the products of two genes in which one modifies the phenotypic expression produced by the other.

epithelium (Gr. *epi*, **on +** *thele*, **nipple**) A thin layer of cells forming a tissue that covers the internal and external surfaces of the body. Simple epithelium consists of the membranes that line the lungs and major body cavities and that are a single cell layer thick. Stratified epithelium (the skin or epidermis) is composed of more complex epithelial cells that are several cell layers thick.

erythrocyte (Gr. *erythros*, **red +** *kytos*, **hollow vessel**) A red blood cell, the carrier of hemoglobin. Erythrocytes act as the transporters of oxygen in the vertebrate body. During the process of their maturation in mammals, they lose their nuclei and mitochondria, and their endoplasmic reticulum is reabsorbed.

estrus (L. *oestrus*, **frenzy**) The period of maximum female sexual receptivity. Associated with ovulation of the egg. Being "in heat."

estuary (L. *aestus*, **tide**) A partly enclosed body of water, such as those that often form at river mouths and in coastal bays, where the salinity is intermediate between that of saltwater and freshwater.

ethology (Gr. *ethos*, **habit or custom +** *logos*, **discourse**) The study of patterns of animal behavior in nature.

euchromatin (Gr. *eu*, **true +** *chroma*, **color**) Chromatin that is extended except during cell division, from which RNA is transcribed.

eukaryote (Gr. *eu*, **true +** *karyon*, **kernel**) A cell that possesses membrane-bounded organelles, most notably a cell nucleus, and chromosomes whose DNA is associated with proteins; an organism composed of such cells. The appearance of eukaryotes marks a major event in the evolution of life, as all organisms on earth other than bacteria and archaea are eukaryotes.

eumetazoan (Gr. *eu*, **true +** *meta*, **with +** *zoion*, **animal**) A "true animal." An animal with a definite shape and symmetry and nearly always distinct tissues.

eutrophic (Gr. *eutrophos*, **thriving**) Refers to a lake in which an abundant supply of minerals and organic matter exists.

evaporation The escape of water molecules from the liquid to the gas phase at the surface of a body of water.

evolution (L. *evolvere*, **to unfold**) Genetic change in a population of organisms over time (generations). Darwin proposed that natural selection was the mechanism of evolution.

exergonic (L. *ex*, **out +** Gr. *ergon*, **work**) Any reaction that produces products that contain less free energy than that possessed by the original reactants and that tends to proceed spontaneously.

exocytosis (Gr. *ex*, **out of +** *kytos*, **cell**) The extrusion of material from a cell by discharging it from vesicles at the cell surface. The reverse of endocytosis.

exoskeleton (Gr. *exo*, **outside +** *skeletos*, **hard**) An external hard shell that encases a body. In arthropods, comprised mainly of chitin.

experiment The test of a hypothesis. An experiment that tests one or more alternative hypotheses and those that are demonstrated to be inconsistent with experimental observation are rejected.

F

facilitated diffusion The transport of molecules across a membrane by a carrier protein in the direction of lowest concentration.

family A taxonomic group ranking below an order and above a genus.

feedback inhibition A regulatory mechanism in which a biochemical pathway is regulated by the amount of the product that the pathway produces.

fermentation (L. *fermentum*, **ferment**) A catabolic process in which the final electron acceptor is an organic molecule.

fertilization (L. *ferre*, **to bear**) The union of male and female gametes to form a zygote.

fitness The genetic contribution of an individual to succeeding generations, relative to the contributions of other individuals in the population.

flagellum, *pl.* **flagella** (L. *flagellum*, **whip**) A fine, long, threadlike organelle protruding from the surface of a cell. In bacteria, a single protein fiber capable of rotary motion that propels the cell through the water. In eukaryotes, an array of microtubules with a characteristic internal $9 + 2$ microtubule structure that is capable of vibratory but not rotary motion. Used in locomotion and feeding. Common in protists and motile gametes. A cilium is a short flagellum.

food web The food relationships within a community. A diagram of who eats whom.

founder effect The effect by which rare alleles and combinations of alleles may be enhanced in new populations.

frequency In statistics, defined as the proportion of individuals in a certain category, relative to the total number of individuals being considered.

fruit In angiosperms, a mature, ripened ovary (or group of ovaries) containing the seeds.

G

gamete (Gr. **wife**) A haploid reproductive cell. Upon fertilization, its nucleus fuses with that of another gamete of the opposite sex. The resulting diploid cell (zygote) may develop into a new diploid individual, or in some protists and fungi, may undergo meiosis to form haploid somatic cells.

gametophyte (Gr. *gamete*, **wife +** *phyton*, **plant**) In plants, the haploid (n), gamete-producing generation, which alternates with the diploid ($2n$) sporophyte.

ganglion, *pl.* **ganglia** (Gr. **a swelling**) A group of nerve cells forming a nerve center in the peripheral nervous system.

gastrulation The inward movement of certain cell groups from the surface of the blastula.

gene (Gr. *genos*, **birth, race**) The basic unit of heredity. A sequence of DNA nucleotides on a chromosome that encodes a polypeptide or RNA molecule and so determines the nature of an individual's inherited traits.

gene expression The process in which an RNA copy of each active gene is made, and the RNA copy directs the sequential assembly of a chain of amino acids at a ribosome.

gene frequency The frequency with which individuals in a population possess a particular gene. Often confused with allele frequency.

genetic code The "language" of the genes. The mRNA codons specific for the 20 common amino acids constitute the genetic code.

genetic drift Random fluctuations in allele frequencies in a small population over time.

genetic map A diagram showing the relative positions of genes.

genetics (Gr. *genos*, birth, race) The study of the way in which an individual's traits are transmitted from one generation to the next.

genome (Gr. *genos*, offspring + L. *oma*, abstract group) The genetic information of an organism.

genomics The study of genomes as opposed to individual genes.

genotype (Gr. *genos*, offspring + *typos*, form) The total set of genes present in the cells of an organism. Also used to refer to the set of alleles at a single gene locus.

genus, *pl.* genera (L. race) A taxonomic group that ranks below a family and above a species.

germination (L. *germinare*, to sprout) The resumption of growth and development by a spore or seed.

gland (L. *glandis*, acorn) Any of several organs in the body, such as exocrine or endocrine, that secrete substances for use in the body. Glands are composed of epithelial tissue.

glomerulus (L. a little ball) A network of capillaries in a vertebrate kidney, whose walls act as a filtration device.

glycolysis (Gr. *glykys*, sweet + *lyein*, to loosen) The anaerobic breakdown of glucose; this enzyme-catalyzed process yields two molecules of pyruvate with a net of two molecules of ATP.

gravitropism (L. *gravis*, heavy + *tropes*, turning) The response of a plant to gravity, which generally causes shoots to grow up and roots to grow down.

greenhouse effect The process in which carbon dioxide and certain other gases, such as methane, that occur in the earth's atmosphere transmit radiant energy from the sun but trap the longer wavelengths of infrared light, or heat, and prevent them from radiating into space.

guard cells Pairs of specialized epidermal cells that surround a stoma. When the guard cells are turgid, the stoma is open; when they are flaccid, it is closed.

gymnosperm (Gr. *gymnos*, naked + *sperma*, seed) A seed plant with seeds not enclosed in an ovary. The conifers are the most familiar group.

H

habitat (L. *habitare*, to inhabit) The place where individuals of a species live.

half-life The length of time it takes for half of a radioactive substance to decay.

haploid (Gr. *haploos*, single + *eidos*, form) The gametes of a cell or an individual with only one set of chromosomes.

Hardy-Weinberg equilibrium After G. H. Hardy, English mathematician, and G. Weinberg, German physician. A mathematical description of the fact that the relative frequencies of two or more alleles in a population do not change because of Mendelian segregation. Allele and genotype frequencies remain constant in a random-mating population in the absence of inbreeding, selection, or other evolutionary forces. Usually stated as: If the frequency of allele A is p and the frequency of allele a is q, then the genotype frequencies after one generation of random mating will always be $(p + q)^2 = p^2 + 2pq + q^2$.

Haversian canal After Clopton Havers, English anatomist. Narrow channels that run parallel to the length of a bone and contain blood vessels and nerve cells.

helper T cell A class of white blood cells that initiates both the cell-mediated immune response and the humoral immune response; helper T cells are the targets of the AIDS virus (HIV).

hemoglobin (Gr. *haima*, blood + L. *globus*, a ball) A globular protein in vertebrate red blood cells and in the plasma of many invertebrates that carries oxygen and carbon dioxide.

herbivore (L. *herba*, grass + *vorare*, to devour) Any organism that eats only plants.

heredity (L. *heredis*, heir) The transmission of characteristics from parent to offspring.

heterochromatin (Gr. *heteros*, different + *chroma*, color) That portion of a eukaryotic chromosome that remains permanently condensed and therefore is not transcribed into RNA. Most centromere regions are heterochromatic.

heterokaryon (Gr. *heteros*, other + *karyon*, kernel) A fungal hypha that has two or more genetically distinct types of nuclei.

heterotroph (Gr. *heteros*, other + *trophos*, feeder) An organism that does not have the ability to produce its own food. *See also* autotroph.

heterozygote (Gr. *heteros*, other + *zygotos*, a pair) A diploid individual carrying two different alleles of a gene on its two homologous chromosomes.

hierarchical (Gr. *hieros*, sacred + *archos*, leader) Refers to a system of classification in which successively smaller units of classification are included within one another.

histone (Gr. *histos*, tissue) A complex of small, very basic polypeptides rich in the amino acids arginine and lysine. A basic part of chromosomes, histones form the core around which DNA is wrapped.

homeostasis (Gr. *homeos*, similar + *stasis*, standing) The maintaining of a relatively stable internal physiological environment in an organism or steady-state equilibrium in a population or ecosystem.

homeotherm (Gr. *homeo*, similar + *therme*, heat) An organism, such as a bird or mammal, capable of maintaining a stable body temperature.

hominid (L. *homo*, man) Human beings and their direct ancestors. A member of the family Hominidae. *Homo sapiens* is the only living member.

homologous chromosome (Gr. *homologia*, agreement) One of the two nearly identical versions of each chromosome. Chromosomes that associate in pairs in the first stage of meiosis. In diploid cells, one chromosome of a pair that carries equivalent genes.

homology (Gr. *homologia*, agreement) A condition in which the similarity between two structures or functions is indicative of a common evolutionary origin.

homozygote (Gr. *homos*, same or similar + *zygotos*, a pair) A diploid individual whose two copies of a gene are the same. An individual carrying identical alleles on both homologous chromosomes is said to be homozygous for that gene.

hormone (Gr. *hormaein*, to excite) A chemical messenger, often a steroid or peptide, produced in a small quantity in one part of an organism and then transported to another part of the organism, where it brings about a physiological response.

hybrid (L. *hybrida*, the offspring of a tame sow and a wild boar) A plant or animal that results from the crossing of dissimilar parents.

hybridization The mating of unlike parents of different taxa.

hydrogen bond A molecular force formed by the attraction of the partial positive charge of one hydrogen atom of a water molecule with the partial negative charge of the oxygen atom of another.

hydrolysis reaction (Gr. *hydro*, water + *lyse*, break) The process of tearing down a polymer by adding a molecule of water. A hydrogen is attached to one subunit and a hydroxyl to the other, which breaks the covalent bond. Essentially the reverse of a dehydration reaction.

hydrophobic (Gr. *hydro*, water + *phobos*, hating) Nonpolar molecules, which do not form hydrogen bonds with water and therefore are not soluble in water.

hydroskeleton (Gr. *hydro*, water + *skeletos*, hard) The skeleton of most soft-bodied invertebrates that have neither an internal nor an external skeleton. They use the relative incompressibility of the water within their bodies as a kind of skeleton.

hypertonic (Gr. *hyper*, above + *tonos*, tension) A cell that contains a higher concentration of solutes than its surrounding solution.

hypha, *pl.* hyphae (Gr. *hyphe*, web) A filament of a fungus. A mass of hyphae comprises a mycelium.

hypothalamus (Gr. *hypo*, under + *thalamos*, inner room) The region of the brain under the thalamus that controls temperature, hunger, and thirst and that produces hormones that influence the pituitary gland.

hypothesis (Gr. *hypo*, under + *tithenai*, to put) A proposal that might be true. No hypothesis is ever proven correct. All hypotheses are provisional—proposals that are retained for the time being as useful but that may be rejected in the future if found to be inconsistent with new information. A hypothesis that stands the test of time—often tested and never rejected—is called a theory.

hypotonic (Gr. *hypo*, under + *tonos*, tension) A solution surrounding a cell that has a lower concentration of solutes than does the cell.

I

inbreeding The breeding of genetically related plants or animals. In plants, inbreeding results from self-pollination. In animals, inbreeding results from matings between relatives. Inbreeding tends to increase homozygosity.

incomplete dominance The ability of two alleles to produce a heterozygous phenotype that is different from either homozygous phenotype.

independent assortment Mendel's second law: The principle that segregation of alternative alleles at one locus into gametes is independent of the segregation of alleles at other loci. Only true for gene loci located on different chromosomes or those so far apart on one chromosome that crossing over is very frequent between the loci.

industrial melanism (Gr. *melas*, black) The evolutionary process in which a population of initially light-colored organisms becomes a population of dark organisms as a result of natural selection.

inflammatory response (L. *inflammare*, to flame) A generalized nonspecific response to infection that acts to clear an infected area of infecting microbes and dead tissue cells so that tissue repair can begin.

integument (L. *integumentum*, covering) The natural outer covering layers of an animal. Develops from the ectoderm.

interneuron A nerve cell found only in the CNS that acts as a functional link between sensory neurons and motor neurons. Also called association neuron.

internode The region of a plant stem between nodes where stems and leaves attach.

interoception (L. *interus*, inner + Eng. *[re]ceptive)* The sensing of information that relates to the body itself, its internal condition, and its position.

interphase That portion of the cell cycle preceding mitosis. It includes the G_1 phase, when cells grow, the S phase, when a replica of the genome is synthesized, and a G_2 phase, when preparations are made for genomic separation.

intron (L. *intra*, within) A segment of DNA transcribed into mRNA but removed before translation. These untranslated regions make up the bulk of most eukaryotic genes.

ion An atom in which the number of electrons does not equal the number of protons. An ion carries an electrical charge.

ionic bond A chemical bond formed between ions as a result of the attraction of opposite electrical charges.

ionizing radiation High-energy radiation, such as X rays and gamma rays.

isolating mechanisms Mechanisms that prevent genetic exchange between individuals of different populations or species.

isotonic (Gr. *isos*, equal + *tonos*, tension) A cell with the same concentration of solutes as its environment.

isotope (Gr. *isos*, equal + *topos*, place) An atom that has the same number of protons but different numbers of neutrons.

J

joint The part of a vertebrate where one bone meets and moves on another.

K

karyotype (Gr. *karyon*, kernel + *typos*, stamp or print) The particular array of chromosomes that an individual possesses.

kinetic energy The energy of motion.

kinetochore (Gr. *kinetikos*, putting in motion + *choros*, chorus) A disk of protein bound to the centromere to which microtubules attach during cell division, linking chromatids to the spindle.

kingdom The chief taxonomic category. This book recognizes six kingdoms: Archaea, Bacteria, Protista, Fungi, Animalia, and Plantae.

L

lamella, *pl.* lamellae (L. a little plate) A thin, platelike structure. In chloroplasts, a layer of chlorophyll-containing membranes. In bivalve mollusks, one of the two plates forming a gill. In vertebrates, one of the thin layers of bone laid concentrically around the Haversian canals.

ligament (L. *ligare*, to bind) A band or sheet of connective tissue that links bone to bone.

linkage The patterns of assortment of genes that are located on the same chromosome. Important because if the genes are located relatively far apart, crossing over is more likely to occur between them than if they are close together.

lipid (Gr. *lipos*, fat) A loosely defined group of molecules that are insoluble in water but soluble in oil. Oils such as olive, corn, and coconut are lipids, as well as waxes, such as beeswax and earwax.

lipid bilayer The basic foundation of all biological membranes. In such a layer, the nonpolar tails of phospholipid molecules point inward, forming a nonpolar zone in the interior of the bilayers. Lipid bilayers are selectively permeable and do not permit the diffusion of water-soluble molecules into the cell.

littoral (L. *litus*, shore) Referring to the shoreline zone of a lake or pond or the ocean

that is exposed to the air whenever water recedes.

locus, *pl.* loci (L. place) The position on a chromosome where a gene is located.

loop of Henle After F. G. J. Henle, German anatomist. A hairpin loop formed by a urine-conveying tubule when it enters the inner layer of the kidney and then turns around to pass up again into the outer layer of the kidney.

lymph (L. *lympha*, clear water) In animals, a colorless fluid derived from blood by filtration through capillary walls in the tissues.

lymphatic system An open circulatory system composed of a network of vessels that function to collect the water within blood plasma forced out during passage through the capillaries and to return it to the bloodstream. The lymphatic system also returns proteins to the circulation, transports fats absorbed from the intestine, and carries bacteria and dead blood cells to the lymph nodes and spleen for destruction.

lymphocyte (Gr. *lympha*, water + Gr. *kytos*, hollow vessel) A white blood cell. A cell of the immune system that either synthesizes antibodies (B cells) or attacks virus-infected cells (T cells).

lyse (Gr. *lysis*, loosening) To disintegrate a cell by rupturing its plasma membrane.

M

macromolecule (Gr. *makros*, large + L. *moliculus*, a little mass) An extremely large molecule. Refers specifically to carbohydrates, lipids, proteins, and nucleic acids.

macrophage (Gr. *makros*, large + *-phage*, eat) A phagocytic cell of the immune system able to engulf and digest invading bacteria, fungi, and other microorganisms, as well as cellular debris.

marrow The soft tissue that fills the cavities of most bones and is the source of red blood cells.

mass flow The overall process by which materials move in the phloem of plants.

mass number The mass number of an atom consists of the combined mass of all of its protons and neutrons.

meiosis (Gr. *meioun*, to make smaller) A special form of nuclear division that precedes gamete formation in sexually reproducing eukaryotes. It results in four haploid daughter cells.

Mendelian ratio After Gregor Mendel, Austrian monk. Refers to the characteristic 3:1 segregation ratio that Mendel observed, in which pairs of alternative traits are expressed in the F_2 generation in the ratio of three-fourths dominant to one-fourth recessive.

menstruation (L. *mens*, month) Periodic sloughing off of the blood-enriched lining of the uterus when pregnancy does not occur.

meristem (Gr. *merizein*, to divide) In plants, a zone of unspecialized cells whose only function is to divide.

mesoderm (Gr. *mesos*, middle + *derma*, skin) One of the three embryonic germ layers that form in the gastrula. Gives rise to muscle, bone, and other connective tissue; the peritoneum; the circulatory system; and most of the excretory and reproductive systems.

mesophyll (Gr. *mesos*, middle + *phyllon*, leaf) The photosynthetic parenchyma of a leaf, located within the epidermis. The vascular strands (veins) run through the mesophyll.

metabolism (Gr. *metabole*, change) The process by which all living things assimilate energy and use it to grow.

metamorphosis (Gr. *meta*, after + *morphe*, form + *osis*, state of) Process in which form changes markedly during postembryonic development—for example, tadpole to frog or larval insect to adult.

metaphase (Gr. *meta*, middle + *phasis*, form) The stage of mitosis characterized by the alignment of the chromosomes on a plane in the center of the cell.

metastasis, *pl.* metastases (Gr. to place in another way) The spread of cancerous cells to other parts of the body, forming new tumors at distant sites.

microevolution (Gr. *mikros*, small + L. *evolvere*, to unfold) Refers to the evolutionary process itself. Evolution within a species. Also called adaptation.

microtubule (Gr. *mikros*, small + L. *tubulus*, little pipe) In eukaryotic cells, a long, hollow cylinder about 25 nanometers in diameter and composed of the protein tubulin. Microtubules influence cell shape, move the chromosomes in cell division, and provide the functional internal structure of cilia and flagella.

mimicry (Gr. *mimos*, mime) The resemblance in form, color, or behavior of certain organisms (mimics) to other more powerful or more protected ones (models), which results in the mimics being protected in some way.

mitochondrion, *pl.* mitochondria (Gr. *mitos*, thread + *chondrion*, small grain) A tubular or sausage-shaped organelle 1 to 3 micrometers long. Bounded by two membranes, mitochondria closely resemble the aerobic bacteria from which they were originally derived. As chemical furnaces of the cell, they carry out its oxidative metabolism.

mitosis (Gr. *mitos*, thread) The M phase of cell division in which the microtubular apparatus is assembled, binds to the chromosomes, and moves them apart. This phase is the essential step in the separation of the two daughter cell genomes.

mole (L. *moles*, mass) The atomic weight of a substance, expressed in grams. One mole is defined as the mass of 6.0222×10^{23} atoms.

molecule (L. *moliculus*, a small mass) The smallest unit of a compound that displays the properties of that compound.

monocot Short for monocotyledon; flowering plant in which the embryos have only one cotyledon, the flower parts are often in threes, and the leaves typically are parallel-veined.

monosaccharide (Gr. *monos*, one + *sakcharon*, sugar) A simple sugar.

morphogenesis (Gr. *morphe*, form + *genesis*, origin) The formation of shape. The growth and differentiation of cells and tissues during development.

motor endplate The point where a neuron attaches to a muscle. A neuromuscular synapse.

multicellularity A condition in which the activities of the individual cells are coordinated and the cells themselves are in contact. A property of eukaryotes alone and one of their major characteristics.

muscle (L. *musculus*, mouse) The tissue in the body of humans and animals that can be contracted and relaxed to make the body move.

muscle cell A long, cylindrical, multinucleated cell that contains numerous myofibrils and is capable of contraction when stimulated.

muscle spindle A sensory organ that is attached to a muscle and sensitive to stretching.

mutagen (L. *mutare*, to change) A chemical capable of damaging DNA.

mutation (L. *mutare*, to change) A change in a cell's genetic message.

mutualism (L. *mutuus*, lent, borrowed) A symbiotic relationship in which both participating species benefit.

mycelium, *pl.* mycelia (Gr. *mykes*, fungus) In fungi, a mass of hyphae.

mycology (Gr. *mykes*, fungus) The study of fungi. A person who studies fungi is called a mycologist.

mycorrhiza, *pl.* mycorrhizae (Gr. *mykes*, fungus + *rhiza*, root) A symbiotic association between fungi and plant roots.

myofibril (Gr. *myos*, muscle + L. *fibrilla*, little fiber) An elongated structure in a muscle fiber, composed of myosin and actin.

myosin (Gr. *myos*, muscle + *in*, belonging to) One of two protein components of myofilaments. (The other is actin.)

N

natural selection The differential reproduction of genotypes caused by factors in the environment. Leads to evolutionary change.

nematocyst (Gr. *nema*, thread + *kystos*, bladder) A coiled, threadlike stinging structure of cnidarians that is discharged to capture prey and for defense.

nephron (Gr. *nephros*, kidney) The functional unit of the vertebrate kidney. A human kidney has more than 1 million nephrons that filter waste matter from the blood. Each nephron consists of a Bowman's capsule, glomerulus, and tubule.

nerve A bundle of axons with accompanying supportive cells, held together by connective tissue.

nerve impulse A rapid, transient, self-propagating reversal in electrical potential that travels along the membrane of a neuron.

neuromodulator A chemical transmitter that mediates effects that are slow and longer lasting and that typically involve second messengers within the cell.

neuromuscular junction The structure formed when the tips of axons contact (innervate) a muscle fiber.

neuron (Gr. nerve) A nerve cell specialized for signal transmission.

neurotransmitter (Gr. *neuron*, nerve + L. *trans*, across + *mitere*, to send) A chemical released at an axon tip that travels across the synapse and binds a specific receptor protein in the membrane on the far side.

neurulation (Gr. *neuron*, nerve) The elaboration of a notochord and a dorsal nerve cord that marks the evolution of the chordates.

neutron (L. *neuter*, neither) A subatomic particle located within the nucleus of an atom. Similar to a proton in mass, but as its name implies, a neutron is neutral and possesses no charge.

neutrophil An abundant type of white blood cell capable of engulfing microorganisms and other foreign particles.

niche (L. *nidus*, nest) The role an organism plays in the environment; realized niche is the niche that an organism occupies under natural circumstances; fundamental niche is the niche an organism would occupy if competitors were not present.

nitrogen fixation The incorporation of atmospheric nitrogen into nitrogen compounds, a process that can be carried out only by certain microorganisms.

nocturnal (L. *nocturnus*, night) Active primarily at night.

node (L. *nodus*, knot) The place on the stem where a leaf is formed.

node of Ranvier After L. A. Ranvier, French histologist. A gap formed at the point where two Schwann cells meet and where the axon is in direct contact with the surrounding intercellular fluid.

nondisjunction The failure of homologous chromosomes to separate in meiosis I. The cause of Down syndrome.

nonrandom mating A phenomenon in which individuals with certain genotypes sometimes mate with one another more commonly than would be expected on a random basis.

notochord (Gr. *noto*, back + L. *chorda*, cord) In chordates, a dorsal rod of cartilage that forms between the nerve cord and the developing gut in the early embryo.

nucleic acid A nucleotide polymer. A long chain of nucleotides. Chief types are deoxyribonucleic acid (DNA), which is double-stranded, and ribonucleic acid (RNA), which is typically single-stranded.

nucleosome (L. *nucleus*, kernel + *soma*, body) The basic packaging unit of eukaryotic chromosomes, in which the DNA molecule is wound around a ball of histone proteins. Chromatin is composed of long strings of nucleosomes, like beads on a string.

nucleotide A single unit of nucleic acid, composed of a phosphate, a five-carbon sugar (either ribose or deoxyribose), and a purine or a pyrimidine.

nucleus (L. *a kernel*, dim. Fr. *nux*, nut) A spherical organelle (structure) characteristic of eukaryotic cells. The repository of the genetic information that directs all activities of a living cell. In atoms, the central core, containing positively charged protons and (in all but hydrogen) electrically neutral neutrons.

O

oocyte (Gr. *oion*, egg + *kytos*, vessel) A cell in the outer layer of the ovary that gives rise to an ovum. A primary oocyte is any of the 2 million oocytes a female is born with, all of which have begun the first meiotic division.

operon (L. *operis*, work) A cluster of functionally related genes transcribed onto a single mRNA molecule. A common mode of gene regulation in prokaryotes; it is rare in eukaryotes other than fungi.

order A taxonomic category ranking below a class and above a family.

organ (L. *organon*, tool) A complex body structure composed of several different kinds of tissue grouped together in a structural and functional unit.

organelle (Gr. *organella*, little tool) A specialized compartment of a cell. Mitochondria are organelles.

organism Any individual living creature, either unicellular or multicellular.

organ system A group of organs that function together to carry out the principal activities of the body.

osmoconformer An animal that maintains the osmotic concentration of its body fluids at about the same level as that of the medium in which it is living.

osmoregulation The maintenance of a constant internal solute concentration by an organism, regardless of the environment in which it lives.

osmosis (Gr. *osmos*, act of pushing, thrust) The diffusion of water across a membrane that permits the free passage of water but not that of one or more solutes. Water moves from an area of low solute concentration to an area with higher solute concentration.

osmotic pressure The increase of hydrostatic water pressure within a cell as a result of water molecules that continue to diffuse inward toward the area of lower water concentration (the water concentration is lower inside than outside the cell because of the dissolved solutes in the cell).

osteoblast (Gr. *osteon*, bone + *blastos*, bud) A bone-forming cell.

osteocyte (Gr. *osteon*, bone + *kytos*, hollow vessel) A mature osteoblast.

outcross A term used to describe species that interbreed with individuals other than those like themselves.

oviparous (L. *ovum*, egg + *parere*, to bring forth) Refers to reproduction in which the eggs are developed after leaving the body of the mother, as in reptiles.

ovulation The successful development and release of an egg by the ovary.

ovule (L. *ovulum*, a little egg) A structure in a seed plant that becomes a seed when mature.

ovum, *pl.* **ova** (L. egg) A mature egg cell. A female gamete.

oxidation (Fr. *oxider*, to oxidize) The loss of an electron during a chemical reaction from one atom to another. Occurs simultaneously with reduction. Is the second stage of the 10 reactions of glycolysis.

oxidative metabolism A collective term for metabolic reactions requiring oxygen.

oxidative respiration Respiration in which the final electron acceptor is molecular oxygen.

P

parasitism (Gr. *para*, beside + *sitos*, food) A symbiotic relationship in which one organism benefits and the other is harmed.

parthenogenesis (Gr. *parthenos*, virgin + Eng. *genesis*, beginning) The development of an adult from an unfertilized egg. A common form of reproduction in insects.

partial pressures (P) The components of each individual gas—such as nitrogen, oxygen, and carbon dioxide—that together constitute the total air pressure.

pathogen (Gr. *pathos*, suffering + Eng. *genesis*, beginning) A disease-causing organism.

pedigree (L. *pes*, foot + *grus*, crane) A family tree. The patterns of inheritance observed in family histories. Used to determine the mode of inheritance of a particular trait.

peptide (Gr. *peptein*, to soften, digest) Two or more amino acids linked by peptide bonds.

peptide bond A covalent bond linking two amino acids. Formed when the positive (amino, or NH_2) group at one end and a negative (carboxyl, or COOH) group at the other end undergo a chemical reaction and lose a molecule of water.

peristalsis (Gr. *peri*, around + *stellein*, to wrap) The rhythmic sequences of waves of muscular contraction in the walls of a tube.

pH Refers to the concentration of H^+ ions in a solution. The numerical value of the pH is the negative of the exponent of the molar concentration. Low pH values indicate high concentrations of H^+ ions (acids), and high pH values indicate low concentrations (bases).

phagocyte (Gr. *phagein*, to eat + *kytos*, hollow vessel) A cell that kills invading cells by engulfing them. Includes neutrophils and macrophages.

phagocytosis (Gr. *phagein*, to eat + *kytos*, hollow vessel) A form of endocytosis in which cells engulf organisms or fragments of organisms.

phenotype (Gr. *phainein*, to show + *typos*, stamp or print) The realized expression of the genotype. The observable expression of a trait (affecting an individual's structure, physiology, or behavior) that results from the biological activity of proteins or RNA molecules transcribed from the DNA.

pheromone (Gr. *pherein*, to carry + [hor]mone) A chemical signal emitted by certain animals as a means of communication.

phloem (Gr. *phloos*, bark) In vascular plants, a food-conducting tissue basically composed of sieve elements, various kinds of parenchyma cells, fibers, and sclereids.

phosphodiester bond The bond that results from the formation of a nucleic acid chain in which individual sugars are linked together in a line by the phosphate groups. The phosphate group of one sugar binds to the hydroxyl group of another, forming an—O—P—O bond.

photon (Gr. *photos*, light) The unit of light energy.

photoperiodism (Gr. *photos*, light + *periodos*, a period) A mechanism that organisms use to measure seasonal changes in relative day and night length.

photorespiration A process in which carbon dioxide is released without the production of ATP or NADPH. Because it produces neither ATP nor NADPH, photorespiration acts to undo the work of photosynthesis.

photosynthesis (Gr. *photos*, light + *-syn*, together + *tithenai*, to place) The process by which plants, algae, and some bacteria use the energy of sunlight to create from carbon dioxide (CO_2) and water (H_2O) the more complicated molecules that make up living organisms.

phototropism (Gr. *photos*, light + *trope*, turning to light) A plant's growth response to a unidirectional light source.

phylogeny (Gr. *phylon*, race, tribe) The evolutionary relationships among any group of organisms.

phylum, *pl.* **phyla** (Gr. *phylon*, race, tribe) A major taxonomic category, ranking above a class.

physiology (Gr. *physis*, nature + *logos*, a discourse) The study of the function of cells, tissues, and organs.

pigment (L. *pigmentum*, paint) A molecule that absorbs light.

pinocytosis (Gr. *pinein*, to drink + *kytos*, cell) A form of endocytosis in which the material brought into the cell is a liquid containing dissolved molecules.

pistil (L. *pistillum*, pestle) Central organ of flowers, typically consisting of ovary, style, and stigma; a pistil may consist of one or more fused carpels and is more technically and better known as the gynoecium.

plankton (Gr. *planktos*, wandering) The small organisms that float or drift in water, especially at or near the surface.

plasma (Gr. form) The fluid of vertebrate blood. Contains dissolved salts, metabolic wastes, hormones, and a variety of proteins, including antibodies and albumin. Blood minus the blood cells.

plasma membrane A lipid bilayer with embedded proteins that control the cell's permeability to water and dissolved substances.

plasmid (Gr. *plasma*, a form or something molded) A small fragment of DNA that replicates independently of the bacterial chromosome.

platelet (Gr. dim of *plattus*, flat) In mammals, a fragment of a white blood cell that circulates in the blood and functions in the formation of blood clots at sites of injury.

pleiotropy (Gr. *pleros*, more + *trope*, a turning) A gene that produces more than one phenotypic effect.

polarization The charge difference of a neuron so that the interior of the cell is negative with respect to the exterior.

polar molecule A molecule with positively and negatively charged ends. One portion of a polar molecule attracts electrons more strongly than another portion, with the result that the molecule has electron-rich (–) and electron-poor (+) regions, giving it magnetlike positive and negative poles. Water is one of the most polar molecules known.

pollen (L. fine dust) A fine, yellowish powder consisting of grains or microspores, each of which contains a mature or immature male gametophyte. In flowering plants, pollen is released from the anthers of flowers and fertilizes the pistils.

pollen tube A tube that grows from a pollen grain. Male reproductive cells move through the pollen tube into the ovule.

pollination The transfer of pollen from the anthers to the stigmas of flowers for fertilization, as by insects or the wind.

polygyny (Gr. poly, many + gyne, woman, wife) A mating choice in which a male mates with more than one female.

polymer (Gr. polus, many + meris, part) A large molecule formed of long chains of similar molecules called subunits.

polymerase chain reaction (PCR) A process by which DNA polymerase is used to copy a sequence of DNA repeatedly, making millions of copies of the same DNA.

polymorphism (Gr. polys, many + morphe, form) The presence in a population of more than one allele of a gene at a frequency greater than that of newly arising mutations.

polynomial system (Gr. polys, many + [bi]nomial) Before Linnaeus, naming a genus by use of a cumbersome string of Latin words and phrases.

polyp A cylindrical, pipe-shaped cnidarian usually attached to a rock with the mouth facing away from the rock on which it is growing. Coral is made up of polyps.

polypeptide (Gr. polys, many + peptein, to digest) A general term for a long chain of amino acids linked end to end by peptide bonds. A protein is a long, complex polypeptide.

polysaccharide (Gr. polys, many + sakcharon, sugar) A sugar polymer. A carbohydrate composed of many monosaccharide sugar subunits linked together in a long chain.

population (L. populus, the people) Any group of individuals of a single species, occupying a given area at the same time.

posterior (L. post, after) Situated behind or farther back.

potential difference A difference in electrical charge on two sides of a membrane caused by an unequal distribution of ions.

potential energy Energy with the potential to do work. Stored energy.

predation (L. praeda, prey) The eating of other organisms. The one doing the eating is called a predator, and the one being consumed is called the prey.

primary growth In vascular plants, growth originating in the apical meristems of shoots and roots, as contrasted with secondary growth; results in an increase in length.

primary plant body The part of a plant that arises from the apical meristems.

primary producers Photosynthetic organisms, including plants, algae, and photosynthetic bacteria.

primary structure of a protein The sequence of amino acids that makes up a particular polypeptide chain.

primordium, pl. primordia (L. primus, first + ordiri, begin) The first cells in the earliest stages of the development of an organ or structure.

productivity The total amount of energy of an ecosystem fixed by photosynthesis per unit of time. Net productivity is productivity minus that which is expended by the metabolic activity of the organisms in the community.

prokaryote (Gr. pro, before + karyon, kernel) A simple organism that is small, single-celled, and has little evidence of internal structure.

promoter An RNA polymerase binding site. The nucleotide sequence at the end of a gene to which RNA polymerase attaches to initiate transcription of mRNA.

prophase (Gr. pro, before + phasis, form) The first stage of mitosis during which the chromosomes become more condensed, the nuclear envelope is reabsorbed, and a network of microtubules (called the spindle) forms between opposite poles of the cell.

protein (Gr. proteios, primary) A long chain of amino acids linked end to end by peptide bonds. Because the 20 amino acids that occur in proteins have side groups with very different chemical properties, the function and shape of a protein is critically affected by its particular sequence of amino acids.

protist (Gr. protos, first) A member of the kingdom Protista, which includes unicellular eukaryotic organisms and some multicellular lines derived from them.

proton A subatomic particle in the nucleus of an atom that carries a positive charge. The number of protons determines the chemical character of the atom because it dictates the number of electrons orbiting the nucleus and available for chemical activity.

protostome (Gr. protos, first + stoma, mouth) An animal in whose embryonic development the mouth forms at or near the blastopore. Also characterized by spiral cleavage.

protozoa (Gr. protos, first + zoion, animal) The traditional name given to heterotrophic protists.

pseudocoel (Gr. pseudos, false + koiloma, cavity) A body cavity similar to the coelom except that it forms between the mesoderm and endoderm.

punctuated equilibrium A hypothesis of the mechanism of evolutionary change that proposes that long periods of little or no change are punctuated by periods of rapid evolution.

Q

quaternary structure of a protein A term to describe the way multiple protein subunits are assembled into a whole.

R

radial symmetry (L. radius, a spoke of a wheel + Gr. summetros, symmetry) The regular arrangement of parts around a central axis so that any plane passing through the central axis divides the organism into halves that are approximate mirror images.

radioactivity The emission of nuclear particles and rays by unstable atoms as they decay into more stable forms. Measured in curies, with 1 curie equal to 37 billion disintegrations a second.

radula (L. scraper) A rasping, tonguelike organ characteristic of most mollusks.

recessive allele An allele whose phenotype effects are masked in heterozygotes by the presence of a dominant allele.

recombination The formation of new gene combinations. In bacteria, it is accomplished by the transfer of genes into cells, often in association with viruses. In eukaryotes, it is accomplished by reassortment of chromosomes during meiosis and by crossing over.

reducing power The use of light energy to extract hydrogen atoms from water.

reduction (L. reductio, a bringing back; originally, "bringing back" a metal from its oxide) The gain of an electron during a chemical reaction from one atom to another. Occurs simultaneously with oxidation.

reflex (L. reflectere, to bend back) An automatic consequence of a nerve stimulation. The motion that results from a nerve impulse passing through the system of neurons, eventually reaching the body muscles and causing them to contract.

refractory period The recovery period after membrane depolarization during which the membrane is unable to respond to additional stimulation.

renal (L. renes, kidneys) Pertaining to the kidney.

repression (L. reprimere, to press back, keep back) The process of blocking transcription by the placement of the regulatory protein between the polymerase and the gene, thus blocking movement of the polymerase to the gene.

repressor (L. reprimere, to press back, keep back) A protein that regulates transcription of mRNA from DNA by binding to the operator and so preventing RNA polymerase from attaching to the promoter.

resolving power The ability of a microscope to distinguish two points as separate.

respiration (L. respirare, to breathe) The utilization of oxygen. In terrestrial vertebrates, the inhalation of oxygen and the exhalation of carbon dioxide.

resting membrane potential The charge difference that exists across a neuron's membrane at rest (about 70 millivolts).

restriction endonuclease A special kind of enzyme that can recognize and cleave DNA molecules into fragments. One of the basic tools of genetic engineering.

restriction fragment-length polymorphism (RFLP) An associated genetic mutation marker detected because the mutation alters the length of DNA segments.

retrovirus (L. *retro*, turning back) A virus whose genetic material is RNA rather than DNA. When a retrovirus infects a cell, it makes a DNA copy of itself, which it can then insert into the cellular DNA as if it were a cellular gene.

ribose A five-carbon sugar.

ribosome A cell structure composed of protein and RNA that translates RNA copies of genes into protein.

RNA polymerase The enzyme that transcribes RNA from DNA.

S

saltatory conduction A very fast form of nerve impulse conduction in which the impulses leap from node to node over insulated portions.

sarcoma (Gr. *sarx*, flesh) A cancerous tumor that involves connective or hard tissue, such as muscle.

sarcomere (Gr. *sarx*, flesh + *meris*, part of) The fundamental unit of contraction in skeletal muscle. The repeating bands of actin and myosin that appear between two Z lines.

sarcoplasmic reticulum (Gr. *sarx*, flesh + *plassein*, to form, mold; L. *reticulum*, network) The endoplasmic reticulum of a muscle cell. A sleeve of membrane that wraps around each myofilament.

scientific creationism A view that the biblical account of the origin of the earth is literally true, that the earth is much younger than most scientists believe, and that all species of organisms were individually created just as they are today.

secondary growth In vascular plants, growth that results from the division of a cylinder of cells around the plant's periphery. Secondary growth causes a plant to grow in diameter.

second messenger An intermediary compound that couples extracellular signals to intracellular processes and also amplifies a hormonal signal.

seed A structure that develops from the mature ovule of a seed plant. Contains an embryo and a food source surrounded by a protective coat.

selection The process by which some organisms leave more offspring than competing ones and their genetic traits tend to appear in greater proportions among members of succeeding generations than the traits of those individuals that leave fewer offspring.

self-fertilization The transfer of pollen from an anther to a stigma in the same flower or to another flower of the same plant.

sepal (L. *sepalum*, a covering) A member of the outermost whorl of a flowering plant. Collectively, the sepals constitute the calyx.

septum, *pl.* septa (L. *saeptum*, a fence) A partition or cross-wall, such as those that divide fungal hyphae into cells.

sex chromosomes In humans, the X and Y chromosomes, which are different in the two sexes and are involved in sex determination.

sex-linked characteristic A genetic characteristic that is determined by genes located on the sex chromosomes.

sexual reproduction Reproduction that involves the regular alternation between syngamy and meiosis. Its outstanding characteristic is that an individual offspring inherits genes from two parent individuals.

shoot In vascular plants, the aboveground parts, such as the stem and leaves.

sieve cell In the phloem (food-conducting tissue) of vascular plants, a long, slender sieve element with relatively unspecialized sieve areas and with tapering end walls that lack sieve plates. Found in all vascular plants except angiosperms, which have sieve-tube members.

soluble Refers to polar molecules that dissolve in water and are surrounded by a hydration shell.

solute The molecules dissolved in a solution. *See also* solution, solvent.

solution A mixture of molecules, such as sugars, amino acids, and ions, dissolved in water.

solvent The most common of the molecules in a solution. Usually a liquid, commonly water.

somatic cells (Gr. *soma*, body) All the diploid body cells of an animal that are not involved in gamete formation.

somite A segmented block of tissue on either side of a developing notochord.

species, *pl.* species (L. kind, sort) A level of taxonomic hierarchy; a species ranks next below a genus.

sperm (Gr. *sperma*, sperm, seed) A sperm cell. The male gamete.

spindle The mitotic assembly that carries out the separation of chromosomes during cell division. Composed of microtubules and assembled during prophase at the centrioles of the dividing cell.

spore (Gr. *spora*, seed) A haploid reproductive cell, usually unicellular, that is capable of developing into an adult without fusion with another cell. Spores result from meiosis, as do gametes, but gametes fuse immediately to produce a new diploid cell.

sporophyte (Gr. *spora*, seed + *phyton*, plant) The spore-producing, diploid ($2n$) phase in the life cycle of a plant having alternation of generations.

stabilizing selection A form of selection in which selection acts to eliminate both extremes from a range of phenotypes.

stamen (L. thread) The part of the flower that contains the pollen. Consists of a slender filament that supports the anther. A flower that produces only pollen is called staminate and is functionally male.

steroid (Gr. *stereos*, solid + L. *ol*, from oleum, oil) A kind of lipid. Many of the

molecules that function as messengers and pass across cell membranes are steroids, such as the male and female sex hormones and cholesterol.

steroid hormone A hormone derived from cholesterol. Those that promote the development of the secondary sexual characteristics are steroids.

stigma (Gr. mark) A specialized area of the carpel of a flowering plant that receives the pollen.

stoma, *pl.* stomata (Gr. mouth) A specialized opening in the leaves of some plants that allows carbon dioxide to pass into the plant body and allows water vapor and oxygen to pass out of them.

stratum corneum The outer layer of the epidermis of the skin of the vertebrate body.

substrate (L. *substratus*, strewn under) A molecule on which an enzyme acts.

substrate-level phosphorylation The generation of ATP by coupling its synthesis to a strongly exergonic (energy-yielding) reaction.

succession In ecology, the slow, orderly progression of changes in community composition that takes place through time. Primary succession occurs in nature on bare substrates, over long periods of time. Secondary succession occurs when a climax community has been disturbed.

sugar Any monosaccharide or disaccharide.

surface tension A tautness of the surface of a liquid, caused by the cohesion of the liquid molecules. Water has an extremely high surface tension.

surface-to-volume ratio Describes cell size increases. Cell volume grows much more rapidly than surface area.

symbiosis (Gr. *syn*, together with + *bios*, life) The condition in which two or more dissimilar organisms live together in close association; includes parasitism, commensalism, and mutualism.

synapse (Gr. *synapsis*, a union) A junction between a neuron and another neuron or muscle cell. The two cells do not touch. Instead, neurotransmitters cross the narrow space between them.

synapsis (Gr. *synapsis*, contact, union) The close pairing of homologous chromosomes that occurs early in prophase I of meiosis. With the genes of the chromosomes thus aligned, a DNA strand of one homologue can pair with the complementary DNA strand of the other.

syngamy (Gr. *syn*, together with + *gamos*, marriage) Fertilization. The union of male and female gametes.

T

taxonomy (Gr. *taxis*, arrangement + *nomos*, law) The science of the classification of organisms.

T cell A type of lymphocyte involved in cell-mediated immune responses and interactions with B cells. Also called a T lymphocyte.

tendon (Gr. *tenon*, stretch) A strap of connective tissue that attaches muscle to bone.

tertiary structure of a protein The three-dimensional shape of a protein. Primarily the result of hydrophobic interactions of amino acid side groups and, to a lesser extent, of hydrogen bonds between them. Forms spontaneously.

test cross A cross between a heterozygote and a recessive homozygote. A procedure Mendel used to further test his hypotheses.

theory (Gr. *theorein*, to look at) A well-tested hypothesis supported by a great deal of evidence.

thigmotropism (Gr. *thigma*, touch + *trope*, a turning) The growth response of a plant to touch.

thorax (Gr. a breastplate) The part of the body between the head and the abdomen.

thylakoid (Gr. *thylakos*, sac + *-oides*, like) A flattened, saclike membrane in the chloroplast of a eukaryote. Thylakoids are stacked on top of one another in arrangements called grana and are the sites of photosystem reactions.

tissue (L. *texere*, to weave) A group of similar cells organized into a structural and functional unit.

trachea, *pl.* tracheae (L. windpipe) In vertebrates, the windpipe.

tracheid (Gr. *tracheia*, rough) An elongated cell with thick, perforated walls that carries water and dissolved minerals through a plant and provides support. Tracheids form an essential element of the xylem of vascular plants.

transcription (L. *trans*, across + *scribere*, to write) The first stage of gene expression in which the RNA polymerase enzyme synthesizes an mRNA molecule whose sequence is complementary to the DNA.

translation (L. *trans*, across + *latus*, that which is carried) The second stage of gene expression in which a ribosome assembles a polypeptide, using the mRNA to specify the amino acids.

translocation (L. *trans*, across + *locare*, to put or place) In plants, the process in which most of the carbohydrates manufactured in the leaves and other green parts of the plant are moved through the phloem to other parts of the plant.

transpiration (L. *trans*, across + *spirare*, to breathe) The loss of water vapor by plant parts, primarily through the stomata.

transposon (L. *transponere*, to change the position of) A DNA sequence carrying one or more genes and flanked by insertion sequences that confer the ability to move from one DNA molecule to another. An element capable of transposition (the changing of chromosomal location).

trophic level (Gr. *trophos*, feeder) A step in the movement of energy through an ecosystem.

tropism (Gr. *trop*, turning) A plant's response to external stimuli. A positive tropism is one in which the movement or reaction is in the direction of the source of the stimulus. A negative tropism is one in which the movement or growth is in the opposite direction.

turgor pressure (L. *turgor*, a swelling) The pressure within a cell that results from the movement of water into the cell. A cell with high turgor pressure is said to be turgid.

U

unicellular Composed of a single cell.

urea (Gr. *ouron*, urine) An organic molecule formed in the vertebrate liver. The principal form of disposal of nitrogenous wastes by mammals.

urine (Gr. *ouron*, urine) The liquid waste filtered from the blood by the kidneys.

V

vaccination The injection of a harmless microbe into a person or animal to confer resistance to a dangerous microbe.

vacuole (L. *vacuus*, empty) A cavity in the cytoplasm of a cell that is bound by a single membrane and contains water and waste products of cell metabolism. Typically found in plant cells.

variable Any factor that influences a process. In evaluating alternative hypotheses about one variable, all other variables are held constant so that the investigator is not misled or confused by other influences.

vascular bundle In vascular plants, a strand of tissue containing primary xylem and primary phloem. These bundles of elongated cells conduct water with dissolved minerals and carbohydrates throughout the plant body.

vascular cambium In vascular plants, the meristematic layer of cells that gives rise to secondary phloem and secondary xylem. The activity of the vascular cambium increases stem or root diameter.

ventral (L. *venter*, belly) Refers to the bottom portion of an animal. Opposite of dorsal.

vertebrate An animal having a backbone made of bony segments called vertebrae.

vesicle (L. *vesicula*, a little (ladder) Membrane-enclosed sacs within eukaryotic cells.

vessel element In vascular plants, a typically elongated cell, dead at maturity, that conducts water and solutes in the xylem.

villus, *pl.* villi (L. a tuft of hair) In vertebrates, fine, microscopic, fingerlike projections on epithelial cells lining the small intestine that serve to increase the absorptive surface area of the intestine.

vitamin (L. *vita*, life + *amine*, of chemical origin) An organic substance that the organism cannot synthesize, but is required in minute quantities by an organism for growth and activity.

viviparous (L. *vivus*, alive + *parere*, to bring forth) Refers to reproduction in which eggs develop within the mother's body and young are born free-living.

voltage-gated channel A transmembrane pathway for an ion that is opened or closed by a change in the voltage, or charge difference, across the cell membrane.

W

water vascular system The system of water-filled canals connecting the tube feet of echinoderms.

whorl A circle of leaves or of flower parts present at a single level along an axis.

wood Accumulated secondary xylem. Heartwood is the central, nonliving wood in the trunk of a tree. Hardwood is the wood of dicots, regardless of how hard or soft it actually is. Softwood is the wood of conifers.

X

xylem (Gr. *xylon*, wood) In vascular plants, a specialized tissue, composed primarily of elongate, thick-walled conducting cells, that transports water and solutes through the plant body.

Y

yolk (O.E. *geolu*, yellow) The stored substance in egg cells that provides the embryo's primary food supply.

Z

zygote (Gr. *zygotos*, paired together) The diploid ($2n$) cell resulting from the fusion of male and female gametes (fertilization).

Arthropods

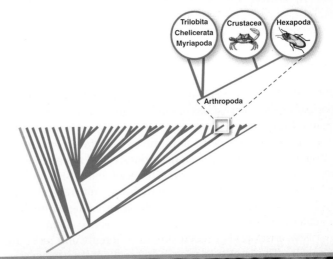

A Winning Combination

Humans suffer staggering economic losses due to insects. Locust outbreaks in Africa seem a thing of the past to many, but this is far from true. Locust populations fluctuate between quiet phases, during which they cover only 16 million square kilometers in 30 African countries, and plague phases, when they cover 29 million square kilometers of land in 60 countries. A swarm of locusts, *Schistocerca gregaria*, contains 40 to 80 million insects per square kilometer. In peak phases, they cover 20% of the earth's land surface and affect the livelihood of one-tenth of the earth's population. The last plague phase was 1986–1989, but the Food and Agriculture Organization (FAO) of the United Nations monitors and maps population sizes continuously to respond quickly to outbreaks (http://www.fao.org/ag/locusts/en/info/info/faq/index.html).

In the western United States and Canada, an outbreak of mountain pine beetles in the 1980s and 1990s killed pines on huge acreages, and the 1973 to 1985 outbreak of spruce budworm in fir/spruce forests killed millions of conifer trees. Since its introduction in the 1920s, a fungus that causes Dutch elm disease, mainly transmitted by European bark beetles, has virtually obliterated American elm trees in North America. Since 2004, another alien invader, the emerald ash borer, a beetle, threatens the continent's ash trees.

These examples remind us of our ceaseless struggle with the dominant group of animals on earth today: insects. Insect species far outnumber all other species of animals combined. Some scientists have estimated that there are 200 million insects for every single human alive today! Insects have an unmatched ability to adapt to all land environments and virtually all climates. Many have exploited freshwater and shoreline habitats, and have evolved extraordinary abilities to survive adverse environmental conditions.

How can we explain the enormous success of these creatures? Insects, like other members of phylum Arthropoda, have a combination of valuable structural and physiological adaptations, including a versatile exoskeleton, metamerism, an efficient respiratory system, and highly developed sensory organs. In addition, many have a waterproof cuticle and an extraordinary ability to survive adverse environmental conditions. We describe these adaptations and others in this chapter.

Spotted spiny lobster, *Panulirus guttatus*.

P hylum Arthropoda (ar-thro-pod´a) (Gr. *arthron,* joint, + *podos,* foot) embraces spiders, scorpions, ticks, mites, crustaceans, millipedes, centipedes, insects, and some smaller groups. In addition its rich fossil record extends back to the mid-Cambrian period (figure 13.1).

Arthropods are coelomate protostomes with well-developed organ systems, and their cuticular exoskeleton containing chitin and tanned protein is a prominent characteristic. Like annelids, they are conspicuously segmented; their ancestral body pattern is a linear series of similar segments, each with a pair of jointed appendages. However, unlike annelids, arthropods have various patterns of segments and appendages. Often segments are combined or fused into functional groups, called **tagmata** (sing., **tagma**), for specialized purposes. The head and thorax are two such tagmata. Appendages, too, are frequently differentiated and specialized for walking, swimming, flying, or eating. Arthropods also differ from annelids in having a very reduced coelom.

Few arthropods exceed 60 cm in length, and most are far smaller. The largest is a Japanese crab (*Macrocheira kaempferi*) with a span of approximately 3.7 m; the smallest is a parasitic mite less than 0.1 mm long.

Arthropods are usually active, energetic animals. Whether judged by their great diversity, their wide ecological distribution, or their vast numbers of species, they are the most abundant and diverse of all animals.

Although arthropods compete with humans for food supplies and spread serious diseases, they are essential pollinators of many food plants, and they also serve as food, yield drugs and dyes, and create such products as silk, honey, and beeswax.

■ Ecological Relationships

In diversity of ecological distribution, arthropods have no rivals. Arthropods occur in all types of environments, from low ocean depths to very high altitudes and from the tropics far into both the north and south polar regions. Some species are adapted for life on land or in fresh, brackish, and marine waters; others live in or on plants and other animals. Most species use flight to move among their favored habitats. Some live in places where no other animal could survive.

Although all feeding types—carnivorous, omnivorous, and herbivorous—occur in this vast group, the majority are herbivorous. Most aquatic arthropods depend on algae for their nourishment, and most land forms live chiefly on plants. Many are parasites.

Why Are Arthropods So Diverse and Abundant?

The following structural and physiological patterns have helped arthropods achieve an amazing degree of diversity:

1. **Versatile exoskeleton.** Arthropods have an exoskeleton, called the cuticle, that is highly protective without sacrificing mobility. The cuticle is an outer covering secreted by underlying epidermis.

   The cuticle consists of an outer, relatively thin **epicuticle** and an inner and thicker **procuticle** (figure 13.2). Both the epicuticle and the procuticle are composed of several layers each. The epicuticle is made of protein and often lipids. The protein is stabilized and hardened by a chemical process called tanning, adding further protection. The procuticle is divided into **exocuticle,** which is secreted before a molt, and **endocuticle,** which is secreted after molting. Both layers of the procuticle contain **chitin** bound with protein. Chitin is a tough, resistant, nitrogenous polysaccharide that is insoluble in water, alkalies, and weak acids. Thus, the procuticle is not only flexible and lightweight but also affords protection, particularly against dehydration. In most crustaceans, some areas of the procuticle are also impregnated with **calcium salts,** which reduce flexibility. In the hard shells of lobsters and crabs, for instance, this calcification is extreme.

A   B

figure 13.1

Fossils of early arthropods. **A,** Trilobite fossils, dorsal view. These animals were abundant in the mid-Cambrian period. **B,** Eurypterid fossil; eurypterids flourished in northern seas from the Ordovician to the Permian period.

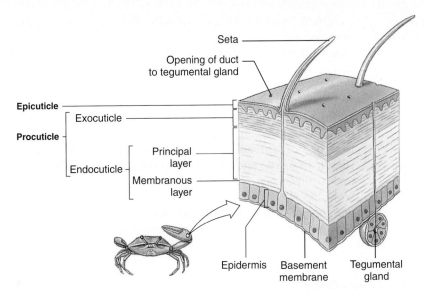

figure 13.2

Structure of crustacean cuticle.

The cuticle may be soft and permeable or may form a veritable coat of armor. Between body segments and between segments of appendages, it is thin and flexible, permitting free movement of joints. In crustaceans and insects, the cuticle forms ingrowths for muscle attachment. It may also line the foregut and hindgut, line and support the tracheae, and be adapted for a variety of purposes.

The nonexpansible cuticular exoskeleton imposes important conditions on growth. To grow, an arthropod must shed its outer covering at intervals and grow a larger one—a process called **ecdysis,** or **molting.** Arthropods molt from four to seven times before reaching adulthood, and some continue to molt after that. Much of an arthropod's physiology centers on molting, particularly in young animals—preparation, molting itself, and then all of the processes that must be completed in the postmolt period. More details of the molting process are given for crustaceans (see p. 247) and for insects (see p. 264).

An exoskeleton is also relatively heavy and becomes proportionately heavier with increasing size. The weight of the exoskeleton tends to limit ultimate body size.

2. **Segmentation and appendages for more efficient locomotion.** Typically, each segment has a pair of jointed appendages, but this arrangement is often modified, with both segments and appendages specialized for adaptive functions. Limb segments are essentially hollow levers that are moved by muscles, most of which are striated for rapid action. The jointed appendages are equipped with sensory hairs and are variously modified for sensory functions, food handling, and swift, efficient walking or swimming.

3. **Air piped directly to cells.** Most land arthropods have a highly efficient tracheal system of air tubes, which delivers oxygen directly to tissues and cells and makes a high metabolic rate possible. Aquatic arthropods breathe mainly by gills.

4. Highly **developed sensory organs.** Sensory organs show great variety, from compound (mosaic) eyes to

---

Characteristics of Phylum Arthropoda

1. **Jointed appendages;** ancestrally, one pair to each segment, but number often reduced; appendages often modified for specialized functions
2. Live in marine, freshwater, and terrestrial habitats; many capable of flight
3. Free-living and parasitic taxa
4. Bilateral symmetry; **segmented body** divided into functional groups called **tagmata:** head and trunk; head, thorax, and abdomen; or cephalothorax and abdomen; definite head
5. Triploblastic body
6. **Reduced coelom** in adult; body cavity consists mostly of hemocoel (spaces in the tissues) filled with blood
7. **Cuticular exoskeleton;** contains protein, lipid, chitin, and often calcium carbonate secreted by underlying epidermis and shed (molted) at intervals; although **chitin** occurs in a few groups other than arthropods, its use is better developed in arthropods
8. **Complete digestive system;** mouthparts modified from ancestral appendages and adapted for different methods of feeding; gut tube shows great specialization by having, in various arthropods, chitinous teeth, compartments, and gastric ossicles

9. **Complex muscular system,** with exoskeleton for attachment, **striated muscles** for rapid actions, smooth muscles for visceral organs; no cilia
10. **Nervous system** similar to that of annelids, with dorsal brain connected by a ring around the gullet to a double nerve chain of ventral ganglia; fused ganglia in some species
11. Well-developed sensory organs; behavioral patterns much more complex than those of most invertebrates, with more **social organization**
12. Parthenogenesis in some taxa
13. **Sexes usually separate,** with paired reproductive organs and ducts; usually internal fertilization; oviparous, ovoviviparous, or viviparous; often with **metamorphosis**
14. Paired excretory glands called **coxal, antennal,** or **maxillary glands** present in some; others have excretory organs called **Malpighian tubules**
15. Respiration by **body surface, gills, tracheae** (air tubes), or **book lungs**
16. **Open circulatory system,** with dorsal **contractile heart,** arteries and hemocoel (blood sinuses)

senses of touch, smell, hearing, balance, and chemical reception. Arthropods are keenly alert to environmental stimuli.

5. **Complex behavior patterns.** Arthropods exceed most other invertebrates in the complexity and organization of their activities. Innate (unlearned) behavior unquestionably controls much of what they do, but many arthropods also demonstrate learned behaviors.

6. **Trophic breadth through metamorphosis.** Many arthropods pass through metamorphic changes, including a larval form quite different from the adult structure. Larval forms are often adapted for eating a different kind of food than adults do, permitting a single species to exploit diverse resources.

Arthropoda is so astonishingly diverse that zoologists have argued over whether all its members belong within a single phylum. Currently, most biologists accept Arthropoda as a monophyletic group, but there is much discussion about which arthropod subphyla are valid. Formerly, arthropods were divided among four subphyla: the extinct Trilobita and the three extant taxa Chelicerata, Crustacea, and Uniramia. The subphylum Uniramia was diagnosed by the shared presence of **uniramous** appendages with a single branch (figure 13.3, *top*) and included insects and myriapods (centipedes, millipedes, and a few less well-known forms). Recent work has questioned the validity of this group, so we divide uniramians into two subphyla: Myriapoda and Hexapoda. Hexapoda contains class Insecta and one other very small

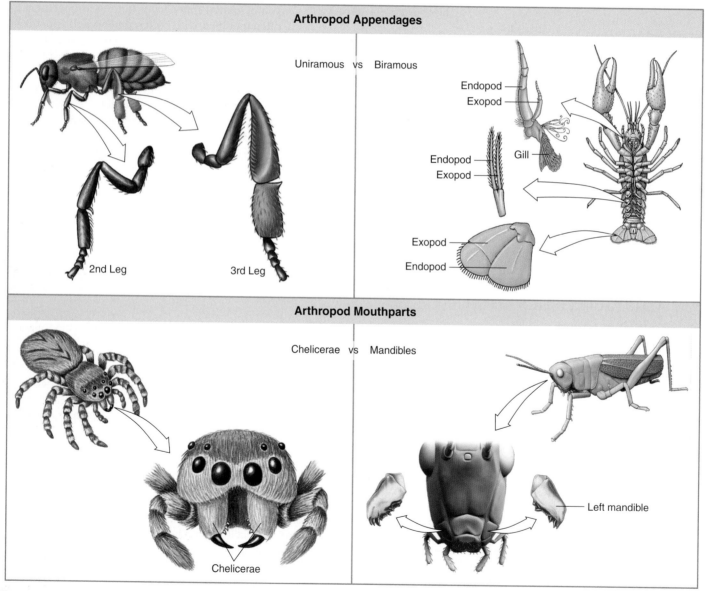

figure 13.3

Two important arthropod characters: Appendages may be uniramous (honey bee leg) or biramous (lobster limb); mouthparts may include chelicerae (spider) or mandibles (grasshopper). Note that the presence or absence of gills is unrelated to appendage form.

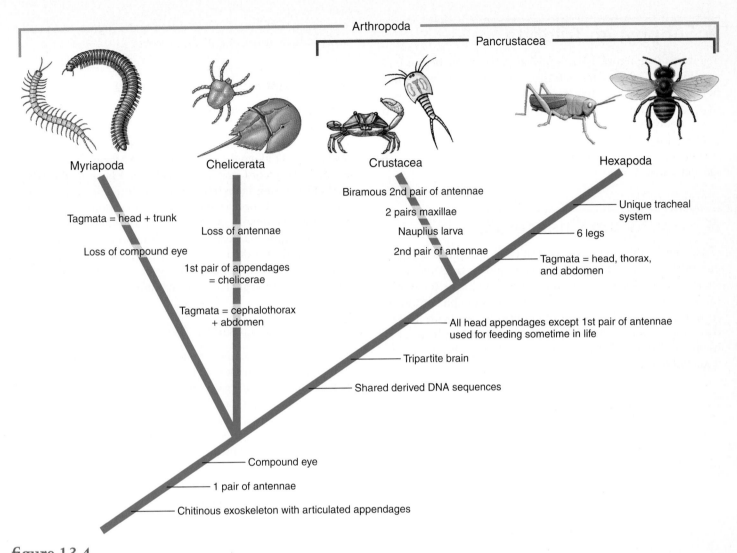

figure 13.4

Cladogram of arthropods showing probable relationships of the four extant subphyla. Only a few synapomorphies are included here. Crustaceans and hexapods are shown as sister taxa, but no branching order for Myriapoda, Chelicerata, or Pancrustacea is specified.

class. Arthropod subphyla themselves are relatively easy to distinguish based on the number of tagmata and the types of appendages present, as outlined next.

Relationships among the subphyla are controversial. One hypothesis proposes that all arthropods possessing a particular mouthpart, called a **mandible,** form a single clade, Mandibulata. This clade includes members of Myriapoda, Hexapoda, and Crustacea. Arthropods that do not have mandibles possess **chelicerae** (see figure 13.3, *bottom*), as exemplified by spiders. Thus, according to the "mandibulate hypothesis," myriapods, hexapods, and crustaceans are more closely related to each other than any of them are to chelicerates. Critics of the mandibulate hypothesis argue that the mandibles in each group are so different from each other that they could not be homologous. The mandibles of crustaceans are multijointed, with chewing or biting surfaces on the mandible bases (called a gnathobasic mandible), whereas those of myriapods and hexapods have a single joint with the biting

surface on the distal edge (called an entire-limb mandible). There are also some differences in the muscles controlling the two types. Proponents of the mandibulate hypothesis respond that the 550-million-year history of the mandibulates makes possible the evolution of diverse mandibles from an ancestral type.

We assume that subphylum Trilobita is the sister taxon to a group containing all other known arthropods. We depict subphylum Crustacea as the sister taxon of subphylum Hexapoda, but do not specify a branching order for subphylum Myriapoda, subphylum Chelicerata, or the combined branch with hexapods and crustaceans (figure 13.4). Evidence that hexapods and crustaceans form a clade emerged from several phylogenetic studies using molecular characters; these studies prompted a reevaluation of the morphological characters in members of both taxa. We unite subphylum Crustacea with subphylum Hexapoda in clade Pancrustacea.

■ Subphylum Trilobita

Trilobites (see figure 13.1A) probably had their beginnings a million or more years before the Cambrian period. They have been extinct some 250 million years, but were abundant during the Cambrian and Ordovician periods. Their name denotes the trilobed shape of the body, caused by a pair of longitudinal grooves. They were largely bottom-dwellers, probably scavengers. Most of them could roll up like pill bugs.

■ Subphylum Chelicerata

Chelicerate arthropods are a very ancient group that includes eurypterids (extinct), horseshoe crabs, spiders, ticks and mites, scorpions, sea spiders, and others. They are characterized by the presence of two tagmata and six pairs of cephalothoracic appendages that include a pair of **chelicerae** (see figure 13.3), a pair of **pedipalps,** and **four pairs of walking legs.** They have no mandibles and no antennae. Most chelicerates suck liquid food from their prey.

Class Merostomata

Subclass Eurypterida

Eurypterids, or giant water scorpions (see figure 13.1B), lived 200 to 500 million years ago, and some were perhaps the largest of all arthropods, reaching a length of 3 m. They had some resemblances to marine horseshoe crabs (figure 13.5) and to scorpions, their terrestrial counterparts.

Subclass Xiphosurida: Horseshoe Crabs

Xiphosurids are an ancient marine group that dates from the Cambrian period. Only three genera (five species) survive today. *Limulus* (L. *limus,* sidelong, askew) (figure 13.5), which lives in shallow water along the North American Atlantic coast, appears in the fossil record practically unchanged back to the Triassic period. Horseshoe crabs have an unsegmented, horseshoe-shaped **carapace** (hard dorsal shield) and a broad abdomen, which has a long, spinelike **telson,** or tailpiece. On some abdominal appendages, **book gills** (flat, leaflike gills) are exposed. Horseshoe crabs can swim awkwardly by means of their abdominal plates and can walk on their walking legs. They feed at night on worms and small molluscs and are harmless to humans.

Class Pycnogonida: Sea Spiders

The curious little marine animals called pycnogonids are much more common than most of us realize. They move on four pairs of long, thin walking legs, drinking juices from hydroids and soft-bodied animals with their large suctorial proboscis (figure 13.6). Their odd appearance is enhanced by a much reduced abdomen attached to an elongated cephalothorax. The small abdomen is completely occupied by the digestive tract, so the gonads extend into the legs. Males often use a pair of legs called **ovigers** to carry the egg masses. Most pycnogonids are only a few millimeters long; they are common in all oceans.

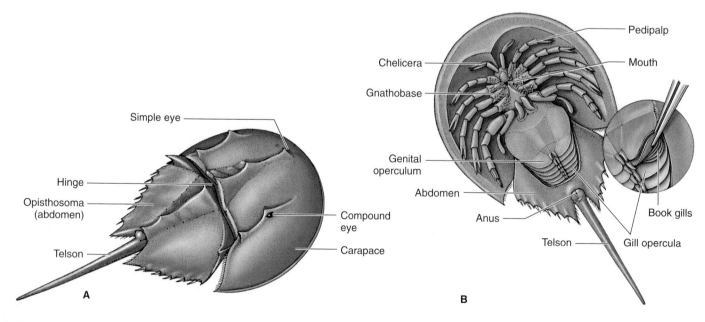

figure 13.5

A, Dorsal view of horseshoe crab *Limulus* (class Merostomata). Individuals grow to 0.5 m in length. **B,** Ventral view of a female.

Class Arachnida

Arachnids (Gr. *arachnē,* spider) are numerous and diverse, with over 80,000 species described so far. They include spiders, scorpions, pseudoscorpions, whip scorpions, ticks, mites, harvestmen (daddy longlegs), and others. The arachnid tagmata are a cephalothorax and an abdomen.

Order Araneae: Spiders

Spiders are a large group of 40,000 recognized species, distributed all over the world. The cephalothorax and abdomen show no external segmentation, and the tagmata are joined by a narrow, waistlike pedicel (figure 13.7).

All spiders are predaceous and feed largely on insects (figure 13.8). Their chelicerae function as fangs and bear ducts from their venom glands, with which they effectively dispatch their prey. Some spiders chase their prey, others ambush them, and many trap them in a net of silk. After a spider seizes its prey with its chelicerae and injects venom, it liquefies the prey's tissues with a digestive fluid and sucks the resulting broth into the stomach. Spiders with teeth at the bases of their chelicerae crush or chew prey, and enzymes from their mouth further aid digestion. Many spiders provision their young with previously captured prey.

Spiders breathe by **book lungs** or **tracheae** or both. Book lungs, which are unique to spiders, consist of many parallel air pockets extending into a blood-filled chamber (see figure 13.7C). Air enters the chamber through a slit in the body wall. Tracheae are a system of air tubes that carry air directly to tissues from openings called **spiracles.** The tracheae of spiders are similar to those of insects (see p. 262), but much less extensive.

Spiders and insects have a unique excretory system of **Malpighian tubules** (see figure 13.7C) that work in conjunction with specialized rectal glands. Potassium and other solutes and waste materials are secreted into the tubules, which drain the fluid, or "urine," into the intestine. Rectal glands reabsorb most of the potassium and water, leaving behind wastes such as uric acid. Through this cycling of water and potassium, species living in dry environments conserve body fluids, producing a nearly dry mixture of urine and feces. Many spiders also have **coxal glands,** which are modified nephridia that open at the coxa, or base, of the first and third walking legs.

Spiders usually have eight **simple eyes,** each provided with a lens, optic rods, and a retina (see figure 13.7B). Chiefly, the eyes perceive moving objects, but some, such as those of the hunting and jumping spiders, may form images. Because vision is usually poor, a spider's awareness of its environment depends especially on its hairlike **sensory setae.** Every seta on its surface is useful in communicating some information about the spider's surroundings, air currents, or changing tensions in its web. By sensing vibrations of its web, a spider can judge the size and activity of its entangled prey or receive a message tapped on a silk thread by a prospective mate.

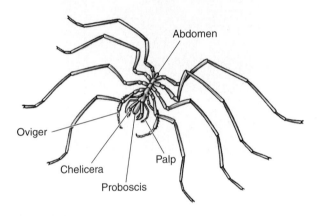

figure 13.6

A pycnogonid, *Nymphon* sp. In this genus, all anterior appendages (chelicerae, palps, and ovigers) are present in both sexes, although ovigers are often not present in females of other genera.

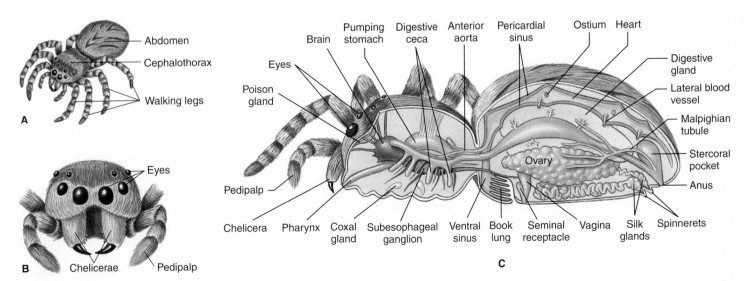

figure 13.7

A, External anatomy of a jumping spider. **B,** Anterior view of head. **C,** Internal anatomy of a female spider.

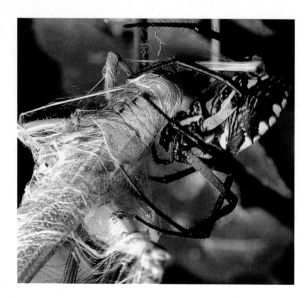

figure 13.8

A grasshopper, snared and helpless in the web of a golden garden spider (*Argiope aurantia*), is wrapped in silk while still alive. If the spider is not hungry, its prize is saved for a later meal.

Web-Spinning Habits   The ability to spin silk is important in the life of a spider, as in some other arachnids as well. Two or three pairs of spinnerets containing hundreds of microscopic tubes connect to special abdominal **silk glands** (see figure 13.7C). A protein secretion emitted as a liquid hardens on contact with air to form a silk thread. Spiders' silk threads are stronger than steel threads of the same diameter and are probably second in tensional strength only to fused quartz fibers. The threads can stretch one-fifth of their length before breaking.

The spider web used for trapping insects is familiar to most people. The webs of some species merely consist of a few strands of silk radiating out from a spider's burrow or place of retreat. Other species spin beautiful, geometric orb webs. Besides making webs, spiders use silk threads to line their nests; form sperm webs or egg sacs; build draglines; make bridge lines, warning threads, molting threads, attachment discs, or nursery webs; or wrap their prey securely (figure 13.8). Not all spiders spin webs for traps. Some, such as crab spiders, hide from their prey (figure 13.9A), whereas wolf spiders, jumping spiders (figure 13.9B), and fisher spiders (figure 13.10), simply chase and catch their prey.

Reproduction   A courtship ritual usually precedes mating. Before mating, a male spins a small web, deposits a drop of sperm on it, and then lifts the package and stores it in special cavities of his pedipalps (second pair of appendages). When he mates, he inserts a pedipalp into a female's genital opening. Sperm are stored in a female's seminal receptacle, sometimes for weeks or months, until eggs are ready. A female lays her fertilized eggs in a silken cocoon, which she may carry or may attach to a web or plant. A cocoon may contain hundreds of eggs, which hatch in approximately 2 weeks. The young usually remain in their egg sac for a few weeks and molt once before leaving it. Several molts occur before adulthood.

A

B

figure 13.9

A, A camouflaged crab spider, *Misumenoides* sp., awaits its insect prey. Its coloration matches the petals among which it lies, thus deceiving insects that visit the flowers in search of pollen or nectar. **B,** A jumping spider, *Eris aurantius*. This species has excellent vision and stalks an insect until it is close enough to leap with unerring precision, fixing its chelicerae into its prey.

Are Spiders Dangerous?   It is truly amazing that such small and helpless creatures as spiders have generated so much unreasoned fear in humans. Spiders are timid creatures that, rather than being enemies to humans, are allies in our continuing conflict with insects. The venom spiders produce to kill prey is usually harmless to humans. Even the most venomous spiders bite only when threatened or when defending their eggs or young. American tarantulas (figure 13.11), despite their fearsome appearance, are not dangerous. They rarely bite, and their bite is not considered serious.

Two spider genera in the United States can inflict severe or even fatal bites: *Latrodectus* (L. *latro*, robber, + *dektes*, biter) and *Loxosceles* (Gr. *loxos*, crooked, + *skelos*, leg). The most important species are *Latrodectus mactans*, or the black widow, and *Loxosceles reclusa*, or the brown recluse. Black widows are moderate to small in size and shiny black, with a bright orange or red "hourglass" on the underside of their abdomen (figure 13.12A). Their venom is neurotoxic, acting on the nervous system. About four or five of each 1000 bites reported are fatal.

figure 13.10

A fisher spider, *Dolomedes triton*, feeds on a minnow. This handsome spider feeds mostly on aquatic and terrestrial insects but occasionally captures small fishes and tadpoles. It pulls its paralyzed victim from the water, pumps in digestive enzymes, and then sucks out the predigested contents.

figure 13.11

A tarantula, *Brachypelma vagans*.

Brown recluse spiders, which are smaller than black widows, are brown, and bear a violin-shaped dorsal stripe on their cephalothorax (figure 13.12B). Their venom is hemolytic rather than neurotoxic, destroying the tissues and skin surrounding a bite. Their bite can be mild to serious and occasionally fatal.

Dangerous spiders in other parts of the world include funnel-web spiders (*Atrax robustus*) in Australia and certain ctenid spiders in South America, such as *Phoneutria fera*. In contrast to most spiders, these are quite aggressive.

Order Scorpionida: Scorpions

Although scorpions are more common in tropical and subtropical regions, some occur in temperate zones. Scorpions are generally

A

B

figure 13.12

A, A black widow spider, *Latrodectus mactans*, suspended on her web. Note the orange "hourglass" on the ventral side of her abdomen. **B,** The brown recluse spider, *Loxosceles reclusa*, is a small venomous spider. Note the small, violin-shaped marking on its cephalothorax. The venom is hemolytic and dangerous.

reclusive, hiding in burrows or under objects by day and feeding at night. They feed largely on insects and spiders, which they seize with chelate pedipalps and rip with jawlike chelicerae.

A scorpion's body consists of a rather short cephalothorax, which bears appendages and from one to six pairs of eyes, and a clearly segmented abdomen without appendages. The abdomen is divided into a broader **preabdomen** and a tail-like **postabdomen,** which ends in a stinging apparatus used to inject venom. The venom of most species is not harmful to humans, although that of certain species of *Androctonus* in Africa and *Centruroides* in Mexico, Arizona, and New Mexico can be fatal.

Scorpions bear well-developed young, which their mother carries on her back until after their first molt (figure 13.13A).

Order Solpugida: Sun or Camel Spiders

Solpugids, sometimes also called solfugids and by such common names as sun, camel, or wind spiders, are nonvenomous

figure 13.13

A, An emperor scorpion (order Scorpionida), *Paninus imperator,* with young, which stay with their mother until their first molt. **B,** A harvestman (order Opiliones). Harvestmen run rapidly on their stiltlike legs. They are especially noticeable during the harvesting season, hence the common name.

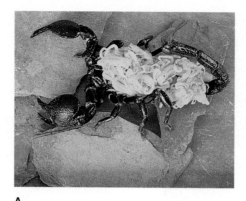

A

B

A Wood tick, *Dermacentor variabilis*

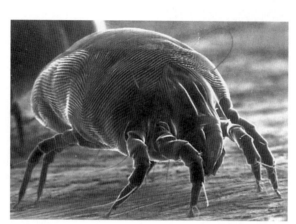

B SEM of house dust mite, *Dermatophagoides farinae*

C Follicle mite, *Demodex follicuorum*

figure 13.14

Ticks and mites are arachnids that often affect humans. **A,** The wood tick, *Dermacentor variabilis*, transmits Rocky Mountain spotted fever and other diseases. **B,** Dust mites, *Dermatophagoides farinae*, often trigger allergic reactions. **C,** The human follicle mite, *Demodex follicuorum*, is tiny (100 to 400 um) and lives in follicles, particularly around the nose and eyes. Its prevalence ranges from about 20% in persons 20 years of age or younger to nearly 100% in the aged.

arachnids that shred prey with their large chelicerae. They are often less than 1 cm long, but some species approach 15 cm. They are common in tropical and subtropical deserts in America, the Middle East, Africa, and Asia.

Order Opiliones: Harvestmen

Harvestmen, often known as "daddy longlegs," are common in the United States and other parts of the world (figure 13.13B). They are easily distinguished from spiders by a broad joining of their abdomen and cephalothorax without the constriction of a pedicel, and by the external segmentation of their abdomen. They have four pairs of long, spindly legs and, without apparent ill effect, can cast off one or more legs if they are grasped by a predator (or human hand). The ends of their chelicerae are pincerlike, and they feed much more as scavengers than do most arachnids.

Order Acari: Ticks and Mites

Acarines differ from all other arachnids in having their cephalothorax and abdomen completely fused, with no external division or segmentation (figure 13.14A). Their mouthparts are on a little anterior projection, or **capitulum.** They occur almost everywhere—in both fresh and salt water, on vegetation, on the ground, and parasitic on vertebrates and invertebrates. Over 40,000 species have been described, many of which are important to humans, but this is probably only a fraction of the species that exist.

Many species of mites are entirely free-living. *Dermatophagoides farinae* (Gr. *dermatos,* skin, + *phago,* to eat, + *eidos,* likeness of form) (figure 13.14B) and related species are denizens of house dust all over the world, sometimes causing allergies and dermatoses. Some mites are marine, but most aquatic species live in fresh water. They have long, hairlike setae on their legs for swimming, and their larvae may be parasitic on aquatic invertebrates. Their sheer abundance gives acarines ecological importance, but many acarines have direct effects on our food supply and health as well. Spider mites (family Tetranychidae) are serious agricultural pests on fruit trees, cotton, clover, and many other plants. Larvae of genus *Trombicula* are called chiggers or redbugs. They feed on dermal tissues of terrestrial vertebrates, including humans, and cause an irritating dermatitis; some species of chiggers transmit a disease called Asiatic scrub typhus. Hair-follicle mites, *Demodex* (figure 13.14C), are apparently nonpathogenic in humans; they infect most of us although we are unaware of them. Other species of *Demodex* and other genera of mites cause mange in domestic animals.

The inflamed welt and intense itching that follow a chigger bite are not caused by a chigger burrowing into the skin, as is popularly believed. Rather, the chigger bites through skin with its chelicerae and injects a salivary secretion containing powerful enzymes that liquefy skin cells. Human skin responds defensively by forming a hardened tube that the larva uses as a sort of drinking straw and through which it gorges itself with host cells and fluid. Scratching usually removes the chigger but leaves the tube, which remains a source of irritation for several days.

Ticks are usually larger than mites. They pierce the skin of vertebrates and suck blood until their bodies become enormously distended; then they drop off and digest their meal. After molting, they are ready for another meal. In addition to disease conditions that they themselves cause, ticks are among the world's premier disease vectors, ranking second only to mosquitos. They carry a greater variety of infectious agents than any other arthropod; such agents include protozoan, rickettsial, viral, bacterial, and fungal organisms. Species of *Ixodes* carry the most common arthropod-borne infection in the United States, Lyme disease (see accompanying note). Species of *Dermacentor* (see figure 13.14A) and other ticks transmit Rocky Mountain spotted fever, a misnamed disease since most cases occur in the eastern United States. *Dermacentor* also transmits tularemia and agents of several other diseases. Texas cattle fever, also called red-water fever, is caused by a protozoan parasite transmitted by the cattle tick *Boophilus annulatus.*

In the 1970s, people in the town of Lyme, Connecticut, experienced an epidemic of arthritis-like symptoms. Subsequently called Lyme disease, it is caused by a bacterium and carried by ticks of the genus *Ixodes*. Thousands of cases are reported each year in Europe and North America, and other cases have been reported from Japan, Australia, and South Africa. Many people bitten by infected ticks recover spontaneously or do not suffer any ill effects. Others, if not treated at an early stage, develop a chronic, disabling disease. Lyme disease is now the leading arthropod-borne disease in the United States.

■ Subphylum Myriapoda

The term **myriapod** (Gr. *myrias,* a myriad, + *podos,* foot) denotes several classes that share a pattern of two tagmata—head and trunk—with paired appendages on most or all trunk segments. Myriapods include Chilopoda (centipedes), Diplopoda (millipedes), Pauropoda (pauropods), and Symphyla (symphylans). We describe only the chilopods and diplopods.

The head of myriapods has only **one pair of antennae,** instead of two. It also has **mandibles** (see figure 13.3, *bottom*) and two pairs of **maxillae** (one pair of maxillae in millipedes). The legs are all **uniramous.**

Respiratory exchange occurs through body surface and tracheal systems, although juveniles, if aquatic, may have gills.

Class Chilopoda: Centipedes

Centipedes are active predators with a preference for moist places such as under logs or stones, where they feed largely on earthworms and insects. Their bodies are somewhat flattened dorsoventrally, and they may contain from a few to 177 segments (figure 13.15). Each segment, except the one behind the head and the last two, bears one pair of appendages. Those of the first body segment are modified to form venom claws, which centipedes use to kill their prey. Most species are harmless to humans.

The centipede head bears a pair of eyes, each consisting of a group of ocelli (simple eyes). Respiration is by tracheal tubes with a pair of spiracles in each segment. Sexes are separate, and all species are oviparous. Young are similar to adults. Familiar genera are the common house centipedes *Scutigera,* with 15 pairs of legs, and *Scolopendra* (figure 13.15), with 21 pairs of legs.

Class Diplopoda: Millipedes

Diplopods, or "double-footed" arthropods, are commonly called millipedes, which means "thousand feet," although they do not literally have a thousand legs (figure 13.16). Their cylindrical bodies contain 25 to 100 segments. The four thoracic segments bear only one pair of legs each, but the abdominal segments each have two pairs, a condition that may have evolved from fusion of segments. Two pairs of spiracles occur on each abdominal segment, each opening into an air chamber that gives rise to tracheal tubes.

Millipedes are less active than centipedes and are generally herbivorous, living on decayed plant and animal matter and sometimes living plants. They prefer dark, moist places under stones and logs. Females lay eggs in a nest and guard them carefully. Larval forms have only one pair of legs per segment.

■ Subphylum Crustacea

The 67,000 or more species of Crustacea (L. *crusta,* shell) include lobsters, crayfishes, shrimp, crabs, water fleas, copepods, and barnacles. Crustaceans compose the only arthropod subphylum that is primarily aquatic; they are mainly

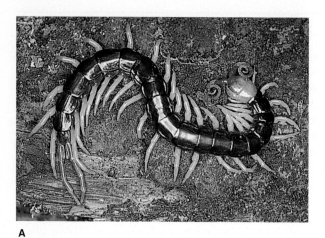

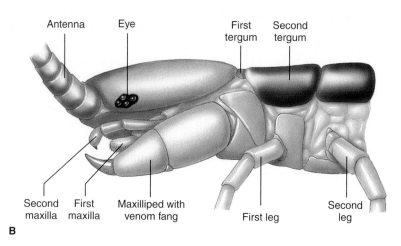

figure 13.15

A, A centipede, *Scolopendra* (class Chilopoda) from the Amazon Basin, Peru. Most segments have one pair of appendages each. The first segment bears a pair of venom claws, which in some species can inflict serious wounds. Centipedes are carnivorous. **B,** Head of a centipede.

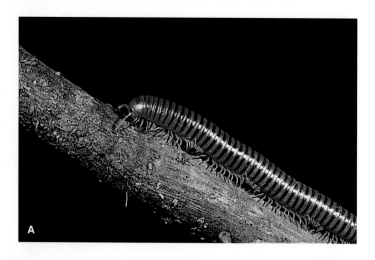

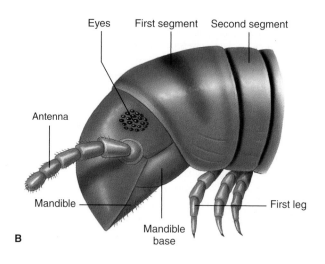

figure 13.16

A, A tropical millipede with warning coloration. Note the typical doubling of appendages on most segments, hence diplosegments. **B,** Head of a millipede.

marine, but many freshwater and a few terrestrial species are known. Most are free-living, but some are sessile, commensal, or parasitic. Crustaceans are often very important components of aquatic ecosystems, and several have considerable economic importance.

Crustaceans are the only arthropods with **two pairs of antennae** (figure 13.17). In addition to antennae and **mandibles,** they have **two pairs of maxillae** on the head, followed by a pair of appendages on each body segment (although appendages on some segments are absent in some groups). All appendages, except perhaps the first antennae (antennules), are primitively **biramous** (see figure 13.3, *top*), and at least some appendages of all present-day adults show that condition. Organs specialized for respiration, if present, are in the form of gills. Malpighian tubules are absent.

Ancestral crustaceans typically had 60 segments or more, but most modern forms tend to have between 16 and 20 segments and increased tagmatization. The major tagmata are **head, thorax,** and **abdomen,** but these are not homologous throughout the subphylum (or even within some classes) because of varying degrees of segment fusion—for example, in the cephalothorax.

In many crustaceans, the dorsal cuticle of the head extends posteriorly and around the sides of the animal to cover or fuse with some or all of the thoracic and abdominal segments. This covering is called a **carapace.** In some groups, the carapace forms clamshell-like valves that cover most or all of the body. In decapods (including lobsters, shrimp, crabs, and others), the carapace covers the entire cephalothorax but not the abdomen. Crustacea has recently expanded to include the

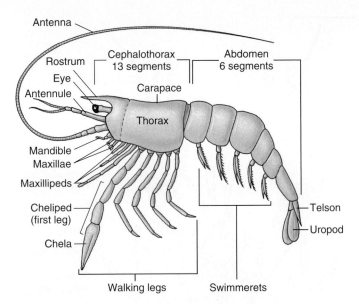

figure 13.17

Archetypical plan of Malacostraca. Note that maxillae and maxillipeds have been separated diagrammatically to illustrate the general plan. Typically, in living animals, only the third maxilliped is visible externally. In order Decapoda, the carapace covers the cephalothorax, as shown here. The head region is beneath the carapace to the left of the dashed line.

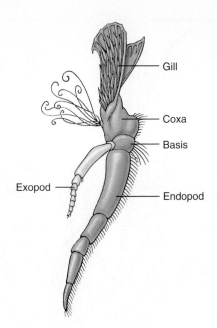

figure 13.18

Parts of a biramous crustacean appendage (third maxilliped of a crayfish).

wormlike pentastomids; these parasites previously were considered a phylum of animals, but are now placed in Crustacea, near the fish lice, subclass Branchiura.

Form and Function

Appendages

Some modifications of crustacean appendages are illustrated by those of crayfishes and lobsters (class Malacostraca, order Decapoda, see p. 254). **Swimmerets,** or abdominal appendages, retain the ancestral biramous condition. Such an appendage consists of inner and outer branches, called the **endopod** and **exopod,** which are attached to one or more basal segments collectively called a protopod (figure 13.18).

There are many modifications of this plan. In the ancestral character state for crustaceans, all trunk appendages are rather similar in structure and adapted for swimming. The evolutionary trend, shown in crayfishes, has been toward a reduced number of appendages and an increased variety of modifications that fit the appendages for many functions. Some appendages are foliaceous (flat and leaflike), as are maxillae; some are biramous, as are swimmerets, maxillipeds, uropods, and antennae; and others have lost one branch and are **uniramous,** as are walking legs.

In crayfishes, the first three pairs of thoracic appendages, called **maxillipeds,** serve along with the two pairs of maxillae as food handlers; the other five pairs of appendages are lengthened and strengthened for walking and defense (figure 13.19). The first pair of walking legs, called **chelipeds,**

are enlarged with a strong claw, or **chela,** for defense. Abdominal swimmerets serve not only for locomotion, but in males the first pair, called gonopods, are modified for copulation, and in females they all serve as a nursery for attached eggs and young. The last pair of appendages, called **uropods,** are wide and serve as paddles for swift backward movements; with the telson, they form a protective device for eggs or young on the swimmerets.

The terminology zoologists use to describe crustacean appendages has not been blessed with uniformity. At least two systems are in wide use. For example, alternative terms to those used in this book are exopodite, endopodite, basipodite, and coxopodite (see figure 13.18). The first and second pairs of antennae may be called antennules and antennae (see figure 13.17), and the first and second maxillae are often called maxillules and maxillae. A rose by any other name…

Ecdysis

The problem of growth despite a restrictive exoskeleton is solved in crustaceans, as in other arthropods, by ecdysis (Gr. *ekdysis,* to strip off), the periodic shedding of old cuticle and formation of a larger new one. Ecdysis occurs most frequently during larval stages and less often as an animal reaches adulthood. Although actual shedding of the cuticle is periodic, the molting process and preparations for it, involving storage of reserves and changes in the integument, are a continuous process lasting most of an animal's life.

During each **premolt** period, the old cuticle becomes thinner as inorganic salts are withdrawn from it and stored

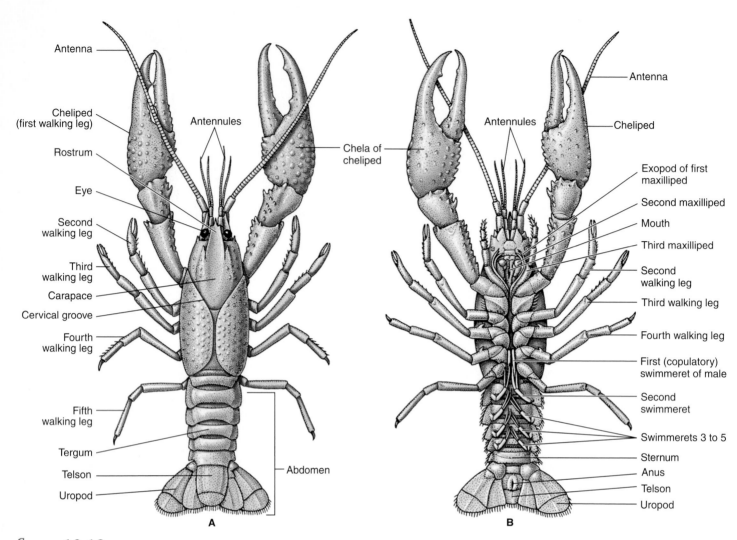

figure 13.19

External structure of crayfishes. **A,** Dorsal view. **B,** Ventral view.

in tissues. Other reserves, both organic and inorganic, also accumulate and are stored. The underlying epidermis begins to grow by cell division; it secretes first a new inner layer of epicuticle and then enzymes that digest away the inner layers of old endocuticle (figure 13.20). Gradually, a new cuticle forms inside the degenerating old one. Finally, actual ecdysis occurs as the old cuticle ruptures, usually along the middorsal line, and the animal backs out (figure 13.21). The animal swells with air or water to stretch the new, larger cuticle to its full size. During the **postmolt** period, the cuticle thickens, its outer layer hardens by tanning, and its inner layer uses salvaged inorganic salts and other constituents for strengthening. Usually an animal is very reclusive during its postmolt period when its defenseless condition makes it particularly vulnerable to predation.

That ecdysis is under hormonal control has been demonstrated in both crustaceans and insects, but the process is often initiated by a stimulus perceived by the central nervous system. In decapods, the stimulus decreases production of a **molt-inhibiting hormone** from neurosecretory cells in the

X-organ of the eyestalk. The sinus gland, also in the eyestalk, releases the hormone. When the level of molt-inhibiting hormone drops, **Y-organs** near the mandibles produce **molting hormone.** This hormone initiates processes leading to premolt. Y-organs are homologous to the prothoracic glands of insects, which produce ecdysone.

Neurosecretory cells are modified nerve cells that secrete hormones. They are widespread in invertebrates and also occur in vertebrates. Cells in the vertebrate hypothalamus and in the posterior pituitary are good examples.

Other Endocrine Functions

Pigments in special branched cells **(chromatophores)** in the epidermis produce body color in crustaceans. Chromatophores change color by concentrating pigment granules in the center of each cell, which causes a lightening effect, or by dispersing pigment throughout each cell, which causes darkening.

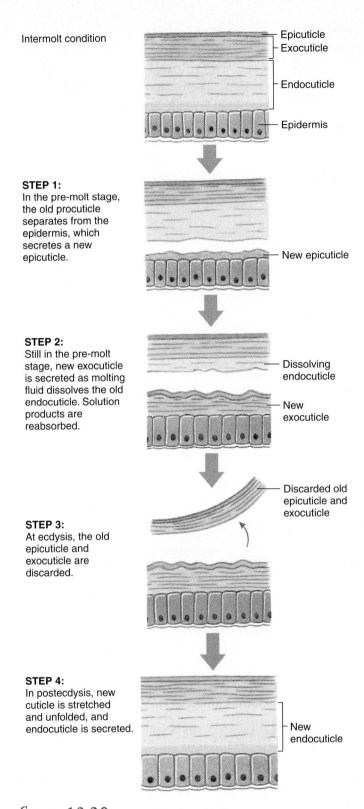

Intermolt condition

— Epicuticle
— Exocuticle

— Endocuticle

— Epidermis

STEP 1:
In the pre-molt stage, the old procuticle separates from the epidermis, which secretes a new epicuticle.

— New epicuticle

STEP 2:
Still in the pre-molt stage, new exocuticle is secreted as molting fluid dissolves the old endocuticle. Solution products are reabsorbed.

— Dissolving endocuticle

— New exocuticle

— Discarded old epicuticle and exocuticle

STEP 3:
At ecdysis, the old epicuticle and exocuticle are discarded.

STEP 4:
In postecdysis, new cuticle is stretched and unfolded, and endocuticle is secreted.

— New endocuticle

figure 13.20

Cuticle secretion and resorption in ecdysis.

Neurosecretory cells in the eyestalk control pigment behavior. Neurosecretory hormones also control pigment in the eyes for light and dark adaptation, and other neurosecretory hormones control rate and amplitude of heartbeat.

Androgenic glands, which are not neurosecretory, occur in male malacostracans, and their secretion stimulates the expression of male sexual characteristics. If androgenic glands are artificially implanted in a female, her ovaries transform to testes and begin to produce sperm, and her appendages begin to acquire male characteristics at the next molt.

Feeding Habits

Feeding habits and adaptations for feeding vary greatly among crustaceans. Many forms can shift from one type of feeding to another depending on environment and food availability, but fundamentally all use the same set of mouthparts. Maxillipeds hold and crush food; mandibles and maxillae shred food and place it in the mouth. In predators, the walking legs, particularly chelipeds, serve in food capture.

Many crustaceans, both large and small, are predatory, and some have interesting adaptations for killing prey. One shrimplike form, *Lygiosquilla,* has on one of its walking legs a specialized digit that can be drawn into a groove and released suddenly to pierce passing prey. Pistol shrimp, *Alpheus,* have one enormously enlarged chela that can be cocked like the hammer of a gun and snapped shut at great speed, forming a cavitation bubble that implodes with a snap sufficient to stun its prey.

The food of crustaceans ranges from plankton, detritus, and bacteria, used by **suspension feeders;** to larvae, worms, crustaceans, snails, and fishes, used by predators; to dead animal and plant matter, used by **scavengers.** Suspension feeders, such as fairy shrimps, water fleas, and barnacles, use their legs, which bear a thick fringe of setae, to create water currents that sweep food particles through the setae, where they are captured. Mud shrimps, *Upogebia,* use long setae on their first two pairs of thoracic appendages to strain food material from water circulated through their burrow by movements of their swimmerets.

Crayfishes have a two-part stomach. The first contains a **gastric mill** in which food, already shredded by the mandibles, is ground further by three calcareous teeth into particles fine enough to pass through a filter of setae in the second part of the stomach; food particles then pass into the intestine for chemical digestion.

Respiration, Excretion, and Circulation

The **gills** of crustaceans vary in shape. They may be treelike, leaflike, or filamentous, and all are provided with blood vessels or sinuses. They are usually attached to appendages and kept ventilated by movement of the appendages through water. The overlapping carapace usually protects the **branchial chambers.** Some smaller crustaceans breathe through their general body surface.

Excretory and osmoregulatory organs in crustaceans are paired glands located in the head, with excretory pores opening at the base of either antennae or maxillae; the glands are thus called **antennal glands** or **maxillary glands,** respectively

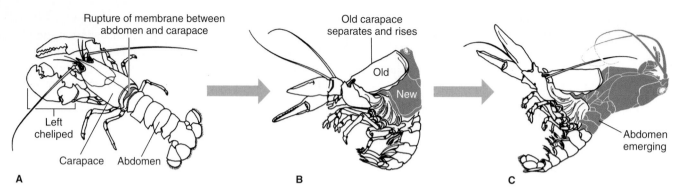

Rupture of membrane between abdomen and carapace

Old carapace separates and rises

Old

New

Abdomen emerging

Left cheliped

Carapace   Abdomen

A   B   C

figure 13.21

Molting sequence in a lobster, *Homarus americanus*. **A,** The membrane between the carapace and the abdomen ruptures, and the carapace begins a slow elevation. This step may take up to 2 hours. **B, C,** Head, thorax, and finally the abdomen are withdrawn. This process usually takes no more than 15 minutes. Immediately after ecdysis, chelipeds are desiccated and the body is very soft. The lobster now begins rapid absorption of water so that within 12 hours its body increases about 20% in length and 50% in weight. Tissue water will be replaced by protein in succeeding weeks.

figure 13.22

Internal structure of a male crayfish.

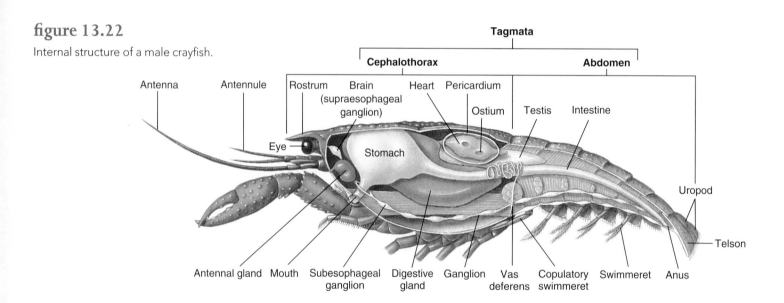

(figure 13.22). The antennal glands of decapods are also called **green glands.** They resemble the coxal glands of chelicerates. Waste products are mostly ammonia with some urea and uric acid. Some wastes diffuse through the gills as well as through the excretory glands.

Circulation, as in other arthropods, is an **open system** consisting of a heart, either compact or tubular, and arteries, which transport blood to different areas of the hemocoel. Some smaller crustaceans lack a heart. An open circulatory system depends less on heartbeats for circulation because movement of organs and limbs circulates blood more effectively in open sinuses than in capillaries. Blood may contain as respiratory pigments either hemocyanin or hemoglobin (hemocyanin in decapods), and it has the property of clotting to prevent loss of blood in minor injuries.

Nervous and Sensory Systems

A cerebral ganglion above the esophagus sends nerves to the anterior sense organs and connects to a subesophageal ganglion by a pair of connectives around the esophagus. A double ventral nerve cord has a ganglion in each segment that sends nerves to the viscera, appendages, and muscles (figure 13.22). Giant fiber systems are common among crustaceans.

Sensory organs are well developed. There are two types of eyes—a median (or nauplius) eye and compound eyes. A **median eye** usually consists of a group of three pigment cups containing retinal cells, and it may or may not have a lens. Median eyes occur in nauplius larvae and in some adult forms, and they may be an adult's only eye, as in copepods.

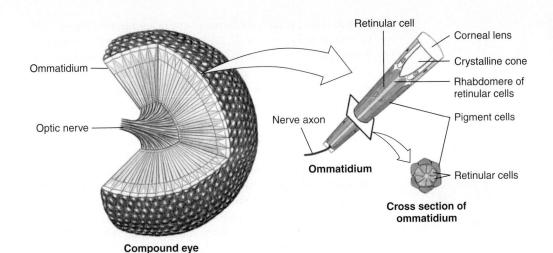

figure 13.23

Compound eye of an insect. *Right,* A single ommatidium is shown enlarged.

Most crustaceans have **compound eyes** similar to insect eyes. In crabs and crayfishes, the eyes are on the ends of movable eyestalks (figure 13.22). Compound eyes are precise instruments, different from vertebrate eyes, and yet especially adept at detecting motion; they can analyze polarized light. The convex corneal surface provides a wide visual field, particularly in stalked eyes where the surface may cover an arc of 200 degrees or more.

Compound eyes are composed of many tapering units called **ommatidia** set close together (figure 13.23). Facets, or corneal surfaces, of the ommatidia give the eye surface the appearance of a fine mosaic. Most crustacean eyes are adapted either to bright or to dim light, depending on their diurnal or nocturnal habits, but some are able, by means of screening pigments, to adapt somewhat to both bright and dim light. The number of ommatidia varies from a dozen or two in some small crustaceans to 15,000 or more in a large lobster. By comparison, some insects have approximately 30,000.

Other sensory organs include statocysts, tactile setae on the cuticle of most of the body, and chemosensitive setae, especially on antennae, antennules, and mouthparts.

Reproduction and Life Cycles

Most crustaceans have separate sexes, and numerous specializations for copulation occur among different groups. Almost all barnacles are monoecious but generally practice cross-fertilization. In some ostracods, males are scarce, and reproduction is usually parthenogenetic. Most crustaceans brood their eggs in some manner—branchiopods and barnacles have special brood chambers, copepods have egg sacs attached to the sides of their abdomen (see figure 13.25C), and malacostracans usually carry eggs and young attached to their appendages.

A crayfish hatchling is a tiny juvenile similar in form to the adult and has a complete set of appendages and segments. However, most crustaceans produce larvae that undergo a series of changes, either gradual or abrupt over a series of molts, to assume adult form (metamorphosis). The ancestral larva of crustaceans is a **nauplius** (pl., **nauplii**) (figure 13.24). It has an unsegmented body, a frontal eye, and three pairs of

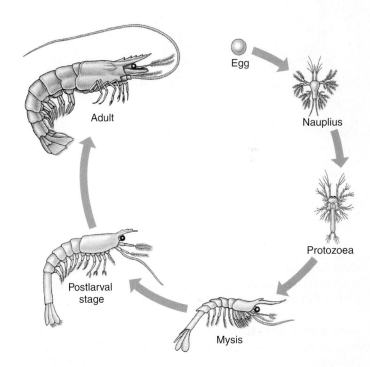

figure 13.24

Life cycle of a Gulf shrimp, *Penaeus.* Penaeids spawn at depths of 40 to 90 m. Young larval forms are planktonic and move inshore to water of lower salinity to develop as juveniles. Older shrimp return to deeper water offshore.

appendages, representing the two pairs of antennae and the mandibles. The developmental stages and postlarvae of different groups of Crustacea are varied and have special names.

Class Branchiopoda

Members of class Branchiopoda (branke-ä´pōd-ə) have several ancestral characteristics. Four orders are recognized: **Anostraca** (fairy shrimp and brine shrimp), which lack a carapace; **Notostraca** (tadpole shrimp such as *Triops*), whose carapace forms a large dorsal shield covering most trunk segments;

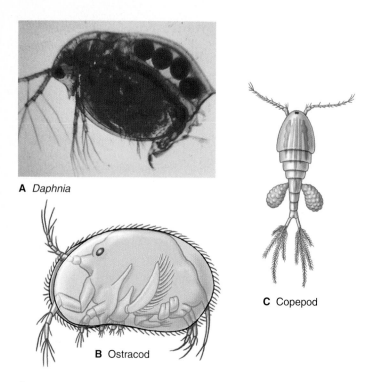

A *Daphnia*

B Ostracod

C Copepod

figure 13.25

A, A water flea, *Daphnia* (order Cladocera), photographed with polarized light. These tiny forms occur in great numbers in northern lakes and are an important component of the food chain leading to fishes. **B,** An ostracod (subclass Ostracoda, class Maxillopoda). **C,** A copepod with attached ovisacs (subclass Copepoda, class Maxillopoda).

Conchostraca (clam shrimp such as *Lynceus*), whose carapace is bivalved and usually encloses the entire body; and **Cladocera** (water fleas such as *Daphnia*, figure 13.25A), with a carapace typically covering the entire body but not the head. Branchiopods have reduced first antennae and second maxillae. Their legs are flattened and leaflike **(phyllopodia)** and are the chief respiratory organs (hence, the name branchiopods). Most branchiopods also use their legs in suspension feeding, and groups other than cladocerans use their legs for locomotion as well. The most important and diverse order is Cladocera, which often forms a large segment of freshwater zooplankton.

Class Maxillopoda

Class Maxillopoda includes a number of crustacean groups traditionally considered classes themselves. Specialists have recognized evidence that these groups form a clade within Crustacea. The typical body plan consists of five cephalic, six thoracic, and usually four abdominal segments plus a telson, but fewer segments are common. Appendages are usually on the abdomen. The eyes of nauplii (when present) have a unique structure termed a **maxillopodan eye.**

Members of subclass **Ostracoda** (os-tra´-kōd-ə) (Gr. *ostrakodes,* having a shell) are, like conchostracans,

enclosed in a bivalved carapace and resemble tiny clams, 0.25 to 8 mm long (figure 13.25B). Ostracods show considerable fusion of trunk segments, and their thoracic appendages are reduced to two or none. Most ostracods crawl or burrow in marine or freshwater sediments. They scavenge food, feed on detritus, or collect suspended particles from the water.

Subclass **Copepoda** (ko-pe´-pōd-ə) (Gr. *kōpē,* oar, + *podos,* foot) is an important group of Crustacea, second only to Malacostraca in number of species. Copepods are small (usually a few millimeters or less in length), rather elongate, tapering toward the posterior end, lacking a carapace, and retaining a simple, median, nauplius eye in adults (figure 13.25C). They have four pairs of rather flattened, biramous, thoracic swimming appendages, and a fifth, reduced pair. Their abdomen bears no legs. Free-living copepods occur in planktonic and benthic habitats. Planktonic species are essential members of marine and freshwater food webs, often dominating the primary consumer level (herbivore) in aquatic communities. Many symbiotic species are known, and parasitic forms may be so highly modified as adults (and may depart so far from the description just given) that they can hardly be recognized as arthropods.

Subclass **Branchiura** (bran-kē-u´ra) (Gr. *branchia,* gills, + *ura,* tail) is a small group of primarily fish parasites that, despite its name, has no gills (figure 13.26A). Members of this group are usually between 5 and 10 mm long and parasitize marine or freshwater fishes. They typically have a broad, shieldlike carapace, compound eyes, four biramous thoracic appendages for swimming, and a short, unsegmented abdomen. The second maxillae have become modified as suction cups (figure 13.26B).

Subclass **Pentastomida** (pen-ta-stom´i-da) (Gr. *pente,* five, + *stoma,* mouth), or tongue worms, consist of about 130 species of wormlike parasites of the respiratory system of vertebrates. Adult pentastomids live mostly in the lungs of reptiles, but one species, *Linguatula serrata* (Gr. *lingua,* tongue), lives in the nasopharynx of canines and felines (and occasionally humans). Although more common in tropical areas, they also occur in North America, Europe, and Australia.

Adult pentastomida range from 1 to 13 cm in length. Transverse rings give their bodies a segmented appearance (figure 13.26C and D). Their body is covered with a nonchitinous cuticle that is molted periodically during larval stages. The anterior end may bear five short protuberances (hence the name Pentastomida). Four of these bear chitinous claws, and the fifth bears the mouth (figure 13.26E). The digestive system is simple and adapted for sucking blood from the host. The nervous system, similar to that of other arthropods, has paired ganglia along the ventral nerve cord. The only sense organs appear to be papillae. There are no circulatory, excretory, or respiratory organs.

Sexes are separate, and females are usually larger than males. A female may produce several million eggs, which pass up the trachea of the host, are swallowed, and exit with feces. Larvae hatch as oval, tailed creatures with four stumpy legs. Most pentastomid life cycles require an intermediate vertebrate host such as a fish, a reptile, or, rarely, a mammal, that is eaten

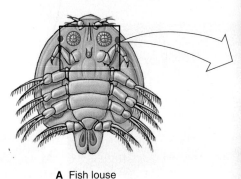

A Fish louse

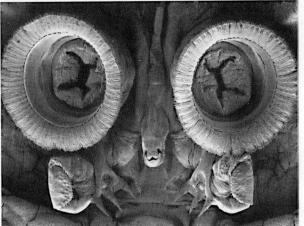

B Anterior, ventral surface of *Argulus nobilis*

figure 13.26

A, Fish lice, in subclass Branchiura, are closely related to pentastomids (**C** and **D**). SEMs of the anterior regions of both animals (**B** and **E**) demonstrate morphological similarities.

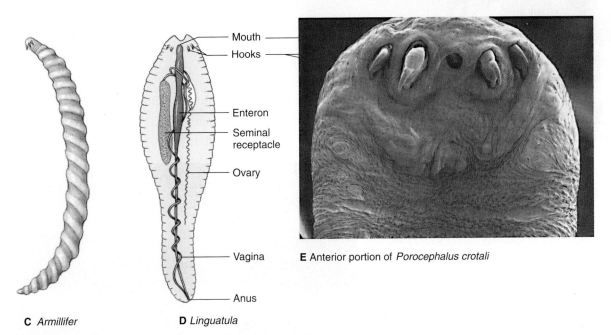

Mouth
Hooks
Enteron
Seminal receptacle
Ovary
Vagina
Anus

E Anterior portion of *Porocephalus crotali*

C *Armillifer*   **D** *Linguatula*

by the definitive vertebrate host. After ingestion by an intermediate host, larvae penetrate the intestine, migrate randomly in the body, and finally metamorphose into nymphs. After growth and several molts, a nymph finally becomes encapsulated and dormant. When eaten by a final host, a juvenile finds its way to a lung, feeds on blood and tissue, and matures.

Several species have been found encysted in humans, the most common being *Armillifer armillatus* (L. *armilla*, ring, bracelet, + *fero*, to bear) (see figure 13.26C), but usually they cause few symptoms. *L. serrata* is a cause of nasopharyngeal pentastomiasis, or "halzoun," a disease of humans in the Middle East and India.

Subclass **Cirripedia** (sir-i-ped´i-a) (L. *cirrus,* curl of hair, + *pedis,* foot) includes barnacles, which are usually enclosed in a shell of calcareous plates, as well as three smaller orders of burrowing or parasitic forms. Barnacles are sessile as adults and may be attached to their substrate directly, as with acorn barnacles (figure 13.27A), or by a stalk, as with gooseneck barnacles (figure 13.27B). Typically, a carapace (mantle) surrounds their

body and secretes a shell of calcareous plates. Their head is reduced, they have no abdomen, and their thoracic legs are long, many-jointed cirri with hairlike setae. The cirri are extended through an opening between the calcareous plates to filter from water small particles on which the animal feeds (figure 13.27B).

Barnacles frequently foul ship bottoms by settling and growing there. There may be so many barnacles that the speed of a ship is reduced 30% to 40%, requiring expensive drydocking while the barnacles are removed.

Class Malacostraca

Class Malacostraca (mal´a-kos´tra-ka) (Gr. *malakos,* soft, + *ostrakon,* shell) is the largest class of Crustacea and shows great diversity. We mention only 4 of its 12 to 13 orders. The trunk of malacostracans usually has eight thoracic and six

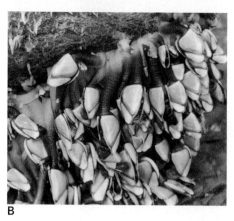

figure 13.27

A, Acorn barnacles, *Semibalanus cariosus* (subclass Cirripedia) are found on rocks along the Pacific Coast of North America. **B,** Common gooseneck barnacles, *Lepas anatifera*. Note the feeding legs, or cirri. Barnacles attach themselves to a variety of firm substrates, including rocks, pilings, and boat bottoms.

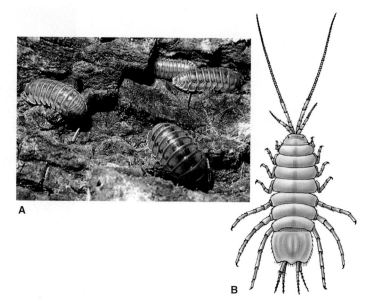

figure 13.28

A, Four pill bugs, *Armadillidium vulgare* (order Isopoda), common terrestrial forms. **B,** Freshwater sow bug, *Caecidotea* sp., an aquatic isopod.

figure 13.29

An isopod parasite (*Anilocra* sp., order Isopoda, class Malacostraca) on a coney (*Cephalopholis fulvus*) inhabiting a Caribbean coral reef.

abdominal segments, each with a pair of appendages. There are many marine and freshwater species.

Isopoda (i-so´pod-ə) (Gr. *isos*, equal, + *podos*, foot) are commonly dorsoventrally flattened, lack a carapace, and have sessile compound eyes. Their abdominal appendages bear gills. Common land forms are sow bugs or pill bugs (*Porcellio* and *Armadillidium*, figure 13.28A), which live under stones and in other damp places. *Asellus* is common in fresh water, and *Ligia* is abundant on sea beaches and rocky shores. Some isopods are parasites of other crustaceans or of fish (figure 13.29).

Members of **Amphipoda** (am-fi´-pod-ə) (Gr. *amphis*, on both sides, + *podos*, foot) resemble isopods in having sessile compound eyes and no carapace. However, they are usually compressed laterally, and their gills are in the thoracic position, as in other malacostracans. The many marine amphipods (figure 13.30) include beach fleas (*Orchestia*), and there are also numerous freshwater species.

Euphausiacea (yu-faws´i-a´se-a) (Gr. *eu*, well, + *phausi*, shining bright, + *acea*, L. suffix, pertaining to) is a group of only about 90 species that comprise the important oceanic plankton known as "krill." Individuals are about 3 to 6 cm long (figure 13.31) and commonly occur in great oceanic swarms, where they are eaten by baleen whales and many fishes.

Decapoda (deca´-pod-ə) (Gr. *deka*, ten, + *podos*, foot) have five pairs of walking legs of which the first is often modified to form pincers **(chelae)** (see figures 13.17 and 13.19). These are lobsters, crayfishes (see figure 13.19), shrimps (see figure 13.24), and crabs, the largest of the crustaceans (figure 13.32). True crabs differ from others in having a broader carapace and a much reduced abdomen (figure 13.32A and C). Familiar examples are fiddler crabs, *Uca*, which burrow in sand just below high-tide level (figure 13.32C); decorator crabs,

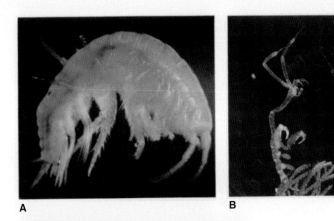

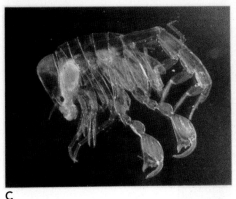

figure 13.30

Marine amphipods. **A,** Free-swimming amphipod, *Anisogammarus* sp. **B,** Skeleton shrimp, *Caprella* sp., shown on a bryozoan colony, resemble praying mantids. **C,** *Phronima*, a marine pelagic amphipod, occupies the tunic of a salp (subphylum Urochordata, see Chapter 15). Swimming by means of its abdominal swimmerets, which protrude from the opening of the barrel-shaped tunic, the amphipod (order Amphipoda, class Malacostraca) maneuvers to catch its prey. The tunic is not seen.

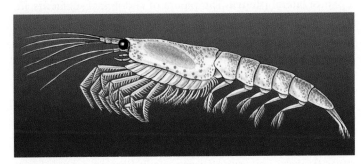

figure 13.31

Meganyctiphanes, order Euphausiacea, "northern krill."

which cover their carapaces with sponges and sea anemones for camouflage; and spider crabs, such as *Libinia*. Hermit crabs (figure 13.32B) have become adapted to living in snail shells; their abdomen, which lacks a hard exoskeleton, is protected by the snail shell.

■ Subphylum Hexapoda

The subphylum Hexapoda is named for the presence of **six legs** in its members. All legs are **uniramous.** Hexapods have **three tagmata**—head, thorax, and abdomen—with appendages on the head and thorax. Abdominal appendages are greatly reduced in size or absent. The subphylum has two classes: Entognatha, a small group whose members have the bases of mouthparts enclosed within the head capsule, and Insecta, an enormous group whose members have the bases of mouthparts visible outside the head capsule (hence, ectognathous mouthparts).

Winged insects are called pterygotes, and wingless insects are called apterygotes. The wingless order Thysanura forms the living sister taxon to all other insects. Insect wings evolved in a common ancestor of the latter clade (figure 13.33). Thysanurans are called primitively wingless to distinguish them from orders whose members do not have wings now, but whose ancestors were winged.

Class Insecta: Insects

Insects are the most numerous and diverse of all groups of arthropods (figure 13.34). There are more species of insects than species in all the other classes of animals combined. The number of insect species named has been estimated at close to 1 million, with thousands, perhaps millions, of other species yet to be discovered and classified.

There are more than 30 orders of insects. Some of the most common ones, such as Diptera and Hymenoptera, are briefly outlined beginning on page 271.

It is difficult to fully appreciate the significance of this extensive group and its role in the biological pattern of animal life. The study of insects **(entomology)** occupies the time and resources of thousands of skilled researchers across the world. The struggle between humans and insect pests seems to be endless, and yet paradoxically, insects are so interwoven into the economy of nature that we would have a difficult time without them.

Insects differ from other arthropods in having **three pairs of legs** and usually **two pairs of wings** on the thoracic region of the body (figure 13.35), although some have one pair of wings or none. In size, insects range from less than 1 mm to 20 cm in length, the majority being less than 2.5 cm long.

Distribution and Adaptability

Insects have occupied practically all habitats that can support life, but relatively few are marine. They are common in brackish water, in salt marshes, and on sandy beaches. They are abundant in fresh water, soils, forests, and plants, and they even occur in deserts and wastelands, on mountaintops, and as parasites in and on the bodies of plants and animals, including other insects.

Their wide distribution is made possible by their powers of flight and their highly adaptable nature. Many insects can easily surmount barriers that are impassable to other animals.

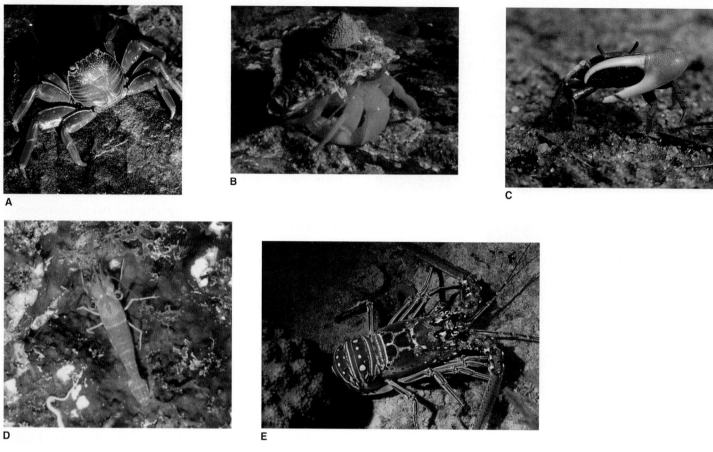

figure 13.32

Decapod crustaceans. **A,** A bright orange tropical rock crab, *Grapsus grapsus,* is a conspicuous exception to the rule that most crabs exhibit cryptic coloration. **B,** A hermit crab, *Elassochirus gilli,* which has a soft abdominal exoskeleton, occupies and carries a snail shell into which it can withdraw for protection. **C,** A male fiddler crab, *Uca* sp., uses its enlarged cheliped in territorial displays and in threat and combat. **D,** A red night shrimp, *Rhynchocinetes rigens,* prowls caves and overhangs of coral reefs, but only at night. **E,** Spiny lobster *Panulirus argus* (order Decapoda, class Malacostraca).

Their small size and well-protected eggs allow them to be carried great distances by wind, water, and other animals.

The amazing adaptability of insects is evidenced by their wide distribution and enormous diversity of species. Such diversity enables this vigorous group to use all available resources of food and shelter.

Much of insects' success is due to the adaptive qualities of their cuticular exoskeleton, as is true of other arthropods as well. However, the great exploitation of terrestrial environments by insects has been made possible by their array of adaptations for withstanding its rigors. For example, to minimize evaporative water loss, their epicuticle has both a waxy layer and a varnish layer, and they can close their spiracles. Insects extract maximal fluid from food and fecal material, and many can retain water produced in oxidative metabolism. Many can enter a resting stage (diapause) and lie dormant during inhospitable conditions.

External Features

Insect tagmata are **head, thorax,** and **abdomen.** The cuticle of each body segment is typically composed of four plates **(sclerites),** a dorsal notum **(tergum),** a ventral **sternum,** and a pair of lateral **pleura.** The pleura of abdominal segments are membranous rather than sclerotized (hardened).

The head usually bears a pair of relatively large compound eyes, a pair of antennae, and usually three ocelli. Mouthparts typically consist of a **labrum,** a pair each of **mandibles** and **maxillae,** a **labium,** and a tonguelike **hypopharynx.** The type of mouthparts an insect possesses determines how it feeds. We discuss some of these modifications in a later section.

The thorax is composed of three segments: **prothorax, mesothorax,** and **metathorax,** each bearing a pair of legs (figure 13.35B). In most insects, the mesothorax and metathorax each bear a pair of wings. The wings consist of a double membrane that contains veins of thicker cuticle, which serve to strengthen the wing. Although these veins vary in their patterns among different species, they often are constant within a species and serve as one means of classification and identification.

The legs of insects are often modified for special purposes. Terrestrial forms have walking legs with terminal

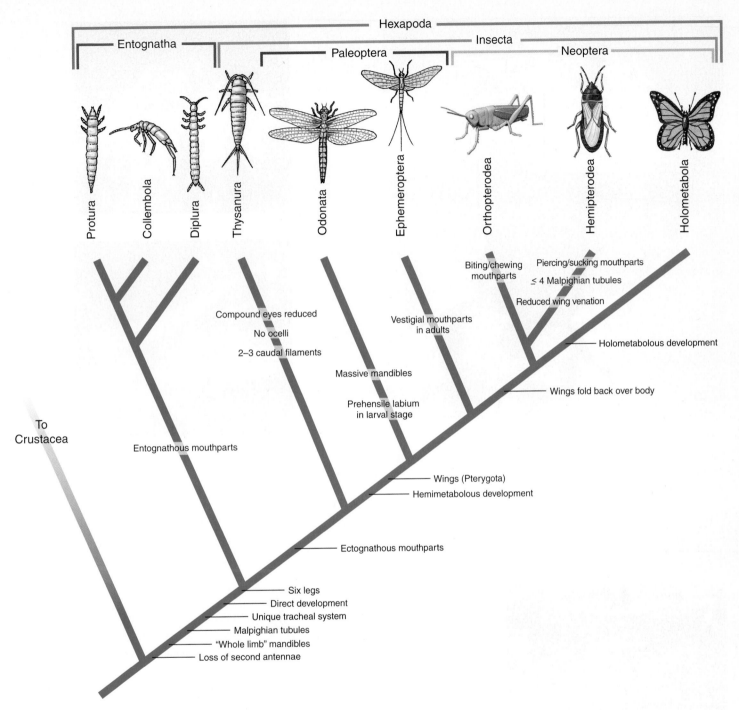

figure 13.33

Cladogram showing hypothetical relationships among hexapods. Many synapomorphies have been omitted. Orders Protura, Collembola, and Diplura are entognathous. These orders, plus Thysanura, originated before the earliest winged ancestors. Orders Odonata and Ephemeroptera form Paleoptera, where wings are outspread. The remaining orders have wings that can fold back over the abdomen (Neoptera). Superorder Orthopterodea includes orders Orthoptera, Blattodea, Phasmatodea, Mantodea, Mantophasmatodea, Isoptera, Plecoptera, Embiidina, and Dermaptera. Hemipterodea includes orders Zoraptera, Psocoptera, Hemiptera, Thysanoptera, and Phthiraptera; and superorder Holometabola encompasses all holometabolous orders.

pads and claws, as in beetles, for example. These pads may be sticky for walking upside down, as in house flies. The hindlegs of grasshoppers and crickets are adapted for jumping (figure 13.35B). In mole crickets, the first pair of legs is modified for burrowing in the ground. Water bugs and many beetles have paddle-shaped appendages for swimming. For grasping prey, the forelegs of a praying mantis are long and strong (figure 13.36).

figure 13.34

Pie diagram indicating the relative numbers of insect species compared to the rest of the animal kingdom and protozoan groups.

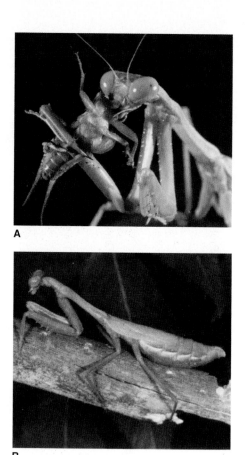

A

B

figure 13.36

A, Praying mantis (order Mantodea), feeding on an insect. **B,** Praying mantis laying eggs.

A

figure 13.35

Class Insecta. **A,** A pair of grasshoppers, *Schistocerca obscura* (order Orthoptera), copulating. The African desert locust mentioned in the chapter prologue (see p. 235) is *Schistocerca gregaria*. **B,** External features of a female grasshopper. The terminal segment of a male with external genitalia is shown in inset.

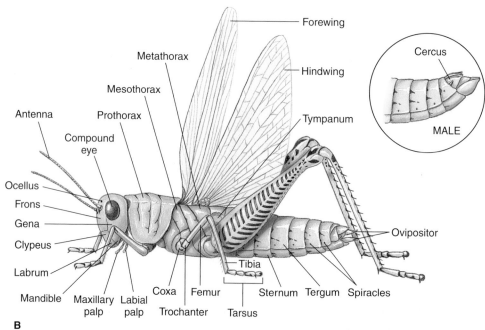

B

Wings and the Flight Mechanism

Insects share the power of flight with birds and flying mammals. However, wings evolved independently in birds, bats, and insects. Insect wings are composed of cuticle and formed by outgrowth from the body wall of the mesothoracic and metathoracic segments.

Most insects have two pairs of wings, but Diptera (true flies, figure 13.37) have only one pair, the hindwings being represented by a pair of small **halteres** (sing., **halter;** balancer) that vibrate and are responsible for equilibrium during flight. Males in order Strepsiptera have only a hind pair of wings and

figure 13.37

House fly, *Musca domestica* (order Diptera). House flies can become contaminated with over 100 human pathogens, and there is strong circumstantial evidence for mechanical transmission of many of them.

an anterior pair of halteres. Males of scale insects also have one pair of wings but no halteres. Some insects are wingless. Ants and termites, for example, have wings only on males, and on females during certain periods; workers (females) are always wingless. Lice and fleas are always wingless.

Wings may be thin and membranous, as in flies and many others; thick and stiff, as in the forewings of beetles; parchmentlike, as in the forewings of grasshoppers; covered with fine scales, as in butterflies and moths; or hairlike structures, as in caddisflies.

Wing movements are controlled by a complex of thoracic muscles. **Direct flight muscles** are attached to a part of the wing itself. **Indirect flight muscles** are not attached to the wing and cause wing movement by altering the shape of the thorax. The wing is hinged at the thoracic tergum and also slightly laterally on a pleural process, which acts as a fulcrum (figure 13.38). In all insects, the upstroke of a wing is effected by contracting indirect muscles that pull the tergum down toward the sternum. Locusts, dragonflies, and cockroaches (figure 13.38A) accomplish the downstroke by contracting direct muscles attached to the wings lateral to the pleural fulcrum. In flies, bees, and midges, all flight muscles are indirect. The downstroke occurs when sternotergal muscles relax and longitudinal muscles of the thorax arch the tergum (figure 13.38B), pulling the tergal articulations upward relative to the pleura. The downstroke in beetles and grasshoppers involves both direct and indirect muscles.

Contraction of flight muscles is governed by two basic types of neural control: **synchronous** and **asynchronous.** Larger insects such as dragonflies and butterflies have synchronous muscles, in which a single volley of nerve impulses stimulates a muscle contraction and thus one wing stroke. Asynchronous muscles occur in other insects. Their mechanism of

figure 13.38

A, Flight muscles of insects such as locusts, dragonflies, and cockroaches, in which upstroke is by indirect muscles and downstroke is by direct muscles. **B,** In insects such as flies, bees, and midges, both upstroke and downstroke are by indirect muscles. **C,** The figure-eight path followed by the wing of a flying insect during the upstroke and downstroke.

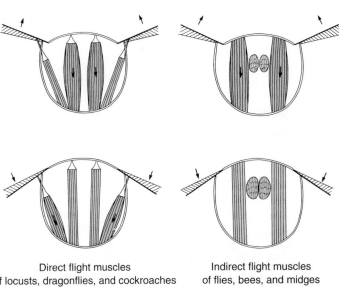

Direct flight muscles of locusts, dragonflies, and cockroaches

A

Indirect flight muscles of flies, bees, and midges

B

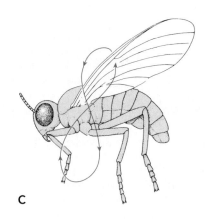

C

action is complex and depends on storage of potential energy in resilient parts of the thoracic cuticle. As one set of muscles contracts (moving the wing in one direction), the cuticle changes shape. When these muscles relax, the cuticle rebounds, stretching the antagonistic set of muscles passively. These muscles then actively contract, (moving the wing in the other direction). Because the muscle contractions are not phase-related to nervous stimulation, only occasional nerve impulses are necessary to keep the muscles responsive to alternating stretch activation. Thus, extremely rapid wing beats are possible. For example, butterflies (with synchronous muscles) may beat as few as four times per second. Insects with asynchronous muscles, such as flies and bees, may vibrate at 100 beats per second or more. Fruit flies, *Drosophila* (Gr. *drosos,* dew, + *philos, loving*), can fly at 300 beats per second, and midges have been clocked at more than 1000 beats per second!

Obviously, flying entails more than simple flapping of wings; a forward thrust is necessary. As the indirect flight muscles alternate rhythmically to raise and lower the wings, the direct flight muscles alter the angle of the wings so that they act as lifting airfoils during both upstroke and downstroke, twisting the leading edge of the wings downward during downstroke and upward during upstroke. This modulation produces a figure-eight movement (see figure 13.38C) that aids in spilling air from the trailing edges of the wings. The quality of the forward thrust depends, of course, on several factors, such as variations in wing venation, how much the wings are tilted, and how they are tapered.

Flight speeds vary. The fastest flyers usually have narrow, fast-moving wings with a pronounced tilt and a strong figure-eight component. Sphinx moths and horse flies are said to achieve approximately 48 km (30 miles) per hour, and dragonflies approximately 40 km (25 miles) per hour. Some insects are capable of long, continuous flights. Migrating monarch butterflies, *Danaus plexippus* (Gr. after Danaus, mythical king of Arabia) (see figure 13.47), travel south for hundreds of miles in the fall, flying at a speed of approximately 10 km (6 miles) per hour.

Internal Form and Function

Nutrition   The digestive system (figure 13.39) consists of a foregut (mouth with salivary glands, **esophagus, crop** for storage, and **proventriculus** for grinding), **midgut** (stomach and gastric ceca), and hindgut (intestine, rectum, and anus). The foregut and hindgut are lined with cuticle, so absorption of food is confined largely to the midgut, although some absorption may occur in all sections. Most insects feed on plant juices and plant tissues, a feeding habit described as **phytophagous.** Some insects feed on specific plants; others, such as grasshoppers, can eat almost any plant. Caterpillars of many moths and butterflies eat the foliage of only certain plants. Certain species of ants and termites cultivate fungus gardens as a source of food.

Many beetles and the larvae of many insects live on dead animals, a feeding habit called **saprophagous.** A number of insects are **predaceous,** catching and eating other insects as well as other types of animals.

Many insects are parasitic as adults or as larvae, and in some cases, both juveniles and adults are parasites. For example, fleas (figure 13.40) live on the blood of mammals as adults, but their larvae are free-living scavengers. Lice (figures 13.41 and 13.42) are parasitic throughout their life cycle. Many parasitic insects are themselves parasitized by other insects, a condition known as **hyperparasitism.**

Larvae of many varieties of wasps live inside the bodies of spiders or other insects (figure 13.43), consuming their hosts and eventually killing them. Because they always destroy their hosts, they are **parasitoids** (a particular type of parasite); typical parasites normally do not kill their hosts. Parasitoid insects are enormously important in controlling other insect populations.

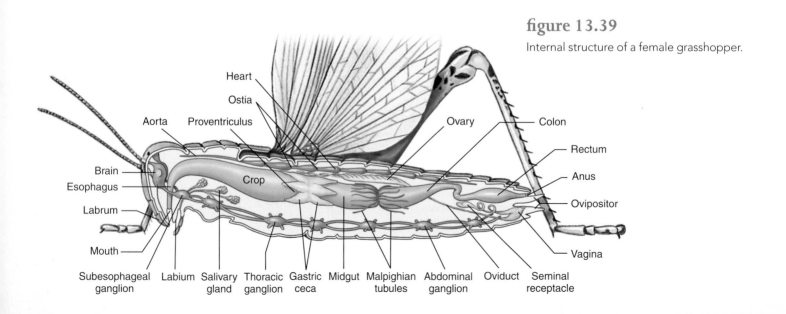

figure 13.39

Internal structure of a female grasshopper.

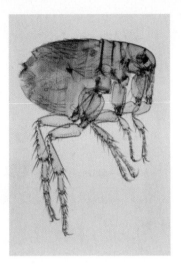

figure 13.40

Female human flea, *Pulex irritans* (order Siphonaptera).

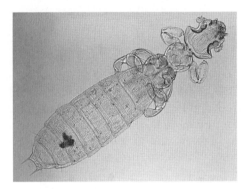

figure 13.41

Gliricola porcelli (order Phthiraptera), a chewing louse of guinea pigs. Antennae are normally held in deep grooves on the sides of the head.

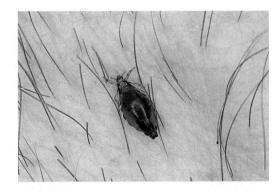

figure 13.42

The head and body louse of humans, *Pediculus humanus* (order Phthiraptera, suborder Anoplura) feeding.

The feeding habits of insects are determined to some extent by their mouthparts, which are highly specialized for each type of feeding.

Biting and **chewing mouthparts,** such as those of grasshoppers and many herbivorous insects, are adapted for

A

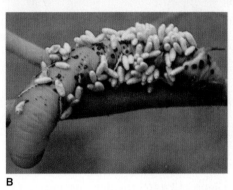

B

figure 13.43

A, Larval stage of a sphinx moth (order Lepidoptera). The more than 100 species of North American sphinx moths are strong fliers and mostly nocturnal feeders. Their larvae, called hornworms because of the large fleshy posterior spine, are often pests of tomatoes, tobacco, and other plants. **B,** Hornworm parasitized by a tiny wasp, *Apanteles,* which laid its eggs inside the caterpillar. The wasp larvae have emerged, and their pupae are on the caterpillar's skin. Young wasps emerge in 5 to 10 days, and the caterpillar usually dies.

seizing and crushing food (figure 13.44). The mandibles of chewing insects are strong, toothed plates with edges that can bite or tear while the maxillae hold the food and pass it toward the mouth. Enzymes secreted by the salivary glands add chemical action to the chewing process.

Sucking mouthparts are greatly varied. House flies and fruit flies have no mandibles; their labium is modified into two soft lobes containing many small tubules that absorb liquids with a capillary action, much as do the holes of a commercial sponge (figure 13.44D; see figure 13.37). Horse flies, however, are fitted not only to soak up surface liquids but to bite into skin with their slender, tapering mandibles and then collect blood. Mosquitos combine **piercing** by means of needlelike stylets and sucking through a food channel (figure 13.44B). In honey bees, the labium forms a flexible and contractile "tongue" covered with many hairs. When a bee plunges its proboscis into nectar, the tip of the tongue bends upward and moves back and forth rapidly. Liquid enters the tube by capillarity and is drawn up the tube continuously by a pumping pharynx. In butterflies and moths, mandibles are usually absent, and maxillae are modified into a long, sucking

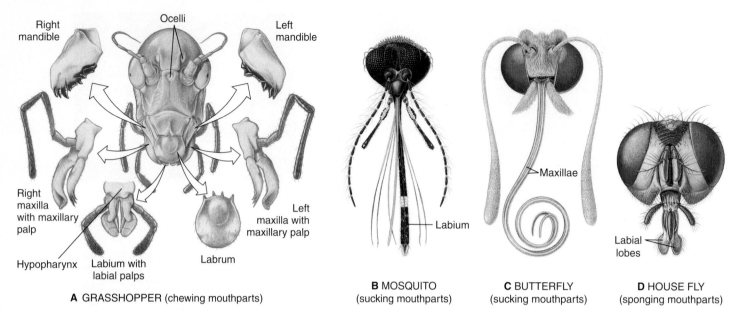

figure 13.44

Four types of insect mouthparts.

proboscis (figure 13.44C) for drawing nectar from flowers. At rest, the proboscis is coiled into a flat spiral. In feeding, it extends, and pharyngeal muscles pump fluid.

Circulation A tubular heart in the pericardial cavity (see figure 13.39) moves **hemolymph,** consisting of plasma and amebocytes, forward through the only blood vessel, a dorsal aorta. The heartbeat is a peristaltic wave. Accessory pulsatory organs help move hemolymph into the wings and legs, and flow is also facilitated by various body movements. Hemolymph apparently has little role in oxygen transport; rather, it distributes substances such as molting hormones and nutrients throughout the body. Oxygen transport is done by the **tracheal system,** an unusual system of tubes that pipe air directly to each cell.

Gas Exchange Terrestrial animals obtain oxygen from the air as it dissolves across a wet membrane. Maintaining a wet membrane in a terrestrial environment is difficult, so gas exchange typically occurs in an internal cavity. The twin goals of an efficient respiratory system are to permit rapid oxygen–carbon dioxide exchange and to restrict water loss. In insects, this is the function of the tracheal system, an extensive network of thin-walled tubes that branch into every part of the body (figure 13.45). Tracheal trunks open to the outside by paired **spiracles,** usually two on the thorax and seven or eight on the abdomen. A spiracle may be a simple hole in the integument, as in primitively wingless insects, but it more often has a valve or other closing mechanism that decreases water loss. Evolution of such a device must have been very important in enabling insects to move into drier habitats.

Tracheae are composed of a single layer of cells and are lined with cuticle that is shed, along with the outer cuticle, during molts. Spiral thickenings of the cuticle, called **taenidia,** support the tracheae and prevent their collapse. Tracheae

branch into smaller tubes, ending in very fine, fluid-filled tubules called **tracheoles** (not lined with cuticle), which branch into a fine network over the cells. Scarcely any living cell is located more than a few micrometers away from a tracheole. In fact, the ends of some tracheoles actually indent the membranes of the cells they supply, so that they terminate close to mitochondria. The tracheal system affords an efficient system of transport without the use of oxygen-carrying pigments in hemolymph.

In some very small insects, gas transport occurs entirely by diffusion along a concentration gradient. As oxygen is used, a partial vacuum develops in the tracheae, drawing air inward through the spiracles. Larger or more active insects employ a ventilation device for moving air in and out of the tubes. Usually muscular movements in the abdomen perform the pumping action that draws air in or expels it.

The tracheal system is primarily adapted for breathing air, but many insects (nymphs, larvae, and adults) live in water.

Although diving beetles, *Dytiscus* (G. *dytikos,* able to swim), can fly, they spend most of their life in water as excellent swimmers. They use an "artificial gill" in the form of a bubble of air held under the first pair of wings. The bubble is kept stable by a layer of hairs on top of the abdomen and is in contact with the spiracles on the abdomen. Oxygen from the bubble diffuses into the tracheae and is replaced by diffusion of oxygen from the surrounding water. However, nitrogen from the bubble diffuses into the water, slowly decreasing the size of the bubble; therefore, diving beetles must surface every few hours to replace the air. Mosquito larvae are not good swimmers but live just below the surface, putting out short breathing tubes like snorkels to the surface for air. Spreading oil on the water, a favorite method of mosquito control, clogs the tracheae with oil and suffocates the larvae. "Rattailed maggots" of syrphid flies have an extensible tail that can stretch as much as 15 cm to the water surface.

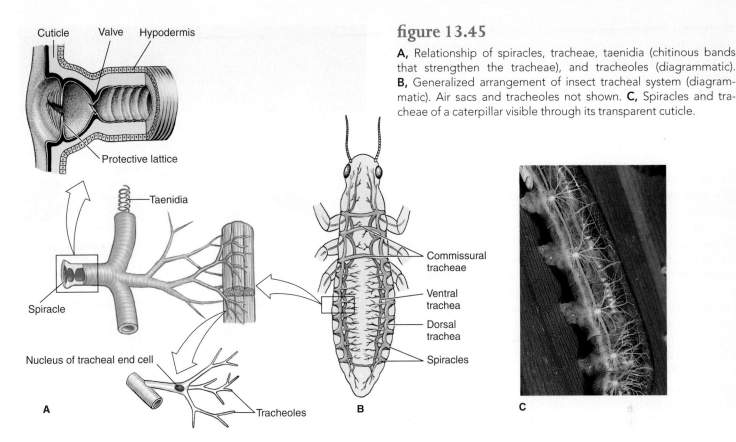

figure 13.45

A, Relationship of spiracles, tracheae, taenidia (chitinous bands that strengthen the tracheae), and tracheoles (diagrammatic). **B,** Generalized arrangement of insect tracheal system (diagrammatic). Air sacs and tracheoles not shown. **C,** Spiracles and tracheae of a caterpillar visible through its transparent cuticle.

In small, soft-bodied aquatic nymphs, gas exchange may occur by diffusion through the body wall, usually into and out of a tracheal network just under the integument. The aquatic nymphs of stoneflies and mayflies are equipped with **tracheal gills,** which are thin extensions of the body wall containing a rich tracheal supply. The gills of dragonfly nymphs are ridges in the rectum (rectal gills) where gas exchange occurs as water enters and leaves.

Excretion and Water Balance   Malpighian tubules (see figure 13.39) are typical of most insects. As in spiders (see p. 241), Malpighian tubules are very efficient, both as excretory organs and as a means of conserving body fluids—an important factor in the success of terrestrial animals.

Because water requirements vary among different types of insects, this ability to cycle water and salts is very important. Insects living in dry environments may resorb nearly all of the water from the rectum, producing a nearly dry mixture of urine and feces. Leaf-feeding insects take in and excrete large quantities of fluid. Freshwater larvae need to excrete water and conserve salts. Insects that feed on dry grains need to conserve water and excrete salt.

Nervous System   The insect nervous system in general resembles that of larger crustaceans, with a similar tendency toward fusion of ganglia (see figure 13.39). Some insects have a giant fiber system. There is also a visceral nervous system that corresponds in function with the autonomic nervous system of vertebrates. Neurosecretory cells in various parts of the brain

have an endocrine function, but except for their role in molting and metamorphosis, little is known of their activity.

Sense Organs   The sensory perceptions of insects are usually keen. Organs receptive to mechanical, auditory, chemical, visual, and other stimuli are well developed and are scattered over the body, but especially on the appendages.

Photoreceptors include both ocelli and compound eyes. Compound eyes are large and constructed of ommatidia, as are those of crustaceans (see p. 251). Apparently, the visual acuity of insect eyes is much lower than that of human eyes, but most flying insects rate much higher than humans in flicker-fusion tests. Flickers of light become fused in human eyes at a frequency of 45 to 55 per second, but in bees and blow flies they do not fuse until 200 to 300 per second. This would be an advantage in analyzing a fast-changing landscape. Most insects have three ocelli on their head, and they also have dermal light receptors on their body surface.

Insects may detect sounds by means of sensitive, hairlike **sensilla** or by relying on tympanic organs sensitive to sonic or ultrasonic sound. Sensilla are modifications in the cuticular surface for reception of sensory stimuli other than light and are supplied with one or more neurons. Tympanic organs, found in grasshoppers (see figure 13.35B), crickets, cicadas, butterflies, and moths, involve a number of sensory cells extending to a thin tympanic membrane that encloses an air space in which vibrations can be detected.

Chemoreceptive sensilla, which are peglike or setae, are especially abundant on the antennae, mouthparts, or legs.

Mechanical stimuli, such as contact pressure, vibrations, and tension changes in the cuticle, are detected by sensilla or by sensory cells in the epidermis. Insects also sense temperature, humidity, body position (proprioception), and gravity.

Reproduction   Sexes are separate in insects, and fertilization is usually internal. Insects have various means of attracting mates. Female moths emit a chemical (pheromone) that males can detect for a great distance—several miles from females. Fireflies use flashes of light; other insects find each other by means of sounds or color signals and by various kinds of courtship behavior.

At the time of copulation, sperm are usually deposited in the vagina of females (see figure 13.35A). In some orders, sperm are encased in spermatophores that may be transferred at copulation or deposited on the substrate to be collected by a female. A male silverfish deposits a spermatophore on the ground, and then spins signal threads to guide a female to it. During the evolutionary transition from aquatic to terrestrial life, spermatophores were widely used, with copulation evolving much later.

Usually sperm are stored in the seminal receptacle of a female in numbers sufficient to fertilize more than one batch of eggs. Many insects mate only once during their lifetime, and none mates more than a few times. Sperm storage allows fertilization to occur much later.

Insects usually lay many eggs. A queen honey bee, for example, may lay more than 1 million eggs during her lifetime. On the other hand, some flies are ovoviviparous and bring forth only a single offspring at a time. Forms that make no provision for care of young usually lay many more eggs than those that provide for their young or those that have a very short life cycle.

Most species lay their eggs in a particular habitat to which they are guided by visual, chemical, or other clues. Butterflies and moths lay their eggs on the specific kind of plant on which their caterpillars must feed. A tiger moth may look for a pigweed, a sphinx moth for a tomato or tobacco plant, and a monarch butterfly for a milkweed plant. Insects whose immature stages are aquatic lay their eggs in water. A tiny braconid wasp lays her eggs on a caterpillar of the sphinx moth where they will feed and pupate in tiny white cocoons (see figure 13.43B). An ichneumon wasp, with unerring accuracy, seeks out a certain kind of larva in which her young will live as internal parasites. Her long ovipositor may have to penetrate 1 to 2 cm of wood to find and deposit her eggs in the larva of a wood wasp or a wood-boring beetle (figure 13.46).

Metamorphosis and Growth

The early development of insects occurs within the eggshell, and hatching young escape from the capsule in various ways. During postembryonic development, most insects change in form; they undergo **metamorphosis.** A number of molts are necessary during the growth period, and each stage between molts is called an **instar.** Although many animals undergo metamorphosis, insects illustrate it more dramatically than any other

figure 13.46

An ichneumon wasp with the end of the abdomen raised to thrust her long ovipositor into wood. She can bore 13 mm or more into wood to find a tunnel made by the larva of a wood wasp or wood-boring beetle. After she lays her eggs in the larva, the wood-boring beetle larva becomes host for the ichneumon larvae. Other ichneumon species attack spiders, moths, flies, crickets, caterpillars, and other insects.

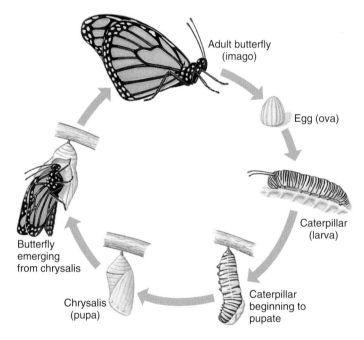

figure 13.47

Holometabolous (complete) metamorphosis in a butterfly, *Danaus plexippus* (order Lepidoptera). Eggs hatch to produce the first of several larval instars. The last larval instar molts to become a pupa. At the pupal molt, an adult emerges.

group. The transformation of a caterpillar into a beautiful moth or butterfly is indeed an astonishing morphological change.

Approximately 88% of insects go through **holometabolous (complete) metamorphosis** (Gr. *holo,* complete, + *metabolē,* change) (figure 13.47), which separates the physiological processes of growth **(larva)** from those of differentiation **(pupa)** and reproduction **(adult).** Each stage functions efficiently without competition with other stages, because the larvae often live in entirely different surroundings and eat different foods than adults. The wormlike larvae, which usually have chewing mouthparts, have various common names, such as caterpillars, maggots, bagworms, fuzzy worms, and grubs. After a series of instars, a larva forms a case or cocoon about itself and becomes a pupa, or chrysalis, a nonfeeding stage in which many insects pass the winter. When the final molt occurs, a full-grown adult emerges (see figure 13.47), pale and with wrinkled wings. In a short time, the wings expand and harden, and the insect flies for the first time. Adults undergo no further molting.

Some insects undergo **hemimetabolous (gradual,** or **incomplete) metamorphosis** (Gr. *hemi,* half, + *metabolē* change) (figure 13.48). These include bugs, scale insects, lice, and grasshoppers, which have terrestrial young, and mayflies, stoneflies (figure 13.49A), and dragonflies (figure 13.49B), which lay their eggs in water. The young are called **nymphs** or simply juveniles (figure 13.49C), and their wings develop externally as budlike outgrowths in the early instars and increase in size as the animal grows by successive molts and becomes a winged adult (figure 13.50). Aquatic nymphs have

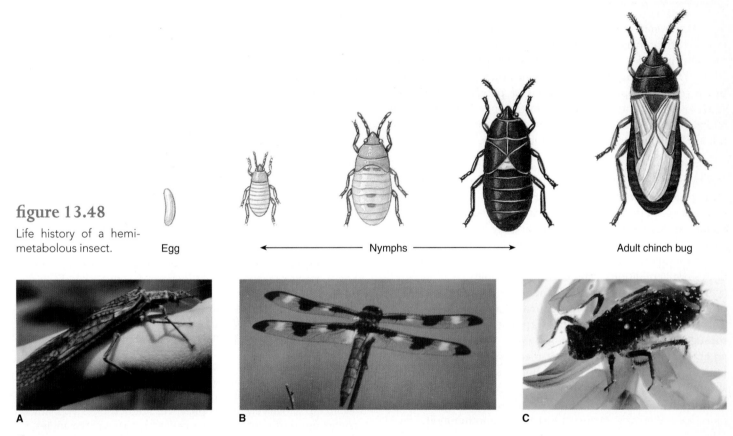

figure 13.48

Life history of a hemimetabolous insect.

Egg   ← Nymphs →   Adult chinch bug

A   B   C

figure 13.49

A, A stonefly, *Perla* sp. (order Plecoptera). **B,** A ten-spot dragonfly, *Libellula pulchella* (order Odonata). **C,** Nymph (juvenile) of a dragonfly. Both stoneflies and dragonflies have aquatic larvae that undergo gradual metamorphosis.

figure 13.50

A, Ecdysis in a cicada, *Tibicen davisi* (order Hemiptera, suborder Auchenorrhyncha). The old cuticle splits along a dorsal midline due to increased blood pressure and air forced into the thorax by muscle contraction. The emerging insect is pale, and its new cuticle is soft. The wings expand as hemolymph is pumped into veins, and the insect enlarges by taking in air. **B,** An adult *Tibicen davisi.*

A   B

tracheal gills or other modifications for aquatic life. The stages are egg, nymph (several instars), and adult.

A few insects, such as silverfish (see figure 13.60) and springtails, undergo direct development. The young, or juveniles, are similar to the adults except in size and sexual maturation. The stages are egg, juvenile, and adult. Such insects include the primitively wingless insects.

In common English usage, people often refer to all insects as "bugs," even extending the word to such nonanimals as bacteria, viruses, and glitches in computer programs. Biologically speaking, however, a bug is a member of order Hemiptera, suborder Heteroptera, and nothing else.

Hormones control and regulate metamorphosis in insects. Three major endocrine organs guide development through juvenile instars and the eventual emergence of adults. These organs and the hormones they produce are the **brain** (ecdysiotropin), the **ecdysial** or **prothoracic glands** (ecdysone), and the **corpora allata** (juvenile hormone). Hormonal control of molting and metamorphosis is the same in holometabolous and hemimetabolous insects.

Diapause   Many animals can enter a state of dormancy during adverse conditions, and the life cycle of many insects includes a long dormant period during which external climatic conditions are too harsh for normal activity. Most insects enter such a stage facultatively when some environmental factor, such as temperature, becomes unfavorable, and the state continues until conditions again become favorable.

However, some species experience a prolonged arrest of growth that is internally programmed and usually seasonal. This type of dormancy is called **diapause** (di´a-poz) (Gr. *dia*, through, dividing into two parts, + *pausis*, a stopping), and it is an important adaptation to adverse environmental conditions. Diapause is usually triggered by some external signal, such as shortening day length. Diapause always occurs at the end of an active growth stage of the molting cycle so that, when the diapause period is over, the insect is ready for another molt.

Behavior and Communication

Insects' keen sensory perceptions make them extremely responsive to many stimuli. The stimuli may be internal (physiological) or external (environmental), and the responses are governed by both the physiological state of the animal and the pattern of nerve pathways involved. Many responses are simple, such as orientation toward or away from a stimulus as occurs when a moth flies toward light, a cockroach avoids light, or carrion flies are attracted to the odor of dead flesh.

Much insect behavior, however, is not a simple matter of orientation but involves a complex series of responses. A pair of dung beetles chew off a bit of dung, roll it into a ball, and roll the ball laboriously to where they intend to bury it after laying their eggs in it (figure 13.51). A female cicada slits the bark of

figure 13.51

Dung beetles, *Canthon pilularis* (order Coleoptera), chew off a bit of dung, roll it into a ball, and then roll it to where they bury it in soil. One beetle pushes while the other pulls. They then lay their eggs in the ball, and the larvae feed on the dung. Dung beetles are black, an inch or less in length, and common in pastures.

a twig and then lays an egg in each of the slits. A female potter wasp (*Eumenes*) scoops up clay into pellets, carries them one by one to her building site, and fashions them into dainty, narrow-necked clay pots, into each of which she lays an egg. Then she hunts and paralyzes a number of caterpillars, pokes them into the opening of a pot, and closes the opening with clay. Each egg, in its own protective pot, hatches to find a well-stocked larder of food awaiting.

Some insects can memorize and perform in sequence tasks involving multiple signals in various sensory areas. Worker honey bees have been trained to walk through mazes that involve five turns in sequence, using such clues as the color of a marker, the distance between two spots, or the angle of a turn. The same is true of ants. Workers of one species of *Formica* learned a six-point maze at a rate only two or three times slower than that of laboratory rats. Foraging trips of ants and bees often wind and loop in a circuitous route, but once the forager has found food, the return trip is relatively direct. One investigator suggested that the continuous series of calculations necessary to figure the angles, directions, distance, and speed of the trip and to convert it into a direct return could involve a stopwatch, a compass, and integral vector calculus. How an insect does it is unknown.

Much insect behavior is "innate," meaning that entire sequences of actions apparently have been programmed. However, more learning is apparently involved than we once thought. A potter wasp, for example, must learn where she has left her pots if she is to return to fill them with caterpillars one at a time. Social insects, which have been studied extensively, are capable of most of the basic forms of learning used by mammals. An exception is insight learning. Apparently insects, when faced with a new problem, cannot reorganize their memories to construct a new response.

Insects communicate with other members of their species by chemical, visual, auditory, and tactile signals. Chemical signals take the form of **pheromones,** which are substances secreted by one individual that affect the behavior or physiological processes of another individual. Examples of pheromones include sex attractants, releasers of certain behavior patterns, trail markers, alarm signals, and territorial markers. Like hormones, pheromones are effective in minute quantities. Social insects, such as bees, ants, wasps, and termites, can recognize a nestmate—or an alien in the nest—by means of identification pheromones. Pheromones determine caste in termites, and to some extent in ants and bees. In fact, pheromones are probably a primary integrating force in populations of social insects. Many insect pheromones have been extracted and chemically identified.

Sound production and **sound reception** (phonoproduction and phonoreception) in insects have been studied extensively, and although not all insects have a sense of hearing, those that do use sounds as warning devices, to advertise territorial claims, or for courtship. For example, the sounds of crickets and grasshoppers function in both courtship and aggression. Male crickets scrape the modified edges of their forewings together to produce their characteristic chirping. The long, drawn-out sound of male cicadas, a call to attract females, is produced by vibrating membranes in a pair of organs located on the ventral side of the basal abdominal segment.

Insects practice many forms of **tactile communication,** such as tapping, stroking, grasping, and antennae touching, which evoke responses varying from recognition to recruitment and alarm. Certain kinds of flies, springtails, and beetles manufacture their own visual signals in the form of **bioluminescence.** The best-known luminescent beetles are fireflies, or lightning bugs (which are neither flies nor bugs, but beetles), which use a flash of light to locate a prospective mate. Each species has its own characteristic flashing rhythm produced on the ventral side of the last abdominal segments. Females flash an answer to the species-specific pattern to attract males. This interesting "love call" has been adopted by species of *Photuris,* which prey on male fireflies of other species they attract (figure 13.52).

Social Behavior In terms of being organized into social groups, insects rank very high in the animal kingdom, and cooperation within such complex groups depends heavily on chemical and tactile communication. However, not all social communities are complex. Some community groups are temporary and uncoordinated, such as hibernating associations of carpenter bees or feeding gatherings of aphids (figure 13.53). Some insects are coordinated for only brief periods, such as the tent caterpillars, *Malacosoma,* that join in building a home web and a feeding net. Still, all these are open communities with social behavior.

In true societies of some orders, such as Hymenoptera (honey bees and ants) and Isoptera (termites), a complex social life occurs. Such societies are closed. They involve all stages of the life cycle, communities are usually permanent, all activities are collective, and reciprocal communication occurs. Division of labor is highly efficient. Such a society is essentially a family

figure 13.52

Firefly femme fatale, *Photuris versicolor,* eating a male *Photinus tanytoxus,* which she has attracted with false mating signals.

figure 13.53

An ant (order Hymenoptera) tending a group of aphids (order Hemiptera, suborder Sternorrhyncha). The aphids feed copiously on plant juices and excrete the excess as a clear liquid rich in carbohydrates ("honey-dew"), which ants cherish as a food.

group in which the mother or perhaps both parents remain with their young, sharing the duties of the group in a cooperative manner. The society usually demonstrates polymorphism, or **caste differentiation.**

Honey bees have one of the most complex social organizations in the insect world. Instead of lasting one season, their organization continues for a more or less indefinite period.

As many as 60,000 to 70,000 honey bees may live in a single hive. Of these, there are three castes: a single, sexually mature female, or **queen**; a few hundred **drones,** which are sexually mature males; and thousands of **workers,** which are sexually inactive genetic females (figure 13.54).

Workers take care of the young, secrete wax with which they build the six-sided cells of the honeycomb, gather nectar from flowers, manufacture honey, collect pollen, and ventilate and guard the hive. One drone, or sometimes more, fertilizes the queen during the mating flight, at which time enough sperm are stored in her seminal receptacle to last her lifetime.

figure 13.54

Queen bee surrounded by her court. The queen is the only egg layer in the colony. The attendants, attracted by her pheromones, constantly lick her body. As food is transferred from these bees to others, the queen's presence is communicated throughout the colony.

Castes are determined partly by fertilization and partly by what is fed to the larvae. Drones develop parthenogenetically from unfertilized eggs (and consequently are haploid); queens and workers develop from fertilized eggs (and thus are diploid; see haplodiploidy, p. 228). Female larvae that will become queens are fed **royal jelly,** a secretion from the salivary glands of nurse workers. Royal jelly differs from the "worker jelly" fed to ordinary larvae, but the components in it that are essential for queen determination have not yet been identified. Honey and pollen are added to the worker diet about the third day of larval life. Pheromones in "queen substance," which is produced by the queen's mandibular glands, prevent female workers from maturing sexually. Workers produce royal jelly only when the level of "queen substance" pheromone in the colony drops. This change occurs when the queen becomes too old, dies, or is removed. Then workers start enlarging a larval cell and feeding a larva royal jelly that produces a new queen.

Honey bees have evolved an efficient system of communication by which, through certain body movements, their scouts inform workers of the location and quantity of food sources.

Termite colonies contain several castes, consisting of fertile individuals, both males and females, and sterile individuals (figure 13.55). Some fertile individuals may have wings and leave the colony, mate, lose their wings, and start a new colony as **king** and **queen.** Wingless fertile individuals may, under certain conditions, substitute for the king or queen. Sterile members are wingless and become **workers** and **soldiers.** Soldiers, which have large heads and mandibles, defend the colony. As in bees and ants, extrinsic factors cause caste differentiation. Reproductive individuals and soldiers secrete inhibiting pheromones that pass throughout the colony to nymphs via a mutual feeding process called **trophallaxis,** so that they become sterile workers. Workers also produce pheromones, and if the level of "worker substance" or "soldier substance" falls, as might happen after an attack by marauding predators, for example, the next generation produces compensating proportions of the appropriate caste.

Ants also have highly organized societies. Superficially, they resemble termites, but they are quite different (belong to a different order) and can be distinguished easily. In contrast to termites, ants are usually dark in color, are hard bodied, and have a constriction posterior to their first abdominal segment.

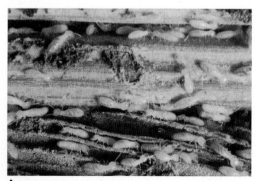

figure 13.55

A, Termite workers, *Reticulitermes flavipes* (order Isoptera), eating yellow pine. Workers are wingless sterile adults that tend the nest and care for the young. **B,** The termite queen becomes a distended egg-laying machine. Here a queen is surrounded by several workers and soldiers.

A   B

Entomologists describe insect societies by borrowing terms commonly used to describe human societies: queen, king, royal, soldier, worker, and caste. Such terms can be misleading by implying a correspondence between human and insect societies that does not exist. For example, in human societies "queen" suggests a position of political power that has no correspondence to the reproductive role of the "queen" of a bee colony. Confusion of these terms led a famous population geneticist, Ronald Fisher, to argue that human societies could achieve greater stability by emulating insect societies, specifically by concentrating reproduction among members of the upper classes. This argument is now considered an embarrassment of his otherwise highly regarded and influential book, *The Genetical Theory of Natural Selection* (1930).

In ant colonies, males die soon after mating, and the queen either starts her own new colony or joins an established colony and does the egg laying. Sterile females are wingless workers and soldiers that do the work of the colony—gather food, care for young, and protect the colony. Many larger colonies may have two or three types of individuals within each caste.

Ants have evolved some striking patterns of "economic" behavior, such as making slaves, farming fungi, herding "ant cows" (aphids or other hemipterans, see figure 13.53), sewing their nests together with silk (figure 13.56), and using tools.

Insects and Human Welfare

Beneficial Insects Although most of us think of insects primarily as pests, humanity would have great difficulty surviving if all insects were suddenly to disappear. Insects are necessary for cross-fertilization (pollination) of many crops. Bees pollinate over $14 billion worth of food crops per year in the United States alone, and this value does not include pollination of forage crops for livestock or pollination by other insects. In addition, some insects produce useful materials—for example, honey and beeswax from bees, silk from silkworms, and shellac from a wax secreted by lac insects.

Very early in their evolution, insects and flowering plants developed mutual adaptations that have functioned to each other's advantage. Insects exploit flowers for food, and flowers exploit insects for pollination. Each floral petal and sepal arrangement is correlated with the sensory adjustment of certain pollinating insects. Among these mutual adaptations are amazing allurements, traps, specialized structures, and precise timing.

Many predaceous insects, such as tiger beetles, aphid lions, ant lions, praying mantids, and lady beetles, destroy harmful insects (figure 13.57A and B). Some insects control harmful ones by parasitizing them or by laying their eggs where their young, when hatched, may devour the host (figure 13.57C).

figure 13.56

A weaver ant nest in Australia.

A

B

C

figure 13.57

Some beneficial insects. **A,** A predaceous stink bug (order Hemiptera) feeds on a caterpillar. Note the sucking proboscis of the bug. **B,** A lady beetle ("ladybug," order Coleoptera). Adults (and larvae of most species) feed voraciously on plant pests such as mites, aphids, scale insects, and thrips. **C,** A parasitic wasp (*Larra bicolor*) attacking a mole cricket. The wasp drives the cricket from its burrow, and then stings and paralyzes it. After the wasp deposits her eggs, the mole cricket recovers and resumes an active life—until it is killed by developing wasp larvae.

A   **B**   **C**

figure 13.58

Insect pests. **A,** Japanese beetles, *Popillia japonica* (order Coleoptera), are serious pests of fruit trees and ornamental shrubs. They were introduced into the United States from Japan in 1917. **B,** Longtailed mealybug, *Pseudococcus longispinus* (order Hemiptera, suborder Sternorrhyncha). Many mealybugs are pests of commercially valuable plants. **C,** Corn ear worms, *Heliothis zea* (order Lepidoptera). An even more serious pest of corn is the infamous corn borer, an import from Europe in 1908 or 1909.

Dead animals are quickly consumed by maggots hatched from eggs laid on carcasses.

Insects and their larvae serve as an important source of food for many birds, fish, and other animals.

Harmful Insects   Harmful insects include those that eat and destroy plants and fruits; examples are grasshoppers, chinch bugs, corn borers, boll weevils, grain weevils, San Jose scale, and scores of others (figure 13.58). Practically every cultivated crop has several insect pests. Humans expend enormous resources in all agricultural activities, in forestry, and in the food industry to counter insects and the damage they engender. Outbreaks of bark beetles or defoliators, such as spruce budworms and gypsy moths, have generated tremendous economic losses and have had a major impact on the composition of forests in the United States. Gypsy moths, introduced into the United States in 1869 in an ill-advised attempt to breed a better silkworm, have spread throughout the Northeast as far south as Virginia and as far west as Minnesota. In outbreak years, they defoliate oak forests; for example, in 1981, they defoliated 13 million acres in 17 northeastern states.

Lice, blood-sucking flies, warble flies, bot flies, and many others attack humans or domestic animals or both. Malaria, carried by the *Anopheles* mosquito (figure 13.59), is still one of the world's major diseases; mosquitos also transmit yellow fever and lymphatic filariasis. Fleas carry plague, which at times in history has eradicated significant portions of the human population. House flies are vectors of typhoid, as are lice for typhus fever; tsetse flies carry African sleeping sickness; and certain blood-sucking bugs, *Rhodnius* and related genera, transmit Chagas disease.

Tremendous destruction of food, clothing, and property is caused by weevils, cockroaches, ants, clothes moths, termites, and carpet beetles. Not the least of the insect pests are bed bugs, *Cimex*, blood-sucking hemipterous insects originally contracted by humans from bats that shared their caves early in human evolution.

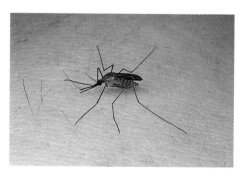

figure 13.59

A mosquito, *Anopheles quadrimaculatus* (order Diptera). *Anopheles* spp. are vectors of malaria.

West Nile virus, a disease agent spread by mosquitos, affects mammals and birds throughout the world. First identified in Uganda in 1937, it spread to North America in 1999. Birds serve as a reservoir for the virus: a bird bitten by an infected mosquito plays host to the virus for 1 to 4 days, during which the virus can be picked up by other mosquitos and spread to new hosts. Human response to infection varies, with about 80% showing no symptoms, close to 20% exhibiting flu-like symptoms such as fever and achiness, and less than 1% developing potentially fatal encephalitis or other possibly permanent neurological effects. Preventing mosquito bites is the best way to avoid infection, so studies of mosquito behavior are useful. For example, researchers wonder whether mosquitos that initially feed on infected birds tend to choose another bird for the next bite, or simply feed opportunistically on any available animal. Understanding virus transmission makes possible mathematical models to predict how and when the disease will spread.

Control of Insects   Because all insects are an integral part of the ecological communities to which they belong, their total destruction would probably do more harm than good. Food chains would be disturbed. Some of our favorite birds would disappear. The biological cycles by which dead animal and plant matter disintegrates and returns to enrich the soil would be seriously impeded. The beneficial roles of insects in our environment are often overlooked, and in our zeal to control the pests, we spray the landscape indiscriminately with extremely effective "broad-spectrum" insecticides that eradicate good, as well as harmful, insects. We have also found, to our dismay, that many chemical insecticides persist in the environment and accumulate as residues in the bodies of animals higher in the food chain. Furthermore, many insects have developed resistance to insecticides in common use.

In recent years, methods of control other than chemical insecticides have been under intense investigation, experimentation, and development. Economics, concern for the environment, and consumer demand are causing thousands of farmers across the United States to use alternative methods to control insect pests, rather than depending strictly on chemicals.

Several types of biological controls have been developed and are under investigation. All of these areas present problems but also show great potential. One method uses bacterial, viral, and fungal pathogens. A bacterium, *Bacillus thuringiensis,* is quite effective in controlling lepidopteran pests (cabbage looper, imported cabbage worm, tomato worm, and gypsy moth). Other strains of *B. thuringiensis* attack insects in other orders, and the species diversity of target insects is being widened by genetic engineering techniques. Genes coding for the toxin produced by *B. thuringiensis* (Bt) have also been introduced into the DNA of the plants themselves, which makes the plants resistant to insect attack, while the Bt is harmless to humans. Genes for Bt and for herbicide resistance have been incorporated into much of the soybeans, corn, cotton, and canola produced in the United States, thus reducing the need for hazardous chemical sprays. However, some insects have now evolved resistance to the toxin. Concerns about the health risks of consuming genetically modified crops have arisen, especially in Europe, but such fears are supported by little scientific evidence.

Classification of Subphylum Hexapoda

Hexapods are divided into orders chiefly on the basis of morphology and developmental features. Entomologists do not all agree on the names of the orders or on the contents of each order. Some tend to combine and others to divide groups. However, the following synopsis of major orders is rather widely accepted.

Class Entognatha

Order Protura (pro-tu´ra) (Gr. *protos,* first, + *oura,* tail). Minute (1 to 1.5 mm); no eyes or antennae; appendages on abdomen as well as thorax; live in soil and dark, humid places; slight, gradual metamorphosis.

Order Diplura (dip-lu´ra) (Gr. *diploos,* double, + *oura,* tail): **japygids.** Usually less than 10 mm; pale, eyeless; have a pair of long terminal filaments or a pair of caudal forceps; live in damp humus or rotting logs; direct development.

Order Collembola (col-lem´bo-la) (Gr. *kolla,* glue, + *embolon,* peg, wedge): **springtails** and **snowfleas.** Small (5 mm or less); no eyes; respiration by trachea or body surface; use a springing organ folded under the abdomen for leaping; abundant in soil; sometimes swarm on pond surface film or on snowbanks in spring; direct development.

Class Insecta

Order Thysanura (thy-sa-nu´ra) (Gr. *thysanos,* tassel, + *oura,* tail): **silverfish** (figure 13.60) and **bristletails.** Small to medium size; large eyes; long antennae; three long terminal cerci; live under stones and leaves and around human habitations; wingless; direct development.

Order Ephemeroptera (e-fem-er-op´ter-a) (Gr. *ephēmeros,* lasting but a day, + *pteron,* wing): **mayflies** (figure 13.61). Wings membranous; forewings larger than hindwings; adult mouthparts vestigial; nymphs aquatic, with lateral tracheal gills; hemimetabolous development.

figure 13.60

Silverfish, *Lepisma* (order Thysanura), is often found in homes.

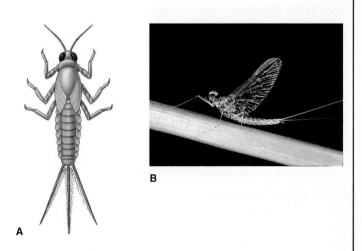

A

B

figure 13.61

Mayfly (order Ephemeroptera). **A,** Nymph. **B,** Adult.

Order Odonata (o-do-na´ta) (Gr. *odontos,* tooth, + *ata,* characterized by): **dragonflies** (see figure 13.49B) and **damselflies.** Large; membranous wings are long, narrow, net-veined, and similar in size; long and slender body; aquatic nymphs have aquatic gills and prehensile labium for capture of prey; hemimetabolous development.

Order Orthoptera (or-thop´ter-a) (Gr. *orthos,* straight, + *pteron* wing): **grasshoppers** (see figure 13.35), **locusts, crickets,** and **katydids.** Wings, when present, have forewings thickened and hindwings folded like a fan under forewings; chewing mouthparts.

Order Blattodea (blə-´tō-dē ə) (L. *blatta,* cockroach, + Gr. *eidos,* form, + *ea,* characterized by): **cockroaches.** Common insects in tropical areas; often infest houses in northern areas; oval, flattened bodies may exceed 5 cm in length; tarsi with 5 segments; wings typically present, often reduced.

Order Phasmatodea (faz-mə-´tō-dēə) (Gr. *phasma,* apparition, + *eidos* form, + *ea,* characterized by): **walkingsticks** and **leaf insects.** Bodies elongated and sticklike or flattened and laterally expanded; herbivorous, tropical forms may be very large (up to 30 cm).

Order Mantodea (man-´tō-dēə) (Gr. *mantis,* soothsayer, + *eidos,* form, + *ea,* characterized by): **mantids** (see figure 13.36). Bodies elongated with raptorial front legs; predatory; may reach 10 cm in length.

Order Mantophasmatodea (man-´tō-faz-mə-´tō-dēə) (an amalgamation of the order names for praying mantids [Mantodea] and walkingsticks [Phasmatodea]): **gladiators.** Secondarily wingless; chewing mouthparts; resemble a combination of a praying mantis and a walkingstick; nocturnal predators on insects and spiders; described in 2002; rare, found in Africa; 6 to 8 species.

Order Dermaptera (der-map´ter-a) (Gr. *derma,* skin, + *pteron,* wing): **earwigs.** Very short forewings; large and membranous hindwings folded under forewings when at rest; chewing mouthparts; forceps-like cerci.

Order Plecoptera (ple-kop´ter-a) (Gr. *plekein,* to twist, + *pteron,* wing): **stoneflies** (see figure 13.49A). Membranous wings; larger and fanlike hindwings; aquatic nymph with tufts of tracheal gills.

Order Isoptera (i-sop´ter-a) (Gr. *isos,* equal, + *pteron,* wing): **termites** (see figure 13.55). Small; membranous, narrow wings similar in size with few veins; wings shed at maturity; erroneously called "white ants"; distinguishable from true ants by broad union of thorax and abdomen; complex social organization; hemimetabolous development.

Order Embiidina (em-bē-ə´ di-nə) (Gr. *embios,* lively, + *eidos,* form, + *ina,* resembling): **webspinners.** Small; male wings membranous, narrow, and similar in size; wingless females; chewing mouthparts; colonial; make silk-lined channels in tropical soil.

Order Psocoptera (so-cop´ter-a) (Gr. *psoco,* rub away, + *pteron,* wing) **(Corrodentia): psocids, book lice,** and **bark lice.** Body usually small, may be as large as 10 mm; membranous, narrow wings with few veins, usually held rooflike over abdomen when at rest; some wingless species; found in books, bark, bird nests, on foliage.

Order Zoraptera (zo-rap´ter-a) (Gr. *zōros,* pure, + *apteryos,* wingless): **zorapterans.** As large as 2.5 mm; membranous, narrow wings usually shed at maturity; colonial and termite-like.

Order Phthiraptera (thī-rap´ter-a) (Gr. *phteir,* louse, + *apteros,* wingless): **lice.** Wingless ectoparasites adapted for clinging to warm-blooded hosts. **Sucking lice** (see figure 13.42) in former order Anoplura now constitute suborder Anoplura, mouthparts adapted for piercing and sucking, includes head lice, crab lice, and body lice. **Chewing lice** (see figure 13.41) in former order Mallophaga now divided among three suborders.

Order Thysanoptera (thy-sa-nop´ter-a) (Gr. *thysanos,* tassel, + *pteron,* wing): **thrips.** Length 0.5 to 5 mm (a few longer); wings, if present, long, very narrow, with few veins, and fringed with long hairs; sucking mouthparts; destructive plant-eaters, but some feed on insects.

Order Hemiptera (he-mip´ter-a) (Gr. *hemi,* half, + *pteron,* wing). Members have unique mouthparts specialized for piercing and sucking. Hemiptera is divided into three suborders: Heteroptera, Auchenorrhyncha, and Sternorrhyncha. Heteroptera contains **true bugs;** size 2 to 100 mm; wings present or absent; forewings with basal portion thickened and partly sclerotized; apical portion membranous; hindwings membranous; at rest, wings held flat over abdomen; many with odorous scent glands; includes water scorpions, water striders, bedbugs, squash bugs, assassin bugs, chinch bugs, stink bugs (see figure 13.57A), plant bugs, lace bugs, and many others. Auchenorrhyncha contains **hoppers** (figure 13.62) and **cicadas** (see figure 13.50); four wings typical if wings are present. Sternorrhyncha contains **whiteflies, psyllids, aphids, mealybugs** (see figure 13.58B), and **scale insects;** four wings typical if wings are present; often have complex life histories; many species are plant pests.

Order Neuroptera (neu-rop´ter-a) (Gr. *neuron,* nerve, + *pteron,* wing): **dobsonflies, ant lions** (figure 13.63), and **lacewings.** Medium to large size; similar, membranous wings with many cross veins; chewing mouthparts; dobsonflies have greatly enlarged mandibles in males and aquatic larvae; ant lion larvae (doodlebugs) make craters in sand to trap ants; holometabolous development.

Order Coleoptera (ko-le-op´ter-a) (Gr. *koleos,* sheath, + *pteron,* wing): **beetles** (see figure 13.58A and B), **fireflies** (see figure 13.52), and **weevils.** The largest order of animals; forewings (elytra) thick, hard, opaque; membranous hindwings folded under forewings at rest;

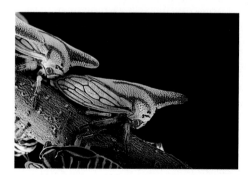

figure 13.62

Oak treehoppers, *Platycotis vittata* (order Hemiptera, suborder Auchenorrhyncha).

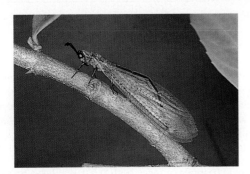

figure 13.63
Adult ant lion (order Neuroptera).

mouthparts for biting and chewing; includes ground beetles, carrion beetles, whirligig beetles, darkling beetles, stag beetles, dung beetles (see figure 13.51), diving beetles, boll weevils, fireflies, lady beetles (ladybugs), others; holometabolous development.

Order Strepsiptera (strep-sip´ter-a) (Gr. *strepsis,* a turning, + *pteron,* wing): **stylops** or **twisted wing parasites.** Females wingless, without eyes or antennae; males have vestigial forewings and fan-shaped hindwings; females and larvae parasites of bees, wasps, and other insects.

Order Mecoptera (me-kop´ter-a) (Gr. *mekos,* length, + *pteron,* wing): **scorpionflies.** Small to medium size; wings long, slender, with many veins; at rest, wings held rooflike over back; males have scorpion-like clasping organ at end of abdomen; carnivorous; live in most woodlands.

Order Lepidoptera (lep-i-dop´ter-a) (Gr. *lepidos,* scale, + *pteron,* wing): **butterflies** and **moths** (see figures 13.47 and 13.58C).

Membranous wings covered with overlapping scales, wings coupled at base; mouthpart is a sucking tube, coiled when not in use; larvae (caterpillars) have chewing mandibles for eating plants, stubby prolegs on the abdomen, and silk glands for spinning cocoons; antennae knobbed in butterflies and usually plumed in moths; holometabolous development.

Order Diptera (dip´ter-a) (Gr. *dis,* two, + *pteron,* wing): **true flies.** Single pair of wings, membranous and narrow; hindwings reduced to inconspicuous balancers (halteres); sucking mouthparts or adapted for sponging, lapping, or piercing; legless larvae called maggots or, when aquatic, wigglers; include crane flies, mosquitos (see figure 13.59), moth flies, midges, fruit flies, flesh flies, house flies (see figure 13.37), horse flies, bot flies, blow flies, gnats, and many others; holometabolous development.

Order Trichoptera (tri-kop´ter-a) (Gr. *trichos,* hair, + *pteron,* wing): **caddisflies.** Small, soft-bodied; wings well-veined and hairy, folded rooflike over hairy body; chewing mouthparts; aquatic larvae construct cases of leaves, sand, gravel, bits of shell, or plant matter, bound together with secreted silk or cement; some make silk feeding nets attached to rocks in streams; holometabolous development.

Order Siphonaptera (si-fon-ap´ter-a) (Gr. *siphon,* a siphon, + *apteros,* wingless): **fleas** (see figure 13.40). Small; wingless; bodies laterally compressed; legs adapted for leaping; no eyes; ectoparasitic on birds and mammals; larvae legless and scavengers; holometabolous development.

Order Hymenoptera (hi-men-op´ter-a) (Gr. *hymen,* membrane, + *pteron,* wing): **ants, bees** (see figure 13.54), and **wasps** (see figure 13.46). Very small to large; membranous, narrow wings coupled distally; subordinate hindwings; mouthparts for lapping liquids and biting; ovipositor sometimes modified into stinger, piercer, or saw; both social and solitary species; most larvae legless, blind, and maggot-like; holometabolous development.

Introduction of natural predators or parasites of the insect pests has had some success. In the United States, vedalia beetles from Australia help control the cottony-cushion scale on citrus plants, and numerous instances of control by using insect parasites have been recorded. However, the introduction of exotic species in order to control insect pests may have unexpected negative consequences, and should be done with caution.

Another approach to biological control is to interfere with the reproduction or behavior of insect pests by sterilizing males or by using naturally occurring organic compounds that act as hormones or pheromones. Such research, although very promising, is slow because of our limited understanding of insect behavior and the problems of isolating and identifying complex compounds that are produced in such minute amounts. Nevertheless, pheromones may play an important role in biological pest control in the future.

A systems approach called **integrated pest management** is practiced with many crops. This approach involves integrating all possible, practical techniques to contain pest infestations at a tolerable level—for example, cultural techniques (resistant plant varieties, crop rotation, tillage techniques, timing of sowing, planting, or harvesting, and others), use of biological controls, and sparing use of insecticides.

Phylogeny and Adaptive Diversification

Phylogeny

Whether phylum Arthropoda is monophyletic has long been controversial. Some scientists have contended that Arthropoda is polyphyletic and that some or all current subphyla are derived from different annelid-like ancestors that have undergone "arthropodization," the crucial hardening of the cuticle to form a stiffened exoskeleton. However, most other zoologists argue that derived similarities of the arthropod subphyla strongly support monophyly.

Biologists assume that the ancestral arthropod had a segmented body with one pair of appendages per segment. During evolution, adjacent segments fused to make body regions

Classification Phylum Arthropoda

Subphylum Trilobita (tri´lo-bi´ta) (Gr. *tri-*, three, + *lobos*, lobe): **trilobites.** All extinct forms; Cambrian to Permian periods; body divided by two longitudinal furrows into three lobes; distinct head, thorax, and abdomen; biramous appendages.

Subphylum Chelicerata (ke-lis´e-ra´ta) (Gr. *chēle*, claw, + *keratos*, a horn): **eurypterids, horseshoe crabs, spiders,** and **ticks.** First pair of appendages modified to form chelicerae; pair of pedipalps and four pairs of legs; no antennae, no mandibles; cephalothorax and abdomen often with segments fused.

Class Merostomata (mer´o-sto´ma-ta) (Gr. *meros*, thigh, + *stomatos*, mouth): **aquatic chelicerates.** Cephalothorax and abdomen; compound lateral eyes; appendages with gills; sharp telson; **subclasses Eurypterida** (all extinct) and **Xiphosurida,** the horseshoe crabs.

Class Pycnogonida (pik´no-gon´i-da) (Gr. *pyknos*, compact, + *gonia*, knee, angle): **sea spiders.** Small (3 to 4 mm), but some reach 500 mm; body chiefly cephalothorax; tiny abdomen; usually four pairs of long walking legs (some with five or six pairs); one pair of subsidiary legs (ovigers) for egg bearing; mouth on long proboscis; four simple eyes; no respiratory or excretory system. Example: *Pycnogonum.*

Class Arachnida (ar-ack´ni-da) (Gr. *arachnē*, spider): **scorpions, spiders, mites, ticks,** and **harvestmen.** Four pairs of legs; segmented or unsegmented abdomen with or without appendages and generally distinct from cephalothorax; respiration by gills, tracheae, or book lungs; excretion by Malpighian tubules or coxal glands; dorsal bilobed brain connected to ventral ganglionic mass with nerves; simple eyes; sexes separate; chiefly oviparous; no true metamorphosis. Examples: *Argiope, Centruroides.*

Subphylum Crustacea (crus-ta´she-a) (L. *crusta*, shell, + *acea*, group suffix): **crustaceans.** Mostly aquatic, with gills; cephalothorax usually with dorsal carapace; biramous appendages, modified for various functions; head appendages consist of two pairs of antennae, one pair of mandibles, and two pairs of maxillae; sexes usually separate; development primitively with nauplius stage.

Class Branchiopoda (brank´ē-o-pod-ə) (Gr. *branchia*, gills, + *podos*, foot): **branchiopods.** Flattened, leaflike swimming appendages (phyllopodia) with respiratory function. Examples: *Triops, Lynceus, Daphnia.*

Class Maxillopoda (mak´sil-o-pod-ə) (L. *maxilla*, jawbone, + Gr. *podos*, foot): **ostracods, copepods, branchiurans,** and **barnacles.** Five cephalic, six thoracic, and usually four abdominal segments; typically no appendages on abdomen; unique maxillopodan eye. Examples: *Cypris, Cyclops, Ergasilus, Argulus, Balanus.*

Class Malacostraca (mal´a-kos´tra-ka) (Gr. *malakos*, soft, + *ostrakon*, shell): **shrimps, crayfishes, lobsters,** and **crabs.** Usually have eight thoracic and six abdominal segments, each with a pair of appendages. Examples: *Armadillidium, Gammarus, Megacytiphanes, Grapsus, Homarus, Panulirus.*

Subphylum Myriapoda (mir-ē-a´pod-ə) (Gr. *myrias*, a myriad, + *podos*, foot): **myriapods.** All appendages uniramous; head appendages consist of one pair of antennae, one pair of mandibles, and one or two pairs of maxillae.

Class Diplopoda (dip´lō-pod-ə) (Gr. *diploos*, double, + *podos*, foot): **millipedes.** Subcylindrical body; head with short antennae and simple eyes; body with variable number of segments; short legs, usually two pairs of legs to a segment; separate sexes. Examples: *Julus, Spirobolus.*

Class Chilopoda (ki´lō-pod-ə) (Gr. *cheilos*, lip, + *podos*, foot): **centipedes.** Dorsoventrally flattened body; variable number of segments, each with one pair of legs; one pair of long antennae; separate sexes. Examples: *Cermatia, Lithobius, Geophilus.*

Class Pauropoda (pāu-rō-pod-ə) (Gr. *pauros*, small, + *podos*, foot): **pauropods.** Minute (1 to 1.5 mm), cylindrical body consisting of double segments and bearing nine or ten pairs of legs; no eyes. Example: *Pauropus.*

Class Symphyla (sim´fi-la) (Gr. *syn*, together, + *phylon*, tribe): **garden centipedes.** Slender (1 to 8 mm) with long, threadlike antennae; body consists of 15 to 23 segments with 10 to 12 pairs of legs; no eyes. Example: *Scutigerella.*

Subphylum Hexapoda (hek´sa-pod-ə) (Gr. *hex*, six, + *podos*, foot): **hexapods.** Body has distinct head, thorax, and abdomen; pair of antennae; mouthparts modified for different food habits; head composed of six fused segments; thorax has three segments; abdomen has variable number of segments, usually 11 somites; thorax has two pairs of wings (sometimes one pair or none) and three pairs of jointed legs; separate sexes; usually oviparous; gradual or abrupt metamorphosis.

Class Entognatha (en´tog-na-tha) (Gr. *entos*, within, inside + *gnathos*, jaw): **entognaths.** Base of mouthparts lies within head capsule; mandibles have one articulation. Example: *Entomobrya.*

Class Insecta (in-sek´ta) (L. *insectus*, cut into): **insects.** Bases of mouthparts exposed and exiting head capsule; mandibles generally have two regions of articulation. Examples: *Drosophila, Bombus, Anopheles* (insect orders listed on pp. 271–273).

(tagmata). How many segments contributed to a head in each group of arthropods? A partial answer to this question comes from studies of *Hox* genes that are highly correlated with specific anterior-posterior differentiation of body parts in bilateral animals. *Hox* gene studies indicate that the first five segments, at least, fused to form the head tagma in all four extant subphyla. It is surprising to find the same pattern of fusion in chelicerates as in other subphyla because a head is not immediately obvious in a chelicerate. Spider bodies have two tagmata: prosoma, or cephalothorax, and opisthosoma, or abdomen. Is the head part of the prosoma? *Hox* gene comparisons indicate that the entire prosoma corresponds to the head of other arthropods.

Another controversial area of arthropod biology for which genetic studies have proved helpful involves the evolution and antiquity of uniramous and biramous appendages. Hexapods and myriapods have uniramous appendages, but trilobites and some crustaceans have biramous appendages. If the ancestral appendage were biramous, then the switch to uniramous appendages might have occurred in one lineage whose descendants now carry this trait. Such reasoning led biologists to group hexapods with myriapods, but phylogenies using molecular characters repeatedly placed hexapods with crustaceans. Is it likely that the uniramous limb evolved more than once? This question would be more easily answered if the genetic basis of limb structure were understood. It is now known that modulation in expression of the *Distal-less (Dll)* gene determines the location of distal ends of arthropod limbs. In each primordial (embryonic) biramous appendage, the gene product of *Dll* can be observed in two groups of cells, each of which becomes a branch of the limb. In a uniramous limb primordium, there is only one such group of cells, and in primordia of phyllopodous limbs (as in class Branchiopoda), there are as many groups expressing *Dll* as there are limb branches. Gene expression can be modified within a lineage, so the number of limb branches is not likely to be an homologous character.

The best explanation for the similarities between crustaceans and insects, such as the basic structure of their ommatidia, is that these two taxa form a clade within Arthropoda. We depict crustaceans and hexapods as sister taxa (see figure 13.4), but some evidence suggests that hexapods arose from *within* the crustacean group, making Crustacea paraphyletic unless it includes hexapods. Insects may be the descendants of freshwater branchiopods. Crustacea now includes members of the former phylum Pentastomida as a subclass. The taxon Pancrustacea includes crustaceans and hexapods.

Phylogenetic placement of subphylum Myriapoda is highly controversial. Awaiting further research, we show a polytomy (multiple branches coming from a single point) in figure 13.4 to describe the relationships among Myriapoda, Chelicerata, and Pancrustacea.

Evolution within hexapods involved specialization of the first three postcephalic body segments (somites) to become locomotor segments (thorax) and a loss or reduction of appendages on the rest of the body (abdomen). The wingless orders traditionally have been regarded as having the most primitive characteristics. Three wingless orders (Diplura, Collembola, and Protura) have their mandibles and first maxillae located deeply in pouches in the head, a condition known as **entognathy.** All other insects are **ectognathous,** including the wingless order Thysanura. Ectognathous insects do not have their mandibles and maxillae in pouches, and they share other synapomorphies. Entognathous and ectognathous insects form sister groups, and Thysanura diverged from a common ancestor of ectognathous insects before the advent of flight, which unites the remaining ectognathous orders (see figure 13.33).

An ancestral winged insect gave rise to three lines, which differed in their ability to flex their wings (see figure 13.33). Two of these (Odonata and Ephemeroptera) have outspread wings. The other line, which has wings that can fold back over the abdomen, branched into three groups: one with hemimetabolous metamorphosis and chewing mouthparts (Orthopterodea); one group with hemimetabolous metamorphosis and usually sucking mouthparts (Hemipterodea); and a group with holometabolous metamorphosis (Holometabola).

How did the first arthropod evolve, and to which other phyla are arthropods closely related? Do all segmented phyla share a segmented common ancestor? A long-held hypothesis states that both annelids and arthropods originated from a common line of coelomate segmented protostomes from which two or more lines then diverged: a protoannelid line with laterally located parapodia and one or more protoarthropod lines with more ventrally located appendages. However, molecular evidence now supports placement of annelids in superphylum Lophotrochozoa and arthropods in superphylum Ecdysozoa. Alignment in separate superphyla implies that metamerism arose independently in the two groups and is a convergent character. Were metameric bodies convergent, the genetic controls and chemical signals used during development of a segmented body should differ among phyla. As discussed on p. 219, very preliminary comparisons suggest that annelids and arthropods do not share mechanisms of segmentation.

Assuming that arthropods belong within Ecdysozoa and are not closely related to annelids, several other phyla do seem allied with them. Phylum Tardigrada may be the sister taxon to arthropods, with phylum Onychophora being the sister taxon to the combined Arthropoda and Tardigrada (see Chapter 12).

Adaptive Diversification

The adaptive trend in arthropods has been toward tagmatization of the body by differentiation or fusion of segments, giving rise to such tagmata as head and trunk; head, thorax, and abdomen; or cephalothorax (fused head and thorax) and abdomen. A series of similar appendages, one pair on each trunk segment, is the primitive character state, still retained by some crustaceans and by myriapods. Derived forms include appendages specialized for specific functions and some appendages lost entirely.

Much of the amazing diversity in arthropods seems to have developed because of modification and specialization of their cuticular exoskeleton and their jointed appendages, thus producing a wide variety of locomotor and feeding adaptations. Whether in the area of habitat, feeding adaptations, means of locomotion, reproduction, or general mode of living, the adaptive achievements of arthropods are truly remarkable.

■ Summary

Arthropoda is the largest, most abundant and diverse phylum in the world. Arthropods are metameric, coelomate protostomes with well-developed organ systems. Most show marked tagmatization. They are extremely diverse and occur in all habitats capable of supporting life. Perhaps more than any other single factor, the success of arthropods is explained by adaptations made possible by their cuticular exoskeleton. Other important elements in their success are jointed appendages, tracheal respiration, efficient sensory organs, complex behavior, metamorphosis, and the ability to fly.

All arthropods must periodically cast off their cuticle (ecdysis) and grow larger before the newly secreted cuticle hardens. Premolt and postmolt periods are hormonally controlled, as are several other structures and functions.

Adaptive diversification of the arthropods has been enormous, and they are extremely abundant.

Members of subphylum Chelicerata have no antennae, and their main feeding appendages are chelicerae. In addition, they have a pair of pedipalps (which may be similar to walking legs) and four pairs of walking legs. A great majority of living chelicerates are in class Arachnida: spiders (order Araneae), scorpions (order Scorpionida), harvestmen (order Opiliones), and ticks and mites (order Acari).

The tagmata of spiders (cephalothorax and abdomen) show no external segmentation and join at a waistlike pedicel. Their chelicerae have venom glands for paralyzing or killing their prey. Spiders can spin silk, which they use for a variety of purposes.

The cephalothorax and abdomen of ticks and mites are completely fused, and the anterior capitulum bears the mouthparts. Ticks and mites are the most numerous arachnids; some are important disease carriers, and others are serious plant pests.

Crustacea is a large, primarily aquatic subphylum of arthropods. Crustaceans bear two pairs of antennae, mandibles, and two pairs of maxillae on the head. Their appendages are primitively biramous, and the major tagmata are head, thorax, and abdomen. Many have a carapace and respire with gills.

Many crustaceans are predators, scavengers, filter feeders, and parasites. Respiration is through the body surface or by gills, and excretory organs take the form of maxillary or antennal glands. Circulation, as in other arthropods, is through an open system of sinuses (hemocoel), and a dorsal, tubular heart is the chief pumping organ. Most crustaceans have compound eyes composed of units called ommatidia.

Members of class Maxillopoda, subclass Copepoda, lack a carapace and abdominal appendages. They are abundant and are some of the most important primary consumers in many freshwater and marine ecosystems.

Most members of subclass Cirripedia (barnacles) are sessile as adults, secrete a shell of calcareous plates, and filter-feed. Subclass Branchiura contains fish lice. Closely related to fish lice are tongue worms; they are parasitic in the lungs and nasal cavities of vertebrates. These members of former phylum Pentastomida now form subclass Pentastomida in class Maxillopoda.

Malacostraca is the largest crustacean class, and the most important orders are Isopoda, Amphipoda, Euphausiacea, and Decapoda. All have both abdominal and thoracic appendages. Decapods include crabs, shrimp, lobster, crayfish, and others; they have five pairs of walking legs (including chelipeds) on their thorax.

The former subphylum Uniramia grouped arthropods having uniramous appendages, one pair of antennae, a pair of mandibles, and two pairs of maxillae (one pair of maxillae in millipedes) on the head. Uniramia has been divided into two subphyla: Myriapoda, in which the animals have head and trunk tagmata, and Hexapoda, in which the tagmata are head, thorax, and abdomen.

Hexapoda is the largest subphylum of the world's largest phylum. Insects are easily recognized by the combination of their tagmata and their possession of three pairs of thoracic legs.

The diversification and abundance of insects are largely explained by several features that allow them to exploit terrestrial habitats, such as a waterproof cuticle and other mechanisms to minimize water loss and their ability to become dormant during adverse conditions.

Feeding habits vary greatly among insects, and an enormous variety of specialized mouthparts reflects their particular feeding habits. Insects breathe by means of a tracheal system, a system of tubes that open by spiracles on the thorax and abdomen. Excretory organs are Malpighian tubules.

Sexes are separate in insects, and fertilization is usually internal. Almost all insects undergo metamorphosis during development. In holometabolous (complete) metamorphosis, the last larval molt gives rise to a nonfeeding stage (pupa). An adult, usually winged, emerges at the final, pupal molt. In hemimetabolous (gradual) metamorphosis, larval instars are called nymphs, and adults emerge at the last nymphal molt. Both types of metamorphosis are hormonally controlled.

Insects are important to human welfare, particularly because they pollinate food crop plants, control populations of other, harmful insects by predation and parasitism, and serve as food for other animals. Many insects harm human interests because they feed on crop plants, and many carry important diseases affecting humans and domestic animals.

A preponderance of morphological and molecular evidence supports monophyly of phylum Arthropoda. The traditional alliance of Crustacea with insects and myriapods in a group called Mandibulata is supported by some morphological evidence, but some molecular data support a clade composed of crustaceans and insects, with myriapods the sister taxon to this clade, or the sister taxon to chelicerates. Wings, hemimetabolous metamorphosis, and holometabolous metamorphosis evolved among ectognathous insects.

Until recently, zoologists grouped Annelida and Arthropoda as descendants of a metameric common ancestor. Molecular evidence suggests that they were derived independently from a protostome ancestor and belong to separate superphyla (Lophotrochozoa and Ecdysozoa). If this hypothesis is supported by further studies, metamerism must have evolved independently in each superphylum.

Review Questions

1. List some characteristics of arthropods that clearly distinguish them from Annelida.
2. Name the subphyla of arthropods, and give a few examples of each.
3. Much of the success of arthropods has been attributed to their cuticle. Why? Describe some other factors that probably contributed to their success.
4. What is a trilobite?
5. What appendages characterize chelicerates?
6. Briefly describe the appearance of each of the following: eurypterids, horseshoe crabs, pycnogonids.
7. Describe the mechanism of each of the following with respect to spiders: feeding, excretion, sensory reception, webspinning, reproduction.
8. Distinguish each of the following orders from each other: Araneae, Scorpionida, Opiliones, Acari.
9. People fear spiders and scorpions, but ticks and mites are far more important medically and economically. Why? Give examples.
10. Which segments and appendages occur on the head of a malacostracan crustacean? What are some other important characteristics of Crustacea?
11. Among the classes of Crustacea, Branchiopoda, Maxillopoda, and Malacostraca are the most important. Distinguish them from each other.
12. Distinguish among subclasses Ostracoda, Copepoda, Branchiura, and Cirripedia in class Maxillopoda.
13. Copepods sometimes are called "insects of the sea" because marine planktonic copepods probably are the most abundant animals in the world. What is their ecological importance?
14. Define each of the following: swimmeret, maxilliped, cheliped, nauplius.
15. Describe molting in Crustacea, including the action of hormones.
16. Explain the mechanism of each of the following with respect to crustaceans: feeding, respiration, excretion, circulation, sensory reception, reproduction.
17. Distinguish the following from each other: Diplopoda, Chilopoda, Insecta.
18. Define each of the following with respect to insects: sclerite, tergum, sternum, labrum, hypopharynx, haltere, instar, diapause.
19. Explain why wings powered by indirect flight muscles can beat much more rapidly than those powered by direct flight muscles.
20. What different modes of feeding do insects use, and how are these reflected in their mouthparts?
21. Describe each of the following with respect to insects: respiration, excretion and water balance, sensory reception, reproduction.
22. Explain the difference between holometabolous and hemimetabolous metamorphosis in insects, including the stages of each.
23. Describe and give an example of each of four ways insects communicate with each other.
24. What castes occur in honey bees and in termites, and what is the function of each? What is trophallaxis?
25. Name several ways in which insects benefit humans and several ways in which they are detrimental.
26. For the past 50 or more years, people have relied on toxic insecticides for control of harmful insects. What problems have arisen as a result? What are the alternatives? Define integrated pest management.
27. What evidence suggests that metamerism evolved independently in Annelida and Arthropoda?
28. We hypothesize that the earliest insects were wingless, making lack of wings the primitive condition. Does winglessness characterize a hexapod class? In what sense is it useful for classification?

Selected References

See also general references on page 423.

Arnett, R. H., Jr., and M. C. Thomas, eds. 2000. American beetles, vol. 1. Boca Raton, Florida, CRC Press.

Arnett, R. H., Jr., M. C. Thomas, P. E. Skelley, and J. H. Franks, eds. 2002. American beetles, vol. 2. Polyphaga: Scarabaeoidea through Curculionoidea. Boca Raton, Florida, CRC Press. *These two volumes present recent detailed keys to families of American beetles; the second edition of volume 1 (2001) includes additions and corrections.*

Averof, M. 1998. Evolutionary biology: origin of the spider's head. Nature **395**:436–437. *Summary of research on homology of the head across arthropod subphyla.*

Brown, K. 2001. Seeds of concern. Sci. Am. **284**:52–57 (Apr.). *The first of four articles that examine the pros and cons of genetically modified crops, including those with genes for insecticidal toxin.*

Brusca, R. C. 2001. Unraveling the history of arthropod biodiversification. Ann. Missouri Bot. Garden **87**:13–25. *An easy-to-read discussion of changes in our understanding of arthropod evolution.*

Downs, A. M. R., K. A. Stafford, and G. C. Coles. 1999. Head lice: prevalence in schoolchildren and insecticide resistance. Parasitol. Today **15**:1–4. *This report is mainly concerned with England, but head lice are one of the most common parasites of American schoolchildren.*

Giribet, G., G. D. Edgecombe, and W. C. Wheeler. 2001. Arthropod phylogeny based on eight molecular loci and morphology. Nature **413**:157–161. *This phylogenetic analysis indicates a close relationship between crustaceans and hexapods, and supports a mandibulate clade.*

Glenner, H., P. F. Thomsen, M. B. Hebsgaard, M. V. Sorensen, and E. Willerslev. 2006. The origin of insects. Science **314**:1883–1884. *The origin of insects as terrestrial crustaceans explains a puzzling aspect of the fossil record.*

Gullan, P. J., and P. S. Cranston. 2005. The insects: an outline of entomology, ed. 3. Malden, Massachusetts, Blackwell Publishing. *An easy-to-use text for general entomology with good figures, modern phylogenies, and data on biogeography.*

Johnson, N. F., and C. Triplehorn. 2005. Borror and DeLong's introduction to the study of insects, ed. 7. Belmont, California, Brooks/Cole Publishing Company. *An up-to-date reference text for the study of insects; keys are included, but some* require specialized knowledge of morphological characters. *See Arnett and Thomas for keys to the American beetle families.*

Lane, R. P., and R. W. Crosskey (eds). 1993. Medical insects and arachnids. London, Chapman & Hall. *This is the best book currently available on medical entomology.*

Lavrov, D. V., W. M. Brown, and J. L. Boore. 2004. Phylogenetic position of the Pentastomida and (pan)crustacean relationships. Proc. Royal Soc. Biol. Sciences B **271**:537–544. *Mitochondrial gene arrangements and sequences indicate that pentastomids are modified crustaceans, and likely related to branchiurans.*

Levine, M. 2002. How insects lose their limbs. Nature **415**:848–849. *A Hox gene product in the abdomen of insects inhibits action of another gene product that is necessary for limb formation.*

Luoma, J. R. 2001. The removable feast. Audubon **103(3)**:48–54. *During May and June, large numbers of horseshoe crabs ascend the shores of U.S. Atlantic states to breed and lay eggs. Since the 1980s, they have been heavily harvested to be chopped up and used for bait. This*

practice has led to serious declines in Limulus *populations, with accompanying declines in populations of migrating shorebirds that feed on* Limulus *eggs.*

Mallatt, J., J. R. Garey, and J. W. Shultz. 2004. Ecdysozoan phylogeny and Bayesian inference: first use of nearly complete 28s and 18s rRNA gene sequences to classify arthropods and their kin. Mol. Phylogenet. Evol. **31**:178–191. *Results indicate that Crustacea is paraphyletic without hexapods, but Pancrustacea is a monophyletic group, that chelicerates and myriapods are sister taxa, and that Panarthropoda is a monophyletic group. There was no support for a mandibulate clade.*

Milius, S. 2007. Not-so-elementary bee mystery. Science News **172**: 56. *A short summary of research into honey bee colony collapse disorder.*

Suter, R. B. 1999. Walking on water. Amer. Sci. **87**:154–159. *Fishing spiders* (Dolomedes) *depend on surface tension to walk on water.*

Telford, S. R. III., and H. K. Goethert. 2004. Emerging tick-borne infections: rediscovered and better characterized, or truly 'new'? Parasitology **129**:S301–S327.

A serious summary of infectious agents carried by ticks.

Versluis, M., B. Schmitz, A. von der Heydt, and D. Lohse. 2000. How snapping shrimp snap: through cavitating bubbles. Science **289**:2114–2117. *When* Alpheus *snaps the claw on its chela shut, it generates a jet of water with a velocity so high that the pressure decreases below the vapor pressure of water, producing a cavitation bubble. As the water pressure rises again, the bubble collapses with a force sufficient to stun or kill prey.*

Westneat, M. W., O. Betz, R. W. Blob, K. Fezzaa, W. J. Cooper, and W. Lee. 2003. Tracheal respiration in insects visualized with synchrotron X-ray imaging. Science **299**:558–560. *Tracheae compress actively, exhaling air, but expand passively.*

Whiting, R. 2004. Phylogenetic relationships and evolution of insects, pp. 330–344. In J. Cracraft and M. J. Donoghue, eds., Assembling the tree of life. New York, Oxford University Press. *A detailed discussion of current hypotheses for insect evolution, including the suggestion that entognathous hexapods do not form a monophyletic group, unlike ectognathous forms.*

■ Custom Website

The *Animal Diversity* Online Learning Center is a great place to check your understanding of chapter material. Visit www.mhhe.com/hickmanad5e for access to key terms, quizzes, and more! Further enhance your knowledge with Web links to chapter-related material.

Explore live links for these topics:

Classification and Phylogeny of Animals
Phylum Arthropoda
Subphylum Chelicerata
Subphylum Crustacea
Subphylum Myriapoda

Subphylum Hexapoda
Class Insecta

Vertebrate Beginnings:
The Chordates

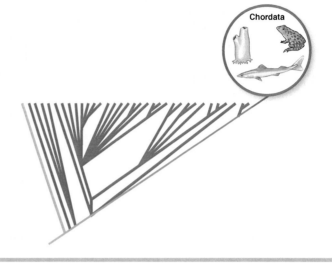

Chordata

Two amphioxus in feeding posture.

It's a Long Way from Amphioxus

Along the more southern coasts of North America, half buried in sand on the sea floor, lives a small, fishlike, translucent animal quietly filtering organic particles from seawater. Inconspicuous, of no commercial value, and largely unknown, this creature is nonetheless one of the famous animals of classical zoology. It is amphioxus, an animal that wonderfully exhibits the five distinctive hallmarks of the phylum Chordata: (1) a dorsal hollow nerve cord overlying (2) a supportive notochord, (3) pharyngeal pouches or slits and (4) an endostyle for filter feeding, and (5) a postanal tail for propulsion. Amphioxus is an animal that might have been designed by a zoologist for the classroom. During the nineteenth century, with interest in vertebrate ancestry running high, many zoologists thought amphioxus bore a close resemblance to the direct ancestor of vertebrates. Its exalted position was later acknowledged by Philip Pope in a poem sung to the tune of "Tipperary." It ends with the refrain:

> It's a long way from amphioxus
> It's a long way to us,
> It's a long way from amphioxus
> To the meanest human cuss.
> Well, it's good-bye to fins and gill slits
> And it's welcome lungs and hair,
> It's a long, long way from amphioxus
> But we all came from there.

But amphioxus's place in the sun was not to endure. One reason is that amphioxus lacks one of the most important vertebrate characteristics—a distinct head with special sense organs and other structures for shifting to an active predatory mode of life. Absence of a head, together with several specialized features, suggests to today's zoologists that amphioxus represents an early departure from vertebrate ancestry. It seems that we are a very long way indeed from amphioxus. Nevertheless, while amphioxus is denied the vertebrate ancestor award, it resembles the chordate condition immediately preceding the origin of vertebrates more closely than any other living animal we know.

T he animals most familiar to most people belong to the phylum Chordata. Humans are members and share the characteristic from which the phylum derives its name—the notochord (Gr. *nōton*, back, + L. *chorda*, cord) (figure 15.1). All members of the phylum possess this structure, either restricted to early development or present throughout life. The notochord is a rodlike, semirigid body of cells enclosed by a fibrous sheath, which extends, in most cases, the length of the body just ventral to the central nervous system. Its primary purpose is to support and stiffen the body, providing skeletal scaffolding for the attachment of swimming muscles.

The structural plan of chordates retains many of the features of nonchordate invertebrates, such as bilateral symmetry, anteroposterior axis, coelom tube-within-a-tube arrangement, metamerism, and cephalization. However, the phylogenetic position of chordates within the animal kingdom has been controversial.

Two lines of descent have been proposed. Earlier speculations that focused on the arthropod-annelid-mollusc group (Protostomia branch) of the invertebrates have fallen from favor. Only members of the echinoderm-hemichordate assemblage (Deuterostomia branch) now deserve serious consideration as the chordate sister group. Chordates share with other deuterostomes several important characteristics: radial cleavage (see p. 59), an anus derived from the first embryonic opening (blastopore) and a mouth derived from an opening of secondary origin, and a coelom primitively formed by fusion of enterocoelous pouches (although in most vertebrates coelom formation is schizocoelus, but independently derived, as an accommodation for their large yolks). These uniquely shared characteristics indicate a natural unity among the Deuterostomia.

Phylum Chordata shows a more fundamental unity of organs and organ systems than do other phyla. Ecologically, chordates are among the most adaptable of organic forms, able to occupy most kinds of habitat. They illustrate perhaps better than any other animal group the basic evolution of new structures, adaptive strategies, and adaptive diversification.

Traditional and Cladistic Classification of the Chordates

Traditional Linnean classification of chordates (see p. 314) provides a convenient way to indicate the taxa included in each major group. However, in cladistic usage, some of the traditional taxa, such as Agnatha and Reptilia, are no longer recognized. Such taxa do not satisfy the cladistic requirement that only **monophyletic** groups are valid taxonomic entities—that is, groups containing all known descendants of a single common ancestor. The reptiles, for example, are considered a **paraphyletic** grouping because their group does not contain all descendants of their most recent common ancestor. The common ancestor of reptiles as traditionally recognized is also the ancestor of birds. As shown in the cladogram (see figure 15.2), reptiles, birds, and mammals compose a monophyletic group called Amniota, so named because all develop from an egg having special extraembryonic membranes, one of which is the amnion. Therefore, according to cladistics, "reptiles" can be used only as a term of convenience to refer to amniotes that are not birds or mammals; there are no derived characters that unite the reptiles to the exclusion of birds and mammals. The reasons nonmonophyletic groups are not used in cladistic taxonomy are explained in Chapter 4 (see p. 83).

The phylogenetic tree of chordates (figure 15.3) and the cladogram of chordates (figure 15.2) provide different kinds of information. The cladogram shows a nested hierarchy of taxa grouped by their shared derived characters. These characters may be morphological, physiological, embryological, behavioral, chromosomal, or molecular. By contrast, the branches of a phylogenetic tree are intended to represent real lineages that occurred in the evolutionary past. Geological information regarding ages of lineages is added to the information from the cladogram to generate a phylogenetic tree for the same taxa.

In our treatment of chordates, we have retained the traditional Linnean classification (see p. 314) because subfields of zoology are organized according to this scheme and because the alternative—thorough revision following cladistic principles—would require extensive change and abandonment of familiar rankings. However, we have tried to use monophyletic taxa as much as possible, because such usage is necessary to reconstruct the evolution of morphological characters in chordates.

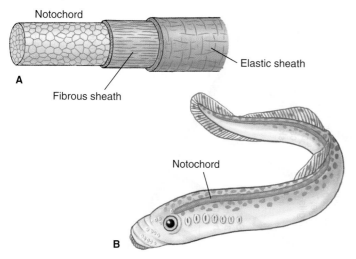

Notochord

Elastic sheath

A

Fibrous sheath

Notochord

B

figure 15.1

A, Structure of the notochord and its surrounding sheaths. Cells of the notochord proper are thick walled, pressed together closely, and filled with a semifluid substance. Their stiffness is caused mainly by the turgidity of fluid-filled cells and surrounding connective tissue sheaths. This primitive type of endoskeleton is characteristic of all chordates at some stage of the life cycle. The notochord provides longitudinal stiffening of the main body axis, a base for trunk muscles, and an axis around which the vertebral column develops. **B,** In hagfishes and lampreys, the notochord persists throughout life, but in other vertebrates it is largely replaced by vertebrae. In mammals, slight remnants are found in the nuclei pulposi of intervertebral discs. The method of notochord formation is different in the various groups of vertebrates. In amphioxus, it originates from the endoderm; in birds and mammals, it arises as an anterior outgrowth of the embryonic primitive streak.

Table 15.1 Traditional Divisions of the Phylum Chordata

Urochordata (tunicates)	Cephalochordata (lancelets)	Myxini (hagfishes)	Petromyzontida (lampreys)	Chondrichthyes (sharks)	Osteichthyes (bony fishes)	Amphibia (amphibians)	Reptilia (reptiles)	Aves (birds)	Mammalia (mammals)

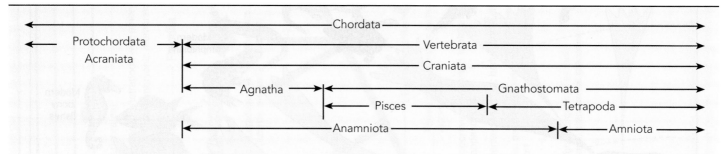

Characteristics
of Phylum Chordata

1. Bilateral symmetry; segmented body; three germ layers; well-developed coelom
2. **Notochord** (a skeletal rod) present at some life stage
3. **Single, dorsal hollow nerve cord;** anterior end of cord usually enlarged to form a brain
4. **Pharyngeal pouches** present at some life stage; in aquatic chordates, these develop into **pharyngeal slits**
5. **Endostyle** in floor of pharynx or a **thyroid gland** derived from the endostyle
6. **Postanal tail,** projecting beyond the anus at some life stage but may or may not persist
7. Complete digestive system
8. **Segmentation,** if present, restricted to outer body wall, head, and tail and not extending into coelom

Several traditional divisions of phylum Chordata used in Linnean classifications are shown in table 15.1. A fundamental separation is Protochordata from the Vertebrata. Since the former lack a well-developed head, they are sometimes called Acraniata. All vertebrates have a well-developed skull case enclosing the brain and also are called Craniata. We should note that some cladistic classifications exclude Myxini (hagfishes) from the group Vertebrata, because they lack vertebrae, but retain them in Craniata because they have a cranium. The vertebrates (craniates) may be variously subdivided into groups based on shared characteristics. Two such subdivisions shown in table 15.1 are: (1) Agnatha, vertebrates lacking jaws (hagfishes and lampreys), and Gnathostomata, vertebrates having jaws (all other vertebrates), and (2) Amniota, vertebrates whose embryos develop within a

fluid-filled sac, the amnion (nonavian reptiles, birds, and mammals), and Anamniota, vertebrates lacking this adaptation (fishes and amphibians). The Gnathostomata in turn can be subdivided into Pisces, jawed vertebrates with appendages, if any, in the form of fins, and Tetrapoda (Gr. *tetras,* four, + *podos,* foot), jawed vertebrates with appendages, if any, in the form of limbs. Note that several of these groupings are paraphyletic (Protochordata, Acraniata, Agnatha, Anamniota, Pisces) and consequently are not accepted in cladistic classifications. Accepted monophyletic taxa are shown at the top of the cladogram in figure 15.2 as a nested hierarchy of increasingly more inclusive groupings.

■ Five Chordate Hallmarks

Five distinctive characteristics that, taken together, set chordates apart from all other phyla are a **notochord,** a **dorsal hollow nerve cord, pharyngeal slits or pouches,** an **endostyle,** and a **postanal tail.** These characteristics are always found at some embryonic stage, although they may change or disappear in later stages of the life cycle.

Notochord

The notochord is a flexible, rodlike structure, extending the length of the body; it is the first part of the endoskeleton to appear in the embryo. The notochord is an axis for muscle attachment, and because it can bend without shortening, it permits undulatory movements of the body. In most protochordates and in jawless vertebrates, the notochord persists throughout life but in all jawed vertebrates it is at least partly replaced by a series of cartilaginous or bony vertebrae.

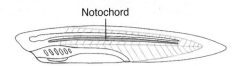

Notochord

Dorsal Hollow Nerve Cord

In most invertebrate phyla that have a nerve cord, it is ventral to the digestive tract and is solid, but in chordates the single cord is dorsal to the digestive tract and notochord and is a tube (although the hollow center may be nearly obliterated during growth). The anterior end becomes enlarged to form the brain in vertebrates. The hollow cord is produced in the embryo by infolding of ectodermal cells on the dorsal side of the body above the notochord. Among vertebrates, the nerve cord passes through the protective neural arches of the vertebrae, and the brain is surrounded by a bony or cartilaginous cranium.

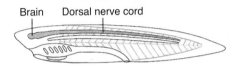

Brain   Dorsal nerve cord

Pharyngeal Pouches or Slits

Pharyngeal slits are openings that lead from the pharyngeal cavity to the outside. They are formed by the inpocketing of the outside ectoderm (pharyngeal grooves) and the evagination, or outpocketing, of the endodermal lining of the pharynx (pharyngeal pouches). In aquatic chordates, the two pockets break through the pharyngeal cavity where they meet to form the pharyngeal slit. In amniotes, some pockets may not break through the pharyngeal cavity, so only grooves are formed instead of slits. In tetrapod (four-limbed) vertebrates, pharyngeal pouches give rise to several different structures, including the Eustachian tube, middle ear cavity, tonsils, and parathyroid glands.

    The perforated pharynx evolved as a filter-feeding apparatus and is used as such in protochordates. Water with suspended food particles is drawn by ciliary action through the mouth and flows out through pharyngeal slits, where food is trapped in mucus. In vertebrates, ciliary action is replaced by muscular pharyngeal contractions that drive water through the pharynx. The addition of a capillary network and thin, gas-permeable walls in the pharyngeal arches led to the development of **internal gills,** completing the conversion of the pharynx from a filter-feeding apparatus in protochordates to a respiratory organ in aquatic vertebrates.

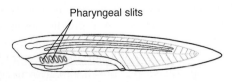

Pharyngeal slits

Endostyle or Thyroid Gland

Until recently, the endostyle was not recognized as a chordate character. However, it or its derivative, the thyroid gland, occurs in all chordates, and in no other animals. The endostyle, located in the pharyngeal floor, secretes mucus that traps small food particles brought into the pharyngeal cavity. An endostyle is present in protochordates and lamprey larvae. Some cells in the endostyle secrete iodinated proteins. These cells are homologous with the iodinated-hormone-secreting thyroid gland of adult lampreys and the remainder of vertebrates. In ancestral chordates, an endostyle and a perforated pharynx work together to create an efficient filter-feeding apparatus.

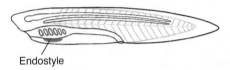

Endostyle

Postanal Tail

A postanal tail, together with somatic musculature and the stiffening notochord, provides the motility that larval tunicates and amphioxus need for their free-swimming existence. As a structure added to the body behind the anus, the tail clearly has evolved specifically for propulsion in water. Its efficiency is later increased in fishes with the addition of fins. A tail is evident in humans only as a vestige (the coccyx, a series of small vertebrae at the end of the spinal column), but most other mammals have a waggable tail as adults.

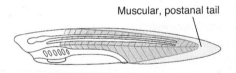

Muscular, postanal tail

■ Ancestry and Evolution

Since the mid-nineteenth century when Darwin's theory of common descent became the focal point for recognizing relationships among groups of living organisms, zoologists have debated the origin of chordates. Zoologists at first speculated that chordates evolved within the protostome clade (annelids and arthropods) but rejected such ideas when they realized that supposed morphological similarities had no developmental basis. Early in the twentieth century, further theorizing became rooted in developmental patterns of animals, and it became apparent that chordates must have originated within the deuterostome branch of the animal kingdom. As explained in Chapter 3 (see p. 62 and figure 3.8), Deuterostomia, a grouping that includes echinoderms, hemichordates, and chordates, has several important embryological features, as well as shared gene sequences, that clearly separate it from Protostomia and establish its monophyly. Thus, deuterostomes are almost certainly a natural grouping of interrelated animals that have their common origin in ancient Precambrian seas. Somewhat later, at the base of the Cambrian period some 570 million years ago, the first distinctive chordates arose from a lineage related to echinoderms and hemichordates (see figure 15.2; see also figure 14.1).

Most early efforts to determine chordate relationships were based on similarities due to analogy rather than homology. Analogous structures perform similar functions but have altogether different origins (such as the wings of birds and butterflies). Homologous structures, on the other hand, share a common origin but may look quite different (at least superficially) and perform quite different functions. For example, all vertebrate forelimbs are homologous because they are derived from a pentadactyl limb of the same ancestor, even though they may be modified as differently as a human's arm and a bird's wing. Homologous structures share a genetic heritage; analogous structures do not. Obviously, only homologous similarities reveal common ancestry.

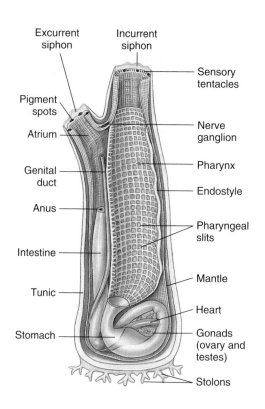

figure 15.4

Structure of a common tunicate, *Ciona* sp.

Subphylum Urochordata (Tunicata)

The urochordates ("tail-chordates"), more commonly called tunicates, include about 1600 species. They live in all seas, from near shoreline to great depths. Most are sessile as adults, although some are free-living. The name "tunicate" describes the usually tough, nonliving **tunic,** or test, that surrounds the animal and contains cellulose (figure 15.4). As adults, tunicates are highly specialized chordates, for in most species only the larval form, which resembles a microscopic tadpole, bears all the chordate hallmarks. During adult metamorphosis, the notochord and the tail disappear, while the dorsal nerve cord is reduced to a single ganglion.

Urochordata is divided into three classes—**Ascidiacea** (Gr. *askiolion,* little bag, + *acea,* suffix), **Appendicularia** (L. *larva,* ghost, + *acea,* suffix), and **Thaliacea** (Gr. *thalia,* luxuriance, + *acea,* suffix). Members of Ascidiacea, commonly called ascidians, or sea squirts, are by far the most common and best known. Ascidians may be solitary, colonial, or compound. All but a few ascidian species are sessile, attached to rocks or other hard substances such as pilings or the bottoms of ships. In some areas, they are among the most abundant of intertidal animals.

Solitary or colonial ascidians are usually spherical or cylindrical forms, each bearing its own tunic. Lining the tunic is an inner membrane, the mantle. On the outside are two projections: an **incurrent siphon** and an **excurrent siphon** (figure 15.4). Water enters the incurrent siphon and passes into the pharynx through the mouth. On the midventral side of the pharynx is a groove, the endostyle, which is ciliated and secretes a sheet of mucus. As the mucous sheet is carried by cilia across the inner surface of the pharynx to the dorsal side, it traps small food particles from water passing through slits in the wall of the pharynx. The mucus with its entrapped food is formed into a rope and passed posteriorly to the esophagus. The water, now largely cleared of food particles, is driven by cilia into the

atrial cavity and finally out the excurrent siphon. Nutrients are absorbed in the midgut, and indigestible wastes are discharged from the anus, located near the excurrent siphon.

The circulatory system consists of a ventral **heart** near the stomach and two large vessels, one on either side of the heart. An odd feature, found in no other chordate, is that the heart drives the blood first in one direction for a few beats, then pauses, reverses, and drives the blood in the opposite direction. The excretory system is a type of nephridium near the intestine. The nervous system is restricted to a **nerve ganglion** and a few nerves that lie on the dorsal side of the pharynx. The animals are hermaphroditic. Germ cells are carried out of the excurrent siphon into the surrounding water, where fertilization occurs.

Of the five chief characteristics of chordates, adult sea squirts have only two: pharyngeal gill slits and an endostyle. However, the larval forms reveal the secret of their true relationship. The tiny tadpole larva (figure 15.5) is an elongate, transparent form with a head and all five chordate characteristics: a notochord, dorsal hollow nerve cord, a propulsive postanal tail, and a large pharynx with an endostyle and gill slits. The larva does not feed but swims for several hours before fastening vertically by adhesive papillae to some solid object. It then metamorphoses to become a sessile adult.

The remaining two classes of Urochordata— **Appendicularia** and **Thaliacea**—are mostly small, transparent animals of the open sea (figure 15.6). Appendicularians, also called larvaceans, are small, tadpolelike forms resembling the larval stage of ascidians. An appendicularian builds and inhabits a hollow, transparent sphere of mucus. Food particles are collected in feeding filters inside the sphere and ingested. Thaliaceans are spindle-shaped or cylindrical forms surrounded by delicate muscle bands. They are mostly carried by ocean

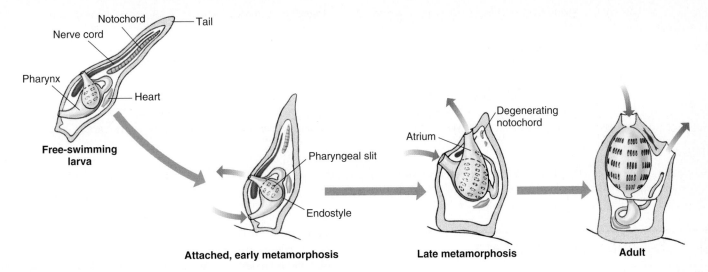

figure 15.5

Metamorphosis of a solitary ascidian from a free-swimming larval stage.

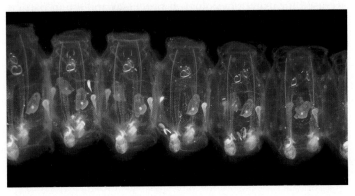

figure 15.6

Salps. The transparent individuals of this delicate, planktonic species are grouped in a chain. Visible within each individual is an opaque gonad, an opaque gut, and a long, serrated gill bar. Class Thaliacea.

currents and, as such, form part of the plankton. Many have luminous organs and emit a beautiful light at night.

■ Subphylum Cephalochordata

Cephalochordates are lancelets: slender, laterally compressed, translucent animals about 3 to 7 cm in length (figure 15.7) that inhabit sandy sediments of coastal waters around the world. Lancelets originally bore the generic name *Amphioxus* (Gr. *amphi*, both ends, + *oxys*, sharp), later surrendered by priority to *Branchiostoma* (Gr. *branchia*, gills, + *stoma*, mouth). The common name amphioxus is still used, however, as a convenient term that encompasses the approximately 29 species in this diminutive subphylum. Five species of amphioxus occur in North American coastal waters.

Amphioxus is especially interesting because it exhibits the five distinctive characteristics of chordates in simple form. Water enters the mouth, driven by cilia in the buccal cavity, and then passes through numerous pharyngeal slits in the pharynx, where food is trapped in mucus, which is then moved by cilia into the intestine. Here, the smallest food particles are separated from the mucus and passed into the **hepatic cecum,** where they are phagocytized and digested intracellularly. As in tunicates, filtered water passes first into an atrium, and then leaves the body by an **atriopore** (equivalent to the excurrent siphon of tunicates).

The closed circulatory system is complex for so simple a chordate. The flow pattern is remarkably similar to that of fishes, although there is no heart. Blood is pumped forward in the ventral aorta by peristaltic-like contractions of the vessel wall, and then passes upward through branchial arteries (aortic arches) in pharyngeal arches to paired dorsal aortas. From there, blood is distributed to the body tissues by capillaries and then collected in veins, which return it to the ventral aorta. Lacking both erythrocytes and hemoglobin, the blood of a lancelet is thought to circulate nutrients but play little role in gas transport. There are no gills specialized for respiration in the pharynx; gas exchange occurs over the surface of the body.

The nervous system is centered around a hollow nerve cord lying above the notochord. Sense organs are simple, including an anterior, unpaired ocellus that functions as a photoreceptor. The anterior end of the nerve cord is not enlarged into the characteristic vertebrate brain.

Sexes are separate. Gametes are released in the atrium, and then pass through the atriopore to the outside, where fertilization occurs. Larvae hatch soon after the eggs are fertilized and gradually assume the shape of adults.

In addition to the five chordate anatomical hallmarks, amphioxus possesses several structural features that resemble the vertebrate plan. Among these are a hepatic cecum, which secretes digestive enzymes, **segmented trunk musculature,** and the basic circulatory pattern of more advanced chordates.

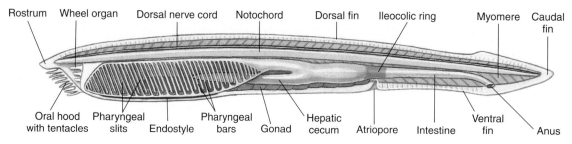

figure 15.7

A lancelet, amphioxus. This filter-feeding cephalochordate possesses the five distinctive chordate characteristics (notochord, dorsal hollow nerve cord, pharyngeal slits, endostyle, and postanal tail).

■ Subphylum Vertebrata

The third subphylum of chordates is the large and diverse Vertebrata, the subject of Chapters 16 through 20. This monophyletic group shares the basic chordate characteristics with the other two subphyla, but in addition it reveals novel homologies that the others do not share. The alternative name of the subphylum, Craniata, more accurately describes the group because all have a cranium (bony or cartilaginous braincase), but some jawless fishes lack vertebrae.

Adaptations That Have Guided Early Vertebrate Evolution

The earliest vertebrates were substantially larger and considerably more active than the protochordates. Modifications of the skeleton and muscles permitted, increased speed and mobility. The higher activity level and size of vertebrates also required structures specialized for locating, capturing, and digesting food as well as adaptations designed to support a high metabolic rate.

Musculoskeletal Modifications

The endoskeleton of vertebrates permits almost unlimited body size, with much greater economy of building materials than the exoskeleton of arthropods. Some vertebrates have become the most massive organisms on earth. The endoskeleton forms an excellent jointed scaffolding for attachment of segmented muscles. The segmented body muscles (myomeres) changed from the V-shaped muscles of cephalochordates to the W-shaped muscles of vertebrates. This more complex folding in the myomeres provides powerful control over a body of extended length.

The endoskeleton was composed initially of cartilage but later of bone. Cartilage, with its fast growth and flexibility, is ideal for constructing the first skeletal framework of all vertebrate embryos. The endoskeleton of living hagfishes, lampreys, sharks, and their kin, and even that of some "bony" fishes, such as sturgeons, is mostly cartilage. Bone may have been adaptive in early vertebrates in several ways. The pres-

ence of bone in the skin of ostracoderms and other ancient fishes certainly provided protection from predators. In addition, bone is structurally stronger than cartilage, making it ideal for muscle attachment in areas of high mechanical stress. One of the most interesting ideas is that bone's original function was mineral storage and regulation. Phosphorus and calcium are used for many physiological processes and are in particularly high demand in organisms with high metabolic rates.

We should note that most vertebrates possess an extensive exoskeleton, although it is highly modified in advanced forms. Some of the most primitive fishes, including the ostracoderms and placoderms, were partly covered by a bony dermal armor. This armor is modified as scales in later fishes. Most vertebrates are further protected with keratinized structures derived from the epidermis, such as reptilian scales, hair, feathers, claws, and horns.

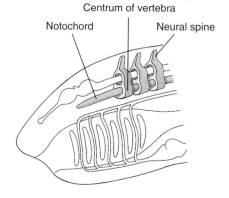

Physiology Upgrade

The vertebrate digestive, respiratory, and circulatory systems are modified to meet an increased metabolic demand. The perforated pharynx evolved as a filter-feeding device in early chordates, using cilia and mucus to move water and to trap small, suspended food particles. In vertebrates, the addition of muscles to the pharynx created a powerful pump for moving water. With the origin of highly vascularized gills, the function of the pharynx shifted primarily to gas exchange. Changes in the gut, including a shift from movement of food by ciliary action to muscular action and the addition of accessory digestive glands, the liver and pancreas, managed the increased amount of food ingested. A ventral, three-chambered heart consisting of a sinus venosus, atrium, and ventricle, as well as the presence of erythrocytes with hemoglobin enhanced transportation of nutrients, gases, and other substances.

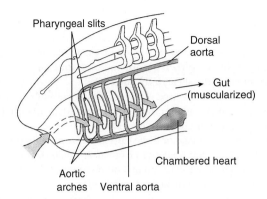

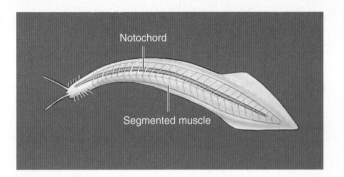

figure 15.8

Pikaia, an early chordate from the Burgess Shale of British Columbia, Canada.

New Head, Brain, and Sensory Systems

When vertebrate ancestors shifted from sessile filter feeding to active predation, new sensory, motor, and integrative controls became essential for locating and capturing larger prey. The anterior end of the nerve cord became enlarged as a **tripartite brain** (forebrain, midbrain, and hindbrain) and protected by a cartilaginous or bony cranium. Paired special sense organs adapted for distance reception evolved. These included eyes with lenses and inverted retinas; pressure receptors, such as paired inner ears designed for equilibrium and sound reception; chemical receptors, including taste and exquisitely sensitive olfactory organs; lateral-line receptors for detecting water vibrations; and electroreceptors for detecting electrical currents that signal prey.

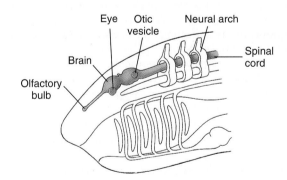

Neural Crest, Ectodermal Placodes, and Hox Genes

Development of the vertebrate head and special sense organs resulted from two embryonic innovations present only in vertebrates: a **neural crest** and **ectodermal placodes.** The neural crest, a population of ectodermal cells lying along the length of the embryonic neural tube, contributes to the formation of many different structures, including most of the cranium, the pharyngeal skeleton, tooth dentine, Schwann cells, and some endocrine glands. Ectodermal placodes (Gr. *placo,* plate) are platelike ectodermal thickenings that appear on either side of the neural tube. These give rise to the olfactory epithelium, the

lens of the eye, inner-ear epithelium, some ganglia and cranial nerves, lateral-line mechanoreceptors, and electroreceptors. Thus, the vertebrate head, with its complex sensory structures located adjacent to the mouth (later equipped with prey-capturing jaws), stemmed from the creation of new cell types.

Recent studies of the distribution of **homeobox** genes that control the body plan of chordate embryos suggest that the *Hox* genes were duplicated at about the time of the origin of vertebrates. Amphioxus and other invertebrates have only one set of *Hox* genes, whereas most living gnathostomes have four sets. Perhaps these additional copies of genes that control body plan provided genetic material free to evolve a more complex kind of animal.

The Search for the Ancestral Vertebrate Stock

Most of the early Paleozoic vertebrate fossils, the jawless ostracoderms (see figure 15.11), share many novel features of organ system development with living vertebrates. These organ systems must have originated in an early vertebrate or invertebrate chordate lineage. Fossil invertebrate chordates are rare and known primarily from two fossil beds—the well-known middle-Cambrian Burgess Shale of Canada (see figure 1.11) and the recently discovered early-Cambrian fossil beds of Chengjiang and Haikou, China. An ascidian tunicate and *Yunnanozoon*, a probable cephalochordate, are known from Chengjiang. Slightly better known is *Pikaia*, a ribbon-shaped, somewhat fishlike creature about 5 cm in length discovered in the Burgess Shale (figure 15.8). The presence of V-shaped myomeres and a notochord clearly identifies *Pikaia* as a chordate. The superficial resemblance of *Pikaia* to living amphioxus suggests that it may be an early cephalochordate. *Haikouella lanceolata*, a small, fishlike creature recently discovered at Haikou, possesses several characters that clearly identify it as a chordate, including notochord, pharynx, and dorsal nerve cord, but it also had characters that are characteristic of vertebrates, including pharyngeal muscles, paired eyes, and an enlarged brain (figure 15.9). However, it is not a

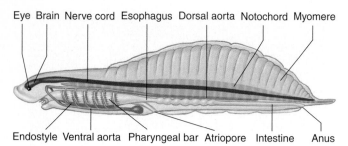

Eye Brain Nerve cord Esophagus Dorsal aorta Notochord Myomere

Endostyle Ventral aorta Pharyngeal bar Atriopore Intestine Anus

figure 15.9

Haikouella, a chordate with several vertebrate features from the early Cambrian shales of Haikou, China. Some zoologists hypothesize that *Haikouella* is the sister group of vertebrates (craniates).

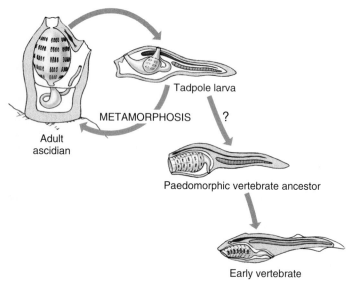

Adult ascidian

METAMORPHOSIS

Tadpole larva

?

Paedomorphic vertebrate ancestor

Early vertebrate

figure 15.10

Garstang's hypothesis of larval evolution. Adult tunicates live on the sea floor but reproduce through a free-swimming tadpole larva. According to this hypothesis, more than 550 million years ago, some larvae became paedomorphic, attaining reproductive maturity in the larval body form. These became cephalized, evolving into the first vertebrates.

vertebrate, because the fossils lack evidence of several diagnostic vertebrate traits, including a cranium and a distinct telencephalon (anterior region of the forebrain). *Haikouella* has been hypothesized to be the sister taxon of vertebrates. Despite recent fossil discoveries of early chordates, many speculations regarding vertebrate ancestry have focused on the living protochordates, in part because they are much better known than the fossil forms.

Garstang's Hypothesis of Chordate Larval Evolution

The chordates have pursued two paths in their early evolution, one path leading to sedentary urochordates and the other to active, mobile cephalochordates and vertebrates. One hypothesis, proposed in 1928 by Walter Garstang of England, suggested

that the chordate ancestral stock was derived by retaining into adulthood the tadpole-like larval form of sessile, tunicate-like animals. At some point, Garstang suggested, the larva failed to metamorphose into an adult tunicate, instead developing gonads and reproducing in the larval stage. With continued evolution, a new group of free-swimming animals appeared, the ancestors of cephalochordates and vertebrates (figure 15.10).

Garstang called this process **paedomorphosis** (Gr. *pais,* child, + *morphē,* form), a term that describes the evolutionary retention of juvenile or larval traits in the adult body. Garstang suggested that evolution may occur in larval stages of animals, in this case leading to the vertebrate lineage. Paedomorphosis is a well-known phenomenon in several different animal groups (paedomorphosis in amphibians is described on p. 349). Although long popular, Garstang's hypothesis is no longer accepted because phylogenies generated from molecular data suggest that sessile ascidians represent a derived body form, and that free-swimming appendicularians are most similar in body form to ancestral chordates.

Paedomorphosis, the displacement of ancestral larval or juvenile features into a descendant adult, can be produced by three different evolutionary-developmental processes: neoteny, progenesis, and postdisplacement. In neoteny, the growth rate of body form is slowed so that the animal does not attain the ancestral adult form when it reaches maturity. Progenesis is precocious maturation of gonads in a larval (or juvenile) body that then stops growing and never attains an adult body form. In postdisplacement, the onset of a developmental process is delayed relative to reproductive maturation, so that an ancestral adult form is not attained by the time of reproductive maturity. Neoteny, progenesis, and postdisplacement thus describe different ways in which paedomorphosis can happen. Biologists use the inclusive term paedomorphosis to describe the results of these evolutionary-developmental processes.

Position of Amphioxus

Zoologists have long considered the cephalochordate amphioxus the closest living relative of vertebrates (see figure 15.2). Amphioxus shares several characters with vertebrates that are absent in urochordates, including segmented myomeres, dorsal and ventral aortas, and branchial arches. However, amphioxus is unlike the most recent common ancestor of vertebrates because it lacks the tripartite brain, chambered heart, special sensory organs, muscular gut and pharynx, and neural crest tissue inferred to have been present in that ancestor. The traditional placement of amphioxus shown in figure 15.2 has become less certain, as some recent phylogenies generated from molecular data suggest that urochordates are the *living* sister group of vertebrates. This hypothesis received further support when neural crest–like cells were discovered in sea squirts, but not in amphioxus. However, the sessile sea squirts clearly are highly derived, and the prevertebrate and ancestral chordate body forms are likely similar to that of modern amphioxus.

The Earliest Vertebrates

The earliest known vertebrate fossils, until recently, were armored jawless fishes called **ostracoderms** (os-trak´o-derm) (Gr. *ostrakon,* shell, + *derma,* skin) from late Cambrian and Ordovician deposits. During the past 10 years, researchers unearthed a number of 530-million-year-old fossils in the amazing Chengjiang deposits belonging to two (possibly the same species) fishlike vertebrates: *Myllokunmingia* and *Haikouichthys*. These fossils push back the origin of vertebrates to at least the early Cambrian period. They show many vertebrate characteristics, including a heart, paired eyes, otic (ear) capsules, and what have been interpreted as rudimentary vertebrae.

The earliest ostracoderms were armored with bone in their dermis and usually lacked the paired fins so important to later fishes for stability (figure 15.11). The swimming movements of one of the early groups, the **heterostracans** (Gr. *heteros,* different, + *ostrakon,* shell), must have been

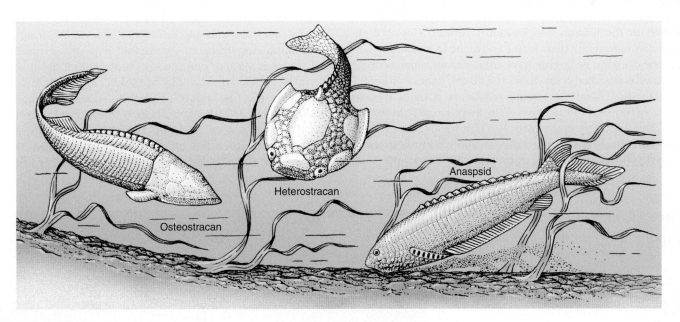

Osteostracan

Heterostracan

Anaspsid

figure 15.11

Three ostracoderms, jawless fishes of Silurian and Devonian times. They are shown as they might have appeared while searching for food on the floor of a Devonian sea. They employed a strong pharyngeal pump to circulate water rather than relying on the much more limiting mode of ciliary action used by their protochordate ancestors (presumably resembling amphioxus in this way).

imprecise, although sufficient to propel them along the ocean floor. With fixed, circular or slitlike mouth openings, they may have filtered small food particles from the water or ocean bottom. However, unlike the ciliary filter-feeding protochordates, ostracoderms sucked water into the pharynx by muscular pumping, an important innovation that suggests to some authorities that ostracoderms may have been active predators that fed on soft-bodied animals.

The term "ostracoderm" does not denote a natural evolutionary assemblage, but instead describes several groups of heavily armored, extinct jawless fishes.

During the Devonian period, the heterostracans underwent a major radiation, producing numerous peculiar-looking forms. Without ever evolving paired fins or jaws, these earliest vertebrates flourished for 150 million years until becoming extinct near the end of the Devonian period.

Coexisting with heterostracans throughout much of the Devonian period were **osteostracans** (Gr. *osteon,* bone, + *ostrakon,* shell). Osteostracans had paired pectoral fins, an innovation that improved swimming efficiency by controlling yaw, pitch, and roll. A typical osteostracan (figure 15.11), was a small animal, seldom exceeding 30 cm in length. It was covered with a heavy, dermal armor of bone, including a single-piece head shield. Examination of internal features of the braincase reveal a sophisticated nervous system and sense organs, similar to those of modern lampreys.

Another group of ostracoderms, the **anaspids** (figure 15.11), were more streamlined than other ostracoderms. These and other ostracoderms enjoyed an impressive diversification in the Silurian and Devonian periods. However, all ostracoderms became extinct by the end of the Devonian period.

For decades, geologists have used strange, microscopic, toothlike fossils called **conodonts** (Gr. *kōnos,* cone, + *odontos,* tooth) to date Paleozoic marine sediments without having any idea what kind of creature originally possessed these elements. The discovery in the early 1980s of fossils of complete conodont animals has changed this situation. With their phosphatized toothlike elements, myomeres, and paired eye and otic capsules, conodonts clearly belong to the vertebrate clade (figure 15.12). Although their exact position in this clade is unclear, they are important in understanding the evolution of early vertebrates.

Early Jawed Vertebrates

All jawed vertebrates, whether extinct or living, are collectively called **gnathostomes** ("jaw mouth") in contrast to jawless vertebrates, which are called **agnathans** ("without jaw"). Gnathostomes are a monophyletic group because the presence of jaws is a derived character state shared by all jawed fishes and tetrapods. Agnathans, however, are defined principally by the absence of jaws, a character that is not unique to jawless fishes because jaws are lacking in vertebrate ancestors. Thus, Agnatha is paraphyletic.

The origin of jaws was one of the most important events in vertebrate evolution. The utility of jaws is obvious: they allow predation on large and active forms of food not available to jawless vertebrates. Ample evidence suggests that jaws arose through modifications of the first or second of the serially repeated cartilaginous gill arches. How did the function of this mandibular arch change from gill support and ventilation to feeding as jaws? Expansion of this arch and evolution of new, associated muscles may have first assisted gill ventilation, perhaps to meet the increasing metabolic demands of early vertebrates. Once enlarged and equipped with extra muscles, the first pharyngeal arch could have easily been modified to serve as jaws in the manner described in figure 15.13.

An additional feature characteristic of all gnathostomes is the presence of paired pectoral and pelvic appendages in the form of fins or limbs. These likely originated as stabilizers to check the yaw, pitch, and roll generated during active swimming. According to the fin-fold hypothesis, paired fins arose from paired continuous, ventrolateral folds or finforming zones. The addition of skeletal supports in the fins enhanced the fins' ability to provide stability during swimming. Evidence for this hypothesis is found in the paired flaps of *Myllokunmingia, Haikouichthys,* and anaspids, and in the multiple paired fins of acanthodians. In one fish lineage, the muscle and skeletal supports in the paired fins became

figure 15.12

Restoration of a conodont. Conodonts superficially resembled amphioxus, but they possessed a much greater degree of encephalization (paired eyes and otic [ear] capsules) and bonelike mineralized elements—all indicating that conodonts were chordates and probably vertebrates. Conodont elements are thought to be part of a food-handling apparatus.

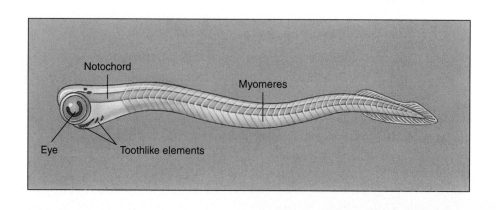

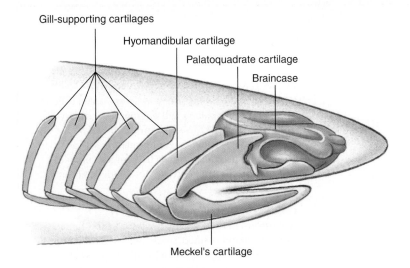

Gill-supporting cartilages
Hyomandibular cartilage
Palatoquadrate cartilage
Braincase
Meckel's cartilage

figure 15.13

How vertebrates got their jaws. Resemblance between the jaws and gill supports of early fishes, such as this Carboniferous shark, suggests that the upper jaw (palatoquadrate) and lower jaw (Meckel's cartilage) evolved from structures that originally functioned as gill supports. The gill supports immediately behind the jaws are hinged like jaws and served to link the jaws to the braincase. Relics of this transformation are seen during the development of modern sharks.

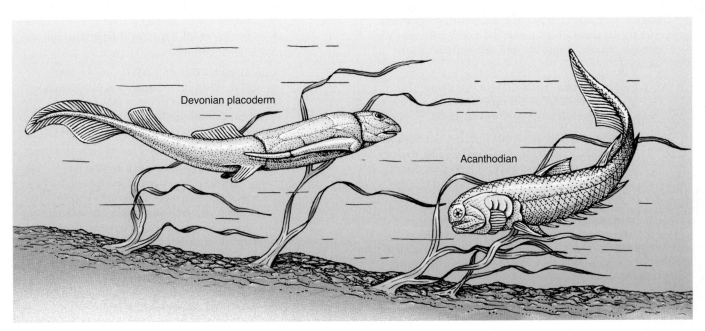

Devonian placoderm

Acanthodian

figure 15.14

Early jawed fishes of the Devonian period, 400 million years ago. Jaws and gill supports from which the jaws evolved develop from neural crest cells, a diagnostic character of vertebrates. Most placoderms were bottom-dwellers that fed on benthic animals, although some were active predators. Acanthodians carried less armor than placoderms and had large, anteriorly placed eyes and prominent spines on paired fins. Most were marine but several species lived in freshwater.

strengthened, adapting them for locomotion on land as limbs. The origin of jaws and paired appendages may be linked to a second *Hox* duplication, near the origin of the gnathostomes. Both jaws and paired fins were major innovations in vertebrate evolution, among the most important reasons for the subsequent major radiations of vertebrates that produced the modern fishes and all tetrapods, including you, the reader of this book.

Among the first jawed vertebrates were the heavily armored **placoderms** (Gr. *plax,* plate, + *derma,* skin). They first appear in the fossil record in the Silurian period (figure 15.14). Placoderms evolved a great variety of forms, some very large (one was 10 m in length!) and grotesque in appearance. They were armored fish covered with diamond-shaped scales or large plates of bone. All became extinct by the end of the Devonian period and appear to have left no descendants. However, **acanthodians** (figure 15.14), a group of early jawed fishes characterized by large, anteriorly-set eyes and fins with large spines, are included in a clade that underwent a great evolutionary diversification into the bony fishes that dominate the waters of the world today.

Classification of Phylum Chordata

Phylum Chordata

Subphylum Urochordata (yur′ō-kor-dä′tə) (Gr. *oura*, tail, + L. *chorda*, cord, + *ata,* characterized by) **(Tunicata): tunicates.** Notochord and nerve cord in free-swimming larva only; ascidian adults sessile, encased in tunic. About 1600 species.

Subphylum Cephalochordata (sef′ə-lō-kor-dä′tə) (Gr. *kephalē*, head, + L. *chorda*, cord): **lancelets (amphioxus).** Notochord and nerve cord found along entire length of body and persist throughout life; fishlike in form. 29 species.

Subphylum Vertebrata (ver′te-brä′tə) (L. *vertebratus*, backboned). **(Craniata): vertebrates.** Bony or cartilaginous cranium surrounding tripartite brain; well-developed head with paired sense organs, usually with vertebrae; heart with multiple chambers; muscularized digestive tract; paired kidneys.

Superclass Agnatha (ag′na-thə) (Gr. *a*, without, + *gnathos*, jaw): **hagfishes, lampreys.** Without true jaws or paired appendages. A paraphyletic group.

Class Myxini (mik-sē′nē) (Gr. *myxa*, slime): **hagfishes.** Four pairs of tentacles around mouth; buccal funnel absent; 1 to 16 pairs of gill openings; slime glands present; vertebrae absent. About 70 species.

Class Petromyzontida (pet′trō-mī-zon′ti′də) (Gr. *petros*, stone, + *myzon*, sucking): **lampreys.** Buccal funnel with keratinized teeth, nasal sac not connected to pharynx; vertebrae present only as neural arches. 38 species.

Superclass Gnathostomata (na′thō-stō′mä-tə) (Gr. *gnathos*, jaw, + *stoma*, mouth): **jawed fishes, tetrapods.** With jaws and (usually) paired appendages.

Class Chondrichthyes (kon-drik′thē-ēz) (Gr. *chondros*, cartilage, + *ichthys*, a fish): **sharks, skates, rays, chimaeras.** Cartilaginous skeleton, intestine with spiral valve; claspers present in males; no swim bladder. About 970 species.

Class Actinopterygii (ak′ti-nop′te-rij′ē-ī) (Gr. *aktis*, ray, + *pteryx*, fin, wing): **ray-finned fishes.** Skeleton ossified; single gill opening covered by operculum; paired fins supported primarily by dermal rays; appendage musculature within body; swim bladder mainly a hydrostatic organ, if present; atrium and ventricle not divided. About 27,000 species.

Class Sarcopterygii (sär-cop-te-rij′ē-ī) (Gr. *sarkos,* flesh, + *pteryx*, fin, wing): **lobe-finned fishes.** Skeleton ossified; single gill opening covered by operculum; paired fins with sturdy internal skeleton and musculature within appendage; diphycercal tail; intestine with spiral valve; usually with lunglike swim bladder; atrium and ventricle at least partly divided. 8 species. Paraphyletic unless tetrapods are included.

Class Amphibia (am-fib′ē-ə) (Gr. *amphi*, both or double, + *bios,* life): **amphibians.** Ectothermic tetrapods; respiration by lungs, gills, or skin; development through larval stage; skin moist, containing mucous glands and lacking scales. About 6000 species.

Class Reptilia (rep-til′ē-ə) (L. *repere*, to creep): **reptiles.** Ectothermic tetrapods possessing lungs; embryo develops within shelled egg; no larval stage; skin dry, lacking mucous glands, and covered by epidermal scales. A paraphyletic group unless birds are included. About 8100 species.

Class Aves (ā′vēz) (L. pl. of *avis*, bird): **birds.** Endothermic vertebrates with front limbs modified for flight; body covered with feathers; scales on feet. About 9700 species.

Class Mammalia (ma-mā′lē-ə) (L. *mamma*, breast): **mammals.** Endothermic vertebrates possessing mammary glands; body more or less covered with hair; brain large, with neocortex; three middle ear bones. About 4800 species.

■ Summary

Phylum Chordata is named for the rodlike notochord that forms a stiffening body axis at some stage in the life cycle of every chordate. All chordates share five distinctive hallmarks that set them apart from all other phyla: notochord, dorsal hollow nerve cord, pharyngeal pouches or slits, endostyle, and postanal tail. Two of the three chordate subphyla are invertebrates and lack a well-developed head. These are Urochordata (tunicates), most of which are sessile as adults, but all of which have a free-swimming larval stage, and Cephalochordata (lancelets), fishlike forms that include the famous amphioxus.

Chordates have evolutionary affinities with echinoderms and hemichordates, although their precise origins have been controversial. Most zoologists now consider the chordate ancestor to have been a small, free-swimming, filter-feeding creature.

Subphylum Vertebrata includes the backboned members of the animal kingdom (hagfishes actually lack vertebrae but are included with the Vertebrata by tradition because they share numerous homologies with vertebrates). As a group, vertebrates are characterized by a well-developed head and comparatively large size, high degree of motility, and distinctive body plan that permitted their exceptional adaptive diversification. Their most important distinguishing features are a living endoskeleton that allows continuous growth and provides a sturdy framework for efficient muscle attachment and action, a muscular pharynx with slits and gills (lost or greatly modified in higher vertebrates) with vastly increased respiratory efficiency, a muscularized gut and chambered heart for meeting higher metabolic demands, and an advanced nervous system with a distinct brain and paired sense organs. Evolution of jaws and paired appendages likely contributed to the incredible success of one group of vertebrates, the gnathostomes.

■ Review Questions

1. What characteristics are shared by the three deuterostome phyla that indicate a monophyletic group of interrelated animals?
2. Explain how use of a cladistic classification for vertebrates changes the major important regroupings of traditional vertebrate taxa (refer to figure 15.2). Why are Agnatha and Reptilia, as traditionally recognized, inconsistent with cladistic principles?
3. Name five hallmarks shared by all chordates, and explain the function of each.
4. In debating the question of chordate origins, zoologists eventually agreed that chordates must have evolved within the deuterostome assemblage rather than from a protostome group as earlier argued. What embryological evidence supports this view?
5. Offer a description of an adult tunicate that would identify it as a chordate, yet distinguish it from any other chordate group.
6. Amphioxus has long been of interest to zoologists searching for a vertebrate ancestor. Explain why amphioxus captured such interest and why it no longer is considered to resemble closely the most recent common ancestor of all vertebrates.
7. Both sea squirts (urochordates) and lancelets (cephalochordates) are filter-feeding organisms. Describe the filter-feeding apparatus of a sea squirt, and explain in what ways its mode of feeding is similar to, and different from, that of amphioxus.
8. Explain why it is necessary to know the life history of a tunicate in order to understand why tunicates are chordates.
9. List three groups of adaptations that guided vertebrate evolution, and explain how each has contributed to the success of vertebrates.
10. In 1928, Walter Garstang hypothesized that tunicates resemble the ancestral stock of the vertebrates. Explain this hypothesis.
11. What is the phylogenetic placement of *Haikouella,* and what evidence supports its placement there?
12. Distinguish between ostracoderms and placoderms. What important evolutionary adaptations first appeared in each group? What are conodonts?
13. Explain how zoologists think the vertebrate jaw evolved.

■ Selected References

See also general references on page 423.

Ahlberg, P. E. 2001. Major events in early vertebrate evolution. London, Taylor & Francis. *Evolution of vertebrates up to the split of major jawed fish groups, incorporating molecular, fossil, and embryological data. This book makes many important contributions, but some of its conclusions are controversial.*

Alldredge, A. 1976. Appendicularians. Sci. Am. **235**:94–102 (July). *Describes the biology of larvaceans, which build delicate houses for trapping food.*

Carroll, R. L. 1997. Patterns and processes of vertebrate evolution. New York, Cambridge University Press. *A comprehensive analysis of the evolutionary processes that have influenced large-scale changes in vertebrate evolution.*

Donoghue, P. C. J., P. L. Forey, and R. J. Aldridge. 2000. Conodont affinity and chordate phylogeny. Biol. Rev. **75**:191–251. *In this summary of early chordate evolution, the authors provide evidence that conodonts are vertebrates and that lampreys and hagfishes do not form a monophyletic group.*

Gee, H. 1996. Before the backbone: views on the origin of the vertebrates. New York, Chapman & Hall. *Outstanding review of the many vertebrate origin hypotheses. Gee links genetic, developmental, and molecular evidence.*

Gould, S. J. 1989. Wonderful life: the Burgess Shale and the nature of history. New York, W. W. Norton & Company. *In this book describing the marvelous Cambrian fossils of the Burgess Shale, Gould "saves the best for last" by inserting an epilogue on Pikaia, the first known chordate.*

Jeffery, W. R., A. G. Strickler, and Y. Yamamoto. 2004. Migratory neural crest-like cells form body pigmentation in a urochordate embryo. Nature **431**:696–699. *Neural-crest-like cells are in sea squirts, supporting a sister-group relationship with vertebrates.*

Long, J. A. 1995. The rise of fishes: 500 million years of evolution. Baltimore, The Johns Hopkins University Press. *An authoritative, liberally illustrated evolutionary history of fishes.*

Maisey, J. G. 1996. Discovering fossil fishes. New York, Henry Holt & Company. *Handsomely illustrated chronology of fish evolution with cladistic analysis of evolutionary relationships.*

Mallatt, J., and J.-Y. Chen. 2003. Fossil sister group of craniates: predicted and found. J. Morph. **258**:1–31. *Reevaluation of Haikaouella lanceolata fossils reveals several features that suggest this is the sister group to craniates.*

Shimeld, S. M., and P. W. H. Holland. 2000. Vertebrate innovations. Proc. Natl. Acad. Sci. **97**:4449–4452. *Focuses on developmental characters, including neural crest, neural placodes, and Hox genes.*

Stokes, M. D., and N. D. Holland. 1998. The lancelet. Am. Sci. **86**(6):552–560. *Describes the historical role of amphioxus in early hypotheses of vertebrate ancestry and summarizes molecular data that rekindled interest in amphioxus.*

■ Custom Website

The *Animal Diversity* Online Learning Center is a great place to check your understanding of chapter material. Visit www.mhhe.com/hickmanad5e for access to key terms, quizzes, and more! Further enhance your knowledge with Web links to chapter-related material.

Explore live links for these topics:

Classification and Phylogeny of Animals
General Chordate References
Subphylum Urochordata
Subphylum Cephalochordata
Subphylum Vertebrata

Systematics and Characteristics of the Craniates
Early Vertebrates

Fishes

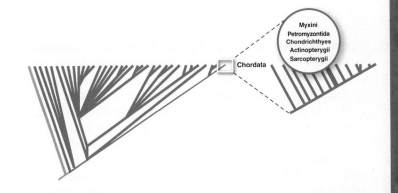

Chordata

Myxini
Petromyzontida
Chondrichthyes
Actinopterygii
Sarcopterygii

What Is a Fish?

In common (and especially older) usage, the term "fish" denotes a mixed assortment of water-dwelling animals. We speak of jellyfish, cuttlefish, starfish, crayfish, and shellfish, knowing full well that when we use the word "fish" in such combinations, we are not referring to a true fish. In earlier times, even biologists did not make such a distinction. Sixteenth-century natural historians classified seals, whales, amphibians, crocodiles, and even hippopotamuses, as well as a host of aquatic invertebrates, as fish. Later biologists were more discriminating, eliminating first the invertebrates and then the amphibians, reptiles, and mammals from the narrowing concept of a fish. Today we recognize a fish as an aquatic vertebrate with gills, appendages, if present, in the form of fins, and usually a skin with scales of dermal origin. Even this modern concept of the term "fish" is used for convenience, not as a taxonomic unit. Fishes do not form a monophyletic group, because the ancestor of land vertebrates (tetrapods) is found within one group of fishes (the sarcopterygians). Thus, fishes can be defined in an evolutionary sense as all vertebrates that are not tetrapods. Because fishes live in a habitat that is basically alien to humans, people have rarely appreciated the remarkable diversity of these vertebrates. Nevertheless, whether appreciated by humans or not, the world's fishes have enjoyed effusive proliferation that has produced an estimated 28,000 living species—more than all other species of vertebrates combined—with adaptations that have fitted them to almost every conceivable aquatic environment. No other animal group threatens their domination of the world's seas, lakes, and streams.

Grey snappers (*Lutjanus griseus*) in the Florida Keys.

The life of a fish is bound to its body form, which is streamlined for movement through water. Suspended in a medium that is 800 times more dense than air, a trout or pike can remain motionless, varying its neutral buoyancy by adding or removing air from its swim bladder. It may dart forward or at angles, using its fins as brakes and tilting rudders. With excellent organs for salt and water exchange, bony fishes can steady and finely tune their body fluid composition in their freshwater or seawater environment. Their gills are the most effective respiratory devices in the animal kingdom for extracting oxygen from a medium that contains less than 1/20 as much oxygen as air. Fishes have excellent olfactory and visual senses and a unique lateral-line system, which has an exquisite sensitivity to water currents and vibrations. Thus, in mastering the physical problems of their element, early fishes evolved a basic body plan and a set of physiological strategies that both shaped and constrained the evolution of their descendants.

The use of *fishes* as the plural form of *fish* may sound odd to most people accustomed to using *fish* in both the singular and the plural. *Fish* refers to one or more individuals of the same species; *fishes* refers to more than one species.

Ancestry and Relationships of Major Groups of Fishes

Fishes are of ancient ancestry, having descended from an unknown free-swimming protochordate ancestor (hypotheses concerning chordate and vertebrate origins are discussed in Chapter 15). The earliest fishlike vertebrates were a paraphyletic assemblage of jawless **agnathan** fishes, the ostracoderms (see figure 15.11). One group of ostracoderms gave rise to the jawed **gnathostomes** (see figure 15.14).

Along with the extinct ostracoderms, the jawless agnathans include the living **hagfishes** and **lampreys,** fishes adapted as scavengers or parasites. Although hagfishes have no vertebrae and lampreys have only rudimentary vertebrae, they nevertheless are included within the subphylum Vertebrata because they have a cranium and many other vertebrate homologies. The ancestry of hagfishes and lampreys is uncertain; they bear little resemblance to the extinct ostracoderms. Although hagfishes and lampreys superficially look much alike, they are in fact so different from each other that zoologists have assigned them to separate taxonomic classes.

All remaining fishes have paired appendages and jaws and are included, along with tetrapods (land vertebrates), in the monophyletic group of gnathostomes. They appear in the fossil record in the late Silurian period with fully formed jaws, and no forms intermediate between agnathans and gnathostomes are known. By the Devonian period, the "age of fishes," several distinct groups of jawed fishes were well represented. One of these, the placoderms (see figure 15.14), became extinct in the subsequent Carboniferous period, leaving no descendants.

A second group, **cartilaginous fishes** of class Chondrichthyes (sharks, rays, and chimaeras), lost the heavy dermal armor of the early jawed fishes and adopted cartilage for the endoskeleton. Most are active predators with sharklike or raylike body forms that changed only slightly over the ages.

Of all the gnathostomes, **bony fishes** (Osteichthyes) radiated most extensively and are the dominant fishes today (figure 16.1). We can recognize two distinct lineages of bony fishes. By far the most diverse are the **ray-finned fishes** (class Actinopterygii), which radiated to form most modern bony fishes. The other group, **lobe-finned fishes** (class Sarcopterygii), contains few living species but includes the sister group of the tetrapods. The lobe-finned fishes are represented today by **lungfishes** and **coelacanths**—meager remnants of important lineages that flourished in the Devonian period (figure 16.1). A classification of major fish taxa is on p. 338.

Living Jawless Fishes

Living jawless fishes include approximately 108 species divided between two classes: Myxini (hagfishes) and Petromyzontida (lampreys). Members of each group lack jaws, internal ossification, scales, and paired fins, and both groups share porelike gill openings and an eel-like body form. In other respects, however, the two groups are morphologically very different. Lampreys have many characters, including vertebrae, extrinsic eye muscles, at least two semicircular canals, and a cerebellum, that they uniquely share with gnathostomes. Thus we take the view that hagfishes form the sister group of a clade that includes lampreys and gnathostomes (figure 16.2).

Hagfishes: Class Myxini

Hagfishes are an entirely marine group that feeds on annelids, molluscs, crustaceans, and dead or dying fishes. They are not parasitic like lampreys, but are scavengers and predators. There are 70 described species of hagfishes, of which the best known in North America are the Atlantic hagfish, *Myxine glutinosa* (Gr. *myxa,* slime) (figure 16.3), and the Pacific hagfish, *Eptatretus stouti* (N.L., *ept,* Gr. *hepta,* seven, + *tretos,* perforated). Although almost completely blind, a hagfish is quickly attracted to food, especially dead or dying fish, by its keenly developed senses of smell and touch. Using two toothed, keratinized plates on its tongue that fold together in a pincerlike action, the hagfish rasps bits of flesh from its prey. For extra leverage, the hagfish often ties a knot in its tail, and then passes the knot forward along its body until it is pressed securely against the side of its prey (figure 16.3D).

Unlike any other vertebrate, the body fluids of hagfishes are in osmotic equilibrium with seawater, as are those of most marine invertebrates. Hagfishes have several other anatomical and physiological peculiarities, including a low-pressure circulatory system served by three accessory hearts in addition to the main heart positioned behind the gills. Hagfishes also are renowned for their ability to generate enormous quantities of slime.

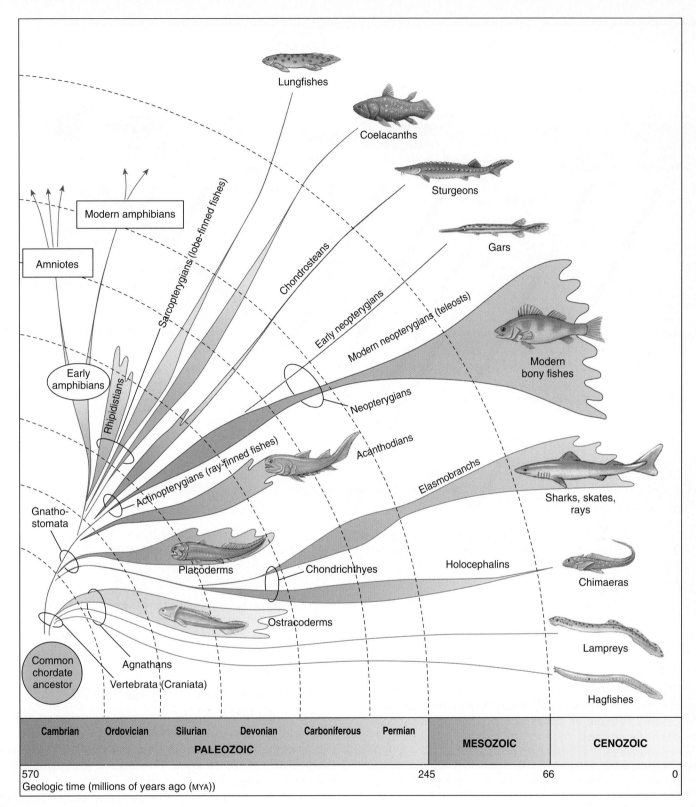

figure 16.1

Graphic representation of the family tree of fishes, showing the evolution of major groups through geological time. Numerous lineages of extinct fishes are not shown. Widened areas in the lines of descent indicate periods of adaptive diversification and the relative number of species in each group. The lobe-finned fishes (sarcopterygians), for example, flourished in the Devonian period, but declined and are today represented by only four surviving genera (lungfishes and coelacanths). Homologies shared by sarcopterygians and tetrapods suggest that they form a clade. Sharks and rays diversified during the Carboniferous period, declined in the Permian, and then diversified again in the Mesozoic era. Johnny-come-latelies in fish evolution are the spectacularly diverse modern fishes, or teleosts, which include most living fishes.

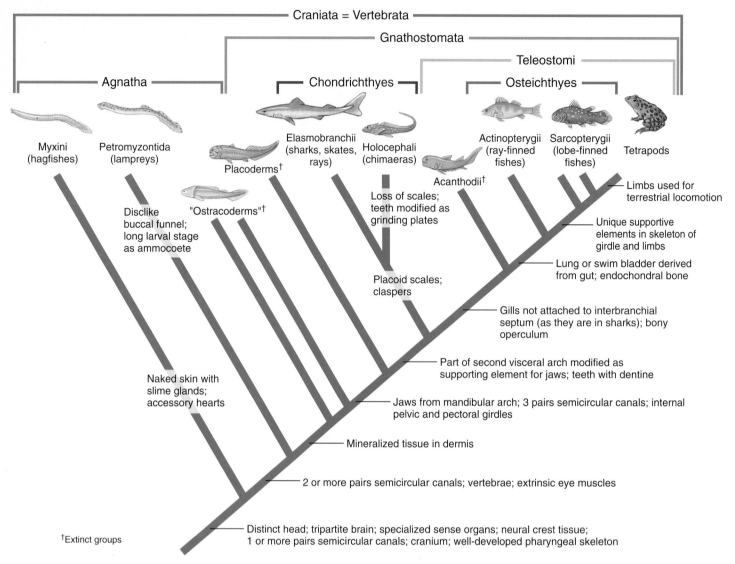

figure 16.2

Cladogram of the fishes, showing the probable relationships of major monophyletic fish taxa. Several alternative relationships have been proposed. Extinct groups are designated by a dagger (†). Some shared derived characters are shown to the right of the branch points. The groups Agnatha and Osteichthyes, although paraphyletic structural grades considered undesirable in cladistic classification, are conveniently recognized in systematics because they share broad structural and functional patterns of organization.

The reproductive biology of hagfishes remains largely a mystery. Females produce small numbers of surprisingly large, yolky eggs 2 to 7 cm in diameter, depending on the species. There is no larval stage.

While the strange features of hagfishes fascinate many people, hagfishes have not endeared themselves to commercial fishermen. In earlier days, when commercial fishing was done mainly by gill nets and set lines, hagfish often bit into the bodies of captured fishes and devoured the contents, leaving behind a useless sack of skin and bones. But as large and efficient trawls came into use, hagfishes ceased to be important pests. Recently, the commercial fishing industry "turned the tables" and began targeting hagfishes as a source of leather for golf bags and boots. Fishing pressure has been so intense that some species have greatly declined.

Lampreys: Class Petromyzontida

Of the 38 described species of lampreys distributed around the world, the best known to North Americans is the destructive marine lamprey, *Petromyzon marinus*, of the Great Lakes (figure 16.4). The name *Petromyzon* (Gr. *petros*, stone, + *myzon*, sucking) refers to the lamprey's habit of grasping a stone with its mouth to hold its position in a current. There are 20 species of lampreys in North America, of which about half are parasitic; the rest are species that never feed after metamorphosis and die soon after spawning.

In North America, all lampreys, marine as well as freshwater forms, spawn in the winter or spring in the shallow gravel of freshwater streams. Males begin building nests and are joined later by females. Using their oral discs to lift stones and pebbles and using vigorous body vibrations to sweep away

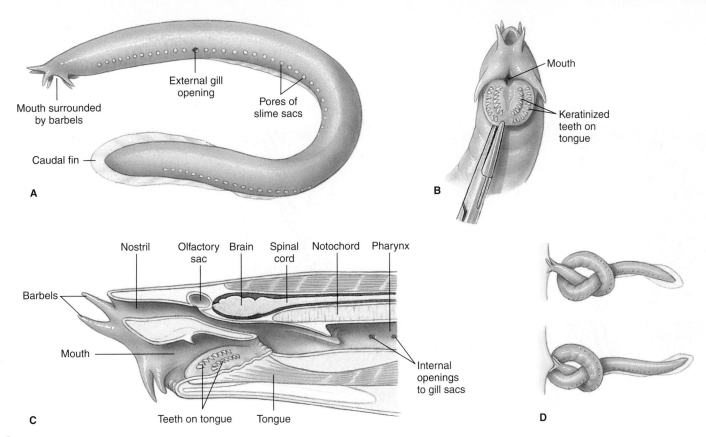

figure 16.3

Atlantic hagfish, *Myxine glutinosa* (class Myxini). **A,** External anatomy. **B,** Ventral view of head, showing keratinized teeth used to grasp food during feeding. **C,** Sagittal section of head region. (Note retracted position of rasping tongue and internal openings into a row of gill sacs.) **D,** Hagfish knotting, showing how it obtains leverage to tear flesh from prey.

Characteristics
of Hagfishes (Myxini)
and Lampreys (Petromyzontida)

1. Slender, eel-like body with **naked skin**
2. Median fins present, but **no paired appendages**
3. **Fibrous** and **cartilaginous skeleton;** notochord persistent; vertebrae absent or reduced
4. **Jaws absent;** biting mouth with keratinized plates in hagfishes; suckerlike oral disc with keratinized teeth in lampreys
5. Heart with sinus venosus, atrium and ventricle; **single circulation;** hagfishes have accessory hearts
6. Five to 16 pairs of gills in hagfishes; 7 pairs of gills in lampreys
7. **Pronephric** and **mesonephric kidneys** in hagfishes; **opisthonephric kidney** in lampreys
8. Dorsal hollow nerve cord with **distinct brain;** 10 pairs of cranial nerves
9. Digestive system with **no distinct stomach**
10. Sense organs of taste, smell, hearing; eyes poorly developed in hagfishes, but moderately developed in adult lampreys; one pair (hagfishes) or two pairs (lampreys) of **semicircular canals**

figure 16.4

Sea lamprey, *Petromyzon marinus*, feeding on body fluids of a dying fish.

light debris, they form an oval depression. As the female sheds eggs into the nest, the male fertilizes them. The sticky eggs adhere to pebbles in the nest and soon become covered with sand. Adults die soon after spawning.

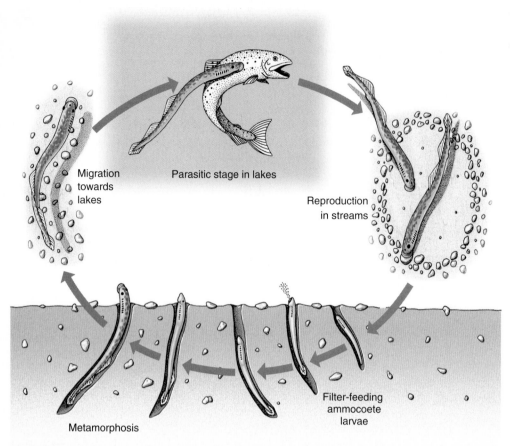

figure 16.5

Life cycle of the "landlocked" form of the sea lamprey *Petromyzon marinus*.

Migration towards lakes

Parasitic stage in lakes

Reproduction in streams

Filter-feeding ammocoete larvae

Metamorphosis

Eggs hatch in about 2 weeks, releasing small larvae called **ammocoetes** (figure 16.5), which stay in the nest until they are approximately 1 cm long; they then burrow into mud or sand and filter-feed on small organisms and fine organic matter. The larvae live from 3 to 7 or more years, and then rapidly metamorphose into adults.

Parasitic lampreys either migrate to the sea, if marine, or remain in fresh water, where they attach themselves by their suckerlike mouth to fish and use their sharp, keratinized teeth to rasp through flesh and suck body fluids. To promote the flow of blood, a lamprey injects an anticoagulant into the wound. When gorged, the lamprey releases its hold but leaves the fish with a large wound that can be fatal. Parasitic freshwater adults live 1 to 2 years before spawning and then die; marine forms live 2 to 3 years.

Nonparasitic lampreys do not feed after emerging as adults, and their digestive tract degenerates to a nonfunctional strand of tissue. Within a few months, they spawn and die.

The landlocked sea lamprey, *Petromyzon marinus*, first entered the Great Lakes after the Welland Canal around Niagara Falls, a barrier to further western migration, was deepened between 1913 and 1918. Moving first through Lake Erie and then to Lakes Huron, Michigan, and Superior, sea lampreys, combined with the effects of overfishing, caused the total collapse of a multimillion-dollar lake trout fishery in the early 1950s. Other less valuable fish species were attacked and destroyed in turn. After reaching peak abundance in 1951 in Lakes Huron and Michigan and in 1961 in Lake Superior, sea lampreys began to decline, due to depletion of their food supply and effective control measures (mainly chemical larvicides placed in selected spawning streams). Lake trout, aided by a restocking program, are now recovering, but wounding rates are still high in some lakes.

Cartilaginous Fishes: Class Chondrichthyes

There are about 970 living species in the class Chondrichthyes, an ancient group that appeared in the Devonian period. Although the chondrichthyans are a much smaller and less diverse assemblage than the bony fishes, their impressive combination of well-developed sense organs, powerful jaws and swimming musculature, and predaceous habits ensures them a secure and lasting niche in the aquatic community. One of their distinctive features is their cartilaginous skeleton. Although their skeletons are extensively calcified, bone is entirely absent throughout the class—a derived feature, since members of Chondrichthyes descended from ancestors having well-developed bone.

Sharks and Rays: Subclass Elasmobranchii

Sharks, which include about 45% of the approximately 937 species in subclass Elasmobranchii, are typically predaceous fishes with five to seven pairs of gill slits and gills and (usually) a spiracle behind each eye. Larger sharks, such as the massive (but harmless) plankton-feeding whale shark, may reach 15 m in length, the largest of all fishes. Dogfish sharks, widely used in zoological laboratories, rarely exceed 1 m.

Although sharks have a sinister appearance and a fearsome reputation, they are at the same time among the most gracefully streamlined of all fishes (figure 16.6). Sharks are heavier than water and will sink if not swimming forward. The asymmetrical **heterocercal tail,** in which the vertebral column turns upward and extends into the dorsal lobe of the tail (see figure 16.14), provides thrust and some lift as it sweeps back and forth in the water, and the broad head and flat pectoral fins act as planes to provide additional lift.

Sharks are well equipped for their predatory life. Their tough, leathery skin is covered with numerous dermal **placoid scales** (see figure 16.13) that are modified anteriorly to form replaceable rows of teeth in both jaws (figure 16.8). Placoid scales in fact consist of dentine enclosed by an enamel-like substance, like teeth of other vertebrates. Sharks use their keen sense of smell to guide them to food. They also may locate prey from long distances by sensing low-frequency vibrations with mechanoreceptors in the **lateral-line system.** This system is composed of special receptor organs (**neuromasts**) in interconnected tubes and pores extending along the sides of the body and over the head (figure 16.9). At close range, a shark switches to vision as its primary method of tracking prey. During the final stage of the attack, sharks are guided to their prey by the bioelectric fields that surround all animals. Electroreceptors, the **ampullae of Lorenzini,** are located on the shark's head.

All chondrichthyans have internal fertilization; sperm is introduced into the female reproductive tract by a modified portion of the male's pelvic fin called a **clasper** (see figure 16.6). Some sharks and all skates, are **oviparous,** laying eggs soon after fertilization. Embryos are nourished from the egg yolk for a long period—up to 2 years in one species—before hatching. Many sharks are **ovoviviparous,** retaining developing young in the uterus, where they are nourished by the contents of their

yolk sac until birth. Others are **viviparous,** meaning that the embryos receive nourishment from the mother via a placenta or secretions from the uterus. Regardless of the initial amount of maternal support, all parental care ends once eggs are laid or young are born.

Characteristics
of Sharks and Rays
(Elasmobranchii)

1. **Body fusiform** (except rays) with a **heterocercal** caudal fin (see figure 16.14)
2. **Mouth ventral** (see figure 16.6); two olfactory sacs that do not connect to the mouth cavity; jaws present
3. Skin with **placoid scales** (see figure 16.13) or naked; teeth **polyphyodont,** of modified placoid scales
4. **Endoskeleton entirely cartilaginous**
5. Digestive system with a J-shaped stomach and **intestine with spiral valve** (figure 16.7)
6. Circulatory system of several pairs of aortic arches; single circulation; heart with sinus venosus, atrium, ventricle, and conus arteriosus
7. Respiration by means of 5 to 7 pairs of gills leading to **exposed gill slits;** no operculum
8. No swim bladder or lung
9. Opisthonephric kidney and rectal gland (figure 16.7); blood isosmotic or slightly hyperosmotic to seawater; **high concentrations of urea and trimethylamine oxide in blood**
10. Brain has two olfactory lobes, two cerebral hemispheres, two optic lobes, a cerebellum, and a medulla oblongata; 10 pairs of cranial nerves; **three pairs of semicircular canals;** senses of smell, vision, vibration reception (lateral-line system), and electroreception well developed
11. Separate sexes; oviparous, ovoviviparous, or viviparous; direct development; **internal fertilization**

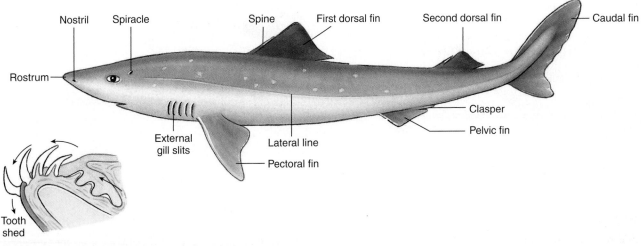

figure 16.6

Male spiny dogfish shark, *Squalus acanthias. Inset:* Section of lower jaw shows new teeth developing inside the jaw. These move forward to replace lost teeth. The rate of replacement varies among species.

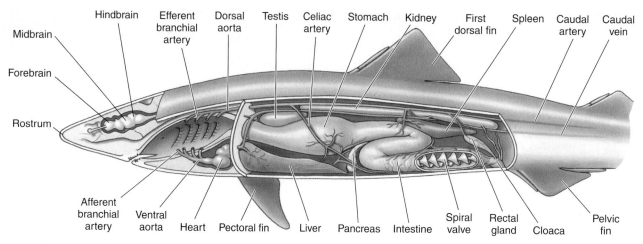

figure 16.7

Internal anatomy of a dogfish shark, *Squalus acanthias*.

figure 16.8

Head of a sand tiger shark, *Carcharias taurus*. Note the series of successional teeth. Also visible below the eye are ampullae of Lorenzini.

More than half of all elasmobranchs are rays, a group that includes skates, stingrays, electric rays, and manta rays. Rays are distinguished by their dorsoventrally flattened bodies and enlarged pectoral fins, which they move in a wavelike fashion to propel themselves (figure 16.10). Gill openings are on the underside of the head, and the large **spiracles** are on top. Respiratory water enters through these spiracles to prevent clogging of the gills, because the mouth is often buried in sand. Teeth are adapted for crushing prey—mainly molluscs, crustaceans, and an occasional small fish.

In stingrays, the slender, whiplike tail is armed with one or more saw-toothed spines that can inflict dangerous wounds. Electric rays have certain muscles on either side of the head, modified into powerful electrical organs, which can produce severe shocks to stun their prey.

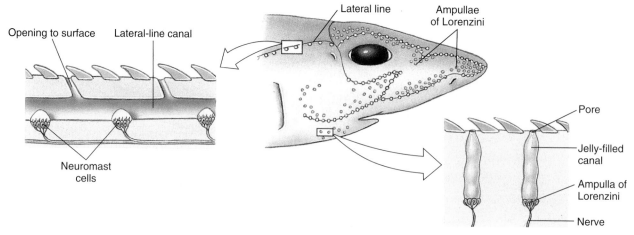

figure 16.9

Sensory canals and receptors in a shark. Ampullae of Lorenzini respond to weak electrical fields, and possibly to temperature, water pressure, and salinity. Lateral-line sensors, called neuromast cells, are sensitive to disturbances in the water, enabling a shark to detect nearby objects by reflected waves in the water.

figure 16.10

Skates and rays are specialized for life on the sea floor. Both **A,** the clearnose skate, *Raja eglanteria,* and **B,** the bluespotted ribbontail ray, *Taeniura lymma,* are flattened dorsoventrally and move by undulations of winglike pectoral fins.

The worldwide shark fishery is experiencing unprecedented pressure, driven by the high price of shark fins for shark-fin soup, an Asian delicacy that may sell for as much as $100.00 per bowl. Coastal shark populations in general have declined so rapidly that "finning" has been outlawed in the United States; other countries, too, are setting quotas to protect threatened shark populations. Even in the Marine Resources Reserve of the Galápagos Islands, one of the world's exceptional wild places, tens of thousands of sharks have been killed illegally for the Asian shark-fin market. Contributing to the threatened collapse of shark fisheries worldwide is the low fecundity of sharks and the long time most sharks require to reach sexual maturity; some species take as long as 35 years.

Chimaeras: Subclass Holocephali

The approximately 33 species of chimaeras (kī-mer´uz; L. monster), distinguished by such suggestive names as ratfish (figure 16.11) and rabbitfish, are remnants of a group that diverged from the earliest shark lineage, which originated at least 360 million years ago (Devonian or Silurian periods of the Paleozoic). Fossil chimaeras first appeared in the Jurassic period, reached their zenith in the Cretaceous and early Tertiary periods (120 million to 50 million years ago), and then declined. Anatomically, they have several features that link them to elasmobranchs, but they possess a suite of unique characters, too. Their food is a mixed diet of molluscs, echinoderms, crustaceans, and fishes. Chimaeras are not commercial species and are seldom caught. Despite their bizarre shape, they are beautifully colored, with a pearly iridescence.

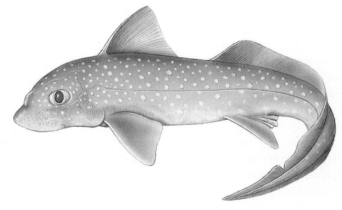

figure 16.11

A spotted ratfish, *Hydrolagus collei,* of the North American west coast. This species is one of the most handsome chimaeras, which tend to be bizarre in appearance.

■ Bony Fishes: The Osteichthyes

In the early to middle Silurian period, a lineage of fishes with bony endoskeletons gave rise to a clade of vertebrates that contains 96% of living fishes and all living tetrapods. Fishes of this clade have traditionally been termed "bony fishes" (**Osteichthyes**). Bony fishes and tetrapods are united by the presence of **endochondral bone** (bone that replaces cartilage developmentally), the presence of lungs or a swim bladder derived from the gut, and several cranial and dental characters. Because traditional usage of the term Osteichthyes does not describe a monophyletic (natural) group (see figure 16.2), most recent classifications, including the one presented on page 338,

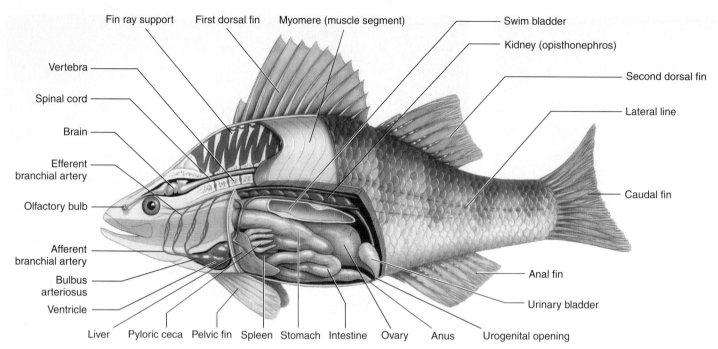

figure 16.12

Anatomy of a yellow perch, *Perca flavescens*, a freshwater teleost fish.

do not recognize this term as a valid taxon. Rather, it is a term of convenience to describe vertebrates with endochondral bone that are conventionally termed "bony fishes."

Fossils of the earliest bony fishes show several structural similarities, including a bony operculum and branchiostegal rays, with acanthodians (see figure 15.14), indicating that they likely descended from a unique common ancestor. By the middle Devonian period, bony fishes already had diversified extensively into two major clades, with adaptations that fitted them for every aquatic habitat except the most inhospitable. One of these clades, the ray-finned fishes (class Actinopterygii), includes teleosts (figure 16.12), the most species-rich clade of living vertebrates. A second clade, the lobe-finned fishes (class Sarcopterygii), is represented today by only eight fishlike vertebrates, the lungfishes and coelacanths (see figures 16.19 and 16.20); however, it includes the sister group of land vertebrates (tetrapods).

Several key adaptations contributed to the diversification of bony fishes. They have an operculum over the gill composed of bony plates and attached to a series of muscles. This feature increases respiratory efficiency because outward rotation of the operculum creates a negative pressure so that water is drawn across the gills, as well as pushed across by the mouth pump. A gas-filled pouch branching from the esophagus provides an additional means of gas exchange in oxygen-poor waters and an efficient means of achieving neutral buoyancy. In fishes that use these pouches primarily for gas exchange, the pouches are called **lungs,** while in fishes that use these pouches primarily for buoyancy, these pouches are called **swim bladders** (see p. 332). Progressive specialization of jaw musculature and skeletal elements involved in suction feeding is another key feature of bony fish evolution.

Ray-Finned Fishes: Class Actinopterygii

Ray-finned fishes are an enormous assemblage containing all of the bony fishes we are familiar with today—almost 27,000 species. The ancestral forms that swam in Devonian waters were small and heavily armored, with ganoid scales (figure 16.13) and heterocercal caudal fins (figure 16.14).

From those earliest ray-finned fishes arose several clades. Bichirs, in the clade Cladistia, have lungs, heavy ganoid scales, and other characteristics similar to those of their bony-fish ancestors (figure 16.15A). The 16 species of bichirs live in fresh waters of Africa. A second group are the **chondrosteans** (Gr. *chondros,* cartilage, + *osteon,* bone), represented by 27 species of freshwater and anadromous sturgeons and paddlefishes (figure 16.15B and C).

The third major group to emerge from the early ray-finned stock were **neopterygians** (Gr. *neos,* new, + *pteryx,* fin). Neopterygians appeared in the late Permian period and diversified extensively during the Mesozoic era when one lineage gave rise to modern bony fishes, the teleosts. The three surviving genera of non-teleost neopterygians are the bowfin *Amia* (Gr. tunalike fish), which inhabits shallow, weedy waters of the Great Lakes and the Mississippi River basin, and the gars *Lepisosteus* (Gr. *lepidos,* scale, + *osteon,* bone) and *Atractosteus* (Gr. *atraktos,* spindle, + *osteon,* bone), both native to eastern and southern North America (figure 16.16). Gars are large, ambush predators with elongate bodies and jaws filled with needlelike teeth.

Teleosts (Gr. *teleos,* complete, + *osteon,* bone), the modern bony fishes (see figure 16.12), form the largest clade of neopterygians. Teleost diversity is astounding, with about 27,000 described species representing about 96% of all living

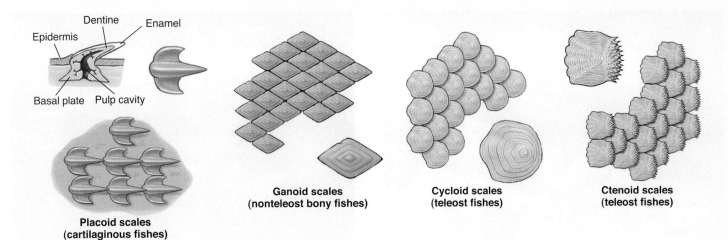

figure 16.13

Types of fish scales. Placoid scales are small, conical, toothlike structures characteristic of Chondrichthyes. Diamond-shaped ganoid scales, present in early bony fishes and living gars, are composed of layers of silvery enamel (ganoin) on the upper surface and bone on the lower. Other bony fishes have either cycloid or ctenoid scales, which are thin and flexible and arranged in overlapping rows.

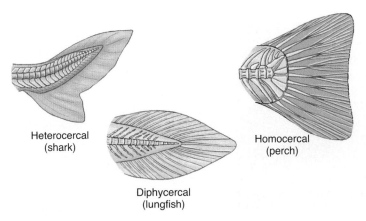

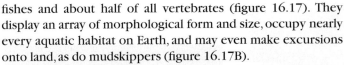

figure 16.14

Types of caudal fins among fishes.

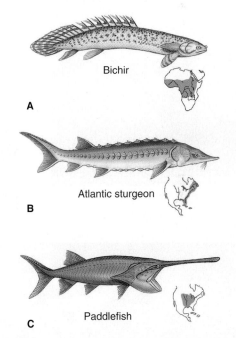

figure 16.15

Ancestral ray-finned fishes of class Actinopterygii. **A,** Bichir, *Polypterus bichir,* of equatorial West Africa is a nocturnal predator. **B,** Atlantic sturgeon, *Acipenser oxyrhynchus* (now uncommon), inhabits Atlantic coastal rivers. **C,** Paddlefish, *Polyodon spathula,* of the Mississippi River basin reaches 2 m and 80 kg.

fishes and about half of all vertebrates (figure 16.17). They display an array of morphological form and size, occupy nearly every aquatic habitat on Earth, and may even make excursions onto land, as do mudskippers (figure 16.17B).

Several morphological trends in the teleost lineage allowed it to diversify into a truly incredible variety of habitats and forms. The heavy dermal armor of primitive ray-finned fishes was replaced by light, thin, flexible **cycloid** and **ctenoid scales** (see figure 16.13). Increased mobility and speed permitted by loss of heavy armor improved predator avoidance and feeding efficiency. The symmetrical shape of the **homocercal** tail (see figure 16.14) of most teleosts focused musculature contractions on the tail, allowing greater speed. Various fins were elaborated into forms that permitted precise steering, camouflage, protection, attachment, or social communication (see figure 16.17C and D). Teleost lineages

demonstrated an increasingly fine control of gas resorption and secretion in the swim bladder, improving control of buoyancy. Changes in jaw suspension enabled the orobranchial cavity to expand rapidly, creating a highly sophisticated suction device. With so many innovations, teleosts have become the most diverse of fishes.

A

B

figure 16.16

Nonteleost neopterygian fishes. **A,** Bowfin, *Amia calva*. **B,** Longnose gar, *Lepisosteus osseus*. Both species frequent slow-moving streams and swamps of eastern North America, where they may hang motionless in the water, ready to snatch passing fishes.

A

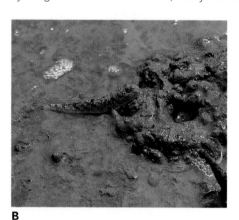

B

figure 16.17

Diversity among teleosts. **A,** Blue marlin, *Makaira nigricans*, is one of the largest teleosts. **B,** Mudskippers, *Periopthalmus* sp., make extensive excursions on land to graze on algae and capture insects; they build nests in which the young hatch and are guarded by the mother. **C,** Protective coloration of the lionfish, *Pterois volitans*, advises caution; the dorsal spines are venomous. **D,** The sucking disc on the sharksucker, *Echeneis naucrates*, is a modification of the dorsal fin.

C

D

Australian lungfish

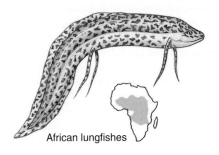

African lungfishes

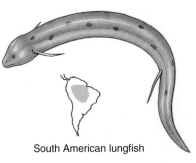

South American lungfish

Characteristics
of Class Actinopterygii

1. **Skeleton with bone of endochondral origin;** caudal fin heterocercal in ancestral forms, usually **homocercal** in descendant forms (see figure 16.14); skin with mucous glands and embedded dermal scales (figure 16.18); scales **ganoid** in ancestral forms; scales **cycloid, ctenoid,** or absent in derived forms (see figure 16.13)
2. Paired and median fins present, **supported by long dermal rays (lepidotrichia);** muscles controlling fin movement within body
3. Jaws present; teeth with enamaloid covering usually present; olfactory sacs do not open into mouth; spiral valve present in ancestral forms, absent in derived forms
4. Respiration primarily by gills supported by arches and covered with an **operculum**
5. **Swim bladder** often present with or without a duct connecting to esophagus, usually functioning in buoyancy
6. Circulation consisting of a heart with a sinus venosus, an undivided atrium, and an undivided ventricle; single circulation; typically four aortic arches; nucleated erythrocytes
7. Excretory system composed of paired opisthonephric kidneys; sexes usually separate; fertilization usually external; larval forms may differ greatly from adults
8. Nervous system consisting of a brain with small cerebrum, optic lobes, and cerebellum; 10 pairs of cranial nerves; three pairs of semicircular canals

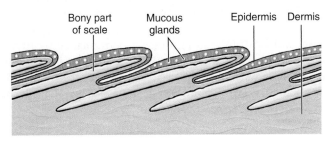

Bony part of scale   Mucous glands   Epidermis   Dermis

figure 16.18
Section through the skin of a bony fish, showing the overlapping scales (yellow). The scales lie in the dermis and are covered by epidermis.

Lobe-Finned Fishes: Class Sarcopterygii

The ancestor of tetrapods lies within a group of extinct sarcopterygian fishes called **rhipidistians,** which included several lineages that flourished in shallow waters in the late Paleozoic era (see figure 17.1). The evolution of tetrapods from rhipidistians is discussed in Chapter 17.

All early sarcopterygians had lungs as well as gills, and a tail of the heterocercal type. However, during the Paleozoic era, the orientation of the vertebral column changed so that the tail became symmetrical and **diphycercal** (see figure 16.14). These fishes had powerful jaws; heavy, enameled scales; and strong, fleshy, paired lobed fins that they may have used like legs to

figure 16.19
Lungfishes are lobe-finned fishes of Sarcopterygii. Extinct Paleozoic lungfishes are most similar in morphology to the Australian lungfish, *Neoceratodus forsteri*. The African lungfishes, *Protopterus* sp., are the best adapted of the three for remaining dormant in mucus-lined cocoons breathing air during prolonged periods of drought.

clamber over woody debris in the water. The sarcopterygian clade today is represented by only eight fish species: six species of lungfishes and two species of coelacanths (figures 16.19 and 16.20).

Neoceratodus (Gr. *neos,* new, + *keratos,* horn, + *odes,* form), the living Australian lungfish, may attain a length of 1.5 m (figure 16.19) and is similar to early forms. This lungfish, unlike its living relatives, normally relies on gill respiration, and cannot survive long out of water. The South American lungfish, *Lepidosiren* (L. *lepidus,* pretty, + *siren,* mythical mermaid), and the African lungfishes, *Protopterus* (Gr. *protos,* first, + *pteron,* wing), can live out of water for long periods of time. *Protopterus* lives in African streams and ponds that are baked hard by the hot tropical sun during the dry season. The fish burrows at the approach of the dry season and secretes a copious slime that mixes with mud to form a hard cocoon in which it remains dormant until rain returns.

Coelacanths also arose in the Devonian period, diversified somewhat, and reached their peak of diversity in the Mesozoic era. At the end of the Mesozoic era, they nearly disappeared but left one remarkable surviving genus, *Latimeria*

Characteristics

of Class Sarcopterygii

1. **Skeleton with bone of endochondral origin;** caudal fin **diphycercal** in living representatives, heterocercal in ancestral forms; skin with embedded dermal scales composed of two layers of bone, a form of dentine called **cosmine,** and a thin layer of enamel in ancestral forms
2. Paired and median fins present; paired fins have a single basal skeletal element and short dermal rays; muscles move paired fins located on appendage
3. Jaws present; teeth are covered with true enamel and typically are crushing plates restricted to palate; olfactory sacs paired, may or may not open into mouth; intestine with spiral valve
4. Gills supported by bony arches and covered with an **operculum**
5. Swim bladder vascularized and used for respiration and buoyancy (fat-filled in coelacanths)
6. Circulation consists of heart with a sinus venosus, two atria, a partly divided ventricle, and a conus arteriosus; **double circulation** with pulmonary and systemic circuits; characteristically five aortic arches
7. Nervous system consists of a cerebrum, a cerebellum, and optic lobes; 10 pairs of cranial nerves; three pairs of semicircular canals
8. Sexes separate; fertilization external or internal

figure 16.20

The coelacanth genus *Latimeria* is a surviving marine relict of a group of lobe-finned fishes that flourished some 350 million years ago.

(figure 16.20). Because the last coelacanths were believed to have become extinct 70 million years ago, one can imagine the astonishment of the scientific world when the remains of a coelacanth were found on a trawl off the coast of South Africa in 1938. An intensive search to locate more specimens was successful off the coast of the Comoro Islands. There, fishermen occasionally catch them at great depths with hand lines, providing specimens for research. This was assumed to be the only population of *Latimeria* until 1998, when the scientific world was again surprised by the capture of a new species of coelacanth in Indonesia, 10,000 km from the Comoros!

"Modern" marine coelacanths are descendants of the Devonian freshwater stock. The tail is diphycercal (see figure 16.14) but possesses a small lobe between the upper and lower caudal lobes, producing a three-pronged structure (figure 16.20).

Coelacanths are a deep metallic blue with irregular white or brassy flecks, providing camouflage against the dark lava-cave reefs that they inhabit. Young are born fully formed after hatching internally from eggs 9 cm in diameter—the largest among bony fishes.

Structural and Functional Adaptations of Fishes

Locomotion in Water

To the human eye, some fishes appear capable of swimming at extremely high speeds, but our judgment is unconsciously tempered by our own experience that water is a highly resistant medium through which to move. Most fishes, such as a trout or a minnow, can swim maximally about 10 body lengths per second, obviously an impressive performance by human standards. Yet, when these speeds are translated into kilometers per hour, we realize that a 30 cm (1 foot) trout can swim only about 10.4 km (6.5 miles) per hour. As a general rule, the larger the fish, the faster it can swim.

Measuring the cruising speeds of fish is best done in a "fish wheel," a large, ring-shaped channel filled with water that is turned at a speed equal and opposite to that of the fish. Much more difficult to measure are the sudden bursts of speed that most fish can make to capture prey or to avoid being captured. A hooked bluefin tuna was once "clocked" at 66 km per hour (41 mph); swordfish and marlin may be capable of incredible bursts of speed approaching, or even exceeding, 110 km per hour (68 mph). Such high speeds can be sustained for no more than 1 to 5 seconds.

The propulsive mechanism of a fish is its trunk and tail musculature. The axial, locomotory musculature is composed of zigzag bands, called **myomeres.** Muscle fibers in each myomere are relatively short and connect the tough connective tissue partitions that separate each myomere from the next. On the surface, myomeres take the shape of a W lying on its side (figure 16.21), but internally the bands are complexly folded and nested so that the pull of each myomere extends over several vertebrae. This arrangement produces more power and

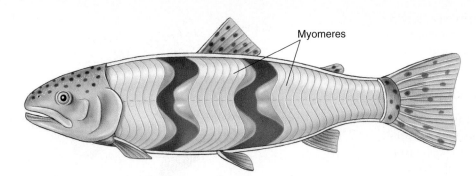

figure 16.21

Trunk musculature of a teleost fish, partly dissected to show the internal arrangement of the muscle bands (myomeres). The myomeres are folded into a complex, nested grouping, an arrangement that favors stronger and more controlled swimming.

finer control of movement since many myomeres are involved in bending a given segment of the body.

Understanding how fishes swim can be approached by studying the motion of a very flexible fish such as an eel (figure 16.22, *left*). The movement is serpentine, not unlike that of a snake, with waves of contraction moving backward along the body by alternate contraction of the myomeres on either side. The anterior end of the body bends less than the posterior end, so that each undulation increases in amplitude as it travels along the body. While undulations move backward, bending of the body pushes laterally against the water, producing a **reactive force** that is directed forward, but at an angle. It can be analyzed as having two components: **thrust,** which is used to overcome drag and propels the fish forward, and **lateral force,** which tends to make the fish's head "yaw," or deviate from the course in the same direction as the tail. This side-to-side head movement is very obvious in a swimming eel or dogfish shark, but many fishes have a large, rigid head with enough surface resistance to minimize yaw.

The movement of an eel is reasonably efficient at low speed, but its body shape generates too much frictional drag for rapid swimming. Fishes that swim rapidly, such as trout, are less flexible and limit body undulations mostly to the caudal region (figure 16.22, *right*). Muscle force generated in the large anterior muscle mass is transferred through tendons to the relatively nonmuscular caudal peduncle and caudal fin where thrust is generated. This form of swimming reaches its highest development in tunas, whose bodies do not flex at all. Virtually all thrust

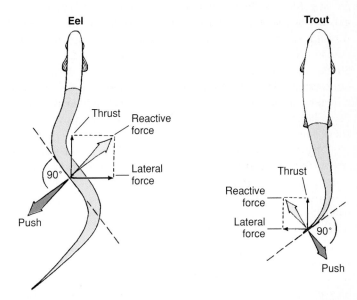

figure 16.22

Movements of swimming fishes, showing the forces developed by an eel-shaped fish and a spindle-shaped fish.

Source: Pough, F. H.; Janis, Christine M; Heiser, John B., VERTEBRATE LIFE, 5th Edition, © 1999. Reprinted by permission of Pearson Education Inc., Upper Saddle River, NJ.

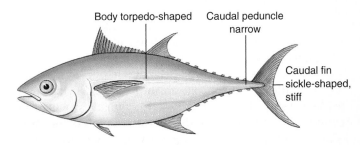

figure 16.23

Bluefin tuna, *Thunnus thynnus*, showing adaptations for fast swimming. Powerful trunk muscles pull on the slender caudal peduncle. Because the body does not bend, all of the thrust comes from beats of the stiff, sickle-shaped caudal fin.

The body temperature of most fishes is the same as their environment, because any heat generated internally is lost quickly into the surrounding water. However, some fishes, such as tunas (figure 16.23) and mako sharks, maintain a high temperature in their swimming muscles and viscera—as much as 10° C warmer than surrounding water. Marlins (see figure 16.17A) and other billfishes elevate the temperature of their brain and retina. Research by F. G. Carey and others explains how these fishes accomplish this kind of thermoregulation, called **regional endothermy.** Heat is generated as a by-product of various activities, including digestion and swimming, or for billfishes, by a specialized heat-generating organ beneath the brain. This heat is conserved with a **rete mirabile,** a parallel bundle of blood vessels arranged to provide a countercurrent flow of blood. High temperatures apparently promote powerful swimming and enhance digestive and nervous system activity. Fishes with regional endothermy are the fastest in the world.

is derived from powerful beats of the caudal fin (figure 16.23). Many fast oceanic fishes, such as marlin, swordfish, amberjacks, and wahoo, have swept-back caudal fins shaped much like a sickle. Such fins are the aquatic counterpart of the high-aspect wings of the swiftest birds (see p. 387). Swimming is the most economical form of animal locomotion, largely because aquatic animals are almost perfectly supported by their medium and need to expend little energy to overcome the force of gravity.

Neutral Buoyancy and the Swim Bladder

All fishes are slightly heavier than water because their skeletons and other tissues contain heavy elements that are present only in trace amounts in natural waters. To keep from sinking, sharks, which lack a swim bladder, must always keep moving forward in the water. The asymmetrical (heterocercal) tail of a shark provides the necessary tail lift as it sweeps through the water, and the broad head and flat pectoral fins (see figure 16.6) act as angled planes to provide additional lift. Sharks also are aided in buoyancy by having very large livers containing a special fatty hydrocarbon called **squalene** with a density of only 0.86 grams per milliliter. The liver thus acts like a large sack of buoyant oil that helps compensate for the shark's heavy body.

By far the most efficient flotation device is a gas-filled space. The swim bladder serves this purpose in bony fishes (figure 16.24). It arose from the paired lungs of early Devonian fishes. Swim bladders are present in most pelagic bony fishes but are absent from tunas, most abyssal fishes, and most bottom-dwellers, such as flounders and sculpins.

By adjusting the volume of gas in its swim bladder, a fish can achieve neutral buoyancy and remain suspended indefinitely at any depth with no muscular effort. If a fish swims to a greater depth, the greater pressure exerted by the surrounding water compresses the gas in the swim bladder, so that the fish becomes less buoyant and begins to sink. Gas must be added to the swim bladder to establish a new equilibrium buoyancy. When a fish swims upward, gas in the bladder expands because of the reduced surrounding water pressure, making the fish more buoyant. Unless gas is removed, the fish continues to ascend with increasing speed as the swim bladder continues to expand.

Gases are removed from the swim bladder in two ways. Some fishes (trout, for example) have a **pneumatic duct** that connects the swim bladder to the esophagus, through which they can expel air. More derived teleosts have lost the pneumatic duct and exchange air in the swim bladder with the blood. Gas is diffused into blood at a highly vascularized region of the swim bladder, the **ovale.** Gas enters the swim bladder at the **gas gland.** The gas gland secretes lactic acid, causing oxygen to be released from hemoglobin. A remarkable network of parallel blood capillaries, the **rete mirabile,** supplies the gas gland and acts as a countercurrent multiplier (figure 16.24). The rete allows oxygen to reach high concentrations in the gas gland, permitting it to diffuse into the swim bladder.

The amazing effectiveness of this device is exemplified by a fish living at a depth of 2400 m (8000 feet). To keep the bladder inflated at that depth, the gas inside (mostly oxygen) must have a pressure exceeding 240 atmospheres, which is much greater than the pressure in a fully charged steel gas

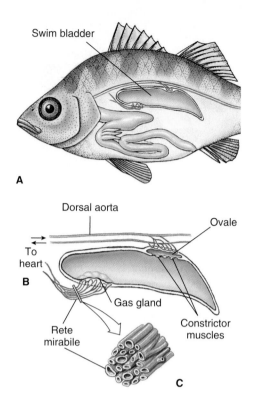

figure 16.24

A, Swim bladder of a teleost fish. The swim bladder lies in the coelom just beneath the vertebral column. **B,** Gas is secreted into the swim bladder by the gas gland. Gas from the blood is moved into the gas gland by the rete mirabile, a complex array of tightly packed capillaries that act as a countercurrent multiplier to increase oxygen concentration. The arrangement of venous and arterial capillaries in the rete is shown in **C.** To release gas during ascent, a muscular valve opens, allowing gas to enter the ovale, from which the gas is removed by diffusion into the blood.

cylinder. Yet the oxygen pressure in the fish's blood cannot exceed 0.2 atmosphere, in equilibrium with the oxygen pressure in the atmosphere at the sea surface.

Respiration

Fish gills are composed of thin filaments, each covered with a thin epidermal membrane that is folded repeatedly into platelike **lamellae** (figure 16.25). These lamellae are richly supplied with blood vessels. The gills are located inside a pharyngeal cavity and are covered with a movable flap called the **operculum.** This arrangement provides excellent protection to delicate gill filaments, streamlines the body, and makes possible a pumping system for moving water through the mouth, across the gills, and out the operculum. Instead of opercular flaps as in bony fishes, elasmobranchs have a series of **gill slits** (see figure 16.6) out of which the water flows. In both elasmobranchs and bony fishes, the branchial mechanism is arranged to pump water continuously and smoothly over the gills, although to an observer it appears that fish breathing is pulsatile.

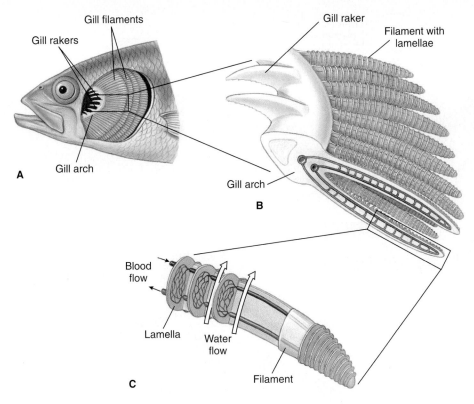

figure 16.25

Gills of a fish. The bony, protective operculum covering the gills has been removed, **A,** to reveal the branchial chamber containing the gills. There are four gill arches on each side, each bearing numerous filaments. **B,** A portion of a gill arch shows gill rakers that project forward to strain food and debris, and gill filaments that project to the rear. **C,** A single gill filament is dissected to show the blood capillaries within the platelike lamellae. The direction of water flow (*large arrows*) is opposite the direction of blood flow.

The direction of water flow is opposite that of blood flow (countercurrent flow), the best arrangement for extracting the greatest possible amount of oxygen from water. Some bony fishes can remove as much as 85% of the dissolved oxygen from water passing over their gills. Very active fishes, such as herring and mackerel, can obtain sufficient water for their high oxygen demands only by swimming forward continuously to force water into their open mouth and across their gills. This process is called ram ventilation.

Osmotic Regulation

Fresh water is an extremely dilute medium with a salt concentration (0.001 to 0.005 gram moles per liter [M]) much below that of the blood of freshwater fishes (0.2 to 0.3 M). Water therefore tends to enter their bodies osmotically, and salt is lost by diffusion outward. Although the scaled and mucus-covered body surface is almost totally impermeable to water, water gain and salt loss do occur across thin membranes of the gills. Freshwater fishes are **hyperosmotic**

regulators with several defenses against these problems (figure 16.26, *top*). First, excess water is pumped out by the kidneys, which are capable of forming very dilute urine. Second, special **salt-absorbing cells** located in the gill epithelium actively move salt ions, principally sodium and chloride, from water to the blood. This absorption, together with salt present in the fish's food, replaces diffusive salt loss. These mechanisms are so efficient that a freshwater fish devotes only a small part of its total energy expenditure to maintaining osmotic balance.

Marine fishes are **hypoosmotic regulators** that encounter a completely different problem. Having a much lower blood salt concentration (0.3 to 0.4 M) than the seawater around them (about 1 M), they tend to lose water and to gain salt. A marine teleost quite literally risks drying out, much like a desert mammal deprived of water. To compensate for water loss, a marine teleost drinks seawater (figure 16.26, *bottom*). Excess salt accompanying the seawater is disposed of in multiple ways. Major sea salt ions (sodium, chloride, and potassium) are carried by the blood to the gills, where they are expelled by special **salt-secretory cells.** The remaining sea salt ions, mostly magnesium, sulfate, and calcium, are voided with feces or excreted by the kidney.

Migration

Freshwater Eels

For centuries, naturalists had been puzzled by the life history of freshwater eels, *Anguilla* (an-gwil´ə) (L. eel), a common and commercially important species inhabiting coastal streams of the North Atlantic. Eels are **catadromous** (Gr. *kata,* down, + *dromos,* running), meaning that they spend most of their lives in fresh water but migrate to the sea to spawn. Each fall, people saw large numbers of eels swimming down rivers toward the sea, but no adults ever returned. Each spring, countless numbers of young eels, called "elvers," each about the size of a wooden matchstick, appeared in coastal rivers and began swimming upstream. Beyond the assumption that eels must spawn somewhere at sea, the location of their breeding grounds was completely unknown.

The first clue was provided by two Italian scientists, Grassi and Calandruccio, who in 1896 discovered that elvers were advanced juvenile eels and that true larval eels were tiny, leaf-shaped, transparent creatures called **leptocephali.** In 1905, Johann Schmidt began a systematic study of eel biology,

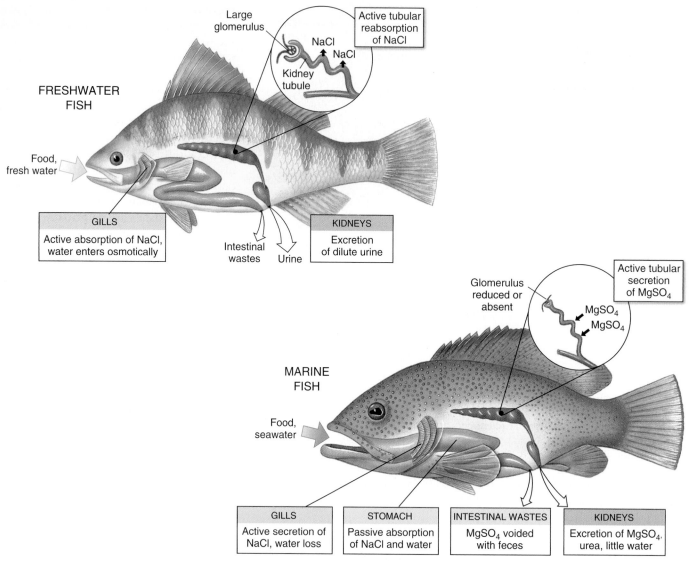

figure 16.26

Osmotic regulation in freshwater and marine bony fishes. *Top:* A freshwater fish maintains osmotic and ionic balance in its dilute environment by actively absorbing sodium chloride (NaCl) across the gills (some salt is gained with food). To flush out excess water that constantly enters the body, the glomerular kidney produces a dilute urine by reabsorbing sodium chloride. *Bottom:* A marine fish must drink seawater to replace water lost osmotically to its salty environment. Sodium chloride and water are absorbed from the stomach. Excess sodium chloride is actively transported outward by the gills. Divalent sea salts, mostly magnesium sulfate ($MgSO_4$), are eliminated with feces and secreted by the tubular kidney.

examining thousands of leptocephali caught in plankton nets from many areas of the Atlantic. By noting where larvae in different stages were captured, Schmidt and his colleagues reconstructed the spawning migration.

When adult eels leave the coastal streams of Europe and North America, they swim to the Sargasso Sea, a vast area of warm oceanic water southeast of Bermuda. Here, at depths of 300 m or more, the eels spawn and die. Minute larvae then begin an incredible journey back to the streams of Europe and North America (figure 16.27). Because the Sargasso Sea is much closer to the American coastline, American eel larvae make their journey in only about one year, compared to

3 years for European eel larvae. Males typically remain in the brackish water of coastal rivers, while females migrate as far as several hundred kilometers upstream. After 6 to 15 years of growth, females, now 1 m long, return to the ocean to join the smaller males in the journey back to the spawning grounds in the Sargasso Sea.

Enzyme electrophoretic analyses of eel larvae confirm not only the existence of separate European and American species but also Schmidt's hypothesis that the European and American eels spawn in partially overlapping areas of the Sargasso Sea.

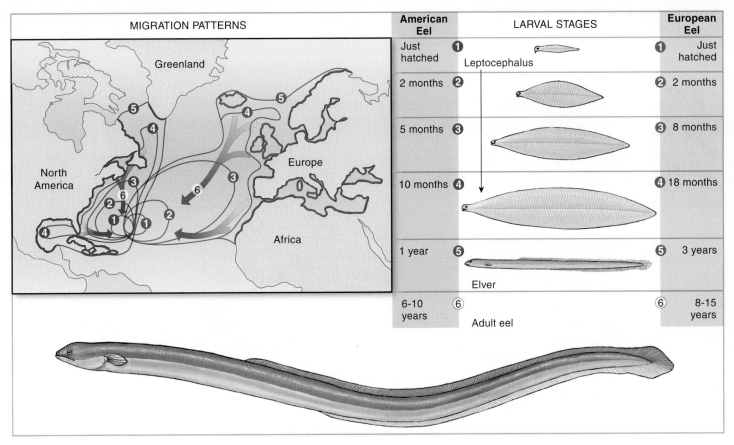

The table in the figure:

American Eel	LARVAL STAGES		European Eel
Just hatched ❶	Leptocephalus ❶		❶ Just hatched
2 months ❷			❷ 2 months
5 months ❸			❸ 8 months
10 months ❹			❹ 18 months
1 year ❺	Elver		❺ 3 years
6-10 years ❻	Adult eel		❻ 8-15 years

figure 16.27

Life histories of American eels, *Anguilla rostrata*, and European eels, *Anguilla anguilla*. Migration patterns of American species are shown in blue. Migration patterns of European species are shown in red. Circled numbers refer to stages of development. Note that American eels complete their larval metamorphosis and sea journey in 1 year, while it requires nearly 3 years for European eels to complete their much longer journey.

Homing Salmon

The life history of salmon is nearly as remarkable as that of freshwater eels and certainly has received far more popular attention. Salmon are **anadromous** (Gr. *anadromous,* running upward), spending their adult lives at sea but returning to fresh water to spawn. Atlantic salmon (*Salmo salar*) and Pacific salmon (six species in the genus *Oncorhynchus* [on-kō-rēnk´us]) follow this practice, but there are important differences among the seven species. Atlantic salmon can make repeated upstream spawning runs. The six Pacific salmon species (sockeye, coho, pink, Chinook, chum, and Japanese masu) each make a single spawning run (figures 16.28 and 16.29), after which they die.

The virtually infallible homing instinct of the Pacific species is legendary. After migrating downstream as a smolt (a juvenile stage; figure 16.29), a sockeye salmon ranges many hundreds of kilometers over the Pacific for nearly 4 years, grows to 2 to 5 kg in weight, and then returns almost unerringly to spawn in the headwaters of its parent stream. Some straying does occur and is an important means of increasing gene flow and populating new streams.

figure 16.28

Migrating Pacific sockeye salmon, *Oncorhynchus nerka*.

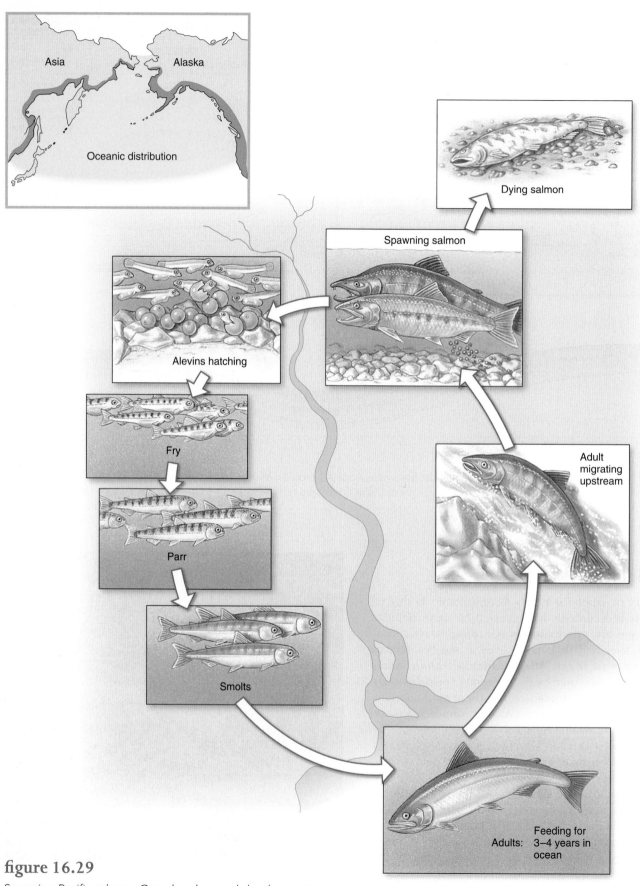

figure 16.29

Spawning Pacific salmon, *Oncorhynchus*, and development of eggs and young.

Experiments by A. D. Hasler and others show that homing salmon are guided upstream by the characteristic odor of their parent stream. When salmon finally reach the spawning beds of their parents (where they themselves were hatched), they spawn and die. The following spring, newly hatched fry transform into smolts before and during the downstream migration. At this time they are imprinted with the distinctive odor of the stream, which is apparently a mosaic of compounds released by the characteristic vegetation and soil in the watershed of the parent stream. They also seem to imprint on odors of other streams that they pass while migrating downriver and use these odors in reverse sequence as a map during the upriver migration as returning adults.

Salmon runs along the Pacific coast of North America have been devastated by a lethal combination of increased siltation from logging, pollution and, especially, the presence of more than 50 hydroelectric dams, which obstruct upstream migration of adult salmon and kill downstream migrants as they pass through the dams' power-generating turbines. In addition, the chain of reservoirs behind the dams, which has converted the Columbia and Snake Rivers into a series of lakes, increases the mortality of young salmon migrating downstream by slowing their passage to the sea. The result is that the annual run of wild salmon is today less than 3% of the 10 to 16 million fish that ascended the rivers 150 years ago. While recovery plans have been delayed by the power industry, environmental groups argue that in the long run losing the salmon will be more expensive to the regional economy than making the changes that will allow salmon stocks to recover.

Reproduction

In a group as diverse as fishes, it is no surprise to find extraordinary variations on the basic theme of sexual reproduction. Most fishes favor a simple theme: they are **dioecious,** with **external fertilization** and **external development** of their eggs and embryos (oviparity). However, as tropical fish enthusiasts are well aware, the ever-popular ovoviviparous guppies and mollies of home aquaria develop in the ovarian cavity of the mother and then are born (figure 16.30). As described earlier in this chapter (see p. 323), some viviparous sharks develop a kind of placental attachment through which the young are nourished during gestation.

Oviparity is the most common mode of reproduction in fishes. Many marine fishes are extraordinarily profligate egg producers. Males and females come together in great schools and, without elaborate courtship behavior, release vast numbers of germ cells into the water to drift with currents. A large female cod may release 4 to 6 million eggs at a single spawning. Less than one in a million will survive the numerous perils of the ocean to reach reproductive maturity.

Unlike the minute, semibuoyant, transparent eggs of pelagic marine teleosts, the eggs of many near-shore and

figure 16.30

Rainbow surfperch, *Hypsurus caryi*, giving birth. All of the West Coast surfperches (family Embiotocidae) are ovoviviparous.

figure 16.31

Male banded jawfish, *Opistognathus macrognathus*, orally brooding its eggs. The male retrieves the female's eggs and incubates them until they hatch. During brief periods when the jawfish is feeding, the eggs are left in the burrow.

bottom-dwelling (benthic) species are larger, yolky, nonbuoyant, and adhesive. Some fishes bury their eggs, many attach them to vegetation, some deposit them in nests, and others even incubate them in their mouths (figure 16.31). Many benthic spawners guard their eggs. Intruders expecting an easy meal of eggs may be met with a vivid and often belligerent display by the guard, which is almost always the male.

Freshwater fishes usually produce nonbuoyant eggs. Fishes such as perch, that provide no parental care simply scatter their myriads of eggs among weeds or along the sediment. Freshwater fishes that do provide some form of egg care, such as bullhead catfishes and some darters, produce fewer, larger eggs that have a better chance for survival.

Elaborate preliminaries to mating are the rule for freshwater fishes. A female Pacific salmon, for example, performs a ritualized mating "dance" with her breeding partner after arriving at the spawning bed in a fast-flowing, gravel-bottomed stream. She then turns on her side and scoops out a nest with her tail. As the eggs are laid by the female, they are fertilized by the male. After the female covers the eggs with gravel, the exhausted fish dies.

Soon after the egg of an oviparous species is fertilized, it absorbs water, and the outer layer hardens. Cleavage follows, and a blastoderm forms astride a relatively enormous yolk mass. Many fishes hatch as larvae, carrying a semitransparent sac of yolk, which provides their food supply until the mouth and digestive tract have developed and the larvae can feed on their own. After a period of growth, a larva undergoes a metamorphosis, especially dramatic in many marine species, including eels (see figure 16.27). Body shape is refashioned, fin and color patterns change, and the larva becomes a juvenile bearing the unmistakable definitive body form of its species.

Classification of Living Fishes

The following Linnean classification of major fish taxa follows that of Nelson (2006). The probable relationships of these traditional groupings, together with the major extinct groups of fishes, are shown in the cladogram in figure 16.2. Other schemes of classification have been proposed. Because of the difficulty of determining relationships among the numerous living and fossil species, we can appreciate why fish classification has undergone, and will continue to undergo, continuous revision.

Phylum Chordata

Subphylum Vertebrata (Craniata)

Superclass Myxinomorphi

Class Myxini (mik-sin´ē) (Gr. *myxa*, slime): **hagfishes.** No jaws or paired fins; mouth with four pairs of tentacles; buccal funnel absent; 1–16 pairs of external gill openings; vertebrae absent; slime glands present. Examples: *Myxine, Epaptretus;* about 70 species, marine.

Superclass Petromyzontomorphi

Class Petromyzontida (pet´trō-mī-zon´ti-də) (Gr. *petros*, stone, + *myzon*, sucking): **lampreys.** No jaws or paired fins; mouth surrounded by keratinized teeth but no barbels; buccal funnel present; seven pairs of external gill openings; vertebrae present only as neural arches. Examples: *Petromyzon, Ichthyomyzon, Lampetra*; 38 species, freshwater and anadromous.

Superclass Gnathostomata (na´thō-stō´mä-tə) (Gr. *gnathos*, jaw, + *stoma*, mouth). Jaws present; paired appendages present (secondarily lost in a few forms); three pairs of semicircular canals; notochord partly or completely replaced by centra.

Class Chondrichthyes (kon-drik´thē-ēz´) (Gr. *chondros*, cartilage, + *ichthys*, fish): **cartilaginous fishes.** Cartilaginous skeleton; teeth not fused to jaws and usually replaced; no swim bladder; intestine with spiral valve; claspers present in males.

Subclass Elasmobranchii (ē-laz´mō-brānk´ē-ī) (Gr. *elasmos*, plated, + *branchia*, gills): **sharks, skates,** and **rays.** Placoid scales or derivatives (scutes and spines) usually present; five to seven gill arches and gill slits in separate clefts along pharynx; upper jaw not fused to cranium. Examples: *Squalus, Raja, Sphyrna;* about 937 species, mostly marine.

Subclass Holocephali (hō-lō-sef´ə-lī) (Gr. *holos*, entire, + *kephalē*, head): **chimaeras** and **ratfishes.** Scales absent; four gill slits covered by operculum; jaws with tooth plates; accessory clasping organ (tentaculum) in males; upper jaw fused to cranium. Examples: *Chimaera, Hydrolagus;* 33 species, marine.

Class Actinopterygii (ak´ti-nop´te-rij´ē-ī) (Gr. *aktis*, ray, + *pteryx*, fin, wing): **ray-finned fishes.** Skeleton ossified; single gill opening covered by operculum; paired fins supported primarily by dermal rays; limb musculature within body; swim bladder mainly a hydrostatic organ, if present; atrium and ventricle not divided; teeth with enameloid covering.

Subclass Cladistia (clə-dis´tē-ə) (Gr. *cladi*, branch): **bichirs.** Rhombic ganoid scales; lungs; spiracle present; dorsal fin consisting of 5–18 finlets. Examples: *Polypterus;* about 16 species, freshwater.

Subclass Chondrostei (kon-dros´tē-ī) (Gr. *chondros*, cartilage, + *osteon*, bone): **paddlefishes, sturgeons.** Skeleton primarily cartilage; caudal fin heterocercal; large scutes or tiny ganoid scales present; spiracle usually present; more fin rays than ray supports. Examples: *Polyodon, Acipenser;* 29 species, freshwater and anadromous.

Subclass Neopterygii (nē´op-te-rij´ē-ī) (Gr. *neo*, new, + *pteryx*, fin, wing): **gars, bowfin,** and **teleosts.** Skeleton primarily bone; caudal fin usually homocercal; scales cycloid, ctenoid, absent, or rarely, ganoid. Fin ray number equal to their supports in dorsal and anal fins. Examples: *Amia, Lepisosteus, Anguilla, Oncorhynchus, Perca;* about 27,000 species, nearly all aquatic habitats.

Class Sarcopterygii (sär-cop-te-rij´-ē-ī) (Gr. *sarkos,* flesh, + *pteryx,* fin, wing): **lobe-finned fishes.** Skeleton ossified; single gill opening covered by operculum; paired fins with sturdy internal skeleton and musculature within appendage; diphycercal tail; intestine with spiral valve; usually with lungs; atrium and ventricle at least partly divided; teeth with enamel covering. Examples: *Latimeria* (coelacanths); *Neoceratodus, Lepidosiren, Protopterus* (lungfishes); 8 species, marine and freshwater. Not monophyletic unless tetrapods are included.

■ Summary

Fishes are gill-breathing aquatic vertebrates with fins for appendages. They include the oldest vertebrates, having originated from a vertebrate chordate ancestor in the Cambrian period or possibly earlier. Five classes of living fishes are recognized. The jawless hagfishes (class Myxini) and lampreys (class Petromyzontida) have an eel-like body form without paired fins, a cartilaginous skeleton, a notochord that persists throughout life, and a disclike mouth adapted for sucking or biting. All other vertebrates have jaws, a major development in vertebrate evolution.

Members of class Chondrichthyes (sharks, skates, rays, and chimaeras) have a cartilaginous skeleton, paired fins, excellent sensory organs, and an active, characteristically predaceous habit. Bony fishes may be divided into two classes. Lobe-finned fishes of the class Sarcopterygii, represented today by lungfishes

and coelacanths, form a paraphyletic group if tetrapods are excluded, as in traditional classification. Terrestrial vertebrates arose from one lineage within this group. The second class is composed of ray-finned fishes (class Actinopterygii), a huge and diverse modern assemblage containing nearly all familiar freshwater and marine fishes.

Modern bony fishes (teleosts) have radiated into approximately 27,000 species that reveal an enormous diversity of adaptations, body form, behavior, and habitat preference. Most fishes swim by undulatory contractions of their body muscles, which generate thrust (propulsive force) and lateral force. Eel-like fishes oscillate the whole body, but in more rapid swimmers the undulations are limited to the caudal region or the caudal fin alone.

Most pelagic bony fishes achieve neutral buoyancy in water using a gas-filled swim

bladder, the most effective gas-secreting device known in the animal kingdom. Gills of fishes, having efficient countercurrent flow between water and blood, facilitate high rates of oxygen exchange. All fishes show well-developed osmotic and ionic regulation, achieved principally by kidneys and gills.

Many fishes are migratory, and some, such as freshwater eels and anadromous salmon, make remarkable migrations of great length and precision. Fishes reveal an extraordinary range of sexual reproductive strategies. Most fishes are oviparous, but ovoviviparous and viviparous fishes are not uncommon. Reproductive investment may be in large numbers of eggs with low survival (many marine fishes) or in fewer eggs with greater parental care for better survival (many freshwater fishes).

■ Review Questions

1. Provide a brief description of fishes, citing characteristics that distinguish them from all other animals.
2. What characteristics distinguish hagfishes and lampreys from all other fishes? How do they differ in morphology from each other?
3. Describe feeding behavior in hagfishes and lampreys. How do they differ?
4. Describe the life cycle of sea lampreys, *Petromyzon marinus,* and the history of their invasion of the Great Lakes.
5. In what ways are sharks well equipped for a predatory life habit?
6. What function does the lateral-line system serve? Where are receptors located?
7. Explain how bony fishes differ from sharks and rays in the following systems or features: skeleton, scales, buoyancy, respiration, and reproduction.

8. Match the ray-finned fishes in the right column with the group to which each belongs in the left column:

    ___Chondrosteans   a. Perch
    ___Nonteleost   b. Sturgeon
        neopterygians   c. Gar
    ___Teleosts   d. Salmon
         e. Paddlefish
         f. Bowfin

9. Make a cladogram that includes the following groups of fishes: chondrosteans, elasmobranchs, hagfishes, holocephalans, lampreys, lungfishes, teleosts. Add the following synapomorphies to the diagram: claspers, cranium, endochondral bone, fleshy fins, jaws, vertebrae.
10. List four characteristics of teleosts that contributed to their incredible evolutionary diversity.
11. Only eight species of lobe-finned fishes are alive today, remnants of a group that flourished in the Devonian

period of the Paleozoic. What morphological characteristics distinguish lobe-finned fishes? What is the literal meaning of Sarcopterygii, the class to which the lobe-finned fishes belong?
12. Give the geographical locations of the three surviving genera of lungfishes, and explain how they differ in their ability to survive out of water.
13. Describe discoveries of living coelacanths. What is the evolutionary significance of the group to which they belong?
14. Compare the swimming movements of eels with those of trout, and explain why the latter are more efficient for rapid locomotion.
15. Sharks and bony fishes approach or achieve neutral buoyancy in different ways. Describe the methods evolved in each group. Why must a teleost adjust the gas volume in its swim bladder

when it swims upward or downward? How is gas volume adjusted?

16. What is meant by "countercurrent flow" as it applies to fish gills?

17. Compare the osmotic problem and the mechanism of osmotic regulation in freshwater and marine bony fishes.

18. Describe the life cycle of freshwater eels. How does the life cycle of American eels differ from that of European eels?

19. How do adult Pacific salmon find their way back to their parent stream to spawn?

20. What mode of reproduction in fishes is described by each of the following terms: oviparous, ovoviviparous, viviparous?

21. Reproduction in marine pelagic fishes and in freshwater fishes is distinctively different. How and why do they differ?

■ Selected References

See also general references on page 423.

Barton, M. 2007. Bond's biology of fishes, ed. 3. Belmont, California, Thomson Brooks/Cole. *A revision of Bond's text that emphasizes anatomy, physiology, and ecology.*

Carey, F. G. 1973. Fishes with warm bodies. Sci. Am. **228**:36–44 (Feb.). *Classic paper about how fishes with regional endothermy keep warm.*

Helfman, G. J., B. B. Collette, and D. E. Facey. 1997. The diversity of fishes. Malden, Massachusetts, Blackwell Science. *This delightful and information-packed textbook focuses on adaptation and diversity and is particularly strong in evolution, systematics, and history of fishes.*

Horn, M. H., and R. N. Gibson. 1988. Intertidal fishes. Sci. Am. **258**:64–70 (Jan.). *Describes the special adaptations of fishes living in a demanding environment.*

Long, J. A. 1995. The rise of fishes: 500 million years of evolution. Baltimore, The Johns Hopkins University Press. *A lavishly illustrated evolutionary history of fishes.*

Martini, F. H. 1998. Secrets of the slime hag. Sci. Am. **279**:70–75 (Oct.). *Biology of the most ancestral living vertebrate.*

Nelson, J. S. 2006. Fishes of the world, ed. 4. New York, John Wiley & Sons, Inc. *Authoritative classification of all major groups of fishes.*

Paxton, J. R., and W. N. Eschmeyer. 1998. Encyclopedia of fishes, ed. 2. San Diego, Academic Press. *Excellent authoritative*

reference that focuses on diversity and is spectacularly illustrated.

Springer, V. G., and J. P. Gold. 1989. Sharks in question. Washington, D.C., Smithsonian Institution Press. *Morphology, biology, and diversity of sharks, richly illustrated.*

Webb, P. W. 1984. Form and function in fish swimming. Sci. Am. **251**:72–82 (July). *Specializations of fish for swimming and analysis of thrust generation.*

Weinberg, S. 2000. A fish caught in time: the search for the coelacanth. London, Fourth Estate. *The exciting history of the coelacanth discoveries.*

■ Custom Website

The *Animal Diversity* Online Learning Center is a great place to check your understanding of chapter material. Visit www.mhhe.com/hickmanad5e for access to key terms, quizzes, and more! Further enhance your knowledge with web links to chapter-related material.

Explore live links for these topics:

Class Myxini
Class Petromyzontida
Subclass Elasmobranchii
Dissection Guides for Elasmobranchs
Vertebrate Laboratory Exercises
Class Osteichthyes

Primitive Bony Fish
Teleosts
Dissection Guides for Teleosts
Fisheries and Conservation Issues Concerning Teleosts
Fisheries
Impact of Humans on the Sea; Harvesting

The Early Tetrapods and Modern Amphibians

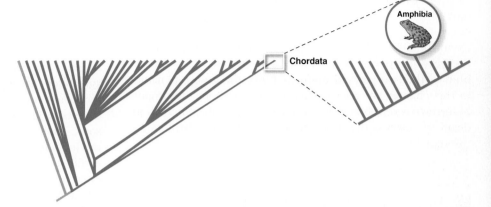

From Water to Land in Ontogeny and Phylogeny

The chorus of frogs beside a pond on a spring evening heralds one of nature's dramatic events. Mating frogs produce masses of eggs, which soon hatch into limbless, gill-breathing tadpole larvae that feed and grow. Then a remarkable transformation occurs. Hindlimbs appear and gradually lengthen. The tail shortens. Larval teeth and gills are lost. Eyelids develop. The forelegs emerge. In a matter of weeks, the aquatic tadpole has completed its metamorphosis to an adult, land-dwelling frog.

By contrast, the evolutionary transition from water to land occurred not in weeks but over millions of years. A lengthy series of alterations cumulatively fitted the vertebrate body plan for life on land. The origin of land vertebrates is no less remarkable for this fact and is unlikely to happen again because well-established competitors would exclude a transitional form.

Amphibians include the only living vertebrates that have a transition from water to land in both their ontogeny (organismal development) and their phylogeny (evolutionary history). Even after some 350 million years of evolution, amphibians remain quasiterrestrial, hovering between aquatic and land environments. Even the amphibians best adapted for a terrestrial existence cannot stray far from moist conditions. Many, however, have developed ways to keep their eggs out of open water where the larvae would be exposed to enemies.

A frog tadpole undergoing metamorphosis.

Adaptation for life on land is a major theme of the remaining vertebrate groups, which form a clade called the superclass Tetrapoda (from the Greek term for "four feet"). Amphibians and amniotes (including nonavian reptiles, birds, and mammals) are the two major extant branches of **tetrapod** phylogeny, which originates in the Devonian period. Many tetrapod lineages have lost one or both of the two pairs of limbs that give the group its name. In this chapter, we review what is known about the origins of terrestrial vertebrates and discuss the amphibian branch in detail. We discuss the major amniote groups in Chapters 18 through 20.

■ Movement onto Land

Movement from water to land is perhaps the most dramatic event in animal evolution, because it involves invasion of a physically hazardous habitat. Life originated in water. Animal bodies are mostly composed of water, and all cellular activities occur in water. Nevertheless, organisms invaded land, carrying their watery composition with them. Vascular plants, pulmonate snails, and tracheate arthropods made this transition much earlier than did vertebrates, and thus generated a food supply that terrestrial vertebrates eventually would use. Although the invasion of land required modification of almost every organ system, aquatic and terrestrial vertebrates retain many structural and functional similarities. Today, we see the transition between aquatic and terrestrial vertebrates most clearly in the many living amphibians that make this transition during their own life histories.

When moving from water to land, animals must accommodate important physical differences in environmental: (1) oxygen content, (2) fluid density, (3) temperature regulation, and (4) habitat diversity. Oxygen is at least 20 times more abundant in air, and it diffuses much more rapidly through air than through water. Consequently, terrestrial animals can obtain oxygen far more easily than aquatic ones can, once they possess appropriately adapted respiratory structures, such as lungs. Air, however, has approximately 1000 times less buoyant density than water and is approximately 50 times less viscous. It therefore provides relatively little support against gravity, requiring terrestrial animals to develop strong limbs and to remodel their skeletons to achieve adequate structural support. Air fluctuates in temperature more readily than does water, and terrestrial environments therefore experience harsh and unpredictable cycles of freezing, thawing, drying, and flooding. Terrestrial animals require behavioral and physiological strategies to protect themselves from thermal extremes.

Despite its hazards, the terrestrial environment offers a great variety of habitats, including forests (boreal, temperate, and tropical), grasslands, deserts, mountains, oceanic islands, and polar regions. Safe shelter for vulnerable eggs and young is found much more readily in many of these terrestrial habitats than in aquatic ones.

■ Early Evolution of Terrestrial Vertebrates

Devonian Origin of Tetrapods

By the Devonian period, beginning about 400 million years ago, bony fishes had diversified to include many freshwater forms. An important combination of characteristics that evolved originally in aquatic habitats now gave its possessors some ability to explore terrestrial habitats. These characteristics included two structures that connected to the pharynx: an air-filled cavity, which functioned as a swim bladder, and paired internal nares (evolutionary origin shown on figure 17.1), which functioned in chemoreception. On land, this combination of structures would be used to draw oxygen-rich air through the nares and into the air-filled cavity, whose surface would permit some respiratory gas exchange with body fluids. The bony elements of paired fins, modified for support and movement on underwater surfaces (evolutionary origin shown on figure 17.2), gained sufficient strength to support the body and to walk on land.

The internal nares, air-filled cavity, and paired limbs of an aquatic tetrapod ancestor therefore were available for modification by later evolution to fit them for terrestrial breathing and support. The air-filled cavity illustrates an important evolutionary principle in which a structure that has evolved by natural selection for an initial utility or role is later recruited or "coopted" for a new role. Note that the air-filled cavities are homologous, with *lung* indicating that the structure's primary role is for air breathing, as it is in terrestrial forms, and *swim bladder* denoting that the structure serves primarily to provide buoyancy during swimming in aquatic animals.

Freshwater habitats are inherently unstable, being prone to evaporation or depletion of the dissolved oxygen needed to support vertebrate life. It is therefore not surprising that multiple fish groups, given a combination of structures that could be coopted for terrestrial breathing and locomotion, evolved some degree of terrestriality. Mudskippers and lungfish are two familiar examples of evolution of terrestriality by fishes; however, only one such transition, occurring in the early Devonian period, provided the ancestral lineage of all tetrapod vertebrates. This lineage ultimately evolved the characteristic tetrapod adaptations to air breathing, including increased vascularization of the air-filled cavity with a rich capillary network to form a lung, and a **double circulation** to direct the deoxygenated blood into the lungs for oxygenation, and the oxygenated blood from the lungs to other body tissues.

Tetrapods evolved limbs in an ancestral aquatic habitat during the Devonian period prior to their evolutionary movement onto land. Although fish fins at first appear very different from the jointed limbs of tetrapods, an examination of the bony elements of the paired fins of the lobe-finned fishes shows that they broadly resemble the homologous structures of amphibian limbs. In *Eusthenopteron,* a Devonian lobe-fin, we can recognize an upper arm bone (humerus) and two forearm

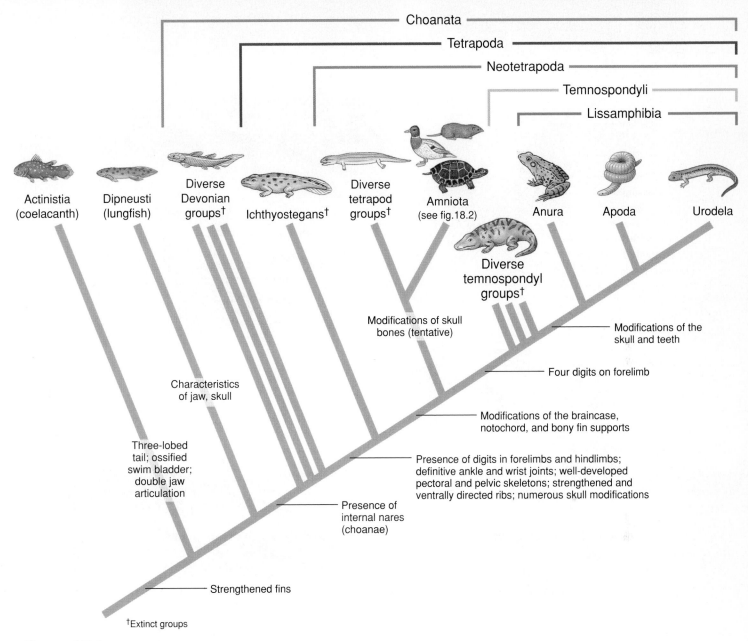

figure 17.1

Tentative cladogram of the Tetrapoda with emphasis on descent of the amphibians. Especially controversial are the relationships of major tetrapod groups (Amniota, Temnospondyli, and diverse early tetrapod groups) and outgroups (Actinistia, Dipneusti, extinct Devonian groups). All aspects of this cladogram are controversial, however, including relationships of the Lissamphibia. The relationships shown for the three groups of Lissamphibia are based on molecular evidence. Extinct groups are marked with a dagger symbol (†).

bones (radius and ulna) as well as other elements that we can homologize with the wrist bones of tetrapods (figure 17.2). *Eusthenopteron* could paddle itself through the bottom mud of pools with its fins, but it could not walk upright because backward and forward movement of the fins was limited to about 20 to 25 degrees. The recently discovered fossil genus *Tiktaalik* is morphologically intermediate between lobe-finned fishes and tetrapods. *Tiktaalik* probably inhabited shallow, oxygen-depleted streams or swamps, using its limbs to support the body while placing its snout above water to breathe air. This form

also might have traversed land. *Acanthostega*, one of the earliest known Devonian tetrapods, had well-formed tetrapod limbs with clearly formed digits on both fore- and hindlimbs, but it was clearly an aquatically adapted form whose limbs were too weakly constructed for proper walking on land. *Ichthyostega*, however, with its fully developed shoulder girdle, bulky limb bones, well-developed muscles, and other adaptations for terrestrial life, must have been able to pull itself onto land, although it probably did not walk very well. Thus, the tetrapods evolved their limbs underwater and only later invaded land.

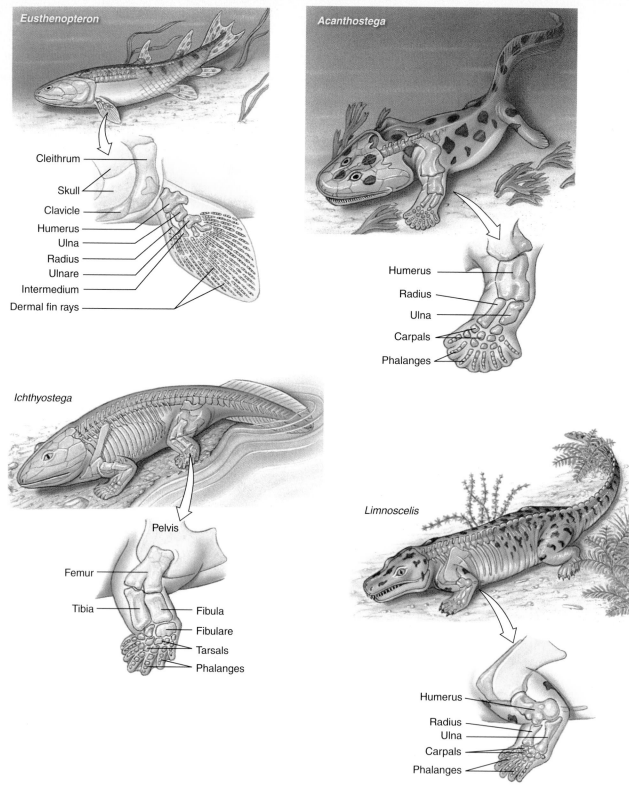

figure 17.2

Evolution of tetrapod limbs. The limbs of tetrapods evolved from the fins of Paleozoic fishes. *Eusthenopteron*, a late Devonian lobe-finned fish, had paired muscular fins supported by bony elements that foreshadowed the bones of tetrapod limbs. The anterior fin contained an upper arm bone (humerus), two forearm bones (radius and ulna), and smaller elements homologous to the wrist bones of tetrapods. As typical of fishes, the pectoral girdle, consisting of the cleithrum, clavicle, and other bones, was firmly attached to the skull. In *Acanthostega*, one of the earliest known Devonian tetrapods (appearing about 360 million years ago), dermal fin rays of the anterior appendage were replaced by eight fully evolved fingers. *Acanthostega* was probably exclusively aquatic because its limbs were too weak for travel on land. *Ichthyostega*, a contemporary of *Acanthostega*, had fully formed tetrapod limbs and must have been able to walk on land. The hindlimb bore seven toes (the number of forelimb digits is unknown). *Limnoscelis*, an anthracosaur of the Carboniferous (about 300 million years ago), had five digits on both fore- and hindlimbs, the basic pentadactyl model that became the tetrapod standard.

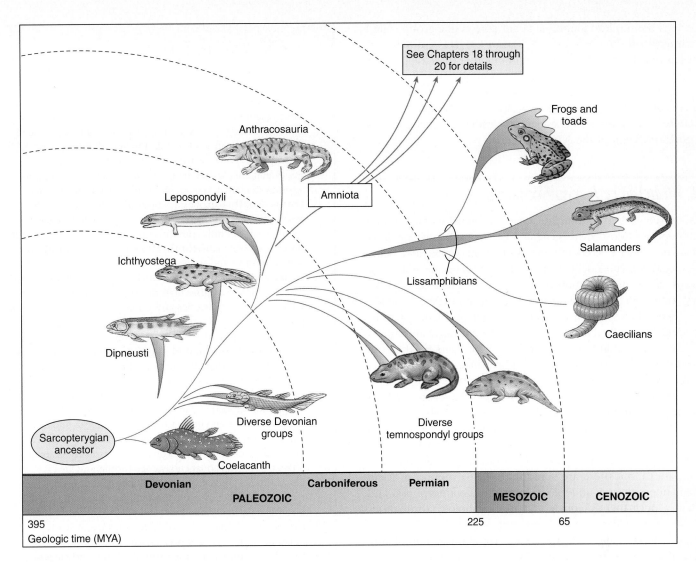

figure 17.3

Early tetrapod evolution and the descent of amphibians. The tetrapods share most recent common ancestry with the extinct Devonian groups; of living groups, the tetrapods are most closely related to the lungfishes. Amphibians share most recent common ancestry with the diverse temnospondyls of the Carboniferous and Permian periods of the Paleozoic era, and the Triassic period of the Mesozoic era.

Evidence points to lobe-finned fishes as the closest relatives of tetrapods; in cladistic terms, they contain the sister group of tetrapods (figure 17.3; see figure 17.1). Both the lobe-finned fishes and early tetrapods such as *Acanthostega* and *Ichthyostega* shared several characteristics of the skull, teeth, and pectoral girdle. *Ichthyostega* (Gr. *ichthys,* fish, + *stegē,* roof or covering, in reference to the roof of the skull, which was shaped like that of a fish) is an early offshoot of tetrapod phylogeny. It possessed several adaptations, in addition to jointed limbs, that equipped it for life on land (see figure 17.2): a stronger backbone and associated muscles to support the body in air, new muscles to elevate the head, strengthened shoulder and hip girdles, a protective rib cage, a more advanced ear structure for detecting airborne sounds, a foreshortened skull, and a lengthened snout. *Ichthyostega* nonetheless resembled aquatic forms in retaining a tail complete with fin rays and in having opercular (gill-covering) bones.

Bones of *Ichthyostega*, the most thoroughly studied of all early tetrapods, were first discovered on an east Greenland mountainside in 1897 by Swedish scientists looking for three explorers lost two years earlier during an ill-fated attempt to reach the North Pole by hot-air balloon. Later expeditions by Gunnar Säve-Söderberg uncovered skulls of *Ichthyostega*, but Säve-Söderberg died, at age 38, before he could examine the skulls. After Swedish paleontologists returned to the Greenland site, where they found the remainder of *Ichthyostega*'s skeleton, Erik Jarvik, one of Säve-Söderberg's assistants, devoted his life's work to producing the detailed description of *Ichthyostega* available to us today.

Evolutionary relationships of early tetrapod groups are still controversial. We present a tentative cladogram (see figure 17.1), which almost certainly will be revised as new data are collected. Several extinct lineages plus the **Lissamphibia,** which contains the modern amphibians, are placed in a group called **temnospondyls** (see figures 17.1 and 17.3). This group generally has only four digits on the forelimb rather than the five digits characteristic of most tetrapods. Lissamphibians diversified during the Carboniferous period to produce ancestors of the three major groups of amphibians alive today: **frogs** (Anura or Salientia), **salamanders** (Caudata or Urodela), and **caecilians** (Apoda or Gymnophiona).

■ Modern Amphibians

The three living amphibian orders comprise more than 6000 species. Most share general adaptations for life on land, including skeletal strengthening. Amphibian larvae and some aquatic adult salamanders use the ancestral lateral-line system for sensory input, but metamorphosed adults use a redesigned olfactory epithelium to sense airborne odors and ears to detect sounds.

Nonetheless, most amphibians meet problems of independent life on land only halfway. In the ancestral amphibian life history, eggs are aquatic, and they hatch to produce an aquatic larval form that uses gills for breathing. A metamorphosis follows in which gills are lost. Metamorphosed amphibians use cutaneous respiration on land, and many have lungs, which are present throughout larval life and then activated at metamorphosis for breathing air. Gas exchange across the skin also aids air breathing and is the primary means of respiration in many terrestrial salamanders. Many amphibians retain this general pattern, but there are some important exceptions. Some salamanders do not undergo a complete metamorphosis and retain a permanently aquatic, larval morphology throughout life. Some caecilians, some frogs, and other salamanders live entirely on land and lack the aquatic larval phase completely. Both alternatives are evolutionarily derived conditions.

Even the most terrestrial amphibians remain dependent on very moist environments. Their skin is thin, and it requires moisture for protection against desiccation in air. Amphibians also require moderately cool environments. As ectotherms, their body temperature is determined by their environment, and varies with its changes, greatly restricting where they can live. Cool and wet environments are especially important for reproduction. Eggs alone are not well protected from desiccation, and they must be shed directly into water or onto moist terrestrial surfaces.

Caecilians: Order Gymnophiona (Apoda)

The order Gymnophiona (jim´no-fī´o-na) (Gr. *gymnos,* naked, + *ophineos,* of a snake) contains approximately 173 species of elongate, limbless, burrowing creatures commonly called **caecilians** (figure 17.4). They occur in tropical forests of South America (their principal home), Africa, India, and Southeast Asia, and many species are aquatic. They possess a long, slender body, many vertebrae, long ribs, no limbs, and a terminal anus; some have small dermal scales in the skin. Eyes are small, and most species are totally blind as adults. Their food consists mostly of worms and small invertebrates, which they find underground.

Characteristics
of Modern Amphibians

1. **Skeleton mostly bony,** with varying numbers of vertebrae; ribs present in some, absent or fused to vertebrae in others
2. Body forms vary greatly among species: salamanders usually have distinct head, neck, trunk, and tail; adult frogs have a compressed body with fused head and trunk and no intervening neck; caecilians have an elongated trunk, not strongly demarcated from the head, and a terminal anus
3. **Limbs usually four (quadrupedal)** in two pairs with associated shoulder/hip girdle, although some forms have a single pair of limbs and others no limbs; webbed feet often present; no true nails; **forelimb usually has four digits** but sometimes five and sometimes fewer
4. **Heart with two atria,** one ventricle, a conus arteriosus, and a sinus venosus; **double circulation** through the heart in which pulmonary arteries and veins supply the lungs (when present) and return oxygenated blood to the heart; skin is abundantly supplied with blood vessels
5. **Skin smooth, moist, and glandular;** integument modified for **cutaneous respiration;** pigment cells (chromatophores) common and of considerable variety; **granular glands** associated with secretion of defensive compounds
6. Respiration by skin and in some forms by gills and/or lungs; presence of gills and lungs varies among species and by developmental stage of some species; aquatic larvae lose gills at metamorphosis if a metamorphosis occurs; many salamanders retain gills and an aquatic existence throughout life
7. Ectothermic (body temperature dependent upon environmental temperature and not modulated by metabolically generated heat)
8. Excretory system consists of paired mesonephric or opisthonephric kidneys; urea is main nitrogenous waste
9. Ear with **tympanic membrane** (eardrum) and **stapes** (columella) for transmitting vibrations to inner ear
10. For vision in air, cornea rather than lens is principal refractive surface for bending light; **eyelids** and **lachrymal glands** protect and wash eyes
11. Mouth usually large, with small teeth in upper or both jaws; paired **internal nostrils** open into a nasal cavity lined with **olfactory epithelium** at anterior part of mouth cavity and enable breathing (in lung-breathing forms)
12. Ten pairs of cranial nerves
13. Separate sexes; fertilization mostly external in frogs and toads but internal via a spermatophore in most salamanders and caecilians; predominantly oviparous, some ovoviviparous or viviparous; metamorphosis usually present; **moderately yolky eggs** (mesolecithal) **with jellylike membrane coverings**

Fertilization is internal, and the male has a protrusible copulatory organ. Eggs are usually deposited in moist ground near water. In some species, eggs are carefully guarded in folds of the body during their development. Some species have aquatic larvae with a tail fin, an open gill slit, and external gills; larval development in other species occurs within the egg. Viviparity also is common in some caecilians, with the embryos obtaining nourishment by eating the wall of the oviduct.

figure 17.4

A, Female caecilian coiled around eggs in a burrow. **B,** Pink-head caecilian (*Herpele multiplicata*), native to western Africa.

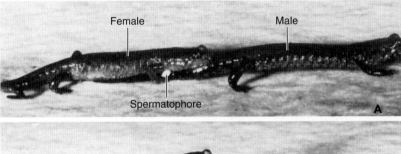
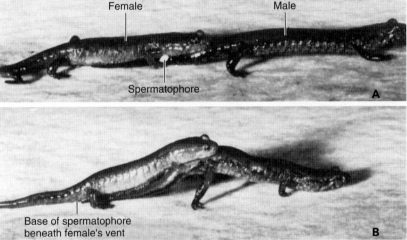

figure 17.5

Courtship and sperm transfer in the pygmy salamander, *Desmognathus wrighti*. After judging the female's receptivity by the presence of her chin on his tail base, the male deposits a spermatophore on the ground, and then moves forward a few paces. **A,** The white mass of the sperm atop a gelatinous base is visible at the level of the female's forelimb. The male moves ahead, the female following until the spermatophore is at the level of her vent. **B,** The female has recovered the sperm mass in her vent, while the male arches his tail, tilting the female upward and presumably facilitating recovery of the sperm mass. The female later uses sperm stored in her body to fertilize eggs internally before laying them.

Salamanders: Order Urodela (Caudata)

Order Urodela (Gr. *oura*, tail, + *delos*, evident) comprises tailed amphibians, approximately 553 species of salamanders. Salamanders occur in almost all northern temperate regions of the world, and they are abundant and diverse in North America. Salamanders also inhabit tropical areas of Central America and northern South America. Salamanders are typically small; most of the common North American salamanders are less than 15 cm long. Some aquatic forms are considerably longer, and Japanese giant salamanders sometimes exceed 1.5 m in length.

Most salamanders have limbs set at right angles to the trunk, with forelimbs and hindlimbs of approximately equal size. In some aquatic and burrowing forms, limbs are rudimentary or absent.

Salamanders are carnivorous both as larvae and as adults, preying on worms, small arthropods, and small molluscs. Like all amphibians, they are **ectothermic** and have a low metabolic rate.

Breeding Behavior

Some salamanders are either aquatic or terrestrial throughout their life cycle, but the ancestral life cycle is metamorphic, having aquatic larvae and terrestrial adults that live in moist places under stones and rotten logs. Eggs of most salamanders are fertilized internally; a female recovers in her vent (common

figure 17.6

Female dusky salamander (*Desmognathus* sp.) attending eggs. Many salamanders care for their eggs, which includes rotating the eggs and protecting them from fungal infections and predation by various arthropods and other salamanders.

opening for anus and reproductive system) a packet of sperm (**spermatophore**) deposited by a male on a leaf or stick (figure 17.5). Aquatic species lay their eggs in clusters or stringy masses in water. Their eggs hatch to produce an aquatic larva having external gills and a finlike tail. Completely terrestrial species deposit eggs in small, grapelike clusters under logs or in excavations in soft moist earth, and many species guard their eggs (figure 17.6). Terrestrial species undergo **direct development.** They bypass the larval stage and hatch as

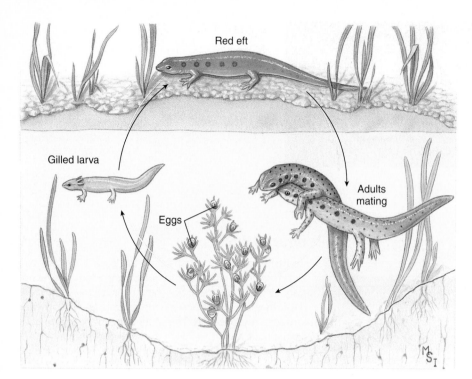

figure 17.7

Life history of the red-spotted newt, *Notophthalmus viridescens* of the family Salamandridae. In many habitats, the aquatic larva metamorphoses into a brightly colored "red eft" stage, which remains on land from one to three years before transforming into a secondarily aquatic adult.

miniature versions of their parents. The most complex salamander life cycle occurs in some American newts, whose aquatic larvae metamorphose to form terrestrial juveniles that later metamorphose again to produce secondarily aquatic, breeding adults (figure 17.7).

Respiration

At various stages of their life history, salamanders may have external gills, lungs, both, or neither of these structures. They also share the general amphibian condition of having extensive vascular nets in their skin for respiratory exchange of oxygen and carbon dioxide with the external environment (called "cutaneous respiration"). Salamanders that have an aquatic larval stage hatch with gills, but lose them later if a metamorphosis occurs. Several diverse lineages of salamanders have evolved permanently aquatic forms that fail to complete metamorphosis and retain their gills and finlike tail throughout life (figure 17.8). Lungs, the most widespread respiratory organ of terrestrial vertebrates, are present from birth in the salamanders that have them, and become the primary means of respiration following metamorphosis. Amphiumas, while having a completely aquatic life history, nonetheless lose their gills before adulthood and then breathe primarily by lungs, raising their nostrils above the water surface to get air.

In contrast to amphiumas, all species of the large family Plethodontidae (see figures 17.5, 17.6, and 17.9) are lungless, and many of these species are entirely terrestrial. Efficiency of cutaneous respiration is increased by penetration of a capillary network into the epidermis or by thinning of the epidermis over superficial dermal capillaries. Cutaneous respiration is supplemented by air pumped into the mouth, where respiratory gases are exchanged across the vascularized membranes of

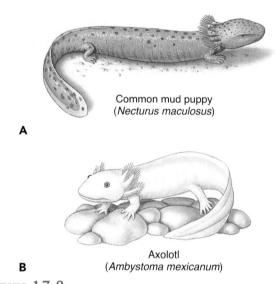

A

Common mud puppy
(*Necturus maculosus*)

B

Axolotl
(*Ambystoma mexicanum*)

figure 17.8

Permanently-gilled, aquatic salamanders. **A,** The mud puppy (*Necturus* sp.) and **B,** the axolotl (*Ambystoma mexicanum*). Some other species of *Ambystoma* are facultatively metamorphic; they may remain permanently gilled or, should their pond habitat evaporate, metamorphose to a terrestrial form that loses its gills and breathes by lungs. The axolotl shown is an albino form commonly used in laboratory experiments but uncommon in natural populations. Evolutionary change from a metamorphosing ancestor to a nonmetamorphosing, permanently-gilled descendant illustrates paedomorphosis (juvenile ancestral characters retained by adult descendants).

the buccal (mouth) cavity (buccopharyngeal breathing). Lungless plethodontids probably originated in streams, where lungs would have been disadvantageous by providing excess buoyancy, and where water is so cool and well oxygenated that cutaneous respiration alone is sufficient for life. It is odd that the most completely terrestrial group of salamanders is one that lacks lungs.

Paedomorphosis

Whereas most salamanders complete their development by metamorphosis to the adult body form, some species reach sexual maturity while retaining their gills, aquatic lifestyle, and other larval characteristics. This condition illustrates **paedomorphosis** (Gr. "child form"), defined as evolution of an adult form that resembles an ancestral juvenile. Some characteristics of an ancestral adult morphology are consequently eliminated. Examples of such nonmetamorphic, permanently-gilled species

figure 17.9

Longtail salamander, *Eurycea longicauda,* a common plethodontid salamander.

are mud puppies of the genus *Necturus* (see figure 17.8A), which live on the bottoms of ponds and lakes, and the **axolotl** of Mexico (see figure 17.8B). These species never metamorphose under any conditions.

Other species of salamanders that reach sexual maturity with larval morphology may metamorphose to terrestrial forms under certain environmental conditions. We find good examples in *Ambystoma tigrinum* and related species from North America. They typically inhabit small ponds that can disappear through evaporation in dry weather. When ponds evaporate, the aquatic form metamorphoses to a terrestrial form, losing its gills and developing lungs. It then can travel across land to find new sources of water in which to live and to reproduce.

Paedomorphosis is an important means of evolutionary diversification, even in salamanders that lack an aquatic larval stage. For example, paedomorphosis provides a means by which some species of the tropical plethodontid genus *Bolitoglossa* evolved adaptations for climbing forest vegetation. The highly webbed feet of *Bolitoglossa rufescens* result from paedomorphic evolution in which development of the digits is greatly reduced (figure 17.10B), making the foot an adhesive surface for attaching the animal to banana trees and other smooth leaves and stems. The ancestral adult foot structure has greater digital development (figure 17.10A and C) and occurs in related species that live mainly on the ground.

Frogs and Toads: Order Anura (Salientia)

The approximately 5283 species of frogs and toads that form the order Anura (Gr. *an,* without, + *oura,* tail) are for most people the most familiar amphibians. The Anura are an old group, known from the Triassic period, 250 million years ago. Frogs and toads occupy a great variety of habitats, despite their aquatic mode of reproduction and water-permeable skin, which

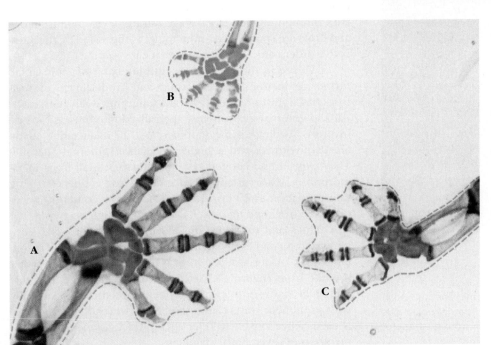

figure 17.10

Foot structure of representatives of three different species of the tropical plethodontid salamander genus *Bolitoglossa.* These specimens have been treated chemically to clear the skin and muscles and to stain the bone red/pink and the cartilage blue. The species having the most fully ossified and distinct digits (**A, C**) live primarily on the forest floor. The species having the pad-like foot caused by restricted digital growth (**B**) climbs smooth leaves and stems using the foot surface to produce suction or adhesion for attachment. The padlike foot evolved by paedomorphosis; it was derived evolutionarily by truncating development of the body, which prevents full digital development.

A

figure 17.11

Two common North American frogs. **A,** Bullfrog, *Litho-bates catesbeianus*, largest American frog and mainstay of the frog-leg epicurean market (family Ranidae). **B,** Green tree frog, *Hyla cinerea*, a common inhabitant of swamps of the southeastern United States (family Hylidae). Note the adhesive pads on the feet.

B

figure 17.12

American toad, *Bufo americanus* of the family Bufonidae. This principally nocturnal yet familiar amphibian feeds on large numbers of insect pests as well as on snails and earthworms. The warty skin contains numerous glands that produce a surprisingly poisonous milky fluid, giving the toad excellent protection from a variety of potential predators.

prevent them from wandering too far from sources of water, and their ectothermy, which bars them from polar and subarctic habitats. The name of the order, Anura, refers to an obvious group characteristic, the absence of tails in adults (although all pass through a tailed larval stage during development). Frogs and toads are specialized for jumping, as suggested by the alternative order name, Salientia, which means leaping.

We see in the appearance and life habit of their larvae further distinctions between Anura and Urodela. Eggs of most frogs hatch into a tadpole having a long, finned tail, both internal and external gills, no legs, specialized mouthparts for herbivorous feeding (some tadpoles and all salamander larvae are carnivorous), and a highly specialized internal anatomy. They look and act altogether differently than adult frogs. Metamorphosis of a frog tadpole to an adult frog is thus a striking transformation. The permanently gilled larval condition never occurs in frogs and toads as it does in salamanders.

Frogs and toads are divided into 44 families. The best-known frog families in North America are Ranidae, which contains most of our familiar frogs (figure 17.11A), and Hylidae, the tree frogs (figure 17.11B). True toads, belonging to family Bufonidae, have short legs, stout bodies, and thick skins usually with prominent warts (figure 17.12). However, the term "toad" is used rather loosely to refer also to thick-skinned, terrestrial members of several other families.

figure 17.13

Conraua goliath (family Petropedetidae) of West Africa, the world's largest frog. This specimen weighed 3.3 kg (approximately 7-1/2 pounds).

The largest anuran is the West African *Conraua goliath,* which is more than 30 cm long from tip of nose to anus (figure 17.13). This giant eats animals as big as rats and ducks. The smallest frogs recorded are *Eleutherodactylus iberia* and *Psyllophryne didactyla,* measuring less than 1 cm in length; they are also the smallest known tetrapods. These tiny frogs, which can be more than covered by a dime, live respectively in Cuba and in the Brazilian rain forest. The largest American frog is the bullfrog, *Lithobates catesbeianus* (see figure 17.11A), which reaches a head and body length of 20 cm.

Habitats and Distribution

Probably the most familiar frogs are species of the ranid genera *Lithobates, Pelophylax* and *Rana* (Gr. frog), which collectively occupy most temperate and tropical regions of the world. They usually live near water, although some, such as the wood frog, *L. sylvatica,* spend most of their time on damp forest floors. The larger bullfrogs, *L. catesbeianus,* and the green frogs, *L. clamitans,* are nearly always in or near permanent water or swamps. Leopard frogs, *L. pipiens* and related species, occur in nearly every state and Canadian province and are the most widespread of all North American frogs. The northern leopard frog, *L. pipiens,* is the species most commonly used in biology laboratories and for classical electrophysiological research.

Frog species are often patchy in distribution, being restricted to certain localities (for instance, to specific streams or pools) and absent or scarce in similar habitats elsewhere. Pickerel frogs (*L. palustris*) are especially noteworthy in this respect. Recent studies show that many populations of frogs worldwide may be declining in numbers and becoming even more geographically fragmented than usual. Causes of decline include high ultraviolet radiation and infections with larval trematodes and fungi.

Most larger frogs are solitary except during breeding season. During breeding periods, most of them, especially males, are very noisy. Each male usually takes possession of a particular perch near water, where he may remain for hours or even days, trying to attract a female to that spot. At times, frogs are mainly silent, and their presence is not detected until they are disturbed. When they enter the water, they dart swiftly to the bottom of the pool, where they kick the substrate to conceal themselves in a cloud of muddy water. In swimming, they hold the forelimbs near the body and kick backward with their webbed hindlimbs, which propel them forward. When they surface to breathe, only the head and foreparts are exposed, and they conceal themselves behind any available vegetation.

Amphibian populations have declined in various parts of the world, although many species thrive. No single explanation fits all declines, although loss of habitat predominates. In some populations, changes are simply random fluctuations caused by periodic droughts and other naturally occurring phenomena. Frog and toad eggs exposed on the surfaces of ponds are especially sensitive to damaging ultraviolet radiation. Climatic changes that reduce water depth at oviposition sites increase the ultraviolet exposure of embryos and make them more susceptible to fungal infection. Declines in population may be accompanied by an increased incidence of malformed individuals, such as frogs with extra limbs. Malformed limbs are often associated with infection by trematodes (see p. 153).

Declines in some amphibian populations are caused by other amphibians. For example, an exotic frog introduced into southern California thrives in its new American home. African clawed frogs, *Xenopus laevis* (figure 17.14), are voracious, aggressive, primarily aquatic frogs that rapidly displace native frogs and fish from waterways. This species was introduced into North America in the 1940s when it was used extensively in human pregnancy tests. Some hospitals dumped surplus frogs into nearby streams, where these prolific breeders flourished and are now considered pests. Similar results occurred when giant toads, *Bufo marinus* (to 23 cm in length), were introduced to Queensland, Australia to control agricultural pests. They rapidly spread, producing numerous ecological changes, including displacement of native anurans.

During winter months, most frogs hibernate in soft mud under pools and streams. Their life processes reach a very low ebb during hibernation, and such energy as they need comes from glycogen and fat stored in their bodies during the spring

figure 17.14

African clawed frog, *Xenopus laevis*. The claws, an unusual feature in frogs, are on the hind feet. This frog has been introduced into California, where it is considered a serious pest.

and summer. More terrestrial frogs, such as tree frogs, hibernate in humus of the forest floor. They tolerate low temperatures, and many actually survive prolonged freezing of all extracellular fluid, representing 35% of their body water. Such frost-tolerant frogs prepare for winter by accumulating glucose and glycerol in their body fluids, which protects tissues from ice-crystal formation.

Adult frogs have numerous enemies, including snakes, aquatic birds, turtles, raccoons, and humans; fish prey upon tadpoles, only a few of which survive to maturity. Some adult frogs defend themselves by feigning death. Most anurans can inflate their lungs so that they are difficult to swallow. When disturbed along the margin of a pond or brook, a frog often remains quite still. When it senses danger, it jumps, not always into the water where enemies may lurk, but into grassy cover on the bank. When held, a frog may cease its struggles for an instant to put its captor off guard and then suddenly leap, voiding its urine. A frog's best protection is its ability to leap and in some species, to use poison glands. Many frogs and toads in the tropics and subtropics are aggressive, jumping and biting at predators. Bullfrogs in captivity do not hesitate to snap at tormenters and can inflict painful bites.

figure 17.15

A male green frog, *Hyla cinerea*, clasps a larger female during the breeding season in a South Carolina swamp. Clasping (amplexus) is maintained until the female deposits her eggs, which are fertilized externally (outside the body). Like most tree frogs, these are capable of rapid and marked color changes; the male here, normally green, has darkened during amplexus.

Life History

Because frogs and toads are ectothermic, they breed, feed, and grow only during warm seasons, often in a predictable annual cycle. With warming spring temperatures and rainfall, males call vociferously to attract females. After a brief courtship, females enter the water and are clasped by the males in a process called **amplexus** (figure 17.15), during which eggs are fertilized externally (after leaving the female's body). As the female lays eggs, the male discharges seminal fluid containing sperm over the eggs to fertilize them. After fertilization, the jelly layers absorb water and swell (figure 17.16). Eggs are laid in large masses, often anchored to vegetation, and then abandoned by the parents. The eggs begin development immediately. Within a few days, the embryos have developed into tiny tadpoles

---

Classification of Class Amphibia

Order Gymnophiona (jim´no-fī´o-na) (Gr. *gymnos,* naked, + *ophioneos,* of a snake) **(Apoda): caecilians.** Body elongate; limbs and limb girdle absent; mesodermal scales present in skin of some; tail short or absent; 95 to 285 vertebrae; pantropical, 3 families, 33 genera, approximately 173 species.

Order Urodela (ūr´uh-dēl´ə) (Gr. *oura,* tail, + *delos,* evident) **(Caudata): salamanders.** Body with head, trunk, and tail; no scales; usually two pairs of equal limbs; 10 to 60 vertebrae;

predominantly Holarctic; 9 living families, 64 genera, approximately 553 species.

Order Anura (uh-nūr´ə) (Gr. *an,* without, + *oura,* tail) **(Salientia): frogs** and **toads.** Head and trunk fused; no tail; no scales; two pairs of limbs; large mouth; lungs; 6 to 10 vertebrae including urostyle (coccyx); cosmopolitan, predominantly tropical; 44 families; 362 genera; approximately 5283 species.

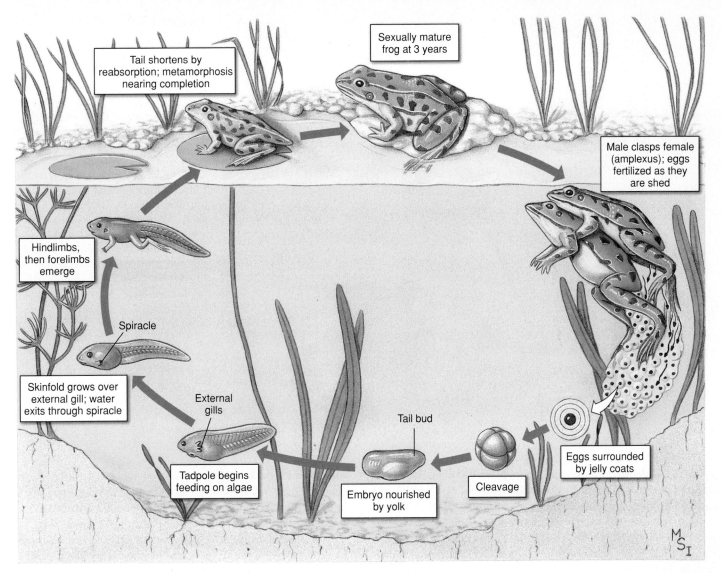

figure 17.16

Life cycle of a leopard frog. The stages marked "cleavage" and "embryo nourished by yolk" are visible through the translucent jelly layers surrounding the egg (not shown).

visible through the translucent jelly layers surrounding them (see figure 17.16). The embryonic tadpoles grow and develop for several weeks before hatching from their eggs to become freeliving. If the eggs were laid in a temporary pond or puddle, tadpoles race against time to complete development before the habitat dries.

At hatching, a tadpole has a distinct head and body with a compressed tail. The mouth is on the ventral side of the head and has keratinized jaws for scraping vegetation from objects for food. Behind the mouth is a ventral adhesive disc for clinging to objects. In front of the mouth are two deep pits, which later become nostrils. Swellings occur on each side of the head, and these later become external gills. There are three pairs of external gills, which later transform into internal gills that become covered with a flap of skin (the operculum) on each side. On the right side, the operculum completely fuses with the body wall, but on the left side a small opening, the **spiracle** (L. *spiraculum,* airhole) permits water to exit after entering the mouth and passing the internal gills. The hindlimbs appear first, whereas the forelimbs are hidden for a time by folds of the operculum. The tail is absorbed, the intestine becomes much shorter, the mouth undergoes a transformation into the adult condition, lungs develop, and the gills are absorbed. Leopard frogs usually complete metamorphosis within three months; a bullfrog takes much longer to complete this process.

The life cycle just described is typical of most temperate-zone anurans but is only one of many alternative patterns in tropical anurans. Some remarkable reproductive strategies of tropical anurans are illustrated in figure 17.17. Some species lay their eggs in foam masses that float on the surface of the water; some deposit their eggs on leaves overhanging ponds and streams into which the emerging tadpoles will drop; some lay

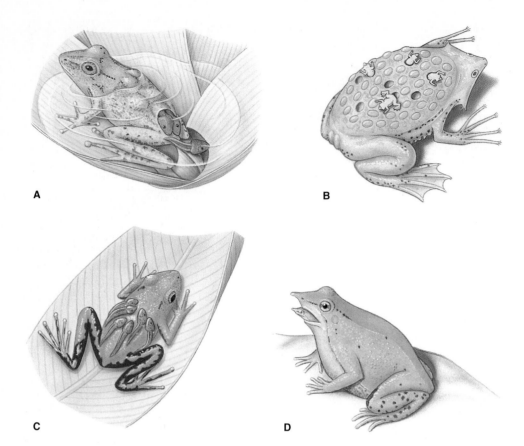

A

B

C

D

figure 17.17

Unusual reproductive strategies of anurans. **A,** A female South American pygmy marsupial frog (*Flectonotus pygmaeus*) carries developing larvae in a dorsal pouch. **B,** A female Surinam frog carries eggs embedded in specialized brooding pouches on the dorsum; froglets emerge and swim away when development is complete. **C,** A male poison-dart frog, *Phyllobates bicolor,* carries tadpoles adhering to its back. **D,** Tadpoles of Darwin's frog, *Rhinoderma darwinii,* develop into froglets in their male parent's vocal pouch. When the froglets are ready to emerge, their father opens his mouth to let them escape.

their eggs in damp burrows; and others place their eggs in water trapped in tree cavities or in water-filled chambers of some bromeliads (epiphytic plants in the tropical forest canopy). While most frogs abandon their eggs, some tend their eggs. Marsupial frogs carry their developing eggs in a pouch on the back (figure 17.17A). In Surinam frogs (figure 17.17B), the male and female do backward somersaults during mating, and eggs and sperm slide into the space between the mating pair. The male presses the fertilized eggs into the female's back, which develops a spongy incubating layer that eventually sloughs once young are hatched. Hatchling poison-dart frogs squirm onto the parent's back to be carried for varying lengths of time (figure 17.16C). Tadpoles of Darwin's frog develop into froglets in the protection of their father's vocal pouch (figure 17.7D).

Although most frogs develop through a larval stage (the tadpole), many tropical frogs have evolved direct development. In direct development, the tadpole stage is bypassed, and the froglet that emerges is a miniature replica of the adult. In the species-rich tropical genus *Eleutherodactylus,* mating occurs on land, and eggs hatch directly into froglets; the aquatic larval stage is eliminated, freeing these frogs from an obligatory association with pools or streams.

■ Summary

Amphibians are ectothermic, primitively quadrupedal vertebrates that have glandular skin and breathe by lungs, by gills, and/or through their skin. They form one of two major phylogenetic branches of living tetrapods, the other one being the amniotes. Living amphibians comprise three major evolutionary groups. Caecilians (order Gymnophiona) are a small tropical group of limbless, elongate forms. Salamanders (order Urodela, or Caudata) are tailed amphibians that have retained the generalized four-legged body plan of their Paleozoic ancestors. Frogs and toads (order Anura) are the largest group of modern amphibians; adults are specialized for a jumping mode of locomotion on land or in water.

Most amphibians have a biphasic life cycle that begins with an aquatic larva followed by metamorphosis to a terrestrial adult that returns to water to lay eggs. Some frogs, salamanders, and caecilians have evolved direct development that omits the aquatic larval stage, and some caecilians have evolved viviparity. Salamanders are unique among amphibians in having evolved several permanently gilled species that retain a larval morphology throughout life, eliminating the terrestrial phase completely. The permanently gilled condition is obligate in some species, but others metamorphose to a terrestrial form only if the pond habitat dries.

Despite adaptations for terrestrial life, the adults and eggs of all amphibians require cool, moist environments if not actual pools or streams. Eggs and adult skin have no effective protection against very cold, hot, or dry conditions, greatly restricting the adaptive diversification of amphibians to environments with moderate temperatures and abundant water.

Review Questions

1. How did the characteristic differences between aquatic and terrestrial environments influence the early evolution of tetrapods?
2. Describe the different modes of respiration used by amphibians. What paradox do the amphiumas and terrestrial plethodontids present regarding the association of lungs with life on land?
3. Evolution of the tetrapod limb was one of the most important advances in vertebrate history. Describe the inferred sequence of its evolution.
4. Compare the general life-history patterns of salamanders with those of frogs. Which group shows a greater variety of evolutionary changes from the ancestral biphasic amphibian life cycle?
5. Give the literal meaning of the name Gymnophiona. What animals are in this amphibian order? Describe their appearance and habitats.
6. What are the literal meanings of the order names Urodela and Anura? What major features distinguish members of these two orders from each other?
7. Describe the breeding behavior of a typical woodland salamander.
8. How is paedomorphosis important to evolutionary diversification of salamanders?
9. Briefly describe the reproductive behavior of frogs. In what important ways do frogs and salamanders differ in their reproduction?

Selected References

See also general references on page 423.

Clack, J. A. 2002. Gaining ground: the origin and evolution of tetrapods. Bloomington, Indiana, Indiana University Press. *An authoritative account of paleontological evidence regarding tetrapod origins.*

Conant, R., and J. T. Collins. 1998. A field guide to reptiles and amphibians: Eastern and Central North America. The Peterson field guide series. Boston, Houghton Mifflin Company. *Updated version of a popular field guide; color illustrations and distribution maps for all species.*

Daeschler, E. B., N. H. Shubin, and F. A. Jenkins, Jr. 2006. A Devonian tetrapod-like fish and the evolution of the tetrapod body plan. Nature **440:**757–763. *Describes Tiktaalik, a fossil intermediate between lobe-finned fishes and tetrapods.*

Duellman, W. E., and L. R. Trueb. 1994. Biology of amphibians. Baltimore, Johns Hopkins University Press. *Important comprehensive sourcebook of information on amphibians, extensively referenced and illustrated.*

Frost, D. R., T. Grant, J. Faivovich, R. H. Bain, A. Haas, C. F. B. Haddad, R. O. De Sá, A. Channing, M. Wilkinson, S. C. Donnellan, C. J. Raxworthy, J. A. Campbell, B. L. Blotto, P. Moler, R. C. Drewes, R. A. Nussbaum, J. D. Lynch, D. M. Green, and W. C. Wheeler. 2006. The amphibian tree of life. Bull. Am. Mus. Nat. Hist. **297:**1–370. *A phylogeny for living amphibians derived from a large compilation of morphological and molecular characters.*

Halliday, T. R., and K. Adler, eds. 2002. Firefly encyclopedia of reptiles and amphibians. Toronto, Canada, Firefly Books. *Excellent authoritative reference work with high-quality illustrations.*

Jamieson, B. G. M. (ed.). 2003. Reproductive biology and phylogeny of Anura. Enfield, New Hampshire, Science Publishers, Inc. *Provides detailed coverage of reproductive biology and early evolutionary diversification of frogs and toads.*

Lannoo, M. (ed.). 2005. Amphibian declines: the conservation status of United States species. Berkeley, California, University of California Press. *A survey of conservation status of American amphibians.*

Lewis, S. 1989. Cane toads: an unnatural history. New York, Dolphin/Doubleday. *Based on an amusing and informative film of the same title that describes the introduction of cane toads to Queensland, Australia, and the unexpected consequences of their population explosion there. "If Monty Python teamed up with National Geographic, the result would be Cane Toads."*

Savage, J. M. 2002. The amphibians and reptiles of Costa Rica. Chicago, University of Chicago Press. *Costa Rica hosts diverse caecilians, frogs, and salamanders. The Organization for Tropical Studies offers students a chance to study this amphibian fauna.*

Sever, D. M. (ed.). 2003. Reproductive biology and phylogeny of Urodela (Amphibia). Enfield, New Hampshire, Science Publishers, Inc. *A thorough review of reproductive biology and evolutionary relationships among salamanders.*

Stebbins, R. C., and N. W. Cohen. 1995. A natural history of amphibians. Princeton, New Jersey, Princeton University Press. *World-wide treatment of amphibian biology, emphasizing physiological adaptations, ecology, reproduction, behavior, and a concluding chapter on amphibian declines.*

Custom Website

The *Animal Diversity* Online Learning Center is a great place to check your understanding of chapter material. Visit www.mhhe.com/hickmanad5e for access to key terms, quizzes, and more! Further enhance your knowledge with web links to chapter-related material.

Explore live links for these topics:

Classification and Phylogeny of Animals
Class Amphibia
Order Gymnophiona
Order Urodela
Order Salientia

Dissection Guides for Amphibians
Conservation Issues Concerning Amphibians

Amniote Origins and Nonavian Reptiles

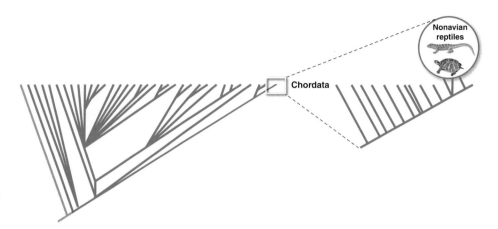

Chordata

Nonavian reptiles

Hatching Komodo lizard, *Varanus komodoensis.*

Enclosing the Pond

Amphibians, with their well-developed limbs, redesigned sensory and respiratory systems, and modifications of the postcranial skeleton for supporting the body in air, have made a notable conquest of land. However, their shell-less eggs, thin, moist skin, and often gilled larvae keep their development hazardously tied to water. The ancestor of a clade containing nonavian reptiles, birds, and mammals evolved an egg better adapted for dry terrestrial conditions. This shelled egg, perhaps more than any other adaptation, unshackled early reptiles from the aquatic environment by freeing the developmental process from dependence on aquatic or very moist terrestrial environments. In fact, the "pond-dwelling" stages were not eliminated but enclosed within a series of extraembryonic membranes that provided complete support for embryonic development. One membrane, the amnion, encloses a fluid-filled cavity, the "pond," which suspends the developing embryo. Another membranous sac, the allantois, serves both as a respiratory surface and as a chamber for storing nitrogenous wastes. Enclosing these membranes is a third membrane, the chorion, through which oxygen and carbon dioxide freely pass. Finally, surrounding and protecting everything is a porous, parchmentlike or leathery shell.

With the last ties to aquatic reproduction severed, conquest of land by vertebrates was ensured. Paleozoic tetrapods that developed this reproductive pattern were ancestors of a single, monophyletic assemblage called Amniota, named after the innermost of the three extraembryonic membranes, the amnion. Before the end of the Paleozoic era, the amniotes diversified into multiple lineages that gave rise to all nonavian reptiles, birds, and mammals.

The paraphyletic class Reptilia (rep-til´ē-ə) (L. *repto,* to creep) includes nearly 8000 species (approximately 340 species in the United States and Canada) occupying a great variety of aquatic and terrestrial habitats, in many of which they are diverse and abundant. Nevertheless, reptiles are perhaps remembered best for what they once were, rather than for what they are now. The "age of reptiles," which lasted for more than 165 million years, saw the diversification of reptilian lineages into a bewildering array of terrestrial and aquatic forms. Among these were herbivorous and carnivorous dinosaurs, many of huge stature and awesome appearance, that dominated animal life on land. Then, during a mass extinction at the end of the Mesozoic era, many reptilian lineages became extinct. Among the lineages to emerge from the Mesozoic extinction are those of today's reptiles. One of these lineages includes the two species of tuataras (*Sphenodon*) of New Zealand, sole survivors of a group that otherwise disappeared 100 million years ago. Their closest living relatives, lizards and snakes, diversified greatly following the Mesozoic era (figure 18.1). The morphology, physiology, and behavior of some reptiles, especially lizards, probably are more similar to the first amniotes than any other living vertebrates. In the next section, we discuss the origin of amniotes, their diversification into various groups, and their adaptations for life on dry land.

Origin and Early Evolution of Amniotes

As mentioned in the prologue to this chapter, amniotes are a monophyletic group that appeared and diversified in the late Paleozoic era. Most zoologists agree that amniotes are most closely related to anthracosaurs, a group of **anamniotes** (vertebrates lacking an amnion) of the early Carboniferous period. Early diversification of amniotes produced three patterns of holes (fenestrae) in the temporal region of the skull. **Anapsid** (Gr. *an,* without, + *apsis,* arch) skulls have no openings in the temporal area of the skull behind the **orbit** (opening in the skull for the eye); thus, the temporal region of the skull is completely roofed by dermal bones (figure 18.2). This skull morphology was present in the earliest amniotes, and in one living group, the turtles, although the anapsid condition in turtles likely evolved secondarily, from ancestors having temporal fenestrae. Two other amniote clades, Diapsida and Synapsida, represent separate evolutionary derivations from the ancestral anapsid condition.

The **diapsid** (Gr. *di,* double, + *apsis,* arch) skull has two temporal openings: one pair located low over the cheeks, and a second pair positioned above the lower pair, in the roof of the skull, and separated from the first by a bony arch (see figure 18.2). Diapsid skulls are present in birds and all amniotes traditionally considered "reptiles," except turtles (see figure 18.1). In many living diapsids (lizards, snakes, and birds), one or both of the bony arches and openings have been lost, perhaps to facilitate skull kinesis (see figure 18.9). The earliest diapsids gave rise to five morphologically distinct clades. The **lepidosaurs** include lizards, snakes, and tuataras. The **archosaurs** include dinosaurs, pterosaurs, and living crocodilians and birds. A third, smaller clade, the **sauropterygians,** includes several extinct aquatic groups, the most conspicuous of which are the large, long-necked plesiosaurs (see figure 18.1). **Ichthyosaurs,** represented by extinct, aquatic, dolphinlike forms (see figure 18.1), form a fourth clade of diapsids. Placement of the last clade, the **turtles,** with diapsids is controversial, although we treat turtles as highly modified members of the clade Diapsida here. Turtle skulls lack temporal fenestrae and are often hypothesized to be the only living descendants of pararept, an early anapsid group. However, other morphological and genetic evidence published over the past 15 years places turtles within the diapsid clade, suggesting that the two pairs of temporal fenestrae characteristic of diapsids were lost early in turtle evolution.

The third skull fenestration condition is **synapsid** (Gr. *syn,* together, + *apsis,* arch), characterized by a single pair of temporal openings located low on the cheeks and bordered by a bony arch (figure 18.2). The synapsid condition occurs in a clade that includes mammals and their extinct relatives, the therapsids and pelycosaurs (see figure 18.1).

What was the functional significance of the temporal openings in early amniotes? In living forms, these openings are occupied by large muscles that elevate (adduct) the lower jaw. Changes in jaw musculature might reflect a shift from suction feeding in aquatic vertebrates to a terrestrial feeding method that required larger muscles to produce more static pressure, for such activities as nipping plant material with the anterior teeth or grinding food with the posterior teeth.

Derived Characters of Amniotes

In addition to several skeletal syanapomorphies in the head, shoulder, and ankle, amniotes have several unique morphological features that support an active, terrestrial lifestyle.

1. **Amniotic egg.** All amniotes have eggs with four extraembryonic membranes: the **amnion, allantois, chorion,** and **yolk sac** (figure 18.3). The amnion encloses the embryo in fluid, cushioning the embryo and providing an aqueous medium for growth. The allantois forms a sac for storage of metabolic wastes. The chorion surrounds the entire contents of the egg, and like the allantois, is highly vascularized. Like eggs of anamniotes, amniotic eggs have a yolk sac for nutrient storage, although the yolk sac tends to be larger in amniotes. Most amniotic eggs are surrounded by a mineralized but often flexible shell, although many lizards and snakes and most mammals lack shelled eggs. The shell forms an important mechanical support, and especially for birds, a semipermeable barrier, which allows passage of gases but limits water loss.

   How did the amniotic egg evolve? It is tempting to think of the amniotic egg as *the* land egg. However, many amphibians lay eggs on land, and many amniotic eggs,

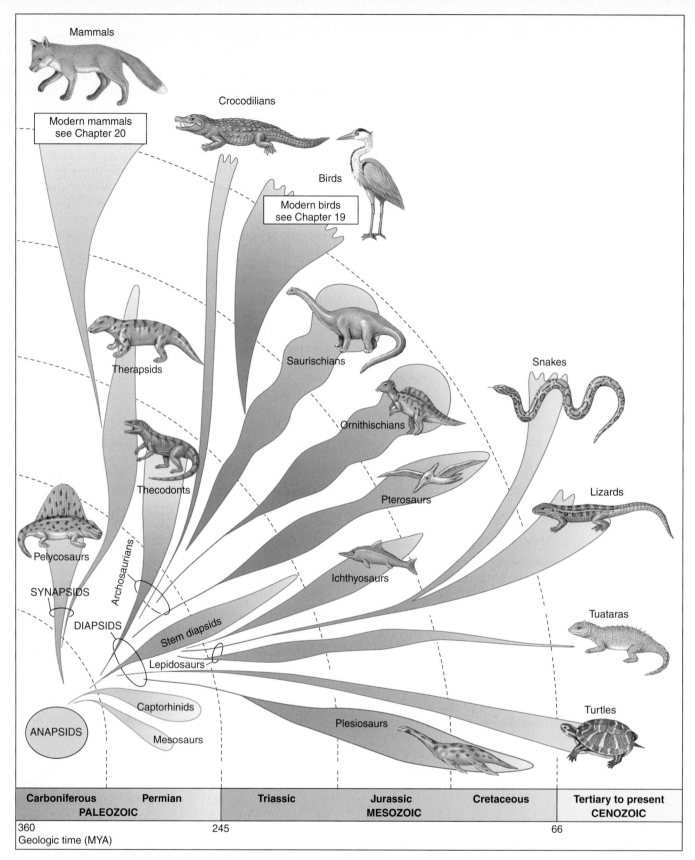

figure 18.1

Evolution of amniotes. The earliest amniotes evolved an amniotic egg, which allowed amniotes to exploit much drier habitats than their ancestors. The living amniotes, which include nonavian reptiles, birds, and mammals, evolved from a lineage of small, lizardlike forms that retained the anapsid skull pattern of early, anamniote tetrapods. One lineage that descended from the early amniotes had a skull pattern called synapsid. Mammals evolved from early synapsids. Birds, squamates, and crocodilians have a skull pattern called diapsid. Turtles have an anapsid skull, although it is probably independently evolved. The great Mesozoic diversification of amniotes may have resulted partly from the increased variety of ecological habitats and the increased ecological productivity of the Mesozoic era.

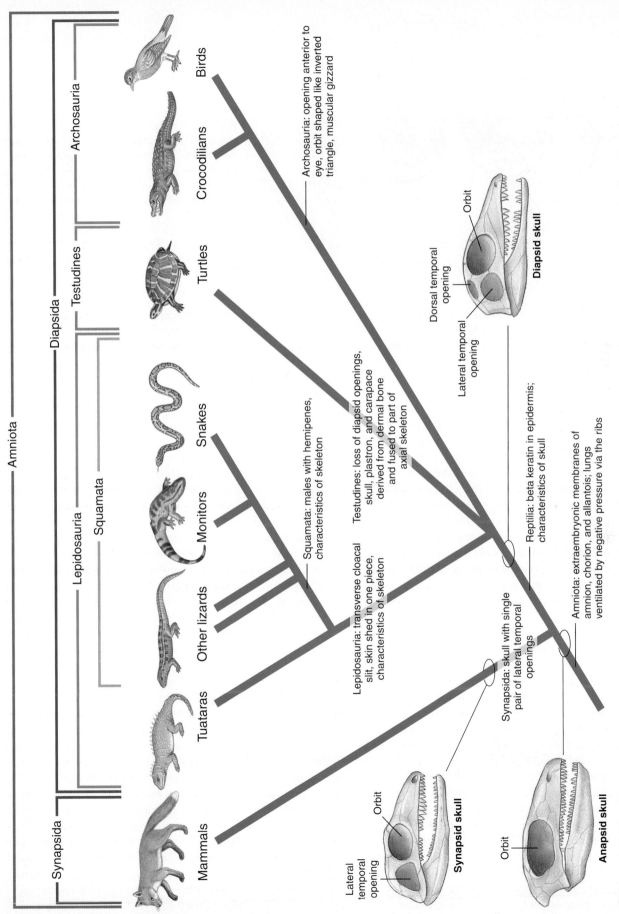

figure 18.2

Cladogram of living Amniota, showing monophyletic groups. Some shared derived characters (synapomorphies) of the groups are given. The skulls represent the ancestral condition of the three groups. Skulls of modern diapsids and synapsids are often highly modified by loss or fusion of skull bones that obscures the ancestral condition. Representative skulls for anapsids are *Nyctiphruetus* of the upper Permian; for diapsids, *Youngina* of the upper Permian; for synapsids, *Aerosaurus*, a pelycosaur of the lower Permian. The relationship of turtles to other reptiles is controversial: some researchers consider them archosaurs; others consider them lepidosaurs or direct living descendants of anapsids.

Labels within figure:

Birds

Crocodilians

Turtles

Snakes

Monitors

Other lizards

Tuataras

Mammals

Amniota

Synapsida

Diapsida

Archosauria

Testudines

Lepidosauria

Squamata

Archosauria: opening anterior to eye, orbit shaped like inverted triangle, muscular gizzard

Squamata: males with hemipenes, characteristics of skeleton

Testudines: loss of diapsid openings, skull, plastron, and carapace derived from dermal bone and fused to part of axial skeleton

Lepidosauria: transverse cloacal slit, skin shed in one piece, characteristics of skeleton

Reptilia: beta keratin in epidermis; characteristics of skull

Amniota: extraembryonic membranes of amnion, chorion, and allantois; lungs ventilated by negative pressure via the ribs

Synapsida: skull with single pair of lateral temporal openings

Dorsal temporal opening

Orbit

Lateral temporal opening

Diapsid skull

Lateral temporal opening

Orbit

Synapsid skull

Orbit

Anapsid skull

359

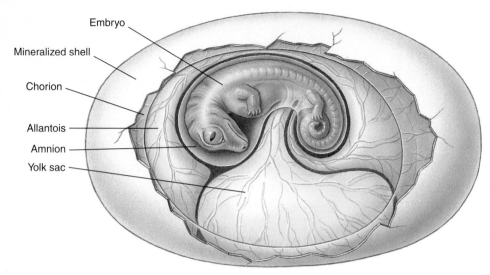

Embryo

Mineralized shell

Chorion

Allantois

Amnion

Yolk sac

figure 18.3

Amniotic egg. The embryo develops within the amnion and is cushioned by amniotic fluid. Food is provided by yolk from the yolk sac, and metabolic wastes are deposited within the allantois. As development proceeds, the allantois fuses with the chorion, a membrane lying against the inner surface of the shell; both membranes are supplied with blood vessels that assist in the exchange of oxygen and carbon dioxide across the porous shell. Because this kind of egg is an enclosed, self-contained system, it is often called a "cleidoic" egg (Gr. *kleidoun*, to lock in).

such as those of turtles, must be buried in moist soil or deposited in areas of high humidity. Still, amniotic eggs can be laid in places too dry for any amphibian; clearly, the evolution of amniotic eggs was a major factor in the success of tetrapods on land. Perhaps a more important selective advantage of the amniotic egg is that it permitted development of a larger, faster-growing embryo. Anamniote eggs are supported mainly by a thick, jelly-like layer. This jelly layer is inadequate to support large eggs and limits movement of oxygen into the eggs. One hypothesis suggests that a first step in the evolution of the amniotic egg was replacement of the jelly layer with a shell, which provided better support and movement of oxygen. Furthermore, calcium deposited in the shell can be dissolved and absorbed by the growing embryo, providing a raw material needed for skeleton construction. This hypothesis is supported by physiological studies, which show that embryos of species with the smallest amniotic eggs have a metabolic rate about three times that of embryos of anamniotes with eggs of the same size.

2. **Rib ventilation of the lungs.** Amphibians, like air-breathing fishes, fill their lungs by *pushing* air from the oral and pharyngeal cavities into the lungs. In contrast, amniotes *draw* air into their lungs (**aspiration**) by expanding the thoracic cavity using costal (rib) muscles or by pulling the liver (with other muscles) posterior.

3. **Thicker and more waterproof skin.** Although skin structure varies widely among living amniotes and anamniote tetrapods, amniote skin tends to be more keratinized and less permeable to water. A wide variety of structures composed of keratin, such as scales, hair, feathers, and claws, project from amniote skin, and the epidermis itself is more heavily keratinized. Keratin protects the skin from physical trauma, and lipids in the skin limit water loss through the skin. Together, keratin and lipids limit the skin's ability to exchange respiratory gases—so, unlike most amphibians, few amniotes use

their skin as a primary respiratory organ. Amniote gas exchange takes place primarily in the lungs, which have considerably more surface area than anamniote lungs.

Changes in Traditional Classification of Reptiles

With increasing use of cladistic methodology in zoology and its insistence on hierarchical arrangement of monophyletic groups (see p. 83), important changes have been made in the classification of amniotes. As traditionally defined, class Reptilia excludes birds, but includes snakes, lizards, tuataras, crocodilians, and turtles, in addition to several extinct groups, such as dinosaurs, plesiosaurs, pterosaurs, and the "mammal-like reptiles." However, birds and reptiles share several derived characters, including certain skull and ankle characteristics as well as the presence of a special type of keratin in the skin called beta keratin, which unites them as a monophyletic group (see figure 18.2). Thus, reptiles as traditionally defined form a **paraphyletic** group because they do not include all descendants of their most recent ancestor.

Crocodilians and birds are sister groups; they are more recently descended from a common ancestor than either is from any other living reptilian lineage. In other words, crocodilians and birds belong to a monophyletic group apart from other reptiles and, according to the rules of cladistics, should be assigned to a clade that separates them from the remaining reptiles. This clade is in fact recognized; it is Archosauria (see figures 18.1 and 18.2), a grouping that also includes the extinct dinosaurs and pterosaurs. Archosaurs, along with their sister group, the lepidosaurs (tuataras, lizards, and snakes), and turtles, form a monophyletic group that cladists call Reptilia. Here we use Reptilia and reptiles in a cladistic fashion to include living amniote groups traditionally termed "reptiles" together with birds and all extinct groups more closely related to these than to mammals. We use the term "nonavian reptiles" to refer to a paraphyletic group that includes the living turtles, lizards, snakes, tuataras, and crocodilians, and a number of extinct groups, including plesiosaurs, ichthyosaurs, pterosaurs, and dinosaurs. Nonavian reptiles are the subject of most of the remainder of this chapter; birds, which form the remainder of clade Reptilia, are discussed in Chapter 19.

Characteristics of Nonavian Reptiles That Distinguish Them from Amphibians

Both amphibians and nonavian reptiles are ectothermic tetrapods, relying on the environment for adjustment of their body temperature. However, they differ in several characteristics, many of which are directly related to the success of nonavian reptiles in dry, terrestrial environments.

1. **Nonavian reptiles have better-developed lungs than do amphibians.** Nonavian reptiles, like other amniotes, rely primarily on lungs for gas exchange. These lungs have more surface area than the lungs of amphibians and are ventilated by drawing air into the lungs, rather than by pushing air into the lungs as amphibians do. Nonavian reptiles expand the thoracic cavity, drawing air into the lungs by expanding the rib cage (lizards and snakes) or by moving internal organs (turtles and crocodiles). Pulmonary respiration is supplemented by respiration in the cloaca or pharynx in many aquatic turtles and by cutaneous respiration in sea snakes and turtles.

2. **Nonavian reptiles have tough, dry, scaly skin that protects against desiccation and physical injury.** Amphibians must maintain a thin, moist skin to permit effective gas exchange. However, this skin makes amphibians vulnerable to dehydration. The shift from skin to lungs as the primary site of respiration permitted the amniotes' skin to become more resistant to desiccation. The skin of nonavian reptiles has an epidermis of varying thickness and a thick, collagen-rich dermis (figure 18.4). The dermis contains chromatophores, color-bearing cells that give many lizards and snakes their colorful hues. This layer, unfortunately for their bearers, is converted into alligator and snakeskin leather, esteemed for expensive pocketbooks and shoes. Resistance to desiccation primarily is provided by hydrophobic lipids in the epidermis. The characteristic scales of nonavian reptiles, formed mostly of beta keratin, provide protection against wear in terrestrial environments. The primarily epidermal scales are not homologous to the scales of fishes, which are mostly bony, dermal structures. In crocodilians, scales remain throughout life, growing gradually to replace wear. In other nonavian reptiles, such as lizards and snakes, new keratinized epidermis grows beneath the old, which is then shed at intervals. Turtles add new layers of keratin under the old layers of the platelike scutes, which are modified scales.

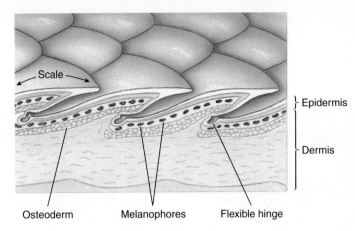

figure 18.4

Section of the skin of a reptile showing overlapping epidermal scales and bony osteoderms in the dermis.

3. **The amniotic egg of nonavian reptiles permits rapid development of large young in relatively dry environments.** As described on page 357, the amniotic egg allows nonavian reptiles to reproduce outside water, although their eggs often require relatively high humidity to avoid desiccation. For many species of nonavian reptiles, egg or embryo development occurs in a female's reproductive tract, providing even greater protection from predators and dehydration, and enabling the mother to manage the embryo's nutritional and other physiological needs.

4. **The jaws of nonavian reptiles are efficiently designed for crushing or gripping prey.** As you may recall from Chapter 16, the jaws of fishes are designed for suction feeding or for quick closure, but once the prey is seized, little static force can be applied. By contrast, the larger jaw muscles of amniotes have a mechanical advantage.

5. **Nonavian reptiles have an efficient and versatile circulatory system and higher blood pressure than amphibians.** In all nonavian reptiles, like other amniotes, the right atrium, which receives oxygen-poor blood from the body, is completely partitioned from the left atrium, which receives oxygen-rich blood from the lungs. Crocodilians have two completely separated ventricles as well (figure 18.5); in other nonavian reptiles, the ventricle is incompletely partitioned into multiple chambers. Even in those forms with incomplete ventricular septa, flow patterns within the heart limit mixing of pulmonary (oxygen-rich) and systemic (oxygen-poor) blood; all nonavian reptiles therefore have two functionally separate circulations. Incomplete separation between the right and left sides of the heart provides the added benefit of permitting blood to bypass the lungs when pulmonary respiration is not occurring (for example, during diving, **hibernation,** or **estivation**).

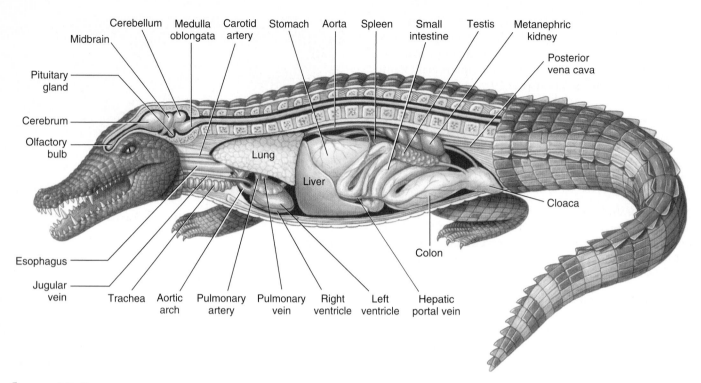

figure 18.5

Internal structure of a male crocodile.

6. **Nonavian reptiles have efficient strategies for water conservation.** Most amphibians excrete their metabolic waste primarily as ammonia. Ammonia is toxic at relatively low concentrations and must be removed in a dilute solution. Thus, it is not adaptive for vertebrates occupying dry, terrestrial environments. Nonavian reptiles excrete their nitrogenous wastes as uric acid. Uric acid is relatively nontoxic, so it can be concentrated without harmful effects. All amniotes, including nonavian reptiles, have metanephric kidneys, but nonavian reptiles (unlike mammals) cannot concentrate their urine in the kidneys. Thus the urinary bladder of nonavian reptiles receives undiluted urine. Water (and most salts) is resorbed in the bladder, and "urine" is voided as a semisolid mass of uric acid. Salts are removed in many nonavian reptiles by salt glands—located near the nose, eyes, or tongue—which secrete a salty fluid that is strongly hyperosmotic to body fluids.

7. **The nervous system of nonavian reptiles is more complex than that of amphibians.** Although the brain of nonavian reptiles is small compared to the brain of other amniotes, the brain of all amniotes has a relatively enlarged cerebrum. Nonavian reptiles have particularly good vision, and many species display brilliant coloration. Smell is not as well developed in some reptiles, but snakes and many lizards use a highly sensitive sense of smell to find prey and mates. In lizards and snakes, olfaction is assisted by a well-developed Jacobson's organ, a specialized olfactory chamber in the roof of the mouth.

Characteristics

of Nonavian Reptiles (Class Reptilia)

1. Body covered with **keratinized epidermal scales** and sometimes bony dermal plates; **integument with few glands**
2. **Two paired limbs, usually with five toes,** and adapted for climbing, running, or paddling; limbs vestigial or absent in snakes and some lizards
3. Skeleton well ossified; ribs with sternum (sternum absent in snakes) forming a complete thoracic basket; **skull with one occipital condyle**
4. Respiration primarily by lungs, which have high surface area and are filled by **aspiration; no gills;** some use cloaca, pharynx, or skin for respiration
5. Circulatory system functionally divided into **pulmonary and systemic circuits;** heart typically consists of a sinus venosus, an atrium completely divided into two chambers, and a ventricle incompletely divided into three chambers; crocodilian heart has a sinus venosus, two atria, and two ventricles
6. Ectothermic; many thermoregulate behaviorally
7. **Metanephric kidney** (paired); **uric acid** main nitrogenous waste
8. Nervous system with optic lobes on dorsal side of brain; **12 pairs of cranial nerves** in addition to nervus terminalis; enlarged cerebrum
9. Sexes separate; **fertilization internal;** copulatory organ a **penis, hemipenes,** or (rarely) absent
10. Eggs covered with calcareous or leathery shells; extraembryonic membranes (**amnion, chorion, yolk sac,** and **allantois**) present during embryonic life; **no aquatic larval stages**

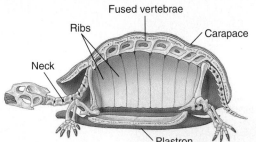
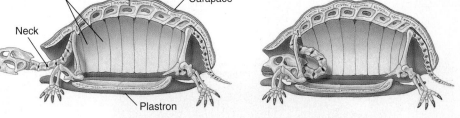

Fused vertebrae

Ribs

Neck

Carapace

Plastron

figure 18.6

Skeleton and shell of a turtle, showing fusion of vertebrae and ribs with the carapace. The long, flexible neck allows the turtle to withdraw its head into its shell for protection.

Characteristics and Natural History of Reptilian Orders

Turtles: Order Testudines

Turtles appear in the fossil record in the Upper Triassic period some 200 million years ago. Since the Triassic, turtles have survived to the present with very little change to their early morphology. They are enclosed in shells consisting of a dorsal **carapace** (Fr., from Sp. *carapacho,* covering) and a ventral **plastron** (Fr., breastplate). As clumsy and unlikely as they appear within their protective shells, they are nonetheless a varied and ecologically diverse group that seems able to adjust to human presence. The shell is so much a part of the animal that it is fused to the thoracic vertebrae and ribs (figure 18.6). Like a medieval coat of armor, the shell offers protection for the head and appendages, which most turtles can retract into it. Because the ribs are fused to the shell, the turtle cannot expand its chest to breathe. Instead, turtles employ certain abdominal and pectoral muscles as a "diaphragm." They draw air inward by contracting limb flank muscles to make the body cavity larger. To exhale, they draw the shoulder girdle back into the shell, thus compressing the viscera and forcing air out of the lungs.

The terms "turtle," "tortoise," and "terrapin" are applied variously to different members of the turtle order. In North American usage, they are all correctly called turtles. The term "tortoise" is frequently applied to land turtles, especially large forms. British usage of the terms is different: "tortoise" is the inclusive term, whereas "turtle" is applied only to the aquatic members.

Lacking teeth, turtle jaws have tough, keratinized plates for gripping food (figure 18.7). Sound perception is poor in turtles, and most turtles are mute (the biblical "voice of the turtle" refers to the turtledove, a bird). Compensating for their poor hearing are good senses of smell and color vision. Turtles are oviparous, and fertilization is internal. All turtles, even marine forms, bury their shelled, amniotic eggs in the ground. An interesting feature of turtle reproduction is that in some turtle families, as in all crocodilians and some lizards, nest temperature determines the sex of the hatchlings. In turtles, low temperatures during incubation produce males, and high temperatures produce females.

figure 18.7

Snapping turtle, *Chelydra serpentina,* showing the absence of teeth. Instead, the jaw edges are covered with a keratinized plate.

Marine turtles, buoyed by their aquatic environment, can reach great size. Leatherbacks are the largest, attaining a length of 2 m and a weight of 725 kg. Green turtles, so named because of their greenish body fat, may exceed 360 kg, although most individuals of this economically valuable and heavily exploited species seldom live long enough to reach anything approaching this size. Some land tortoises weigh several hundred kilograms; examples include the giant tortoises of the Galápagos Islands (figure 18.8) that so intrigued Darwin during his visit there in 1835. Most tortoises move rather slowly; one hour of determined trudging carries a large Galápagos tortoise approximately 300 m. Low metabolism may explain the longevity of turtles, for some live more than 150 years.

Lizards, and Snakes: Order Squamata

Squamates are the most recent and diverse products of diapsid evolution, comprising approximately 95% of all known living nonavian reptiles. Lizards appeared in the fossil record as early as the Jurassic period, but they did not begin their diversification until the Cretaceous period of the Mesozoic era when the dinosaurs were at the climax of their diversification. Snakes

figure 18.8

Mating Galápagos tortoises, *Geochelone elaphantopus*. The male has a concave plastron that fits over the highly convex carapace of the female, helping to provide stability during mating. Males utter a roaring sound during mating, the only time they are known to emit vocalizations.

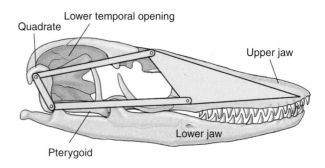

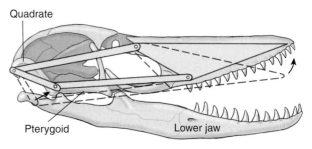

figure 18.9

Kinetic diapsid skull of a modern lizard (monitor lizard, *Varanus* sp.), showing the jaws closed (*top*) and open (*bottom*). Movable joints allow the snout and upper jaw to move on the rest of the skull. The quadrate bone can move at its dorsal end and ventrally at both the lower jaw and the pterygoid bone. The front part of the braincase is also flexible, allowing the snout to be raised or depressed. Note that the lower temporal opening is very large, with no lower border; this modification of the diapsid condition, common in modern lizards, provides space for expansion of large jaw muscles. The upper temporal opening lies dorsal and medial to the postorbital-squamosal arch and is not visible in this drawing.

figure 18.10

The tokay, *Gekko gecko*, of Southeast Asia has a true voice and is named after its strident, repeated *to-kay, to-kay* call.

appeared during the late Jurassic period, probably evolving from a group of lizards whose descendants include the Gila monster and monitor lizards. Two specializations in particular characterize snakes: (1) extreme elongation of the body with accompanying displacement and rearrangement of internal organs, and (2) specializations for eating large prey.

Skulls of squamates are modified from the ancestral diapsid condition by loss of dermal bone ventral and posterior to the lower temporal opening. This modification has allowed the evolution in most lizards and snakes of a **kinetic skull** having movable joints (figure 18.9). These joints, located at the posterior of the quadrate and pterygoid bones, palate, and roof of the skull, allow the snout to be tilted. Specialized mobility of the skull enables squamates to seize and manipulate their prey. It also increases the effective closing force of the jaw musculature. The skull of snakes is even more kinetic than that of lizards. Such exceptional skull mobility is considered a major factor in the diversification of lizards and snakes.

Lizards: Suborder Sauria

Lizards are an extremely diverse group that includes terrestrial, burrowing, aquatic, arboreal, and aerial members. Among the more familiar groups in this varied suborder are **geckos** (figure 18.10), small, agile, mostly nocturnal forms with adhesive toe pads that enable them to walk upside down and on vertical surfaces; **iguanas,** often brightly colored New World lizards with ornamental crests, frills, and throat fans, including the remarkable marine iguana of the Galápagos Islands (figure 18.11); **skinks,** which have elongate bodies, an armor of tight-fitting

osteoderms, and reduced limbs in many species; **monitors,** large, active predators that include the largest lizard, the Komodo dragon, *Varanus komodoensis* (see photo on p. 356); and **chameleons,** a group of arboreal lizards, mostly of Africa and Madagascar. Chameleons are entertaining creatures that catch insects with a sticky-tipped tongue that can be flicked accurately and rapidly to a distance greater than the length

figure 18.11

A large male marine iguana, *Amblyrhynchus cristatus*, of the Galápagos Islands, feeding underwater on algae. This is the only marine lizard in the world. It has special salt-removing glands in the eye orbits and long claws that enable it to cling to the bottom while feeding on small red and green algae, its principal diet. It may dive to depths exceeding 10 m (33 feet) and remain submerged more than 30 minutes.

figure 18.12

A chameleon snares a dragonfly. After cautiously edging close to its target, the chameleon suddenly lunges forward, anchoring its tail and feet to the branch. A split second later, it launches its sticky-tipped, foot-long tongue to trap the prey. The eyes of this common European chameleon, *Chamaeleo chamaeleon*, are swiveled forward to provide binocular vision and excellent depth perception.

of their body (figure 18.12). The great majority of lizards have four limbs and relatively short bodies, but in many, the limbs are reduced, and a few, such as glass lizards (figure 18.13), are completely limbless.

Most lizards have movable eyelids, whereas a snake's eyes are permanently covered with a transparent cap. Lizards have keen vision for daylight (retinas rich in both cones and rods),

figure 18.13

A glass lizard, *Ophisaurus* sp., of the southeastern United States. This legless lizard feels stiff and brittle to the touch and has an extremely long, fragile tail that readily fractures when the animal is struck or seized. Most specimens, such as this one, have only a partly regenerated tip to replace a much longer tail previously lost. Glass lizards can be readily distinguished from snakes by the deep, flexible groove running along each side of the body. They feed on worms, insects, spiders, birds' eggs, and small nonavian reptiles.

although one group, the nocturnal geckos, has retinas composed entirely of rods. Most lizards have an external ear opening that snakes lack. However, as with other nonavian reptiles, hearing does not play an important role in the lives of most lizards. Geckos are exceptions because the males are strongly vocal (to announce territory and to discourage the approach of other males), and they must, of course, hear their own vocalizations.

Many lizards occupy the world's hot and arid regions, aided by adaptations that make desert life possible. Lipids in their thick skin minimize water loss. Little water is lost in their urine because they primarily excrete uric acid, as do other groups that are successful in arid habitats (birds, insects, and pulmonate snails). Some, such as Gila monsters of the southwestern United States deserts, store fat in their tails, and then use the fat during droughts to produce energy and metabolic water (figure 18.14).

Lizards, like nearly all nonavian reptiles, are **ectothermic,** adjusting their body temperature by moving among different microclimates. Because cold climates provide few opportunities for ectotherms to raise their body temperature, relatively few nonavian reptile species live in these habitats. Ectotherms use considerably less energy than endotherms; therefore, nonavian reptiles are successful in ecosystems with low productivity and warm climates, such as tropical deserts, dry, open forests, and grasslands. Thus, ectothermy is not an "inferior" characteristic of nonavian reptiles, but rather is a successful strategy for coping with specific environmental challenges.

The amphisbaenians, or "worm lizards," are lizards highly specialized for a **fossorial** (burrowing) life. Amphisbaenia means "double walk," in reference to their peculiar ability to

The Mesozoic World of Dinosaurs

In 1842, when the English anatomist Richard Owen coined the term *dinosaur* ("fearfully great lizard") to describe fossil Mesozoic reptiles of gigantic size, only three poorly known dinosaur genera were distinguished. New and marvelous fossil discoveries quickly followed, and by 1887 zoologists were able to distinguish two groups of dinosaurs—Saurischia and Ornithischia—based on differences in the structure of the pelvic girdles. The Saurischia ("lizard-hipped") had a simple, three-pronged pelvis with hip bones arranged much as they are in other nonavian reptiles. A large, bladelike ilium was attached to one or two sacral vertebrae. The pubis and ischium extended ventrally and posteriorly, respectively, and all three bones met at the hip socket. The Ornithischia ("bird-hipped") had a somewhat more complex pelvis. The ilium and ischium were arranged similarly in ornithischians and saurischians, but the ornithischian pubis was a narrow, rod-shaped bone with anteriorly and posteriorly directed processes lying alongside the ischium. Oddly, while the ornithischian pelvis, as the name suggests, was similar to that of birds, birds are of the saurischian lineage.

Dinosaurs and their living relatives, the birds, are archosaurs ("ruling lizards"), a group that includes crocodilians and pterosaurs (refer to the classification of amniotes on p. 371). As traditionally recognized, dinosaurs are a paraphyletic group because they do not include birds, which are descended from the theropod dinosaur lineage.

From among the various archosaurian diversifications of the Triassic there emerged a lineage with limbs drawn under the body to provide an upright posture. This lineage gave rise to the earliest dinosaurs of the Late Triassic period. In *Herrerasaurus,* a bipedal dinosaur from Argentina, we see one of the most distinctive characteristics of dinosaurs: walking upright on pillarlike legs, rather than on legs splayed outward like those of modern amphibians and nonavian reptiles. This arrangement allowed the legs to support the great weight of the body while providing an efficient and rapid stride.

Two groups of saurischian dinosaurs have been proposed based on differences in feeding habits and locomotion: the carnivorous and bipedal theropods, and the herbivorous and quadrupedal sauropods. *Coelophysis* was an early theropod with a body form typical of all theropods: powerful hindlimbs with three-toed feet; a long, heavy, counterbalancing tail; slender, grasping forelimbs; a flexible neck; and a large head with jaws armed with daggerlike teeth. Large predators such as *Allosaurus,* common during the Jurassic, were replaced by even more massively built carnivores of the Cretaceous, such as *Tyrannosaurus,* which reached a length of 12.5 m (42 ft), stood nearly 6 m high, and weighed more than 7200 kg (8 tons). Not all predatory saurischians were massive; several were swift and nimble, such as *Velociraptor* ("speedy predator") of the Upper Cretaceous.

Herbivorous saurischians, the quadrupedal sauropods, appeared in the Late Triassic. Although early sauropods were small- and medium-sized dinosaurs, those of the Jurassic and Cretaceous attained gigantic proportions and were the largest terrestrial vertebrates ever to have lived. *Brachiosaurus* reached 25 m (82 ft) in length and may have weighed more than 30,000 kg (33 tons). Even larger sauropods have been discovered; *Argentinosaurus* was 40 m (132 ft) long and weighed at least 80,000 kg. With long necks and long front legs, the sauropods were the first vertebrates adapted to feed on trees. They reached their greatest diversity in the Jurassic and began to decline in over-all abundance and diversity during the Cretaceous.

The second group of dinosaurs, the Ornithischia, were all herbivorous. Although more varied, even grotesque, in appearance than saurischians, the ornithischians are united by several derived skeletal features that indicate common ancestry. The huge back-plated *Stegosaurus* of the Jurassic is a well-known example of armored ornithischians, which comprised two of the five major groups of ornithischians. Even more shielded with bony plates than stegosaurs were the heavily built ankylosaurs, "armored tanks" of the dinosaur world. As the Jurassic gave way to the Cretaceous, several groups of unarmored ornithischians appeared, although many bore impressive horns. The steady increase in ornithiscian diversity in the Cretaceous paralleled a concurrent gradual decline in giant sauropods, which had flourished in the Jurassic. *Triceratops* is representative of horned dinosaurs that were common in the Upper Cretaceous. Even more prominent in the Upper Cretaceous were the hadrosaurs, such as *Parasaurolophus,* which probably lived in large herds. Many hadrosaurs had skulls elaborated with crests that probably functioned as vocal resonators to produce species-specific calls.

Dinosaurs likely provided considerably more parental care than most other non-avian reptilians. Because both crocodilians and birds, members of the clade Archosauria in which dinosaurs are contained (see figure 18.1), share complex parental care, it is likely that dinosaurs exhibited similar behavior. Fossil nests of dinosaurs have been discovered for several groups. In one case, a fossil adult of the small theropod *Oviraptor* was found with a nest of eggs. Originally it was hypothesized that the adult was a predator on the eggs (*Oviraptor* means "egg seizer"). But later, an embryo in similar eggs was found and identified as *Oviraptor,* indicating that the adult was probably with its own eggs! Examination of baby *Maiasaura* (a hadrosaur) found in a nest revealed considerable wear on their teeth, suggesting that the babies had remained in the nest and possibly been fed by adults during part of their early life.

Sixty-five million years ago, the last Mesozoic dinosaurs became extinct, leaving birds and crocodilians as the only surviving lineages of archosaurs. The demise of dinosaurs coincided with a large asteroid impact on the Yucatán peninsula that would have produced worldwide environmental upheaval. An alternative explanation, supported by many paleontologists, suggests that extinctions were caused by less catastrophic environmental changes at the close of the Cretaceous. However, these hypotheses do not explain why dinosaurs became extinct, while many other vertebrate lineages persisted. We continue to be fascinated by the awe-inspiring, often staggeringly large creatures that dominated the Mesozoic era for 165 million years—an incomprehensibly long period of time. Today, inspired by clues from fossils and footprints from a lost world, scientists continue to piece together the puzzle of how the various dinosaur groups arose, behaved, and diversified.

SAURISCHIANS

ORNITHISCHIANS

66 MYA

CRETACEOUS

Titanosaurus
12 m (40 ft)

Velociraptor
1.8 m (6 ft)

Parasaurolophus (duck-billed dinosaur)
10 m (33 ft)

Triceratops
9 m (30 ft)

144 MYA

JURASSIC

Brachiosaurus
25 m (82 ft)

Allosaurus
11 m (35 ft)

Stegosaurus
9 m (30 ft)

Ilium

Ischium

Pubis

208 MYA

TRIASSIC

Coelophysis
3 m (10 ft)

Ilium

Ischium

Pubis

Herrerasaurus 4 m (13 ft)
One of the oldest known
dinosaurs. Has characteristics
of both saurischians and
ornithischians.

245 MYA

figure 18.14

A Gila monster, *Heloderma suspectum*, of southwestern United States desert regions. The Gila monster and its relative, the Mexican beaded lizard, are the only venomous lizards known. These brightly colored, clumsy-looking lizards feed principally on birds' eggs, nesting birds, mammals, and insects. Unlike venomous snakes, the Gila monster secretes venom from glands in its lower jaw. The chewing bite is painful to humans but seldom fatal.

figure 18.15

An amphisbaenian, or "worm lizard." Amphisbaenians are burrowing forms with a solidly constructed skull used as a digging tool. The species pictured, *Amphisbaena alba*, is widely distributed in South America.

move backward nearly as effectively as forward. Amphisbaenians appear so different from other lizards that, until recently, they were placed in a separate suborder, Amphisbaenia. However, phylogenetic analyses of morphological and molecular data show that they are highly modified lizards. Amphisbaenians have elongate, cylindrical bodies of nearly uniform diameter, and most lack any trace of external limbs (figure 18.15). Their eyes are usually hidden underneath the skin, and they have no external ear openings. Their skull is solidly built and either conical or spade-shaped, which aids in tunneling through the soil. The skin is formed into numerous, independently moving rings that can grip the soil, creating a movement not unlike that of earthworms. Amphisbaenians have an

figure 18.16

The great mobility of a snake's jaws and cranial bones is evident in this snake, *Dasypeltis*, swallowing an egg.

extensive distribution in South America and tropical Africa; one species occurs in the United States.

Snakes: Suborder Serpentes

Snakes are limbless and usually lack both pectoral and pelvic girdles (the latter persists as a vestige in pythons, boas, and some other snakes). The numerous vertebrae of snakes, shorter and wider than those of most tetrapods, permit quick lateral undulations through grass and over rough terrain. Ribs increase the rigidity of the vertebral column, providing more resistance to lateral stresses.

In addition to the highly kinetic skull that enables snakes to swallow prey several times their own diameter (figure 18.16), snakes differ from lizards in having no movable eyelids (snakes' eyes are permanently covered with upper and lower transparent eyelids fused together) and no external ear openings. Most snakes have relatively poor vision, but arboreal snakes possess excellent binocular vision, which is useful for tracking prey through branches where scent trails are difficult to follow (figure 18.17). Snakes' internal ears are mainly sensitive to sounds in a limited range of low frequency (100 to 700 Hz). Snakes are also quite sensitive to vibrations conducted through the ground.

Nevertheless, most snakes employ chemical senses rather than vision or vibration to hunt their prey. In addition to the usual olfactory areas in the nose, which are not well developed, snakes have a pair of pitlike **Jacobson's organs** in the roof of the mouth. These organs are lined with an olfactory epithelium and are richly innervated. The **forked tongue,** flicked through the air, collects scent molecules (figure 18.18); the tongue is then drawn past Jacobson's organs; finally, information is then transmitted to the brain, where scents are identified.

Boids (pythons and boas) and pit vipers have special heat-sensitive **pit organs** on their heads, located between their nostrils and eyes (figure 18.19). These pits are supplied with a dense packing of free nerve endings from the fifth cranial

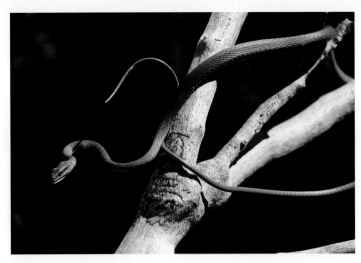

figure 18.17

A parrot snake, *Leptophis ahaetulla*. The slender body of this Central American tree snake is an adaptation for sliding along branches without weighing them down.

figure 18.18

A blacktail rattlesnake, *Crotalus molossus,* flicks its tongue to smell its surroundings. Scent particles trapped on the tongue's surface are transferred to Jacobson's organs, olfactory organs in the roof of the mouth. Note the heat-sensitive pit organ between the nostril and the eye.

nerve. They are exceedingly sensitive to radiant energy (long-wave infrared) and can distinguish temperature differences smaller than 0.003°C from a radiating surface. The pits are used to track warm prey and to aim strikes, which are as effective in total darkness as in daylight.

Most snakes capture their prey by grabbing it with their mouth and swallowing it while it is still alive. Swallowing a struggling, kicking, biting animal is dangerous, so most snakes that swallow prey alive specialize on small prey, such as worms, insects, fish, frogs, and, less frequently, small mammals. Many of these snakes, which may be quite fast, locate prey by actively foraging. Snakes that first kill their prey by constriction

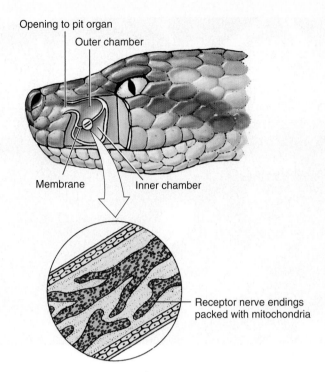

figure 18.19

Pit organ of rattlesnake, a pit viper. Cutaway shows the location of a deep membrane that divides the pit into inner and outer chambers. Heat-sensitive nerve endings are concentrated in the membrane.

(figure 18.20) often specialize on larger, often mammalian, prey. The largest constrictors are able to kill and swallow prey as large as deer, leopards, and crocodilians. However, because muscle rearrangements that permit constricting also reduce speed of travel, most constrictors ambush their prey.

Other snakes kill their prey before swallowing it by injecting it with venom. Less than 20% of all snakes are venomous, although venomous species outnumber nonvenomous species by 4 to 1 in Australia. Venomous snakes are usually divided into five families, based in part on type of fangs. Vipers (family Viperidae) have large, movable, tubular fangs at the front of their mouth (figure 18.21). The fangs lie in a membranous sheath when the mouth is closed. When a viper strikes, a special muscle and bone lever system erects the fangs as the mouth opens (figure 18.21). Fangs are driven into prey by the thrust, and venom is injected into the wound through a canal in the fangs. A viper immediately releases its prey after the bite and follows it until it is paralyzed or dead. Vipers of the old world lack facial heat-sensing pits. Snakes of subfamily Crotalinae within family Viperidae are called **pit vipers** because they possess pit organs on their heads (see figure 18.19). All best-known North American venomous snakes are pit vipers, including rattlesnakes (see figure 18.18), water moccasins, and copperheads. Each year in the United States approximately 7000 bites from pit vipers are reported, causing only about 5 deaths.

figure 18.20

Nonvenomous African house snake, *Boaedon fuluginosus*, constricting a mouse before swallowing it.

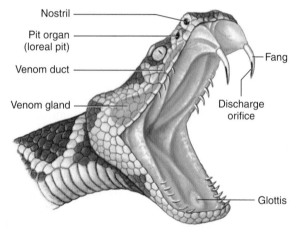

figure 18.21

Head of a rattlesnake showing the venom apparatus. The venom gland, a modified salivary gland, is connected by a duct to the hollow fang.

A second family of venomous snakes (family Elapidae) has short, permanently erect fangs in the front of the mouth and includes cobras (figure 18.22), mambas, coral snakes, and kraits. Smaller groups include the highly venomous sea snakes (family Hydrophiidae) and the poorly known fossorial mole vipers (family Atractaspididae). The large family Colubridae, which contains most familiar (and nonvenomous) snakes, does include a few venomous species, including

figure 18.22

Spectacled, or Indian, cobra (*Naja naja*). Cobras erect the front part of the body when startled and as a threat display. Although the cobra's strike range is limited, all cobras are dangerous because of the extreme toxicity of their venom.

the rear-fanged African boomslang and the twig snake, both of which cause some human fatalities.

Even the saliva of harmless snakes possesses limited toxic qualities, and it is logical that there was a natural selection for this toxic tendency as snakes evolved. Snake venoms have traditionally been divided into two types. The **neurotoxic** type acts mainly on the nervous system, affecting the optic nerves (causing blindness) or the phrenic nerve of the diaphragm (paralyzing the muscles of respiration). The **hemorrhagin** type destroys red blood cells and blood vessels and causes extensive hemorrhaging of blood into tissue spaces. In fact, most snake venoms are complex mixtures of various substances that attack different organs in specific ways.

Although sea snakes and the Australian tiger snake have perhaps the most toxic of snake venoms, several larger snakes are more dangerous. The aggressive king cobra, which may exceed 5.5 m in length, is the largest and probably the most dangerous of all venomous snakes. It is estimated that, worldwide, 50,000–60,000 people die from snakebite each year. Most of the deaths occur in India, Pakistan, Myanmar, and nearby countries where poorly shod people frequently contact venomous snakes and do not get immediate medical attention following a snake bite. The snakes primarily responsible for deaths in these areas are Russell's viper, the saw-scaled viper, and several species of cobras.

Most snakes are **oviparous** (L. *ovum*, egg, + *parere*, to bring forth) species that lay their shelled, elliptical eggs beneath rotten logs, under rocks, or in holes in the ground. Most of the remainder, including all American pit vipers except the tropical bushmaster, are **ovoviviparous** (L. *ovum*, egg, + *vivus*, living, + *parere*, to bring forth), giving birth to well-formed young. Very few snakes exhibit placental **viviparity** (L. *vivus*, living, + *parere*, to bring forth); in these snakes, the

Classification of Living Nonavian Reptiles

The following Linnean classification agrees with the genealogical relationships of living nonavian reptiles shown in figure 18.2. Relationships of turtles to other diapsids are controversial.

Subclass Diapsida (dī-ap′si-də) (Gr. *di*, double, + *apsis*, arch): **diapsids.** Amniotes having a skull with two temporal openings.

> **Order Testudines (tes-tū′di-nēz)** (L. *testudo*, tortoise) **(Chelonia): turtles.** Body in a bony case of dorsal carapace and ventral plastron; jaws with keratinized beaks instead of teeth; vertebrae and ribs fused to overlying carapace; temporal openings lost; approximately 300 species.

> **Superorder Lepidosauria (le-pi-dō-sor′ē-ə)** (Gr. *lepidos*, scale, + *sauros*, lizard). Characterized by sprawling posture; no bipedal specializations; diapsid skull often modified by loss of one or both temporal arches; transverse cloacal slit; skin shed in one piece.

> > **Order Squamata (skwä-mā′tə)** (L. *squamatus*, scaly, + *ata*, characterized by): **snakes and lizards.** Skin composed of keratinized epidermal scales or plates, which are shed; quadrate movable; skull kinetic (except in amphisbaenians); vertebrae usually concave in front; paired copulatory organs.

> > > **Suborder Lacertilia (la-sur-til′ē-ə)** (L. *lacerta*, lizard) **(Sauria): lizards.** Body slender, usually with four limbs but many species lack one or both pairs of limbs; rami of lower jaw fused; eyelids movable; amphisbaenians have eyes hidden beneath skin; external ear present; this paraphyletic suborder contains approximately 4800 species.

> > > **Suborder Serpentes (sur-pen′tēz)** (L. *serpere*, to creep): **snakes.** Body elongate; limbs, ear openings, and middle ear absent; mandibles joined anteriorly by ligaments; eyelids fused into transparent spectacle; tongue forked and protrusible; left lung reduced or absent; approximately 2900 species.

> > **Order Sphenodonta (sfē′nō-don′tə)** (Gr. *sphen*, wedge, + *odontos*, tooth): **tuataras.** Primitive diapsid skull; vertebrae biconcave; quadrate immovable; parietal eye present; two extant species in *Sphenodon.*

> **Superorder Archosauria (ärk′ō-sor′ē-ə)** (Gr. *archon*, ruling, + *sauros*, lizard). Lineage tending toward bipedalism; orbit shaped like an upside-down triangle; anteorbital fenestra (opening in the skull anterior to the orbit) and gizzard present; ventricle fully divided; parental care of young.

> > **Order Crocodilia (krok′ə-dil′ē-ə)** (L. *crocodilus*, crocodile): **crocodilians.** Skull elongate and massive; nares terminal; secondary palate present; four-chambered heart; vertebrae usually concave in front; forelimbs usually with five digits; hindlimbs with four digits; quadrate immovable; advanced social behavior; 23 species.

placenta permits exchange of materials between the embryonic and maternal bloodstreams.

Tuataras: Order Sphenodonta

The order Sphenodonta contains two living species of the genus *Sphenodon* (Gr. *sphenos*, wedge, + *odontos*, tooth) of New Zealand (figure 18.23). Tuataras are sole survivors of the sphenodontid lineage that diversified modestly during the early Mesozoic but declined toward the end of that era. Tuataras were once widespread throughout the two main islands of New Zealand but are now restricted to small islets of Cook Strait and off the northeast coast of North Island.

Tuataras are lizardlike forms, measuring 66 cm long or less, that live in burrows they often share with sea birds called petrels. They are slow-growing animals with long lives; one is recorded to have lived 77 years.

Tuataras have captured the interest of zoologists because of numerous features that are almost identical to those of early Mesozoic diapsids 200 million years old. These features include a diapsid skull with two temporal openings bounded by complete arches, and a well-developed median parietal "third eye." *Sphenodon* represents one of the slowest rates of morphological evolution known among vertebrates.

figure 18.23

Tuatara, *Sphenodon* sp., a living representative of order Sphenodonta. This "living fossil" has, on top of its head, a well-developed parietal "eye" with retina, lens, and nervous connections to the brain. Although covered with scales, this third eye is sensitive to light. The parietal eye may have been an important sense organ in early reptiles. Tuataras are found today only on certain islands off the coast of New Zealand.

Crocodiles, Alligators, Caimens, and Gharials: Order Crocodilia

Modern crocodilians and birds are the only surviving representatives of the archosaurian lineage that gave rise to the great Mesozoic diversification of dinosaurs and their kin. Crocodilians differ little in structural details from crocodilians of the early Mesozoic. Having remained mostly unchanged for nearly 200 million years, crocodilians face an uncertain future in a world dominated by humans.

All crocodilians have an elongate, robust, well-reinforced skull and massive jaw musculature arranged to provide a wide gape and rapid, powerful closure. Teeth are set in sockets, a type of dentition that was typical of Mesozoic archosaurs as well as the earliest birds. Another adaptation, found in no other vertebrate except mammals, is a complete secondary palate. This innovation allows a crocodilian to breathe when its mouth is filled with water or food (or both).

Estuarine crocodiles (*Crocodylus porosus*) of southern Asia, and Nile crocodiles (*C. niloticus*) of Africa (figure 18.24A) grow to great size (adults weighing 1000 kg have been reported) and are swift and aggressive. Crocodiles are known to attack animals as large as cattle, deer, and people. Alligators (figure 18.24B) are less aggressive than these crocodiles and far less dangerous to people. In the United States, *Alligator mississipiensis* is the only species of alligator; *Crocodylus acutus,* restricted to extreme southern Florida, is the only species of crocodile.

Male alligators emit loud bellows in the mating season, unusual among nonavian reptiles. Crocodilians are oviparous. The female usually lays 20 to 50 eggs in a mass of dead vegetation or buries them in sand, and then guards them. Unlike other nonavian reptiles, crocodilians provide extensive parental care. The mother hears vocalizations from hatching young and responds by opening the nest to allow the hatchlings to escape. Young are guarded by their mother for two years or more after hatching. Although the young are capable of catching their own food immediately after hatching, they also may feed on small pieces that fall from food the mother is eating. As with many turtles and some lizards, the incubation temperature of the eggs determines the sex ratio of the offspring. However, unlike turtles (see p. 363), low nest temperatures produce only females, whereas high nest temperatures produce only males.

A

B

figure 18.24

Crocodilians. **A,** Nile crocodile, *Crocodylus niloticus*, basking. The lower jaw tooth fits *outside* the slender upper jaw; alligators lack this feature. **B,** American alligator, *Alligator mississipiensis*, an increasingly noticeable resident of rivers, bayous, and swamps of the southeastern United States.

■ Summary

Amniotes diverged from a group of early tetrapods during the late Paleozoic era, about 300 million years ago. Their success as terrestrial vertebrates is attributed to several adaptations, especially the amniotic egg. The amniotic egg, with its shell and four extraembryonic membranes—the amnion, allantois, chorion, and yolk sac—permits rapid development of embryos in terrestrial environments. Additional amniote adaptations that permit occupation of dry environments include a thick, water-resistant skin, excretion of urea or uric acid, and complex lungs ventilated by trunk muscles.

Before the end of the Paleozoic era, amniotes diversified to form three groups distinguished by skull structure: anapsids, which lack temporal fenstrae; synapsids, which have one pair of temporal fenstrae, and diapsids, which have two pairs of temporal fenstrae. Mammals evolved from early synapsids. Early diapsids gave rise to all living nonavian reptiles (tentatively including turtles) and to birds. There are no living descendants of Paleozoic anapsids. One clade of diapsids, the archosaurs, underwent a worldwide diversification during the Mesozoic Era into large and morphologically diverse forms.

Turtles (order Testudines), with their distinctive shells, have changed little in anatomy since the Triassic period. Turtles are a small group of long-lived terrestrial, semiaquatic, aquatic, and marine species. They lack teeth, and instead bear keratinized plates on their jaws. All are oviparous, and all, including marine forms, bury their eggs.

Lizards and snakes (order Squamata) represent 95% of all living nonavian reptiles. Lizards are a diversified and successful group, particularly in hot climates. They are distinguished from snakes by having united lower jaw halves, movable eyelids, and external ear openings. Lizards and snakes are ectothermic, regulating their temperature by moving among different microenvironments. Most lizards and snakes are oviparous, although viviparity is not uncommon, especially in cooler climates. Amphisbaenians are a small group of tropical lizards specialized for burrowing. They have ringed, usually limbless bodies and a solid skull.

Snakes, which evolved from one group of lizards, are characterized by elongate, limbless bodies and a highly kinetic skull that allows them to swallow prey several times larger than their own diameter. Most snakes rely on chemical senses, including Jacobson's organ, to hunt prey, rather than on visual and auditory senses. Two groups of snakes (pit vipers and boids) have unique infrared-sensing organs for tracking prey.

Tuataras of New Zealand (order Sphenodonta) represent a relict genus and sole survivor of a group that otherwise disappeared 100 million years ago. They bear several features that are almost identical to those of Mesozoic fossil diapsids.

Crocodiles, alligators, caimens, and gharials (order Crocodilia) are the only living nonavian representatives of the archosaurian lineage that gave rise to the extinct dinosaurs and the living birds. Crocodilians have several adaptations for a carnivorous, semiaquatic life, including a massive skull with powerful jaws, and a secondary palate. They have the most complex parental care of any living nonavian reptile.

■ Review Questions

1. What are the four membranes associated with amniotic eggs? What is the function of each of these membranes?
2. How do the skin and respiratory systems of amniotes differ from those of their early tetrapod ancestors?
3. Amniotes are divided into three groups based on their skull morphologies. What are these three groups, and how do the skulls differ? Which living amniotes, if any, originated from each of these three groups?
4. Why are "reptiles," as traditionally defined, a paraphyletic group? How has cladistic taxonomy revised Reptilia to make it monophyletic?
5. Describe ways in which nonavian reptiles are more functionally or structurally suited for terrestriality than amphibians.
6. Describe the principal structural features of turtles that would distinguish them from any other nonavian reptilian order.
7. How might nest temperature affect egg development in turtles? In crocodilians?
8. What is meant by a "kinetic" skull, and what benefit does it confer? How are snakes able to eat such large prey?
9. In what ways are the special senses of snakes similar to those of lizards, and in what ways have they evolved for specialized feeding strategies?
10. What are amphisbaenians? What morphological adaptations do they have for burrowing?
11. Distinguish ornithiscian and saurischian dinosaurs, based on their hip anatomy. Was a dinosaur's style of parental care more like a lizard's or a crocodilian's?
12. How do crocodilians breathe when their mouths are full of food?
13. What is the function of Jacobson's organ in snakes and lizards?
14. What is the function of the "pit" in pit vipers?
15. What are the differences in structure or location of fangs in a rattlesnake, a cobra, and an African boomslang?
16. Most snakes are oviparous, but some are ovoviviparous or have placental viviparity. Compare these methods of reproduction in squamates. In what climate is viviparity more common?
17. Why are tuataras (*Sphenodon*) of special interest to biologists? Where would you have to go to see one in its natural habitat?
18. From which diapsid lineage have crocodilians descended? What other major fossil and living vertebrate groups belong to this same lineage? In what structural and behavioral ways do crocodilians differ from other living nonavian reptiles?

■ Selected References

See also general references on page 423.

Alvarez, W., and F. Asaro. 1990. An extraterrestrial impact. Sci. Am. **263**:78–84 (Oct.). *This article and an accompanying article by V. E. Courtillot, "A volcanic eruption," present opposing interpretations of the cause of the Cretaceous mass extinction that led to the demise of the dinosaurs.*

Cogger, H. G., and R. G. Zweifel, eds. 1998. Reptiles and amphibians. San Diego, Academic Press. *This comprehensive and lavishly illustrated volume was written by some of the best-known herpetologists in the field.*

Crews, D. 1994. Animal sexuality. Sci. Am. **270**:108–114 (Jan.). *The reproductive strategies of reptiles, including nongenetic sex determination, provide insights into the origins and functions of sexuality.*

Greene, H. W. 1997. Snakes: the evolution of mystery in nature. Berkeley, University of California Press. *Beautiful photographs accompany a well-written volume for the scientist or novice.*

Halliday, T. R., and K. Adler, eds. 2002. Firefly encyclopedia of reptiles and amphibians. Richmond Hill, Ontario, Firefly Books Ltd. *Comprehensive and beautifully illustrated treatment of the reptilian groups with helpful introductory sections on origins and characteristics.*

Lohmann, K. J. 1992. How sea turtles navigate. Sci. Am. **266:**100–106 (Jan.). *Recent evidence suggests that sea turtles use the earth's magnetic field and the direction of ocean waves to navigate back to their natal beaches to nest.*

Mattison, C. 1995. The encyclopedia of snakes. New York, Facts on File, Inc. *Generously illustrated book treating evolution, physiology, behavior, and classification of snakes.*

Norman, D. 1991. Dinosaur! New York, Prentice-Hall. *Highly readable account of the life and evolution of dinosaurs, with fine illustrations.*

Paul, G. 2000. The Scientific American book of dinosaurs. New York, St. Martin's Press. *Essays emphasizing functional morphology, behavior, evolution, and extinction of dinosaurs.*

Pianka, E. R., and L. J. Vitt. 2003. Lizards: windows to the evolution of diversity. Berkeley, University of California Press. *Hundreds of color photographs highlight a discussion of behavior and evolution of lizards.*

Pough, F. H., R. M. Andrews, J. E. Cadle, M. L. Crump, A. H. Savitzky, and K. D. Wells. 2003. Herpetology, ed. 3. Upper Saddle River, New Jersey, Prentice-Hall. *A comprehensive textbook treating diversity, physiology, behavior, ecology, and conservation of reptiles and amphibians.*

Sumida, S. S., and K. L. M. Martin, eds. 1997. Amniote origins: completing the transition to land. San Diego, Academic. *Discusses the diversity, evolution, ecology, and adaptive morphology of early amniotes, with special emphasis on the origin of the amniotic egg.*

■ Custom Website

The *Animal Diversity* Online Learning Center is a great place to check your understanding of chapter material. Visit www.mhhe.com/hickmanad5e for access to key terms, quizzes, and more! Further enhance your knowledge with web links to chapter-related material.

Explore live links for these topics:

Class Reptilia
Order Testudines
Marine Turtles
Order Crocodilia
Suborder Lacertilia

Suborder Serpentes
Order Sphenodonta
Superorder Archosauria and Related
　　Mesozoic Reptiles
Dissection Guides for Reptiles
Conservation Issues Concerning Reptiles

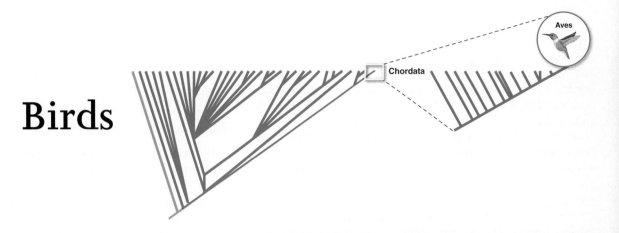

Birds

Long Trip to a Summer Home

Perhaps it was ordained that birds, having mastered flight, often use this power to make long seasonal migrations. Moving between southern wintering regions and northern summer breeding regions with long summer days and an abundance of insects provides parents with ample food to rear their young. Predators of birds are not so abundant in the far North, and a brief once-a-year appearance of vulnerable young birds does not encourage buildup of predator populations. Migration also vastly increases the amount of space available for breeding and reduces aggressive territorial behavior. Finally, migration favors homeostasis—the balancing of internal physiological processes—by allowing birds to avoid climatic extremes.

Still, the wonder of the migratory pageant remains, and there is much yet to learn about its mechanisms. What determines the timing of migration, and what induces each bird to store sufficient fuel for the journey? How did the sometimes difficult migratory routes originate, and what cues do birds use in navigation? It is instinct that drives the migratory waves in spring and fall—instinctive obedience that carries most birds successfully to their northern nests, while countless others fail and die, winnowed by the ever-challenging environment.

Flock of dunlins, *Calidris alpina*, in flight.

O f the vertebrates, birds (class Aves, ā´vēz; L. pl. of *avis*, bird) are the most noticeable, the most melodious, and many think the most beautiful. With more than 9700 species distributed over nearly the entire earth, birds far outnumber any other vertebrate group except fishes. Birds occur in forests and deserts, in mountains and prairies, and on all oceans. Four species are known to have visited the North Pole, and one, a skua, was seen at the South Pole. Some birds live in total darkness in caves, finding their way by echolocation, and others dive to depths greater than 45 m to prey on aquatic life.

The single unique feature that distinguishes birds from other living animals is their feathers. If an animal has feathers, it is a bird; if it lacks feathers, it is not a bird. Feathers also were present in some theropod dinosaurs, but these feathers were not capable of supporting flight.

There is great uniformity of structure among birds. Despite approximately 150 million years of evolution, during which they proliferated and adapted to specialized ways of life, we have no difficulty recognizing a living bird as a bird. In addition to feathers, all birds have forelimbs modified into wings (although not always used for flight); all have hindlimbs adapted for walking, swimming, or perching; all have keratinized beaks; and all lay eggs. The reason for this great structural and functional uniformity is that birds evolved into flying machines, which greatly restricts morphological diversity so much more evident in other vertebrate classes.

A bird's entire anatomy is designed around flight. An airborne life for a large vertebrate is a highly demanding evolutionary challenge. A bird must, of course, have wings for lift and propulsion. Bones must be light and hollow and yet serve as a rigid airframe. The respiratory system must be highly efficient to meet the intense metabolic demands of flight. A bird must have a rapid and efficient digestive system to process an energy-rich diet; it must have a high metabolic rate; and it must have a high-pressure circulatory system. Above all, birds must have a finely tuned nervous system and acute senses, especially superb vision, to handle the complex demands of headfirst, high-velocity flight.

■ Origin and Relationships

Approximately 147 million years ago, a flying animal drowned and settled to the bottom of a shallow marine lagoon in what is now Bavaria, Germany. It was rapidly covered with a fine silt and eventually fossilized. There it remained until discovered in 1861 by a workman splitting slate in a limestone quarry. The fossil was approximately the size of a crow, with a skull not unlike that of modern birds except that the beaklike jaws bore small, bony teeth set in sockets like those of dinosaurs (figure 19.1). The skeleton was decidedly reptilian, with a long bony tail, clawed fingers, and abdominal ribs. It might have been classified as a theropod dinosaur except that it carried an unmistakable imprint of **feathers,** those marvels of biological engineering that only birds possess. Named *Archaeopteryx lithographica* (är-kē-op´ter-iks lith-ō-graf´e-kə; Gr., meaning "ancient wing inscribed in stone"), the fossil was an especially fortunate discovery because it demonstrated beyond reasonable doubt the phylogenetic relatedness of birds and theropod dinosaurs.

A

B

figure 19.1

Archaeopteryx, a 147-million-year-old relative of modern birds. **A,** Cast of the most nearly perfect fossil of *Archaeopteryx,* which was discovered in a Bavarian stone quarry. Ten specimens of *Archaeopteryx* have been discovered, the most recent one described in 2007. **B,** Reconstruction of *Archaeopteryx.*

Characteristics

of Class Aves

1. Body usually spindle shaped, with four divisions: head, neck, trunk, and tail; **neck disproportionately long** for balancing and food gathering
2. Limbs paired; **forelimbs usually modified for flying;** posterior pair variously adapted for perching, walking, and swimming; foot with four toes (two or three toes in some)
3. Epidermal **covering of feathers** and **leg scales;** thin integument of epidermis and dermis; no sweat glands; oil or preen gland at base of tail; **pinna of ear rudimentary**
4. **Fully ossified skeleton with air cavities;** skull bones fused with **one occipital condyle;** each jaw covered with a keratinized sheath, forming a **beak; no teeth;** ribs with strengthening, uncinate processes; posterior caudal vertebrae reduced and fused as the **pygostyle;** pelvic girdle a **synsacrum;** erythrocytes sternum usually well developed with keel; **single bone in middle ear**
5. Nervous system well developed, with 12 pairs of cranial nerves and brain with **large cerebellum and optic lobes**
6. Circulatory system consists of four-chambered heart with two atria and two ventricles; completely **separate pulmonary and systemic circuits; right aortic arch persisting;** nucleated erythrocytes
7. **Endothermic**
8. Respiration by slightly expansible lungs, with thin **air sacs** among the visceral organs and skeleton; **syrinx (voice box)** near junction of trachea and bronchi
9. Excretory system includes metanephric kidneys; ureters open into cloaca; **no bladder;** semisolid urine; uric acid main nitrogenous waste
10. Sexes separate; testes paired, with the vas deferens opening into the cloaca; **females have left ovary and oviduct only;** copulatory organ (penis) only in ducks, geese, paleognathids, and a few others
11. Fertilization internal; **amniotic eggs with much yolk and hard, calcareous shells;** embryonic membranes in egg during development; **incubation external;** young active at hatching **(precocial)** or helpless and naked **(altricial);** sex determined by females (females heterogametic)

Zoologists had long recognized the similarity of birds and nonavian reptiles because of their many shared morphological, developmental, and physiological homologies. The distinguished English zoologist Thomas Henry Huxley was so impressed with these affinities that he called birds "glorified reptiles" and classified them with a group of dinosaurs called theropods that displayed several birdlike characteristics (figures 19.2 and 19.3). Theropod dinosaurs share many derived characters with birds, the most obvious of which is the elongate, mobile, S-shaped neck.

Dromeosaurs, a group of theropods that includes *Velociraptor,* share many additional derived characters with birds, including a furcula (fused clavicles) and lunate wrist bones that permit swiveling motions used in flight (figure 19.3).

Additional evidence linking birds to dromeosaurs comes from recently described fossils from late Jurassic and early Cretaceous deposits in Liaoning Province, China. These spectacular dromeosaur-like fossils include some with filaments, such as *Sinosauropteryx,* and some with feathers, such as *Protarchaeopteryx* and *Caudipteryx.* These feathered dinosaurs could not fly, however, because they had short forelimbs and symmetrical vaned feathers (the flight feathers of modern flying birds are asymmetrical). Clearly, these filaments and feathers were not used for flight; perhaps they were used for thermoregulation or were colorful and used in social displays. Fossils from Spain and Argentina, representing birds more derived than *Archaeopteryx,* document the development of the keeled sternum and alula (see figure 19.5), loss of teeth, and fusion of bones characteristic of modern birds. A phylogenetic approach to classification would group birds with theropod dinosaurs. With this view, dinosaurs are not extinct—they are with us today as birds!

Living birds (Neonithes) are divided into two groups: (1) **Paleognathae** (Gr. *palaios,* ancient, + *gnathos,* jaw) are large, flightless, ostrichlike birds and kiwis, often called **ratite** birds, that have a flat sternum with poorly developed pectoral muscles. (2) **Neognathae** (Gr. *neos,* new, + *gnathos,* jaw) are flying birds that have a keeled sternum on which powerful flight muscles insert. There are a number of flightless neognathus birds, some of which lack a keeled sternum. Flightlessness has appeared independently among many groups of birds; the fossil record reveals flightless wrens, pigeons, parrots, cranes, ducks, auks, and even a flightless owl. Penguins are flightless although they use their wings to "fly" through water (see figure 4.6). Flightlessness has almost always evolved on islands, where few terrestrial predators occur. Flightless birds living on continents today are the large paleognathids (ostrich, rhea, cassowary, emu), which can run fast enough to escape predators. Ostriches can run 70 km (42 miles) per hour, and claims of speeds of 96 km (60 miles) per hour have been made. The evolution of flightless birds is discussed on pp. 17–18.

The bodies of flightless birds are dramatically redesigned to remove restrictions for flight. The keel of the sternum is lost, and heavy flight muscles (as much as 17% of the body weight of flying birds), as well as other specialized flight apparatus, disappear. Because body weight is no longer a restriction, flightless birds tend to become large. Several extinct flightless birds were enormous: the giant moas of New Zealand weighed more than 225 kg (500 pounds), and elephantbirds of Madagascar, the largest birds that ever lived, probably weighed nearly 450 kg (about 1000 pounds) and stood nearly 2 m tall.

Structural and Functional Adaptations for Flight

Just as an airplane must be designed and built according to rigid aerodynamic specifications, so too must birds meet stringent structural requirements in order to stay airborne. Flight by humans became possible when they developed an internal

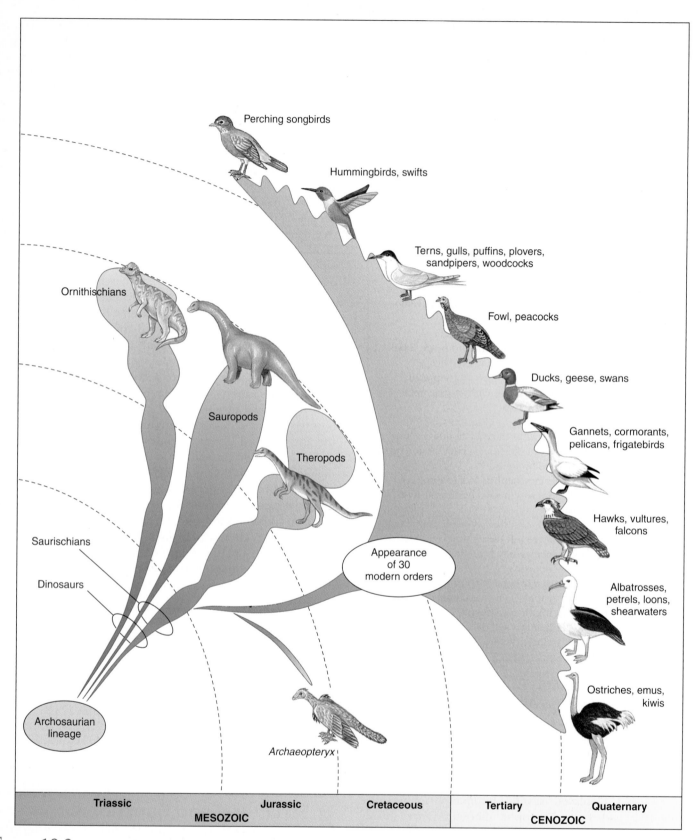

figure 19.2

Evolution of modern birds. Of 30 living bird orders, 9 of the more important are shown. The earliest known bird, *Archaeopteryx,* lived in the Upper Jurassic period about 147 million years ago. *Archaeopteryx* uniquely shares many specialized aspects of its skeleton with the smaller theropod dinosaurs and is considered to have evolved within the theropod lineage. Evolution of modern bird orders occurred rapidly during the Cretaceous and early Tertiary periods.

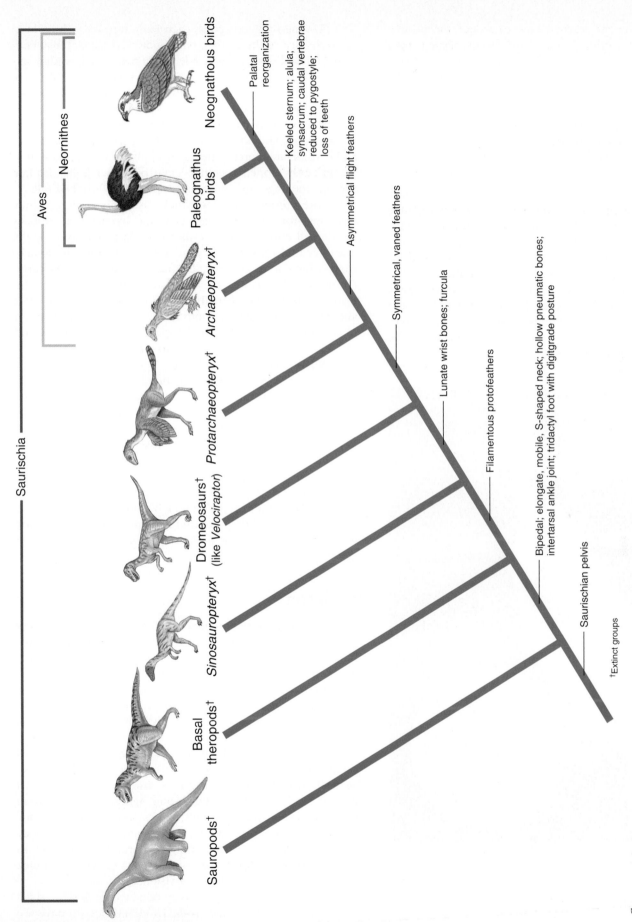

figure 19.3

Cladogram of Saurischia, illustrating the relationship of several taxa to modern birds. Shown are a few of the shared derived characters, mostly related to flight, that were used to construct the genealogy. The ornithischians are the sister group to the saurischians, and all are members of the clade Archosauria (see figures 18.1 and 18.2).

Sauropods†

Basal
theropods†

Sinosauropteryx†

Dromeosaurs†
(like Velociraptor)

Protarchaeopteryx†

Archaeopteryx†

Paleognathus
birds

Neognathous birds

Saurischia

Aves

Neornithes

Palatal
reorganization

Keeled sternum; alula;
synsacrum; caudal vertebrae
reduced to pygostyle;
loss of teeth

Asymmetrical flight feathers

Symmetrical, vaned feathers

Lunate wrist bones; furcula

Filamentous protofeathers

Bipedal; elongate, mobile, S-shaped neck; hollow pneumatic bones;
intertarsal ankle joint; tridactyl foot with digitgrade posture

Saurischian pelvis

†Extinct groups

combustion engine and learned how to reduce the weight-to-power ratio to a critical point. Birds accomplished flight millions of years ago, and many of their adaptations for flying contribute to that same ratio: more power and less weight. But birds must do much more than fly. Unlike airplanes, birds also must feed themselves, convert food into high-energy fuel, escape predators, repair their own injuries, maintain a constant body temperature, and reproduce.

Feathers

Feathers are very lightweight, and yet they possess remarkable toughness and tensile strength. Most bird feathers are **contour feathers,** vaned feathers that cover and streamline the bird's body. A contour feather consists of a hollow **quill,** or **calamus,** emerging from a skin follicle, and a **shaft,** or **rachis,** which is a continuation of the quill and bears numerous **barbs** (figure 19.4). Barbs are arranged in closely parallel fashion and spread diagonally outward from both sides of the central shaft to form a flat, expansive, webbed surface, the **vane.** There may be several hundred barbs in a vane.

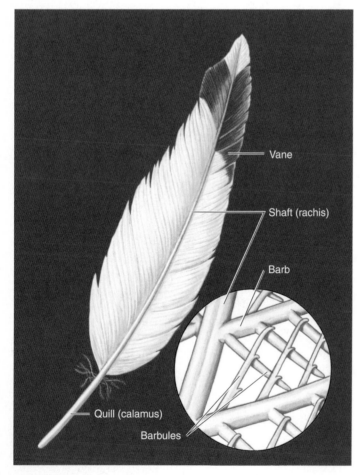

figure 19.4

Contour feather. Inset enlargement of the vane shows the minute hooks on the barbules that cross-link loosely to form a continuous surface of vane.

Through a microscope, each barb appears to be a miniature replica of the feather, with numerous parallel filaments called **barbules** set in each side of the barb and spreading laterally from it. There may be 600 barbules on each side of a barb, adding up to more than 1 million barbules for the feather. Barbules of one barb overlap the barbules of a neighboring barb in a herringbone pattern and are held together with great tenacity by tiny hooks. Should two adjoining barbs become separated—and considerable force is needed to pull the vane apart—they are instantly zipped together again by drawing the feather through the fingertips. Birds do this preening with their bill.

Like a reptile's scale, to which it is homologous, a feather develops from an epidermal elevation overlying a nourishing dermal core. However, rather than flattening like a scale, a feather bud rolls into a cylinder and sinks into the follicle from which it is growing. During growth, pigments (lipochromes and melanin) are added to epidermal cells. As the feather enlarges and nears the end of its growth, the soft shaft and barbs are transformed into hard structures by deposition of keratin. The protective sheath splits apart, allowing the end of a feather to protrude and barbs to unfold.

When fully grown, a feather, like mammalian hair, is a dead structure. Shedding, or molting, of feathers is a highly orderly process; feathers are discarded gradually, which avoids appearance of bare spots. Flight and tail feathers are lost in exact pairs, one from each side, so that balance is maintained. Replacements emerge before the next pair is lost, and most birds can continue to fly unimpaired during the molting period; however, many water birds (ducks, geese, loons, and others) lose all their primary feathers at once and are grounded during the molt. Many prepare for molting by moving to isolated bodies of water where they can find food and more easily escape enemies. Nearly all birds molt at least once a year, usually in late summer after nesting season.

Skeleton

A major structural requirement for flight is a light, yet sturdy skeleton (figure 19.5A). Compared with the earliest known bird, *Archaeopteryx* (figure 19.5B), bones of modern birds are phenomenally light, delicate, and laced with air cavities. Such **pneumatized** bones (figure 19.6) are nevertheless strong. The skeleton of a frigate bird with a 2.1 m (7-foot) wingspan weighs only 114 grams (4 ounces), less than the weight of all its feathers.

As archosaurs, birds evolved from ancestors with diapsid skulls (see p. 359). However, skulls of modern birds are so specialized that it is difficult to see any trace of the original diapsid condition. A bird's skull is built lightly and mostly fused into one piece. A pigeon's skull weighs only 0.21% of its body weight; by comparison, a rat's skull weighs 1.25% of its body weight. The braincase and orbits are large in bird skulls to accommodate a bulging brain and large eyes needed for quick motor coordination and superior vision.

In *Archaeopteryx,* both jaws contained teeth set in sockets, an archosaurian characteristic. However, modern birds are

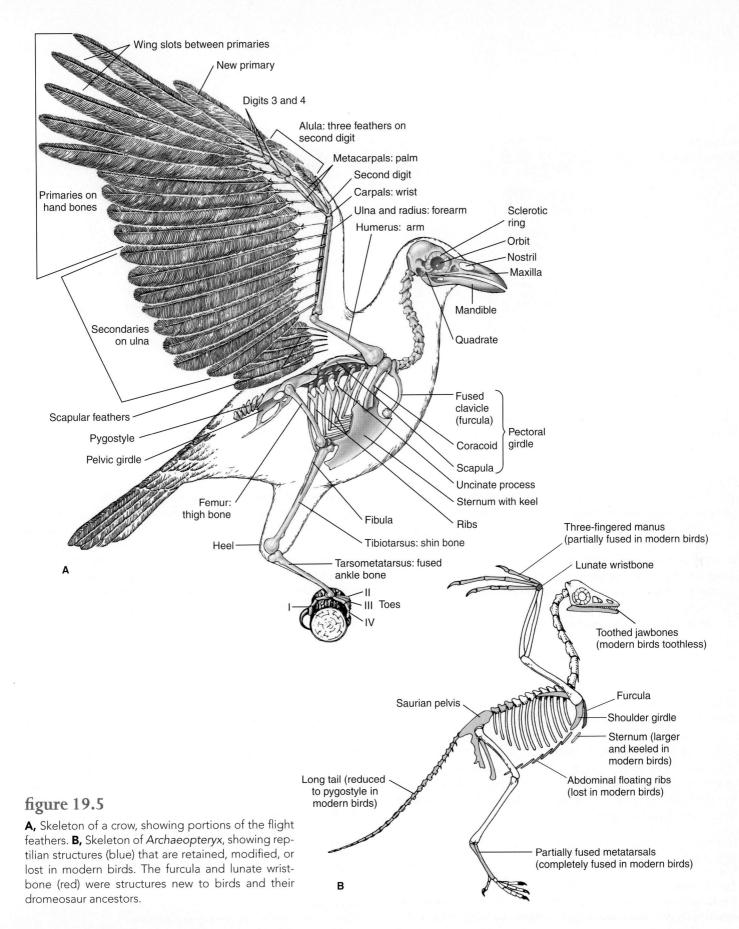

Wing slots between primaries

New primary

Digits 3 and 4

Alula: three feathers on second digit

Metacarpals: palm

Second digit

Carpals: wrist

Ulna and radius: forearm

Humerus: arm

Sclerotic ring

Orbit

Nostril

Maxilla

Mandible

Quadrate

Primaries on hand bones

Secondaries on ulna

Scapular feathers

Pygostyle

Pelvic girdle

Fused clavicle (furcula)

Coracoid

Scapula

} Pectoral girdle

Uncinate process

Sternum with keel

Femur: thigh bone

Fibula

Ribs

Heel

Tibiotarsus: shin bone

Tarsometatarsus: fused ankle bone

II
I   III Toes
IV

A

Three-fingered manus (partially fused in modern birds)

Lunate wristbone

Toothed jawbones (modern birds toothless)

Furcula

Shoulder girdle

Sternum (larger and keeled in modern birds)

Saurian pelvis

Abdominal floating ribs (lost in modern birds)

Long tail (reduced to pygostyle in modern birds)

Partially fused metatarsals (completely fused in modern birds)

B

figure 19.5

A, Skeleton of a crow, showing portions of the flight feathers. **B,** Skeleton of *Archaeopteryx*, showing reptilian structures (blue) that are retained, modified, or lost in modern birds. The furcula and lunate wristbone (red) were structures new to birds and their dromeosaur ancestors.

figure 19.6

Hollow wing bone of a songbird, showing stiffening struts and air spaces that replace bone marrow. Such pneumatized bones are remarkably light and strong.

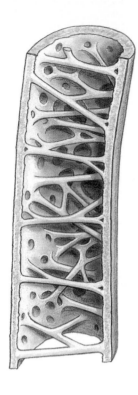

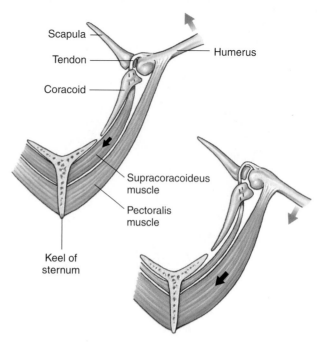

figure 19.7

The flight muscles of a bird are arranged to keep the center of gravity low in the body. Both of the major flight muscles are anchored on the sternum keel. Contraction of the pectoralis muscle pulls the wing downward. Then, as the pectoralis relaxes, the supracoracoideus muscle contracts and, acting as a pulley system, pulls the wing upward.

completely toothless, having instead a keratinous beak molded around the bony jaws. The mandible is a complex of several bones hinged to provide a double-jointed action, which permits the mouth to gape widely. Most birds have kinetic skulls (kinetic skulls of lizards are described on p. 364) with a flexible attachment between upper jaw and skull. This attachment allows the upper jaw to move slightly, thus increasing the gape.

The most distinctive feature of the vertebral column is its rigidity. Most vertebrae, except the **cervicals** (neck vertebrae), are fused together, and along with the pelvic girdle, form a stiff but light framework to support the legs and to provide rigidity for flight. To assist in this rigidity, ribs are braced against each other with uncinate processes (see figure 19.5A). Except in flightless birds, the sternum bears a large, thin keel that provides an attachment for powerful flight muscles. Fused clavicles form an elastic **furcula** that apparently stores energy as it flexes during wing beats. The asymmetrical flight feathers and distinct furcula of *Archaeopteryx* indicate that it could fly, but the small sternum, offering relatively little area for flight muscle attachment, suggests that it was not a strong flier (see figure 19.5B).

Bones of the forelimbs are highly modified for flight. They are reduced in number, and several are fused together. Despite these alterations, a bird wing is clearly a rearrangement of the basic vertebrate tetrapod limb from which it arose (see figure 17.1), and all the elements—arm, forearm, wrist, and fingers—are represented in modified form (see figure 19.5A).

Muscular System

Locomotor muscles of wings are relatively massive to meet demands of flight. The largest of these is the **pectoralis,** which depresses the wings in flight. Its antagonist is the

supracoracoideus muscle, which raises the wing (figure 19.7). Surprisingly, perhaps, this latter muscle is not located on the backbone (anyone who has been served the back of a chicken knows that it offers little meat) but is positioned under the pectoralis on the breast. It is attached by a tendon to the upper side of the humerus of the wing so that it pulls from below by an ingenious "rope-and-pulley" arrangement. Both the pectoralis and the supracoracoideus are anchored to the keel of the sternum. Positioning the main muscle mass low in the body improves aerodynamic stability.

From the main leg muscle mass in the thigh, thin but strong tendons extend downward through sleevelike sheaths to the toes. Consequently, the feet are nearly devoid of muscles, explaining the thin, delicate appearance of a bird's leg. This arrangement places the main muscle mass near a bird's center of gravity and at the same time allows great agility to the slender, lightweight feet. Because the feet are composed mostly of bone, tendon, and tough, scaly skin, they are highly resistant to damage from freezing. When a bird perches on a branch, an ingenious toe-locking mechanism (figure 19.8) is activated, which prevents the bird from falling off its perch even when asleep. The same mechanism causes the talons of a hawk or owl to automatically sink deeply into its prey as the legs bend under the impact of the strike. The powerful grip of a bird of prey was described by L. Brown.[1]

---

[1]Brown, L. 1970, Eagles, New York, Arco Publishing.

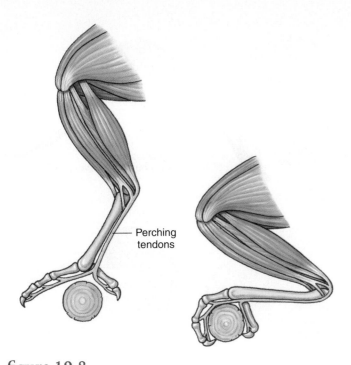

figure 19.8

Perching mechanism of a bird. When a bird settles on a branch, tendons automatically tighten, closing the toes around the perch.

When an eagle grips in earnest, one's hand becomes numb, and it is quite impossible to tear it free, or to loosen the grip of the eagle's toes with the other hand. One just has to wait until the bird relents, and while waiting one has ample time to realize that an animal such as a rabbit would be quickly paralyzed, unable to draw breath, and perhaps pierced through and through by the talons in such a clutch.

Digestive System

Birds process an energy-rich diet rapidly and thoroughly with efficient digestive equipment. A shrike can digest a mouse in 3 hours, and berries pass completely through the digestive tract of a thrush in just 30 minutes. Although many animal foods find their way into diets of birds, insects comprise by far the largest component. Because birds lack teeth, foods that require grinding are reduced in the gizzard. Salivary glands are poorly developed and mainly secrete mucus for lubricating food and the slender, horn-covered **tongue.** There are few taste buds, although all birds can taste to some extent. From the short **pharynx,** a relatively long, muscular, elastic **esophagus** extends to the **stomach.** Many birds have an enlargement **(crop)** at the lower end of the esophagus, which serves as a storage chamber.

In pigeons, doves, and some parrots, the crop not only stores food but also produces a lipid- and protein-rich "milk," composed of sloughed epithelial cells of the crop lining. For a few days after hatching, the helpless young are fed regurgitated crop milk by both parents.

The stomach proper consists of a **proventriculus,** which secretes gastric juice, and a muscular **gizzard,** a region specialized for grinding food. To assist in grinding food, birds swallow gritty objects or pebbles, which lodge in the gizzard. Certain birds of prey, such as owls, form pellets of indigestible materials, mainly bones and fur, in the proventriculus and eject them through the mouth. At the junction of the small intestine with the colon are paired **ceca;** these are well developed in herbivorous birds in which they serve as fermentation chambers. The terminal part of the digestive system is the **cloaca,** which also receives genital ducts and ureters.

Beaks of birds are strongly adapted to specialized food habits—from generalized types, such as the strong, pointed beaks of crows and ravens, to grotesque, highly specialized beaks in flamingos, pelicans, and avocets (figure 19.9). The beak of a woodpecker is a straight, hard, chisel-like device. Anchored to a tree trunk, with its tail serving as a brace, a woodpecker delivers powerful, rapid blows to excavate nest cavities or to expose burrows of wood-boring insects. It then uses its long, flexible, barbed tongue to seek insects in their galleries. A woodpecker's skull is especially thick to absorb shock.

Circulatory System

The general plan of circulation in birds is not greatly different from that of mammals, although it evolved independently. Their four-chambered heart is large with strong ventricular walls; thus birds share with mammals a complete separation of respiratory and systemic circulations. Their heartbeat is extremely fast, and as in mammals an inverse relationship occurs between heart rate and body weight. For example, a turkey has a heart rate at rest of about 93 beats per minute, a chicken has a rate of 250 beats per minute, and a black-capped chickadee has a rate of 500 beats per minute when asleep, which may increase to a phenomenal 1000 beats per minute during exercise. Blood pressure in birds is roughly equivalent to that in mammals of similar size. Birds' blood contains **nucleated biconvex erythrocytes.** (Mammals, the only other endothermic vertebrates, have enucleate biconcave erythrocytes that are somewhat smaller than those of birds.) **Phagocytes,** or mobile ameboid cells of blood, are particularly efficient in birds in repairing wounds and destroying microbes.

Respiratory System

The respiratory system of birds differs radically from lungs of nonavian reptiles and mammals and is marvelously adapted for meeting the high metabolic demands of flight. In birds, the finest branches of the bronchi, rather than ending in saclike alveoli as in mammals, are tubelike **parabronchi** through which air flows continuously. Also unique is the extensive system of nine interconnecting **air sacs** that are located in pairs in the thorax and abdomen and even extend by tiny tubes into the centers of long bones (figure 19.10A). Air sacs are

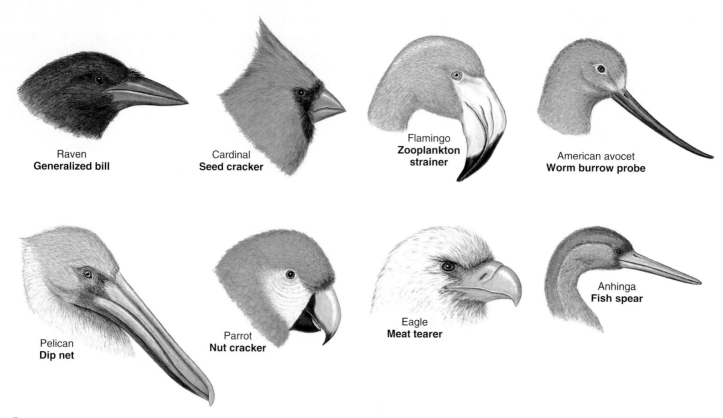

figure 19.9

Some bills of birds showing a variety of adaptations.

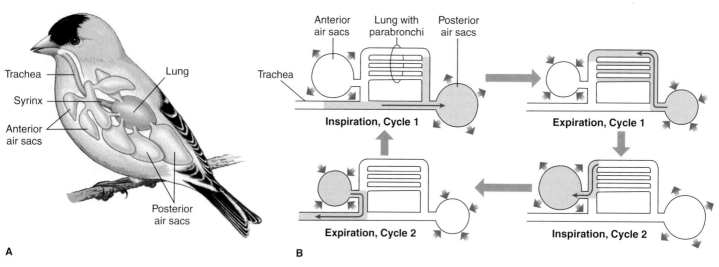

A

B

figure 19.10

Respiratory system of a bird. **A,** Locations of the lungs and air sacs. One side of the bilateral air sac system is shown. **B,** Movement of a single volume of air through a bird's respiratory system. Two full respiratory cycles are required to move air through the system.

connected to the lungs in such a way that most of the inspired air bypasses the lungs and flows directly into the posterior air sacs, which serve as reservoirs for fresh air. On expiration, this oxygenated air is passed through the lungs and collected in the anterior air sacs. From there, it flows directly to the outside. Thus, it takes two respiratory cycles for a single breath of air to pass through the respiratory system (figure 19.10B). The advantage of such a system is that an almost continuous stream of oxygenated air is passed through a system of richly vascularized parabronchi.

The remarkable efficiency of a bird's respiratory system is emphasized by bar-headed geese that routinely migrate over the Himalayan mountains and have been sighted flying over Mt. Everest (8848 meters or 29,141 feet) under conditions that are severely hypoxic to humans. The geese reach altitudes of 9000 meters in less than a day, without the acclimatization that is absolutely essential for humans even to approach the upper reaches of Mt. Everest.

Excretory System

The relatively large, paired metanephric kidneys are composed of many thousands of **nephrons,** each consisting of a renal corpuscle and a nephric tubule. As in other vertebrates, urine is formed by glomerular filtration followed by selective modification of the filtrate in the tubule.

Like nonavian reptiles, birds excrete their nitrogenous wastes as uric acid rather than urea. In shelled eggs, all excretory products must remain within the eggshell with the growing embryo. Uric acid crystallizes from solution and can be stored harmlessly in the allantois. Because of uric acid's low solubility, a bird can excrete 1 g of uric acid in only 1.5 to 3 ml of water, whereas a mammal may require 60 ml of water to excrete 1 g of urea. Concentration of uric acid occurs almost entirely in the cloaca, where it is combined with fecal matter, and the water is reabsorbed. Bird kidneys are much less efficient than those of mammals in removing salts, especially sodium, potassium, and chloride. The kidneys of most birds concentrate salts only slightly greater than that of blood, but most mammals concentrate salts 4 to 8 times that of blood, and some desert rodents concentrate salts to nearly 25 times that of blood.

To compensate for the weak solute-concentrating ability of the kidneys, some birds, especially marine birds, use extrarenal mechanisms to excrete salts gained from the food they eat and the seawater they drink. Excess salt is removed from their blood by special **salt glands,** one located above each eye (figure 19.11). These glands are capable of excreting a highly concentrated solution of sodium chloride—up to twice the concentration of seawater. The salt solution runs out the internal or external nostrils, giving gulls, petrels, and other sea birds a perpetually runny nose.

Nervous and Sensory System

The design of a bird's nervous and sensory system reflects the complex problems of flight and a highly visible existence, in which the bird must gather food, mate, defend territory, incubate and rear young, and correctly distinguish friend from foe. Its brain has well-developed **cerebral hemispheres, cerebellum,** and **optic lobes.** The **cerebral cortex**—chief coordinating center of a mammalian brain—is thin, unfissured, and poorly developed in birds. The core of the cerebrum, the **dorsal ventricular ridge,** has enlarged into the principal

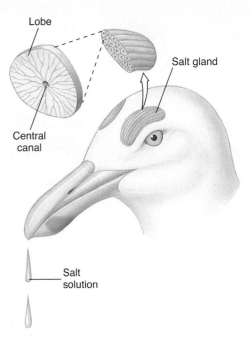

figure 19.11

Salt glands of a marine bird (gull). One salt gland is located above each eye. Each gland consists of several lobes arranged in parallel. One lobe is shown in cross section, much enlarged. Salt is secreted into many radially arranged tubules, and then flows into a central canal that leads into the nose.

integrative center, controlling such activities as eating, singing, flying, and complex reproductive behavior. Relatively intelligent birds, such as crows and parrots, have larger cerebral hemispheres than do less intelligent birds, such as chickens and pigeons. The **cerebellum** is a crucial coordinating center where muscle-position sense, equilibrium sense, and visual cues are assembled and used to coordinate movement and balance. The **optic lobes,** laterally bulging structures of the midbrain, form a visual apparatus comparable to the visual cortex of mammals.

Although the senses of smell and taste are poor in some birds, they are relatively well developed in many other birds, such as carnivorous birds, flightless birds, oceanic birds, and waterfowl. Birds have good hearing and superb vision, the keenest in the animal kingdom. The organ of hearing, the **cochlea,** is much shorter than the coiled mammalian cochlea, and yet birds can hear roughly the same range of sound frequencies as humans. Actually, a bird's ear far surpasses that of humans in its capacity to distinguish differences in intensities and to respond to rapid fluctuations in pitch.

A bird's eye resembles that of other vertebrates in gross structure but is relatively larger, less spherical, and almost immobile; instead of turning their eyes, birds turn their heads with their long flexible necks to scan the visual field. The light-sensitive **retina** (figure 19.12) is generously equipped with rods (for dim light vision) and cones (for color vision).

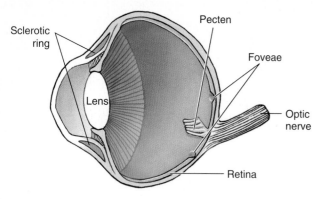

figure 19.12

A hawk's eye has all the structural components of a mammalian eye, plus a peculiar pleated structure, or pecten, thought to provide nourishment to the retina. The extraordinarily keen vision of hawks is attributed to the extreme density of cone cells in the foveae: 1.5 million per fovea compared to 0.2 million for humans.

Cones predominate in day birds, and rods are more numerous in nocturnal birds. A distinctive feature of a bird's eye is the **pecten,** a highly vascularized organ attached to the retina and jutting into the vitreous humor (figure 19.12). The pecten is thought to provide nutrients and oxygen to the eye.

The **fovea,** or region of keenest vision on the retina, is in a deep pit (in birds of prey and some others), which requires the bird to focus exactly on the subject. Many birds, moreover, have two sensitive spots (foveae) on the retina (figure 19.12): a central one for sharp monocular views and a posterior one for binocular vision. The visual acuity of a hawk is about eight times that of humans (enabling a hawk to see clearly a crouching rabbit 2 km away), and an owl's ability to see in dim light is more than 10 times that of a human.

Many birds can see at ultraviolet wavelengths, enabling them to view environmental features inaccessible to humans but accessible to insects (such as flowers with ultraviolet-reflecting "nectar guides" that attract pollinating insects). Several species of ducks, hummingbirds, kingfishers, and passerines (songbirds) can see at near ultraviolet (UV) wavelengths down to 370 nm (human eyes filter out ultraviolet light below 400 nm). For what purpose do birds use their UV-sensitivity? Some, such as hummingbirds, may be attracted to nectar-guiding flowers, but for others, the benefit derived from UV-sensitivity is a matter of conjecture.

■ Flight

What prompted evolution of flight, birds' ability to rise free of earthbound concerns, as almost every human has dreamed of doing? The air was a relatively unexploited habitat stocked with flying insects for food. Flight also offered escape from terrestrial predators and opportunity to travel rapidly and widely to establish new breeding areas and to benefit from year-round favorable climate by migrating north and south with the seasons.

Bird Wing as a Lift Device

A bird's wing is an airfoil subject to recognized laws of aerodynamics. It is streamlined in cross section, with a slightly concave lower surface (**cambered**) and with small, tight-fitting feathers where the leading edge meets the air. Air slips smoothly over the wing, creating lift with minimum drag. Some lift is produced by positive pressure against the undersurface of the wing, but on the upper side, where the airstream must travel farther and faster over a convex surface, negative pressure is created that provides more than two-thirds of the total lift.

The lift-to-drag ratio of an airfoil is determined by the angle of attack (angle of tilt) and by airspeed (figure 19.13A). A wing carrying a given load can pass through the air at high speed and small angle of attack or at low speed and larger angle of attack. As speed decreases, lift can be increased by increasing the angle of attack, but drag forces also increase. When the angle of attack becomes too steep, turbulence appears on the upper surface, lift is destroyed, and stalling occurs (figure 19.13B). Stalling can be delayed or prevented by the presence of a **wing slot** along the leading edge so that a layer of rapidly moving air is directed across the upper wing surface (figure 19.13C). Wing slots were and still are used in aircraft traveling at low speed. In birds, two kinds of wing slots have developed: (1) the **alula,** or group of small feathers on the thumb (see figures 19.5A and 19.16), which provides a mid-wing slot, and (2) **slotting between the primary feathers,** which provides a wing-tip slot. In many songbirds, these together provide stall-preventing slots for nearly the entire outer (and aerodynamically more important) half of the wing.

Flapping Flight

Two forces are required for flapping flight: a vertical *lifting* force to support the bird's weight, and a horizontal *thrusting* force to move the bird forward against resistive forces of friction. Thrust is provided mainly by primary feathers at the wing tips, while secondary feathers of the highly cambered inner wing, which do not move so far or so fast, act as an airfoil, providing mainly lift. Greatest power is applied on the downstroke. The primary feathers bend upward and twist to a steep angle of attack, biting into the air like a propeller (figure 19.14). The entire wing (and the bird's body) is pulled forward. On the upstroke, the primary feathers bend in the opposite direction so that their upper surfaces twist into a positive angle of attack to produce thrust, just as the lower surfaces did on the downstroke. A powered upstroke is essential for hovering flight, as in hummingbirds (figure 19.15), and is important for fast, steep takeoffs by small birds with elliptical wings.

Basic Forms of Bird Wings

Bird wings vary in size and form because successful exploitation of different habitats has imposed special aerodynamic requirements. Four types of bird wings are easily recognized: elliptical, high-aspect, dynamic soaring, and high-lift (figure 19.16).

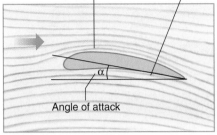

Lowest pressure and greatest lift where air flow is fastest

Smaller area of high pressure and lift beneath wing

α

Angle of attack

A Air flow around wing

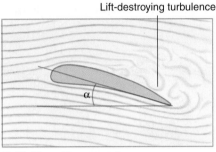

Lift-destroying turbulence

α

B Stalling at low speed

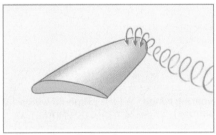

Wing slot directs fast-moving air over wing surface

C Preventing stall with wing slots

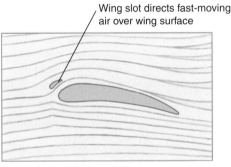

D Formation of wing tip vortex

figure 19.13

Air patterns formed by the airfoil, or wing, moving from right to left. **A,** At low speed, the angle of attack (α) must increase to maintain lift, but this increases the threat of stalling. **B, C,** Low-speed stalling can be prevented with wing slots. **D,** Wing tip vortex, a turbulence that tends to develop at high speeds, reduces flight efficiency. The effect is reduced in wings that sweep back and taper to a tip.

Elliptical Wings

Birds such as flycatchers, warblers, doves, woodpeckers, and magpies, which must maneuver in forested or brushy habitats, have elliptical wings (figure 19.16A). This type has a **low-aspect ratio** (ratio of length to average width). Wings of the highly maneuverable British Spitfire fighter plane of World War II fame conformed closely to the outline of a sparrow's wing. Elliptical wings have both an alula and slotting between the primary feathers; this slotting helps prevent stalling during sharp turns, low-speed flight, and frequent landing and takeoff. Each separated primary feather behaves as a narrow wing with a high angle of attack, providing high lift at low speed. The high maneuverability of elliptical wings is exemplified by the tiny chickadee, which, if frightened, can change course within 0.03 second.

High-Aspect Ratio Wings

Birds that feed during flight, such as swallows, hummingbirds, and swifts, or those that make long migrations, such as plovers, sandpipers, terns, and gulls (figure 19.16B), have wings that sweep back and taper to a slender tip. They are rather flat in section, have a high-aspect ratio, and lack wing-tip slotting. Sweepback and wide separation of wing tips reduce "tip vortex" (see figure 19.13D), a drag-creating turbulence that tends to develop at wing tips at faster speeds. This type of wing is aerodynamically efficient for high-speed flight but cannot easily keep a bird airborne at low speeds. The fastest birds, such as sandpipers clocked at 175 km (109 miles) per hour, belong to this group.

Dynamic Soaring Wings

Oceanic soaring birds, including albatrosses, shearwaters, and gannets (figure 19.16C), also have high-aspect ratio wings, shaped like those of sailplanes. Such long, narrow wings lack slots and are adapted for **dynamic soaring.** Dynamic soaring only can be done over seas with strong, reliable winds, and it exploits different wind speeds near the ocean surface (slow) and well above the surface (fast). A bird that uses dynamic soaring begins a downwind glide from an elevated position, gaining speed as it descends. Near the surface of the ocean, it turns into the wind and rises into stronger winds. Although its velocity relative to the ocean slows, the strong winds over its wings provide the lift to keep it aloft.

High-Lift Wings

Hawks, vultures, eagles, owls, and ospreys (figure 19.16D)—predators that carry heavy loads—have wings with slotting, alulas, and pronounced camber, all of which promote high lift at low speed. Many of these birds are land soarers, with broad, slotted wings that provide the sensitive response and maneuverability required for static soaring in the capricious air currents over land.

figure 19.14

In the normal flapping flight of strong fliers such as ducks, the wings sweep downward and forward fully extended. Thrust is provided by primary feathers at the wing tips. To begin the upbeat, the wing is bent, bringing it upward and backward. The wing then extends, ready for the next downbeat.

figure 19.15

The secret of a hummingbird's ability to change direction instantly, or to hang motionless in the air while sipping nectar from a flower, lies in its wing structure. The wing is nearly rigid, but hinged at the shoulder by a swivel joint and powered by a supracoracoideus muscle that is unusually large for the bird's size. When hovering, the wing moves in a sculling motion. The leading edge of the wing moves forward on the forward stroke, and then swivels nearly 180 degrees at the shoulder to move backward on the backstroke. The effect is to provide lift without propulsion on *both* forward and backstrokes.

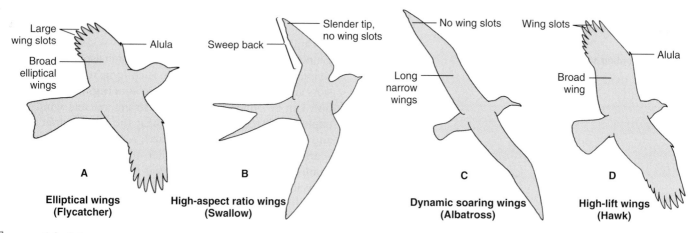

A Elliptical wings (Flycatcher)

B High-aspect ratio wings (Swallow)

C Dynamic soaring wings (Albatross)

D High-lift wings (Hawk)

figure 19.16

Four basic forms of bird wings.

■ Migration and Navigation

We described advantages of migration in the prologue to this chapter. Not all birds migrate, of course, but most North American and European species do, and the biannual journeys of some are truly extraordinary undertakings.

Migration Routes

Most migratory birds have well-established routes trending north and south. Since most birds (and other animals) breed in the Northern Hemisphere, where most of the earth's landmass is concentrated, most birds migrate south for the northern

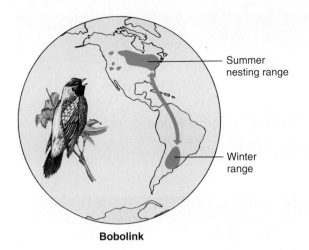

Bobolink

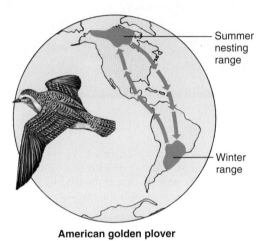

American golden plover

figure 19.17

Migrations of bobolinks, *Dolichonyx oryzivorus*, and American golden plovers, *Pluvialis dominica*. Bobolinks commute 22,500 km (14,000 miles) each year between their nesting sites in North America and their range in Argentina, where they spend the northern winters, a phenomenal feat for such a small bird. Although the breeding range has extended to colonies in western areas, these birds take no shortcuts but adhere to the ancestral seaboard route. American golden plovers fly a loop migration, striking out across the Atlantic in their southward autumnal migration but returning in the spring by way of Central America and the Mississippi Valley because ecological conditions are more favorable at that time.

winter and north in the northern summer to nest. Of the 4000 or more species of migrant birds, most breed in the more northern latitudes of the hemisphere. Certain birds use different routes in the fall and spring (figure 19.17). Some, especially certain aquatic species, complete their migratory routes in a very short time. Others, however, make a leisurely trip, often stopping along the way to feed. Some warblers are known to take 50 to 60 days to migrate from their winter quarters in Central America to their summer breeding areas in Canada.

Some species are known for their long-distance migrations. Arctic terns, the greatest globe spanners of all, breed north of the Arctic Circle during the northern summer and then migrate to Antarctic regions for the northern winter. This species is also known to take a circuitous route in migrations from North America, flying to the coastlines of Europe and Africa and then to winter quarters, a trip that may exceed 18,000 km (11,200 miles).

Many small songbirds, such as warblers, vireos, thrushes, flycatchers, sparrows, and shorebirds, such as sandpipers and plovers, also make great migratory treks (figure 19.17). Migratory birds that nest in Europe or Central Asia spend the northern winter in Africa.

Stimulus for Migration

Humans have known for centuries that the onset of reproductive cycles in birds is closely related to season. Only relatively recently, however, has it been shown that lengthening days of late winter and early spring stimulate development of gonads and accumulation of fat—both important internal changes that predispose birds to migrate northward. Increasing day length stimulates the anterior lobe of the pituitary into activity. Release of pituitary gonadotropic hormone in turn sets in motion a complex series of physiological and behavioral changes, stimulating gonadal growth, fat deposition, migration, courtship and mating behavior, and care of the young.

Direction Finding in Migration

Numerous experiments suggest that most birds navigate chiefly by sight. Birds recognize topographical landmarks and follow familiar migratory routes—a behavior assisted by flock migration, during which the navigational resources and experience of older birds can be pooled. In addition to visual navigation, birds have a variety of orientation cues at their disposal. Birds have a highly accurate sense of time. Numerous studies support a hypothesis that birds can navigate by the earth's magnetic field. In the early 1970s, W. T. Keeton showed that flight bearings of homing pigeons were significantly disturbed by magnets attached to the birds' heads, or by minor fluctuations in the geomagnetic field. Until recently, the nature and position of a magnetic receptor remained a mystery. Deposits of a magnetic substance called magnetite (Fe_3O_4) have been discovered in the beaks of pigeons. Recent experiments showed that a pigeon could discriminate between the presence and absence of a magnetic anomaly, but not when its upper beak was anesthetized, nor when its trigeminal nerve, which innervates the upper beak, was severed.

Experiments by German ornithologists G. Kramer and E. Sauer and American ornithologist S. Emlen demonstrated convincingly that birds can navigate by celestial cues: the sun by day and the stars by night. Using special circular cages, Kramer concluded that birds maintain compass direction by referring to the sun, regardless of the time of day (figure 19.18). This process is called **sun-compass navigation** (*azimuth*, compass bearing of the sun). Sauer's and Emlen's ingenious planetarium experiments also strongly suggest that some birds,

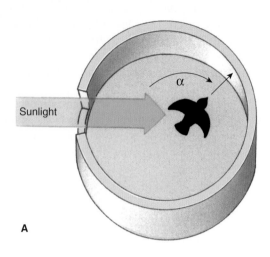

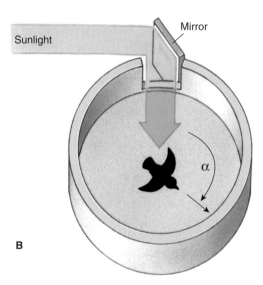

figure 19.18

Gustav Kramer's experiments with sun-compass navigation in starlings. **A,** In a windowed, circular cage, the bird fluttered to align itself in the direction it would normally follow if it were free. **B,** When the true angle of the sun is deflected with a mirror, the bird maintains the same relative position to the sun. This shows that these birds use the sun as a compass. The bird navigates correctly throughout the day, changing its orientation to the sun as the sun moves across the sky.

figure 19.19

Cooperative feeding behavior by white pelicans, *Pelecanus onocrotalus.* **A,** Pelicans form a horseshoe to drive fish together. **B,** Then they plunge simultaneously to scoop fish in their huge bills. These photographs were taken 2 seconds apart.

Social Behavior and Reproduction

The adage says "birds of a feather flock together," and many birds are indeed highly social creatures. Especially during the breeding season, sea birds gather, often in enormous colonies, to nest and to rear young. Land birds, with some conspicuous exceptions (such as starlings and rooks), tend to be less gregarious than sea birds during breeding and to seek isolation for rearing their brood. But these same species that covet separation from their kind during breeding may aggregate for migration or feeding. Togetherness offers advantages: mutual protection from enemies, greater ease in finding mates, less opportunity for individual straying during migration, and mass huddling for protection against low night temperatures during migration. Certain species, such as pelicans (figure 19.19), use cooperative behavior to feed. At no time are the highly organized social interactions of birds more evident than during the breeding season, as they establish territorial claims, select mates, build nests, incubate and hatch their eggs, and rear their young.

Reproductive System

During most of the year, **testes** of male birds are tiny, bean-shaped bodes, but during the breeding season, they enlarge

probably many, are able to detect and navigate by the North Star axis around which the constellations appear to rotate.

Some remarkable feats of bird navigation still defy rational explanation. Most birds undoubtedly use a combination of environmental and innate cues to migrate. Migration is a rigorous undertaking. The target is often small, and natural selection relentlessly eliminates individuals that make errors in migration, leaving only the best navigators to propagate the species.

figure 19.20

Copulation in waved albatrosses, *Diomeda irrorata*. In most bird species, males lack a penis. A male passes sperm by standing on the back of a female and pressing his cloaca against that of the female.

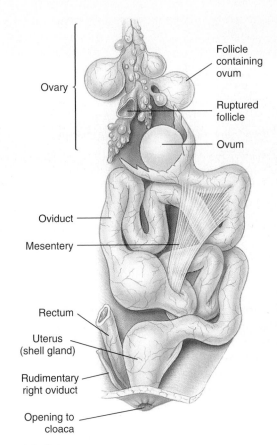

figure 19.21

Reproductive system of a female bird. For most birds, only the left ovary and reproductive tract are functional. The corresponding structures on the right dwindle to vestiges.

greatly, to as much as 300 times their nonbreeding size. Because males of most species lack a penis, copulation is a matter of bringing cloacal surfaces into contact, usually while the male stands on the back of the female (figure 19.20).

In females of most birds, only the **left ovary and oviduct** develop (figure 19.21); those on the right dwindle to vestigial structures (loss of one ovary is another adaptation of birds for reducing weight). Eggs discharged from the ovary enter the oviduct, which runs posteriorly to the cloaca. While eggs are passing down the oviduct, **albumin,** or egg white, from special glands is added to them; farther down the oviduct, shell membrane, shell, and shell pigments are secreted around the egg. Fertilization occurs in the upper oviduct several hours before layers of albumin, shell membranes, and shell are added. Sperm remain alive in the female oviduct for many days after a single mating.

Mating Systems

Two types of mating systems are **monogamy,** in which an individual has only one mate, and **polygamy,** in which an individual has more than one mate during a breeding period. Monogamy is rare in most animal groups, but it is common in birds; more than 90% are monogamous. A few bird species, such as swans and geese, choose partners for life and often remain together throughout the year. Seasonal monogamy is more common as the great majority of migrant birds pair only during the breeding season, living independent lives the rest of the year and perhaps choosing a different mate the next breeding season.

One reason monogamy is much more common among birds than among mammals is that male and female birds are equally adept at most aspects of parental care. Male mammals do not gestate the young and do not lactate; thus they can provide little help in caring for the young. Female and male birds, by contrast, can alternate care of the nest and young, which permits one parent to be at the nest at all times. For some species, a female remains on the nest for months at a time and is fed by the male. This constant attendance to the nest may be particularly important in species that would experience high loss of eggs or young to predators or rival birds if a nest were left unguarded. For many bird species, the high demands on a male to care for the young or his mate preclude the establishment of nests with additional females.

Although most birds have a monogamous mating system, either member of a pair may mate with an individual that is not the partner. Recent DNA analyses have shown that most passerine species frequently are "unfaithful," engaging in extra-pair copulations. As a result, nests of many of these monogamous species contain a sizeable portion (30% or more) of young with fathers other than the attendant male. Why do individuals engage in extra-pair copulations? By mating with an individual of better genetic quality, fitness of the offspring can be improved. Also, mating with multiple partners increases the

figure 19.22
Dominant male sage grouse, *Centrocercus urophasianus*, surrounded by several hens that have been attracted by his "booming" display.

figure 19.23
Anna's hummingbird, *Calypte anna*, feeding its young in its nest, which is constructed of plant down and spider webs and decorated on the outside with lichens. A female builds a nest, incubates two pea-sized eggs, and rears the young with no assistance from a male. Anna's hummingbird, a common resident of California, is the only hummingbird to overwinter in the United States.

genetic variation of the offspring. By mating with additional partners, a male is not only able to father more offspring, but also benefits by having the extra-pair female provide parental care to his offspring.

The most common form of polygamy in birds is **polygyny** ("many females"), in which a male has more than one female mate. In many species of grouse, males gather in a collective display ground, or **lek,** which is divided into individual territories, each vigorously defended by a displaying male (figure 19.22). In a lek, there is nothing of value to the female except the male, and all he can offer are his genes, for only females care for the young. Usually a dominant male and several subordinate males occur in a lek. Competition among males for females is intense, but females appear to choose the dominant male for mating because, presumably, social rank correlates with genetic quality.

Nesting and Care of Young

To produce offspring, nearly all birds lay eggs that must be incubated by one or both parents. Most duties of incubation fall on females, although in many instances both parents share the task, and occasionally only males incubate the eggs.

Most birds build some form of nest in which to rear their young. Some birds simply lay eggs on bare ground or rocks, making no pretense of nest building. Others build elaborate nests, such as the pendant nests constructed by orioles, the delicate lichen-covered mud nests of hummingbirds (figure 19.23) and flycatchers, the chimney-shaped mud nests of cliff swallows, the floating nests of rednecked grebes, and the huge sand and vegetation mounds of Australian brush turkeys. Most birds take considerable pains to conceal their nests from enemies. Nest parasites, such as brown-headed cowbirds and European cuckoos, build no nests at all but simply lay their eggs in the nests of birds smaller than themselves. When their eggs hatch, the foster parents care for the cowbird young, which outcompete the host's own hatchlings.

Altricial
One-day-old meadowlark

Precocial
One-day-old ruffed grouse

figure 19.24
Comparison of 1-day-old altricial and precocial young. The altricial meadowlark (*left*) is born nearly naked, blind, and helpless. The precocial ruffed grouse (*right*) is covered with down, alert, strong-legged, and able to feed itself.

Newly hatched birds are of two types: **altricial** and **precocial** (figure 19.24). Altricial young, which are naked and unable to walk or see at birth, remain in the nest for a week or more. Precocial young, including quail, fowl, ducks, and most water birds, are covered with down when hatched and can run or swim as soon as their plumage is dry. Young of both types require care from parents for some time after hatching. Parents of altricial species must carry food to their young almost constantly, for young birds may eat more than their weight each day. Some young are not easily categorized as altricial or precocial because they are intermediate in development at birth. For example, gulls and terns are born covered with down and with their eyes open, but are unable to leave the nest for some time.

Although it may seem that precocial chicks have all the advantages, with their greater ability to find food and escape predation, altricial chicks have an advantage of their own. Altricial chicks grow faster, perhaps due to the higher growth potential of immature tissue.

■ Humans and Bird Populations

Activities of people may cause spectacular changes in bird distribution. Both starlings (figure 19.25) and house sparrows have been accidentally or deliberately introduced into numerous countries, making them the two most abundant bird species on earth, with the exception of domestic fowl.

Humans also are responsible for the extinction of many bird species. More than 140 species of birds have, since 1681, followed the last dodo to extinction. Many were victims of changes in their habitat or competition with introduced species. Overhunting contributed to the extinction of some species, among them passenger pigeons, which only a century ago darkened skies over North America in numbers estimated in the billions (figure 19.26).

Today, game bird hunting is a well-managed renewable resource in the United States and Canada, and while hunters kill millions of game birds each year, none of the 74 bird species legally hunted are endangered. Hunting interests, by acquiring large areas of wetlands for migratory bird refuges and sanctuaries, have contributed to the recovery of both game and nongame birds.

Of particular concern is the recent sharp decline in songbirds in the United States and southern Canada. According to the records of ornithologists and amateur birdwatchers, many songbird species that were abundant as recently as 40 years ago are now suddenly scarce. There are several reasons for the decline. Intensification of agriculture, permitted by the use of herbicides, pesticides, and fertilizers, has deprived ground-nesting birds of

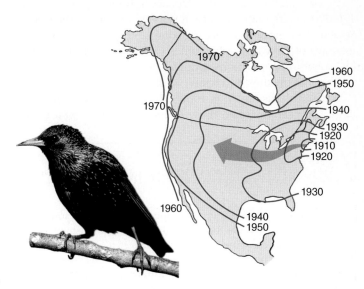

figure 19.25

Colonization of North America by starlings, *Sturnus vulgaris*, after the introduction of 120 birds into Central Park in New York City in 1890. There are now perhaps 200 million starlings in the United States alone, testimony to the great reproductive potential of birds. Starlings are omnivorous, eating mostly insects in spring and summer and shifting to wild fruits in the fall.

figure 19.26

Sport-shooting of passenger pigeons in Louisiana during the nineteenth century before establishment of state and federal hunting regulations. In addition to clearing the hardwood forests that served as nesting habitats, relentless sport and market hunting eventually dropped the population too low to sustain colonial breeding. The last passenger pigeon died in captivity in 1914.

fields that were formerly left fallow. Excessive fragmentation of forests throughout much of the United States has increased exposure of nests of forest-dwelling species to nest predators, such as blue jays, raccoons, and opossums, and to nest parasites, such as brown-headed cowbirds. House cats also kill millions of small birds every year. From a study of radio-collared farm cats in Wisconsin, researchers estimated that, in that state alone, cats may kill 19 million songbirds in a single year.

The rapid loss of tropical forests—approximately 170,000 square kilometers each year, an area about the size of Washington state—is depriving some 250 species of songbird migrants of their wintering homes. Of all long-term threats facing songbird populations, tropical deforestation is the most serious and the most intractable to change.

Some birds, such as robins, house sparrows, and starlings, can accommodate these changes, and may even thrive

Lead poisoning of waterfowl is a side effect of hunting. Before long-delayed federal regulations in 1991 required nonlead shot for all inland and coastal waterfowl hunting, shotguns scattered more than 3000 tons of lead each year in the United States alone. When waterfowl eat the pellets (which they mistake for seeds or grist), the pellets are ground and eroded in their gizzards, facilitating absorption of lead into their blood. Lead poisoning paralyzes or weakens birds, leading to death by starvation. Today, birds are still dying from ingesting lead shot that accumulated over the years.

on them, but for most birds the changes are adverse. Terborgh (1992) warns that unless we take leadership in managing our natural resources wisely we soon could be facing the "silent spring" that Rachel Carson envisioned in 1962.

Classification of Living Birds of Class Aves

Class Aves contains about 9700 species distributed among 30 orders of living birds. Understanding the relationships of living birds, and consequently placing them in a classification, has been difficult because of the apparent rapid diversification of birds in the Cretaceous and early Tertiary periods. Prior to the study of Sibley and Alquist (1990), which used DNA hybridization, classification had been primarily based on morphological similarity. New attempts at discovering the higher relationships of birds have utilized many kinds of data, but especially mitochondrial DNA (mtDNA) and nuclear DNA sequences. The classification and numbers of living bird species that we present here mostly follow that of Gill (2006), which itself is based on Sibley and Alquist's study and many other, more recent, phylogenetic reconstructions.

Class Aves (L. *avis,* bird)

> **Superorder Paleognathae** (Gr. *palaios,* ancient, + *gnathos,* jaw). Modern birds with primitive archosaurian palate. Ratites, which include ostriches, rheas, cassowaries, emus, and kiwis (with unkeeled sternum), and tinamous (with keeled sternum).

>> **Order Struthioniformes** (strŭ´thē-on-i-for´mēz) (L. *struthio,* ostrich, + *forma,* form): **ostrich.** The ostrich, *Struthio camelus* (figure 19.27), of Africa, is the largest living bird, with some specimens 2.4 m tall and weighing 135 kg. The feet have only two toes of unequal size covered with pads, which enable the birds to travel rapidly over sandy ground.

>> **Order Rheiformes** (rē´i-for-mēz) (Gr. *rhea,* rhea, + form): **rheas.** Two species of large, flightless birds found in grasslands of South America.

>> **Order Casuariiformes** (kas´u-er-i-for´mēz) (Mal. *casuar,* cassowary, + form): **cassowaries** and **emu.** The three species of cassowaries occupy forests of northern Australia and New Guinea. The emu is the second largest living bird species, and is confined to Australia. All are flightless.

figure 19.27

Ostrich, *Struthio camelus* (order Struthioniformes), of Africa, the largest of all living birds.

Order Dinornithiformes (din´or-nith´i-for-mēz) (Gr. *din*, terrible, + *ornith*, bird, + form): **kiwis.** Kiwis, about the size of a domestic fowl, are unusual in having only the mere vestige of a wing. This order also includes the extinct, flightless moas, some of which reached 2 m at the shoulder. Three living species, all in New Zealand.

Order Tinamiformes (tin-am´i-for´mēz) (N.L. *Tinamus*, type genus, + form): **tinamous.** Ground-dwelling, grouselike birds of Central and South America. About 47 species.

Superorder Neognathae (Gr. *neos*, new, + *gnathos*, jaw). Modern birds with flexible palate.

Order Anseriformes (an´ser-i-for´mēz) (L. *anser*, goose, + form): swans, **geese,** and **ducks.** The members of this order have broad bills with filtering ridges at their margins, a foot web restricted to the front toes, and a long breastbone with a low keel. About 162 species, worldwide distribution.

Order Galliformes (gal´li-for´mēz) (L. *gallus*, cock, + form): **quail, grouse, pheasants, ptarmigans, turkeys,** and **domestic fowl.** Chickenlike ground-nesting herbivores with strong beaks and heavy feet. The bobwhite quail, *Colinus virginianus*, occurs across the eastern half of the United States. The ruffed grouse, *Bonasa umbellus*, occupies the same region, but in woods instead of the open pastures and grain fields the bobwhite frequents. About 290 species, worldwide distribution.

Order Sphenisciformes (sfē-nis´i-for´mēz) (Gr. *Sphēniskos*, dim. of *sphen*, wedge, from the shortness of the wings, + form): **penguins.** Web-footed marine swimmers of southern seas from Antarctica north to the Galápagos Islands. Although penguins have a keeled sternum, they use their wings as paddles for swimming rather than for flight. About 17 species.

Order Gaviiformes (gā´vē-i-for´mēz) (L. *gavia*, bird, probably sea mew, + form): **loons.** The five species of loons are remarkable swimmers and divers with short legs and heavy bodies. They live exclusively on fish and small aquatic forms. The familiar great northern diver, *Gavia immer*, is found mainly in northern waters of North America and Eurasia.

Order Podicipediformes (pōd´i-si-ped´i-for´-mēz) (L. *podex*, rump, + *pes, pedis*, foot): **grebes.** Short-legged divers with lobate-webbed toes. The pied-billed grebe, *Podilymbus podiceps*, is a familiar example of this order. Grebes are most common in old ponds where they build their raftlike floating nests. Twenty-two species, worldwide distribution.

Order Phoenicopteriformes (fē´ni-cop-ter´i-for´mēz) (Gr. *phoenico*, reddish-purple, + *pter*, wing, + form): **flamingos** (figure 19.28). Large, colorful, wading birds that use lamellae in their beaks to strain zooplankton from the water. Five species.

Order Procellariiformes (prō-sel-lar´ē-i-for´mēz) (L. *procella*, tempest, + form): **albatrosses, petrels, fulmars,** and **shearwaters.** All are marine birds with hooked beaks and tubular nostrils. In wingspan (more than 3.6 m in some), albatrosses are the largest flying birds. About 112 species, worldwide distribution.

figure 19.28

Greater flamingos, *Phoenicopterus ruber* (order Phoenicopteriformes), on an alkaline lake in East Africa.

Order Pelecaniformes (pel-e-can´i-for´mēz) (Gr. *pelekan*, pelican, + form): **pelicans, cormorants, gannets, boobies,** and **others.** Colonial fish-eaters with throat pouch and all four toes of each foot included within the web. About 65 species, worldwide distribution, especially in the tropics.

Order Ciconiiformes (si-ko´nē-i-for´mēz) (L. *ciconia*, stork, + form): **herons, bitterns, storks, ibises, spoonbills,** and **vultures.** Long-necked, long-legged, mostly colonial waders and vultures. A familiar eastern North American representative is the great blue heron, *Ardea herodias*, which frequents marshes and ponds. About 116 species, worldwide distribution.

Order Falconiformes (fal´ko-ni-for´mēz) (L. *falco*, falcon, + form): **eagles, hawks, falcons, condors,** and **buzzards.** Diurnal birds of prey. All are strong fliers with keen vision and sharp, curved talons. About 304 species, worldwide distribution.

Order Gruiformes (gru´i-for´mēz) (L. *grus*, crane, + form): **cranes, rails, coots,** and **gallinules.** Mostly prairie and marsh breeders. About 212 species, worldwide distribution.

Order Charadriiformes (kä-ra-drē´i-for´mēz) (N.L. *Charadrius*, genus of plovers, + form): **gulls** (figure 19.29), **oyster catchers, plovers, sandpipers, terns, woodcocks, turnstones, lapwings, snipe, avocets, phalaropes, skuas, skimmers, auks,** and **puffins.** All are shorebirds. They are strong fliers and are usually colonial. About 367 species, worldwide distribution.

Order Columbiformes (kō-lum´bē-i-for´mēz) (L. *columba*, dove, + form): **pigeons** and **doves.** All have short necks, short legs, and a short, slender bill. The flightless dodo, *Raphus cucullatus*, of the Mauritius Islands became extinct in 1681. About 308 species, worldwide distribution.

Order Psittaciformes (sit´ta-sē´-for´mēz) (L. *psittacus*, parrot, + form): **parrots** and **parakeets.** Birds with hinged and movable upper beak, fleshy tongue. About 364 species, pantropical distribution.

(continued)

(continued)

figure 19.29

Laughing gulls, *Larus atricilla* (order Charadriiformes), in flight.

figure 19.30

Ground finch, *Geospiza fuliginosa* (order Passeriformes), one of the famous Darwin's finches of the Galápagos Islands.

Order Opisthocomiformes (ō-pis′thō-co-mi-for′mēz) (Gr. *opistho,* back, + L. *comos,* with long hair, + form): **hoatzin.** The relationship of the single species in this order to other birds is uncertain. The young of this South American, herbivorous bird use the large claws on their wings to climb trees.

Order Musophagiformes (myū′sō-fa′ji-for′mēz) (L. *musa,* banana, + Gr. *phagō,* to eat, + form): **turacos.** Medium to large birds of dense forest or forest edge having a conspicuous patch of crimson on the spread wing, brightly colored bill, and short and rounded wings. Twenty-three species restricted to Africa.

Order Cuculiformes (ku-ku′li-for′mēz) (L. *cuculus,* cuckoo, + form): **cuckoos** and **roadrunners.** European cuckoos, *Cuculus canorus,* lay their eggs in nests of smaller birds, which rear the young cuckoos. American cuckoos, black-billed and yellow-billed, usually rear their own young. About 138 species, worldwide distribution.

Order Strigiformes (strij′i-for′mēz) (L. *strix,* screech owl, + form): **owls.** Nocturnal predators with large eyes, powerful beaks and feet, and silent flight. About 180 species, worldwide distribution.

Order Caprimulgiformes (kap-ri-mul′ji-for′mēz) (L. *caprimulgus,* goatsucker, + form): **goatsuckers, nighthawks,** and **whippoorwills.** Night and twilight feeders with small, weak legs and wide mouths fringed with bristles. Whippoorwills, *Antrostomus vociferus,* are common in the woods of the eastern states, and nighthawks, *Chordeiles minor,* are often seen and heard in the evening flying around city buildings. About 118 species, worldwide distribution.

Order Apodiformes (ə-pōd′i-for′mēz) (Gr. *apous,* footless, + form): **swifts** and **hummingbirds.** Small birds with short legs and rapid wingbeat. The familiar chimney swift, *Chaetura pelagia,* fastens its nest in chimneys by means of saliva. A swift in China builds a nest of saliva that Chinese people use for soup making. Most species of hummingbirds occur in the tropics, but there are 14 species in the United States, of which only one, the ruby-throated hummingbird, occurs in the eastern part of the country. About 429 species, worldwide distribution.

Order Coliiformes (kä-lē′i-for′mēz) (Gr. *kolios,* green woodpecker, + form): **mousebirds.** Small crested birds of uncertain relationship. Six species restricted to southern Africa.

Order Trogoniformes (trō-gon′i′-for′mēz) (Gr. *trōgon,* gnawing, + form): **trogons.** Richly colored, long-tailed birds. About 39 species, pantropical distribution.

Order Coraciiformes (kä-rä′sē′i′for′mēz) (N.L. *coracii* from Gr. *korakias,* a kind of raven, + form): **kingfishers, hornbills, and others.** Birds that have strong, prominent bills and nest in cavities. In the eastern half of the United States, belted kingfishers, *Megaceryle alcyon,* are common along most waterways of any size. About 209 species, worldwide distribution.

Order Piciformes (pis′i-for′mēz) (L. *picus,* woodpecker, + form): **woodpeckers, toucans, puffbirds, and honeyguides.** Birds having highly specialized bills and two toes extending forward and two backward. All nest in cavities. Many species of woodpeckers inhabit North America, the most common being flickers and woodpeckers (downy, hairy, red-bellied, redheaded, and yellow-bellied). The largest is the pileated woodpecker, usually found in mature forests. About 398 species, worldwide distribution.

Order Passeriformes (pas-ser′i-for′mēz) (L. *passer,* sparrow, + form): **perching songbirds.** This is the largest order of birds, containing 56 families and 60% of all birds. Most have a highly developed syrinx (voice box). Their feet are adapted for perching on thin stems and twigs. The young are altricial. To this order belong many birds with beautiful songs, such as thrushes, warblers, finches (figure 19.30), mockingbirds, meadowlarks, and hosts of others. Others of this order, such as swallows, magpies, starlings, crows, ravens, jays, nuthatches, and creepers, have no songs worthy of the name. About 5750 species, worldwide distribution.

Summary

The more than 9700 species of living birds are feathered, egg-laying, endothermic vertebrates whose forelimbs are modified as wings. Birds are closest phylogenetically to theropods, a group of Mesozoic dinosaurs with several birdlike characteristics. The oldest known fossil bird, *Archaeopteryx* from the Jurassic period of the Mesozoic era, had numerous reptilian characteristics and was almost identical to certain theropod dinosaurs except that it had feathers. It is probably the sister taxon of modern birds.

Adaptations of birds for flight are of two kinds: those reducing body weight and those promoting more power for flight. Feathers, the hallmark of birds, are complex derivatives of reptilian scales that combine lightness with strength, water repellency, and high insulative value. Body weight is further reduced by elimination of some bones, fusion of others (also providing rigidity for flight), and the presence in many bones of hollow, air-filled spaces. The light, keratinized bill, replacing the heavy jaws and teeth of reptiles, serves as both hand and mouth for birds and is variously adapted for different feeding habits.

Adaptations that provide power for flight include high metabolic rate and high body temperature coupled with an energy-rich diet; a highly efficient respiratory system consisting of air sacs arranged to provide a constant, one-way flow of air through the lungs; powerful flight and leg muscles arranged to place muscle weight near the bird's center of gravity; and an efficient, high-pressure circulation.

Birds have keen eyesight, good hearing, and superb coordination for flight. Their metanephric kidneys produce uric acid as the principal nitrogenous waste.

Birds fly by applying the same aerodynamic principles as an airplane and using similar equipment: wings for lift, support, and propulsion; a tail for steering and landing control; and wing slots for control at low speed. Flightlessness in birds is unusual but has evolved independently in several bird orders, usually on islands where terrestrial predators are absent; all flightless species are derived from flying ancestors.

Bird migration refers to regular movements between summer nesting places and wintering regions. Spring migration to the north, where more food is available for nestlings, enhances reproductive success. Birds use many cues for finding direction during migration, including an innate sense of direction and the ability to navigate by the sun, stars, or earth's magnetic field.

The highly developed social behavior of birds is manifested in vivid courtship displays, mate selection, territorial behavior, and incubation of eggs and care of the young. Most birds have a monogamous mating system, although extra-pair copulations are common. Young hatch at various levels of development; altricial young are naked and helpless, while precocial young are feathered and able to walk and to feed themselves.

Review Questions

1. Explain the significance of the discovery of *Archaeopteryx*. Why did this fossil demonstrate beyond reasonable doubt that birds are grouped phylogenetically with dinosaurs?
2. The special adaptations of birds contribute to two essentials for flight: more power and less weight. Explain how each of the following contributes to one or both of these two essentials: feathers, skeleton, muscle distribution, digestive system, circulatory system, respiratory system, excretory system, reproductive system.
3. How do marine birds rid themselves of excess salt?
4. In what ways are a bird's ears and eyes specialized for the demands of flight?
5. Explain how a bird wing is designed to provide lift. What design features help prevent stalling at low flight speeds?
6. Describe four basic forms of bird wings. How does wing shape correlate with flight speed and maneuverability?
7. What are advantages of seasonal migration for birds?
8. Describe different navigational resources birds may use in long-distance migration.
9. What are some advantages of social aggregation among birds?
10. More than 90% of all bird species are monogamous. Explain why monogamy is much more common among birds than among mammals.
11. Briefly describe an example of polygyny among birds.
12. Define altricial and precocial as they relate to birds.
13. Offer some examples of how human activities have affected bird populations.

Selected References

See also general references on page 423.

Ackerman, J. 1998. Dinosaurs take wing. National Geographic **194** (1):74–99. *Beautifully illustrated synopsis of dinosaur-to-bird evolution.*

Bennett, P. M., and I. F. F. Owens. 2002. Evolutionary ecology of birds: life histories, mating systems, and extinction. Oxford, UK, Oxford University Press. *A phylogenetic approach to understanding how natural and sexual selection have led to the incredible diversity of bird mating systems.*

Brooke, M., and T. Birkhead, eds. 1991. The Cambridge encyclopedia of ornithology. New York, Cambridge University Press. *Comprehensive, richly illustrated treatment that includes a survey of all modern bird orders.*

Elphick, J., ed. 1995. The atlas of bird migration: tracing the great journeys of the world's birds. New York, Random House. *Lavishly illustrated collection of maps of birds' breeding and wintering areas,* migration routes, and many facts about each bird's migration journey.

Emlen, S. T. 1975. The stellar-orientation system of a migratory bird. Sci. Am. **233:** 102–111 (Aug.). *Describes fascinating research with indigo buntings, revealing their ability to navigate by the center of celestial rotation at night.*

Feduccia, A. 1996. The origin and evolution of birds. New Haven, Yale University Press. *An updated successor to the author's The Age of Birds (1980) but more comprehensive; rich source of information on evolutionary relationships of birds.*

Gill, F. B. 2006. Ornithology, ed. 3. New York, W. B. Freeman and Company. *Popular,*

comprehensive, and accurate ornithology text.

Mora, C. V., M. Davison, J. M. Wild, and M. W. Walker. 2004. Magnetoreception and its trigeminal mediation in the homing pigeon. Nature **432:**508–511. *Pigeons can discriminate between the presence and absence of a magnetic anomaly.*

Norbert, U. M. 1990. Vertebrate flight. New York, Springer-Verlag. *Detailed review of mechanics, physiology, morphology, ecology, and evolution of flight. Covers bats as well as birds.*

Sibley, C. G., and J. E. Ahlquist. 1990. Phylogeny and classification of birds: a study in molecular evolution. New Haven, Yale University

Press. *A comprehensive application of DNA annealing experiments to the problem of resolving avian phylogeny.*

Terborgh, J. 1992. Why American songbirds are vanishing. Sci. Am. **266:**98–104 (May). *The number of songbirds in the United States has been dropping sharply. The author suggests reasons why.*

Waldvogel, J. A. 1990. The bird's eye view. Am. Sci. **78:**342–353 (July–Aug.). *Birds possess visual abilities unmatched by humans. So how can we know what they really see?*

Wellnhofer, P. 1990. *Archaeopteryx.* Sci. Am. **262:**70–77 (May). *Description of perhaps the most important fossil ever discovered.*

■ Custom Website

The *Animal Diversity* Online Learning Center is a great place to check your understanding of chapter material. Visit www.mhhe.com/hickmanad5e for access to key terms, quizzes, and more! Further enhance your knowledge with web links to chapter-related material.

Explore live links for these topics:

Classification and Phylogeny of Animals
Class Aves
Marine Birds
Dissection Guides for Birds

Conservation Issues Concerning Birds
Movement of Populations

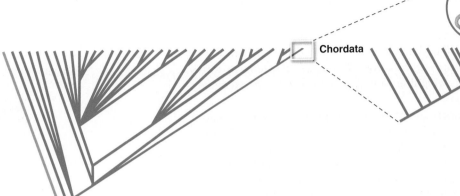

Mammals

Chordata

Mammalia

The Tell-Tale Hair

Hair evolved in a common ancestor of all mammals and has been retained to varying degrees in all species descended from that ancestor. Hair is therefore diagnostic for mammals; except in some pathological conditions, all mammals have hair at some point in their lives, and hair occurs in no other living organisms. Even those living mammals with no obvious hair, such as whales, usually have a few hairs on their bodies. Mammalian hair has undergone numerous adaptive modifications for diverse uses. Mammals use hair for concealment, behavioral signaling, waterproofing, and buoyancy; their hair may serve as sensitive vibrissae on their snouts or as prickly quills. Perhaps the most important use of their hair is thermal insulation, helping to maintain a high, constant body temperature in all climates, and thus support a high level of activity.

Mammals are among the most active animals, exhibiting speed and endurance in aquatic, aerial, and terrestrial habitats. They maintain this activity in nearly all environmental conditions, including cool nights, baking deserts, frigid polar seas, and icy winters. Numerous evolutionary innovations underlie this exuberant adaptive diversification. In addition to hair, mammals uniquely possess a set of middle ear bones for transmitting sounds to the inner ear, mammary glands for nourishing newborns, a large brain with a unique covering of the cerebrum (the neocortex), a diaphragm for efficient ventilation of lungs, and adaptations for a highly developed sense of smell. Most mammals have an intrauterine, vascular placenta for feeding the embryo, specialized teeth and jaw musculature for processing food, and an upright gait for rapid and efficient locomotion.

Juvenile grizzly bear, *Ursus arctos horribilis*.

Mammals, with their highly developed nervous system and numerous adaptations, occupy almost every environment on earth that supports life. Although not a large group (about 5400 species, compared with more than 9700 species of birds, 28,000 species of fishes, and 1,100,000 species of insects), class Mammalia (ma-mā´lē-ə; L. *mamma,* breast) is among the most biologically differentiated groups in the animal kingdom. Mammals are exceedingly diverse in size, shape, form, and function. They range in size from Kitti's hognosed bat, weighing only 2 g, to blue whales, exceeding 170 metric tons.

Despite their adaptability, and in some instances because of it, mammals have been influenced by humans more than any other group of animals. We have domesticated numerous mammals for food and clothing, as beasts of burden, and as pets. We use millions of mammals each year in biomedical research. We have introduced alien mammals into new habitats, occasionally with benign results but more frequently with disastrous effects. Although history provides us with numerous warnings, we continue to overcrop valuable wild stocks of mammals. The whaling industry has threatened itself with total collapse by exterminating its own resource—a classic example of self-destruction in the modern world, in which competing segments of an industry are intent only on reaping all they can today as though tomorrow's supply were of no concern whatever. In some cases, destruction of a valuable mammalian resource has been deliberate, such as the officially sanctioned (and tragically successful) policy during the Indian wars of exterminating bison to drive the Plains Indians into starvation. Although commercial hunting has declined, the ever-increasing human population with accompanying destruction of wild habitats has harassed and disfigured the mammalian fauna. In 2007, 512 species of mammals were listed as "critically endangered" or "endangered" by the International Union for Conservation of Nature and Natural Resources (IUCN), including many bats, cetaceans, cats, and primates.

We are becoming increasingly aware that our presence on this planet makes us responsible for the character of our natural environment. Since our welfare has been and continues to be closely related to that of the other mammals, it is clearly in our interest to preserve the natural environment of which all mammals, ourselves included, are a part. We need to remember that nature can do without humans but humans cannot exist without nature.

Origin and Evolution of Mammals

The evolutionary descent of mammals from their earliest amniote ancestors is perhaps the most fully documented transition in vertebrate history. From the fossil record, we can trace the derivation over 150 million years of endothermic, furry mammals from their small, ectothermic, hairless ancestors. Mammals and their closest fossil relatives have a pair of openings in the temporal region of the skull associated with

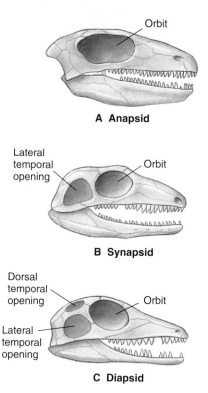

A Anapsid

B Synapsid

C Diapsid

figure 20.1

Skulls of early amniotes, showing the pattern of temporal openings that distinguish the three groups.

attachment of mandibular muscles. This condition identifies them as **synapsids,** one of three major groups of amniotes that diversified during the late Paleozoic era (figure 20.1B; see p. 357 for coverage of the other two groups, anapsids and diapsids).

The earliest synapsids included diverse herbivorous and carnivorous forms often collectively called **pelycosaurs** (figures 20.2 and 20.3). Pelycosaurs share a general outward resemblance to lizards, but this resemblance is misleading. Pelycosaurs are not closely related to lizards, which are diapsids, nor are they a monophyletic group. From one group of early carnivorous synapsids arose the **therapsids** (figure 20.3), the only synapsid group to survive beyond the Paleozoic era. With therapsids, we see for the first time an efficient erect gait with upright limbs positioned beneath the body rather than sprawled to the side, as in lizards. Since stability was reduced by raising the animal from the ground, the muscular coordination center of the brain, the cerebellum, assumed an expanded role. Changes in the morphology of the skull and jaw-closing muscles increased feeding efficiency. Therapsids diversified into numerous herbivorous and carnivorous forms, but most early forms disappeared during a great extinction at the end of the Permian period.

One therapsid group to survive into the Mesozoic era was the **cynodonts** (figures 20.2 and 20.3). Cynodonts evolved several features that supported a high metabolic rate: increased and specialized jaw musculature, permitting a stronger bite; several skeletal changes, supporting greater agility; heterodont

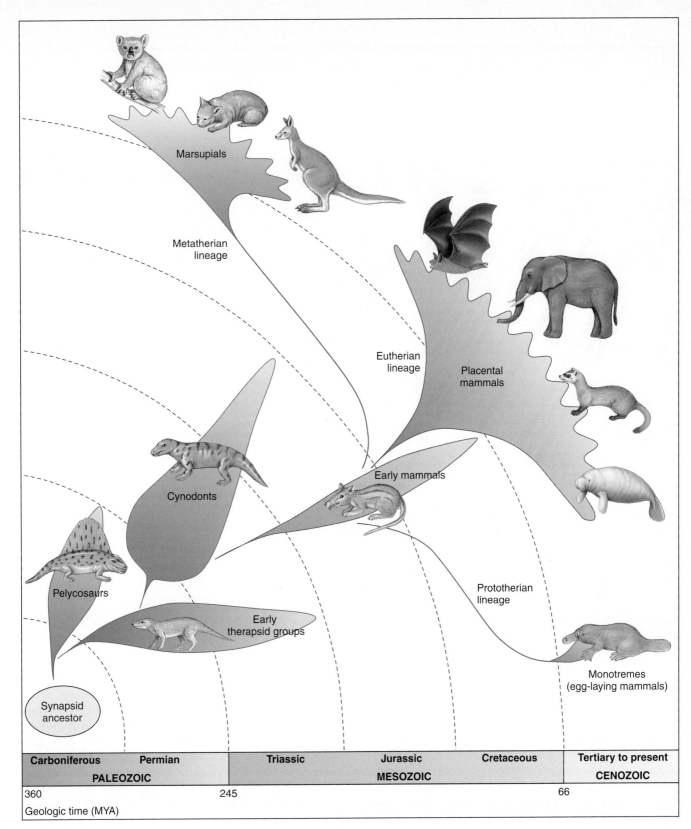

Carboniferous | **Permian** | **Triassic** | **Jurassic** | **Cretaceous** | **Tertiary to present**

PALEOZOIC | **MESOZOIC** | **CENOZOIC**

360 | 245 | 66

Geologic time (MYA)

figure 20.2

Evolution of major groups of synapsids. The synapsid lineage, characterized by lateral temporal openings in the skull, began with pelycosaurs, early amniotes of the Permian period. Pelycosaurs diversified extensively and evolved changes in jaws, teeth, and body form that presaged several mammalian characteristics. These trends continued in their successors, the therapsids, especially in cynodonts. One lineage of cynodonts gave rise in the Triassic to early mammals. Fossil evidence, as currently interpreted, indicates that all three groups of living mammals—monotremes, marsupials, and placentals—are derived from the same cynodont lineage. The great diversification of modern placental orders occurred during the Cretaceous and Tertiary periods.

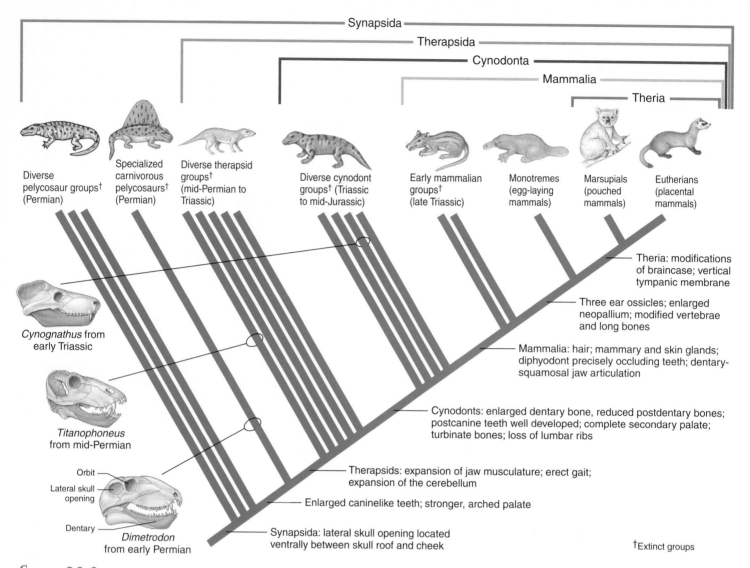

figure 20.3

Abbreviated cladogram of synapsids, emphasizing origins of important characteristics of mammals (shown to the right of the cladogram). Extinct groups are indicated by a dagger (†). The skulls show progressive increase in size of the dentary bone relative to other bones in the lower jaw.

teeth, permitting better food processing; **turbinate bones** in the nasal cavity, aiding retention of body heat (figure 20.4); and a bony, hard (secondary) palate (figure 20.4), enabling an animal to breathe while holding prey in its mouth or chewing food. The secondary palate would be important to subsequent mammalian evolution by permitting the young to breathe while suckling. Loss of lumbar ribs in cynodonts is correlated with the evolution of a **diaphragm** and also may have provided greater dorsoventral flexibility to the spinal column.

The earliest mammals of the late Triassic period were small, mouse- or shrew-sized animals with enlarged crania, redesigned jaws, and a new type of dentition, called **diphyodont,** in which teeth are replaced only once (deciduous and permanent teeth). This condition contrasts with the ancestral amniote pattern of continual tooth replacement throughout life (polyphodont teeth). Two bones, the articular and

the quadrate, which previously served as the jaw joint, were reduced in size and relocated in the middle ear, becoming the malleus and incus, respectively. The earliest mammals were almost certainly endothermic, although their body temperature would have been lower than that of modern placental mammals. Hair was essential for insulation, and the presence of hair implies that sebaceous and sweat glands must have evolved at this time to condition hair and to facilitate thermoregulation. The fossil record is silent on the appearance of mammary glands, but they must have evolved before the end of the Triassic.

Oddly, early mammals of the Late Triassic, having developed nearly all novel attributes of modern mammals, had to wait for another 150 million years before they could achieve their great diversity. While dinosaurs became diverse and abundant, all nonmammalian synapsid groups became extinct. Mammals survived mostly as shrewlike, probably nocturnal creatures. Then, in the Cretaceous period, but especially during the Eocene epoch that began about 58 million years ago, modern mammals began to diversify rapidly. The great Cenozoic diversification of mammals is partly attributed to numerous habitats vacated by the extinction of many amniote groups at the end of the Cretaceous. Mammalian diversification was almost certainly promoted by the facts that mammals were agile, endothermic, intelligent, and adaptable, and that they gave birth to living young, which they protected and nourished from their own milk supply, thus dispensing with vulnerable eggs laid in nests.

Class Mammalia includes 29 orders: one order containing **monotremes** (Prototheria), seven orders of **marsupials** (Metatheria), and 21 orders of **placentals** (Eutheria). A complete classification is on pp. 418–420.

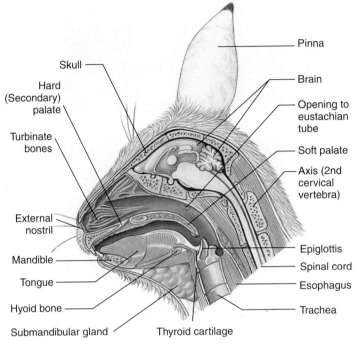

figure 20.4

Sagittal section of the head of a rabbit. The secondary palate, which consists of bony (hard) and nonbony (soft) regions, separates the routes of air (dorsal) and food (ventral).

Structural and Functional Adaptations of Mammals

Integument and Its Derivatives

Mammalian skin and especially its modifications distinguish mammals as a group. As the interface between an animal and its environment, skin is strongly molded by an animal's way of life. In general, skin is thicker in mammals than in other classes of vertebrates, although as in all vertebrates it is composed of **epidermis** and **dermis** (figure 20.5). The epidermis is thinner where it is well protected by hair, but in places that are subject to much contact and use, such as the palms or soles, its outer layers become thick and filled with a type of fibrous protein called **keratin.**

Hair

Hair is especially characteristic of mammals, although humans are not very hairy creatures, and hair in whales is reduced to a few sensory bristles on the snout. A hair grows from a hair follicle that, although epidermal in origin, is sunk into the dermis of the skin (figure 20.5). A hair grows continuously by rapid proliferation of cells in a follicle. As a hair shaft is pushed upward, new cells are carried away from their source of nourishment and die, becoming filled with keratin, the protein that also constitutes nails, claws, hooves, and feathers.

Mammals characteristically have two kinds of hair forming their **pelage** (fur coat): (1) dense and soft **underhair** for insulation, and (2) coarse and longer **guard hair** for protection against wear and to provide coloration. Underhair traps a layer of insulating air. In aquatic mammals, such as fur seals, otters, and beavers, underhair is so dense that it is almost impossible to wet. In water, guard hairs become wet and mat down, forming a protective blanket over the underhair (figure 20.6).

When a hair reaches a certain length, it stops growing. Normally it remains in its follicle until a new growth starts, whereupon it falls out. Most mammals experience periodic molts of the entire coat. In humans, hair is shed and replaced throughout life (although replacement is not assured, as evidenced by balding males!).

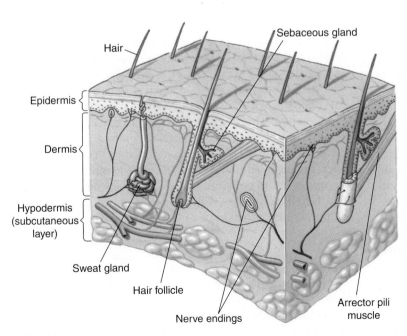

figure 20.5

Structure of human skin (epidermis and dermis) and hypodermis, showing hair and glands.

figure 20.6

American beaver, *Castor canadensis*, gnawing on an aspen tree. This second largest rodent (the South American capybara is larger) has a heavy waterproof pelage consisting of long, tough guard hairs overlying the thick, silky underhair so valued in the fur trade. Order Rodentia, family Castoridae.

A hair is more than a strand of keratin. It consists of three layers: the medulla or pith in the center of the hair, the cortex with pigment granules next to the medulla, and the outer cuticle composed of overlapping scales. Hair of different mammals shows a considerable range of structure. It may be deficient in cortex, like the brittle hair of deer, or it may be deficient in medulla, like the hollow, air-filled hairs of a wolverine. Hairs of rabbits and some others are scaled to interlock when pressed together. Curly hair, such as that of sheep, grows from curved follicles.

In the simplest cases, such as foxes and seals, the pelage is shed every summer. Most mammals have two annual molts, one in spring and one in fall. Summer coats are always much thinner than winter coats and in some mammals may be a different color. Several northern mustelid carnivores, such as weasels, have white winter coats and brown summer coats. It was once hypothesized that the white pelage of arctic animals conserved body heat by reducing radiation loss; in fact, dark and white pelages radiate heat equally well. The white winter pelage of arctic animals is simply camouflage in a land of snow. The varying hare of North America has three annual molts: the white winter coat is replaced by a brownish-gray summer coat, and this is replaced in autumn by a grayer coat, which is soon shed to reveal the white winter coat beneath (figure 20.7).

Most mammals wear somber colors that disguise their presence. Often a species is marked with "salt-and-pepper" coloration or a disruptive pattern that helps make it inconspicuous in its natural surroundings. Examples are the spots of leopards and fawns and the stripes of tigers. Skunks advertise their presence with conspicuous warning coloration.

The hair of mammals has become modified to serve many purposes. Bristles of hogs, spines of porcupines and their kin, and vibrissae on the snouts of most mammals are examples. **Vibrissae,** commonly called "whiskers," are really sensory hairs that provide a tactile sense to many mammals. The slightest

A

B

figure 20.7

Snowshoe, or varying, hare, *Lepus americanus* in **A,** brown summer coat, and **B,** white winter coat. In winter, extra hair growth on the hind feet broadens the animal's support in snow. Snowshoe hares are common residents of the taiga and are an important food for lynxes, foxes, and other carnivores. Population fluctuations of hares and their predators are closely related. Order Lagomorpha, family Leporidae.

movement of a vibrissa generates impulses in sensory nerve endings that travel to special sensory areas in the brain. Vibrissae are especially long in nocturnal and burrowing animals.

Porcupines, hedgehogs, echidnas, and a few other mammals have developed an effective and dangerous spiny armor. When cornered, the common North American porcupine turns its back toward its attacker and lashes out with its barbed tail. The lightly attached quills break off at their bases when they enter the skin and, aided by backward-pointing hooks on the tips, work deeply into tissues. Dogs are frequent victims (figure 20.8), but fishers, wolverines, and bobcats are able to flip the porcupine onto its back to expose vulnerable underparts.

Horns and Antlers

Several kinds of horns or hornlike structures occur in mammals. **True horns** of the family Bovidae (for example, sheep and cattle) are hollow sheaths of keratinized epidermis that embrace a core of bone arising from the skull. True horns are not shed, usually are not branched (although they may be greatly curved), grow continuously, and occur in both sexes.

Antlers of the deer family Cervidae are branched and composed of solid bone when mature. During their annual spring growth, antlers develop beneath a covering of highly vascular soft skin called **velvet** (figure 20.9). When growth of antlers is complete just before the breeding season, blood vessels constrict, and the stag tears off the velvet by rubbing its antlers against trees. Antlers are shed after the breeding season. New buds appear a few months later to herald the next set of antlers. For several years, each new pair of antlers is larger and more elaborate than the previous set. Annual growth of antlers places a strain on mineral metabolism, since during the growing season an older moose or elk must accumulate 50 or more pounds of calcium salts from its vegetable diet.

Horns of the pronghorn antelope (family Antilocapridae) are similar to the true horns of bovids, except the keratinized portion is forked and shed annually. Giraffe horns are similar to antlers but retain their integumentary covering and are not shed. Rhinoceros horn consists of hairlike, keratinized filaments that arise from dermal papillae cemented together, but they are not attached to the skull.

Trade in rhino products, especially the horn, has pushed Asian and African rhinos to the brink of extinction. Rhino horn is valued in China as an agent for reducing fever and for treating heart, liver, and skin disease, and in North India as an aphrodisiac. Such supposed medicinal values are totally without pharmacological basis. The principal use of rhino horns is to fashion handles for ceremonial daggers called jambiyas in the Middle East. Between 1970 and 1997, horns from 22,350 rhinos were imported into northern Yemen alone. An international ban prohibiting the trade of rhino horn has reduced, but not eliminated, the now illegal trade, and populations continue to suffer.

Glands

Of all vertebrates, mammals have the greatest variety of integumentary glands. Most fall into one of four classes: sweat, scent, sebaceous, or mammary. All are derivatives of epidermis.

Sweat glands are tubular, highly coiled glands that occur over much of the body surface in most mammals (see figure 20.5). They are absent in other vertebrates. There are two kinds of sweat glands: eccrine and apocrine. **Eccrine glands** secrete a watery fluid that, if evaporated on the skin's surface, draws heat away from the skin and cools it. Eccrine glands occur in hairless regions, especially foot pads, in most mammals, although in horses and most primates they are scattered over the body. **Apocrine glands** are larger than eccrine glands and have longer and more convoluted ducts. Their secretory coil is in the dermis and extends deep into the hypodermis. They always open into a hair follicle or where a hair once was. Apocrine glands develop near sexual puberty and are restricted (in humans) to the axillae (armpits), mons pubis, breasts, prepuce, scrotum, and external auditory canals. In contrast to the watery secretions of eccrine glands, apocrine secretions are milky fluids, whitish or yellow in color, that dry on the

figure 20.8

Dogs are frequent victims of the porcupine's impressive armor. Unless removed (usually by a veterinarian), the quills continue to work their way deeper into the flesh, causing great distress and possibly even leading to the victim's death.

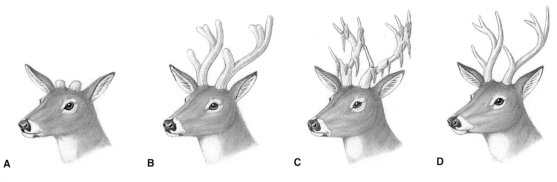

A   B   C   D

figure 20.9

Annual growth of buck deer antlers. **A,** Antlers begin to grow in late spring, stimulated by pituitary gonadotropins. **B,** The bone grows very rapidly until halted by a rapid rise in testosterone production by the testes. **C,** The skin (velvet) dies and sloughs off. **D,** Testosterone levels peak during the fall breeding season. The antlers are shed in January as testosterone levels subside.

Characteristics
of Mammals

1. Body mostly covered with **hair,** but reduced in some
2. **Integument** with **sweat, scent, sebaceous,** and **mammary glands**
3. Skull with **two occipital condyles; turbinate bones** in nasal cavity; jaw joint between the squamosal and dentary bones; middle ear with **three ossicles** (malleus, incus, stapes); **seven cervical vertebrae** (except in some xenarthrans [edentates] and manatees); **pelvic bones fused**
4. Mouth with **diphyodont teeth** (milk, or deciduous, teeth replaced by a permanent set of teeth); teeth **heterodont** in most (varying in structure and function); lower jaw a **single enlarged bone (dentary)**
5. Movable eyelids and **fleshy external ears (pinnae)**
6. Circulatory system consisting of a four-chambered heart, **persistent left aortic arch,** and nonnucleated, biconcave **red blood cells**
7. Respiratory system composed of lungs with alveoli and larynx; **secondary palate** (anterior bony palate and posterior continuation of soft tissue, the soft palate) separates air and food passages (see figure 20.4); **muscular diaphragm** for air exchange separates thoracic and abdominal cavities
8. Excretory system consisting of metanephric kidneys and ureters that usually open into a bladder
9. Brain highly developed, especially **cerebral cortex** (a highly folded superficial layer of the cerebrum); 12 pairs of cranial nerves
10. Endothermic and homeothermic
11. Cloaca distinctive only in monotremes (present, but shallow in marsupials)
12. Separate sexes; reproductive organs include a penis, testes (usually in a scrotum), ovaries, oviducts, and uterus; sex determination by chromosomes (male is heterogametic)
13. Internal fertilization; embryos develop in a **uterus** with **placental attachment** (except in monotremes); **fetal membranes (amnion, chorion, allantois)**
14. Young nourished by **milk from mammary glands**

skin to form a film. Apocrine glands are not involved in heat regulation. Their activity is correlated with certain aspects of the reproductive cycle.

Scent glands occur in nearly all mammals. Their location and functions vary greatly. They are used for communication with members of the same species, for marking territorial boundaries, for warning, or for defense. Scent-producing glands are located in orbital, metatarsal, and interdigital regions; at the base of the tail; and in the penis. The most odoriferous of all glands are those of skunks, which open by ducts into the anus; their secretions can be discharged forcefully for 2 to 3 m. During mating season, many mammals produce strong scents for attracting the opposite sex. Humans also are endowed with scent glands. However, we tend to dislike our own scent, a concern that has stimulated a lucrative deodorant industry to produce an endless array of soaps and odor-masking concoctions.

Sebaceous glands are intimately associated with hair follicles (see figure 20.5), although some are free and open directly onto the surface. The cellular lining of a gland is discharged in the secretory process and must be renewed for further secretion. These gland cells become distended with a fatty accumulation, then die, and are expelled as a greasy mixture called **sebum** into the hair follicle. Called a "polite fat" because it does not turn rancid, sebum keeps skin and hair pliable and glossy. Most mammals have sebaceous glands over their entire body; in humans, they are most numerous in the scalp and on the face.

Mammary glands, for which mammals are named, occur on all female mammals and in a rudimentary form on all male mammals. In the embryo, they develop by thickening of the epidermis to form a milk line along each side of the abdomen. On certain parts of these lines, the mammae appear while the intervening parts of the ridge disappear. Mammary glands increase in size at maturity, becoming considerably larger during pregnancy and subsequent nursing of young. In human females, adipose tissue begins to accumulate around mammary glands at puberty to form the breast. In most mammals, milk is secreted from mammary glands via nipples, but monotremes lack nipples and simply secrete milk into a depression on the mother's belly where it is lapped by the young.

Food and Feeding

Mammals exploit an enormous variety of food sources; some mammals require highly specialized diets, whereas others are opportunistic feeders that thrive on diversified diets. Food habits and physical structure are thus inextricably linked. A mammal's adaptations for attack and defense and its specializations for finding, capturing, chewing, swallowing, and digesting food all determine its shape and habits.

Teeth, perhaps more than any other single physical characteristic, reveal the life habit of a mammal (figure 20.10). All mammals have teeth (with few exceptions), and their modifications are correlated with what the mammal eats.

As mammals evolved during the Mesozoic, major changes occurred in teeth and jaws. Unlike the uniform **homodont** dentition of the first synapsids, mammalian teeth became differentiated to perform specialized functions such as cutting, seizing, gnawing, tearing, grinding, and chewing. Teeth differentiated in this manner are called **heterodont.** Mammalian teeth are differentiated into four types: **incisors (I),** with simple crowns and sharp edges, used mainly for snipping or biting; **canines (C),** with long conical crowns, specialized for piercing; **premolars (PM)** and **molars (M)** with compressed crowns and one or more cusps, suited for shearing, slicing, crushing, or grinding. The ancestral tooth formula, which expresses the number of each tooth type in one-half of the upper and lower jaw, was I 3/3, C 1/1, PM 4/4, and M 3/3. Members of order Insectivora, some omnivores, and most carnivores come closest to this ancestral pattern (figure 20.10).

Most mammals grow just two sets of teeth: a temporary set, called **deciduous teeth,** or **milk teeth,** which is replaced

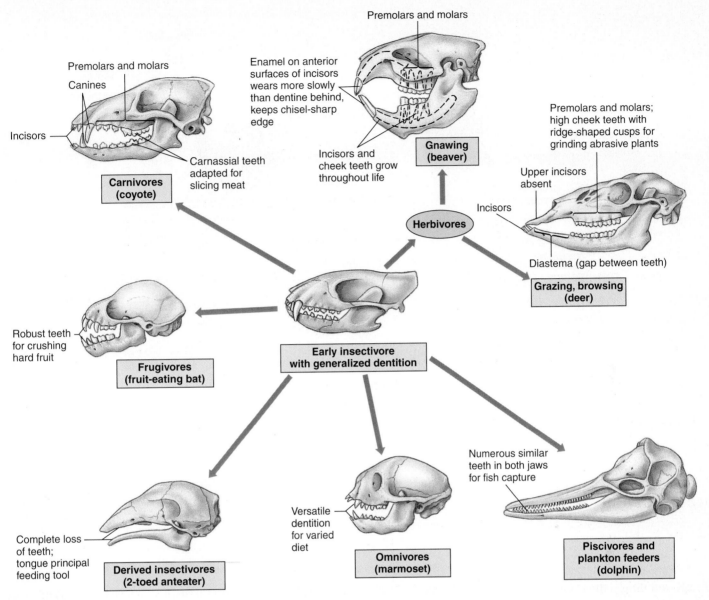

figure 20.10

Feeding specializations of major trophic groups of placental mammals. Early placentals were insectivores; all other types are descended from them.

by a permanent set when the skull has grown large enough to accommodate a full set. Only incisors, canines, and premolars are deciduous; molars are never replaced and the single permanent set must last a lifetime.

Feeding Specializations

The feeding, or trophic, apparatus of a mammal—teeth and jaws, tongue, and digestive tract—is adapted to the animal's particular feeding habits. Mammals are customarily divided among four basic trophic categories—insectivores, carnivores, omnivores, and herbivores—but many other feeding specializations have evolved in mammals, as in other living organisms, and feeding habits of many mammals defy exact classification.

The principal feeding specializations of mammals are shown in figure 20.10.

Insectivorous mammals, such as shrews, moles, anteaters, and most bats, feed on a variety of insects and other small invertebrates. Most insectivorous mammals have teeth with pointed cusps, permitting them to puncture the exoskeleton or skin of their prey. Some insectivores completely lack teeth (figure 20.10).

Herbivorous mammals that feed on grasses and other vegetation form two main groups: (1) **browsers** and **grazers,** such as ungulates (hooved mammals, including horses, deer, antelope, cattle, sheep, and goats), and (2) **gnawers,** including many rodents as well as rabbits and hares. In herbivores, canines are absent or reduced in size, whereas molars, which

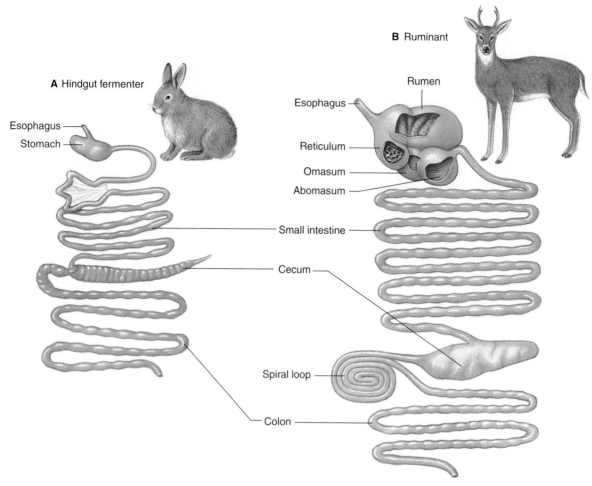

figure 20.11

Digestive tracts of two mammals. **A,** In rabbits, digestion of cellulose by microorganisms takes place in the cecum and colon. **B,** In ruminants, digestion of cellulose by microorganisms takes place in the rumen.

are adapted for grinding, are broad and usually high-crowned. Rodents have chisel-sharp incisors that grow throughout life and must be worn away to keep pace with their continual growth (figure 20.10).

Herbivores have a number of adaptations for processing their fibrous diet of plant food. **Cellulose,** the structural carbohydrate of plants, is composed of long chains of glucose molecules and therefore is a potentially nutritious food resource. However, no vertebrates synthesize cellulose-splitting enzymes **(cellulases).** Instead, herbivorous vertebrates harbor anaerobic bacteria and protozoa that produce cellulase in fermentation chambers in their gut. Simple carbohydrates, proteins, and lipids produced by the microorganisms can be absorbed by the host animal, and the host can digest the microorganisms as well.

Fermentation in some herbivores, such as rabbits, horses, zebras, elephants, some primates, and many rodents, occurs primarily in the colon and in a spacious side pocket, or diverticulum, called a **cecum** (figure 20.11A). Although some absorption occurs in the colon and cecum, fermentation occurs posterior to the small intestine, where nutrients are

absorbed, so many nutrients are lost in feces. Rabbits and many rodents eat their fecal pellets **(coprophagy),** giving food a second pass through the gut to extract additional nutrients.

Ruminants (cattle, bison, buffalo, goats, antelopes, sheep, deer, giraffes, and okapis) have a huge **four-chambered stomach** (figure 20.11B). As a ruminant feeds, grass passes down the esophagus to the **rumen,** where it is digested by microorganisms and then formed into small balls of cud. At its leisure, the ruminant returns a cud to its mouth and chews it deliberately and at length to crush the fiber. Swallowed again, the food returns to the rumen where the cellulolytic bacteria and protozoa continue fermentation. The pulp passes to the **reticulum,** and then to the **omasum,** where water-soluble food and microbial products are absorbed. The remainder proceeds to the **abomasum** ("true" acid stomach) and small intestine, where proteolytic enzymes are secreted and normal digestion occurs. Perhaps because ruminants are particularly good at extracting nutrients from forage, they are the primary large herbivores in ecosystems where food is scarce, such as tundras and deserts.

figure 20.12

Lionesses, *Panthera leo*, eating a wildebeest. Lacking stamina for a long chase, lions stalk prey and then charge suddenly, surprising their prey. After gorging themselves, lions sleep and rest for periods as long as one week before eating again. Order Carnivora, family Felidae.

Herbivores generally have large, long digestive tracts and must eat a considerable amount of plant food to survive. An African elephant weighing 6 tons must consume 135 to 150 kg (300 to 400 pounds) of rough fodder each day to obtain sufficient nourishment for life.

Carnivorous mammals, which feed mainly on herbivores, include foxes, dogs, weasels, wolverines, fishers, and cats. Carnivores are well-equipped with biting and piercing teeth and powerful clawed limbs for killing their prey. Since their protein diet is more easily digested than the fibrous food of herbivores, their digestive tract is shorter, and the cecum is small or absent. Carnivores organize their feeding into discrete meals rather than feeding continuously (as do most herbivores) and therefore have much more leisure time (figure 20.12).

Note that the terms "insectivore" and "carnivore" have two different uses in mammals: to describe diet and to denote specific taxonomic orders of mammals. For example, not all carnivores belong to the order Carnivora (many marsupials and cetaceans are carnivorous), and not all members of the order Carnivora are carnivorous. Many are opportunistic feeders, and some, such as pandas, are strict vegetarians.

Omnivorous mammals use both plants and animals for food. Examples are pigs, raccoons, many rodents, bears, and most primates, including humans. Many carnivorous forms also eat fruits, berries, and grasses when hard pressed. Foxes, which usually feed on mice, small rodents, and birds, eat frozen apples, beechnuts, and corn when their normal food sources are scarce.

Migration

Migration is a more difficult undertaking for mammals than for birds or fishes, because terrestrial locomotion is more energetically expensive than swimming or flying. Not surprisingly, few terrestrial mammals make regular seasonal migrations, instead centering their activities in a defined and limited home range. Nevertheless, some striking terrestrial mammalian migrations occur, especially in northern North America.

The barren-ground caribou of Canada and Alaska undertakes direct and purposeful mass migrations spanning 160 to 1100 km (100 to 700 miles) twice annually (figure 20.13). From winter ranges in boreal forests (taiga), they migrate rapidly in late winter and spring to calving ranges on the barren grounds (tundra). Calves are born in mid-June. As summer progresses, caribou are increasingly harassed by warble and nostril flies that bore into their flesh, by mosquitos that drink their blood (estimated at a liter per caribou each week during the height of the mosquito season), and by wolves that prey on their calves. They move southward in July and August, feeding little along the way. In September, they reach the taiga and feed there almost continuously on low ground vegetation. Mating (rut) occurs in October.

The longest mammalian migrations are made by oceanic seals and whales. One of the most remarkable migrations is that of northern fur seals, which breed on the Pribilof Islands approximately 300 km (185 miles) off the coast of Alaska and north of the Aleutian Islands. From wintering grounds off southern California, females journey as much as 2800 km (1740 miles) across open ocean, arriving in spring at the Pribilofs where they congregate in enormous numbers (figure 20.14). Young are born within a few hours or days after the cows arrive. Then bulls, having already arrived and established territories, collect harems of cows, which they guard with vigilance. After calves have been nursed for approximately three months, cows and juveniles leave for their long migration southward. Bulls do not follow but remain in the Gulf of Alaska during winter.

Caribou have suffered a drastic decline in numbers since the middle 1800s, when their population reached several million. By 1958, less than 200,000 remained in Canada. The decline has been attributed to several factors, including habitat alteration due to exploration and development in the North, but especially excessive hunting. For example, the western Arctic herd in Alaska exceeded 250,000 caribou in 1970. Following five years of heavy unregulated hunting, a 1976 census revealed only about 75,000 animals remaining. After hunting was restricted, the herd had increased to 340,000 by 1988 and to 490,000 in 2006. However, this recovery is threatened by proposed expansion of oil extraction in several Alaskan wildlife refuges, including the Arctic National Wildlife Refuge. The Porcupine caribou herd, which calves on the Arctic National Wildlife Refuge, numbers about 123,000, down by about one-third since 1989.

Although we might expect bats, the only winged mammals, to use their gift of flight to migrate, few of them do. Most spend their winters in hibernation. Four species of American bats that migrate spend their summers in northern or western states and their winters in the southern United States or Mexico.

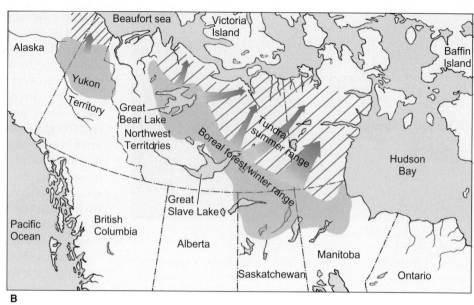

figure 20.13

Barren-ground caribou, *Rangifer tarandus*, of Canada and Alaska. **A,** Adult male caribou in autumn pelage and antlers in velvet. **B,** Summer and winter ranges of some major caribou herds in Canada and Alaska. (Other herds not shown occur on Baffin Island and in western and central Alaska.) The principal spring migration routes are indicated by arrows; routes vary considerably from year to year. The same species is known as reindeer in Europe. Order Artiodactyla, family Cervidae.

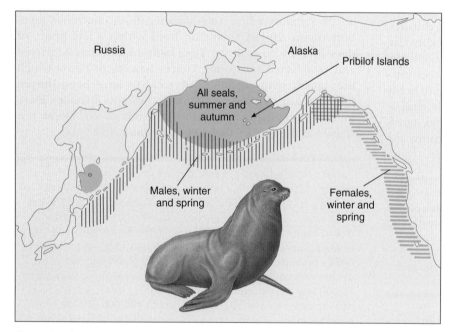

figure 20.14

Annual migrations of northern fur seals, *Callorhinus ursinus*, showing the separate wintering grounds of males and females. Both males and females of the large Pribilof population migrate in early summer to the Pribilof Islands, where females give birth to their pups and then mate with males. Order Carnivora, family Otariidae.

Flight and Echolocation

Many mammals scamper about in trees with amazing agility; some can glide from tree to tree, and one group, bats, is capable of full flight. Gliding and flying evolved independently in several groups of mammals, including marsupials, rodents, flying lemurs, and bats. Flying squirrels (figure 20.15) actually glide rather than fly, using the gliding skin (patagium) that extends from the sides of their body.

Bats are mostly nocturnal or crepuscular (active at twilight), and thus hold a niche unoccupied by most birds. Their achievement is attributed to two features: flight and the capacity to navigate by echolocation. Together, these adaptations enable bats to move quickly while avoiding obstacles in absolute darkness, to locate and to catch insects with precision, and to find their way deep into caves (a habitat largely unexploited by other mammals and birds) where they sleep during the daytime hours.

When in flight, a bat emits short pulses 5 to 10 msec in duration in a narrow directed beam from its mouth or nose (figure 20.16). Each pulse is frequency modulated; it is highest at the beginning, up to 100,000 Hz (hertz, cycles per second), and sweeps down to perhaps 30,000 Hz at the end. Sounds at this frequency are ultrasonic to human ears, which have an upper limit of about 20,000 Hz. When bats search for prey, they produce about 10 pulses per second. If prey is detected, the rate increases rapidly up to 200 pulses per second in the final phase of approach and capture. Pulses are spaced so that the echo of each is received before the next pulse is emitted, an adaptation that prevents jamming. Since transmission-to-reception time decreases as a

figure 20.15

Northern flying squirrel, *Glaucomys sabrinus*, gliding in for a landing. The area of the undersurface is nearly trebled when the gliding skin is spread. Glides of 40 to 50 m are possible. Good maneuverability during flight is achieved by adjusting the position of the gliding skin with special muscles. Flying squirrels are nocturnal and have superb night vision. Order Rodentia, family Sciuridae.

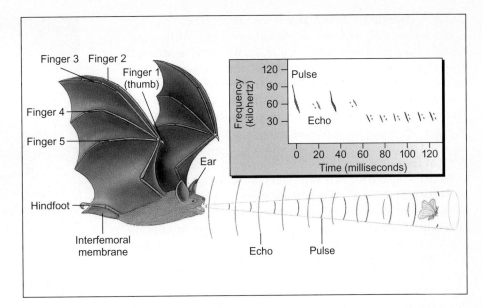

figure 20.16

Echolocation of an insect by a little brown bat, *Myotis lucifugus*. Frequency-modulated pulses are directed in a narrow beam from the bat's mouth. As the bat nears its prey, it emits shorter, lower signals at a faster rate. Order Chiroptera, family Vespertilionidae.

bat approaches an object, the bat can increase pulse frequency to obtain more information about an object. Pulse length also is shortened as the bat nears an object. Some prey of bats—certain nocturnal moths, for example—have evolved ultrasonic detectors to sense and avoid approaching bats.

The external ears of bats are large, like hearing trumpets, and shaped variously in different species. Less is known about the inner ear of bats, but it obviously receives the ultrasonic sounds emitted. A bat builds a mental image of its surroundings from echo scanning that approaches the resolution of a visual image perceived by the eyes of a diurnal animal.

Some bats, including the approximately 170 species of Old World fruit bats, lack echolocation abilities. Even so, most remain nocturnal, using large eyes and olfaction to find their meals of fruits, flowers, and nectar. Vampire bats have razor-sharp incisors used to shave away the epidermis of their prey, exposing underlying capillaries. After infusing an anticoagulant to keep blood flowing, the bat laps its meal and stores it in a specially modified stomach.

Reproduction

Most mammals have definite mating seasons, usually in winter or spring and timed so that birth and the rearing of young occur at the most favorable time of the year. Many male mammals are capable of fertile copulation at any time, but female fertility is restricted to a certain time during the periodic or **estrous cycle.** Females only copulate with males during a relatively brief period called **estrus** or heat (figure 20.17).

figure 20.17

African lions, *Panthera leo*, mating. Lions breed at any season, although predominantly in spring and summer. During the short period a female is receptive, she may mate repeatedly. Three or four cubs are born after gestation of 100 days. Once the mother introduces cubs into the pride, they are treated with affection by both adult males and females. Cubs go through an 18- to 24-month apprenticeship learning how to hunt and then are frequently driven from the pride to manage themselves. Order Carnivora, family Felidae.

There are three different patterns of reproduction in mammals, represented by monotremes, marsupials, and placental mammals. Monotremes are (oviparous) mammals, such as the duck-billed platypus, which has one breeding season each year.

Embryos develop for 10–12 days in the uterus, where they are nourished by yolk supplies deposited prior to ovulation and by secretions from the mother. A thin, leathery shell is secreted around the embryos before the eggs are laid. The platypus lays its eggs in a burrow, where they hatch in a relatively underdeveloped state after about 12 days. After hatching, the young feed on milk produced by the mother's mammary glands. Because monotremes have no nipples, the young lap milk secreted onto the belly fur of the mother.

Marsupials are pouched, viviparous mammals that exhibit a second pattern of reproduction. Although only eutherians are called "placental mammals," marsupials do have a transient type of placenta called a **choriovitteline** or **yolk sac placenta.** Embryos (blastocysts) of a marsupial are first encapsulated by shell membranes and float freely for several days in uterine fluid. After "hatching" from the shell membranes, embryos of most marsupials do not implant, or "take root" in the uterus as they would in eutherians, but erode shallow depressions in the uterine wall in which they lie and absorb nutrient secretions from the mucosa through the vascularized yolk sac. Gestation (the intrauterine period of development) is brief in marsupials, and therefore all marsupials give birth to tiny young that are effectively still embryos, both anatomically and physiologically (figure 20.18). However, early birth is followed by a prolonged interval of lactation and parental care (figure 20.19).

The third pattern of reproduction is that of viviparous placental mammals, eutherians. In placentals, the reproductive investment is in prolonged gestation, unlike marsupials in which the reproductive investment is in prolonged lactation (figure 20.19). Like marsupials, most placental embryos initially receive nutrients through a yolk sac placenta. The yolk sac placenta may persist, as in mice, but usually is transitory and quickly replaced by a **chorioallantoic placenta,** formed from the chorionic and allantoic membranes. In eutherians, both types of placentae are extensively vascularized. The numerous capillaries of the placenta and the mother's uterus are close, but do not connect, and allow nutrients, respiratory gases, wastes, and other molecules to diffuse between the maternal and embryonic circulation. Length of gestation is longer in placentals than in marsupials, and in larger mammals than in smaller mammals. For example, mice have a gestation period of 21 days; rabbits and hares, 30 to 36 days; cats and dogs, 60 days; cattle, 280 days; and elephants, 22 months (the longest). Important exceptions include baleen whales, the largest mammals, whose gestation period is only 12 months, and small bats no larger than mice, whose gestation period extends 4 to 5 months. The condition of the young at birth also varies. An antelope bears its young well-furred, eyes open, and able to run. Newborn mice, however, are blind, naked, and helpless. We all know how long

figure 20.18

Opossums, *Didelphis marsupialis*, 15 days old, fastened to teats in mother's pouch. When born after a gestation period of only 12 days, they are the size of honey bees. They remain attached to the nipples for 50 to 60 days. Order Didelphimorpha, family Didelphidae.

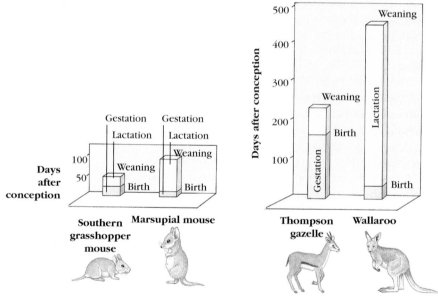

figure 20.19

Comparison of gestation and lactation periods between matched pairs of ecologically similar species of marsupial and placental mammals. The graph shows that marsupials have shorter intervals of gestation and much longer intervals of lactation than do similar species of placentals.

it takes a human baby to gain its footing. Human growth is in fact slower than that of any other mammal, and this is one of the distinctive attributes that sets us apart from other mammals.

Delayed implantation lengthens the gestation period of many mammals. The blastocyst remains dormant while its implantation in the uterine wall is postponed for periods of a few weeks to several months. For many mammals (for example, bears, seals, weasels, badgers, bats, and many deer), delayed implantation is a device for extending gestation so that the young are born at a time of year best for their survival.

■ Mammalian Populations

A population of animals includes all members of a species that share a particular space and can potentially interbreed. All mammals (like other organisms) live in ecological communities, each composed of numerous populations of different animal and plant species. Each species is affected by the activities of other species and by other changes, especially climatic, that occur. Thus populations are always changing in size. Populations of small mammals are lowest before breeding season and greatest just after addition of new members. Beyond these expected changes in population size, mammalian populations may fluctuate due to other causes.

Irregular fluctuations are commonly produced by variations in climate, such as unusually cold, hot, or dry weather, or by natural catastrophes, such as fires, hailstorms, and hurricanes. These are **density-independent** causes because they affect a population whether it is crowded or dispersed. However, the most spectacular fluctuations are **density-dependent,** associated with population crowding. These extreme limits to growth are discussed in Chapter 2 (see p. 42).

Cycles of abundance are common among many rodent species. Among the best-known examples are mass migrations of Scandinavian and arctic North American lemmings following population peaks. Lemmings (figure 20.20) breed all year, although more in summer than in winter. The gestation period is only 21 days; young born at the beginning of summer are weaned in 14 days and can reproduce by the end of summer. At the peak of their population density, having devastated vegetation by tunneling and grazing, lemmings begin long, mass migrations to find new undamaged habitats for food and space. They swim across streams and small lakes as they go, but cannot distinguish these from large lakes, rivers, and the sea, in which they drown. Since lemmings are the main diet of many carnivorous mammals and birds, any change in lemming population density affects their predators as well.

The renowned fecundity of small rodents and the effect of removing natural predators from rodent populations are felicitously expressed in this excerpt from Thornton Burgess's "Portrait of a Meadow Mouse."

> He's fecund to the nth degree
> In fact this really seems to be
> His one and only honest claim
> To anything approaching fame.
> In just twelve months, should all survive,
> A million mice would be alive—
> His progeny. And this, 'tis clear,
> Is quite a record for a year.
> Quite unsuspected, night and day
> They eat the grass that would be hay.
> On any meadow, in a year,
> The loss is several tons, I fear.
> Yet man, with prejudice for guide,
> The checks that nature doth provide
> Destroys. The meadow mouse survives
> And on stupidity he thrives.

Varying hares (snowshoe rabbits) of North America show 10-year cycles in abundance. The well-known fecundity of rabbits enables them to produce litters of three or four young as many as five times per year. The density may increase to 4000 hares competing for food in each square mile of northern forest. Predators (owls, minks, foxes, and especially lynxes) also increase (figure 20.21). Then the population crashes precipitously for reasons that have long puzzled scientists. Rabbits die in great numbers, not from lack of food or from an epidemic disease, but apparently from some density-dependent psychogenic cause. As crowding increases, hares become more aggressive, show signs of fear and defense, and stop breeding. The entire population reveals symptoms of pituitary-adrenal gland exhaustion, an endocrine imbalance called "shock disease," which causes death. These dramatic crashes are not well understood. Whatever the causes, population crashes that follow superabundance, although harsh, permit vegetation to

figure 20.20

Collared lemming, *Dicrostonyx* sp., a small rodent of the far north. Populations of lemmings fluctuate widely. Order Rodentia, family Cricetidae.

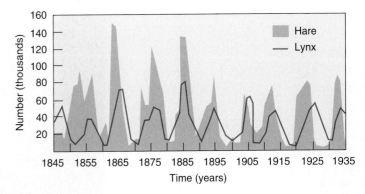

figure 20.21

Changes in population size of varying hare and lynx in Canada as indicated by pelts received by the Hudson's Bay Company. Abundance of lynx (predator) follows that of the hare (prey).

recover, providing survivors with a much better chance for successful breeding.

In his book *The Arctic* (1974. Montreal, Infacor, Ltd.), the Canadian naturalist Fred Bruemmer describes the growth of lemming populations in arctic Canada: "After a population crash one sees few signs of lemmings; there may be only one to every 10 acres. The next year, they are evidently numerous; their runways snake beneath the tundra vegetation, and frequent piles of rice-sized droppings indicate the lemmings fare well. The third year one sees them everywhere. The fourth year, usually the peak year of their cycle, the populations explode. Now more than 150 lemmings may inhabit each acre of land and they honeycomb it with as many as 4000 burrows. Males meet frequently and fight instantly. Males pursue females and mate after a brief but ardent courtship. Everywhere one hears the squeak and chitter of the excited, irritable, crowded animals. At such times they may spill over the land in manic migrations."

■ Human Evolution

Darwin devoted an entire book, *The Descent of Man and Selection in Relation to Sex*, largely to human evolution. The idea that humans share common descent with apes and other animals was repugnant to the Victorian world, which responded with predictable outrage (see figure 1.17). When Darwin's views were first debated, few human fossils had been unearthed, but the current accumulation of fossil evidence has strongly vindicated Darwin's hypothesis that humans descend from other primates. All primates share certain significant characteristics: grasping fingers on all four limbs, flat fingernails instead of claws, and forward-pointing eyes with binocular vision and excellent depth perception. The following synopsis highlights probable relationships of major primate groups.

The earliest primate was probably a small, nocturnal animal similar in appearance to a tree shrew. This ancestral primate lineage split into two lineages, one of which gave rise to lemurs and lorises, and the other to tarsiers (figure 20.22), monkeys (figure 20.23), and apes (figure 20.24). Traditionally, the lemurs, lorises, and tarsiers have been called the **prosimians,** a paraphyletic group, and the apes and monkeys have been called **simians.** Prosimians and many simians are arboreal (tree-dwelling), which is probably the ancestral lifestyle for both groups. Flexible limbs are essential for active animals moving through trees. Grasping hands and feet, in contrast to the clawed feet of squirrels and other rodents, enable primates to grip limbs, to hang from branches, to seize food and to manipulate it, and most significantly, to use tools. Primates have highly developed sense organs, especially acute, binocular vision, and proper coordination of limb and finger muscles to assist their active arboreal life. Of course, sense organs are no better than the brain that processes the sensory information. Precise timing, judgment of distance, and alertness are supported by a large cerebral cortex.

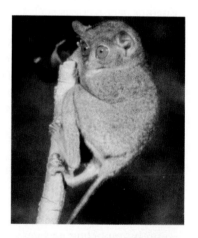

figure 20.22

A prosimian, the Mindanao tarsier, *Tarsius syrichta carbonarius,* of Mindanao Island in the Philippines. Order Primates, family Tarsiidae.

figure 20.23

Monkeys. **A,** Red-howler monkeys, *Alovatta seniculus,* order Primates, family Cebidae, an example of New World monkeys. **B,** The olive baboon, *Papio homadryas,* order Primates, family Cercopithecidae, an example of Old World monkeys.

A   B

figure 20.24

Gorillas, *Gorilla gorilla*, order Primates, family Hominidae, are examples of apes.

The earliest simian fossils appeared in Africa some 40 million years ago. Many of these primates became day-active rather than nocturnal, making vision the dominant special sense, now enhanced by color perception. We recognize three major simian clades: (1) New World monkeys of South America (ceboids), including howler monkeys (see figure 20.23A), spider monkeys, and tamarins; (2) Old World monkeys (cercopithecoids), including baboons (see figure 20.23B), mandrills, and colobus monkeys; and (3) apes (figure 20.24). In addition to their geographic separation, Old World monkeys differ from New World monkeys in lacking a grasping tail while having close-set nostrils and better opposable and grasping thumbs.

Apes, which differ from Old World monkeys in lacking a tail, include gibbons, orangutans, gorillas, chimpanzees, bonobos, and humans. Except for gibbons, all apes belong to the family Hominidae and are here called **hominids.** Chimpanzees and bonobos form the living sister group to modern humans (see figure 4.7). All fossil hominid species that are phylogenetically closer to living humans than to chimpanzees and bonobos are referred to here as **humans.** Apes first appear in 20-million-year-old fossils. At this time, woodland savannas were arising in Africa, Europe, and North America. Perhaps motivated by the greater abundance of food on the ground, these apes left the trees and became largely terrestrial. Because of the benefits of standing upright (better view of predators, freeing of hands for using tools, defense, caring for young, and gathering food), emerging hominids gradually evolved upright posture.

Evidence of the earliest humans of this period is sparse. In 2001, the desert sands of Chad yielded one of the most astonishing and important discoveries of modern paleontology, a remarkably complete skull of a hominid, *Sahelanthropus tchadensis* (Sahel hominid of Chad), dated at nearly 7 million years ago (figure 20.25). Although its brain is no larger than that of a chimp (between 320 and 380 cm³), its relatively small canine teeth, massive brow ridges, and features of the face and cranium suggest that the skull is that of a human. Until this skull was discovered, the earliest known human was *Ardipithecus ramidus,* from the sands of Ethiopia, dated at about 4.4 million years (figure 20.25). *Ardipithecus ramidus* is a mosaic of apelike and humanlike traits, with indirect evidence that it may have been bipedal.

The most celebrated early human fossil is a 40% complete skeleton of a female *Australopithecus afarensis* (figure 20.26). Unearthed in 1974 and named "Lucy" by its discoverer, Donald Johanson, *A. afarensis* was a short, bipedal human with a brain size slightly larger than that of a chimpanzee (figure 20.27). Numerous fossils of these species, dating from 3.7 to 3.0 million years ago, are now known. In 1995, *Australopithecus anamensis* was discovered in the Rift Valley of Kenya. Many researchers hypothesize that this species, which lived between 4.2 and 3.9 million years ago, is an intermediate between *A. ramidus* and *A. afarensis* (Lucy).

In the last two decades, there has been an explosion of australopithecine fossil finds, with eight putative species requiring interpretation. Most of these species are known as gracile australopithecines because of their relatively light build, especially in the skull and teeth (although all were more robust than modern humans). The gracile australopithecines are generally considered more closely related to early *Homo* species and, by extension, to the lineage leading to modern humans. In 1998, a partial skull, dated at 2.5 million years ago, was discovered in Ethiopia. Named *Australopithecus garhi*, this species has been suggested as the missing link between *Australopithecus* and *Homo*, although its phylogenetic position is controversial. Coexisting with the earliest species of *Homo* was a different lineage of robust australopithecines that lived between 2.5 and 1.2 million years ago. These "robust" australopithecines, including *Paranthropus robustus* (see figure 20.25), had heavy jaws, skull crests, and large back molars used for chewing coarse roots and tubers. They are an extinct branch in hominid evolution and not part of our own human lineage.

Although researchers are divided over who the first members of *Homo* were, and indeed how to define the genus *Homo*, the earliest *known* species of the genus was *Homo habilis* ("handy man"). *Homo habilis* had a larger brain than the australopithecines (see figure 20.25) and unquestionably used stone tools.

About 1.5 million years ago, *Homo erectus* appeared, a large hominid standing 150 to 170 cm (5 to 5.5 feet) tall, with a low but distinct forehead and strong brow ridges. Its brain capacity was about 1000 mm³, intermediate between the brain capacity of *H. habilis* and modern humans (see figure 20.25). *Homo erectus* had a successful and complex culture and became widespread throughout the tropical and temperate

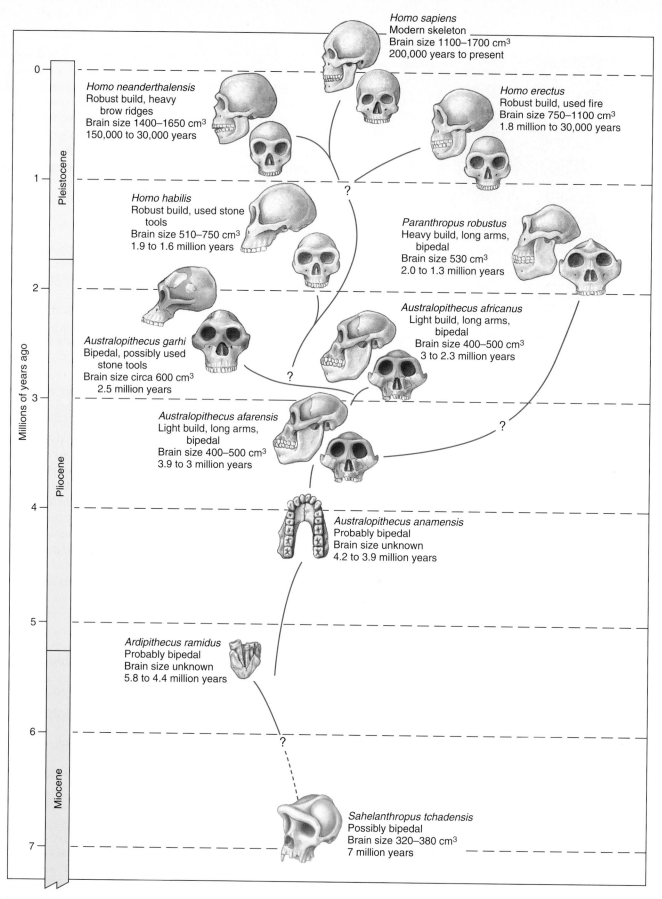

figure 20.25

Hominid skulls, showing several of the best-known lines preceding modern humans (*Homo sapiens*).

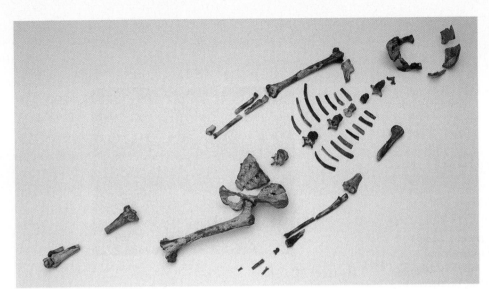

figure 20.26

Lucy (*Australopithecus afarensis*), the most nearly complete skeleton of an early human ever found. Lucy is dated at 3.2 million years old. A nearly complete skull of *A. afarensis* was discovered in 1994.

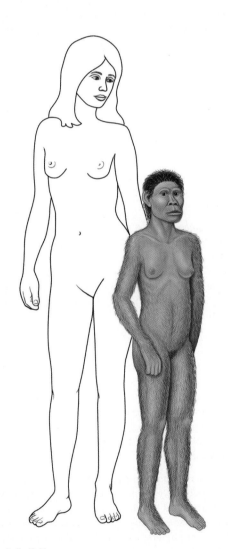

figure 20.27

A reconstruction of the appearance of Lucy (*right*) compared with a modern human (*left*).

Old World. Their brain shape, revealed by casts of skulls, suggests that limited speech was possible, and charcoal deposits indicate that they controlled and used fire. Another amazing hominid find was announced in 2004: *Homo floresiensis*, a species only 1 m tall, from the island of Flores, Indonesia. This species apparently arose from *H. erectus* and became extinct only about 13,000 years ago.

The lineage leading to *Homo sapiens* ("wise man") diverged from *H. erectus* perhaps 800,000 years ago, in Africa. One group of well-known humans, the Neandertals, *Homo neanderthalensis*, arose about 150,000 years ago and occupied most of Europe and the Middle East. Neandertals had a brain size similar to that of modern humans and invented more sophisticated stone tools than *H. erectus*. Their robust, heavily muscled bodies allowed them to survive the cold climates of the Ice Age and to hunt large Pleistocene mammals. About 30,000 years ago, the Neandertals were replaced by modern humans, tall people with a culture very different from that of Neandertals. Implement crafting developed rapidly, and human culture became enriched with aesthetics, artistry, and sophisticated language.

Biologically, *Homo sapiens* is a product of the same processes that have directed the evolution of every organism since life began. Mutation, isolation, genetic drift, and natural selection have operated for us as they have for other animals. We are nonetheless unique in having a nongenetic cultural evolution that provides constant feedback between past and future experience. Our symbolic languages, capacity for conceptual thought, knowledge of our history, and ability to manipulate our environment emerge from this nongenetic cultural endowment. Finally, we owe much of our cultural and intellectual achievements to our arboreal ancestry, which gave us binocular vision, superb visuotactile discrimination, and manipulative use of our hands. If horses (with one toe instead of five fingers) had human mental capacity, could they have accomplished what humans have?

Classification of Living Mammalian Orders

This classification follows that of Wilson and Reeder (2005). Of the 29 recognized mammalian orders, three smaller marsupial orders and ten smaller placental orders are omitted.

Class Mammalia

Subclass Prototheria (prō´tō-thir´ē-ə) (Gr. *prōtos*, first, + *thēr*, wild animal).

Infraclass Ornithodelphia (or-ni´-thō-del´fē-ə) (Gr. *ornis*, bird, +*delphys*, womb). Monotreme mammals.

Order Monotremata (mon´ō-trē-mä´tä) (Gr. *monos*, single, + *trēma*, hole): **egg-laying (oviparous) mammals: duck-billed platypus,** and **echidnas.** Five species in this order from Australia, Tasmania, and New Guinea. Spiny anteaters, or echidnas, *Tachyglossus*, have a long, narrow snout adapted for feeding on ants, their chief food.

Subclass Theria (thir´ē-a) (Gr. *thēr*, wild animal).

Infraclass Metatheria (met´ə-thir´ē-ə) (Gr. *meta*, after, + *thēr*, wild animal). Marsupial mammals.

Order Didelphimorphia (di´del-fi-mor´fē-ə) (Gr. *di*, two, + *delphi*, uterus, + *morph*, form): **American opossums.** These mammals, like other marsupials, are characterized by an abdominal pouch, or marsupium, in which they rear their young. Most species occur in Central and South America, but one species, the Virginia opossum, is widespread in North America; 87 species.

Order Dasyuormorphia (das-ē-yur´ō-mor´fē-ə) (Gr. *dasy*, hairy, + *uro*, tail, + *morph*, form): **Australian carnivorous mammals.** In addition to a number of larger carnivores, this order includes a number of marsupial "mice," all of which are carnivorous. Confined to Australia, Tasmania, and New Guinea; 71 species.

Order Peramelemorphia (per´ə-mel-e-mor´fē-ə) (Gr. *per*, pouch, + *mel*, badger, + *morph*, form): **Bandicoots.** Like placentals, members of this group have a chorioallantoic placenta and a high rate of reproduction for marsupials. Confined to Australia, Tasmania, and New Guinea; 21 species.

Order Diprotodontia (di´prō-tō-don´-tē-ə) (Gr. *di*, two, + *pro*, front, + *odont*, tooth): **Koala, wombats, possums, wallabies,** and **kangaroos.** Diverse marsupial group containing some of the largest and most familiar marsupials. Present in Australia, Tasmania, New Guinea, and many islands of the East Indies; 143 species.

Infraclass Eutheria (yū-ther´ē-ə) (Gr. *eu*, true, + *thēr*, wild animal). Placental mammals.

Order Soricomorpha (sor´i-cō-mor´fə) (L. *soric* shrew, + *morph*, form): **shrews** (figure 20.28) and **moles.**

figure 20.28

A shorttail shrew, *Blarina brevicauda*, eating a grasshopper. This tiny but fierce mammal, with a prodigious appetite for insects, mice, snails, and worms, spends most of its time underground and so is seldom seen by humans. Shrews resemble the insectivorous ancestors of placental mammals. Order Soricomorpha, family Soricidae.

Small, sharp-snouted animals, which feed principally on insects; 428 species.

Order Chiroptera (kī-rop´ter-ə) (Gr. *cheir*, hand, + *pteron*, wing): **bats.** Flying mammals with forelimbs modified into wings. Most are nocturnal insect-eaters and navigate by echolocation, but fruit bats of the Old World tropics are diurnal; 1116 species.

Order Primates (prī-mā´tēz or prī´māts) (L. *prima*, first): **prosimians, monkeys,** and **apes.** First in the animal kingdom in brain development with especially large cerebral cortex. Most species are arboreal, with large eyes, binocular vision, grasping hands, and five digits (usually with flat nails) on both forelimbs and hindlimbs; two suborders; 376 species.

Suborder Strepsirhini (strep´sə-rī-nē) (Gr. *strepsō*, to turn, twist, + *rhinos*, nose): **lemurs, aye-ayes, lorises, pottos,** and **bush babies.** Seven families of arboreal primates concentrated on Madagascar, but with species in Africa, Southeast Asia, and Malay peninsula. All have a wet, naked region surrounding comma-shaped nostrils, long nonprehensile tail, and second toe provided with a claw; 88 species.

Suborder Haplorhini (hap´lō-rī-nē) (Gr. *haploos*, single, simple, + *rhinos*, nose): **tarsiers, marmosets, New and Old World monkeys, gibbons, gorilla, chimpanzee, orangutan,** and **human.** Six families, all except tarsiers, are in the clade Anthropoidea. Haplorhine primates have dry, hairy noses, ringed nostrils, and differences in skull morphology

figure 20.29
Nine-banded armadillo, *Dasypus novemcintus*. During the day, this nocturnal species occupies long tunnels, which it digs using powerful, clawed forelimbs. Order Cingulata, family Dasypodidae.

figure 20.30
A pika, *Ochotona princeps,* atop a rockslide in Alaska. This little rat-sized mammal does not hibernate but prepares for winter by storing dried grasses beneath boulders. Order Lagomorpha, family Ochotonidae.

figure 20.31
Grizzly bear, *Ursus arctos horribilis,* of Alaska. Grizzlies, once common in the lower 48 states, are now confined largely to northern wilderness areas. Order Carnivora, family Ursidae.

that distinguish them from strepsirhine primates; 288 species.

Order Cingulata (sin´gyū-lätə) (L. *cingul,* belt): **armadillos** (figure 20.29). Insectivorous mammals with small, peglike teeth and beltlike bands of armor. Inhabit South and Central America; the nine-banded armadillo is expanding its range in the southern United States; 21 species.

Order Lagomorpha (lag´ō-mor´fə) (Gr. *lagos,* hare, + *morphē,* form): **rabbits, hares,** and **pikas** (figure 20.30). Dentition resembling that of rodents but with four upper incisors rather than two; 92 species.

Order Rodentia (rō-den´tē-ə) (L. *rodere,* to gnaw): **gnawing mammals: squirrels, rats,** and **woodchucks.** Most numerous of all mammals both in numbers and species. Characterized by two upper and two lower chisel-like incisors that grow continually and are adapted for gnawing; 2277 species.

Order Carnivora (car-niv´or-ə) (L. *caro,* flesh, + *vorare,* to devour): **flesh-eating mammals: dogs, wolves, cats, bears** (figure 20.31), **weasels, seals, sea lions,** and **walruses.** All except the giant panda have predatory habits, and their teeth are especially adapted for tearing flesh; most have canines for killing prey; worldwide except in Australian and Antarctic regions; 286 species.

Order Proboscidea (prō´bo-sid´ē-ə) (Gr. *proboskis,* elephant's trunk, from *pro,* before, + *boskein,* to feed): **proboscis mammals: elephants.** Largest of living land animals, with two upper incisors elongated as tusks and well-developed molar teeth. Three extant species: Indian elephant, with relatively small ears, and two species of African elephants, with large ears.

Order Perissodactyla (pe-ris´sō-dak´til-ə) (Gr. *perissos,* odd, + *dactylos,* toe): **odd-toed hoofed mammals: horses, asses, zebras, tapirs,** and **rhinoceroses.** Mammals with an odd number (one or three) of toes,

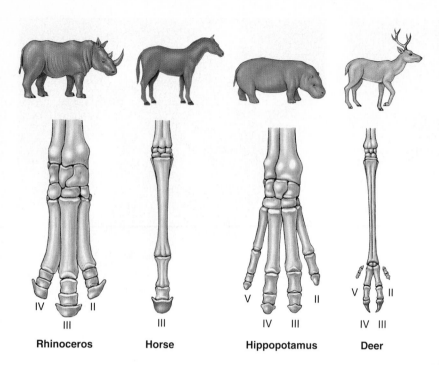

figure 20.32

Odd-toed and even-toed ungulates. Rhinoceroses and horses (order Perissodactyla) are odd-toed; hippopotamuses and deer (order Artiodactyla) are even-toed. Lighter, faster mammals run on only one or two toes.

each with a keratinized hoof (figure 20.32). All are herbivorous. Both Perissodactyla and Artiodactyla often called **ungulates,** or hoofed mammals, with teeth adapted for grinding plants; 17 species.

Order Artiodactyla (är´tē-ō-dak´til-ə) (Gr. *artios,* even, + *daktylos,* toe): **even-toed hoofed mammals: swine, camels, deer and their allies, hippopotamuses, antelopes, cattle, sheep,** and **goats.** Each toe sheathed in a cornified hoof. Most species have two toes, although hippopotamuses and some others have four (figure 20.32). Many, such as cattle, deer, and sheep, have horns or antlers. Most are ruminants; 240 species.

Order Cetacea (se-tā´shē-ə) (L. *cetus,* whale): **whales** (figure 20.33), **dolphins,** and **porpoises.** Anterior limbs of cetaceans are modified into broad flippers; posterior limbs are absent. Nostrils are represented by a single or double blowhole on top of the head. There is no hair except for a few on the muzzle, skin glands are absent except for mammary glands and those of the eye, and there is no external ear; 84 species.

figure 20.33

Humpback whale, *Megaptera novaeangliae,* breaching. Among the most acrobatic of whales, humpbacks appear to breach to stun fish schools or to communicate information to other herd members. Order Cetacea, family Balaenopteridae.

■ Summary

Mammals are endothermic and homeothermic vertebrates whose bodies are insulated by hair and who nurse their young with milk. The approximately 5400 species of mammals descend from the synapsid lineage of amniotes that arose during the Carboniferous period of the Paleozoic era. Their evolution is traced from pelycosaurs of the Permian period to therapsids of the late Permian and Triassic periods of the Mesozoic era. One group of therapsids, the cynodonts, gave rise during the Triassic to the mammals.

Mammalian evolution was accompanied by the appearance of many important derived characteristics, among these enlarged brain with greater sensory integration, high metabolic rate, endothermy, heterodont teeth, and many changes in the skeleton that supported a more active life. Mammals diversified rapidly during the Tertiary period of the Cenozoic era.

Mammals are named for the glandular milk-secreting organs of females (rudimentary in males), a unique adaptation that, combined with prolonged parental care, buffers infants from demands of foraging for themselves and eases the transition to adulthood. Hair, the integumentary outgrowth that covers most mammals, serves variously for mechanical protection, thermal insulation, protective coloration, and waterproofing. Mammalian skin is rich in glands: sweat glands that function in evaporative cooling, scent glands used in social interactions, and sebaceous glands that secrete lubricating skin oil. All placental mammals have deciduous teeth that are replaced by permanent teeth (diphyodont dentition). Four groups of teeth—incisors, canines, premolars, and molars—may be highly modified in different mammals for specialized feeding tasks, or they may be absent.

Food habits of mammals strongly influence their body form and physiology. Insectivores have pointed teeth for piercing the exoskeleton of insects and other small invertebrates. Herbivorous mammals have specialized teeth for grinding cellulose and silica-rich plants and have specialized regions of the gut for harboring bacteria that digest cellulose. Carnivorous mammals have adaptations, including specialized jaw muscles and teeth, for killing and processing their prey, mainly herbivorous mammals. Omnivores feed on both plant and animal foods and have a variety of tooth types.

Some marine, terrestrial, and aerial mammals migrate; some migrations, such as those of fur seals and caribou, are extensive. Migrations are usually made toward climatic conditions favorable for finding food, mating, or rearing young.

Mammals with true flight, the bats, are mainly nocturnal and thus avoid direct competition with birds. Most employ ultrasonic echolocation to navigate and to feed in darkness.

The only living egg-laying mammals are monotremes of the Australian region. After hatching, young are nourished with their mother's milk. All other mammals are viviparous. Embryos of marsupials have brief gestation periods, are born underdeveloped, and complete their early growth in the mother's pouch, nourished by milk. The remaining mammals are eutherians, mammals that develop a sophisticated placental attachment between mother and embryos through which embryos are nourished for a prolonged period.

Mammal populations fluctuate due to both density-dependent and density-independent causes, and some mammals, particularly rodents, may experience extreme cycles in population density. The unqualified success of mammals as a group cannot be attributed to greater organ system perfection, but rather to their impressive overall adaptability.

Humans are primates, a mammalian group that descends from a shrewlike ancestor. The common ancestor of all modern primates was arboreal and had grasping fingers and forward-facing eyes capable of binocular vision. Primates diversified over the last 80 million years to form two major groups: (1) lemurs and lorises and (2) tarsiers, monkeys, and apes (including humans). Chimpanzees and bonobos form the living sister group of humans.

Humans appeared in Africa about 7 million years ago, and gave rise to several species of australopithecines, which persisted for more than 3 million years. Australopithecines gave rise to, and coexisted with, *Homo habilis*, the first user of stone tools. *Homo erectus* appeared about 1.8 million years ago and was eventually replaced by modern humans, *Homo sapiens*.

■ Review Questions

1. Describe the evolution of mammals, tracing their synapsid lineage from early amniote ancestors to true mammals. How would you distinguish the skull of a synapsid from that of a diapsid?

2. Describe structural and functional adaptations in early amniotes that foreshadowed the mammalian body plan. Which mammalian attributes were especially important to successful diversification of mammals?

3. Hair is hypothesized to have evolved in therapsids as an adaptation for insulation, but modern mammals have adapted hair for several other purposes. Describe these.

4. What is distinctive about each of the following: horns of bovids, antlers of deer, and horns of rhinos? Describe the growth cycle of antlers.

5. Describe the location and principal function(s) of each of the following skin glands: sweat glands (eccrine and apocrine), scent glands, sebaceous glands, and mammary glands.

6. Define the terms "diphyodont" and "heterodont," and explain how both terms apply to mammalian dentition.

7. Describe the food habits of each of the following groups: insectivores, herbivores, carnivores, and omnivores. Give the common names of some mammals belonging to each group.

8. Most herbivorous mammals depend on cellulose as their main energy source, and yet no mammal synthesizes cellulose-splitting enzymes. How are the digestive tracts of mammals specialized for symbiotic digestion of cellulose?

9. How does fermentation differ between horses and cattle?

10. Describe the annual migrations of barren-ground caribou and fur seals.

11. Explain what is distinctive about the life habit and mode of navigation in bats.

12. Describe and distinguish patterns of reproduction in monotremes, marsupials, and placental mammals. What aspects of mammalian reproduction are present in *all* mammals but in no other vertebrates?

13. What is the difference between density-dependent and density-independent fluctuations in the sizes of mammalian populations?

14. Describe the hare-lynx population cycle, considered a classic example of a prey-predator relationship (see figure 20.21). From your examination of the cycle, formulate a hypothesis to explain the oscillations.

15. What anatomical characteristics distinguish primates from other mammals?

16. What role does the fossil named "Lucy" play in reconstruction of human evolutionary history?

17. In what ways do the genera *Australopithecus* and *Homo,* which coexisted for at least 1 million years, differ?

18. When did the different species of *Homo* appear, and how did they differ socially?

19. What major attributes make the human position in animal evolution unique?

■ Selected References

See also general references on page 423.

Feldhamer, G. A., L. C. Drickamer, S. H. Vessey, J. F. Merritt, and C. Krajewski. 2007. Mammalogy: adaptation, diversity, and ecology, ed. 3. Baltimore, Johns Hopkins University Press. *Modern, well-illustrated textbook.*

Grzimek's encyclopedia of mammals (vol. 1–5). 1990. New York, McGraw-Hill Publishing Company. *Valuable source of information on all mammalian orders.*

Kemp, T. S. 2005. The origin and evolution of mammals. Oxford, Oxford University Press. *Readable account of mammal evolution from the origin of synapsids in the Paleocene through modern times.*

Macdonald, D., ed. 1984. The encyclopedia of mammals. New York, Facts on File Publications. *Coverage of all mammalian orders and families, enhanced with fine photographs and color artwork.*

Nowak, R. M. 1999. Walker's mammals of the world, ed. 6. Baltimore, The Johns Hopkins University Press. *The definitive illustrated reference work on mammals, with descriptions of all extant and recently extinct species.*

Pilbeam, D., R. D. Martin, and D. Jones. 1994. Cambridge encyclopedia of human evolution. New York, Cambridge University Press. *Comprehensive and informative encyclopedia written for nonspecialists. Highly readable and highly recommended.*

Preston-Mafham, R., and K. Preston-Mafham. 1992. Primates of the world. New York, Facts on File Publications. *A small "primer" with high-quality photographs and serviceable descriptions.*

Rismiller, P. D., and R. S. Seymour. 1991. The echidna. Sci. Am. **294:**96–103 (Feb.). *Recent studies of this fascinating monotreme have revealed many secrets of its natural history and reproduction.*

Suga, N. 1990. Biosonar and neural computation in bats. Sci. Am. **262:**60–68 (June). *How the bat nervous system processes echolocation signals.*

Templeton, A. R. 2002. Out of Africa again and again. Nature **416:**45–51. *A comprehensive analysis of molecular genetic data indicating that humans have evolved as a cohesive lineage for the past 1.7 million years, with multiple migrations of populations out of Africa.*

Wilson, D. E., and D. Reeder, eds. 2005. Mammal species of the world: a taxonomic and geographic reference, 3. ed. Baltimore, Johns Hopkins University Press. *An authoritative compilation of the world's mammal species.*

■ Custom Website

The *Animal Diversity* Online Learning Center is a great place to check your understanding of chapter material. Visit www.mhhe.com/hickmanad5e for access to key terms, quizzes, and more! Further enhance your knowledge with web links to chapter-related material.

Explore live links for these topics:

Classification and Phylogeny of Animals
Class Mammalia
Marine Mammals
Cat Dissections
Rat Dissections

Fetal Pig Dissections
Vertebrate Laboratory Exercises
Conservation Issues Concerning Mammals

Glossary

This glossary lists definitions, pronunciations, and derivations of the most important recurrent technical terms, units, and names (excluding taxa) used in this text.

A

abiotic (ā´bī-ät´ik) (Gr. *a*, without, + *biōtos*, life, livable) Characterized by the absence of life.

abomasum (ab´ō-mā´səm) (L. *ab*, from, + *omasum*, paunch) Fourth and last chamber of the stomach of ruminant mammals.

aboral (ab-o´rəl) (L. *ab*, from, + *os*, mouth) Region of an animal opposite the mouth.

acanthodians (a´kan-thō´dē-əns) (Gr. *akantha*, prickly, thorny) Group of jawed fishes, characterized by large spines in their fins, from Lower Silurian to Lower Permian.

acclimatization (ə-klī´mə-tə-zā-shən) (L. *ad*, to, + Gr. *klima*, climate) Gradual physiological adjustment of an organism in response to relatively long-lasting environmental changes.

aciculum (ə-sik´ū -ləm) (L. *acicula*, dim. of *acus*, a point) Supporting structure in notopodium and neuropodium of some polychaetes.

acoelomate (a-sēl´ə-māt´) (Gr. *a*, not, + *koilōma*, cavity) Without a coelom, as in flatworms and proboscis worms.

acontium (ə-kän´chē-əm), pl. **acontia** (Gr. *akontion*, dart) Threadlike structure bearing nematocysts located on mesentery of sea anemone.

adaptation (L. *adaptatus*, fitted) Anatomical structure, physiological process, or behavioral trait that evolved by natural selection and improves an organism's ability to survive and leave descendants.

adaptive radiation Evolutionary diversification that produces numerous ecologically disparate lineages from a single ancestral one, especially when this diversification occurs within a short interval of geological time.

adaptive zone A characteristic reaction and mutual relationship between environment and organism ("way of life") demonstrated by a group of evolutionarily related organisms.

adductor (ə-duk´tər) (L. *ad*, to, + *ducere*, to lead) A muscle that draws a part toward a median axis, or a muscle that draws the two valves of a mollusc shell together.

adipose (ad´ə-pōs) (L. *adeps*, fat) Fatty tissue; fatty.

aerobic (a-rō´bik) (Gr. *aēr*, air, + *bios*, life) Oxygen-dependent form of respiration.

afferent (af´ə-rənt) (L. *ad*, to, + *ferre*, to bear) Adjective meaning leading or bearing toward some organ—for example, nerves conducting impulses toward the brain or blood vessels carrying blood toward an organ; opposed to efferent.

age structure An accounting of the ages of individuals in a population at a particular time and place.

agnathan (ag-nā´-thən) (Gr. *a*, without, + *gnathos*, jaw) A jawless fish of the paraphyletic superclass Agnatha of the phylum Chordata.

alate (ā´lāt) (L. *alatus*, wing) Winged.

albumin (al-bū´mən) (L. *albuman*, white of egg) Any of a large class of simple proteins that are important constituents of vertebrate blood plasma and tissue fluids and also present in milk, whites of eggs, and other animal substances.

allantois (ə-lan´tois) (Gr. *allas*, sausage, + *eidos*, form) One of the extraembryonic membranes of the amniotes that functions in respiration and excretion in birds and nonavian reptiles and plays an important role in the development of the placenta in most mammals.

allele (ə-lēl´) (Gr. *allēlōn*, of one another) Alternative forms of genes coding for the same trait; situated at the same locus in homologous chromosomes.

allelic frequency An estimation of the proportion of gametes produced in a population (gene pool) that contains a particular allelic form of a particular gene.

allopatric (Gr. *allos*, other, + *patra*, native land) In separate and mutually exclusive geographical regions.

allopatric speciation The hypothesis that new species are formed by dividing an ancestral species into geographically isolated subpopulations that evolve **reproductive barriers** between them through independent evolutionary divergence from their common ancestor.

altricial (al-tri´shəl) (L. *altrices*, nourishers) Referring to young animals (especially birds) having the young hatched in an immature dependent condition.

alula (al´y ə-lə) (L. dim of *ala*, wing) The first digit or thumb of a bird's wing, much reduced in size.

alveolate (al-vē´ ə-lāt) (L. dim. of *alveus*, cavity, hollow) Any member of a protozoan clade having alveolar sacs; includes ciliates, apicomplexans, and dinoflagellates.

alveoli (al-vē´ ə-lī) Pockets or spaces bounded by membrane or epithelium.

ambulacra (am´byə-lak´r ə) (L. *ambulare*, to walk) In echinoderms, radiating grooves where podia of the water-vascular system characteristically project outside the organism.

ameboid (ə-mē´boid) (Gr. *amoibē*, change, + *oid*, like) Ameba-like in putting forth pseudopodia.

amebozoa (ə-mē´bō-zō´ ə) (Gr. *amoibē*, change, + *zōon*, animal) Protozoan clade containing slime molds and amebas with lobose pseudopodia.

amensalism (ā-men´s əl-iz´ əm) An asymmetric competitive interaction between two species in an ecological community in which only one of the species is affected.

amictic (ə-mik´tic) (Gr. *a*, without, + *miktos*, mixed or blended) Pertaining to female rotifers, which produce only diploid eggs that cannot be fertilized, or to the eggs produced by such females; contrasts with **mictic**.

ammocoetes (am-ə-sēd´ēz) (Gr. *ammos*, sand, + *koitē*, bed) The filter-feeding larval stage of lampreys.

amnion (am´nē-än) (Gr. *amnion*, membrane around the fetus) The innermost of the extra-embryonic membranes forming a fluid-filled sac around the embryo in amniotes.

bat/āpe/ärmadillo/herring/fēmale/finch/līce/crocodile/crōw/cȯin/duck/ūnicorn/tüna/ə indicates unaccented vowel sound "uh" as in mammal, fishes, cardinal, heron, vulture/stress as in bi-ol´o-gy, bi´o-log´i-cal

amniote (am´nē-ōt) Having an amnion; as a noun, an animal that develops an amnion in embryonic life; refers collectively to nonavian reptiles, birds, and mammals. Adj., **amniotic.**

amphid (am´fəd) (Gr. *amphidea,* anything that is bound around) One of a pair of anterior sense organs in certain nematodes.

amplexus (am-plek´səs) (L., embrace) The embrace of frogs or toads in which males fertilize aggs as they leave the female's body.

ampulla (am-pūl´ə) (L., flask) Membranous vesicle; dilation at one end of each semicircular canal containing sensory epithelium; muscular vesicle above the tube foot in water-vascular system of echinoderms.

anadromous (an-ad´rə-məs) (Gr. *anadromos,* running upward) Refers to fishes that migrate up streams from the sea to spawn.

anaerobic (an´ə-rō´bik) (Gr. *an,* not, + *aēr,* air, + *bios,* life) Not dependent on oxygen for respiration.

analogy (L. *analogous,* ratio) Similarity of function but not of origin.

anamniote (an´am-nē-ōt) A vertebrate that lacks an amniotic membrane around the embryo. Includes fishes and amphibians.

anapsids (ə-nap´səds) (Gr. *an,* without, + *apsis,* arch) Extinct amniotes in which the skull lacks temporal openings.

ancestral character state The condition of a taxonomic character inferred to have been present in the most recent common ancestor of a taxonomic group being studied cladistically.

androgenic gland (an´drō-jen´ək) (Gr. *anēr,* male, + *gennaein,* to produce) Gland in Crustacea that causes development of male characteristics.

annulus (an´yəl-əs) (L., ring) Any ringlike structure, such as superficial rings on leeches.

antenna (L., sail yard) A sensory appendage on the head of arthropods, or the second pair of two such pairs of structures in crustaceans.

antennal gland Excretory gland of Crustacea located in the antennal metamere.

anterior (L. comparative of *ante,* before) The head of an organism or (as the adjective) toward that end.

anthropoid (an´thrə-poyd) (Gr. *anthrōpos,* man, + *eidos,* form) Resembling humans, especially the great apes.

aperture (ap´ər-chər) (L. *apertura* from *aperire,* to uncover) An opening; the opening into the first whorl of a gastropod shell.

apical (ā´pə-kl) (L. *apex,* tip) Pertaining to the tip or apex.

apical complex A certain combination of organelles found in the protozoan phylum Apicomplexa.

apocrine (ap´ə-krən) (Gr. *apo,* away, + *krinein,* to separate) Applies to a type of mammalian sweat gland that produces a viscous secretion by breaking off a part of the cytoplasm of secreting cells.

apopyle (ap´ə-pīl) (Gr. *apo,* away from, + *pylē,* gate) In sponges, opening of the radial canal into the spongocoel.

aposematic (ap-ə-si-mat´ik) A conspicuous condition that serves as a warning; for example, the bright colors of a Monarch butterfly's wings warn potential predators that the butterfly is distasteful.

arboreal (är-bōr´ē-əl) (L. *arbor,* tree) Living in trees.

archaeocyte (ar´kē-ə-sīt) (Gr. *archaios,* beginning, + *kytos,* hollow vessel) Ameboid cells of varied function in sponges.

archenteron (ärk-en´tə-rän) (Gr. *archē,* beginning, + *eneron,* gut) The main cavity of an embryo in the gastrula stage; it is lined with endoderm and represents the future digestive cavity.

archosaur (är´kə-sor) (Gr. *archōn,* ruling, + *sauros,* lizard) A clade of diapsid vertebrates that includes the living crocodiles and birds and the extinct pterosaurs and dinosaurs.

Aristotle's lantern Masticating apparatus of some sea urchins.

artiodactyl (är´tē-ō-dak´təl) (Gr. *artios,* even, + *daktylos,* toe) One of an order of mammals with two or four digits on each foot.

asconoid (Gr. *askos,* bladder) Simplest form of sponges, with canals leading directly from the outside to the interior.

asexual Without distinct sexual organs; not involving formation of gametes.

asymmetric competition See **amensalism.**

atoke (ā´tōk) (Gr. *a,* without, + *tokos,* offspring) Anterior, nonreproductive part of a marine polychaete, as distinct from the posterior, reproductive part (epitoke) during the breeding season.

atrium (ā´trē-əm) (L. *atrium,* vestibule) One of the chambers of the heart. Also, the tympanic cavity of the ear. Also, the large cavity containing the pharynx in tunicates and cephalochordates.

auricle (aw´ri-kl) (L. *auricula,* dim. of *auris,* ear) One of the less muscular chambers of the heart; atrium; the external ear, or pinna; any earlike lobe or process.

auricularia (ə-rik´u-lar´ē-ə) (L. *auricula,* a small ear) Type of larva found in Holothuroidea.

autogamy (aw-täg´ə-mē) (Gr. *autos,* self, + *gamos,* marriage) Condition in which the gametic nuclei produced by meiosis fuse within the same organism that produced them to restore the diploid number.

autotomy (aw-tät´ə-mē) (Gr. *autos,* self, + *tomos,* a cutting) Detachment of a part of the body by the organism itself.

autotroph (aw´tō-trōf) (Gr. *autos,* self, + *trophos,* feeder) Organism that makes its organic nutrients from inorganic raw materials.

autotrophic nutrition (Gr. *autos,* self, + *trophia,* denoting nutrition) Nutrition characterized by the ability to use simple inorganic substances to synthesize more complex organic compounds, as in green plants and some bacteria.

axial (L. *axis,* axle) Relating to the axis, or stem; on or along the axis.

axocoel (aks´ə-sēl) (Gr. *axon,* axle, + *koilos,* hollow) Anterior coelomic compartment in echinoderms; corresponds to protocoel.

axolotl (ak´sə-lot´l) (Nahuatl *atl,* water, + *xolotl,* doll, servant, spirit) Salamanders of the species *Ambystoma mexicanum,* which do not metamorphose and which retain aquatic larval characteristics throughout adulthood.

axon (ak´sän) (Gr. *axōn*) Elongate extension of a neuron that conducts impulses away from the cell body and toward the synaptic terminals.

axoneme (aks´ə-nēm) (L. *axis,* axle, + Gr. *nēma,* thread) The microtubules in a cilium or flagellum, usually arranged as a circlet of nine pairs; enclosing one central pair; also, the microtubules of an axopodium.

axopodium (ak´sə-pō´dē-əm) (Gr. *axon,* an axis, + *podion,* small foot) Long, slender, more or less permanent pseudopodium in certain amebas. (Also called an **axopod.**)

axostyle (aks´ō-stīl) Tubelike organelle in some flagellate protozoa, extending from the area of the kinetosomes to the posterior end, where it often protrudes.

B

basal body Also called kinetosome or blepharoplast, a cylinder of nine triplets of microtubules found basal to a flagellum or cilium; same structure as a centriole.

basal disc Aboral attachment site on a cnidarian polyp.

basis, basipodite (bā´səs, bā-si´pō-dīt) (Gr. *basis,* base, + *pous, podos,* foot) The distal or second joint of the protopod of a crustacean appendage.

benthos (ben´thōs) (Gr., depth of the sea) Organisms that live along the substrate underlying seas and lakes. Adj., **benthic.** Also, the submerged substrate itself.

Bilateria (bī´lə-tir´-ē-ə) (L. *bi-,* two, + *latus,* side) Bilaterally symmetrical animals.

binary fission Mode of asexual reproduction in which the animal splits into two approximately equal offspring.

binomial nomenclature The Linnean system of naming species in which the first word is the name of the genus (first letter capitalized) and the second word is the specific epithet (uncapitalized), usually an adjective modifying the name of the genus. Both of these words are written in italics.

biogenetic law A statement postulating a characteristic relationship between **ontogeny** and **phylogeny.** Examples include Haeckel's law of **recapitulation** and Von Baer's law that general characteristics (those shared by many species) appear earlier in ontogeny than more restricted ones; neither of these statements is universally true.

biogeochemical cycle A description of the flow of elementary matter, such as carbon or phosphorus, through the component parts of an ecosystem and its **abiotic** environment, including the amount of an element present at the various stages of a **food web.**

biological species concept A reproductive community of populations (reproductively isolated from others) that occupies a specific niche in nature.

bioluminescence Method of light production by living organisms; usually, certain proteins (luciferins), in the presence of oxygen and an enzyme (luciferase), are converted to oxyluciferins with liberation of light.

biomass (Gr. *bios*, life, + *maza*, lump or mass). The weight of total living organisms or of a species population per unit of area.

biome (bī´ōm) (Gr. *bios*, life, + *ōma*, abstract group suffix) Complex of plant and animal communities characterized by climatic and soil conditions; the largest ecological unit.

biosphere (Gr. *bios*, life, + *sphaira*, globe) That part of earth containing living organisms.

biotic (bī-ät´ik) (Gr. *biōtos*, life, livable) Of or relating to life.

bipinnaria (L. *bi*, double, + *pinna*, wing, + *aria*, like or connected with) Free-swimming, ciliated, bilateral larva of the asteroid echinoderms; develops into the brachiolaria larva.

biradial symmetry Type of radial symmetry in which only two planes passing through the oral-aboral axis yield mirror images because some structure is paired.

biramous (bī-rām´əs) (L. *bi*, double, + *ramus*, a branch) Adjective describing appendages with two distinct branches; contrasted with uniramous, unbranched.

blastocoel (blas´tə-sēl) (Gr. *blastos*, germ, + *koilos*, hollow) Cavity of the blastula.

blastomere (Gr. *blastos*, germ, + *meros*, part) An early cleavage cell.

blastopore (Gr. *blastos*, germ, + *poros*, passage, pore) External opening of the archenteron in the gastrula.

blastula (Gr. *blastos*, germ, + *ula*, dim) Early embryological state of many animals; consists of a hollow mass of cells.

blepharoplast (blə-fä´rə-plast) (Gr. *blepharon*, eyelid, + *plastos*, formed) See **basal body.**

book gill Respiratory structure of aquatic chelicerates (Arthropoda) in which many thin, blood-filled gills are layered like the pages of a book. Gas exchange occurs as seawater passes between each pair of gills.

book lung Respiratory structure of terrestrial chelicerates (Arthropoda) in which many thin-walled air pockets extend into a blood-filled chamber in the abdomen.

BP Before the present.

brachial (brāk´ē-əl) (L. *brachium*, forearm) Referring to the arm.

branchial (brank´ē-əl) (Gr. *branchia*, gills) Referring to gills.

brown bodies Remnants of the lophophore and digestive tract of a degenerating adult ectoproct left behind in the chamber as a new lophophore and digestive tract are formed.

buccal (buk´əl) (L. *bucca*, cheek) Referring to the mouth cavity.

budding Reproduction in which the offspring arises as a small outgrowth from the parent. Failure of the offspring to separate from the parent leads to colony formation.

bursa, pl. **bursae** (M.L. *bursa*, pouch, purse made of skin) A saclike cavity. In ophiuroid echinoderms, pouches opening at bases of arms and functioning in respiration and reproduction (genitorespiratory bursae).

C

caecilian (si-sil´-yən) Denotes any member of the amphibian order Gymnophiona (also called Apoda).

calyx (kā´-liks) (L., bud cup of a flower) Any of various cup-shaped zoological structures.

capitulum (ka-pi´chə-ləm) (L., small head) Term applied to small, headlike structures of various organisms, including projection from body of ticks and mites carrying mouthparts.

carapace (kar´ə-pās) (F. from Sp. *carapacho*, shell) Shieldlike plate covering the cephalothorax of certain crustaceans; dorsal part of the shell of a turtle.

carinate (kar´ə-nāt) (L. *carina*, keel) Having a keel; in particular, the flying birds with a keeled sternum for the insertion of flight muscles.

carnivore (kar´nə-vōr´) (L. *carnivorus*, flesh-eating) One of the mammals of the order Carnivora. Also, any organism that eats animals. Adj., **carnivorous.**

carrying capacity The maximum number of individuals of a particular species that can persist under specified environmental conditions.

cartilage (L. *cartilago*; akin to L. *cratis*, wickerwork) Translucent elastic tissue that forms most of the skeleton of embryos, very young vertebrates, and adult cartilaginous fishes, such as sharks and rays; in adult amniotes, much of it is converted into bone.

caste (kast) (L. *castus*, pure, separated) One of the polymorphic forms within an insect society; each caste has its specific duties, such as queen, worker, soldier, and others.

catadromous (kə-tad´rə-məs) (Gr. *kata*, down, + *dromos*, a running) Refers to fishes that migrate from fresh water to the ocean to spawn.

catastrophic species selection Differential survival among species during a time of mass extinction based on character variation that permits some species but not others to withstand severe environmental disturbances, such as those caused by an asteroid impact.

caudal (käd´l) (L. *cauda*, tail) Constituting, belonging to, or relating to a tail.

cecum (sē´kəm) (L. *caecus*, blind) A blind pouch at the beginning of the large intestine; any similar pouch.

cellulase (sel´ū-lās) (L. *cella*, small room) Enzyme that cleaves cellulose; only synthesized by bacteria and some protists.

cellulose (sel´ū-lōs) (L. *cella*, small room) Chief polysaccharide constituent of the cell wall of green plants and some fungi; an insoluble carbohydrate $(C_6H_{10}O_5)_n$ that is converted to glucose by hydrolysis.

centriole (sen´trē-ōl) (Gr. *kentron*, center of a circle, + L. *ola*, small) Minute cytoplasmic organelle usually found in the centrosome and considered the active division center of the animal cell; organizes spindle fibers during mitosis and meiosis. Same structure as basal body or kinetosome.

cephalization (sef´-li-zā´shən) (Gr. *kephalē*, head) The evolutionary process by which specialization, particularly of the sensory organs and appendages, became localized in the head end of animals.

cephalothorax (sef´ə-lä-thō´raks) (Gr. *kephalē*, head, + *thorax*) A body division found in many Arachnida and higher Crustacea in which the head is fused with some or all of the thoracic segments.

cerata (sə-ra´tə) (Gr. *keras*, a horn, bow) Dorsal processes on some nudibranchs for gas exchange.

cercaria (ser-kar´ē-ə) (Gr. *kerkos*, tail, + L. *aria*, like or connected with) Tadpolelike juveniles of trematodes (flukes).

cervical (sər´və-kəl) (L. *cervix*, neck) Relating to a neck.

character (kar´ik-tər) A component of phenotype (including specific molecular, morphological, behavioral, or other features) used by systematists to diagnose species or higher taxa, or to evaluate phylogenetic relationships among different species or higher taxa, or relationships among populations within a species.

character displacement Differences in morphology or behavior within a species caused by competition with another species; characteristics typical of one species differ according to whether the other species is present or absent from a local community.

chela (kēl´ə) (Gr. *chēlē*, claw) Pincerlike claw.

chelicera (kə-lis´ə-rə), pl. **chelicerae** (Gr. *chēlē*, claw, + *keras*, horn) One of a pair of the most anterior head appendages on members of subphylum Chelicerata.

chelipeds (kēl´ə-peds) (Gr. *chēlē*, claw, + L. *pes*, foot) Pincerlike first pair of legs in most decapod crustaceans; specialized for seizing and crushing.

chemoautotroph (kē-mō-aw´tō-trōf) (Gr. *chemeia*, transmutation, + *autos*, self, + *trophos*, feeder) An organism utilizing inorganic compounds as a source of energy.

chitin (kī´tən) (Fr. *chitine*, from Gr. *chitōn*, tunic) A hard substance that forms part of the cuticle of arthropods and occurs sparingly in certain other invertebrates; a nitrogenous polysaccharide insoluble in water, alcohol, dilute acids, and the digestive juices of most animals.

chloragogen cells (klōr´ ə-gog-ən) (Gr. *chlōros,* light green, + *agōgos,* a leading, a guide) Modified peritoneal cells, greenish or brownish, clustered around the digestive tract of certain annelids; apparently they aid in elimination of nitrogenous wastes and in food transport.

chlorophyll (klō´r ə-fil) (Gr. *chlōros,* light green, + *phyllōn,* leaf) Green pigment found in cyanobacteria, plants, and some flagellates; necessary for photosynthesis.

chloroplast (Gr. *chlōros,* light green, + *plastos,* molded) A plastid containing chlorophyll and usually other pigments; found in cytoplasm of plant cells.

choanoblast (kō-an´ ə-blast) (Gr. *choanē,* funnel, + *blastos,* germ) One of several cellular elements within the syncytial tissue of a hexactinellid sponge.

choanocyte (kō-an´ ə-sīt) (Gr. *choanē,* funnel, + *kytos,* hollow vessel) One of the flagellate collar cells that line cavities and canals of sponges.

choanoflagellate (kō-an´ ə-fla-jel´ āt) Any member of a protozoan clade having a single flagellum surrounded by a column of microvilli; some form colonies, and all are included within the larger clade of opisthokonts.

chorioallantoic placenta (kō´ rē-ō-al´ an-tō´ -ic) (Gr. *chorion,* skin, + *allas,* sausage) Type of placenta that occurs in placental mammals and some marsupials; a structure modified from the embryonic chorionic and allantoic membranes through which materials are exchanged between the embryo and the mother.

chorion (kō´ rē-on) (Gr. *chorion,* skin) The outer layer of the double membrane that surrounds the embryo of reptiles, birds, and mammals; in mammals, it contributes to the placenta.

choriovitelline placenta (kor´ ē-ō-vi´ təl-ən) Gr. *chorion,* skin, + *vittel* yolk of an egg) An often transitory placenta that forms during the early developmental stages of marsupials and placental mammals. Also called the "yolk sac placenta," it is formed from the yolk sac and chorionic membrane of the embryo.

chromatophore (krō-mat´ ə-fōr) (Gr. *chrōma,* color, + *herein,* to bear) Pigment cell, usually in the dermis, in which usually the pigment can be dispersed or concentrated.

chromosomal theory of inheritance The well-established principle, initially proposed by Sutton and Boveri in 1903–1904, that nuclear chromosomes are the physical bearers of genetic material in eukaryotic organisms. It is the foundation for modern evolutionary genetics.

chrysalis (kris´ ə-lis) (L., from Gr. *chrysos,* gold) The pupal stage of a butterfly.

cilium (sil´ ē-əm), pl. **cilia** (L., eyelid) A hairlike, vibratile organellar process found on many animal cells. Cilia may be used for moving particles along the cell surface or, in ciliate protozoans, for locomotion.

cirrus (sir´ əs) (L., curl) Hairlike tuft on an insect appendage; locomotor organelle of

fused cilia; male copulatory organ of some invertebrates.

clade (klād) (Gr. *klados,* branch) A taxon or other group consisting of a particular ancestral lineage and all of its descendants, forming a distinct branch on a phylogenetic tree.

cladistics (klad-is´ təks) (Gr. *klados,* branch, sprout) A system of arranging taxa by analysis of primitive and derived characteristics so that the arrangement will reflect phylogenetic relationships.

cladogram (klād´ ə-gram) (Gr. *klados,* branch, + *gramma,* letter) A branching diagram showing the pattern of sharing of evolutionarily derived characters among species or higher taxa.

clasper Digitiform projection on the medial side of the pelvic fins of male chondrichthians and some placoderms; used as an intromittent organ to transfer sperm to the female reproductive tract.

clitellum (kli-tel´ əm) (L. *clitellae,* pack-saddle) Thickened, saddlelike portion of certain midbody segments of many oligochaetes and leeches.

cloaca (klō-ā´ kə) (L., sewer) Posterior chamber of the digestive tract in many vertebrates, receiving feces and urogenital products. In certain invertebrates, a terminal portion of the digestive tract that serves also as a respiratory, excretory, or reproductive duct.

cloning (klō´ ning) Production of genetically identical organisms by asexual reproduction.

cnida (nī´ də) (Gr. *knidē,* nettle). Stinging or adhesive organelles formed within cnidocytes in phylum Cnidaria; nematocysts are a common type.

cnidoblast (nī´ də´ -blast) (Gr. *knidē,* nettle, + Gr. *blastos,* germ) A cnidocyte is called a cnidoblast during the time when a cnida is forming within it.

cnidocil (nī´ dō-sil) (Gr. *knidē,* nettle, + L. *cilium,* hair) Triggerlike spine on a nematocyst.

cnidocyte (nī´ dō-sīt) (Gr. *knidē,* nettle, + *kytos,* hollow vessel) Modified interstitial cell that holds the cnida.

coccidian (kok-sid´ ē-ən) (Gr. *kokkis,* kernel, grain) Intracellular protozoan parasite belonging to a class within phylum Apicomplexa; the organism causing malaria is an example.

cochlea (kōk´ lē-ə) (L., snail, from Gr. *kochlos,* a shellfish) A tubular cavity of the inner ear containing the essential organs of hearing; occurs in crocodiles, birds, and mammals; spirally coiled in mammals.

cocoon (kə-kün´) (Fr. *cocon,* shell) Protective covering of a resting or developmental stage, sometimes including its contents; for example, the cocoon of a moth or the protective covering for the developing embryos in some annelids.

coelenteron (sē-len´ tər-on) (Gr. *koilos,* hollow, + *enteron,* intestine) Internal cavity of a cnidarian; gastrovascular cavity; archenteron.

coelom (sē´ lōm) (Gr. *koilōma,* cavity) The body cavity in triploblastic animals, lined with mesodermal peritoneum.

coelomate (sē´ lōm-āt) Animals that possess a **coelom;** also called eucoelomate.

coelomoduct (sē-lō´ m ə-dukt) (Gr. *koilos,* hollow, + *ductus,* a leading) Duct that carries gametes or excretory products (or both) from the coelom to the exterior.

cohort (kō´ hort) All organisms of a population born within a specified time interval.

collagen (käl´ ə-jən) (Gr. *kolla,* glue, + *genos,* descent) Tough, fibrous protein occurring in vertebrates as the chief constituent of collagenous connective tissue; also occurs in invertebrates—for example, the cuticle of nematodes.

collar bodies Extensions of choanoblasts bearing flagellated collars in hexactinellid sponges.

collar cells Cells having a single flagellum surrounded by a ring of microvilli. Sponge choanocytes are collar cells, as are choanoflagellates, but collar cells also occur outside these taxa.

collencyte (käl´ ən-sīt) (Gr. *kolla,* glue, + *kytos,* hollow vessel) Type of cell in sponges that secretes fibrillar collagen.

colloblast (käl´ ə-blast) (Gr. *kolla,* glue, + *blastos,* germ) A glue-secreting cell on the tentacles of ctenophores.

comb plate One of the plates of fused cilia arranged in rows for ctenophore locomotion.

commensalism (kə-men´ səl-iz´ əm) (L. *com,* together with, + *mensa,* table) A relationship in which one individual lives close to or on another and benefits, and the host is unaffected; often symbiotic.

common descent Darwin's theory that all forms of life are derived from a shared ancestral population through a branching of evolutionary lineages.

community (L. *communitas,* community, fellowship) An assemblage of species that are associated in a common environment and interact with each other in a self-sustaining and self-regulating relationship.

comparative biochemistry Studies of the structures of biological macromolecules, especially proteins and nucleic acids, and their variation within and among related species to reveal homologies of macromolecular structure.

comparative cytology Studies of the structures of chromosomes within and among related species to reveal homologies of chromosomal structure.

comparative method Use of patterns of similarity and dissimilarity among species or populations to infer their phylogenetic relationships; use of phylogeny to examine evolutionary processes and history.

comparative morphology Studies of organismal form and its variation within and among related species to reveal homologies of organismal characters.

competition Some degree of overlap in ecological niches of two populations in the same community, such that both depend on the same food source, shelter, or other resources, and negatively affect each other's survival.

competitive exclusion An ecological principle stating that two species whose niches are very similar cannot coexist indefinitely in the same community; one species is driven to extinction by competition between them.

conjugation (kon´jū-gā´shən) (L. *conjugare,* to yoke together) Temporary union of two ciliate protozoa while they are exchanging chromatin material and undergoing nuclear phenomena leading to binary fission. Also, formation of cytoplasmic bridges between bacteria for transfer of plasmids.

conodont (kōn´ə-dänt) (Gr. *kōnos,* cone, + *odontos,* tooth) Toothlike element from a Paleozoic animal now considered an early marine chordate.

conspecific (L. *com,* together, + species) Of the same species.

consumer (kən-sū´-mer) Organism whose energy and matter are acquired by eating other organisms, which may be **primary producers, herbivores,** or **carnivores.**

contractile vacuole Clear, fluid-filled cell vacuole in protozoa and a few metazoa; collects water and releases it to the outside in a cyclical manner, for osmoregulation and some excretion.

control That part of a scientific experiment to which the experimental variable is not applied, but similar to the experimental group in all other respects.

coprophagy (ko-prō´fā´-jē) (Gr. *kopros,* dung, + *phagein,* to eat) Feeding on dung or excrement as a normal behavior among animals; reingestion of feces.

copulation (Fr., from L. *copulare,* to couple) Sexual union to facilitate fertilization of eggs by sperm.

corneum (kor´nē-əm) (L. *corneus,* horny) Outermost epithelial layer of dead, keratinized cells. Also called stratum corneum.

corona (kə-rō´nə) (L., crown) Head or upper portion of a structure; ciliated disc on anterior end of rotifers.

corpora allata (kor´pə-rə əl-la´tə) (L. *corpus,* body, + *allatum,* aided) Endocrine glands in insects that produce juvenile hormone.

cortex (kor´teks) (L., bark) The outer layer of a structure.

coxa, coxopodite (kox´ə, kox´-ə pō´-dīt) (L. *coxa,* hip, + Gr. *pous, podos,* foot) The proximal joint of an insect or arachnid leg; in crustaceans, the proximal joint of the protopod.

Cretaceous extinction A **mass extinction** that occurred 65 million years ago in which 76% of existing species, including all dinosaurs, became extinct, marking the end of the Mesozoic era.

crop Region of the esophagus specialized for storing food.

cryptobiotic (Gr. *kryptos,* hidden, + *biōticus,* pertaining to life) Living in concealment; refers to insects and other animals that live in secluded situations, such as underground or in wood; also, tardigrades and some nematodes, rotifers, and others that survive harsh environmental

conditions by assuming for a time a state of very low metabolism.

crystalline style Rod containing digestive enzymes present in the stomach of a bivalve.

ctene (tēn) (Gr. *kteis, ktenos,* comb) Fused cilia that form a comb plate in members of phylum Ctenophora.

ctenoid scales (tēn´oid) (Gr. *kteis, ktenos,* comb) Thin, overlapping dermal scales of teleost fishes; exposed posterior margins have fine, toothlike spines.

cuticle (kū´ti-kəl) (L. *cutis,* skin) Protective, noncellular, organic layer secreted by the external epithelium (hypodermis) of many invertebrates. In vertebrates, the term refers to the epidermis or outer skin.

Cuvierian tubules (*Cuvier,* 19th-century French comparative vertebrate anatomist) Sticky, often toxic elongate internal organs of holothurians expelled to entangle potential predators; these can be regenerated.

cyanobacteria (sī-an´ō-bak-ter´ē-ə) (Gr. *kyanos,* a dark-blue substance, + *bakterion,* dim. of *baktron,* a staff) Photosynthetic prokaryotes, also called blue-green algae, cyanophytes.

cycloid scales (sī´kloid) (Gr. *kyklos,* circle) Thin, overlapping dermal scales of teleost fishes; posterior margins are smooth.

cynodonts (sin´ə-dänts) (Gr. *kynodōn,* canine tooth) Group of mammal-like carnivorous synapsids of the Upper Permian and Triassic periods.

cyst (sist) (Gr. *kystis,* a bladder, pouch) Resistant, quiescent stage of an organism, usually with a secreted wall.

cysticercus (sis´tə-ser´kəs) (Gr. *kystis,* bladder, + *kerkos,* tail) Type of juvenile tapeworm having an invaginated and introverted scolex contained in a fluidfilled bladder.

cystid (sis´tid) (Gr. *kystis,* bladder) In an ectoproct, the dead secreted outer parts plus the adherent underlying living layers.

cytopharynx (Gr. *kytos,* hollow vessel, + *pharynx,* throat) Short, tubular gullet in ciliate protozoa.

cytoplasm (sī´tə-plasm) (Gr. *kytos,* hollow vessel, + *plasma,* mold) The living matter of the cell, excluding the nucleus.

cytoproct (sī´tə-prokt) (Gr. *kytos,* hollow vessel, + *prōktos,* anus) Site on a protozoan where indigestible matter is expelled.

cytopyge (sī´tə-pīj) (Gr. *kytos,* hollow vessel, + *pyge,* rump or buttocks) In some protozoa, localized site for expulsion of wastes.

cytostome (sī´tə-stōm) (Gr. *kytos,* hollow vessel, + *stoma,* mouth) The cell mouth in many protozoa.

D

dactylozooid (dak-til´ə-zō-id) (Gr. *dakos,* bite, sting, + *tylos,* knob, + *zōon,* animal) Polyp of a colonial hydroid specialized for defense or killing food.

Darwinism Theory of evolution emphasizing common descent of all living organisms, gradual change, multiplication of species, and natural selection.

data, sing. **datum** (Gr. *dateomai,* to divide, cut in pieces) The results of a scientific experiment, or descriptive observations, upon which a conclusion is based.

deciduous (də-sij´ü-wəs) (L. *deciere,* to fall off) Shed at the end of a growing period.

decomposer (dē´-kəm-pō´zər) **Consumer** that breaks organic matter into soluble components available to plants at the base of the food web; most are bacteria or fungi.

deduction (L. *deductus,* led apart, split, separated) Reasoning from the general to the particular, from given premises to their necessary conclusion.

definitive host The host in which sexual reproduction of a symbiont occurs; if no sexual reproduction, then the host in which the symbiont becomes mature and reproduces; contrast intermediate host.

deme (dēm) (Gr., populace) A local population of closely related animals.

demography (də-mäg´rə-fē) (Gr. *demos,* people, + *graphy*) The properties of the rate of growth and the age structure of populations.

density-dependent Biotic environmental factors, such as predators and parasites, whose effects on a population vary according to the number of organisms in the population.

density-independent Abiotic environmental factors, such as fires, floods, and temperature changes, whose effects on a population are unaffected by the number of organisms in the population.

deposit feeders Aquatic organisms that consume detritus and small organisms in soil and other sediments.

derived character state Condition of a taxonomic character inferred by cladistic analysis to have arisen within a taxon being examined cladistically rather than having been inherited from the most recent common ancestor of all members of the taxon.

dermal (Gr. *derma,* skin) Pertaining to the skin; cutaneous.

dermal ostia (Gr. *derma,* skin, + L. *ostium,* door) Incurrent pores in a sponge.

dermis The inner, sensitive mesodermal layer of skin; corium.

determinate cleavage Type of cleavage, usually spiral, in which the fate of the blastomeres is determined very early in development; see **mosaic development.**

detorsion (L. *de,* down, from, + *torquere,* to twist) Developmental process in post-veliger stage of certain gastropod molluscs whereby orientation of internal organs resulting from torsion is altered to resemble a state prior to torsion; anus and mantle cavity are posterior after detorsion.

detritus (də-trī´tus) (L., that which is rubbed or worn away) Any fine particulate debris of organic or inorganic origin.

Deuterostomia (dū´tə-rō-stō´mē-ə) (Gr. *deuteros,* second, secondary, + *stoma,* mouth) A group of higher phyla in which cleavage is indeterminate and primitively radial. The endomesoderm is enterocoelous, and the mouth is derived away from the blastopore. Includes Echinodermata, Chordata, and Hemichordata; contrasts with **Protostomia.**

diapause (dī´ə-pawz) (Gr. *diapausis,* pause) Period of arrested development in the life cycle of insects and certain other animals in which physiological activity is very low and the animal is highly resistant to unfavorable external conditions.

diapsids (dī-ap´səds) (Gr. *di,* two, + *apsis,* arch) Amniotes in which the skull bears two pairs of temporal openings; includes nonavian reptiles and birds. The temporal openings are evolutionarily lost in turtles.

dictyosome (dik´tē-ə-sōm) (Gr. *diction,* to throw, + *sōma,* body). A part of the secretory system of endoplasmic reticulum in protozoa; also called Golgi bodies.

diffusion (L. *diffusion,* dispersion) Movement of particles or molecules from an area of high concentration of the particles or molecules to an area of lower concentration.

digitigrade (dij´ə-tə-grād) (L. *digitus,* finger, toe, + *gradus,* step, degree) Walking on the digits, with the posterior part of the foot raised; contrasts with **plantigrade.**

dimorphism (dī-mor´fizm) (Gr. *di,* two, + *morphē,* form) Existence within a species of two distinct forms according to color, sex, size, organ structure, or behavior. Occurrence of two kinds of zooids in a colonial organism.

dinoflagellate (dī-nō-fla´jə-lāt) (Gr. *dinos,* whirling, + L. *flagellum,* a whip). Any member of a protozoan clade having two flagella, one in the equatorial region of the body and the other trailing; cells naked or with a test of cellulose plates.

dioecious (dī-esh´əs) (Gr. *di,* two, + *oikos,* house) Having male and female organs in separate individuals.

diphycercal (dif´i-sər´kəl) (Gr. *diphyēs,* twofold, + *kerkos,* tail) A tail that tapers to a point, as in lungfishes; vertebral column extends to tip without upturning.

diphyodont (dī-fī´ə-dänt) (Gr. *diphyēs,* twofold, + *odous,* tooth) Having successive sets of deciduous and permanent teeth.

diploblastic (di´plə-blas´tək) (Gr. *diploos,* double, + *blastos,* bud) Organism with two germ layers, endoderm and ectoderm.

diploid (dip´lòid) (Gr. *diploos,* double, + *eidos,* form) Having the somatic (double, or 2n) number of chromosomes or twice the number characteristic of a gamete of a given species.

diplomonad (dip´lō-mō´nad) (Gr. *diploos,* double, + *monos,* lone, single) Any member of a protozoan clade having four kinetosomes and lacking mitochondria.

direct development A postnatal ontogeny primarily featuring growth in size rather than a major change in body shape or organs present; a life history that lacks **metamorphosis.**

directional selection Natural selection that favors one extreme value of a continuously varying trait and disfavors other values.

disruptive selection Natural selection that simultaneously favors two different extreme values of a continuously varying trait but disfavors intermediate values.

distal (dis´təl) Farther from the center of the body than a reference point.

DNA barcoding Technique for identifying organisms to species using sequence information of a standard gene present in all animals. The mitochondrial gene encoding cytochrome *c* oxidase I (*COI*) is often used.

domain (dō-mān´) An informal taxonomic rank above the Linnean kingdom; Archaea, Bacteria, and Eucarya are ranked as domains.

dorsal (dor´səl) (L. *dorsum,* back) Toward the back, or upper surface, of an animal.

double circulation A blood-transport system having a distinct pulmonary circuit of blood vessels separate from the circuit of blood vessels serving the remainder of the body.

dual-gland adhesive organ Organs in the epidermis of most turbellarians, with three cell types: viscid and releasing gland cells and anchor cells.

E

eccrine (ek´rən) (Gr. *ek,* out of, + *krinein,* to separate) Applies to a type of mammalian sweat gland that produces a watery secretion.

ecdysiotropin (ek-dī-zē-ə-trō´pən) (Gr. *ekdysis,* to strip off, escape, + *tropos,* a turn, change) Hormone secreted in brain of insects that stimulates prothoracic gland to secrete molting hormone. Prothoracicotropic hormone; brain hormone.

ecdysis (ek-dī´-sis) (Gr. *ekdysis,* to strip off, escape) Shedding of outer cuticular layer; molting, as in insects or crustaceans.

ecdysone (ek-dī´sōn) (Gr. *ekdysis,* to strip off) Molting hormone of arthropods; stimulates growth and ecdysis; produced by prothoracic glands in insects and Y-organs in crustaceans.

ecdysozoan protostome (ek-dī´-sō-zō´ən prō´tə-stōm) (Gr. *ekdysis,* to strip off, escape, + *zōon,* animal. Gr. *protos,* first, + *stoma,* mouth) Any member of a clade within Protostomia whose members shed the cuticle as they grow; includes arthropods, nematodes, and several smaller phyla.

ecological pyramid A quantitative measurement of a **food web** in terms of amount of **biomass,** numbers of **organisms,** or energy at each of the different **trophic** levels present (**producers, herbivores,** first-level **carnivores,** higher-level carnivores).

ecology (Gr. *oikos,* house, + *logos,* discourse) Part of biology that concerns the relationship between organisms and their environment.

ecosystem (ek´ō-sis-təm) (eco[logy] from Gr. *oikos,* house, + system) An ecological unit comprising both the biotic communities and the nonliving (abiotic) environment, which interact to produce a stable system.

ectoderm (ek´tō-derm) (Gr. *ektos,* outside, + *derma,* skin) Outer layer of cells of an early embryo (gastrula stage); one of the germ layers, also sometimes used to include tissues derived from ectoderm.

ectognathous (ek´tō-nā´thəs) (Gr. *ektos,* outside, without, + *gnathos,* jaw) Derived character shared by most insects; mandibles and maxillae not in pouches.

ectolecithal (ek´tō-les´ə-thəl) (Gr. *ektos,* ouside, + *ekithos,* yolk) Yolk for nutrition of the embryo contributed by cells that are separate from the egg cell and are combined with the zygote by envelopment within the eggshell.

ectoparasite (ek´tō-par´ə-sīt) **Parasite** that resides on the outside surface of its host organism; contrasts with **endoparasite.**

ectoplasm (ek´tō-pla-zm) (Gr. *ektos,* outside, + *plasma,* form) The cortex of a cell or that part of cytoplasm just under the cell surface; contrasts with **endoplasm.**

ectothermic (ek´tō-therm´ic) (Gr. *ektos,* outside, + *thermē,* heat) Having a variable body temperature derived from heat acquired from the environment; contrasts with **endothermic.**

efferent (ef´ə-rənt) (L. *ex,* out, + *ferre,* to bear) Leading or conveying away from some organ—for example, nerve impulses conducted away from the brain, or blood conveyed away from an organ; contrasts with **afferent.**

egestion (ē-jes´chən) (L. *egestus,* to discharge) Act of dispelling indigestible or waste matter from the body by any normal route.

elephantiasis (el-ə-fən-tī´ə-səs) Disfiguring condition caused by chronic infection with filarial worms *Wuchereria bancrofti* and *Brugia malayi.*

Eltonian pyramid An **ecological pyramid** showing numbers of organisms at each of the **trophic** levels.

embryogenesis (em´brē-ō-jen´ə-səs) (Gr. *embryon,* embryo, + *genesis,* origin) The origin and development of the embryo; embryogeny.

emigrate (L. *emigrare,* to move out) To move *from* one area to another to establish residence.

encystment Process of cyst formation.

endemic (en-dem´ik) (Gr. *en,* in, + *demos,* populace) Geographically restricted to a certain region or country; native to a restricted area; not introduced.

endoderm (en´də-dərm) (Gr. *endon,* within, + *derma,* skin) Innermost germ layer of an embryo, forming the primitive gut; also may refer to tissues derived from endoderm.

endognathous (en´dō-nā-thəs) (Gr. *endon,* within, + *gnathous,* jaw) Ancestral character in insects (orders Diplura, Collembola, and Protura) in which the mandibles and maxillae are located in pouches.

endolecithal (en´dō-les´ə-thəl) (Gr. *endon,* within, + *lekithos,* yolk) Yolk for nutrition of the embryo incorporated into the egg cell itself.

endoparasite (en´dō-par´ə-sīt) Parasite that resides inside the body of its host organism; contrasts with **ectoparasite.**

endoplasm (en´dō-pla-zm) (Gr. *endon,* within, + *plasma,* mold or form) The portion of cytoplasm that immediately surrounds the nucleus.

endopod, endopodite (en´dō-päd, en-dop´ə-dīt) (Gr. *endon,* within, + *pous, podos,* foot) Medial branch of a biramous crustacean appendage.

endoskeleton (Gr. *endon,* within, + *skeletos,* hard) Skeleton or supporting framework within the living tissues of an organism; contrasts with **exoskeleton.**

endostyle (en´dō-stīl) (Gr. *endon,* within, + *stylos,* a pillar) Ciliated groove(s) in the floor of the pharynx of tunicates, cephalochordates, and larval lampreys; used for accumulating and moving food particles to the stomach.

endosymbiosis A symbiosis in which the symbiont lives inside its host; origin of eukaryotes, in which one prokaryote (symbiont) came to live inside another prokaryote (host), and symbionts eventually became organelles, such as mitochondria, of the host.

endothermic (en´dō-therm´ik) (Gr. *endon,* within, + *therme,* heat) Having a body temperature determined by heat derived from an animal's own oxidative metabolism; contrasts with **ectothermic.**

energy budget Economic analysis of the energy used by an organism, partitioned into **gross productivity, net productivity,** and **respiration.**

enterocoel (en´tər-ō-sēl´) (Gr. *enteron,* gut, + *koilos,* hollow) Type of coelom formed by the outpouching of a mesodermal sac from the endoderm of the primitive gut.

enterocoelomate (en´ter-ō-sēl´ō-māt) (Gr. *enteron,* gut, + *koilōma,* cavity, + Engl. *ate,* state of) Animal having an enterocoel, such as an echinoderm or a vertebrate.

enterocoelous mesoderm formation Embryonic formation of mesoderm by a pouchlike outfolding from the archenteron, which then expands and obliterates the blastocoel, thus forming a large cavity, the coelom, lined with mesoderm.

enteron (en´tə-rän) (Gr., intestine) The digestive cavity.

entognathy (en´tə-nā-thē) Bases of mouthparts enclosed within the head capsule in insect orders Collembola, Diplura and Protura.

entomology (en´tə-mol´ə-jē) (Gr. *entoma,* an insect, + *logos,* discourse) Study of insects.

ephyra (ef´ə-rə) (Gr. *Ephyra,* Greek city) Juvenile medusa budded from a strobilating polyp in class Scyphozoa, phylum Cnidaria.

epidermis (ep´ə-dər´məs) (Gr. *epi,* on, upon, + *derma,* skin) The outer, nonvascular layer of skin of ectodermal origin; in invertebrates, a single layer of ectodermal epithelium.

epipod, epipodite (ep´ə-päd, e-pi-pō´-dīt) (Gr. *epi,* on, upon, + *pous, podos,* foot) Lateral process on the protopod of a crustacean appendage, often modified as a gill.

epistome (ep´i-stōm) (Gr. *epi,* on, upon, + *stoma,* mouth) Flap over the mouth in some lophophorates bearing the protocoel.

epithelium (ep´i-thē´lē-um) (Gr. *epi,* on, upon, + *thēlē,* nipple) Cellular tissue covering a free surface or lining a tube or cavity.

epitoke (ep´i-tōk) (Gr. *epitokos,* fruitful) Posterior part of a marine polychaete when swollen with developing gonads during the breeding season; contrast with **atoke.**

erythrocyte (ə-rith´rō-sīt) (Gr. *erythros,* red, + *kytos,* hollow vessel) Red blood cell; has hemoglobin to carry oxygen from lungs or gills to tissues; during formation in mammals, erythrocytes lose their nuclei, whereas those of other vertebrates retain the nuclei.

estivation (es´tə-vā´shen) (L. *aestivates,* to spend the summer) A state of dormancy during the summer when temperatures are high, food is scarce and/or dehydration threatens. Metabolism and breathing rate decrease.

estrous cycle Periodic episodes of estrus, or "heat," when females of most mammalian species become sexually receptive.

estrus (es´trəs) (L. *oestrus,* gadfly, frenzy) The period of heat, or rut, especially of the female during ovulation of the eggs. Associated with maximum sexual receptivity.

eukaryotic, eucaryotic (ū´ka-rē-ot´ik) (Gr. *eu,* good, true, + *karyon,* nut, kernel) Organisms whose cells characteristically contain a membrane-bound nucleus or nuclei; contrasts with **prokaryotic.**

eumetazoan (ü-met-ə-zō´ən) (Gr. *eu,* good, true, + *meta,* after, + *zōon,* animal) Any multicellular animal with distinct germ layers that form true tissues; animals beyond the cellular grade of organization.

euryhaline (ū-rə-hā´līn) (Gr. *eurys,* broad, + *hals,* salt) Able to tolerate wide ranges of saltwater concentrations.

euryphagous (yə-rif´ə-gəs) (Gr. *eurys,* broad, + *phagein,* to eat) Eating a large variety of foods.

eurytopic (ū-rē-tōp´ik) (Gr. *eurys,* broad, + *topos,* place) Describes an organism with a wide environmental range.

eutely (u´tē-lē) (Gr. *euteia,* thrift) Condition of a body composed of a constant number of cells or nuclei in all adult members of a species, as in rotifers, acanthocephalans, and nematodes.

evagination (ē-vaj-ə-nā´shən) (L. *e,* out, + *vagina,* sheath) An outpocketing from a hollow structure.

evolution (L. *evolvere,* to unfold) All changes in the characteristics and diversity of life on earth throughout its history.

evolutionary sciences Empirical investigation of ultimate causes in biology using the comparative method.

evolutionary species concept A single lineage of ancestral-descendant populations that maintains its identity from other such lineages and has its own evolutionary tendencies and historical fate; differs from the biological species concept by explicitly including a time dimension and including asexual lineages.

evolutionary taxonomy System of classification, formalized by George Gaylord Simpson, that groups species into Linnean higher taxa representing a hierarchy of distinct adaptive zones; such taxa may be monophyletic or paraphyletic but not polyphyletic.

exaptation (ek-sap´-tā´shən) Evolutionary cooption of an organismal or molecular character for a biological role unrelated to the character's evolutionary origin. Bird feathers are considered an exaptation for flight because they originated prior to avian flight but provided utility for flight following its origin; contrasts with **adaptation;** bird feathers are considered an adaptation for the biological role of thermoregulation.

exopod, exopodite (ex´ə-päd, ex-äp´ō-dīt) (Gr. *exō,* outside, + *pous, podos,* foot) Lateral branch of a biramous crustacean appendage.

exoskeleton (ek´sō-skel´ə-tən) (Gr. *exō,* outside, + *skeletos,* hard) Supporting structure secreted by ectoderm or epidermis; external, not enveloped by living tissue, as opposed to endoskeleton; in vertebrates, a supporting structure formed within the integument.

experiment (L. *experiri,* to try) A trial made to support or to disprove a hypothesis.

experimental method General procedure for testing hypotheses by predicting how a biological system will respond to a disturbance, making the disturbance under controlled conditions, and then comparing the observed results with the predicted ones.

experimental sciences Empirical investigation of proximate causes in biology using the **experimental method.**

extrinsic factor An environmental variable that influences the biological properties of a population, such as observed number of individuals or rate of growth.

extrusome (eks´trə-sōm) (L. *extrusus,* driven out, + *soma,* body) Any membrane-bound organelle used to extrude something from a protozoan cell.

eyelid (ī´-lid) A thin surface of skin and muscle that can be closed to protect an eye from light, abrasion, and/or desiccation. Appears in many but not all terrestrial vertebrates.

F

filipodium (fi´li-pō´dē-əm) (L. *filum,* thread, + Gr. *pous, podos,* foot) Type of pseudopodium that is very slender and may branch but does not rejoin to form a mesh.

filter feeding Any feeding process by which particulate food is filtered from water in which it is suspended.

fission (L. *fissio,* a splitting) Asexual reproduction by division of the body into two or more parts.

fitness Degree of adjustment and suitability for a particular environment. Genetic fitness is the relative contribution of a genotype to the next generation; organisms with high genetic fitness are those favored by natural selection.

flagellum (fl ə-jel′ əm), pl. **flagella** (L., a whip) Whiplike organelle of locomotion.

flame cell Specialized hollow excretory or osmoregulatory structure composed of one or several small cells containing a tuft of flagella (the "flame") and situated at the end of a minute tubule; connected tubules ultimately open to the outside. See **protonephridium.**

fluke (O.E. *flōc,* flatfish) Member of class Trematoda or class Monogenera. Also, certain of the flatfishes (order Pleuronectiformes).

food chain Movement of energy from plant compounds to organisms that eat plants, then to other organisms that eat the plant feeders, and possibly further through a linear series of organisms that feed and are then eaten by others. Food chains connect and branch to form **food webs.**

food vacuole A digestive organelle in the cell.

food web An analysis relating species in an ecological community according to how they acquire nutrition, such as by fixing atmospheric carbon **(producers),** consuming producers **(herbivores),** consuming herbivores (first-level **carnivores**), or consuming carnivores (higher-level carnivores).

foraminiferan (fo-ra-mə-nif′-ə-rən) (L. *foramin,* hole, perforation, + *fero,* to bear) Granuloreticulosean amebas bearing a test with many openings.

fossil (fos′ əl) Any remains or impression of an organism from a past geological age that has been preserved by natural processes, usually by mineralization in the earth's crust.

fossorial (fä-sōr′ ē-əl) (L. *fossor,* digger) Adapted for digging.

fouling Contamination of feeding or respiratory areas of an organism by excrement, sediment, or other matter. Also, accumulation of sessile marine organisms on the hull of a boat or ship so as to impede its movement through water.

fovea (fō′ vē-ə) (L., a small pit) Small pit or depression, especially the fovea centralis, a small, rodless pit in the retina of some vertebrates; a point of acute vision.

frog (fräg′) Denotes any member of the amphibian order Anura (also called Salientia).

frontal plane Plane parallel to the main axis of the body and at right angles to the sagittal plane.

fundamental niche A variety of roles potentially performed by an organism or population in an ecological community; limits on such roles are set by the intrinsic biological attributes of an organism or population. See also **niche** and **realized niche.**

funnel The tube from which a jet of water exits the mantle cavity of a cephalopod mollusc.

G

gamete (ga′ mēt, gə-mēt′) (Gr. *gamos,* marriage) A mature haploid sex cell; usually male and female gametes can be distinguished. An egg or a sperm.

gametic meiosis Meiosis that occurs during formation of the gametes, as in humans and other metazoa.

gametocyte (g ə-mēt′ ə-sīt) (Gr. *gametēs,* spouse, + *kytos,* hollow vessel) The mother cell of a gamete; an immature gamete.

ganglion (gang′ lē-ən), pl. **ganglia** (Gr., little tumor) Aggregation of nerve tissue containing nerve cells.

ganoid scales (ga′ noyd) (Gr. *ganos,* brightness) Thick, bony, rhombic scales of some bony fishes; not overlapping.

gastrocoel (gas′ trō-sēl) (Gr. *gastēr,* stomach, + *koilos,* hollow) Embryonic cavity forming in gastrulation that becomes the adult gut; also called an archenteron.

gastrodermis (gas′ trō-dər′ mis) (Gr. *gastēr,* stomach, + *derma,* skin) Lining of the digestive cavity of cnidarians.

gastrovascular cavity (Gr. *gastēr,* stomach, + L. *vasculum,* small vessel) Body cavity in certain lower invertebrates that functions in both digestion and circulation and has a single opening serving as both mouth and anus.

gastrozooid (gas′ trō-zō-id) (Gr. *gastēr,* stomach, + *zoon,* animal). Embryonic cavity forming in gastrulation that becomes the adult gut; also called an archenteron.

gastrula (gas′ trə-lə) (Gr. *gastēr,* stomach, + L. *ula,* dim.) Embryonic stage, usually cap- or sac-shaped, with walls of two layers of cells surrounding a cavity (archenteron) with one opening (blastopore).

gemmule (je′ mūl) (L. *gemma,* bud, + *ula,* dim.) Asexual, cystlike reproductive unit in freshwater sponges; formed in summer or autumn and capable of overwintering.

gene (Gr. *genos,* descent) The part of a chromosome that is the hereditary determiner and is transmitted from one generation to another. Specifically, a gene is a nucleic acid sequence (usually DNA) that encodes a functional polypeptide or RNA sequence.

gene pool Collection of all the alleles of all the genes in a population.

genetic drift Change in allelic frequencies by chance processes in the evolution of animals. In small populations, one allele may drift to fixation, becoming the only representative of that gene locus.

genotype (jēn′ ə-tīp) (Gr. *genos,* offspring, + *typos,* form) The genetic constitution, expressed and latent, of an organism; the total set of genes present in the cells of an organism; contrasts with **phenotype.**

genus (jē′ nus), pl. **genera** (L., race) Group of related species with the taxonomic rank between family and species.

germinative zone The site immediately following the scolex on the body of a mature tapeworm where new proglottids are produced.

germ layer In the animal embryo, one of three basic layers (ectoderm, endoderm, mesoderm) from which the various organs and tissues arise in the multicellular animal.

germovitellarium (jer′ mə-vit-əl-ar′ ē-əm) (L. *germen,* a bud, offshoot, + *vitellus,* yolk) Closely associated ovary (germarium) and yolk-producing structure (vitellarium) in rotifers.

germ plasm The germ cells of an organism, as distinct from the somatoplasm; the hereditary material (genes) of the germ cells.

gestation (je-stā′ shən) (L. *gestare,* to bear) Period during which offspring are carried in the uterus.

glochidium (glō-kid′ ē-əm) (Gr. *glochis,* point, + *idion,* dimin. suffix) Bivalved larval stage of freshwater mussels.

glycogen (glī′ kə-jən) (Gr. *glykys,* sweet, + *genes,* produced) A polysaccharide constituting the principal form in which carbohydrate is stored in animals; animal starch.

gnathobase (nath′ ə-bās′) (Gr. *gnathos,* jaw, base) Median basic process on certain appendages in some arthropods, usually used for biting or crushing food.

gnathostomes (nath′ ə-stōmz) (Gr. *gnathos,* jaw, + *stoma,* mouth) Vertebrates with jaws.

gonad (gō′ nad) (N.L. *gonas,* a primary sex organ) Organ that produces gametes (ovary in the female and testis in the male).

gonangium (gō-nan′ jē-əm) (N.L. *gonas,* primary sex organ, + *angeion,* dimin. of vessel) Reproductive zooid of hydroid colony (Cnidaria).

gonoduct (Gr. *gonos,* seed, progeny, + duct) Duct leading from a gonad to the exterior.

gonophore (gon′ ə-for) (Gr. *gonos,* seed, progeny, + *phoros,* bearer). Sexual reproductive structure developing from reduced medusae in some hydrozoans; it may be retained on the colony or released.

gonopore (gän′ ə-pōr) (Gr. *gonos,* seed, progeny, + *poros,* an opening) Genital pore found in many invertebrates.

grade (L. *gradus,* step) Level of organismal complexity or adaptive zone characteristic of a taxonomic group.

gradualism (graj′ ə-wal-iz′ əm) A component of Darwin's evolutionary theory postulating that evolution occurs by the temporal accumulation of small, incremental changes by populations, usually across very long periods of geological time; it opposes claims that evolution can occur by mutations having large and discontinuous phenotypic effects.

granular glands Integumentary structures of modern amphibians associated with secretion of defensive compounds.

granuloreticulosan (gran′ yə-lō-rə-tik-yə-lō′sən) (L. *granulus,* small grain, + *reticulum,* a net) Any member of a protozoan clade having branched and netlike pseudopodia; includes foraminiferans.

green gland Excretory gland of certain Crustacea; the antennal gland.

gregarine (gre-ga-rin´) (L. *gregarious*, belonging to a herd or flock) Protozoan parasites belonging to class Gregarinea within phylum Apicomplexa; these organisms infect the guts or body cavities of invertebrates.

gross productivity Measurement of the total energy assimilated by an organism.

ground substance The matrix in which connective tissue fibers are embedded.

growth rate The proportion by which a population changes in numbers of individuals at a given time by reproduction and possibly by immigration.

guild (gild) (M.E. *gilde*, payment, tribute) Species of a local community that partition resources through character displacement to avoid niche overlap and competition, such as Galápagos finch communities whose component species differ in beak size for specializing on different-sized seeds.

gynecophoric canal (gī´nə-kə-fōr´ik) (Gr. *gynē*, woman, + *pherein*, to carry) Groove in male schistosomes (certain trematodes) that carries the female.

H

habitat (L. *habitare*, to dwell) The place where an organism normally lives or where individuals of a population live.

halter (hal´tər), pl. **halteres** (hal-ti´rēz) (Gr., leap) In Diptera, small, club-shaped structure on each side of the metathorax representing the hind wings; thought to be sense organ for balancing; also called a balancer.

haplodiploidy (Gr. *haploos*, single, + *diploos*, double, + *eidos*, form) Reproduction in which haploid males are produced parthenogenetically and diploid females develop from fertilized eggs.

haploid (Gr. *haploos*, single) The reduced, or n, number of chromosomes, typical of gametes, as opposed to the diploid, or 2n, number found in somatic cells. In certain groups, some mature organisms have a haploid number of chromosomes.

Hardy-Weinberg equilibrium Mathematical demonstration that the Mendelian hereditary process does not change the populational frequencies of alleles or genotypes across generations, and that change in allelic or genotypic frequencies requires factors such as natural selection, genetic drift in finite populations, recurring mutation, migration of individuals among populations, and nonrandom mating.

hemal system (hē´məl) (Gr. *haima*, blood) System of small vessels in echinoderms; function unknown.

hemimetabolous (he´mē-mə-ta´bə-ləs) (Gr. *hēmi*, half, + *metabolē*, change) Refers to gradual metamorphosis during development of insects, without a pupal stage.

hemocoel (hē´mə-sēl) (Gr. *haima*, blood, + *koilos*, hollow) Main body cavity of arthropods; may be subdivided into sinuses, through which blood flows.

hemoglobin (Gr. *haima*, blood, + L. *globulus*, globule) Iron-containing respiratory pigment occurring in vertebrate red blood cells and in blood plasma of many invertebrates; a compound of an iron porphyrin heme and a protein globin.

hemolymph (hē´mə-limf) (Gr. *haima*, blood, + L. *lympha*, water) Fluid composed of blood plasma and lymph residing in the coelom or hemocoel of invertebrates having open circulatory systems.

herbivore ([h]erb´ə-vōr´) (L. *herba*, green crop, + *vorare*, to devour) Any organism subsisting on plants. Adj., **herbivorous.**

hermaphrodite (hər-maf´rə-dīt) (Gr. *hermaphroditos*, containing both sexes; from Greek mythology, Hermaphroditos, son of Hermes and Aphrodite) An organism with both male and female functional reproductive organs. **Hermaphroditism** may refer to an aberration in species that normally have separate male and female individuals; **monoecism** implies that this is the normal condition for the species.

heterocercal (het´ər-o-sər´kəl) (Gr. *heteros*, different, + *kerkos*, tail) In some fishes, a tail with the upper lobe larger than the lower, and the end of the vertebral column somewhat upturned in the upper lobe, as in sharks.

heterochrony (het´ə-rō-krōn-ē) (Gr. *heteros*, different, + *chronos*, time) Evolutionary change in the relative time of appearance or rate of development of characteristics from ancestor to descendant.

heterodont (het´ə-rō-dänt) (Gr. *heteros*, different, + *odous*, tooth) Having teeth differentiated into incisors, canines, and molars for different purposes.

heterolobosea (het´ə-rō-lo-bō´sē-ə) (Gr. *heteros*, other, different, + *lobos*, lobe). Protozoan clade in which most members can assume both ameboid and flagellate forms.

heterostracans (Gr. *heteros*, different, + *ostrakon*, shell) Group of extinct fishes with dermal armor and no jaws or paired fins; known from the Ordovician to Devonian periods.

heterotroph (het´ə-rō-trōf) (Gr. *heteros*, different, + *trophos*, feeder) Organism that obtains both organic and inorganic raw materials from the environment in order to live; includes most animals and those plants that do not have photosynthesis.

heterozygous Describes an organism in which homologous chromosomes contain different allelic forms (often dominant and recessive) of a gene; derived from a zygote formed by union of gametes of dissimilar allelic constitution.

hexamerous (hek-sam´ər-əs) (Gr. *hex*, six, + *meros*, part) Six parts; specifically, symmetry based on six or multiples thereof.

hibernation (L. *hibernus*, wintry) Condition, especially of mammals, of passing the winter in a torpid state in which the body temperature drops nearly to freezing and the metabolism drops close to zero.

hierarchical system Scheme that arranges organisms into a series of taxa of increasing inclusiveness, as illustrated by Linnean classification.

histology (hi-stäl´-ə-jē) (Gr. *histos*, web, tissue, + *logos*, discourse) Study of the microscopic anatomy of tissues.

holometabolous (hō´lō-mə-ta´bə-ləs) (Gr. *holo*, complete, + *metabolē*, change) Complete metamorphosis during development.

holophytic nutrition (hō-lō-fit´ik) (Gr. *holo*, whole, + *phyt*, plant) Occurs in green plants and certain protozoa and involves synthesis of carbohydrates from carbon dioxide and water in the presence of light, chlorophyll, and certain enzymes.

holozoic nutrition (hō-lō-zō´ik) (Gr. *holo*, whole, + *zoikos*, of animals) Type of nutrition involving ingestion of liquid or solid organic food particles.

homeobox (hō´mē-ō-box) (Gr. *homolos*, like, resembling, + L. *buxus*, boxtree [used in the sense of enclosed, contained]) A highly conserved 180-base-pair sequence found in homeotic genes, regulatory sequences of protein-coding genes that regulate development.

homeotic genes (hō-mē-ät´ik) (Gr. *homolos*, like, resembling) Genes, identified through mutations, that give developmental identity to specific body segments.

homeothermic (hō´mē-ō-thər´mik) (Gr. *homeo*, alike, + *thermē*, heat) Having a nearly uniform body temperature, regulated independent of the environmental temperature; "warm-blooded."

home range The area over which an animal ranges in its activities. Unlike territories, home ranges are not defended.

hominid (häm´ə-nid) (L. *homo, hominis*, man) A member of the family Hominidae, which includes chimpanzees, gorillas, humans, orangutans, and extinct forms descended from their most recent common ancestor.

homocercal (hō´mə-ser´kəl) (Gr. *homos*, same, common, + *kerkos*, tail) A tail with the upper and lower lobes symmetrical and the vertebral column ending near the middle of the base, as in most teleost fishes.

homodont (hō´mō-dänt) (Gr. *homos*, same, + *odous*, tooth) Having all teeth similar in form.

homology (hō-mäl´ə-jē) (Gr. *homologos*, agreeing) Similarity of parts or organs of different organisms caused by evolutionary derivation from a corresponding part or organ in a remote ancestor, and usually having a similar embry-onic origin. May also refer to a matching pair of chromosomes. Serial homology is the corre-spondence in the same individual of repeated structures having the same origin and develop-ment, such as the appendages of arthropods. Adj., **homologous.**

homonoid (häm´ə-noyd) Relating to the Homi-noidea, a superfamily of primates to which the great apes and humans belong.

homoplasy (hō´mō-plā´sē) Phenotypic similar-ity among characteristics of different species or populations (including molecular, morpho-logical, behavioral, or other features) that does not accurately represent patterns of common evolutionary descent (= nonhomologous similarity); it is produced by evolutionary parallelism, convergence, and/or reversal, and is revealed by incongruence among different characters on a cladogram or phylogenetic tree.

hyaline (hī´ə-lən) (Gr. *hyalos,* glass) Adj., glassy, translucent. Noun, a clear, glassy, structureless material occurring in cartilage, vitreous bodies, mucin, and glycogen, for example.

hydatid cyst (hī-da´təd) (Gr. *hydatis,* watery vesicle) Type of cyst formed by juveniles of certain tapeworms (*Echinococcus*) in their vertebrate hosts.

hydranth (hī´dranth) (Gr. *hydōr,* water, + *anthos,* flower) Nutritive zooid of hydroid colony.

hydrocoel (hī´drə-sēl) (Gr. *hydōr,* water, + *koilos,* hollow) Second or middle coelomic compart-ment in echinoderms; left hydrocoel gives rise to water-vascular system.

hydrocoral (Gr. *hydōr,* water, + *korallion,* coral) Certain members of the cnidarian class Hydro-zoa that secrete calcium carbonate, resembling true corals.

hydrogenosomes (hī-drə-jen´ə-sōmz) Small organelles in certain anaerobic protozoa that produce molecular hydrogen as an end prod-uct of energy metabolism.

hydroid The polyp form of a cnidarian as distin-guished from the medusa form. Any cnidarian of the class Hydrozoa, order Hydroida.

hydrostatic skeleton A mass of fluid or plastic parenchyma enclosed within a muscular wall to provide the support necessary for antago-nistic muscle action; for example, parenchyma in acoelomates and perivisceral fluids in pseudo-coelomates serve as hydrostatic skeletons.

hydrothermal vent A submarine hot spring; sea-water seeping through the sea floor is heated by magma and expelled back into the sea through a hydrothermal vent.

hyperosmotic (Gr. *hyper,* over, + *ōsmos,* impulse). Describes a solution that contains a greater concentration of dissolved particles than another solution to which it is compared; gains water through a selectively permeable membrane from a solution containing fewer particles; contrasts with **hypoosmotic.**

hyperparasitism A parasite itself parasitized by another parasite.

hypodermis (hī´pə-dər´mis) (Gr. *hypo,* under, + L. *dermis,* skin) The cellular layer lying beneath

and secreting the cuticle of annelids, arthro-pods, and certain other invertebrates.

hypoosmotic (Gr. *hypo,* under, + *ōsmos,* impulse). Describes a solution that contains a lesser concentration of dissolved particles than another solution to which it is compared; loses water through a selectively permeable membrane from a solution containing more particles; contrasts with **hyperosmotic.**

hypostome (hī´pə-stōm) (Gr. *hypo,* under, + *stoma,* mouth) Name applied to a structure in various invertebrates (such as mites and ticks), located at the posterior or ventral area of the mouth; elevation supporting the mouth of a hydrozoan.

hypothesis (Gr. *hypothesis,* foundation, supposi-tion) A statement or proposition that can be tested by observation or experiment.

hypothetico-deductive method The central procedure of scientific inquiry in which a pos-tulate is advanced to explain a natural phenomenon and then subjected to observa-tional or experimental testing that potentially could reject the postulate.

I

ichthyosaur (ik´thē-ō-sor) (Gr. *ichthyo,* fish, + *saur,* lizard) Aquatic, Mesozoic reptiles char-acterized by a porpoiselike body, but having a vertical tail and large eyes.

immediate cause See **proximate cause.**

inbreeding The tendency among members of a population to mate preferentially with close relatives.

indeterminate cleavage Type of embryonic development in which the fate of the blastom-eres is not determined very early as to tissues or organs, as occurs, for example, in echino-derms and vertebrates.

indigenous (in-dij´ə-nəs) (L. *indigna,* native) Pertains to organisms that are native to a par-ticular region; not introduced.

induction (L. *inducere, inductum,* to lead) Rea-soning from the particular to the general; deriv-ing a general statement (hypothesis) based on individual observations. In embryology, the alteration of cell fates as the result of interac-tion with neighboring cells.

infraciliature (in´frə-sil´ē-ə-chər) (L. *infra,* below, + *cilia,* eyelashes) The organelles just below the cilia in ciliate protozoa.

inheritance of acquired characteristics The discredited Lamarckian notion that organisms, by striving to meet the demands of their envi-ronments, obtain new adaptations and pass them by heredity to their offspring.

instar (inz´tär) (L., form) Stage in the life of an insect or other arthropod between molts.

integument (in-teg´ū-mənt) (L. *integumentum,* covering) An external covering or enveloping layer.

intermediary meiosis Meiosis that occurs neither during gamete formation nor immedi-ately after zygote formation, resulting in both

haploid and diploid generations, such as in fora-miniferan protozoa.

intermediate host A host in which some devel-opment of a symbiont occurs, but in which maturation and sexual reproduction do not occur (contrasts with **definitive host**).

internal nostrils Palatal structures connecting the nasal cavity and throat in lungfishes and tetrapod vertebrates; used for olfaction and/or breathing when the mouth is closed.

interstitial (in´tər-sti´shəl) (L. *inter,* among, + *sistere,* to stand) Situated in the interstices or spaces between structures such as cells, organs, or grains of sand.

intracellular (in-trə-sel´yə-lər) (L. *intra,* inside, + *cellula,* chamber) Occurring within a body cell or within body cells.

intrinsic growth rate Exponential growth rate of a population; the difference between the density-independent components of the birth and death rates of a natural population with stable age distribution.

intrinsic rate of increase See **intrinsic growth rate.**

introvert (L. *intro,* inward, + *vertere,* to turn) The anterior narrow portion that can be withdrawn (introverted) into the trunk of a sipunculid worm.

iteroparity (i´tər-o-pā´ri-tē´) A life history in which individual organisms of a population normally reproduce more than one time before dying; contrasts with **semelparity.**

J

Jacobson's organ (*Jacobson,* 19th-century Danish surgeon and anatomist) Chemosensory organ in the roof of the mouth of many terres-trial vertebrates; odors are transferred to this organ, also called the vomeronasal organ, by the tongue.

juvenile hormone Hormone produced by the corpora allata of insects; among its effects are maintenance of larval or nymphal characteris-tics during development.

K

keratin (ker´ə-tən) (Gr. *kera,* horn, + *in,* suffix of proteins) A scleroprotein found in epider-mal tissues and modified into hard structures such as horns, hair, and nails.

keystone species Species (typically a predator) whose removal leads to reduced species diver-sity within the community.

kinetoplast (kī-nēt´ə-plast) (Gr. *kinētos,* moving, + *plastos,* molded, formed) Cellular organelle that functions in association with a kinetosome at the base of a flagellum; pre-sumed to be derived from a mitochondrion.

kinetosome (kin-et´ə-sōm) (Gr. *kinētos,* mov-ing, + *sōma,* body) The self-duplicating granule at the base of a flagellum or cilium;

similar to centriole; also called a basal body or blepharoplast.

L

labium (lā´bē-əm) (L., a lip) The lower lip of an insect formed by fusion of the second pair of maxillae.

labrum (lā´brəm) (L., a lip) The upper lip of insects and crustaceans situated above or in front of the mandibles; also refers to the outer lip of a gastropod shell.

labyrinthodont (lab´ə-rin´thə-dänt) (Gr. *labyrinthos*, labyrinth, + *odous, odontos*, tooth) Group of Paleozoic amphibians containing the temnospondyls and the anthracosaurs.

lachrymal glands (lak´rə-məl) (L. *lacrimia*, tear) Structures in terrestrial vertebrates that secrete tears to lubricate the eyes.

lacunar system Netlike set of circulatory canals filled with fluid in an acanthocephalan.

Lamarckism Hypothesis, as expounded by Jean-Baptiste de Lamarck, of evolution by acquisition during an organism's lifetime of characteristics that are transmitted to offspring.

lamella (lə-mel´ə) (L. dim. of *lamina*, plate) One of the two plates forming a gill in a bivalve mollusc. One of the thin layers of bone laid concentrically around an osteon (Haversian canal). Any thin, platelike structure.

larva (lar´və), pl. **larvae** (L., a ghost) An immature stage that is quite different from the adult.

lateral (L. *latus*, the side, flank) Of or pertaining to the side of an animal; a *bilateral* animal has two sides.

lateral-line system Sensory organ that detects water vibrations; consists of neuromast organs in canals and grooves on the head and sides of the body of fishes and some amphibians.

lek (lek) (Sw., play, game) Area where animals assemble for communal courtship display and mating.

lemniscus (lem-nis´kəs) (L., ribbon) One of a pair of internal projections of the epidermis from the neck region of Acanthocephala, which functions in fluid control in the protrusion and invagination of the proboscis.

lepidosaurs (lep´ə-dō-sors) (L. *lepidos*, scale, + *sauros*, lizard) A group of diapsid reptiles that appeared in the Permian period and that includes the modern snakes, lizards, and tuataras.

leptocephalus (lep´tə-sef´ə-ləs), pl. **leptocephali** (Gr. *leptos*, thin, + *kephalē*, head) Transparent, ribbonlike migratory larva of the European or American eel.

limiting resource A particular source of nutrition, energy, or living space whose scarcity is causally associated with a population having fewer individuals than otherwise expected in a particular environment.

lobopodium (lō´b ə-pō´dē-əm) (Gr. *lobos*, lobe, + *pous, podos*, foot) Blunt, lobelike pseudopodium.

lobosea (lə-bō´sē-ə) (Gr. *lobos*, lobe) A protozoan clade comprising amebas with lobopodia.

lophophore (lōf´ə-fōr) (Gr. *lophos*, crest, + *phoros*, bearing) Tentacle-bearing ridge or arm within which is an extension of the coelomic cavity in lophophorate animals (ectoprocts, brachiopods, and phoronids).

lophotrochozoan protostome (lō´fō-trō´kō-zō´ən) (Gr. *lophos*, crest, + *trochos*, wheel, + *zōon*, animal) Any member of a clade within Protostomia whose members generally possess either a trochophore larva or a lophophore; examples are annelids, molluscs, and ectoprocts.

lorica (lor´ə-kə) (L. *lorica*, corselet) A secreted, protective covering, as in phylum Loricifera.

lymph (limf) (L. *lympha*, water) The interstitial (intercellular) fluid in the body; also, the fluid in the lymphatic space.

M

macroevolution (L. *makros*, long, large, + *evolvere*, to unfold) Evolutionary change on a grand scale, encompassing the origin of novel designs, evolutionary trends, adaptive radiation, and mass extinction.

macrogamete (mak´rə-gam´ēt) (Gr. *makros*, long, large, + *gamos*, marriage) The larger of the two gamete types in a heterogametic species, considered the female gamete.

macronucleus (ma´krō-nū´klē-əs) (Gr. *makros*, long, large, + *nucleus*, kernel) The larger of the two kinds of nuclei in ciliate protozoa; controls all cell function except reproduction.

madreporite (ma´drə-pōr´īt) (Fr. *madrépore*, reef-building coral, + *ite*, suffix for some body parts) Sievelike structure that is the intake of the water-vascular system of echinoderms.

malacostracan (mal´ə-käs´trə-kən) (Gr. *malako*, soft, + *ostracon*, shell) Any member of the crustacean subclass Malacostraca, which includes both aquatic and terrestrial forms of crabs, lobsters, shrimps, pillbugs, sand fleas, and others.

malaria (mə-lar´ē-ə) (It. *malaria*, bad air) Disease marked by periodic chills, fever, anemia, and other symptoms; caused by *Plasmodium* spp.

Malpighian tubules (mal-pig´ē-ən) (Marcello Malpighi, Italian anatomist, 1628–94) Blind tubules opening into the hindgut of nearly all insects and some myriapods and arachnids and functioning primarily as excretory organs.

mandible (L. *mandibula*, jaw) One of the lower jaw bones in vertebrates; one of the head appendages in arthropods.

mantle Soft extension of the body wall in certain invertebrates—for example, brachiopods and

molluscs—which usually secretes a shell; thin body wall of tunicates.

manubrium (mə-nü´brē-əm) (L., handle) The portion projecting from the oral side of a jellyfish medusa, bearing the mouth; oral cone; presternum or anterior part of sternum; handlelike part of malleus of ear.

marsupial (mär-sü´pē-əl) (Gr. *marsypion*, little pouch) One of the pouched mammals of the subclass Metatheria.

mass extinction Relatively short interval of geological time in which a large portion (75–95%) of existing species or higher taxa are eliminated nearly simultaneously.

mastax (mas´tax) (Gr., jaws) Pharyngeal mill of rotifers.

matrix (mā´triks) (L. *mater*, mother) The extracellular substance of a tissue, or that part of a tissue into which an organ or process is set.

maxilla (mak-sil´ə) (L. dim. of *mala*, jaw) One of the upper jawbones in vertebrates; one of the head appendages in arthropods.

maxilliped (mak-sil´ə-ped) (L. *maxilla*, jaw, + *pes*, foot) One of the pairs of head appendages located just posterior to the maxilla in crustaceans; a thoracic appendage that has become incorporated into the feeding mouthparts.

medial (mē´dē-əl) Situated, or occurring, in the middle.

medulla (mə-dül´ə) (L., marrow) The inner portion of an organ in contrast to the cortex, or outer portion. Also, hindbrain.

medusa (mə-dü´-sə) (Gr. mythology, female monster with snake-entwined hair) A jellyfish, or the free-swimming stage that reproduces sexually in the life cycle of cnidarians.

Mehlis glands (me´ləs) Glands of uncertain function surrounding the junction of yolk duct, oviduct, and uterus in trematodes and cestodes.

meiosis (mī-ō´səs) (Gr. from *meioun*, to make small) The nuclear changes by means of which the chromosomes are reduced from the diploid to the haploid number; in animals, usually occurs in the last two divisions in the formation of the mature egg or sperm.

melanin (mel´ə-nin) (Gr. *melas*, black) Black or dark-brown pigment found in plant or animal structures.

membranelle Tiny, membrane-like structure; may be formed by fused cilia.

merozoite (me´rə-zō´īt) (Gr. *meros*, part, + *zōon*, animal) A very small trophozoite at the stage just after cytokinesis has been completed in multiple fission of a protozoan.

mesenchyme (me´zn-kīm) (Gr. *mesos*, middle, + *enchyma*, infusion) Embryonic connective tissue; irregular or amebocytic cells often embedded in gelatinous matrix.

mesocoel (mēz´ō-sēl) (Gr. *mesos*, middle, + *koilos*, hollow) Middle body coelomic compartment in some deuterostomes, anterior in lophophorates; corresponds to hydrocoel in echinoderms.

mesoderm (me´zə-dərm) (Gr. *mesos*, middle, + *derma*, skin) The third germ layer, formed in the gastrula between the ectoderm and endoderm; gives rise to connective tissues, muscle, urogenital and vascular systems, and the peritoneum.

mesoglea (mez´ō-glē´ə) (Gr. *mesos*, middle, + *glia*, glue) The layer of jellylike or cement material between the epidermis and gastrodermis in cnidarians and ctenophores.

mesohyl (me´zō-hil) (Gr. *mesos*, middle, + *hyle*, a wood) Gelatinous matrix surrounding sponge cells; also called mesoglea, mesenchyme.

mesonephros (me-zō-nef´rōs) (Gr. *mesos*, middle, + *nephros*, kidney) The middle of three pairs of embryonic renal organs in vertebrates. Functional kidney of embryonic amniotes; its collecting duct is a Wolffian duct. Adj., **mesonephric.**

mesosome (mez´ə-sōm) (Gr. *mesos*, middle, + *sōma*, body) The portion of the body in lophophorates and some deuterostomes that contains the mesocoel.

metacercaria (me´tə-sər-ka´rē-ə) (Gr. *meta*, after, + *kerkos*, tail, + L. *aria*, connected with) Fluke juvenile (cercaria) that has lost its tail and become encysted.

metacoel (met´ə-sēl) (Gr. *meta*, after, + *koilos*, hollow) Posterior coelomic compartment in some deuterostomes and lophophorates; corresponds to somatocoel in echinoderms.

metamere (met´ə-mēr) (Gr. *meta*, after, + *meros*, part) A repeated body unit along the longitudinal axis of an animal; a somite or segment.

metamerism (mə-ta´-mə-ri´zəm) (Gr. *meta*, between, after, + *meros*, part) Being composed of serially repeated parts (metameres); serial segmentation.

metamorphosis (Gr. *meta*, after, + *morphē*, form, + *osis*, state of) Sharp change in form during postembryonic development— for example, tadpole to frog, or larval insect to adult.

metanephridium (me´tə-nə-fri´di-əm) (Gr. *meta*, after, + *nephros*, kidney) Type of tubular nephridium with the inner open end draining the coelom and the outer open end discharging to the exterior.

metapopulation dynamics The structure of a large population that comprises numerous semi-autonomous subpopulations, termed demes, with some limited movement of individuals among demes. Demes of a metapopulation are often geographically distinct.

metasome (met´ə-sōm) (Gr. *meta*, after, behind, + *sōma*, body) The portion of the body in lophophorates and some deuterostomes that contains the metacoel.

metazoa (met-ə-zō´ə) (Gr. *meta*, after, + *zōon*, animal) Multicellular animals.

microevolution (mī´krō-ev-ə-lü-shən) (L. *mikros*, small, + *evolvere*, to unfold) A change in the gene pool of a population across generations.

microfilariae (mīk´rə-fil-ar´ē-ē) (Gr. *mikros*, small, + L. *filum*, a thread) Born alive, partially developed juvenile filarial worms (phylum Nematoda).

microgamete (mīk´rə-ga´-mēt) (Gr. *mikros*, small, + *gamos*, marriage) The smaller of the two gamete types in a heterogametic species, considered the male gamete.

micron (µ) (mī´-krän) (Gr. neuter of *mikros*, small) One-thousandth of a millimeter; about 1/25,000 of an inch. Now largely replaced by micrometer (µ).

microneme (mī´krə-nēm) (Gr. *mikros*, small, + *nēma*, thread) One type of structure forming the apical complex in phylum Apicomplexa; slender and elongate, leading to the anterior; thought to function in host-cell penetration.

micronucleus Small nucleus found in ciliated protozoa; controls the reproductive functions of these organisms.

microsporidian (mī´krō-spo-rid´ē-ən) (Gr. *micros*, small, + *spora*, seed, + *idion*, dim. suffix) Any member of a protozoan clade comprising intracellular parasites with a distinctive spore morphology.

microthrix See **microvillus.**

microtubule (Gr. *mikros*, small, + L. *tubule*, pipe) Long, tubular cytoskeletal element with an outside diameter of 20 to 27 nm. Microtubules influence cell shape and play important roles during cell division.

microvillus (Gr. *mikros*, small, + L. *villus*, shaggy hair) Narrow, cylindrical cytoplasmic projection from epithelial cells; microvilli form the brush border of several types of epithelial cells. Also, microvilli with unusual structure cover the surface of cestode tegument (also called **microthrix** [pl. **microtriches**]).

mictic (mik´tik) (Gr. *miktos*, mixed or blended) Pertaining to haploid egg of rotifers or the females that lay such eggs.

mimic (mim´ik) (Gr. *mimicus*, imitator) Species whose morphological or behavioral characteristics copy those of another species because those characteristics deter shared predators.

miracidium (mīr´ə-sid´ē-əm) (Gr. *meirakidion*, youthful person) Minute, ciliated larval stage in the life of flukes.

mitochondrion (mīt´ō-kän´drē-ən) (Gr. *mitos*, a thread, + *chondrion*, dim. of *chondros*, corn, grain) Cellular organelle in which aerobic metabolism occurs.

mitosis (mī-tō´səs) (Gr. *mitos*, thread, + *osis*, state of) Nuclear division in which chromosomal material is equally divided both qualitatively and quantitatively between the two resulting nuclei; ordinary cell division.

model (mod´l) (Fr. *modèle*, pattern) A species whose morphological or behavioral characteristics are copied by another species because those characteristics deter shared predators.

modular (mäj´ə-lər) Describes the structure of a colony of genetically identical organisms that are physically associated and produced asexually by cloning.

molting Shedding of the outer cuticular layer; see **ecdysis.**

monoecious (mə-nē´shəs) (Gr. *monos*, single, + *oikos*, house) Having both male and female gonads in the same organism; hermaphroditic.

monogamy (mə-näg´ə-mē) (Gr. *monos*, single, + *gamos*, marriage) The condition of having a single mate at any one time. Adj., **monogamous.**

monophyly (män´ō-fi´lē) (Gr. *monos*, single, + *phyle*, tribe) Condition occurring when a taxon or other group of organisms contains the most recent common ancestor of the group and all of its descendants. Adj., **monophyletic.**

monotreme (mä´nō-trēm) (Gr. *monos*, single, + *trēma*, hole) Egg-laying mammal of the order Monotremata.

morphogenesis (mor´fə-je´nə-səs) (Gr. *morphē*, form, + *genesis*, origin) Development of the architectural features of organisms; formation and differentiation of tissues and organs.

morphology (Gr. *morphē*, form, + *logos*, discourse) The science of structure. Includes cytology, the study of cell structure; histology, the study of tissue structure; and anatomy, the study of gross structure.

mosaic development Embryonic development characterized by independent differentiation of each part of the embryo; determinate cleavage.

mucus (mū´kəs) (L. *mucus*, nasal mucus) Viscid, slippery secretion rich in mucins produced by secretory cells such as those in mucous membranes. Adj., **mucous.**

multiple fission Mode of asexual reproduction in some protistans in which the nuclei divide more than once before cytokinesis occurs.

multiplication of species The Darwinian theory that the evolutionary process generates new species through a branching of evolutionary lineages derived from an ancestral species.

mutation (mū-tā´shən) (L. *mutare*, to change) Stable and abrupt change of a gene; the heritable modification of a character.

mutualism (mü´chə-wə-li´zəm) (L. *mutuus*, lent, borrowed, reciprocal) Type of interaction in which two different species derive benefit from their association and in which the association is necessary to both; often symbiotic.

myocyte (mī´ə-sīt) (Gr. *mys*, muscle, + *kytos*, hollow vessel) Contractile cell (pinacocyte) in sponges.

myofibril (Gr. *mys*, muscle, + L. dim. of *fibra*, fiber) Contractile filament within muscle or muscle fiber.

myomere (mī´ə-mēr) (Gr. *mys*, muscle, + *meros*, part) A muscle segment of successive segmental trunk musculature.

myotome (mī´ə-tōm) (Gr. *mys*, muscle, + *tomos*, cutting) A voluntary muscle segment in cephalochordates and vertebrates; that part of a somite destined to form muscles; the muscle group innervated by a single spinal nerve.

N

nacre (nā´kər) (F., mother-of-pearl) Inner most lustrous layer of a mollusc shell, secreted by mantle epithelium. Adj., **nacreous.**

nares (na´rēz), sing. **naris** (L., nostrils) Openings into the nasal cavity, both internally and externally, in the head of a vertebrate.

natural selection The interactions between organismal character variation and the environment that cause differences in rates of survival and reproduction among varying organisms in a population; leads to evolutionary change if variation is heritable.

nauplius (naw´plē-əs) (L., a kind of shellfish) Free-swimming microscopic larval stage of certain crustaceans, with three pairs of appendages (antennules, antennae, and mandibles) and a median eye. Characteristic of ostracods, copepods, barnacles, and some others.

nekton (nek´tən) (Gr. neuter of *nēktos*, swimming) Term for actively swimming organisms, essentially independent of wave and current action; contrasts with **plankton.**

nematocyst (ne-mat´ə-sist) (Gr. *nēma*, thread, + *kystis*, bladder) Stinging organelle of cnidarians.

neo-Darwinism (nē´ō´där´wə-niz´əm) A modified version of Darwin's evolutionary theory that eliminates elements of the Lamarckian inheritance of acquired characteristics and pangenesis that were present in Darwin's formulation; this theory originated with August Weissmann in the late nineteenth century and, after incorporating Mendelian genetic principles, has become the currently favored version of Darwinian evolutionary theory.

neopterygian (nē-äp´tə-rij´ē-ən) (Gr. *neos*, new, + *pteryx*, fin) Any of a large group of bony fishes that includes most modern species.

nephridium (nə-frid´ē-əm) (Gr. *nephridios*, of the kidney) One of the segmentally arranged, paired excretory tubules of many invertebrates, notably the annelids. In a broad sense, any tubule specialized for excretion and/or osmoregulation; with an external opening and with or without an internal opening.

nephron (ne´frän) (Gr. *nephros*, kidney) Functional unit of kidney structure of vertebrates, consisting of Bowman's capsule, an enclosed glomerulus, and the attached uriniferous tubule.

nephrostome (nef´rə-stōm) (Gr. *nephros*, kidney, + *stoma*, mouth) Ciliated, funnel-shaped opening of a nephridium.

nested hierarchy Ordering of species into a series of increasingly more inclusive clades according to the taxonomic distribution of synapomorphies.

net productivity The energy stored by an organism, equal to the energy assimilated (**gross productivity**) minus the energy used for metabolic maintenance (**respiration**).

neural crest Populations of ectodermally derived embryonic cells that differentiate into many skeletal, neural, and sensory structures; unique to vertebrates.

neuroglia (nü-räg´lē-ə) (Gr. *neuron*, nerve, + *glia*, glue) Tissue supporting and filling the spaces between the nerve cells of the central nervous system.

neuromast (Gr. *neuron*, sinew, nerve, + *mastos*, knoll) Cluster of sense cells on or near the surface of a fish or amphibian that is sensitive to vibratory stimuli and water current.

neuron (Gr., nerve) A nerve cell.

neuropodium (nü´rə-pō´dē-əm) (Gr. *neuron*, nerve, + *pous, podos*, foot) Lobe of parapodium nearer the ventral side in polychaete annelids.

neurosecretory cell (nü´rō-sə-krē´tə-rē) Any cell (neuron) of the nervous system that produces a hormone.

niche (nich´) The role of an organism in an ecological community; its unique way of life and its relationship to other biotic and abiotic factors.

niche overlap A comparison of two species that quantifies the proportion of each species' resources also utilized by the other species.

notochord (nō´tə-kord´) (Gr. *nōtos*, back, + *chorda*, cord) Elongated cellular cord, enclosed in a sheath, that forms the primitive axial skeleton of chordate embryos, adult cephalochordates, and jawless vertebrates.

notopodium (nō´tə-pō´dē-əm) (Gr. *nōtos*, back, + *pous, podos*, foot) Lobe of parapodium nearer the dorsal side in polychaete annelids.

nucleolus (nü-klē´ə-ləs) (dim. of L. *nucleus*, kernel) Deeply staining body within the nucleus of a cell and containing RNA; nucleoli are specialized portions of certain chromosomes that carry multiple copies of the information to synthesize ribosomal RNA.

nucleoplasm (nü´klē-ə-pla´zəm) (L. *nucleus*, kernel, + Gr. *plasma*, mold) Protoplasm of nucleus, as distinguished from cytoplasm.

nucleus (nü´klē-əs) (L. *nucleus*, a little nut, the kernel) The organelle in eukaryotes that contains the chromatin and is bounded by a double membrane (nuclear envelope).

nurse cells Single cells or layers of cells surrounding or adjacent to other cells or structures for which the nurse cells provide nutrients or other molecules (for example, for insect oocytes or *Trichinella* spp. juveniles).

nymph (L. *nympha*, nymph, bride) Immature stage (following hatching) of a hemimetabolous insect that lacks a pupal stage.

O

ocellus (ō-sel´əs) (L. dim. of *oculus*, eye) A simple eye or eyespot in many types of invertebrates.

octomerous (ok-tom´ər-əs) (Gr. *oct*, eight, + *meros*, part) Eight parts; specifically, symmetry based on eight.

odontophore (ō-don´tə-for´) (Gr. *odous*, tooth, + *pherein*, to carry) Tooth-bearing organ in molluscs, including the radula, radular sac, muscles, and cartilages.

olfactory epithelium A specialized chemosensory surface tissue inside the nasal cavities of aquatic and terrestrial vertebrates.

omasum (ō-mā´səm) (L., paunch) The third compartment of the stomach of a ruminant mammal.

ommatidium (ä´mə-tid´ē-əm) (Gr. *omma*, eye, + *idium*, small) One of the optical units of the compound eye of arthropods.

omnivore (äm´nə-vōr) (L. *omnis*, all, + *vorare*, to devour) Animal whose diet includes a variety of animal and plant material.

oncosphere (än´kō-sfiər) (Gr. *onkinos*, a hook, + *sphaira*, ball) Rounded larva common to all cestodes; bears hooks.

ontogeny (än-tä´jə-nē) (Gr. *ontos*, being, + *geneia*, act of being born, from *genēs*, born) The course of development of an individual from egg to senescence.

oocyst (ō´ə-sist) (Gr. *ōion*, egg, + *kystis*, bladder) Cyst formed around zygote of malarial parasite and related organisms.

oocyte (ō´ə-sīt) (Gr. *ōion*, egg, + *kytos*, hollow) Stage in formation of ovum, just preceding first meiotic division (primary oocyte) or just following first meiotic division (secondary oocyte).

ookinete (ō-ə-kī´nēt) (Gr. *ōion*, egg, + *kinein*, to move) Motile zygote of malarial parasites.

operculum (ō-per´kū-ləm) (L., cover) The gill cover in bony fishes; keratinized plate in some snails.

opisthaptor (ō´pəs-thap´tər) (Gr. *opisthen*, behind, + *haptein*, to fasten) Posterior attachment organ of a monogenetic trematode.

opisthokont (ō-pis´thō-kont) (G. *opisthen*, behind, + *kontos*, a pole) Any member of the eukaryotic clade comprising fungi, microsporidians, choanoflagellates, and metazoans; if present, flagellated cells possess a single posterior flagellum.

oral disc The end of a cnidarian polyp bearing the mouth.

oral lobe Flaplike extension of the mouth of a scyphozoan medusa that aids in feeding.

organelle (Gr. *organon*, tool, organ, + L. *ella*, dimin. suffix) Specialized part of a cell; literally, a small organ that performs functions analogous to organs of multicellular animals.

organism (or´-gə-niz´-əm) A biological individual composed of one or more cells, tissues, and/or organs whose parts are interdependent in producing a collective physiological system. Organisms of the same species may form **populations.**

osculum (os´kū-ləm) (L. *osculum*, a little mouth) Excurrent opening in a sponge.

osmoregulation Maintenance of proper internal salt and water concentrations in a cell or in the body of a living organism; active regulation of internal osmotic pressure.

osmosis (oz-mō´sis) (Gr. *ōsmos*, act of pushing, impulse) The flow of solvent (usually water) through a semipermeable membrane.

bat/āpe/ärmadillo/herring/fēmale/finch/līce/crocodile/crōw/cóin/duck/ūnicorn/tüna/ə indicates unaccented vowel sound "uh" as in mammal, fishes, cardinal, heron, vulture/stress as in bi-ol´o-gy, bi´o-log´i-cal

osmotroph (oz´mə-trōf) (Gr. *ōsmos*, a thrusting, impulse, + *trophē*, to eat) Heterotrophic organism that absorbs dissolved nutrients.

osphradium (äs-frā´dē-əm) (Gr. *osphradion*, strong smell) Sense organ in aquatic snails and bivalves that tests incoming water.

ossicles (L. *ossiculum*, small bone) Small separate pieces of echinoderm endoskeleton. Also, tiny bones of the middle ear of vertebrates.

osteostracans (os-tēe-os´trə-kəns) (Gr. *osteon*, bone, + *ostrakon*, shell) Group of jawless, extinct fishes with dermal armor and pectoral fins known from the Silurian and Devonian periods.

ostium (L., door) Opening.

ostracoderm (os-trak´ō-derm) (Gr. *ostrakon*, shell, + *derma*, skin) A paraphyletic group of extinct, jawless fishes with dermal armor known from the late Cambrian to Devonian periods.

otolith (ōt´ə-lith´) (Gr. *ous, otos*, ear, + *lithos*, stone) Calcareous concretions in the membranous labyrinth of the inner ear of lower vertebrates or in the auditory organ of certain invertebrates.

outgroup In phylogenetic systematic studies, a species or group of species closely related to but not included within a taxon whose phylogeny is being studied, and used to polarize variation of characters and to root the phylogenetic tree.

outgroup comparison Method for determining the polarity of a character in cladistic analysis of a taxonomic group. Character states found within the group being studied are judged ancestral if they occur also in related taxa outside the study group (= outgroups); character states that occur only within the taxon being studied but not in outgroups are judged to have been derived evolutionarily within the group being studied.

oviger (ō´vi-jər) (L. *ovum*, egg, + *gerere*, to bear) Leg that carries eggs in pycnogonids.

oviparity (ō´və-pa´rət-ē) (L. *ovum*, egg, + *parere*, to bring forth) Reproduction in which eggs are released by the female; development of offspring occurs outside the maternal body. Adj., **oviparous** (ō-vip´ə-rəs).

ovipositor (ō´ve-päz´ət-ər) (L. *ovum*, egg, + *positor*, builder, placer, + *or*, suffix denoting agent or doer) In many female insects, a structure at the posterior end of the abdomen for laying eggs.

ovoviviparity (ō´vo-vī-və-par´ə-tē) (L. *ovum*, egg, + *vivere*, to live, + *parere*, to bring forth) Reproduction in which eggs develop within the maternal body without additional nourishment from the parent and hatch within the parent or immediately after laying. Adj., **ovoviviparous** (ō-vo-vī-vip´ə-rəs).

ovum (L. *ovum*, egg) Mature female germ cell (egg).

P

paedomorphosis (pē-dō-mor´fə-səs) (Gr. *pais*, child, + *morphē*, form) Displacement of ancestral juvenile features to later stages of the ontogeny of descendants.

pangenesis (pan-jen´ə-sis) (Gr. *pan*, all, + *genesis*, descent) Darwin's discredited hypothesis that hereditary factors are produced by individual body parts according to the organism's use of those parts, and collected in the germ cells for transmission to offspring.

papilla (pə-pil´ə), pl. **papillae** (L., nipple) Small, nipplelike projection. A vascular process that nourishes the root of a hair, feather, or developing tooth.

papula (pa´pü-lə), pl. **papulae** (L., pimple) Respiratory processes on skin of sea stars; also, pustules on skin.

parabasal bodies Cellular organelles similar to Golgi bodies, presumed to function as part of the secretory system in endoplasmic reticulum.

parabasalid (pa´rə-bə´sa-lid) (Gr. *para*, beside, + *basis*, body) Any member of the protozoan clade diagnosed by having a flagellum and parabasal bodies.

parabronchi (par-ə-bron´kī) (Gr. *para*, beside, + *bronchos*, windpipe) Fine air-conduction pathways of the bird lung.

paraphyly (par´ə-fi´lē) (Gr. *para*, before, + *phyle*, tribe) The condition that occurs when a taxon or other group of organisms contains the most recent common ancestor of all members of the group but excludes some descendants of that ancestor. Adj., **paraphyletic.**

parapodium (pa´rə-pō´dē-əm) (Gr. *para*, beside, + *pous, podos*, foot) One of the paired lateral processes on each side of most segments in polychaete annelids; variously modified for locomotion, respiration, or feeding.

parasite (par´ə-sīt) Organism that lives physically on or in, and at the expense of, another organism.

parasitism (par´ə-sit´iz-əm) (Gr. *parasitos*, from *para*, beside, + *sitos*, food) The condition of an organism living in or on another organism (host) at whose expense the parasite is maintained; destructive symbiosis.

parasitoid Organism that is a typical parasite early in its development but that finally kills the host during or at the completion of development; refers to many insect parasites of other insects.

parenchyma (pə-ren´kə-mə) (Gr., anything poured in beside) In simpler animals, a spongy mass of vacuolated mesenchyme cells filling spaces between viscera, muscles, or epithelia; in some, the cells are cell bodies of muscle cells. Also, the special-ized tissue of an organ as distinguished from the supporting connective tissue.

parenchymula (pa´rən-kīm´yə-lə) (Gr. *para*, beside, + *enchyma*, infusion) Flagellated, solid-bodied larva of some sponges.

parietal (pä-rī´-ə-təl) (L. *paries*, wall) Something next to, or forming part of, a wall of a structure.

parthenogenesis (pär´thə-nō-gen´ə-sis) (Gr. *parthenos*, virgin, + L. from Gr. *genesis*, origin) Unisexual reproduction involving the production of young by females not fertilized by males; common in rotifers, cladocerans, aphids,

bees, ants, and wasps. A parthenogenetic egg may be diploid or haploid.

pecten (L., comb) Any of several types of comblike structures on various organisms; for example, a pigmented, vascular, and comblike process that projects into the vitreous humor from the retina at a point of entrance of the optic nerve in the eyes of all birds and many reptiles.

pectoral (pek´tə-rəl) (L. *pectoralis*, from *pectus*, the breast) Of or pertaining to the breast or chest, to the pectoral girdle, or to a pair of keratinized shields of the plastron of certain turtles.

pedalium (pə-dal´ē-əm) (Gr. *pedalion*, a prop, rudder) The flattened, bladelike base of a tentacle or group of tentacles in the cnidarian class Cubozoa.

pedal laceration Asexual reproduction in sea anemones; a form of fission.

pedicel (ped´ə-sel) (L. *pediculus*, little foot) A small or short stalk or stem. In insects, the second segment of an antenna or the waist of an ant.

pedicellaria (ped´ə-sə-lar´ē-ə) (L. *pediculus*, little foot, + *aria*, like or connected with) One of many minute, pincerlike organs on the surface of certain echinoderms.

pedipalps (ped´ə-palps´) (L. *pes, pedis*, foot, + *palpus*, stroking, caress) Second pair of appendages of arachnids.

peduncle (pē-dun´kəl) (L. *pedunculus*, dim. of *pes*, foot) A stalk. Also, a band of white matter joining different parts of the brain.

pelage (pel´ij) (Fr., fur) Hairy covering of mammals.

pelagic (pə-laj´ik) (Gr. *pelagos*, the open sea) Pertaining to the open ocean.

pellicle (pel´ə-kəl) (L. *pellicula*, dim. of *pelis*, skin) Thin, translucent, secreted envelope covering many protozoa.

pelycosaur (pel´ə-kō-sor) (Gr. *pelyx*, basin, + *sauros*, lizard) Any of a group of Permian synapsids characterized by homodont dentition and sprawling limbs.

pen A flattened, flexible internal support in a squid; a remnant of the ancestral shell.

pentadactyl (pen-tə-dak´təl) (Gr. *pente*, five, + *daktylos*, finger) Having five digits, or five fingerlike parts, to the hand or foot.

perennibranchiate (pə-rən´ə-brank´ē-ət) (L. *perennis*, throughout the year, + Gr. *branchia*, gills) Having permanent gills, relating especially to certain paedomorphic salamanders.

periostracum (pe-rē-äs´trə-kəm) (Gr. *peri*, around, + *ostrakon*, shell) Outer keratinized layer of a mollusc shell.

peripheral (pə-ri´fər-əl) (Gr. *peripherein*, to move around) Structure or location distant from center, near outer boundaries.

periproct (per´ə-präkt) (Gr. *peri*, around, + *prōktos*, anus) Region of aboral plates around the anus of echinoids.

perisarc (per´ə-särk) (Gr. *peri*, around, + *sarx*, flesh) Sheath covering the stalk and branches of a hydroid.

perissodactyl (pə-ris´ə-dak´təl) (Gr. *perissos*, odd, + *daktylos*, finger, toe) Pertaining to an order of ungulate mammals with an odd number of digits.

peristomium (per´ ə-stō´mē-əm) (Gr.*peri*, around, + *stoma*, mouth) One of two parts forming the annelid head; it bears the mouth.

peritoneum (per´ ə-tə-nē´ əm) (Gr.*peritonaios*, stretched around) The membrane that lines the coelom and covers the coelomic viscera.

Permian extinction A **mass extinction** that occurred 245 million years ago in which 96% of existing species became extinct, marking the end of the Paleozoic era.

perpetual change The most basic theory of evolution, stating that the living world is neither constant nor cycling, but is always undergoing irreversible modification through time.

phagocyte (fag´ ə-sīt) (Gr.*phagein*, to eat, + *kytos*, hollow vessel) Any cell that engulfs and devours microorganisms or other particles.

phagocytosis (fag´ ə-sī-tō´səs) (Gr.*phagein*, to eat, + *kytos*, hollow vessel) The engulfment of a particle by a phagocyte or a protozoan.

phagosome (fa´gə-sōm) (Gr.*phagein*, to eat, + *sōma*, body) Membrane-bound vessel in cytoplasm containing food material engulfed by phagocytosis.

phagotroph (fag´ ə-trōf) (Gr.*phagein*, to eat, + *trophē*, food) Heterotrophic organism that ingests solid particles for food.

pharynx (far´inks), pl. **pharynges** (Gr.*pharynx*, gullet) The part of the digestive tract between the mouth cavity and the esophagus that, in vertebrates, is common to both the digestive and the respiratory tracts. In cephalochordates, the gill slits open from it.

phenetic taxonomy (fə-ne´tik) (Gr.*phaneros*, visible, evident) Uses overall similarity to classify organisms into taxa; contrasts with classification based explicitly on reconstruction of phylogeny.

phenotype (fē´ nə-tīp) (Gr.*phainein*, to show) The visible or expressed characteristics of an organism; controlled by the genotype, but not all genes in the genotype are expressed.

pheromone (fer´ ə-mōn) (Gr.*pherein*, to carry, + *hormōn*, exciting, stirring up) Chemical substance released by one organism that influences the behavior or physiological processes of another organism.

photoautotroph (fō-tō-aw´ tō-trōf) (Gr.*phōtos*, light, + *autos*, self, + *trophos*, feeder) Organism requiring light as a source of energy for making organic nutrients from inorganic raw materials.

photosynthesis (fō-tō-sin´thə-sis) (Gr.*phōs*, light, + *synthesis*, action or putting together) The synthesis of carbohydrates from carbon dioxide and water in chlorophyll-containing cells exposed to light.

phototaxis (fō-tō-tak´sis) (Gr.*phōtos*, light, + *taxis*, arranging, order) A taxis in which light is the orienting stimulus. Involuntary tendency for an organism to turn toward (positive) or away from (negative) light.

phototrophs (fō-tō-trōfs) (Gr.*phōtos*, light, + *trophē*, nourishment) Organisms capable of using CO_2 in the presence of light as a source of metabolic energy.

phyletic gradualism A model of evolution in which morphological evolutionary change is continuous and incremental and occurs mainly within unbranched species or lineages over long periods of geological time; contrasts with **punctuated equilibrium.**

phylogenetic species concept An irreducible (basal) cluster of organisms, diagnosably distinct from other such clusters, and within which there is a parental pattern of ancestry and descent.

phylogenetic systematics See **cladistics.**

phylogenetic tree A diagram whose branches represent evolutionary lineages; depicts the common descent of species or higher taxa.

phylogeny (fī´läj´ ə-nē) (Gr.*phylon*, tribe, race, + *geneia*, origin) The origin and diversification of any taxon, or the evolutionary history of its origin and diversification, usually presented as a dendrogram.

phylum (fī´ləm), pl. **phyla** (N.L. from Gr. *phylon*, race, tribe) A chief taxonomic category, between kingdom and class, into which are grouped organisms of common descent that share a fundamental pattern of organization.

physiology (L.*physiologia*, natural science) Branch of biology covering the organic processes and phenomena of an organism or any of its parts or a particular body process.

phytoflagellates (fī-tə-fla´jə-lāts) Members of the former class Phytomastigophorea, plantlike flagellates.

phytophagous (fī-täf´ ə-gəs) (Gr.*phyton*, plant, + *phagein*, to eat). Feeding on plants.

pinacocyte (pin´a-kō-sīt´) (Gr.*pinax*, tablet, + *kytos*, hollow vessel) Flattened cells comprising dermal epithelium in sponges.

pinna (pin´ ə) (L., feather, sharp point) The external ear. Also, a feather, wing, fin, or similar part.

pinocytosis (pin´o-sī-tō´sis, pīn´o-sī-tō´sis) (Gr. *pinein*, to drink, + *kytos*, hollow vessel, + *osis*, condition) Acquisition of fluid by a cell; cell drinking.

placenta (plə-sen´tə) (L., flat cake) The vascular structure, both embryonic and maternal, through which the embryo and fetus are nourished while in the uterus.

placoderms (plak´ə-dərmz) (Gr.*plax*, plate, + *derma*, skin) A group of heavily armored jawed fishes of the Lower Devonian to Lower Carboniferous periods.

placoid scale (pla´kȯid) (Gr.*plax, plakos*, tablet, plate) Type of scale found in cartilaginous fishes, composed of a basal plate of dentine embedded in the skin and a backward-pointing spine tipped with enamel.

plankton (plank´tən) (Gr. neuter of *planktos*, wandering) The passively floating animal and plant life of a body of water; contrasts with **nekton.**

plantigrade (plan´tə-grād´) (L.*planta*, sole, + *gradus*, step, degree) Pertaining to animals that walk on the whole surface of the foot (for example, humans and bears); contrasts with **digitigrade.**

planula (plan´yə-lə) (N.L. dim. from L.*planus*, flat) Free-swimming, ciliated larval type of cnidarians; usually flattened and ovoid, with an outer layer of ectodermal cells and an inner mass of endodermal cells.

planuloid ancestor (plan´yə-lȯid) (L.*planus*, flat, + Gr. *eidos*, form) Hypothetical form representing ancestor of Cnidaria and Platyhelminthes.

plasma membrane (plaz´mə) (Gr.*plasma*, a form, mold) Living, external, limiting, protoplasmic structure that regulates the exchange of nutrients across the cell surface.

plasmid (plaz´məd) (Gr.*plasma*, a form, mold) Small circle of DNA that a bacterium may carry in addition to its genomic DNA.

plastron (plast´trən) (Fr.*plastron*, breast plate) Ventral body shield of turtles; structure in corresponding position in certain arthropods; thin film of gas retained by epicuticle hairs of aquatic insects.

pleura (plü´rə) (Gr., side, rib) The membrane that lines each half of the thorax and covers the lungs.

podium (pō´dē-əm) (Gr.*pous, podos*, foot) A footlike structure—for example, the tube foot of echinoderms.

poikilothermic (pȯi-ki´lə-thər´mik) (Gr.*poikilos*, variable, + thermal) Pertaining to animals whose body temperature is variable and fluctuates with that of the environment; cold-blooded; contrasts with **ectothermic.**

polarity (Gr.*polos*, axis) In systematics, the ordering of alternative states of a taxonomic character from ancestral to successively derived conditions in an evolutionary transformation series. In developmental biology, the tendency for the axis of an ovum to orient corresponding to the axis of the mother. Also, condition of having opposite poles; differential distribution of gradation along an axis.

Polian vesicles (pō´lē-ən) (From G. S. Poli, 1746–1825, Italian naturalist) Vesicles opening into a ring canal in most asteroids and holothuroids.

polyandry (pol´ē-an´drē) (Gr.*polys*, many, + *anēr*, man) Having more than one male mate at one time.

polygamy (pə-lig´ ə-mē) (Gr.*polys*, many, + *gamos*, marriage) Having more than one mate at one time.

polygyny (pə-lij´ ə-nē) (Gr.*polys*, many, + *gynē*, woman) Having more than one female mate at one time.

polymorphism (pä´lē-mor´fi-zəm) (Gr.*polys*, many, + *morphē*, form) The presence in a species of more than one structural type of individual; genetic variation in a population.

polyp (päl´əp) (Fr. *polype*, octopus, from L. *polypus*, many-footed) The sessile stage in the life cycle of cnidarians.

polyphyletic (pä´lē-fi-let´-ik) (Gr. *polys*, many, + *phylon*, tribe) Derived from more than one ancestral source; contrasts with monophyletic and paraphyletic.

polyphyly (pä´lē-fi´lē) (Gr. *polys*, full, + *phylon*, tribe) The condition that a taxon or other group of organisms does not contain the most recent common ancestor of all members of the group, implying that it has multiple evolutionary origins; such groups are not valid as formal taxa and are recognized as such only through error.

polyphyodont (pä-lē-fi´ə-dänt) (Gr. *polyphyes*, manifold, + *odous*, tooth) Having several sets of teeth in succession.

polypide (pä´lē-pīd) (L. *polypus*, polyp) An individual or zooid in a colony, specifically in ectroprocts, that has a lophophore, digestive tract, muscles, and nerve centers.

population (L. *populus*, people) A group of organisms of the same species inhabiting a specific geographical locality.

porocyte (pō´rə-sīt) (Gr. *porus*, passage, pore, + *kytos*, hollow vessel) Type of cell in asconoid sponges through which water enters the spongocoel.

portal system (L. *porta*, gate) System of large veins beginning and ending with a bed of capillaries; for example, the hepatic portal and renal portal systems in vertebrates.

positive assortative mating Tendency of an individual to mate preferentially with others whose phenotypes are similar to its own.

posterior (L., latter) Situated at or toward the rear of the body; in bilateral forms, the end of the main body axis opposite the head.

preadaptation The possession of a trait that coincidentally predisposes an organism for survival in an environment different from those encountered in its evolutionary history.

precocial (prē-kō´shəl) (L. *praecoquere*, to ripen beforehand) Referring (especially) to birds whose young are covered with down and are able to walk when newly hatched.

predaceous, predacious (prē-dā´shəs) (L. *praedator*, a plunderer; *praeda*, prey) Living by killing and consuming other animals; predatory.

predation (prə-dā´shən) Interaction between species in an ecological community in which members of one species (prey) serve as food for another species (**predator**).

predator (pred´ə-tər) (L. *praedator*, a plunderer; *praeda*, prey) Organism that preys on other organisms for its food.

prehensile (prē-hen´səl) (L. *prehendere*, to seize) Adapted for grasping.

primary producer Species whose members begin **productivity** by acquiring energy and matter from **abiotic** sources, as for example when plants synthesize sugars from water and carbon dioxide using solar energy (see **photosynthesis**).

primate (prī´māt) (L. *primus*, first) Any mammal of the order Primates, which includes the

tarsiers, lemurs, marmosets, monkeys, apes, and humans.

primitive (L. *primus*, first) Primordial; ancient; little evolved; characteristics closely approximating those possessed by early ancestral types.

proboscis (prō-bäs´əs) (Gr. *pro*, before, + *boskein*, feed) A snout or trunk. Also, a tubular sucking or feeding organ with the mouth at the end, as in planarians, leeches, and insects. Also, the sensory and defensive organ at the anterior end of certain invertebrates.

producers (L. *producere*, to bring forth) Organisms, such as plants, able to produce their own food from inorganic substances.

production In ecology, the energy accumulated by an organism that becomes incorporated into new biomass.

productivity (prō´duk-tiv´-ət-ē) Property of a biological system measured by the amount of energy and/or materials that it incorporates.

proglottid (prō-glät´əd) (Gr. *proglōttis*, tongue tip, from *pro*, before, + *glōtta*, tongue, + *id*, suffix) Portion of a tapeworm containing a set of reproductive organs; usually corresponds to a segment.

prokaryotic, procaryotic (pro-kar´ē-ät´ik) (Gr. *pro*, before, + *karyon*, kernel, nut) Not having a membrane-bound nucleus or nuclei. Prokaryotic cells characterize bacteria and cyanobacteria.

pronephros (prō-nef´rōs) (Gr. *pro*, before, + *nephros*, kidney) Most anterior of three pairs of embryonic renal organs of vertebrates; functional only in adult hagfishes and larval fishes and amphibians; vestigial in mammalian embryos. Adj., **pronephric.**

prosimian (prō-sim´ē-ən) (Gr. *pro*, before, + L. *simia*, ape) Any member of a group of arboreal primates including lemurs, tarsiers, and lorises but excluding monkeys, apes, and humans.

prosopyle (prōs´-ə-pīl) (Gr. *prosō*, forward, + *pylē*, gate) Connections between the incurrent and radial canals in some sponges.

prostomium (prō-stō´mē-əm) (Gr. *pro*, before, + *stoma*, mouth) In most annelids and some molluscs, that part of the head located in front of the mouth.

protein (prō´tēn, prō´tē-ən) (Gr. *protein*, from *proteios*, primary) A macromolecule consisting of carbon, hydrogen, oxygen, and nitrogen and usually containing sulfur; composed of chains of amino acids joined by peptide bonds; present in all cells.

prothoracic glands Glands in the prothorax of insects that secrete the hormone ecdysone.

prothoracicotropic hormone See **ecdysiotropin.**

protist (prō´-tist) (Gr. *prōtos*, first) A member of the kingdom Protista, generally considered to include the protozoa and eukaryotic algae.

protocoel (prō-tō-sēl) (Gr. *prōtos*, first, + *koilos*, hollow) The anterior coelomic compartment in some deuterostomes; corresponds to the axocoel in echinoderms.

protocooperation Mutually beneficial interaction between organisms in which the interaction is

not physiologically necessary to the survival of either.

protonephridium (prō-tō-nə-frid´ē-əm) (Gr. *prōtos*, first, + *nephros*, kidney) Primitive osmoregulatory or excretory organ consisting of a tubule terminating internally with a flame bulb or solenocyte; the unit of a flame bulb system.

proton pump Active transport of hydrogen ions (protons) across an inner mitochondrial membrane during cellular respiration.

protopod, protopodite (prō´-tō-päd, prō´-tō-pō-dīt) (Gr. *prōtos*, first, + *pous, podos*, foot) Basal portion of crustacean appendage, containing coxa and basis.

protostome (prō´tō-stōm) (Gr. *protos*, first, + *stoma*, mouth) A member of the group Protostomia. Protostome taxa have recently been divided into ecdysozoan protostomes and lophotrochozoan protostomes.

Protostomia (prō-tō-stō´mē-ə) (Gr. *prōtos*, first, + *stoma*, mouth) A clade in which cleavage is determinate, the mouth is derived at or near the blastopore, and a coelom (when present) is formed by proliferation of mesodermal bands that later split (schizocoely). Phyla within the clade are divided between two subgroups: Lophotrochozoa and Ecdysozoa. Lophotrochozoans, exemplified by annelids and molluscs, share spiral cleavage and derive the mesoderm from a particular blastomere (called 4d). Ecdysozoans (arthropods and related taxa) have a unique cleavage pattern and do not form mesoderm from the 4d cell. Contrasts with **Deuterostomia.**

proventriculus (pro´ven-trik´ū-ləs) (L. *pro*, before, + *ventriculum*, ventricle) In birds, the glandular stomach between the crop and gizzard. In insects, a muscular dilation of the foregut armed internally with chitinous teeth.

proximal (L. *proximus*, nearest) Situated toward or near the point of attachment; opposite of distal, distant.

proximate cause (L. *proximus*, nearest, + *causa*) The factors that underlie the functioning of a biological system at a particular place and time, including those responsible for metabolic, physiological, and behavioral functions at the molecular, cellular, organismal, and population levels. Immediate cause.

pseudocoelom (sü´də-sē-lōm) (Gr. *pseudēs*, false, + *koilos*, hollow) Body cavity not lined with peritoneum and not a part of the blood or digestive systems; embryonically derived from the blastocoel.

pseudopodium (sü´də-pō´dē-əm) (Gr. *pseudēs*, false, + *podion*, small foot, + *eidos*, form) A temporary cytoplasmic protrusion extended from a protozoan or ameboid cell and serving for locomotion or for engulfing food.

punctuated equilibrium Model of evolution in which morphological evolutionary change is discontinuous, being associated primarily with discrete, geologically instantaneous events of speciation that lead to phylogenetic branching; morphological evolutionary stasis characterizes species between episodes of speciation; contrasts with **phyletic gradualism.**

5, 17, 18

Music with 2 RH Positions

Assign with pages 68–69.

Some pieces keep the LH position throughout, but change RH positions.

LH & RH in C POSITION

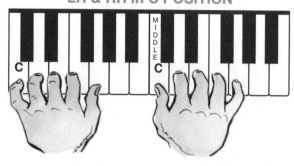

LH in C POSITION   RH in G POSITION

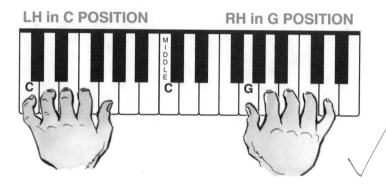

1. Write the name of the key played by each RH finger in C POSITION:

KEY	C	D	E	F	G
RH FINGER	1	2	3	4	5

2. Write the name of the key played by each LH finger in C POSITION:

KEY	C	D	E	F	G
LH FINGER	5	4	3	2	1

3. Write the name of the key played by each RH finger in G POSITION:

KEY	G	A	B	C	D
RH FINGER	1	2	3	4	5

The Fox

4. Look at the music and decide what positions are used for each line. Fill in the boxes.

5. Play.

RH = _____ POSITION

mf
1. Said the fox on a star - ry night,
2. Moon and stars gon-na give me light,
3. Hope I don't get a tum - my ache,
f "Go - in' to the town - O!
Go - in' to the town - O!
Go - in' to the town - O!"

LH = _____ POSITION

Fine

RH = _____ POSITION

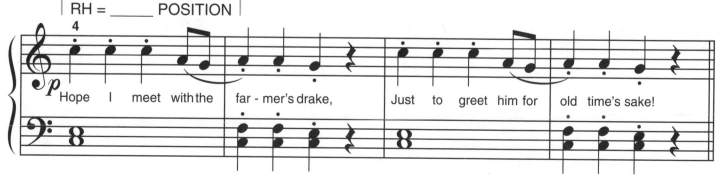

p
Hope I meet with the far - mer's drake, Just to greet him for old time's sake!

*Repeat for 2nd verse, then play to **D.C. al Fine**, ending with 3rd verse at **Fine**.

D.C. al Fine

Music with 2 LH Positions

Some pieces keep the RH position throughout, but change LH positions.

1. Write the name of the key played by
   each LH finger in G POSITION:

5/10/18

LH & RH in G POSITION

KEY	G	A	B	C	D
LH FINGER	5	4	3	2	1

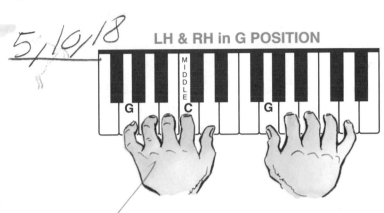

2. Write the name of the key played by
   each RH finger in G POSITION:

KEY	G	A	B	C	D
RH FINGER	1	2	3	4	5

LH in C POSITION   **RH in G POSITION**

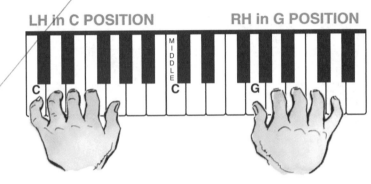

3. Write the name of the key played by
   each LH finger in C POSITION:

KEY	C	D	E	F	G
LH FINGER	5	4	3	2	1

A Merry Song

4. Look at the music and decide what positions
   are used for each line. Fill in the boxes.

5. Play.

KEY OF C MAJOR
Key Signature: no #, no ♭

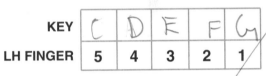

RH = _____ POSITION

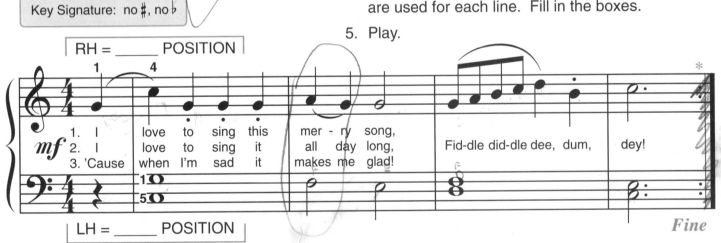

1. I love to sing this mer-ry song,
2. I love to sing it all day long,
3. 'Cause when I'm sad it makes me glad!

Fid-dle did-dle dee, dum, dey!

mf

Fine

LH = _____ POSITION

f I love to sing it when I'm glad; I love to sing it when I'm sad;

LH = _____ POSITION

D.C. al Fine

*Repeat for 2nd verse, then play to **D.C. al Fine**, ending with 3rd verse at **Fine**.

5, 3, 18

Assign with page 66.

The Key of G Major

The **G MAJOR SCALE** has **ONE SHARP, F#**.

A piece based on the G MAJOR SCALE is in the **KEY OF G MAJOR.**

Instead of placing a # before every F in the piece, the # is indicated at the beginning, in the **KEY SIGNATURE.**

Sharps or flats given in the key signature are effective throughout the piece.

1. Draw a circle around the notes that are made # by the key signatures.
2. Play both G major scales.

KEY SIGNATURE:
One sharp (F#)

KEY SIGNATURE:
One sharp (F#)

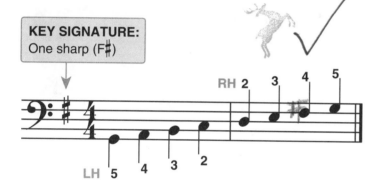

Sea Chanty

1. The key signature applies to all F's, on ANY line or space. Circle the notes affected by the key signature.

2. Play. Use the G TETRACHORD POSITION shown at the top of this page.

IIII IIII

Allegro moderato

mf
1. 'Twas a Fri - day morn when we set
2. When the Cap - tain spied a fair mer -

sail, And we were not far from the land,
maid, With a comb and glass in her hand.

4, 20/18

4, 26/18

Assign with page 65.

The Major Scale

The **MAJOR SCALE** is made of **TWO TETRACHORDS** joined by a whole step.

1. Write the letter names of the notes of the C MAJOR SCALE on the keyboard below.

2. Play the 1st tetrachord with LH 5 4 3 2, and the 2nd tetrachord with RH 2 3 4 5.

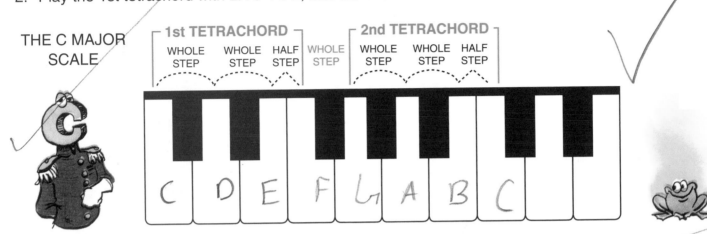

THE C MAJOR SCALE

3. Write the letter names of the notes of the G MAJOR SCALE on the keyboard below.

4. Play the 1st tetrachord with LH 5 4 3 2, and the 2nd tetrachord with RH 2 3 4 5.

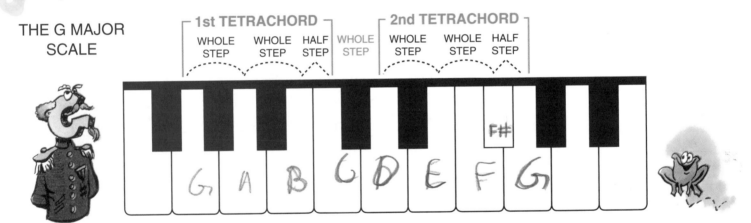

THE G MAJOR SCALE

5. Write tetrachords beginning on each of the following notes.

6. Play as follows: 1st tetrachord with LH 5 4 3 2, 2nd with RH 2 3 4 5.
   2nd tetrachord with LH 5 4 3 2, 3rd with RH 2 3 4 5.
   3rd tetrachord with LH 5 4 3 2, 4th with RH 2 3 4 5.

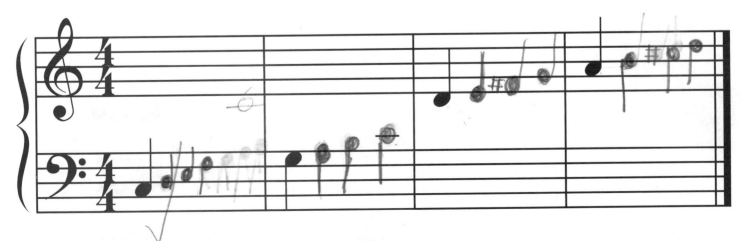

Tetrachords

4/12/18

Assign with page 64.

A **TETRACHORD** is a series of **FOUR NOTES** having a pattern of

WHOLE STEP, WHOLE STEP, HALF STEP.

WHOLE STEP   WHOLE STEP   HALF STEP

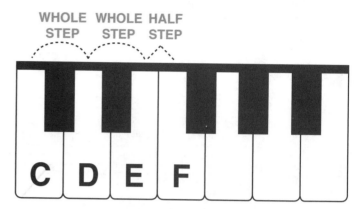

The four notes of a tetrachord must always be **NEIGHBORING LETTERS** of the **MUSICAL ALPHABET.**

1. Study the TETRACHORDS on the keyboards below and answer these questions:

   • Does each consist of WHOLE STEP, WHOLE STEP, HALF STEP?   Answer: __Yes__

   • Are the notes of each tetrachord NEIGHBORING LETTERS of the musical alphabet?
     Answer: __no__

   • Underline the correct spelling of the **D** tetrachord: D E G♭ G   ⟨D E F♯ G⟩

   • Underline the correct spelling of the **A** tetrachord: A B D♭ D   ⟨A B C♯ D⟩

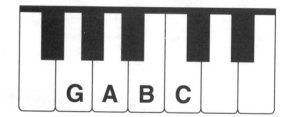

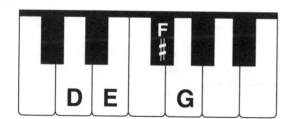

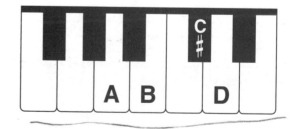

2. Write tetrachords beginning on each of the following notes:

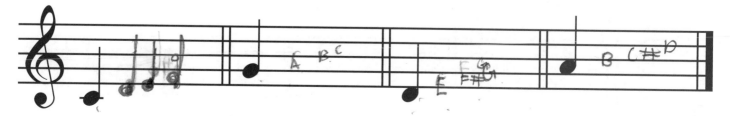

Steps to Progress

Get everything on this page correct and you will never
have trouble with HALF STEPS & WHOLE STEPS!

1. Write ½ for each HALF STEP and 1 for each WHOLE STEP.

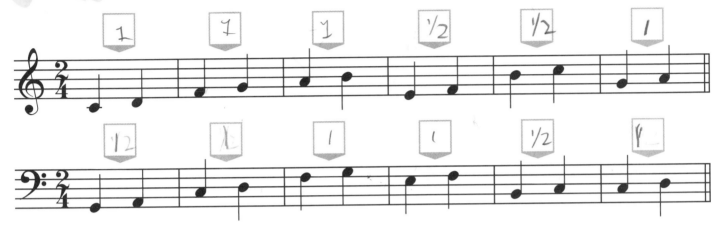

Some tricky ones:

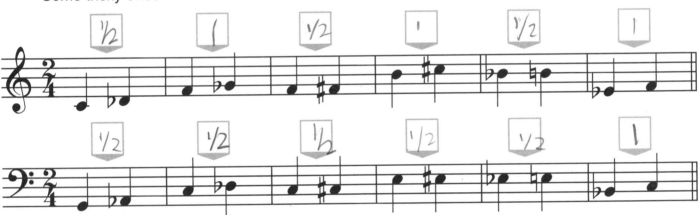

2. Change the following HALF STEPS to WHOLE STEPS by adding
   one accidental (♯, ♭ or ♮) before the second note of each measure.

3. Change the following WHOLE STEPS to HALF STEPS by adding
   one accidental before the second note of each measure.

3/29/18

Assign with page 62.

Whole Steps

A **WHOLE STEP** is equal to 2 half steps.
Skip one key—black or white.

WHOLE STEPS • ONE KEY BETWEEN

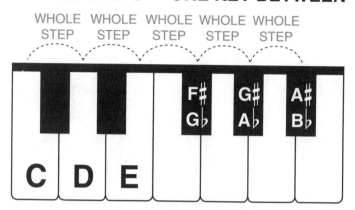

1. Write the names on the keys, continuing up the keyboard in WHOLE STEPS.
   Use SHARPS for the black keys.

2. Write the names on the keys, continuing up the keyboard in WHOLE STEPS.
   Use FLATS for the black keys.

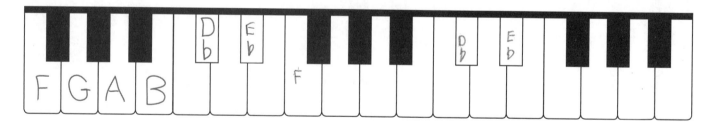

3. In the following squares write ½ for each HALF STEP and 1 for each WHOLE STEP indicated by the arrows.

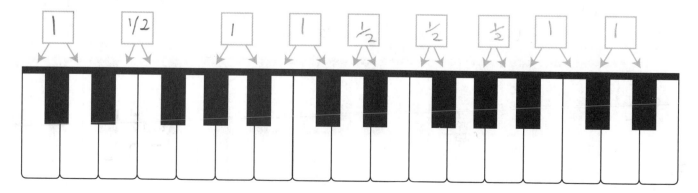

Half Steps

3/29/18

A **HALF STEP** is the distance from any key
to the very next key above or below,
whether black or white.

HALF STEPS • NO KEY BETWEEN

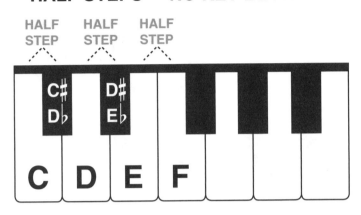

The SHARP SIGN ♯ raises a note a half step (play the next key to the right).

The FLAT sign ♭ lowers a note a half step (play the next key to the left).

The NATURAL sign ♮ cancels a sharp or flat!

1. Make some NATURAL SIGNS. Trace the first sign, then draw 6 more.

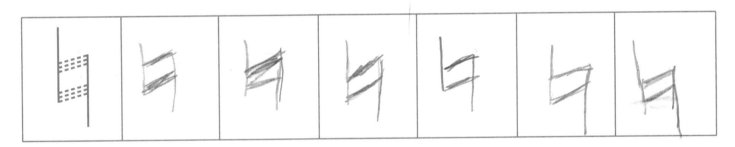

Each black key may be named 2 ways.   EXAMPLE: **C♯ = D♭**

These white keys may also be named 2 ways: **C = B♯   F = E♯   B = C♭   E = F♭**

2. Write 2 different names for each indicated key, as shown in the first 2 examples:

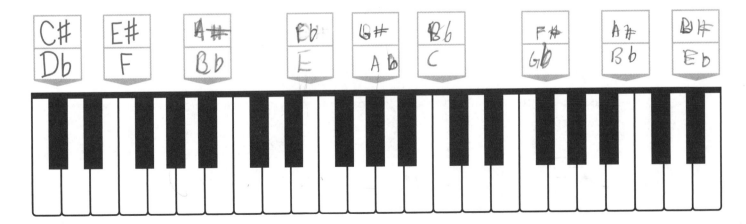

Assign with page 59.

Note Review

Notes on LINES

G B D F A C E G B D F

Notes in SPACES

A C E G B D F A C E

1. Write the names of the notes in the boxes.
2. Play. Use LH 3 for notes below middle C. Use RH 3 for notes on or above middle C.

O Bury Me Not on the Lone Prairie

Middle D Position

1. Write the names of the notes in the boxes.
2. Play.

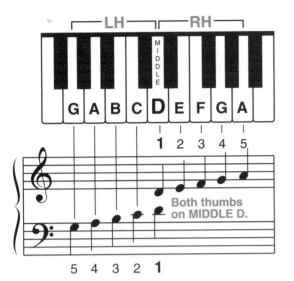

Both thumbs on MIDDLE D.

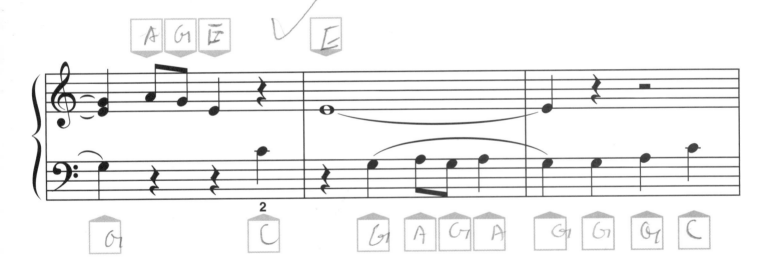

Moderato

mf

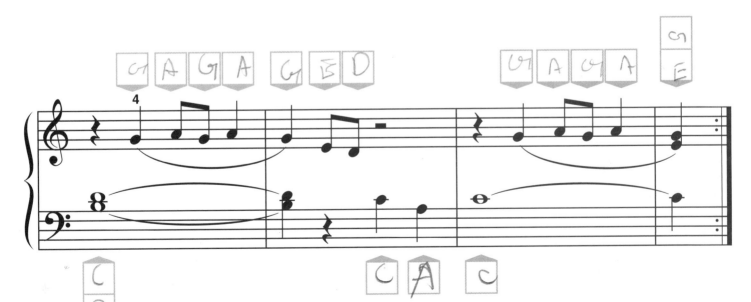

More about Eighths

3,22,18

Assign with pages 56–57.

> ♪ This is an **EIGHTH REST.**
> It means REST for the value of an EIGHTH NOTE.
>
> Pairs of EIGHTH NOTES are joined with a beam:
>
> Single EIGHTH NOTES have a FLAG instead of a beam:

1. Make these quarter notes into SINGLE EIGHTH NOTES. Trace the first flag, then add flags to the other notes.

2. Trace the first EIGHTH REST, then draw eighth rests between the other notes.

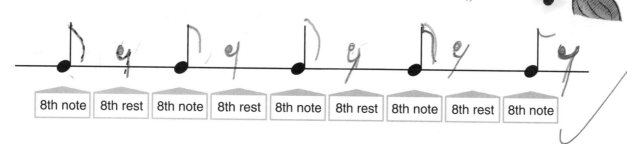

| 8th note | 8th rest | 8th note | 8th rest | 8th note | 8th rest | 8th note | 8th rest | 8th note |

Reviewing Note & Rest Values

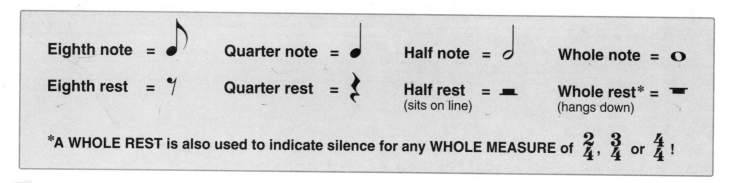

| Eighth note = ♪ | Quarter note = ♩ | Half note = 𝅗𝅥 | Whole note = 𝅝 |
| Eighth rest = ♪ | Quarter rest = 𝄽 | Half rest = ▬ (sits on line) | Whole rest* = ▬ (hangs down) |

*A WHOLE REST is also used to indicate silence for any WHOLE MEASURE of $\frac{2}{4}$, $\frac{3}{4}$ or $\frac{4}{4}$!

3. Complete these measures by adding only ONE REST to each measure:

The Damper Pedal

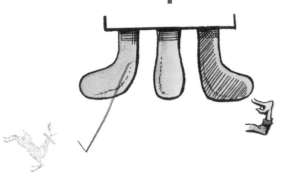

Use the RIGHT FOOT on the RIGHT PEDAL, called the **DAMPER PEDAL.**

This sign shows when the damper pedal is to be used:

Pedal down   **hold pedal**   **Pedal up**

The music on this page helps you to develop freedom of movement at the keyboard. The hands play in a new position in each measure. LH & RH play in either clef.

You will learn how the pedal connects the notes together, LEGATO, even while the hands are changing positions.

G-B-D-F'S

The first note of each measure is G. The notes in each measure are a 3rd apart.

1. Write the names of the notes in the boxes.
2. Play. (Stems down = LH. Stems up = RH.) Hold the pedal down through the entire line.

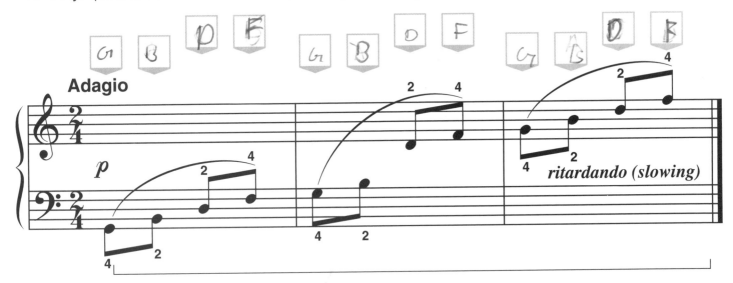

A-C-E-G'S

The first note of each measure is A. The notes in each measure are a 3rd apart.

3. Write the names of the notes in the boxes.
4. Play. (Stems down = LH. Stems up = RH.) Hold the pedal, as indicated.

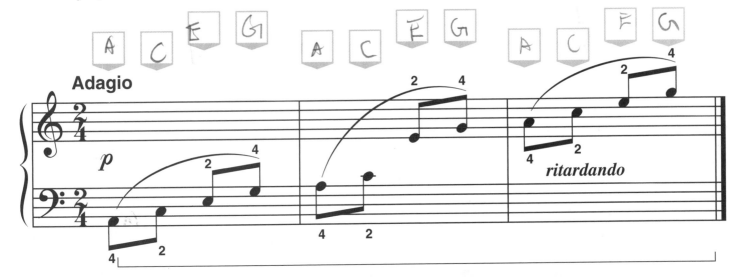

3/20/18

Assign with page 51.

G Positions for LH

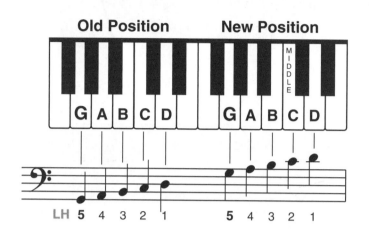

Old Position **New Position**

G A B C D   G A B C D

LH 5 4 3 2 1   5 4 3 2 1

The Big Rock Candy Mountain

1. Write the note names in the boxes ABOVE the notes.
   This will help you learn the NEW G POSITION.

2. Write the note names in the boxes BELOW the notes.
   This reviews the old G POSITION.

3. Play & count.

4. Play and say or sing the words.

Allegro

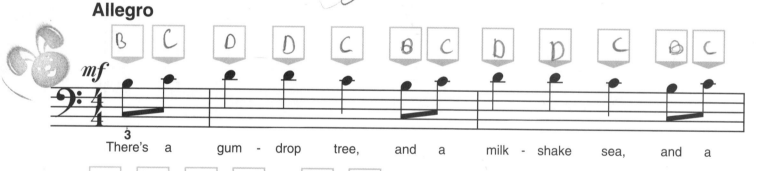

B C D D C B C D D C B C

mf

There's a gum - drop tree, and a milk - shake sea, and a

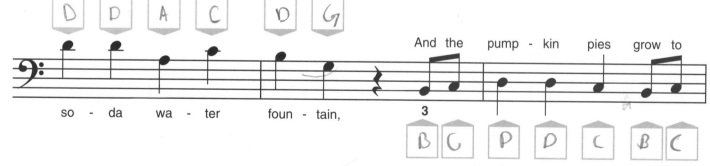

D D A C D G

so - da wa - ter foun - tain,

And the pump - kin pies grow to

B G D D C B C

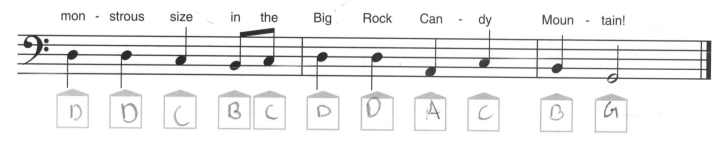

mon - strous size in the Big Rock Can - dy Moun - tain!

D D C B C D D A C B G

How's Your Italian?

Many Italian terms are used in music in almost every country in the world.
You have learned a lot of them already. Let's see how much Italian you now know.

Draw lines connecting the dots on the matching boxes.

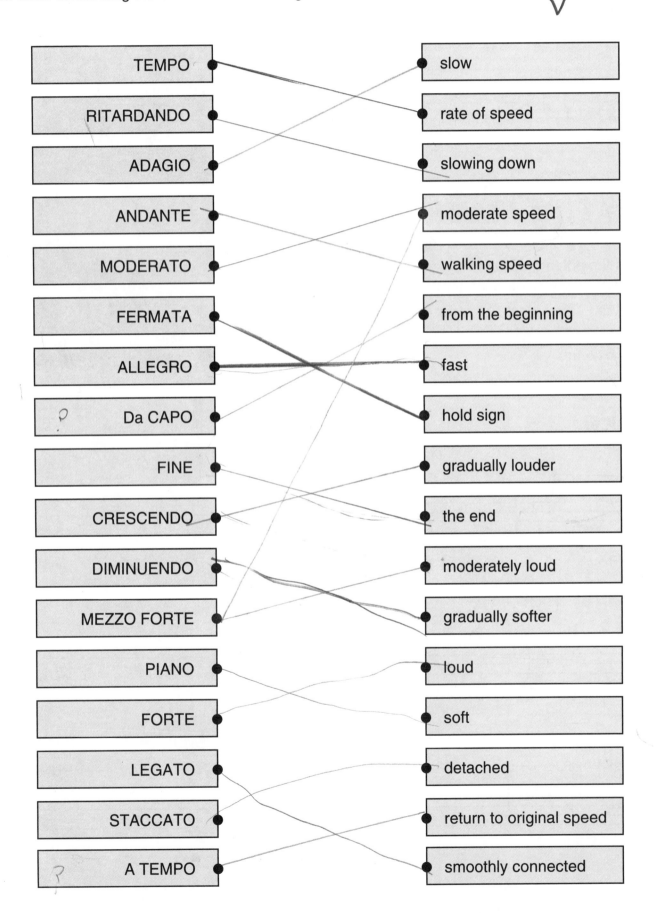

TEMPO	slow
RITARDANDO	rate of speed
ADAGIO	slowing down
ANDANTE	moderate speed
MODERATO	walking speed
FERMATA	from the beginning
ALLEGRO	fast
Da CAPO	hold sign
FINE	gradually louder
CRESCENDO	the end
DIMINUENDO	moderately loud
MEZZO FORTE	gradually softer
PIANO	loud
FORTE	soft
LEGATO	detached
STACCATO	return to original speed
A TEMPO	smoothly connected

$\frac{2}{4}$ means **2** beats to each measure.
a **QUARTER NOTE** gets ONE beat.

Assign with page 48.

Kookaburra

1. Add bar lines.
2. Play. Observe the accent sign >, which means play that one note or chord LOUDER.

Allegro moderato

mf Koo - ka - bur - ra sits on an old gum tree, Mer - ry, mer - ry

A whole rest is used to indicate a whole measure of silence in $\frac{2}{4}$ time.

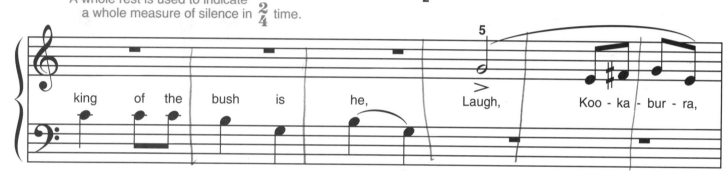

king of the bush is he, Laugh, Koo - ka - bur - ra,

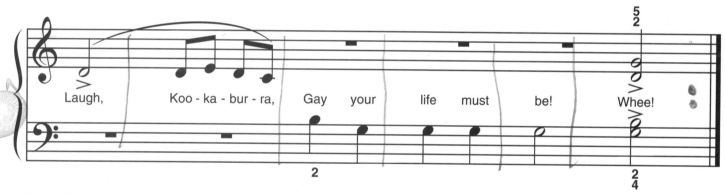

Laugh, Koo - ka - bur - ra, Gay your life must be! Whee!

3. In the three lines below, add time signatures at the beginning of each line.
4. Clap (or tap) the rhythm of each line, counting aloud.
5. Say the words of each line in rhythm.

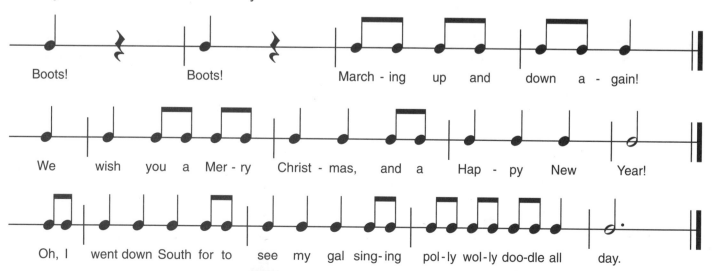

Boots! Boots! March - ing up and down a - gain!

We wish you a Mer - ry Christ - mas, and a Hap - py New Year!

Oh, I went down South for to see my gal sing - ing pol - ly wol - ly doo - dle all day.

Eighth Notes

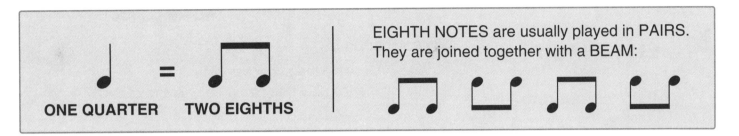

ONE QUARTER　**TWO EIGHTHS**

EIGHTH NOTES are usually played in PAIRS.
They are joined together with a BEAM:

1. Change these quarter notes to EIGHTH NOTES
   by adding a BEAM to each pair:

To count music containing eighth notes, divide each beat into 2 parts:

count: "one-and" or "quar-ter" for each quarter note;
count: "one-and" or "two-8ths" for each pair of eighth notes.

2. Play the following while you count aloud: "One-and, one-and," etc.
   Play again, counting "Quar-ter, quar-ter," etc.

MIDDLE C POSITION

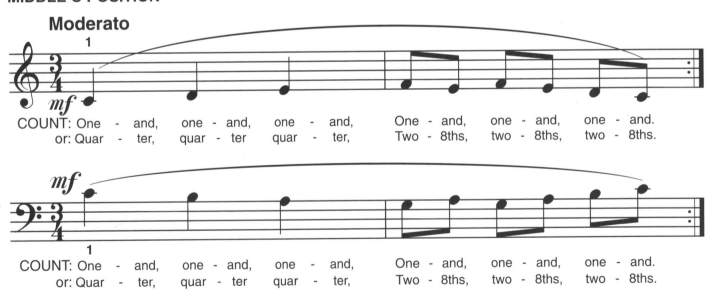

COUNT: One - and,　one - and,　one - and,　One - and,　one - and,　one - and.
or: Quar - ter,　quar - ter　quar - ter,　Two - 8ths,　two - 8ths,　two - 8ths.

COUNT: One - and,　one - and,　one - and,　One - and,　one - and,　one - and.
or: Quar - ter,　quar - ter　quar - ter,　Two - 8ths,　two - 8ths,　two - 8ths.

3. Write one note equal to the sum of each pair of tied notes:

Tempo Marks

31/18

Assign with pages 43–44.

The following Italian words are TEMPO MARKS. They tell how fast or slow to play.

ALLEGRO = Quickly, happily.   **ANDANTE** = Moving along ("walking").   **ADAGIO** = Slowly.

MODERATO = Moderately. The word *moderato* is sometimes used with one of the other words.
Example: **Allegro moderato** = moderately fast.

Three Short Pieces in MIDDLE C POSITION

1. Read the words to each of these 3 short pieces, then decide on the best TEMPO marks and DYNAMIC signs and add them.
2. Add bar lines.
3. At the end of each piece, add a sign that means REPEAT.
4. Play the pieces.

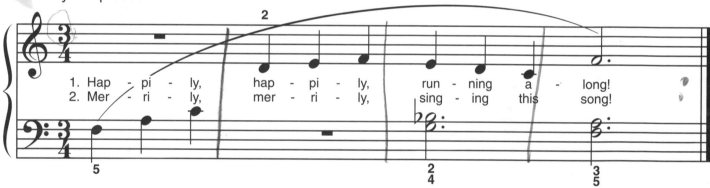

1. Hap - pi - ly, hap - pi - ly, run - ning a - long!
2. Mer - ri - ly, mer - ri - ly, sing - ing this song!

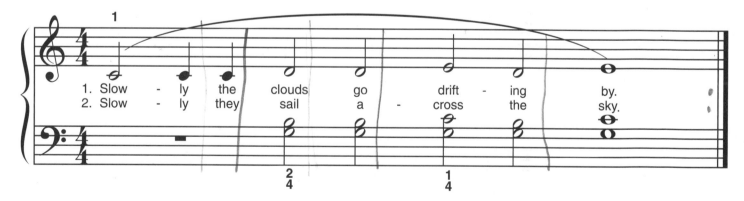

1. Slow - ly the clouds go drift - ing by.
2. Slow - ly they sail a - cross the sky.

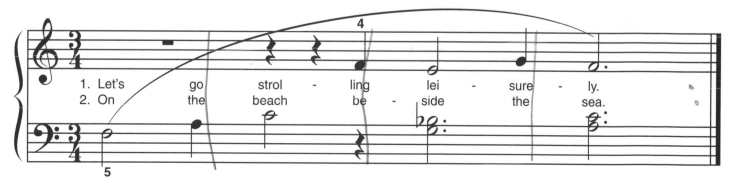

1. Let's go strol - ling lei - sure - ly.
2. On the beach be - side the sea.

Reviewing Middle C Position

Prelude on Middle C

This is an attractive recital piece!
1. Write the note names in the boxes.
2. Play.

Moderately fast

Assign with page 40.

Staccato Is the Opposite of Legato!

STACCATO notes are SEPARATED or DETACHED.

STACCATO is indicated by a **DOT** over or under a note:

LEGATO notes are SMOOTHLY CONNECTED.

LEGATO is indicated by a **SLUR** over or under a group of notes:

1. Write **S** under each staccato note below.

2. Write **L** under each legato note below.

1. First you hop, hop, then go smooth-ly up and down a - gain.
2. Hop, hop, hop, hop, then play as le - ga - to as you can.

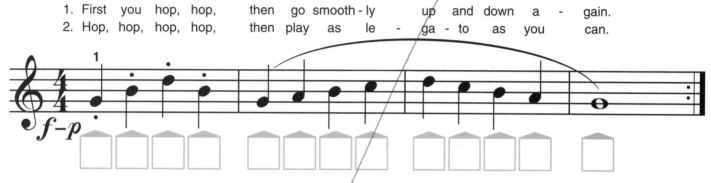

3. Play the above. Carefully observe the staccato and legato signs.

Sometimes LEGATO notes are connected smoothly to a STACCATO note. In such a case only the LAST note is played staccato, while the rest are played legato:

L L L S L L L S L S L S L S S S

Indian Voices

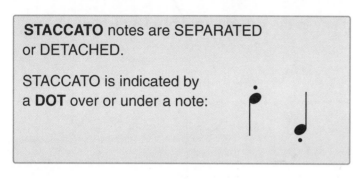

4. Write **L** under each legato note.

5. Write **S** under each staccato note.

1. In - dian voi - ces, Hear them ring - ing! Hi - yah, yah, yah! Hi - yah, yah, yah!
2. In - dians danc - ing, In - dians sing - ing! Hi - yah, yah, yah! Hi - yah, yah, yah!

3. Play the above. Observe everything.

Flats

The **FLAT SIGN** ♭ before a note means play the next key to the left, whether black or white.

1. Make some FLAT SIGNS.

    First, draw one vertical line.   Then add the heavier curved line.

    Draw 4 flat signs here.

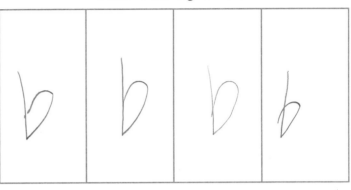

2. Write the names of the ♭ keys in the boxes:

B♭   E♭   A♭   D♭   G♭

3. Change each of these notes into a flat note. Play each with RH 3 or LH 3.

    Be sure to CENTER the flat sign on the line or space of the note to be flatted: Place the flat BEFORE the note:

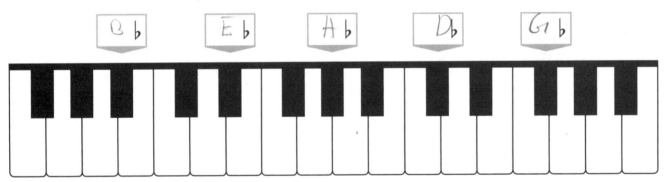

4. Can you read this motto?   ALWAYS  AND YOU'LL NEVER 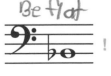 !

Sharps

Assign with page 36.

The **SHARP SIGN** ♯ before a note means play the next key to the right, whether black or white.

1. Make some SHARP SIGNS:

First, draw the two vertical lines.

Then add the heavy slanting lines.

Draw 4 sharp signs here.

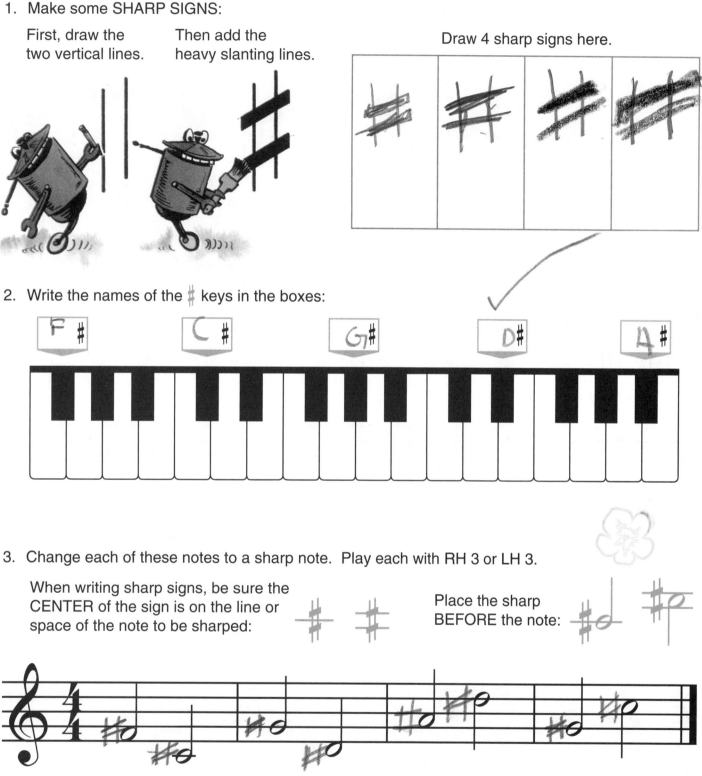

2. Write the names of the ♯ keys in the boxes:

F♯   C♯   G♯   D♯   A♯

3. Change each of these notes to a sharp note. Play each with RH 3 or LH 3.

When writing sharp signs, be sure the CENTER of the sign is on the line or space of the note to be sharped:

Place the sharp BEFORE the note:

Reviewing Rests

**RESTS
are
signs of
SILENCE!**

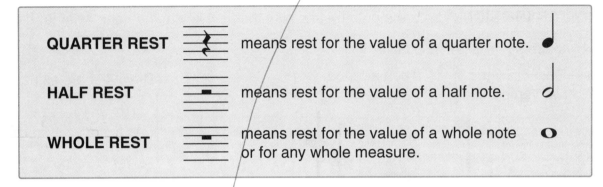

QUARTER REST	𝄽	means rest for the value of a quarter note.	♩
HALF REST	▬	means rest for the value of a half note.	♩
WHOLE REST	▬	means rest for the value of a whole note or for any whole measure.	𝅝

Look! No Hands!

This piece should be very easy to play. Could YOU play it without a mistake?
Be careful! There is already a MISTAKE IN EVERY MEASURE!

1. CORRECT EACH MISTAKE by writing exactly ONE REST in each incomplete measure.

Very softly

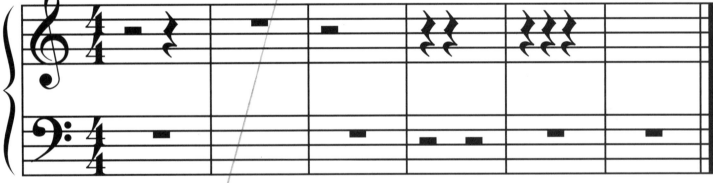

2. Name these rests. Use Q for QUARTER, H for HALF, and W for WHOLE.

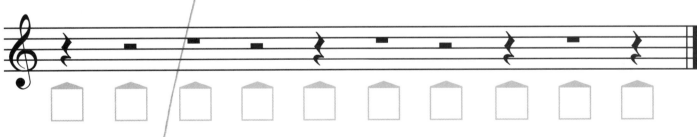

3. In the square below each rest, write the number of counts it receives in 𝄴 time.

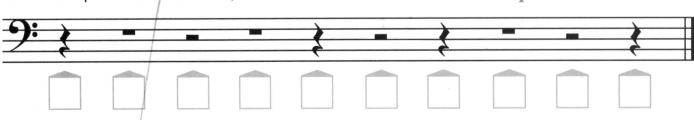

2/13/18

Incomplete Measure

Assign with page 34.

When a piece begins with an INCOMPLETE MEASURE, the missing counts are found in the LAST MEASURE.

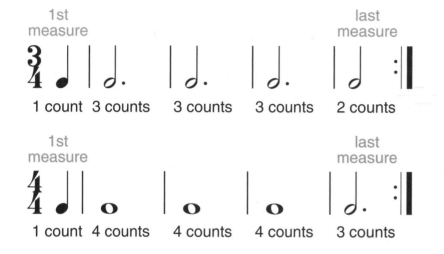

1st measure   last measure

3/4   1 count   3 counts   3 counts   3 counts   2 counts

When you repeat the piece, you will have exactly one COMPLETE measure when you go from the LAST measure to the FIRST measure!

1st measure   last measure

4/4   1 count   4 counts   4 counts   4 counts   3 counts

---

1. In each of these *PONY SONGS* the last note is missing. The name of the missing note is in the box above the measure. Add the note, giving it its proper value.

2. Write the note names in the empty boxes, then play both songs, counting aloud.

Pony Song No. 1

Moderately fast

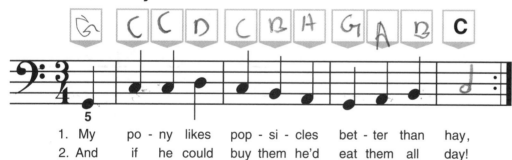

G C C D C B A G A D **C**

1. My   po - ny   likes   pop - si - cles   bet - ter   than   hay,
2. And   if   he   could   buy them he'd   eat them all   day!

Pony Song No. 2

Moderately fast

D B G A C B G   D B G A B **G**

1. My pop gave me some mon - ey   To   buy   my   po - ny   hay.
2. My po - ny looked so   fun - ny,   As   loud - ly   he   said, "Neigh!"

Melodic Intervals in G Position

1. Write the names of the notes in the squares above the staffs.
2. Write the names of the intervals in the boxes below the staffs.

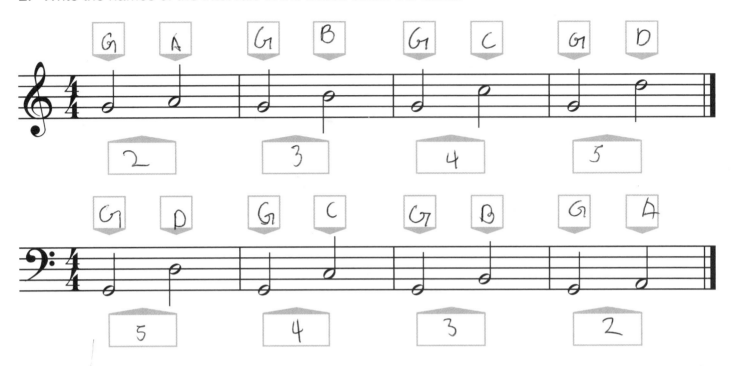

Harmonic Intervals in G Position

3. Write the names of the notes in the squares above the staffs. Write the name of the lower note in the lower square, and the name of the higher note in the higher square.

4. Write the names of the intervals in the boxes below the staffs.

G Position

Assign with page 32.

2, 8, 18   2/1/18

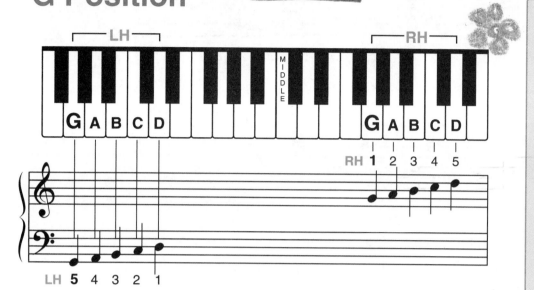

1. Write the LH notes in the BASS staff, under the squares. Use QUARTER NOTES. Turn the stems of G A B & C **UP**. Turn the stem of D **DOWN.**

2. Write the RH notes in the TREBLE staff, over the squares. Use QUARTER NOTES. Turn the stems of G & A **UP**. Turn the stems of B C & D **DOWN.**

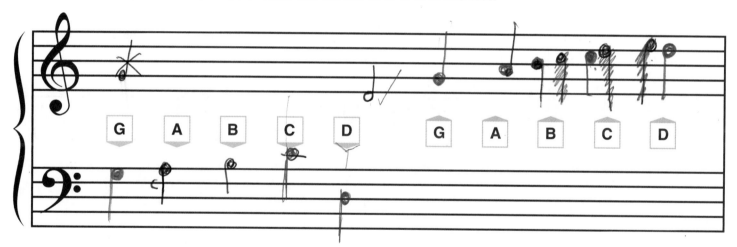

G A B C D G A B C D

Spelling Game

3. Write the name of each note in the square below it to spell familiar words.

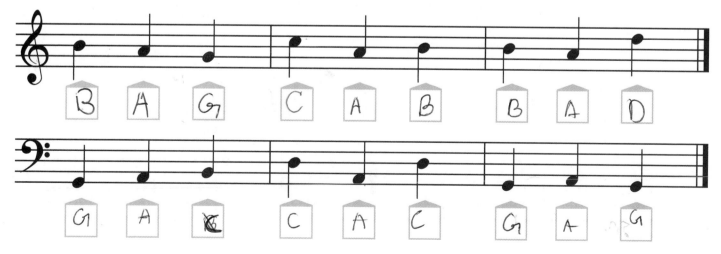

B A G C A B B A D

G A C C A C G A G

Measuring 5ths

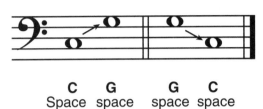

When you skip 3 white keys, the interval is a **5th.**

5ths are written LINE-LINE or SPACE-SPACE.

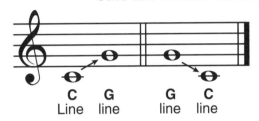

C   G   G   C
Line line   line line

C   G   G   C
Space space   space space

1. Trace the arrows between the notes while saying the words above the notes.

2. Write the note name under each note, then play, saying "Up a 5th," etc.

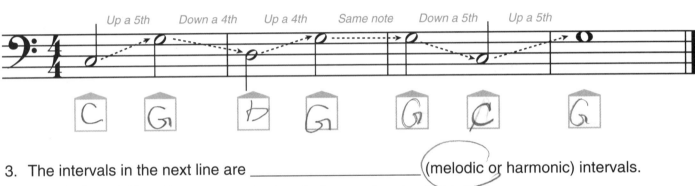

Up a 5th   Down a 4th   Up a 4th   Same note   Down a 5th   Up a 5th

C   G   D   G   G   C   G

3. The intervals in the next line are _____ (melodic or harmonic) intervals.

4. Write the name of the interval in the box below each pair of notes.

5th   4th   3rd   2nd   2nd   3rd   4th   5th

5. The intervals in the next line are _____ (melodic or harmonic) intervals.

6. Write the name of each interval in the box below it.

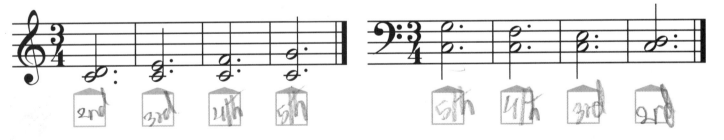

2nd   3rd   4th   5th   5th   4th   3rd   2nd

7. In each measure below, add one note to make the indicated harmonic interval.

2nd   3rd   4th   5th   5th   4th   3rd   2nd

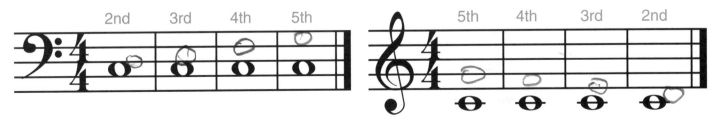

Assign with pages 30–31.

Assign with page 29.

Whole Rests

> ▬ This is a **WHOLE REST.**
>
> It means REST FOR THE VALUE OF
> A WHOLE NOTE or any WHOLE MEASURE.

1. Fill in the 2nd WHOLE REST, then draw 5 more.
   The WHOLE REST hangs down from the 4th line of the staff.

2. In *SILENT MARCH* and *SILENT WALTZ,* add a WHOLE REST
   to each measure that doesn't have one.

Silent March

Moderately fast

p

Silent Waltz

Moderately fast

p

3. Play *SILENT MARCH* with LH and count.
4. Play *SILENT WALTZ* with RH and count.

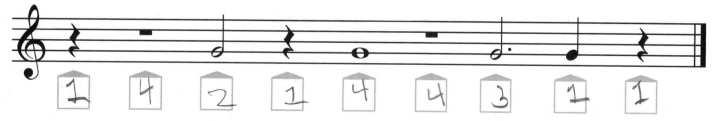

5. Below each rest or note write the number of counts it receives in $\frac{4}{4}$ time.

Measuring 4ths

1,25,18

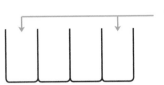

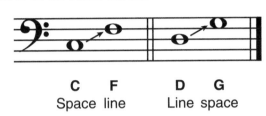

When you skip 2 white keys, the interval is a **4th.**

4ths are written LINE-SPACE or SPACE-LINE.

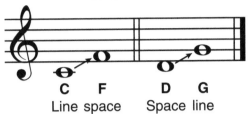

C	F	D	G
Line space	Space line		

C	F	D	G
Space line	Line space		

1. Trace the arrows between the notes while saying the words above the notes.

2. Write the note name under each note, then play, saying "Up a 4th," etc.

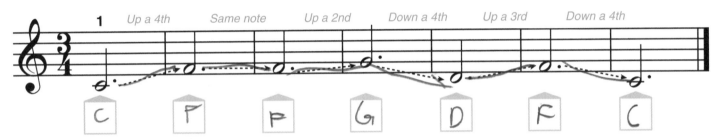

Up a 4th   Same note   Up a 2nd   Down a 4th   Up a 3rd   Down a 4th

C   F   F   G   D   F   C

3. The intervals in the next line are ___melodic___ (melodic or harmonic) intervals.

4. Write the name of the interval in the box below each pair of notes.

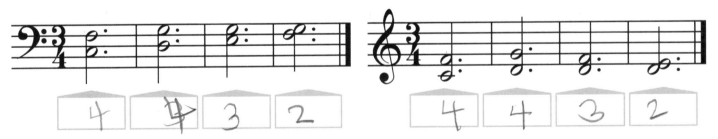

4   3   2   3   2   3   4   4

5. The intervals in the next line are ___harmonic___ (melodic or harmonic) intervals.

6. Write the name of each interval in the box below it.

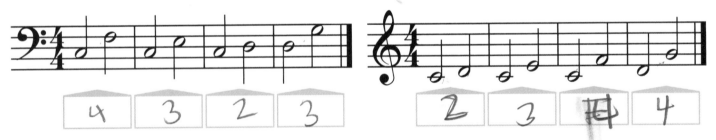

4   4   3   2   4   4   3   2

7. In each measure below, write another note to make the indicated harmonic interval.

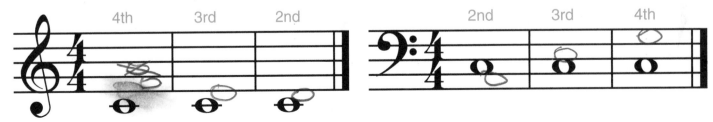

4th   3rd   2nd   2nd   3rd   4th

Review—Musical Matching

Assign with pages 26–27.

Draw each of the above signs in the correct squares below.
Draw each sign TWICE; once in the LEFT column and once in the RIGHT column.

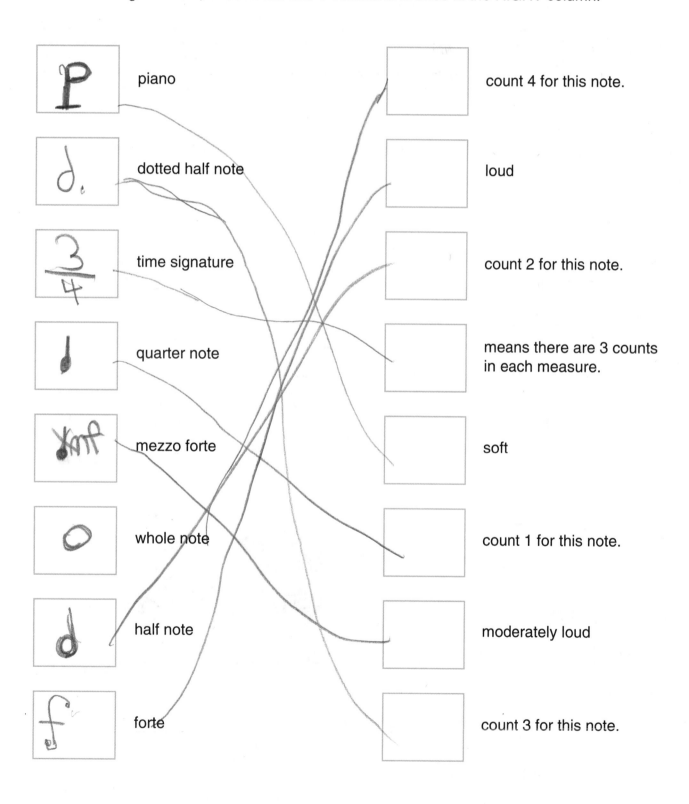

piano

dotted half note

time signature

quarter note

mezzo forte

whole note

half note

forte

count 4 for this note.

loud

count 2 for this note.

means there are 3 counts in each measure.

soft

count 1 for this note.

moderately loud

count 3 for this note.

1, 18, 18

Quarter Rests

> **RESTS** are signs of SILENCE.
>
> This is a **QUARTER REST.**
> It means REST FOR THE VALUE
>   OF A QUARTER NOTE.
>
> Count "1" or "**QUARTER**" for each quarter rest!

1. Trace the 2nd quarter rest, then draw 5 more.

2. Under each note or rest in the following line of music, write the number of counts it receives.

3. Play and count.

4. Add the values of the notes or rests in each problem and put
   the total below each line, as shown in the first example.

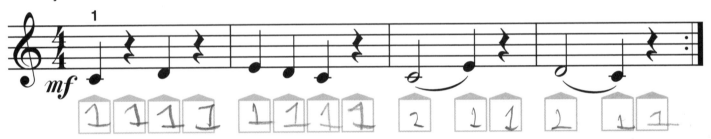

Fish Talk

Moderately slow

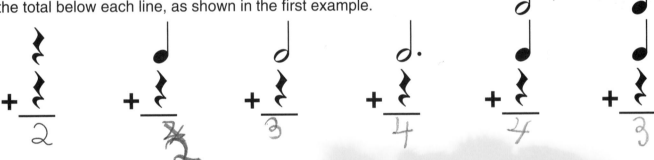

1. When my gold - fish   talks to me, he   says, "_____."
2. He's as qui - et   as can be, he   says, "_____."

5. Play *FISH TALK* and COUNT.

6. Play and sing or say the words. Make a fish face with your mouth for each rest, if you wish.

Melodic Intervals

Assign with page 24.

When notes are played separately they make a MELODY.

We call the intervals between melody notes MELODIC INTERVALS.

1. After each note, add another HALF NOTE making a melodic interval ABOVE the given note, as indicated.

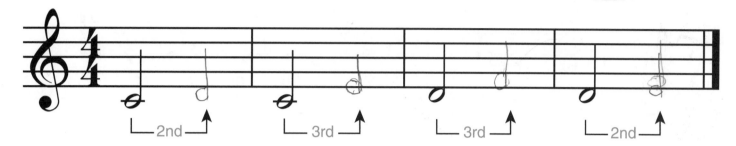

2. After each note, add another HALF NOTE making a melodic interval BELOW the given note, as indicated.

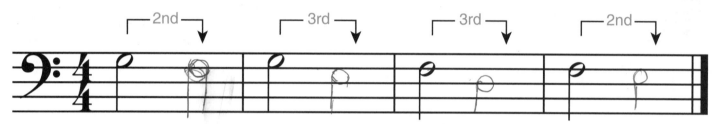

Harmonic Intervals

When notes are played together they make HARMONY.

We call the intervals between these notes HARMONIC INTERVALS.

The notes of **HARMONIC 2nds** are written SIDE-BY-SIDE, touching:

The notes of **HARMONIC 3rds** are written ONE ABOVE THE OTHER: 𝄞

3. Above each note, add another WHOLE NOTE making a harmonic interval ABOVE the given note, as indicated.

4. Below each note, add another WHOLE NOTE making a harmonic interval BELOW the given note, as indicated.

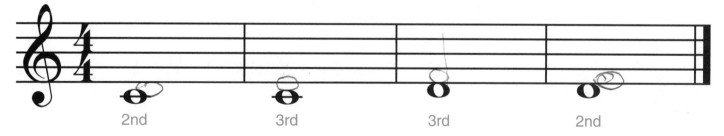

Measuring 3rds

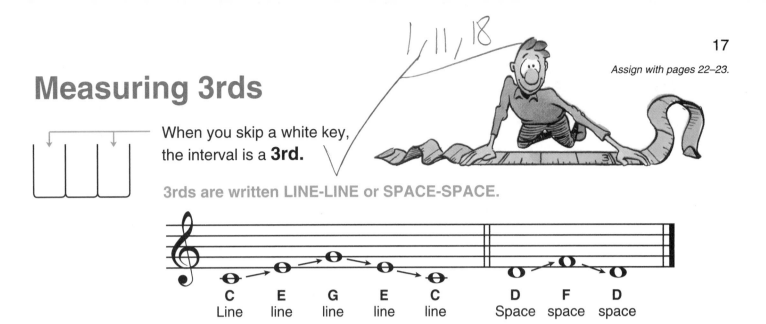

When you skip a white key, the interval is a **3rd.**

3rds are written LINE-LINE or SPACE-SPACE.

C	E	G	E	C		D	F	D
Line	line	line	line	line		Space	space	space

1. Trace the arrows between the notes while saying the words above the notes.

2. Write the note name under each note, then play, saying "Up a 3rd," etc.

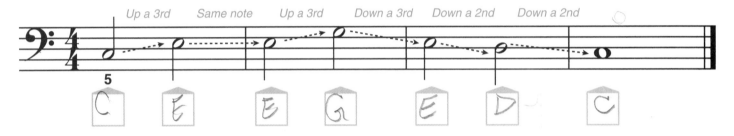

Up a 3rd   Same note   Up a 3rd   Down a 3rd   Down a 2nd   Down a 2nd

C   E   E   G   E   D   C

3. Write the name of the interval (2nd or 3rd) in the box below each pair of notes, as shown in the first box.

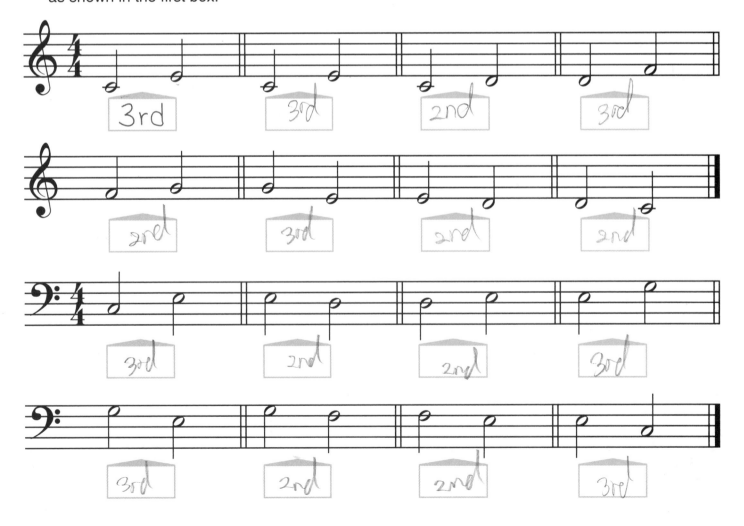

3rd   3rd   2nd   3rd

2nd   3rd   2nd   2nd

3rd   2nd   2nd   3rd

3rd   2nd   2nd   3rd

Tied Notes & Slurred Notes

Assign with page 21.

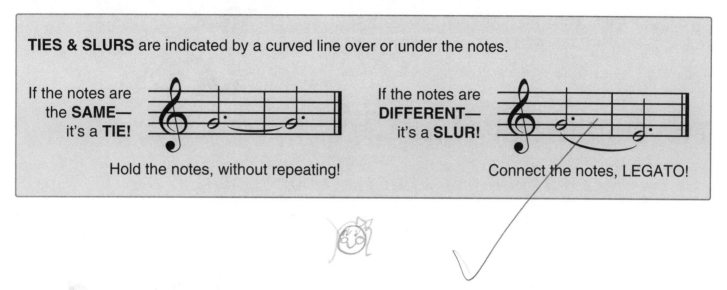

TIES & SLURS are indicated by a curved line over or under the notes.

If the notes are the **SAME**— it's a **TIE!**

Hold the notes, without repeating!

If the notes are **DIFFERENT**— it's a **SLUR!**

Connect the notes, LEGATO!

1. Write **TIE** or **SLUR** in the box under each pair of notes, as shown in the first box:

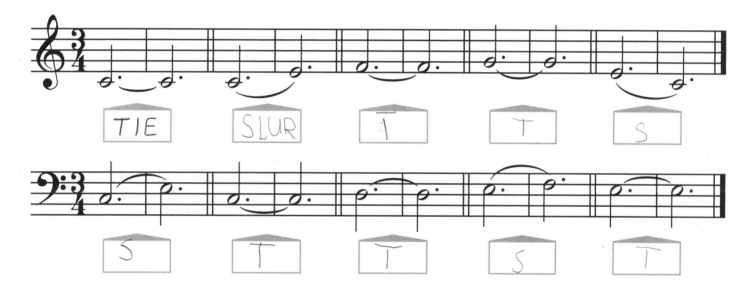

TIE SLUR T T S

S T T S T

2. How long would you hold the key down for each pair of tied notes?
   In the blank spaces, write the TOTAL number of counts for each pair of tied notes.

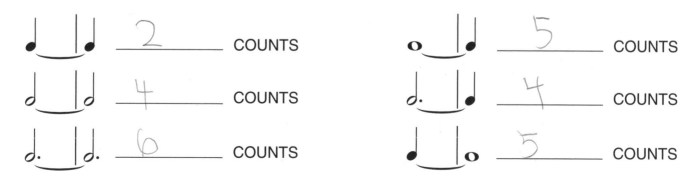

_____2_____ COUNTS

_____4_____ COUNTS

_____6_____ COUNTS

_____5_____ COUNTS

_____4_____ COUNTS

_____5_____ COUNTS

A NEW TIME SIGNATURE

3/4 means **3** beats to each measure.
a **QUARTER NOTE** ♩ gets ONE beat.

The Dotted Half Note ♩.

COUNT 2 for the HALF NOTE + 1 for the DOT!   COUNT: "1 - 2 - 3"

| 3/4 | One, | one, | one, | One | two | three, | One | two, | one, | One, | one | two. |

The notes in each measure must add up to **3** COUNTS!

1. After the 3/4 below, draw a DOTTED HALF NOTE over each "one."

2. Add BAR LINES. Put a DOUBLE BAR at the end.

3/4

One - two - three, | One - two - three, | One - two - three, | One - two - three. ‖

3. In the square below each note, write the number of counts it receives.

o   ♩.   ♩   ♩   ♩.   ♩   ♩.   o   ♩   ♩.

[4] [3] [2] [1] [3] [2] [3] [4] [1] [3]

4. Under each line, write ONE NOTE equal in value to the sum of the TWO NOTES above it,
as shown in the first example.

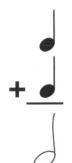  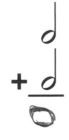 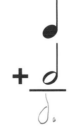  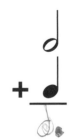

14

Measuring 2nds

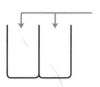

Assign with page 18.

The distance from any white key to the next white key, up or down, is called a **2nd.**

2nds are written LINE-SPACE or SPACE-LINE.

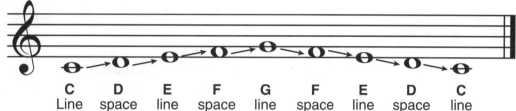

C	D	E	F	G	F	E	D	C
Line	space	line	space	line	space	line	space	line

1. Trace the arrows between the notes while saying the words above the notes ("Up a 2nd," etc.).
2. Write the note name under each note, then play, saying "Up a 2nd," etc.

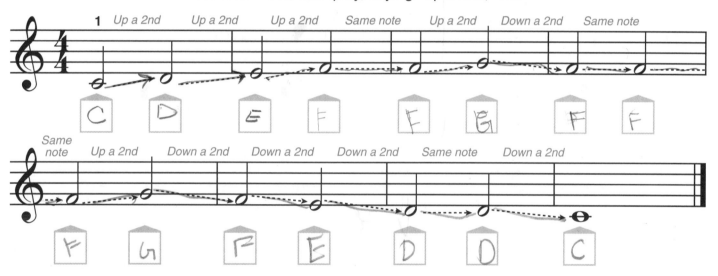

3. Draw notes under the arrows as indicated by the directions above the staff ("Up a 2nd," etc.).
   Use HALF NOTES for each note except the last in measure 8.
   Use a WHOLE NOTE for the last note.
4. Write the note name under each note, then play, saying "Up a 2nd," etc.

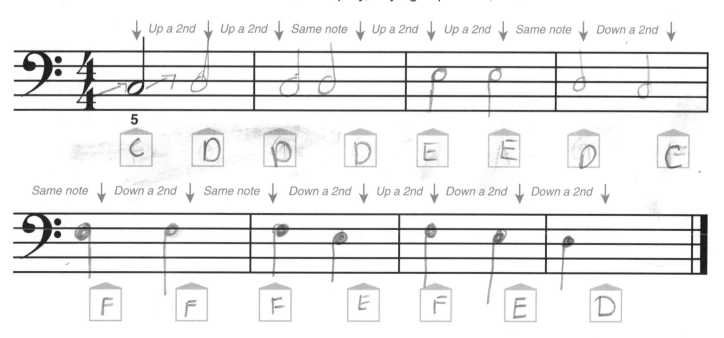

C Position on the Grand Staff

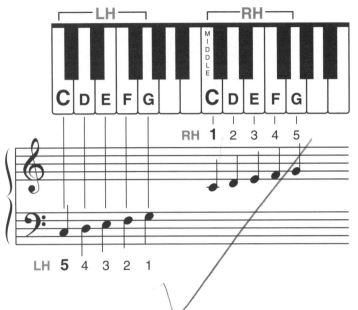

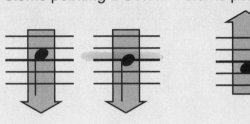

RH plays notes in the TREBLE STAFF.

LH plays notes in the BASS STAFF.

Notes ABOVE or ON the middle line have stems pointing DOWN.

Notes BELOW the middle line have stems pointing UP.

1. Write the LH notes in the BASS staff under the squares. Use QUARTER NOTES.
   Turn the stem of the C UP. Turn the stems of the D E F & G DOWN.

2. Write the RH notes in the TREBLE staff over the squares. Use QUARTER NOTES.
   Turn all the stems UP.

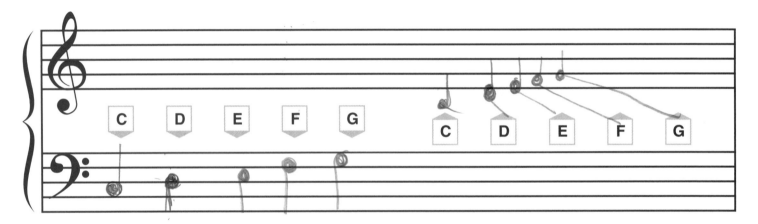

C D E F G   C D E F G

Spelling Game

3. Write the name of each note in the square below it.
   The letters in each group of squares will spell a familiar word.

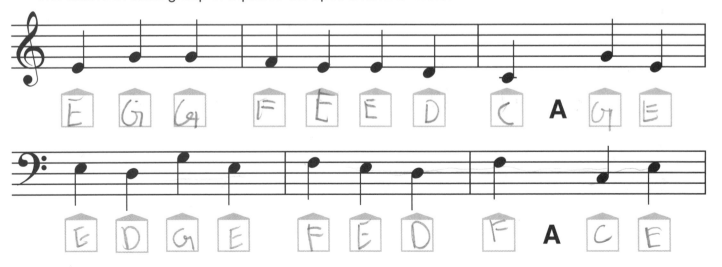

E G G   F E E D   C A G E

E D G E   F E D   F A C E

12

The Grand Staff

The TREBLE STAFF and the BASS STAFF combine to make the GRAND STAFF.

1. Print the letter names on this keyboard, beginning with the lowest A and ending
    with the highest G. You should use the complete MUSICAL ALPHABET 3 times.

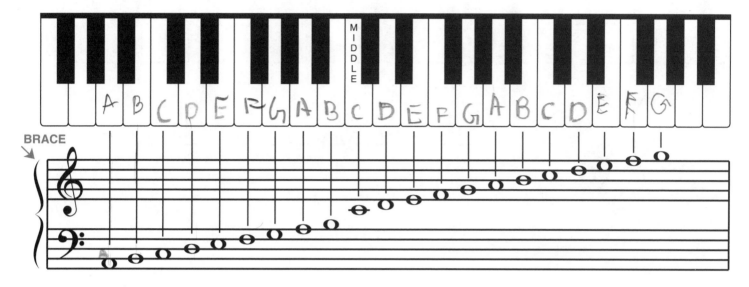

The TREBLE & BASS staffs
are joined together with
a BRACE and a BAR LINE
to make a GRAND STAFF.

2. Trace these 3 BRACES.

3. Draw 3 BRACES
    without tracing.

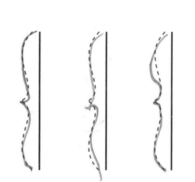

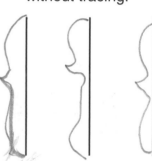

4. Join the beginning and the end of the two staffs below by tracing the bar lines,
    then trace the BRACE at the beginning to complete the GRAND STAFF.

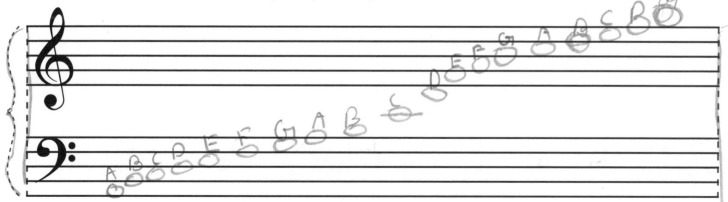

5. Write ALL the notes on the GRAND STAFF above. Use WHOLE NOTES.
    Begin with the lowest space. Keep the notes very close together so they look
    the same as in the staff at the top of this page.

6. Print the name over each note.

The Treble Clef Sign

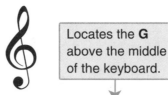

Locates the **G** above the middle of the keyboard.

12, 14, 17

This is the G line.

The clef sign curls around the G line.

1. Trace this treble clef sign:

START HERE

END HERE

2. Trace a whole line of TREBLE CLEF signs. Begin below the staff.
   Curl the end of the sign around the G LINE.

3. Draw a line of TREBLE CLEF signs without tracing.

4. Write the name of each note in the square below it.

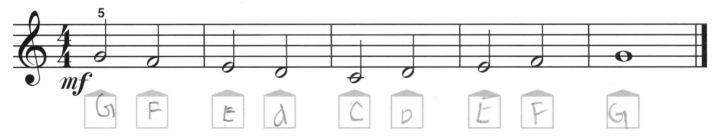

5. Play the above as you say the note names.

Assign with page 12.

The Bass Clef Sign 𝄢

Locates the **F** below the middle of the keyboard.

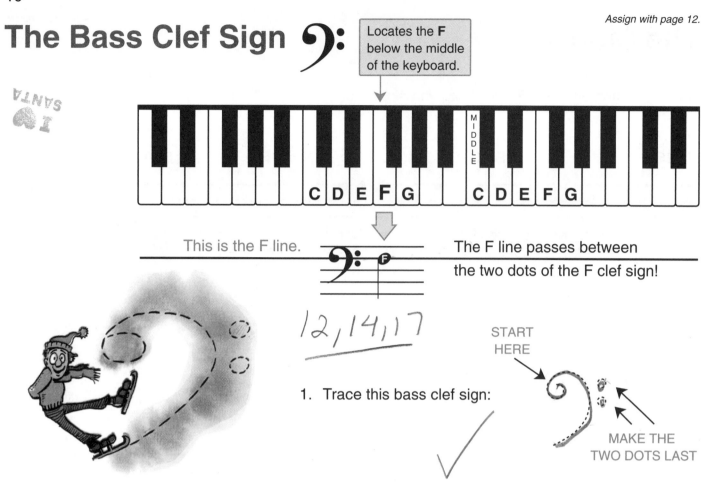

This is the F line.   The F line passes between the two dots of the F clef sign!

12, 14, 17

1. Trace this bass clef sign:

START HERE

MAKE THE TWO DOTS LAST

2. Trace a whole line of BASS CLEF signs. Always begin on the F line. The two dots are in the TOP TWO SPACES.

3. Draw a line of BASS CLEF signs without tracing.

4. Write the name of each note in the square below it.

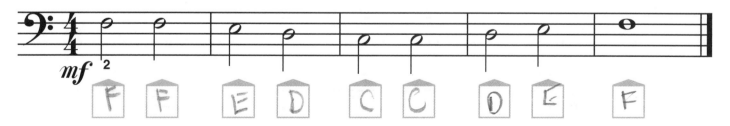

mf 2

F F F   E D   C C   D E   F

5. Play the above as you say the note names.

The Staff

Music is written on a **STAFF** of 5 lines and 4 spaces.

LINES	LINE NOTES	SPACES	SPACE NOTES

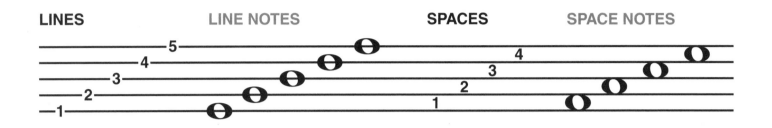

1. Write numbers 1 to 5 on the
   5 lines of the following staff.
   Begin on the bottom line.

2. Draw a WHOLE NOTE on each LINE.

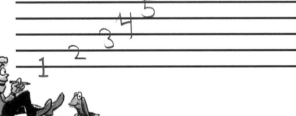

3. Write numbers 1 to 4 in the
   4 spaces of the following staff.
   Begin in the lowest space.

4. Draw a WHOLE NOTE in each SPACE.

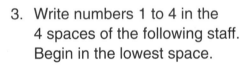

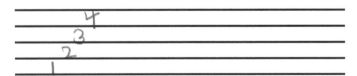

5. Draw a whole note on a LINE above each L, and in a SPACE above each S.
   Use ALL the lines and spaces.

 L S S L L S L S L

Assign with page 11.

Middle C Position

The C nearest the middle of the keyboard (under the name of the piano) is called "Middle C."

In **MIDDLE C POSITION**, both thumbs are on **Middle C.**

MIDDLE C POSITION

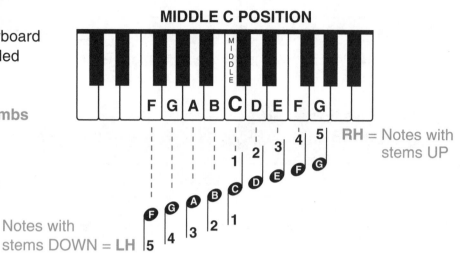

RH = Notes with stems UP

Notes with stems DOWN = **LH**

Roller Coaster

Middle C Position

1. Add RH finger numbers OVER all notes with STEMS UP.
2. Add LH finger numbers UNDER all notes with STEMS DOWN.

NEW DYNAMIC SIGN

mf *(mezzo forte)* = moderately loud

3. Add a sign under the first note of *ROLLER COASTER* that means play MODERATELY LOUD.
4. Play *ROLLER COASTER.*

The Time Signature

Music has numbers at the beginning called the **TIME SIGNATURE**.
The **TOP NUMBER** tells the number of beats in each measure.
The **BOTTOM NUMBER** tells the kind of note that gets ONE beat.

$\frac{4}{4}$ means **4** beats to each measure.

a **QUARTER NOTE** ♩ gets ONE beat.

BAR LINE

◄——————— MEASURE ———————► ◄——————— MEASURE ———————►

One, one, one two, One two three four.

The notes in each measure must add up to **4 COUNTS!**

1. How many **QUARTER NOTES** can you have in each measure of $\frac{4}{4}$ time? ___4___
   Fill these measures with QUARTER NOTES.

2. How many **HALF NOTES** can you have in each measure of $\frac{4}{4}$ time? ___2___
   Fill these measures with HALF NOTES.

3. How many **WHOLE NOTES** can you have in each measure of $\frac{4}{4}$ time? ___1___
   Fill each measure with a WHOLE NOTE.

4. Add only ONE NOTE to each measure to make it complete.

Assign with page 8.

F is on the LEFT
of any
3 black key group!

7. Find all the **F**'s on this keyboard. Print an **F** on each one.

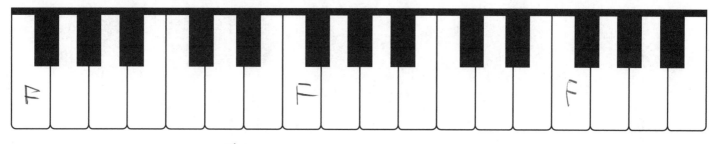

G is between the
1st & 2nd keys
of any
3 black key group!

8. Find all the **G**'s on this keyboard. Print a **G** on each one.

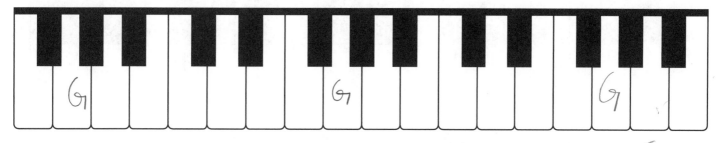

9. On the keyboard below, print the names of the keys in this order:

1. All the C's.
2. All the E's.
3. All the D's.

4. All the F's.
5. All the B's.

6. All the A's.
7. All the G's.

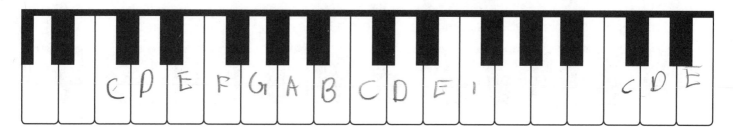

Check: Are all the notes in the order of the MUSICAL ALPHABET?

C is on the LEFT
of any
2 black key group!

4. Find all the **C**'s on this keyboard. Print a **C** on each one.

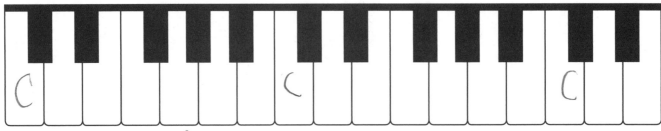

D is in the MIDDLE
of any
2 black key group!

5. Find all the **D**'s on this keyboard. Print a **D** on each one.

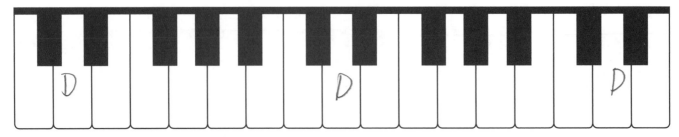

E is on the RIGHT
of any
2 black key group!

6. Find all the **E**'s on this keyboard. Print an **E** on each one.

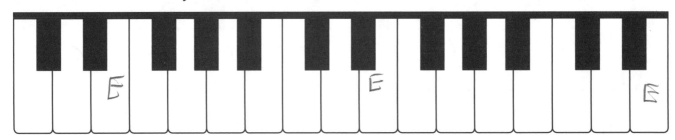

Assign with page 8.

Name That Key!

The **MUSICAL ALPHABET** has 7 letters: A B C D E F G

1. Write the MUSICAL ALPHABET in the squares on this keyboard. Begin with **A.**

A B C D E F G

A is between the
2nd & 3rd keys
of any
3 black key group!

2. Find all the **A**'s on this keyboard. Print an **A** on each one.

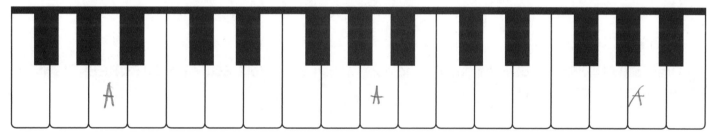

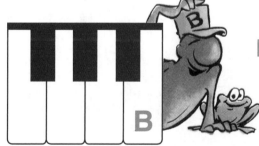

B is on the RIGHT
of any
3 black key group!

3. Find all the **B**'s on this keyboard. Print a **B** on each one.

Note-Stems and Bar Lines

Note-stems that point **UP**
are on the **RIGHT** side
of the note-head!

Note-stems that point **DOWN**
are on the **LEFT** side
of the note-head!

1. Add note-stems POINTING UP.

2. Add note-stems POINTING DOWN.

3. Draw a **BAR LINE** dividing each of the above examples into **2 EQUAL MEASURES**
   (4 notes in each measure).

4. Draw a **DOUBLE BAR** after the last note of each of the above examples.
   Notice that the double bar has one THIN line and one THICK line. It is used at the END.

5. Play EXAMPLE 1. Use RH 3 on any key you choose. Count aloud as you play.

6. Play EXAMPLE 2. Use LH 3 on any key you choose. Count aloud as you play.

How Many Counts?

7. In the square below each note, write the number of counts the note receives.

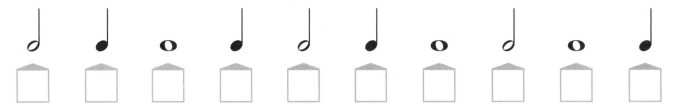

Time to Count!

*Assign before page 7 of
LESSON BOOK, Complete Level 1.*

Draw an oval.
THIS IS A WHOLE NOTE!

Draw a stem.
IT'S A HALF NOTE!

Make it black.
IT'S A QUARTER NOTE!

1. Draw 7 more **WHOLE NOTES** in the space below.

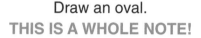

2. Add a **STEM** to each of the above notes. What kind of notes are they now? _____

3. Make each note **BLACK.** What kind of notes are they now?_____

4. Draw a **QUARTER NOTE** over each "one."

One,   one,   one,   one,   One,   one,   one,   one.

5. Count "one" or "quarter" for each quarter note, as you clap (or tap) **ONCE** for each note.

6. Draw a **HALF NOTE** over each "one."

One - two,   one - two,   One - two,   one - two.

7. Count "one-two" or "half-note" for each half note, as you clap (or tap) **ONCE** for each note.

8. Draw a **WHOLE NOTE** over each "one."

One - two - three - four,   One - two - three - four.

9. Count "one-two-three-four" or "whole-note-hold-down" for each whole note,
    as you clap (or tap) **ONCE** for each note.

NOTE TO TEACHERS: All rhythm exercises in this book are based on time signatures in which a quarter note gets one count.

Alfred's Basic Piano Library

Piano

Theory Book
Complete Level 1

FOR THE LATER BEGINNER

Instructions for Use

1. This THEORY BOOK may be assigned at the student's first lesson, or when the student reaches page 7 of the LESSON BOOK, COMPLETE LEVEL 1.

2. This book is coordinated page by page with LESSON BOOK, Complete Level 1, and all assignments should be made according to the instructions in the upper right hand corner of each page of the THEORY BOOK.

3. Theory lessons should be completed by the student *at home.* All assigned pages should be checked by the teacher at the next lesson.

4. Supplementary use of FLASH CARDS (available separately) is recommended.

Willard A. Palmer • Morton Manus • Amanda Vick Lethco

Third Edition
Copyright © MM by Alfred Music
All rights reserved.   Produced in USA.
ISBN 0-88284-827-5

Illustrations by David Silverman (Painted by Cheryl Hennigar)

= 1 =

The Amazon Basin, September 1987

At noon, the clouds clinging to the top of Cerro Gordo broke free and scattered. Far above, in the upper reaches of the forest canopy, Whittlesey could see golden tints of sunlight. Animals—probably spider monkeys—thrashed and hooted above his head and a macaw swooped low, squawking obscenely.

Whittlesey stopped next to a fallen jacaranda tree and watched Carlos, his sweating camp assistant, catch up.

"We will stop here," he said in Spanish. "*Baja la caja.* Put down the box."

Whittlesey sat down on the fallen tree and pulled off his right boot and sock. Lighting a cigarette, he applied its tip to the forest of ticks on his shin and ankle.

Carlos unshouldered an old army packboard, on which a wooden crate was awkwardly lashed.

"Open it, please," said Whittlesey.

Carlos removed the ropes, unsnapped a series of small brass clasps, and pulled off the top.

The contents were packed tightly with the fibers of an

indigenous plant. Whittlesey pulled aside the fibers, exposing some artifacts, a small wooden plant press, and a stained leather journal. He hesitated a moment, then drew a small but exquisitely carved figurine of a beast from the shirt pocket of his field jacket. He hefted the artifact in his hand, admiring again its workmanship, its unnatural heaviness. Then he placed it reluctantly in the crate, covered everything with the fibers, and reattached the lid.

From his rucksack, Whittlesey took out a folded sheet of blank paper, which he opened on his knee. He brought a battered gold pen out of his shirt pocket and began writing:

Upper Xingú
Sept. 17, 1987

Montague,
I've decided to send Carlos back with the last crate and go on alone in search of Crocker. Carlos is trustworthy, and I can't risk losing the crate should anything happen to me. Take note of the shaman's rattle and other ritual objects. They seem unique. But the figurine I've enclosed, which we found in a deserted hut at this site, is the proof I've been looking for. Note the exaggerated claws, the reptilian attributes, the hints at *bipedalia*. The Kothoga exist, and the Mbwun legend is not mere fabrication.

All my field notes are in this notebook. It also contains a complete account of the breakup of the expedition, which you will of course know about by the time this reaches you.

Whittlesey shook his head, remembering the scene that had played itself out the day before. That idiotic bastard, Maxwell. All he'd cared about was getting those specimens he'd stumbled on back to the Museum undamaged. Whittlesey laughed silently to himself. Ancient eggs. As if they were anything more than worthless seed pods. Maxwell should have been a paleobiologist instead of a physical anthropologist. How ironic they'd packed up and left a mere thousand yards from his *own* discovery.

In any case, Maxwell was gone now, and the others with him. Only Carlos and Crocker, and two guides, had stayed. Now there was just Carlos. Whittlesey returned to the note.

> Use my notebook and the artifacts, as you see fit, to help restore my good standing with the Museum. But above all else, take care of this figurine. I am convinced that its worth to anthropology is incalculable. We discovered it yesterday by accident. It seems to be the centerpiece of the Mbwun cult. However, there is no other trace of habitation nearby. This strikes me as odd.

Whittlesey paused. He hadn't described the discovery of the figurine in his field notes. Even now, his mind resisted the memory.

Crocker had wandered off the trail for a better look at a jacamar; otherwise they'd never have found the hidden path, slanting down steeply between moss-slick walls. Then, that crude hut, half-buried among ancient trees, in the wet vale where daylight barely penetrated... The two Botocudo guides, normally chattering nonstop to each other in Tupian, shut up immediately. When questioned by Carlos, one of them just muttered something about a guardian of the hut, and a curse on anybody who violated its secrets. Then, for the first time, Whittlesey had heard them speak the word *Kothoga*. Kothoga. The shadow people.

Whittlesey was skeptical. He'd heard talk of curses before—usually, right before a request for higher wages.

But when he emerged from the hut, the guides were gone.

. . . Then that old woman, blundering out of the forest. She was probably Yanomamo, obviously not Kothoga. But she knew of them. *She had seen them.* The curses she'd hinted at . . . And the way she'd just melted back into the forest, more like a jaguar yearling than a septuagenarian.

Then, they turned their attention to the hut.

The hut . . . Gingerly, Whittlesey allowed himself to remember. It was flanked by two stone tablets with identical carvings of a beast sitting on its haunches. Its claw held something weathered and indistinguishable. Behind the hut lay an overgrown garden, a bizarre oasis of bright color amid the green fastness.

The floor of the hut was sunken several feet, and Crocker almost broke his neck on the way in. Whittlesey followed him more carefully, while Carlos simply knelt in the entranceway. The air inside was dark and cool and smelt of decaying earth. Switching on his flashlight, Whittlesey saw the figurine sitting on a tall earthen mound in the middle of the hut. Around its base lay a number of strangely carved discs. Then the flashlight reached the walls.

The hut had been lined with human skulls. Examining a few of the closest, Whittlesey noticed deep scratch marks he could not immediately understand. Ragged holes yawned through the tops. In many cases, the occipital bone at the base of the skull was also smashed and broken off, the heavy squamosal bones completely gone.

His hand shook, and the flashlight failed. Before he switched it on again, he saw dim light filtering through thousands of eye sockets, dust motes swimming sluggishly in the heavy air.

Afterward, Crocker decided he needed a short walk— to be alone for a while, he'd told Whittlesey. But he hadn't come back.

The vegetation here is very unusual. The cycads and ferns look almost primordial. Too bad there isn't time for more careful study. We've used a particularly resilient variety as packing material for the crates; feel free to let Jörgensen take a look, if he's interested.

I fully expect to be with you at the Explorer's Club a month from now, celebrating our success with a brace of dry martinis and a good Macanudo. Until then, I know I can entrust this material and my reputation to you.

Your colleague,

Whittlesey

He inserted the letter beneath the lid of the crate.

"Carlos," he said, "I want you to take this crate back to Pôrto de Mós, and wait for me there. If I'm not back in two weeks, talk to Colonel Soto. Tell him to ship it back with the rest of the crates by air to the Museum, as agreed. He will draw your wages."

Carlos looked at him. "I do not understand," he said. "You will stay here alone?"

Whittlesey smiled, lit a second cigarette, and resumed killing ticks. "Someone has to bring the crate out. You should be able to catch up with Maxwell before the river. I want a couple of days to search for Crocker."

Carlos slapped his knee. "*Es loco!* I can't leave you alone. *Si te dejo atrás, te morirías.* You will die here in the forest, *Señor,* and your bones will be left to the howler monkeys. We must go back together, that is best."

Whittlesey shook his head impatiently. "Give me the Mercurochrome and the quinine, and the dried beef from your pack," he said, pulling the filthy sock back on and lacing his boot.

Carlos started unpacking, still protesting. Whittlesey

ignored him, absently scratching insect bites on the back
of his neck and staring up toward Cerro Gordo.

"They will wonder, *Señor*. They will think I left you.
It will be very bad for me," Carlos said rapidly, placing
the items in Whittlesey's pack. "The cabouri flies will
eat you alive," he continued, moving over to the crate
and lashing it shut. "You will catch malaria again, and
die this time. I will stay with you."

Whittlesey stared at the shock of snow-white hair
plastered to Carlos's sweaty forehead. That hair had
been pure black yesterday, before Carlos looked into the
hut. Carlos met his gaze for a moment, then lowered his
eyes.

Whittlesey stood up. *"Adiós,"* he said, and disappeared into the bush.

By late afternoon, Whittlesey noticed that the thick, low
clouds had returned to shroud Cerro Gordo. For the last
several miles, he had been following an ancient trail of
unknown origin, barely a narrow alley in the brush. The
trail cleverly worked its way through the blackwater
swamps surrounding the base of the *tepui,* the soggy,
jungle-clotted plateau that lay ahead. The trail had the
logic of a human trail, Whittlesey thought. It moved with
obvious purpose; animal tracks often wandered. And it
was heading for a steep ravine in the shoulder of the
approaching *tepui.* Crocker must have come this way.

He stopped to consider, unconsciously fingering the
talisman—a gold arrow overlaid by another of silver—
that had hung around his neck since childhood. Besides
the hut, they'd seen no sign of human habitation for the
last several days except a long-deserted root-gatherer vil-
lage. Only the Kothoga could have created this path.

As he approached the plateau, he could see a few
braids of water cascading down its steep flanks. He
would camp at the bottom tonight, and make the thou-
sand-meter ascent in the morning. It would be steep,

muddy, and possibly dangerous. If he met the Kothoga—well, he would be trapped.

But he had no reason to think the Kothoga tribe was savage. After all, it was this other creature, Mbwun, to which local myth cycles ascribed all the killing and savagery. Strange—an unknown creature, supposedly controlled by a tribe nobody had seen. *Could Mbwun actually exist?* he wondered. Conceivably, a small remnant could be alive in this vast rain forest; the area was virtually unexplored by biologists. Not for the first time, he wished that Crocker hadn't taken his own Mannlicher .30 06 when he'd left camp.

But first, Whittlesey realized, he had to locate Crocker. Then he could search for the Kothoga, prove they hadn't died out centuries before. He'd be famous—the discoverer of an ancient people, living in a kind of Stone Age purity deep in the Amazon, on a plateau that floated above the jungle like Arthur Conan Doyle's *The Lost World.*

There was no reason to fear the Kothoga. *Except that hut . . .*

Suddenly, a sharp sickly smell assailed his nostrils, and he stopped. There was no mistaking it—a dead animal, and a big one. He took a dozen steps as the smell intensified. His heart quickened with anticipation: perhaps the Kothoga had butchered an animal nearby. There might be artifacts left at the site—tools, weapons, perhaps even something ceremonial in nature.

He crept forward. The sweet nauseating reek grew stronger. He could see sunlight in a patch of canopy high above his head—the sure sign of a nearby clearing. He stopped and tightened his pack, not wanting to be hampered in case he had to move fast.

The narrow trail, walled in by brush, leveled off and took a sudden turn into the head of the small clearing. There, on the opposite side, was the carcass of the animal. The base of the tree it lay against had been ritually carved with a spiral, and a bundle of bright green parrot feathers lay on top of the gaping, greasy brown rib cage.

But as he walked closer, he saw that the carcass was wearing a khaki shirt.

A cloud of fat flies roared and swarmed about the open rib cage. Whittlesey noticed that a severed left arm was lashed to the tree trunk with a fibrous rope, the palm sliced open. A number of spent cartridge casings lay around the body. Then he saw the head. It lay face up under the corpse's armpit, the back of the skull torn away, the cloudy eyes staring upward, the cheeks bulging.

Whittlesey had found Crocker.

Instinctively, Whittlesey began stumbling backward. He saw how rows of claws had flayed the body with obscene, inhuman strength. The corpse looked stiff. Perhaps—if God was merciful—the Kothoga had already departed.

Assuming it was the Kothoga.

Then he noticed that the rain forest, normally overflowing with the sounds of life, was silent. With a start, he turned to face the jungle. Something was moving in the towering brush at the edge of the clearing, and two slitted eyes the color of liquid fire took shape between the leaves. With a sob and a curse, he drew his sleeve across his face and looked again. The eyes had vanished.

There was no time to lose—he had to get back down the trail, away from this place. His path back into the forest lay directly ahead. He'd have to make a run for it.

Just then he saw something on the ground he hadn't noticed before, and he heard movement, ponderous yet horrifyingly stealthy, through the brush in front of him.

= 2 =

Belém, Brazil, July 1988

This time, Ven was pretty sure the dock foreman was onto him.

He stood well back in the shadows of the warehouse alley, watching. Light rain obscured the bulky outlines of the tethered freighters and narrowed the dock lights into pinpoints. Steam rose as the rain hit the hot deckboards, bringing with it the faint odor of creosote. From behind him came the nocturnal sounds of the port: the staccato bark of a dog; faint laughter leavened with Portuguese phrases; calypso music from the waterfront bars on the avenida.

It had been such a sweet deal. He'd come down when Miami got too hot, taking the long route. Here, it was mostly light trade, small freighters bound up and down the coast. The dock crew always needed stevedores, and he'd loaded boats before. He'd said his name was Ven Stevens, and no one questioned it. They wouldn't have believed a first name of Stevenson, anyway.

The setup had all the right ingredients. He'd had

plenty of practice in Miami, plenty of time to sharpen his instincts. Those instincts paid off down here. Deliberately, he spoke Portuguese badly, haltingly, so he could read eyes and gauge responses. Ricon, junior assistant to the harbormaster, was the last link Ven had needed.

Ven was alerted when a shipment was coming in from upriver. Usually he'd just be given two names: incoming and outgoing. He always knew what to look for, the boxes were always the same. He'd see that they were safely off-loaded and stowed in the warehouse. Then, he just made sure they were the last cargo loaded onto the designated freighter headed for the States.

Ven was naturally cautious. He'd kept a close eye on the dock foreman. Once or twice he'd had a feeling, like a warning bell in his brain, that the foreman suspected something. But each time Ven had eased up a little, and in a few days the warning bell had gone away.

Now he checked his watch. Eleven o'clock. He heard a door opening, then closing, from around the corner. Ven drew himself up against the wall. Heavy footfalls sounded against wooden planking, then the familiar form passed under a streetlight. When the footsteps receded, Ven peered around the corner. The office was dark, deserted, as he knew it would be. With a last glance, he edged around the corner of the building, onto the docks.

An empty backpack slapped damply against his shoulders with each step. As he walked, Ven reached into a pocket, withdrew a key, and clenched it tightly. That key was his lifeline. Before he'd spent two days on the docks, he'd had an impression made of it.

Ven passed a small freighter berthed along the wharf, its heavy hawsers dripping black water onto rusted bitts. The ship seemed deserted, not even a harbor watch on deck. He slowed. The warehouse door lay directly ahead, near the end of the main pier. Ven glanced quickly over his shoulder. Then, with a quick turn of his hand, he unlocked the metal door and slipped inside.

Pulling the door closed, he let his eyes grow accustomed to the darkness. Halfway home. He just had to finish up in here and get the hell out.

As soon as possible. Because Ricon was growing greedy, cruzeiros running through his hands like water. Last time, he'd made a crack about the size of his cut. Just that morning, Ricon and the foreman had been talking fast and low, the foreman looking over at Ven. Now, Ven's instincts told him to get away.

Inside, he saw the darkened warehouse resolve itself into a vague landscape of cargo containers and packing crates. He couldn't chance a flashlight, but it didn't matter: he knew the layout well enough to walk it in his dreams. He moved forward carefully, threading a path through the vast mountains of cargo.

At last, he saw the landmark he'd been waiting for: a battered-looking stack of crates, six large and one small, stacked in a forlorn corner. Two of the larger crates were stenciled MNH, NEW YORK.

Months before, Ven had asked about these crates. The quartermaster's boy had told him the story. Seemed the crates had come downriver from Pôrto de Mós the previous fall. They'd been scheduled for air shipment to a New York museum, but something had happened to the people who'd made the arrangements—the apprentice couldn't say exactly what. But payment hadn't come through in time, and now the crates were snarled in a mass of red tape, seemingly forgotten.

Except by Ven. There was just enough room behind the forgotten crates for him to stash his shipments until the outgoing freighters were loading.

The warm night breeze came in from a broken window high in the wall, stirring the sweat on Ven's forehead. He smiled in the darkness. Just the other week, he'd learned that soon the crates would finally be shipped back to the States. But he'd be long gone by then.

Now, he checked his own cache. Just a single box this

time, whose contents would fit nicely into the corners of his backpack. He knew where the markets were and what to do. And he'd be doing it—somewhere far away— very soon.

As he was about to squeeze behind the large crates, Ven stopped abruptly. There was a strange odor here: something earthy, goatish, decaying. A lot of odd cargoes had come through the port, but none smelling quite like this.

His instincts were going off five-alarm, yet he couldn't detect anything wrong or out of place. He slid forward, between the Museum cargo and the wall.

He stopped again. Something wasn't right back here. Something wasn't right at all.

He heard, rather than saw, something moving in the cramped space. The pungent odor welled forward, blanketing him with its rotten stench. Suddenly, he was slammed against the wall with terrific force. Pain exploded in his chest and gut. He opened his mouth to scream, but something was boiling in his throat, and then a stab like lightning tore through his skull, leaving only darkness behind.

MUSEUM OF
UNNATURAL
MYSTERY

PART ONE

= 3 =

New York, Present Day

The red-haired kid was clambering onto the platform, calling his younger brother a chicken, reaching toward the elephant's foot. Juan eyed him silently, easing himself forward just as the kid's hand touched the exhibit.

"Yo!" Juan yelled, breaking into a trot. "Hey, no touching the elephants." The boy looked scared and snatched back his hand; he was still at an age where a uniform impressed him. Older ones—fifteen, sixteen—would give Juan the finger sometimes. They knew he was only a museum guard. Lousy fucking job. One of these days he was going to finish that equivalency shit and take the police exam.

He watched suspiciously as red-hair and little brother walked around the cases in the darkened hall, looking at the stuffed lions. At the case full of chimps, the boy started hooting and scratching under his arms, showing off for junior's benefit. Where the hell were the parents?

Now Billy, the redhead, tugged his little brother into a chamber filled with African artifacts. A row of masks with flat wooden teeth leered at them from a showcase. "Wow!" exclaimed Billy's kid brother.

"That's *dumb*," said Billy. "We're going to see the dinosaurs."

"Where's Mommy?" said the kid, screwing his head around.

"Aw, she got lost," said Billy. "Come on."

They began to move through a vast, echoing hall filled with totem poles. At the far end, a woman holding a red flag was leading the final tour group of the day, her voice shrill. To Billy's younger brother, the hall smelled faintly spooky, like smoke and old tree roots. When the group disappeared around a corner, the hall fell silent.

The last time they had been there, Billy remembered, they had seen the biggest brontosaurus in the world, and a tyrannosaurus and a trachydent. At least, that's what he thought it was called, a trachydent. The teeth on the tyrannosaurus must have been ten feet long. That was just about the greatest thing Billy had ever seen. But he didn't remember seeing these totem poles. Maybe the dinosaurs were through the next door. But that led only to the boring Hall of Pacific Peoples, full of jades and ivories and silks and bronze statues.

"Now look what you did," said Billy.

"What?"

"You made me get lost, that's what," said Billy.

"Mommy's gonna be *real* mad," the kid said.

Billy snorted. They weren't supposed to meet his parents until closing time, on the big front steps. He'd find his way out, no problem.

They wound through several more dusty rooms, down a narrow flight of stairs, and into a long dim hall. Thousands of little stuffed birds lined the walls from floor to ceiling, white cotton poking out of sightless eyes. The hall was empty and smelled of mothballs.

"I know where we are," said Billy, hopefully, peering into the dimness.

The kid started to snuffle.

"Shut up," said Billy. The snuffling stopped.

The hall took a sharp dogleg, ending in a darkened cul-de-sac full of dust and empty display cases. There were no visible exits except back through the hall of dead birds. The footfalls of the children echoed hollowly, far from the other Sunday tourists. Against the far side of the chamber stood a rolling barricade of canvas and wood, pretending unsuccessfully to be a wall. Letting go of his brother's hand, Billy walked up and peered behind the barricade.

"I been here before," he said confidently. "They've closed this place off, but it was open last time. I bet we're right below the dinosaurs. Lemme just see if there's a way up."

"You're not supposed to go back there," the kid brother warned.

"Listen, stupid, I'm going. And you'd better wait." Billy ducked behind the barricade, and a few moments later the kid heard the squeal of metal as a door was pulled open.

"Hey!" came Billy's voice. "There's a spiral staircase here. It only goes down, but it's cool. I'm gonna try it out."

"Don't! Billy!" the kid cried, but the only answer was retreating footsteps.

The kid started to bawl, his thin voice rising in the gloom of the hall. After a few minutes he fell to hiccupping, sniffed loudly, and sat down on the floor. He started pulling on a little flap of rubber that was coming off the toe of his sneaker, working it loose.

Suddenly, he looked up. The hall was silent and airless. The lights in the cases threw black shadows on the floor. A forced-air duct thumped and began to rumble somewhere. Billy was gone for real now. The kid started to cry again, louder this time.

Maybe it would be okay if he followed Billy. Maybe it wasn't such a scary thing after all. Maybe Billy had gone ahead and found his parents, and they were waiting for him, there on the other side. But he had to hurry. The Museum was probably closed by now.

He stood up and slipped behind the partition. The hall continued on, the cases filled with the dust and mold of long-neglected exhibits. An ancient metal door on one side of the hall was slightly ajar.

The kid walked up to it and peered in. Behind the door was the top landing of a narrow spiral staircase that circled downward out of sight. It was even dustier here, and there was a strange smell in the air that made his nose wrinkle. He didn't want to stand on those steps, at all. But Billy was down there.

"Billy!" he called. "Billy, come up! *Please!*"

In the cavernous gloom, his echoes were the only answer. The child sniffled, then gripped the railing and began walking slowly down into darkness.

= 4 =

Monday

As Margo Green rounded the corner of West Seventy-second Street, the early morning sun struck her square in the face. She looked down a minute, blinking; then, tossing her brown hair back, she crossed the street. The New York Museum of Natural History loomed before her like an ancient fortress, its vast Beaux Arts facade climbing ponderously above a row of copper beeches.

Margo turned down the cobbled driveway that led to the staff entrance. She walked past a loading dock and headed for the granite tunnel leading to the interior courtyards of the Museum. Then she slowed, wary. Flickering stripes of red light were painting the mouth of the tunnel in front of her. At the far end, she could see ambulances, police cars, and an Emergency Services vehicle, all parked at random.

Margo entered the tunnel and walked toward a glass pillbox. Normally, old Curly the guard would be dozing in his chair at this time of the morning, propped up against the pillbox corner, a blackened calabash pipe resting on his ample front. But today he was awake and standing. He slid the door open. "Morning, Doctor," he said. He called everyone 'doctor,' from graduate students to the Museum Director, whether they owned that title or not.

"What's up?" Margo asked.

"Don't know," Curly said. "They just got here two minutes ago. But I guess I'd better see your ID this time."

Margo rummaged in her carryall, wondering if she even had her ID. It had been months since someone had asked to see it. "I'm not sure I've got it with me," she said, annoyed that she hadn't cleaned her bag of last winter's detritus. Her carryall had recently won 'messiest bag in the Museum' status from her friends in the Anthro Department.

The pillbox telephone rang, and Curly reached for it. Margo found her ID and held it up to the window, but Curly ignored her, his eyes wide as he listened to the receiver.

He put it down without saying a word, his whole body rigidly at attention.

"Well?" Margo asked. "What's happened?"

Curly removed his pipe. "You don't want to know," he said.

The phone rang again and Curly grabbed it.

Margo had never seen the guard move so quickly. She shrugged, dropped the ID back in her bag, and walked on. The next chapter of her dissertation was coming due, and she couldn't afford to lose a single day. The week before had been a write-off—the service for her father, the formalities, the phone calls. Now, she couldn't lose any more time.

Crossing the courtyard, she entered the Museum through the staff door, turned right, and hurried down a long basement corridor toward the Anthropology Department. The various staff offices were dark, as they always were until nine-thirty or ten o'clock.

The corridor took an abrupt right angle, and she stopped. A band of yellow plastic tape was stretched across the corridor. Margo could make out the printing: NYPD CRIME SCENE—DO NOT CROSS. Jimmy, a guard usually assigned to the Peruvian Gold Hall, was standing in front of the tape with Gregory Kawakita, a young Assistant Curator in the Evolutionary Biology Department.

"What's going on here?" Margo asked.

"Typical Museum efficiency," Kawakita said with a wry smile. "We've been locked out."

"Nobody's told me nothing, except to keep everyone out," the guard said nervously.

"Look," Kawakita said, "I'm giving a presentation to the NSF next week, and this day's going to be a long one. Now, if you'll let me—"

Jimmy looked uncomfortable. "I'm just doing my job, okay?"

"Come on," Margo said to Kawakita. "Let's get some coffee up in the lounge. Maybe someone there will know what's going on."

"First I want to hunt down a men's room, if I can find one that isn't sealed off," Kawakita responded irritably. "I'll meet you there."

The door to the staff lounge, which was never closed, was closed today. Margo put her hand on the knob, wondering if she should wait for Kawakita. Then she opened the door. It would be a cold day in hell when she needed *him* as backup.

Inside, two policemen were talking, their backs turned to her. One sniggered. "What was that, number six?" he said.

"Lost count," the other replied. "But he can't have any more breakfast to bring up." As the officers moved apart, Margo got a look at the lounge behind them.

The large room was deserted. In the kitchen area at the far end, someone was leaning over the sink. He spat,

wiped his mouth, and turned around. Margo recognized
Charlie Prine, the new conservation expert in the Anthro
Department, hired on a temporary grant six months before to restore objects for the new exhibition. His face
was ashen and expressionless.

Moving to Prine's side, the officers propelled him
gently forward.

Margo stood aside to let the group pass. Prine walked
stiffly, like a robot. Instinctively, Margo's eyes traveled
downward.

Prine's shoes were soaked in blood.

Watching her vacantly, Prine registered the change of
expression. His eyes followed hers; then he stopped so
suddenly that the cop behind plowed into his back.

Prine's eyes grew large and white. The policemen
grabbed his arms and he resisted, neighing in panic.
Quickly, they moved him out of the room.

Margo leaned against the wall, willing her heart to
slow down as Kawakita came in, followed by several
others. "Half this Museum must be sealed off," he said,
shaking his head and pouring himself a cup of coffee.
"Nobody can get into their offices."

As if on cue, the Museum's ancient PA system
wheezed into operation. "*Attention please. All nonsup-
port personnel currently on the premises please report
to the staff lounge.*"

As they sat down, more staffers entered in twos and
threes. Lab technicians, for the most part, and assistant
curators without tenure; too early for the really important
people. Margo watched them detachedly. Kawakita was
talking but she couldn't hear him.

Within ten minutes, the room was packed. Everyone
was talking at once: expressing outrage that their offices
were off-limits, complaining about how no one was telling them anything, discussing each new rumor in
shocked tones. Clearly, in a museum where nothing exciting ever seemed to happen, they were having the time
of their lives.

Kawakita gulped his coffee, made a face. "Will you look at that sediment?" He turned toward her. "Been struck dumb, Margo? You haven't said a word since we sat down."

Haltingly, she told him about Prine. Kawakita's handsome features narrowed. "My God," he finally said. "What do you suppose happened?"

As his baritone voice boomed, Margo realized that the conversation in the lounge had died away. A heavyset, balding man in a brown suit was standing in the doorway, a police radio shoved into one pocket of his ill-fitting jacket, an unlit cigar protruding from his mouth. Now he strode through, followed by two uniformed policemen.

He centered himself at the front of the room, hiked up his pants, removed his cigar, picked a piece of tobacco off his tongue, and cleared his throat. "May I have your attention, please," he said. "A situation has arisen that's going to require you to bear with us for a while."

Suddenly, a voice rang out accusingly from the back of the room. "Ex-*cuse* me, Mister? . . ."

Margo craned her neck over the crowd. "Freed," Kawakita whispered. Margo had heard of Frank Freed, a testy Ichthyology curator.

The man in brown turned to look at Freed. "Lieutenant D'Agosta," he rapped out. "New York City Police Department."

It was a reply that would have shut most people up. Freed, an emaciated man with long gray hair, was undaunted. "Perhaps," he said sarcastically, "we may be informed of what exactly is going on around here? I think we have a right . . ."

"I'd *like* to brief you on what happened," D'Agosta resumed. "But at this point, all we can say is that a body has been found on the premises, under circumstances we are currently investigating. If—"

At the explosion of talk, D'Agosta wearily held up his hand.

"I can only tell you that a homicide squad is on the scene and that an investigation is in progress," he continued. "Effective immediately, the Museum is closed. For the time being, no one may enter, and no one may leave. We expect this to be a very temporary condition."

He paused. "If a homicide has occurred, there is a possibility, a *possibility,* that the killer is still inside the Museum. We would merely ask you to remain here an hour or two while a sweep is conducted. A police officer will be around to take your names and titles."

In the stunned silence that followed, he left the room, closing the door behind him. One of the remaining policemen dragged a chair over to the door and sat down heavily in it. Slowly, the conversations began to resume. "We're being locked in here?" Freed cried out. "This is outrageous."

"Jesus," Margo breathed. "You don't suppose Prine is a murderer?"

"Scary thought, isn't it?" Kawakita said. He stood up and went to the coffee machine, beating the last drops out of the urn with a savage blow. "But not as scary as the thought of being unprepared for my presentation."

Margo knew Kawakita, young fast-track scientist that he was, would never be unprepared for anything.

"Image is everything today," Kawakita went on. "Pure science alone doesn't get the grants anymore."

Margo nodded again. She heard him, and she heard the swirl of voices around them, but none of it seemed important. Except for the blood on Prine's shoes.

= 5 =

"Listen up," the policeman said an hour later. "You're free to go now. Just be sure to stay out of the areas behind the yellow tape."

Margo raised her head from her arms with a start as a hand landed on her shoulder. Tall, lanky Bill Smithback clutched two spiral notebooks in the other hand, and his brown hair looked, as usual, as if he'd just gotten out of bed. A chewed pencil was tucked behind one ear, his collar was unbuttoned and his grimy tie knot pulled down. The perfect caricature of a hard-driving journalist, and Margo suspected he cultivated the look. Smithback had been commissioned to write a book about the Museum, focusing on the *Superstition* exhibition that would open next week.

"Unnatural doings at the Natural History Museum," Smithback muttered darkly in her ear as he folded himself into a chair beside her. He slapped his notebooks on the table, and a flood of handwritten papers, unlabeled computer diskettes, and photocopied articles covered with yellow highlighting spilled across the Formica surface.

"Hello, Kawakita!" Smithback said jovially, slapping him on the shoulder. "Seen any tigers lately?"

"Only the paper variety," Kawakita replied dryly.

Smithback turned to Margo. "I suppose you must know all the gory details by now. Pretty nasty, huh?"

"They didn't tell us anything," Margo said. "All we've heard is some talk about a killing. I guess Prine must have done it."

Smithback laughed. "Charlie Prine? That guy couldn't kill a six-pack, let alone a biped. No, Prine just found the body. Or should I say, *them*."

"Them? What are you talking about?"

Smithback sighed. "You really *don't* know anything, do you? I was hoping you'd heard something, sitting in here for hours." He sprang up and went over to the coffee urn. He tipped and rattled and cursed it and came back empty handed. "They found the Director's wife, stuffed in a glass case in the Primate Hall," he said after settling himself in the chair again. "Been there twenty years before anyone noticed."

Margo groaned. "Let's hear the real story, Smithback," she said.

"All right, all right," he sighed. "Around seven-thirty this morning, the bodies of two young boys were found dead in the Old Building basement."

Margo pressed a hand to her mouth.

"How did you learn all this?" Kawakita demanded.

"While you two were cooling your heels in here, the rest of the world was stuck outside on Seventy-second Street," Smithback went on. "They'd shut the gates on us. The press was out there, too. Quite a few, in fact. The upshot is, Wright's going to give a press conference in the Great Rotunda at ten to quell the rumors. All that zoo talk. We've got ten minutes."

"Zoo talk?" Margo pressed.

"It's a zoo around *here*. Oh, God. What a mess."

Smithback was savoring not telling what he knew. "Seems the murders were pretty savage. And you know the press: They've always assumed you've got all sorts of animals locked up in here."

"I think you're actually enjoying this," Kawakita smiled.

"A story like this would add a whole new dimension to my book," Smithback went on. "The shocking true account of the grisly Museum killings, by William Smithback, Junior. Wild, voracious beasts roaming deserted corridors. It could be a best-seller."

"This isn't funny," Margo snapped. She was thinking that Prine's laboratory wasn't far from her own office in the Old Building basement.

"I know, I know," Smithback said good-humoredly. "It *is* terrible. The poor kids. But I'm still not sure I believe it. It's probably some gimmick of Cuthbert's to boost publicity for the exhibition." He sighed, then started guiltily. "Hey, Margo—I was really sorry to hear about your father. I meant to tell you earlier."

"Thanks." Margo's smile held little warmth.

"Listen, you two," Kawakita said, rising, "I really have to—"

"I heard you were thinking of leaving," Smithback continued to Margo. "Dropping your dissertation to work at your father's company, or something." He looked at her curiously. "Is that true? I thought your research was finally getting somewhere."

"Well," Margo said, "yes and no. Dissertation's dragging a bit these days. I've got my weekly eleven o'clock with Frock today. He'll probably forget, as usual, and schedule something else, especially with this tragedy. But I hope I do get in to see him. I found an interesting monograph on the Kiribitu classification of medicinal plants."

She realized that Smithback's eyes had already started to wander, and reminded herself once again that most people had no interest in plant genetics and ethnopharmacology. "Well, I've got to get ready." Margo stood up.

"Hold on a minute!" Smithback said, scrambling to gather up his papers. "Don't you want to see the press conference?"

As they left the staff lounge, Freed was still complaining to anyone who would listen. Kawakita, already trotting down the hall ahead of them, waved over his shoulder as he rounded a bend and disappeared from sight.

They arrived in the Great Rotunda to find the press conference already in progress. Reporters surrounded Winston Wright, Director of the Museum, poking microphones and cameras in his direction, voices echoing crazily in the cavernous space. Ippolito, the Museum's Security Director, stood at the Director's side. Clustered around the periphery were other Museum employees and a few curious school groups.

Wright stood angrily in the quartz lights, fielding shouted questions. His usually impeccable Savile Row suit was rumpled, and his thin hair was drooping over one ear. His pale skin was gray, and his eyes looked bloodshot.

"No," Wright was saying, "apparently they thought their children had already left the Museum. We had no prior warning. . . . No, we do *not* keep live animals in the Museum. Well, of course, we have some mice and snakes for research purposes, but no lions or tigers or anything of that sort. . . . No, I haven't seen the bodies. . . . I don't know what kind of mutilation there was, if any. . . . I don't have the expertise to address that subject, you'll have to wait for the autopsies. . . . I want to emphasize that there's been no official statement made by the police. . . . Until you stop shouting I won't answer any more questions. . . . No, I said we do *not* have wild animals in the Museum. . . . Yes, that includes bears. . . . No, I'm not going to give any names. . . . How could I possibly answer that question? . . . This press conference is over. . . . I said this press conference is *over*. . . . Yes, of course we are cooperating in every way with the police. . . . No, I don't see any reason why this should delay the opening of the new exhibition. Let me emphasize that the opening of *Superstition* is right on schedule. . . . We have *stuffed* lions, yes, but if you're trying to imply. . . . They were shot in Africa seventy-five years ago, for Heaven's sake! The zoo? We have no affiliation with the zoo. . . . I'm simply not going to respond to any more outrageous suggestions along those lines. . . . Will the gentleman from the *Post* please stop shouting? . . . The police are interviewing the scientist who found the bodies, but I have no information on that. . . . No, I don't have anything more to add, except that we're doing everything we can. . . . Yes it was tragic, of course it was. . . ."

The press began to fan out, heading past Wright into the Museum proper.

Wright turned angrily toward the security director. "Where the hell were the police?" Margo heard him snap. As he turned, he said over his shoulder, "if you see Mrs. Rickman, tell her to come to my office immediately." And he stalked out of the Great Rotunda.

= 6 =

Margo moved deeper into the Museum, away from the public areas, until she reached the corridor called 'Broadway.' Stretching the entire length of the Museum—six city blocks—it was said to be the longest single hallway in New York City. Old oaken cabinets lined the walls, punctuated every thirty feet by frosted-glass doors. Most of these doors had curators' names in gold leaf edged in black.

Margo, as a graduate student, had only a metal desk and a bookshelf in one of the basement labs. *At least I have an office,* she thought, turning off from the corridor and starting down a narrow flight of iron stairs. One of her graduate-student acquaintances had only a tiny battered school desk, wedged between two massive freezers in the Mammalogy Department. The woman had to wear heavy sweaters to work, even at the height of August.

A security guard at the bottom of the stairwell waved her on, and she moved down a dim tunnel, flanked on both sides by mounted horse skeletons in ancient glass cases. No police tape was in sight.

In her office, Margo dropped her carryall beside her desk and sat down. Most of the lab was actually storage for South Seas artifacts: Maori shields, war canoes, and cane arrows stuffed into green metal cabinets that stretched from floor to ceiling. A hundred-gallon fish tank, a simulated swamp belonging to the Animal Behavior Department, perched on an iron frame underneath a battery of lights. It was so overpopulated with algae and weeds that Margo had only rarely been able to catch sight of a fish peering out through the murk.

Next to her desk was a long worktable with a row of dusty masks. The conservator, a sour young woman, worked in angry silence, spending what seemed barely three hours each day at her task. Margo figured it took her about two weeks to conserve each mask, judging by the slow turnover. The particular mask collection she was assigned to contained five thousand such masks, but it didn't seem to concern anyone that, at the rate she was going, the project would take close to two centuries to complete.

Margo logged onto her computer terminal. A message in green letters appeared, swimming into focus out of the depths of the CRT:

HELLO MARGO GREEN@BIOTECH@STF
WELCOME BACK TO MUSENET
DISTRIBUTED NETWORKING SYSTEM,
RELEASE 15-5
COPYRIGHT © 1989–1995 NYMNH AND CERE-
BRAL SYSTEMS INC.
CONNECTING AT 10:24:06 03-27-95
PRINT SERVICE ROUTED TO LJ56

YOU HAVE NO MESSAGE(S) WAITING

She went into word-processing mode and called up her notes, preparing to review them before her meeting with Frock. Her adviser often seemed preoccupied during these weekly meetings, and Margo was constantly scrambling to give him something new. The problem was, there usually wasn't anything new—just more articles read, dissected, and stuffed into the computer; more lab work; and maybe . . . *maybe* . . . another three or four pages of her dissertation. She understood how somebody could end up a permanent rider on the government-grant gravy train, or what the scientists derisively referred to as an ABD—All But Dissertation.

When Frock had first agreed to act as her adviser two years before, she half suspected some mistake had been made. Frock—intellect behind the Callisto Effect, occupier of the Cadwalader Chair in Statistical Paleontology at Columbia University, Chairman of the Evolutionary Biology Department at the Museum—had chosen her as a research student, an honor awarded to only a handful each year.

Frock started his career as a physical anthropologist. Confined to a wheelchair by childhood polio, he had nonetheless done pioneering fieldwork that was still the basis of many textbooks. After several severe bouts with malaria made further field research impossible, Frock diverted his ferocious energy to evolutionary theory. In the mid 1980s, he had started a firestorm of controversy with a radical new proposal. Combining chaos theory and Darwinian evolution, Frock's hypothesis disputed the commonly held belief that life evolved gradually. Instead, he postulated that evolution was sometimes much less gradual; he held that short-lived aberrations—"monster species"—were sometimes an offshoot of evolution. Frock argued that evolution wasn't always caused by random selection, that the environment itself could cause sudden, grotesque changes in a species.

Although Frock's theory was backed by a brilliant series of articles and papers, much of the scientific world remained dubious. If bizarre forms of life exist, they asked, where are they hiding? Frock replied that his theory predicted rapid demise of genera as well as rapid development.

The more the experts called Frock misguided, even crazy, the more the popular press embraced his idea. The theory became known as the Callisto Effect, after the Greek myth in which a young woman is suddenly transformed into a wild creature. Although Frock deplored the widespread misconceptions of his work, he shrewdly used his celebrity to further his academic efforts. Like many brilliant curators, Frock was consumed by his research; sometimes, Margo suspected, everything else, including her work, bored him.

Across the room, the conservator got up and—without a word—left for lunch, a sure sign that it was approaching eleven o'clock. Margo scribbled a few sentences on a sheet of paper, cleared the screen, and scooped up her notebook.

Frock's office was in the southwest tower, at the end of an elegant, Edwardian fifth-floor corridor; an oasis far from the labs and computer workstations that characterized much of the behind-the-scene Museum. The heavy oak door of the inner office read simply, DR. FROCK.

Margo knocked.

She heard a great clearing of the throat and the low rumble of a wheelchair. The door opened slowly and the familiar ruddy-complexioned face appeared, bushy eyebrows knitted in surprise. Then his gaze brightened.

"Of course, it's Monday. Come in." He spoke in a low voice, touching her wrist with a plump hand and motioning her to an overstuffed chair. Frock was dressed, as usual, in a somber suit, white shirt, and loud paisley tie. His thick brush of white hair looked ruffled.

The walls of his office were lined with old, glass-fronted bookcases, many of the shelves filled with relics and oddities from his early years in the field. Books were piled in enormous, tottering stacks against a wall. Two large bow windows looked out over the Hudson River. Upholstered Victorian chairs sat on the faded Persian carpet, and on Frock's desk lay several copies of his latest book, *Fractal Evolution.*

Next to the books, Margo recognized a large chunk of gray sandstone. Embedded in its flat surface was a deep depression, oddly smudged and elongated along one end with three large indentations at the other. According to Frock, this was a fossil footprint of a creature unknown to science: the single piece of physical evidence to support his theory of aberrant evolution. Other scientists differed: Many didn't believe it was a fossil at all, calling it "Frock's folly." Most of them had never seen it.

"Clear away that stuff and sit down," Frock said, wheeling back to his favorite spot under one of the bow windows. "Sherry? No, of course, you never do. Silly of me to forget."

On the indicated chair lay several back issues of *Nature* and the typescript of an unfinished article titled "Phyletic Transformation and the Tertiary 'Fern Spike.' " Margo moved them to a nearby table and sat down, wondering if Dr. Frock would mention something about the deaths of the two little boys.

He looked at her for a moment, motionless. Then he blinked, and sighed. "Well, Miss Green," he said. "Shall we begin?"

Disappointed, Margo flipped open her notebook. She skimmed her notes, then began explaining her analysis of Kiribitu plant classification and how it related to her next dissertation chapter. As she spoke, Frock's head gradually dropped to his chest and his eyes closed. A stranger might think him asleep, but Margo knew Frock was listening with intense concentration.

When she finished, he roused himself slowly. "Classification of medicinal plants by use, rather than appearance," he murmured at last. "Interesting. That article reminds me of an experience I had among the Ki tribe of Bechuanaland." Margo waited patiently for the reminiscence that was sure to follow.

"The Ki, as you know"—Frock always assumed his listener was as familiar with a subject as he was—"at one time used the bark of a certain bush as a headache remedy. Charrière studied them in 1869 and noted their use of this bush in his field journals. When I showed up three quarters of a century later, they had stopped using the remedy. They believed instead that headaches were caused by sorcery." He shifted in his wheelchair.

"The accepted remedy was now for the kinfolk of the headache victim to identify the sorcerer and, naturally, go off and murder him. Of course, the kin of the dead sorcerer were then required to avenge this death, so they often went right back and killed the person with the headache. You can imagine what eventually happened."

"What?" Margo asked, assuming Frock was about to explain how all of this fit into her dissertation.

"Why," Frock said, spreading his hands, "it was a medical miracle. People stopped getting headaches."

His generous shirtfront shook with laughter. Margo laughed too—for the first time that day, she realized.

"Well, so much for primitive medicine," Frock said a little wistfully. "Back then, fieldwork was still fun." He paused for a minute. "There will be a whole section on the Ki tribe in the new *Superstition* exhibition, you know," he went on. "Of course, it will be terribly played up for mass consumption. They've brought in some young fellow fresh from Harvard to curate the show. Knows more about computers and mass-marketing than pure science, I'm told."

Frock shifted again in his wheelchair. "In any case, Miss Green, I think what you've described will make a fine addition to your work. I suggest you obtain some samples of the Kiribitu plants from the herbarium and proceed from there."

Margo was gathering her papers when Frock suddenly spoke again. "Bad business this morning."

Margo nodded.

Frock remained silent for a moment. "I fear for the Museum," he said finally.

Surprised, Margo said, "They were brothers. It's a tragedy for the family. But things will die down soon—they always do."

"I think not," Frock said. "I've heard something about the condition of the bodies. The force used was . . . of a nonnormal nature."

"Surely *you* don't think it was a wild animal?" Margo asked. Perhaps Frock was as crazy as everyone said.

Frock smiled. "My dear, I make no assumptions. I will await further evidence. For the moment, I simply hope this unpleasantness will not influence your decision on whether to remain with the Museum. Oh, yes, I've heard about it, and I was very sorry to get the news of your father's death. But you've displayed three gifts that are indispensable to a first-class researcher: a sense of what to look for, a sense of where to look for it, and the zeal to see your theories through." He moved the wheelchair closer to her. "Academic zeal is just as important as zeal in the field, Miss Green. Always remember that. Your technical training, your lab work, has been excellent. It would be a shame if our profession were to lose someone of your talents."

Margo felt a mix of gratitude and resentment. "Thank you, Dr. Frock," she replied. "I appreciate the kind words—and your concern."

The scientist waved his hand, and Margo said goodbye. But at the door, she heard Frock speak again.

"Miss Green?" he asked.

"Yes?"

"Please be watchful."

= 7 =

Outside she nearly collided with Smithback. He leaned toward her, winking roguishly. "How about lunch?"

"No," said Margo. "Too busy." Twice in one day— she wasn't sure she could stand such a full dose of Smithback.

"Come on," he urged. "I've got some more grisly details about the murders."

"It figures." She quickened her pace down the hall, irritated that her curiosity was aroused.

Smithback grabbed her arm. "I hear they're serving a delicious aged and oven-dried lasagna in the cafeteria." He steered her toward the elevator.

The lunchroom was filled with the usual crowd of curators, beefy guards talking loudly, and assorted technicians and preparators in white lab coats. One curator was passing specimens around to a table of fellow scientists, who were murmuring in admiration and interest. Margo took a closer look. The specimens were pickled parasitic worms, coiled in jars of cloudy formaldehyde.

They sat down and Margo tried to saw through the crust of her lasagna.

"Just like I promised," Smithback said, picking up a piece in his hand and biting off a corner with a crunch. "Been on the steam table since nine o'clock this morning, at least."

He chewed noisily. "Well, the police finally made it official. There were two murders here last night. Brilliant to have figured it out! And you remember all those questions the reporters asked about wild animals? Well, there's also a chance they *were* mauled to death by a wild animal."

"Not while I'm eating," Margo said.

"That's right. Literally shredded, by the sound of it." Margo looked up. *"Please."*

"I kid you not," Smithback continued. "And the heat is on to get this thing *solved*, particularly with the big exhibition coming up. I hear the cops have even enlisted a special coroner. Someone who reads gaping claw wounds like Helen Keller reads braille."

"Damn it, Smithback," Margo said and dropped her fork. "I'm sick of this—your cavalier attitude and your gory particulars while I'm having lunch. Can't I eat first and hear about this stuff later?"

"As I was saying," Smithback continued, ignoring the outburst, "she's supposedly an expert on big cats. Dr. Matilda Ziewicz. Some name, huh. Sounds fat."

Despite her annoyance, Margo suppressed a smile. Smithback might be a jerk, but at least he was a funny jerk. She shoved her tray away. "Where'd you hear all this?" she asked.

Smithback grinned. "I have my sources." He shoveled another piece of lasagna into his mouth. "Actually, I ran into a friend who writes for the *News*. Somebody got the story from a contact in the NYPD. It's going to be all over the afternoon papers. Can you imagine Wright's face when he sees that? Oh, God."

Smithback cackled for a moment before filling his

mouth again. He'd finished his own and was starting on Margo's. For a thin guy, he ate like a beast.

"But how could there be a wild animal loose in the Museum?" Margo asked. "That's absurd."

"Yeah? Well, get this: They've got someone in here with a bloodhound, trying to track the son of a bitch."

"Now you're joking."

"Hey, not me. Ask any of the security guards. There's a million square feet in this joint where a big cat or something could be roaming, including five miles of forced-air ducts big enough for a *man* to crawl around in. And under the Museum is a warren of abandoned tunnels. They're taking it seriously."

"Tunnels?"

"Yup. Didn't you read my article in last month's magazine? The first Museum was built on an artesian swamp that couldn't be permanently drained. So they built all these tunnels to divert the water. Then, when the original Museum burned down in 1911, they built the present Museum on top of the old Museum's basement. The subbasement is huge, multileveled ... much of it isn't even electrified. I doubt if there's anybody still alive who really knows their way around down there."

Smithback munched the last piece of lasagna and pushed the tray aside. "And then, there're the usual rumors about the Museum Beast."

Anybody who worked in the Museum had heard that story. Maintenance men working late-night shifts saw it out of the corners of their eyes. Assistant curators wandering down dimly lit corridors on their way to specimen vaults saw it moving in the shadows. Nobody knew what it was, or where it had come from, but some claimed the beast had killed a man several years before.

Margo decided to change the subject. "Is Rickman still giving you trouble?" she asked.

At the mention of the name, Smithback grimaced. Margo knew that Lavinia Rickman, the Chief of Public Relations for the Museum, had hired Smithback to write

his book. She had also worked out the Museum's cut of
the advance and royalties. Although Smithback wasn't
happy about the contractual details, the exhibition promised to be such a blockbuster that book sales, riding on
the success of the exhibit, could easily climb into six
figures. It hadn't been a bad deal for Smithback at all,
Margo thought, given the only modest success of his
previous book on the Boston Aquarium.

"Rickman? Trouble?" Smithback snorted. "Oh, God.
She's the definition of trouble. Listen, I want to read you
something." He pulled a sheaf of papers out of a notebook.

" 'When Dr. Cuthbert pitched the idea for an exhibition on Superstition to the Museum Director, Wright
was very impressed. It had all the makings of a blockbuster exhibition, something on the level of *The Treas-
ures of King Tut* or *The Seven Levels of Troy.* That meant
big money for the Museum, Wright knew, and an un-
paralleled opportunity to raise funds from corporate and
government sponsorship. But some older curators were
unconvinced; they thought the exhibit smacked of sen-
sationalism.' "

Smithback stopped. "Look what Rickman did." He
pushed the paper over to her. A big line sliced across
the paragraph and a marginal note in fat red marker read:
OUT!

Margo giggled.

"What's so funny?" Smithback demanded. "She's
butchering my manuscript. Look at this." He jabbed his
finger at another page.

Margo shook her head. "What Rickman wants is a
snow job for the Museum. You two won't ever see eye
to eye."

"She's driving me crazy. She's taking out everything
that's the slightest bit controversial. She wants me to
spend all my time talking to that nerd who's curating
the exhibition. She knows that he'll only say what his
boss Cuthbert tells him to." He leaned forward conspir-

atorially. "You've never seen such a company man in your life." He looked up, and groaned. "Oh, God, here he comes now."

A young, slightly overweight man with horn-rimmed glasses materialized at their table, holding a tray balanced on a shiny leather briefcase. "May I join you?" he asked shyly. "I'm afraid this is practically the only seat left in the house."

"Sure," said Smithback. "Have a seat. We were just talking about you, anyway. Margo, meet George Moriarty. He's the guy who's curating the *Superstition* exhibition."

Smithback shook the papers at Moriarty. "Look what Rickman did to my manuscript. The only things she didn't touch were *your* quotations."

Moriarty scanned the pages and looked at Smithback with almost childlike gravity. "I'm not surprised," he said. "Why air the Museum's dirty linen, anyway?"

"Come on, George. This is what makes for an interesting story!"

Moriarty turned to Margo. "You're the graduate student working on ethnopharmacology, aren't you?" he asked.

"That's right," she said, flattered. "How did you know?"

"I'm interested in the subject." He smiled and looked at her briefly. "The exhibition has several cases devoted to pharmacology and medicine. I wanted to talk to you about one of them, actually."

"Sure. What did you have in mind?" She looked at Moriarty more closely. He was about as average a Museum character as she could imagine: average height, a little pudgy, hair an average brown. His rumpled tweed jacket sported the heather tones that were regulation Museum-issue. The only things unusual about him were his large wristwatch, shaped like a sundial, and his eyes: an unusually clear hazel, shining with intelligence from behind his horn-rims.

Smithback sat forward, shifted irritably in his chair, and stared at the two. "Well," he said, "I'd like to stay on and witness this charming scene, but I'm interviewing someone in the Bug Room on Wednesday, and I need to finish my current chapter. George, don't sign any movie contracts for that exhibition of yours without talking to me first." He stood up with a snort and made for the door, threading a complex path between tables as he went.

= 8 =

Jonathan Hamm peered down the basement corridor through a thick pair of glasses that badly needed cleaning. Leather leashes were wrapped around his black-gloved hands, and two hounds sat obediently at his feet. His assistant tracker stood beside him. Next to the assistant was Lieutenant D'Agosta, holding soiled, heavily creased blueprints, his two deputies leaning against the wall behind him. Police-issue pump-action Remington 12-gauges hung off their shoulders.

D'Agosta rustled through the blueprints. "Can't the dogs smell which way to go?" he asked irritably.

Hamm let out a long breath. "*Hounds*. They're hounds. And they're not on a scent. They haven't been on a good scent since we began. Or rather, they've been on too many scents."

D'Agosta grunted, withdrew a sodden cigar from his jacket pocket, and began to raise it toward his mouth. Hamm caught his eye.

"Oh yeah," said D'Agosta. He pushed the cigar back into his pocket.

Hamm sniffed the air. It was damp, which was good. But that was the only good thing about this little picnic. First, there was the usual stupidity of the police. *What kind of dogs are these?* they'd asked. *We wanted blood-hounds.* These *were* hounds, he'd explained, a blue-tick hound and a black-and-tan coonhound. Given the right conditions, these hounds could track a lost hiker after a three-foot blizzard. *But these,* thought Hamm, *aren't exactly the right conditions.*

As usual, the crime scene had been fouled up. Chemicals, spray paint, chalk, a thousand people tramping in and out. Besides, the area around the base of the staircase had been literally bathed in blood; even now, eighteen hours or so after the crime, the smell hung heavily in the air, agitating the hounds.

They first tried to follow the scent from the crime scene itself. When that failed, Hamm suggested they ".cut for scent," making a perimeter loop around the crime scene, hoping to pick up the trail as it exited.

The hounds had never been trained to work indoors. Naturally, they were confused. But it wasn't his fault. The police wouldn't even tell him if they were looking for a human or an animal. Perhaps they didn't know themselves.

"Let's go this way," said D'Agosta.

Hamm passed the leashes to his assistant, who started walking ahead, the hounds nosing the ground.

Next, the hounds had bayed up a storage room full of mastodon bones, and the paradichlorobenzene preservative that poured out when they opened the door had caused a half-hour delay while the hounds recovered their sense of smell. And that was just the first of a series of storage rooms full of animal pelts, gorillas in formaldehyde, a freezer full of dead zoo specimens, a whole vault full of human skeletons.

They came to an archway with an open metal door

leading onto a descending stone stairway. The walls were covered with a crust of lime, and the stairway was dark.

"That must be the dungeon," one of the policemen said, with a guffaw.

"This goes to the subbasement," D'Agosta said, consulting the blueprints. He motioned to one of the officers, who handed him a long flashlight.

The shallow stairs ended in a tunnel made of herringbone brickwork, its arched ceiling barely the height of a man. The tracker moved forward with the dogs, D'Agosta and Hamm behind. The two policemen came last.

"There's water on the floor," said Hamm.

"So what?" D'Agosta said.

"If there's been any water flowing through here there won't be any scent."

"I was told to expect puddles of water down here," D'Agosta replied. "It only floods when it rains, and it hasn't rained."

"That's reassuring," said Hamm.

They reached a place where four tunnels came together, and D'Agosta halted to consult the blueprints.

"Somehow I thought you'd need to look at that," Hamm said.

"Oh, yeah?" D'Agosta said. "Well, I've got a surprise for you. These blueprints don't cover the subbasement."

When one of the dogs whined and began furiously sniffing, Hamm came suddenly to attention. "This way. Quick."

The dogs whined again. "They've got something!" said Hamm. "It's a clear scent, it must be. Look at their hackles rise! Keep the light up here, I can't see a blessed thing."

The dogs were straining, pulling forward, noses up and sniffing the air ahead.

"You see, you see!" Hamm said. "It's an air scent.

Feel the fresh air on your cheek? I should have brought the spaniels. They're unbeatable with an air scent!''

The policemen slid past the dogs, one beaming his flashlight, the other carrying his shotgun at the ready. Ahead the tunnel forked again, and the dogs lunged to the right, breaking into a trot.

"Hold it, Mr. Hamm, there might be a killer out there," D'Agosta said.

The dogs suddenly broke into a deafening baying. "Sit!" cried the assistant. "Heel! Castor! Pollux! *Heel,* damn you!" The dogs lunged forward, paying no attention. "Hamm, I need a hand here!"

"What's gotten into you?" cried Hamm, wading into the frantic dogs, trying to grab their collars. "Castor, *heel*!"

"Shut them up!" snapped D'Agosta.

"He's loose!" cried the assistant, as one of the dogs bolted into the darkness. They rushed after the retreating sound of the dog.

"You smell it?" Hamm said, stopping short. "Christ Jesus, you *smell* it?"

A pungent, goatish odor suddenly enveloped them. The other dog was frantic with excitement, leaping and twisting and suddenly breaking free.

"Pollux! *Pollux!*"

"Wait!" said D'Agosta. "Forget the fucking dogs for a second. Let's proceed with a little order here. You two, get in front again. Safeties off.''

The two men pumped their shotguns.

In the echoing darkness ahead of them, the barking faltered, then stopped. There was a moment of silence. Then a terrible, unearthly shriek, like the screeching of tires, leapt from the inky tunnel. The two police officers looked at each other. The sound ended as suddenly as it began.

"Castor!" Hamm cried. "Oh, my God! He's been hurt!"

"Get back, Hamm, goddammit!" barked D'Agosta.

At that moment a shape suddenly hurtled at them from the darkness, and there were two stunning blasts from the shotguns, two flashes of light accompanied by deafening roars. The rumble echoed and died in the tunnel, and there was an intense silence.

"You fucking idiot, you just shot my hound," said Hamm quietly. Pollux lay five feet from them, blood pouring freely from his ruined head.

"He was coming right at me . . ." began one of the officers.

"Jesus Christ," said D'Agosta, "Stow that shit. There's still something out there."

They found the other dog a hundred yards down the tunnel. He was torn nearly in half, guts strung out in crazy patterns.

"Jesus, will you look at that," said D'Agosta.

Hamm said nothing.

Just beyond the body the tunnel branched. D'Agosta continued to stare at the dog. "Without the dogs, there's no way of knowing which way it went," he said at last. "Let's get the hell out of here and let forensics deal with this mess."

Hamm said nothing.

= 9 =

Moriarty, suddenly alone with Margo in the cafeteria, seemed even more uncomfortable. "So?" Margo prompted, after a brief silence.

"Actually, I really *did* want to talk to you about your work." He paused.

"You did?" Margo was unused to anyone showing interest in her project.

"Well, indirectly. The primitive medicine cases for the exhibition are complete, except one. We've got this terrific collection of shamanistic plants and artifacts from the Cameroons we want to display in the last case, but they're badly documented. If you'd be willing to take a look . . . ?"

"I'd love to," Margo said.

"Great! When?"

"Why not now? I've got some time."

They left the staff cafeteria and moved down a long basement hall lined with rumbling steam pipes and padlocked doors. One of the doors bore the label DINOSAUR STOREROOM 4—UPPER JURASSIC. Most of the Museum's dinosaur bone and other fossil collections were stored here in the basement, since—she had heard—the great weight of petrified bone would cause the upper floors to collapse.

"The collection's in one of the sixth-floor vaults," Moriarty said apologetically as they entered a service elevator. "I hope I can find it again. You know what a warren of storage rooms they've got up there."

"Have you heard anything more about Charlie Prine?" Margo asked quietly.

"Not much. Apparently he's not a suspect. But I don't think we'll see him back here for quite a while. Dr. Cuthbert told me before lunch that he was severely traumatized." Moriarty shook his head. "What an awful thing."

On the fifth floor, Margo followed Moriarty along a wide passageway and up a flight of metal stairs. The narrow, labyrinthine catwalks that made up this section of the sixth floor had been built directly underneath the Museum's long pitched roofs. On either side were rows of low metal doors, behind which lay the hermetically sealed vaults of the perishable anthropology collections. In earlier times, a poisonous cyanic compound had periodically been pumped into the vaults to kill vermin and bacteria; now, artifact preservation was handled with subtler methods.

As the two threaded their way along the catwalks, they passed a number of objects stacked against the walls: a carved war canoe, several totems, a row of slitted log drums. Even with one million square feet of storage space, every square inch had been utilized, including stairwells, corridors, and the offices of junior curators. Of fifty million artifacts and specimens, only about 5 percent was on exhibition; the rest was available only to scientists and researchers.

The New York Museum of Natural History consisted

not of a single building, but several large buildings, connected over the years to form one sprawling, rambling structure. As Margo and Moriarty passed from one of the buildings into another, the ceiling ascended, and the catwalk became a branching corridor. A dim light filtered down from a row of dirty skylights, illuminating shelves filled with plaster casts of aboriginal faces.

"God, this place is huge," said Margo, feeling a sudden cold thrust of fear, glad that she was seven stories above the dark spaces where the little boys had met their deaths.

"Largest in the world," Moriarty said, unlocking a door stenciled CEN. AFRICA, D-2.

He switched on a naked, 25-watt bulb. Peering in, Margo could see a tiny room stuffed with masks, shaman's rattles, painted and beaded skins, and a group of long sticks topped by grimacing heads. Along one wall was a row of wooden cabinets. Moriarty nodded toward them.

"The plants are in there. This other stuff is the shaman paraphernalia. It's a great collection, but Eastman, the guy who assembled the Cameroon stuff, wasn't exactly the most careful anthropologist when it came to documentation."

"This is incredible," said Margo. "I had no idea—"

"Listen," Moriarty interrupted, "when we began researching this exhibition, you wouldn't *believe* the things we found. There are close to a hundred anthropology vaults in this section alone, and I swear some of them haven't been opened in forty years."

Moriarty was suddenly more confident and animated. Margo decided that if he dumped the tweed jacket, shed a few pounds, and swapped the horn-rims for contacts, he could almost be cute.

But Moriarty was still talking. "Just last week, we found one of only a couple of existing examples of Yukaghir pictograph writing—right next door! As soon as I get time, I'll be writing a note for the *JAA*."

Margo smiled. He was so excited, he could have been talking about discovering an unknown Shakespeare play. She was sure that only a dozen readers of the *Journal of American Anthropology* would be interested. But Moriarty's enthusiasm was refreshing.

"Anyway," Moriarty said, pushing his glasses up his nose, "I just need someone to help me make sense of this Cameroon stuff for the display case write-up."

"What do you want me to do?" Margo asked, temporarily forgetting the next chapter of her dissertation. His enthusiasm was infectious.

"That's easy," said Moriarty. "I've got the rough script for the case right here."

He extracted a document from his briefcase. "See," he said, running a finger down the covering sheet, "this sets out what, ideally, we want the case to say. We call it the story line. All you have to do is flesh this out, plugging in a few of the artifacts and some of the plants."

Margo scanned the document. It was starting to sound a little more time-consuming than she'd anticipated. "How long do you think this will take, by the way?"

"Oh, ten to fifteen hours, max. I've got the accession listings and some descriptive notes right here. But we've got to hurry. The opening is just a few days away."

Back came the memory of her next chapter. "Now wait a minute," she said. "This is a big job, and I've got a dissertation to write."

The dismay on Moriarty's face was almost comical. It hadn't even occurred to him that she might have other things to do. "You mean you can't help?"

"Maybe I can squeeze it in," she murmured.

His face brightened. "Great! Listen, while we're on the sixth floor, let me show you some of the other stuff up here."

He led her to another vault and inserted a key. The door rasped open to a dazzling display of painted buffalo skulls, rattles, feather bundles, and even a row of what she recognized as raven skeletons tied up with rawhide.

"Jesus," Margo breathed.

"There's a whole religion in here," Moriarty said. "Wait till you see what we're putting on display. This is just the stuff left behind. We've got one of the best Sun Dance shirts anywhere. And look at this!" He pulled open a drawer. "Original wax cylinder recordings of the Sun Dance cycle songs, every one. Recorded in 1901. We've put them on tape, and we're going to play them in the Sioux room. What do you think? *Great* exhibition, huh?"

"It's certainly caused a fuss in the Museum," Margo replied cautiously.

"Actually, there isn't as much controversy as people seem to make out," Moriarty said. "There's no reason why science and entertainment can't meet as friends."

Margo couldn't resist. "I'll bet your boss Cuthbert put you up to *that* line."

"He's always felt that exhibitions should be more accessible to the general public. People may attend this because they expect ghosts and goblins and a spooky show—and they'll get them. But they'll go away with more than you might expect. Besides, the show's going to generate a lot of cash for the Museum. What's wrong with that?"

"Nothing," Margo smiled. She'd leave the baiting to Smithback.

But Moriarty wasn't finished. "I know the word *superstition* has a bad connotation in some people's minds," he said. "It smacks of exploitation. And it's true that some of the effects we're putting together for the show are . . . well . . . a bit sensational. But an exhibit called *Aboriginal Religion* just wouldn't sell, would it?" He looked at her with mute appeal.

"I don't think anyone objects to the title," Margo said. "I guess there are a few people who don't feel your ends are truly scientific."

He shook his head. "Just the crusty old curators and the crackpots. Like Frock, for example. They chose the *Superstition* exhibition over his proposal for one on evolution. So of course he doesn't have a good word to say about it."

Margo's smile faded. "Dr. Frock is a pretty brilliant anthropologist," she said.

"Frock? Dr. Cuthbert says he's gone off the deep end. 'The man's bloody daft,' he says." Moriarty imitated Cuthbert's Scottish accent. The sound echoed unpleasantly down the dim corridors.

"I don't think Cuthbert is half the genius *you* feel he is," Margo said.

"Now please, Margo. He's top rate."

"Not compared to Dr. Frock, he isn't. What about the Callisto Effect?" Margo asked. "That's some of the most cutting-edge work being done today."

"Does he have a single speck of proof to back up his speculations? Have you seen evidence of any unknown, monstrous species roaming the earth?" Moriarty shook his head again, sending his glasses plunging dangerously down his nose. "Theoretical hype. I mean, theory has its place, but it has to be backed up with fieldwork. And that sidekick of his, Greg Kawakita, just encourages Frock with that extrapolation program he's developing. I suppose Kawakita's got his own reasons. But it's pretty sad, really, to see a great mind take such a bad detour. I mean, just look at Frock's new book. *Fractal Evolution?* Even the title sounds more like a kid's computer game than science."

Margo listened with rising indignation. Perhaps Smithback had been right about Moriarty, after all. "Well," she said, "considering my affiliations to Dr. Frock, I don't suppose you'd want me messing with your exhibit. I might add too much hype to the script." She turned and walked briskly out the door and down the corridor.

Moriarty looked shocked. Too late, he remembered that Frock was her major advisor. He danced after her.

"Oh, no, no, I didn't mean—" he stammered. "Please, I was just . . . You know that Frock and Cuthbert don't get along. I guess I've picked up some of that."

He looked so horrified that Margo felt her anger fade.

"I didn't know they had *that* much of a problem with each other," she said, allowing Moriarty to stop her.

"Oh, yes. From way back. You know that ever since Frock came forward with this Callisto Effect, his star has been falling in the Museum. Now he's a department head in name only, and Cuthbert pulls the strings. Of course, I've just heard one side of the story. I'm very sorry, really. You *will* do the case for me, right?"

"On the condition," Margo countered, "that you get me out of this maze. I've got to get back to work."

"Oh, sure. Sorry," Moriarty said. The gaffe had brought back all of his shyness, and as they began retracing their way to the fifth floor, he was silent.

"So tell me more about your exhibition." Margo tried to put him at ease. "I've heard a little about some fabulously rare artifacts that will be on display."

"I guess you must mean the Kothoga tribe material," Moriarty said. "Only one expedition has ever found any traces of them. The figurine of their mythical beast Mbwun is—well, it's one of the centerpieces of the show." He hesitated. "Or I should say, it *will* be one of the centerpieces. It's not on display yet."

"Really?" Margo asked. "Isn't that waiting till the last minute?"

"The situation is kind of unusual," Moriarty replied. "But listen, Margo, this isn't for public consumption." They had returned to the catwalks, and Moriarty led her down the long corridors, speaking low. "There's been a lot of high-level interest in the Kothoga artifacts recently. People like Rickman, Dr. Cuthbert . . . even Wright, apparently. There's been controversy over whether the material should be included in the exhibition. Surely you've heard the stories of a curse on the figurine, that sort of nonsense?"

"Not much," Margo said.

"The expedition that found the Kothoga material met with tragedy," Moriarty continued, "and nobody's been near the stuff since. It's still in the original crates. Just last week, all the crates were taken from the basement area where they'd sat all these years and moved to the Secure Area. Nobody's had access to them since, and I haven't been able to prepare the final displays."

"But why were they moved?" Margo pressed.

They entered the elevator. Moriarty waited until the door had closed before answering. "Apparently, the crates had been recently tampered with."

"What? You mean somebody had broken in?"

Moriarty stared at Margo, his owlish face wearing its look of perpetual surprise. "I didn't say that," he replied.

He turned the key, and the elevator lurched downward.

= 10 =

D'Agosta wished with all his heart that the double-chili-
cheeseburger in his stomach would disappear. Not that
it was bothering him—yet—but it was an unwelcome
presence.

The place smelled like they all did. In fact it stank.
All the disinfectants in the world couldn't cover up the
smell of death. And the vomit-green walls in the Medical
Examiner's Office didn't help things any. Nor did the
large gurney, currently empty, sitting like an uninvited
guest under the bright lights of the autopsy suite.

His thoughts were interrupted as a large woman entered, two men following close behind. D'Agosta noticed stylish glasses, blonde hair escaping from under a
surgeon's cap. The woman strode over and held out her
hand, her red lipstick creased in a professional smile.

"Dr. Ziewicz," she said, with a crushing grip. "You
must be D'Agosta. This is my assistant, Dr. Fred
Gross." Ziewicz indicated a short, skinny man. "And

this is our photographer, Delbert Smith.'' Delbert nodded, clutching a 4×5 Deardorff to his chest.

"So, Dr. Ziewicz, you come here often?'' D'Agosta
asked, suddenly eager to say something, anything, to
stall the inevitable.

"NYME's my home away from home,'' Ziewicz replied with the same smile. "My field is—how shall I
put it—special forensics. For just about everybody. We
do our thing and ship them back out. Then I read about
what it all means in the papers.'' She looked at him
speculatively. "You've, ah, seen this kind of thing before, right?''

"Oh yeah,'' said D'Agosta. "All the time.'' The
burger in his gut felt like a lead ingot. Why didn't he
think ahead, remember what his afternoon schedule was
before chowing down like a damned hog?

"That's good.'' Ziewicz consulted her clipboard.
"Let's see, parental consent? Good. Looks like everything's in order. Fred, start with 5-B.''

She began slipping on latex gloves, three pairs, a
mask, goggles, and a plastic apron. D'Agosta did likewise.

Gross wheeled the gurney over to the morgue bank
and slid out 5-B. The indistinct shape under the plastic
looked strangely short to D'Agosta, with an odd bulge
at one end. Gross slid the cadaver and its tray onto the
gurney, wheeled the cart under the lights, checked the
toe tag, and locked down the wheels. He placed a stainless-steel bucket under the gurney's outlet pipe.

Ziewicz was fiddling with the microphone hanging
above the body.

"Testing, one two three . . . Fred, this mike is totally
dead.''

Fred bent over the reel-to-reel. "I can't understand it,
everything's turned on.''

D'Agosta cleared his throat. "It's unplugged,'' he
said.

There was a short silence.

"Well," said Ziewicz, "I'm glad there's someone here who's not a scientist. If you have any questions or comments, Mr. D'Agosta, please state your name and speak clearly toward the microphone. Okay? Everything goes on the tape. I'm just going to describe the state of the body first, and then we'll start cutting."

"Got it," D'Agosta replied tonelessly. *Cutting.* It was one thing when a dead body was just lying there at the scene. But when they started cutting into it, peeling the layers away—he'd never gotten used to that.

"Are we up and running? Good. This is Dr. Matilda Ziewicz and Dr. Frederick Gross, and the date is Monday, March 27, at two-fifteen in the afternoon. We are joined by Detective Sergeant—?"

"Lieutenant Vincent."

"Lieutenant Vincent D'Agosta, of the NYPD. We have here—"

Fred read off the tag. "William Howard Bridgeman, number 33-A45."

"I am now removing the covering." The thick plastic crackled.

There was a short silence. D'Agosta had a sudden flash of the gutted dog he'd seen that morning. *The trick is not to think too much. Don't think about your own Vinnie, eighth birthday just next week.*

Dr. Ziewicz took a deep breath. "We have here a Caucasian male, a boy, age about, ah, ten to twelve years, height, well, I can't give a height for this one because it's decapitated. Maybe four feet ten inches, maybe five feet? Weight, about ninety pounds. This is very approximate. The state of the body is such that I can see no other identifying marks. Eye color and facial features indeterminate due to massive head trauma."

"No anterior wounds or marks on the feet, legs, or genitals. Fred, please sponge off the abdominal area . . . thank you. There are an undetermined number of large lacerations proceeding from the left anterior pectoral region at a hundred and ninety degree angle downward through the costals, sternum, and terminating at the right anterior abdominal region. This is a massive wound, perhaps two feet long and a foot wide. It appears that the pectoralis minor and pectoralis major are separated from the external thoracic cavity, the external and internal intercostals are separated, and the body is eviscerated to a great degree. The sternal process has been split and the rib cage exposed. Massive hemorrhaging in the aortal— it's hard to see before cleaning and exploration.

"Fred, clean the edge of the thoracic cavity. The viscera that are clearly exposed and fully protuberant are the stomach, small and large intestines. The retroperitoneal organs appear to be in situ.

"Sponge the neck off, Fred. The neck area shows signs of trauma, some bruising, perhaps indicative of extravasation, possible spinal dislocation.

"Now for the head . . . dear God."

In the silence, Fred cleared his throat.

"The head is decapitated between the axial process and the atlas. The entire occipital portion of the calvarium and half the parietal process have been crushed, or rather seemingly punched through and removed, by means unknown, leaving a hole perhaps ten inches in diameter. The skull is empty. The entire brain appears to have fallen out or been extracted through this hole . . . The brain, or what is left of it, is in a pan here to the right of the head, but there is no indication of its original position vis-à-vis the body."

"It was found in pieces near the body," said D'Agosta.

"Thank you, Lieutenant. But where's the rest of it?"

"That's all there was."

"No. Something's missing. You got full scene-of-crime series for this?"

"Of course," said D'Agosta, trying not to show his annoyance.

"The brain is severely traumatized. Fred, bring me a number 2 scalpel and transverse speculum. The brain appears to have been severed at the medulla oblongata. The pons Varolii is intact, but separate. The cerebellum shows surface lacerations but is otherwise intact. There is little evidence of bleeding, indicating postmortem trauma. There's the body of fornix, attached. The cerebrum has been completely severed from the mesencephalon and the mesencephalon has been bisected and—look, Fred, there's no thalamoid region. And no pituitary. That's what's missing.''

"What's that?'' asked D'Agosta. He willed himself to look more closely. The brain, sitting in a stainless-steel pan, looked a hell of a lot more liquid than solid. He turned away. Baseball. Think about baseball. A pitch, the sound of a bat . . .

"The thalamus and the hypothalamus. The body's regulator.''

"The body's regulator,'' repeated D'Agosta.

"The hypothalamus regulates body temperature, blood pressure, heartbeat, and the metabolism of fats and carbohydrates. Also the sleep-wake cycle. We think it holds the centers of pleasure and pain. It's a very complicated organ, Lieutenant.'' She looked fixedly at him, anticipating a question. D'Agosta mumbled dutifully, "How does it do all that?''

"Hormones. It secretes hundreds of regulatory hormones into the brain and bloodstream.''

"Yeah,'' D'Agosta replied. He stepped back. The baseball soaring deep into center field, the center fielder dropping back, glove raised . . .

"Fred come over here and look at this,'' Ziewicz said sharply.

Fred bent over the pan. "It looks like . . . Well, I don't know . . .''

"Come on, Fred,'' Ziewicz coaxed.

"Well, it looks almost like—'' Fred paused. "Like a bite was taken out.''

"Exactly. Photographer!'' Delbert rushed forward.

"Get this. Looks just like when one of my kids takes a bite out of a cake."

D'Agosta leaned forward, but he could see nothing special in the gray, bloody mess.

"It's semicircular, like a human's, but it appears larger, more ragged than you'd expect. We'll take sections. Let's test for the presence of salivase enzymes, Fred, just in case. Take this to the lab, tell them to flash-freeze it and microsection here, here, and here. Five sections each. Stain at least one with eosinophil. Stain one with salivase activating enzyme. Anything else you or they can think of."

As Fred left, Ziewicz continued. "I am now bisecting the cerebrum. The posterior lobe is bruised, consistent with removal from the cranium. Photograph. The surface shows three parallel lacerations or incisions, approximately four millimeters apart, about half an inch deep. I am parting the first incision. Photograph. Lieutenant, see how these lacerations start wide and then converge? What do you think?"

"I don't know," D'Agosta said, peering a little closer. *It's just a dead brain,* he thought.

"Long fingernails, maybe? Sharpened fingernails? I mean, do we have a homicidal psychopath on our hands?"

Fred returned from the lab, and they continued working on the brain for what seemed an eternity to D'Agosta. Finally, Ziewicz told Fred to put it in the refrigerator.

"I will now examine the hands," she spoke into the microphone. She removed a plastic bag from the right hand and carefully resealed it. Then she lifted the hand, rotated it, examined the fingernails. "There is foreign matter under the thumb, index, and ring fingers. Fred, three well slides."

"He's just a kid," D'Agosta said. "You'd expect his fingernails to be dirty."

"Perhaps, Lieutenant," Ziewicz replied. She scraped

the material into small depressions in the slides, one finger at a time. "Fred, the stereozoom? I want to look at this."

Ziewicz placed the slide on the stage, peered down, and adjusted the instrument.

"Normal fingernail dirt under the thumb, from the looks of it. Same with the others. Fred, full analysis, just in case."

There was nothing of interest on the left hand.

"I will now," Ziewicz continued, "examine the longitudinal trauma to the anterior portion of the body. Del, photographs, here, here, and here, and whatever else you think will show the wound best. Close-ups of the areas of penetration. It looks like the killer has done our Y-incision for us, wouldn't you say, Lieutenant?"

"Yeah," D'Agosta said, swallowing hard.

There were a series of rapid flashes.

"Forceps," Ziewicz continued. "Three ragged lacerations begin just above the left nipple in the greater pectoral, penetrating and eventually separating the muscle. I am opening and probing the first laceration at the point of entry. Clamp there, Fred.

"I am now probing the wound. There is unidentified foreign matter here. Fred, a glassine? It looks like clothing material, perhaps from the victim's shirt. Photograph."

The flash popped, and then she held up a small piece of what looked like bloody lint, dropping it into the glassine envelope. She continued probing in silence for a few moments.

"There is another piece of foreign material deep in the muscle, about four centimeters directly below the right nipple. It is lodged on a rib. It appears to be hard. Photograph. Stick a flag in there, Fred."

She extracted it and held it up, a bloody lump poised at the end of the long forceps.

D'Agosta ventured forward. "What is it? Rinse it off, maybe, and see?"

She glanced at him with a slight smile. "Fred, bring me a beaker of sterile water."

As she dipped the object in and stirred, the water turned brownish red.

"Keep the water, we'll see if there's anything else in it," she said, holding her find to the light.

"Jesus H. Christ," said D'Agosta. "It's a claw. A fucking claw."

Ziewicz turned to her assistant. "That will be a charming snippet of monologue for our tape, won't it, Fred?"

= 11 =

Margo dumped her books and papers on the sofa and glanced at the clock perched atop the television: ten-fifteen. She shook her head. What an unbelievable, horrible day. Staying all those extra hours had only netted three new paragraphs on her dissertation. And she still had to work on the display-case copy for Moriarty. She sighed, sorry she'd ever agreed to the project.

Reflected neon light from a liquor store across the avenue struggled through the lone window of Margo's living room, throwing the room into electric-blue chiaroscuro. She turned on the small overhead light and leaned against the door, scanning the disorder slowly. Normally, she was neat to excess. But now after just one week of neglect, textbooks, letters of sympathy, legal documents, shoes, and sweaters were scattered across the furniture. Empty cartons from the Chinese restaurant downstairs lay neglected in the sink. Her old Royal typewriter and a fan of research papers were spread out on the hardwood floor.

The shabby neighborhood—not-yet-gentrified upper Amsterdam Avenue—had given her father another reason why she should return home to Boston. "This is no place for a girl like you to live, Midge," he had said, using her childhood nickname. "And that Museum is no place to work. Cooped up day after day with all those dead, stuffed creatures, things in jars. What kind of a life is that? Come back and work for me. We'd get you a house in Beverly, maybe Marblehead. You'll be happier there, Midge, I know you will."

When she noticed her answering machine was blinking, Margo pressed the message button.

"It's Jan," the first message began. "I got back into town today, and I just heard. Listen, I'm really, really sorry to hear about your father's death. I'll call back later, okay? I want to talk to you. Bye."

She waited. Another voice came on. "Margo, this is your mother." And then a click.

She squeezed her eyes tightly for a moment, then took a deep breath. She wouldn't call Jan, not just yet. And she wouldn't return her mother's call, either; not until tomorrow, at least. She knew what her mother would say: *You have to come home to your father's business. It's what he would have wanted. You owe it to both of us.*

Turning away, she settled herself cross-legged in front of the typewriter, and stared at the curators' notes, catalogue data, and accession listings Moriarty had given her. It was due the day after tomorrow, he'd said, and the next chapter of her dissertation was due the following Monday.

She glanced at the papers for another minute or two, collecting her thoughts. Then she began to type. A few moments later, she stopped and stared into the dusk. She remembered how her father used to make omelettes—the only thing he knew how to cook—on Sunday mornings. "Hey, Midge," he would always say. "Not bad for an old ex-bachelor, huh?"

Several of the lights outside had been shut off as the shops closed. Margo looked out at the graffiti, the boarded-up windows. Maybe her father was right: Poverty wasn't much fun.

Poverty. She shook her head, remembering the last time she'd heard that word, remembering the expression on her mother's face as she'd pronounced it. The two of them had been sitting in the cool, dark office of her father's executor, listening to all the complex reasons why her father's debt-to-equity ratio and lack of estate planning was forcing liquidation—unless some family member were to step in to keep his business afloat.

She wondered about the parents of the two little boys. *They must have had high hopes for their children, too,* she thought. Now, they'll never know disappointment. Or happiness. Then her thoughts moved to Prine. And the blood on his shoes.

She got up and turned on more lights. Time to start dinner. Tomorrow, she'd lock herself in her office, get that chapter finished. Work on the Cameroon write-up for Moriarty. And put off making a decision—for one more day, at least. By next week's meeting with Frock, she promised herself, she'd have made up her mind.

The telephone rang. Automatically, she picked it up.

"Hello," she said. She listened for a moment. "Oh. Hello, Mother."

= 12 =

Night came early to the Museum of Natural History. As five o'clock neared, the early spring sun was already setting. Inside, the crowds began to thin. Tourists, schoolchildren, and harried parents streamed down the marble staircases toward the exits. Soon the echoes and shouts and clatter of footsteps in the vaulted halls died away. One by one, the exhibit cases went dark, and as the night wore on, the remaining lights threw crazed shadows across the marble floors.

A lone guard wandered along a hall, making his rounds, swinging a long key chain and humming. It was the beginning of his shift, and he was dressed in the standard Museum-issue blue-and-black guard uniform. Long ago the novelty of the Museum had worn off.

The whole joint gives me the creeps, he thought. *Look at that son of a bitch in there. Goddamn native shit. Who the hell would pay to look at this stuff? Half of it's got curses on it, anyway.*

The mask leered at him out of a dark case. He hurried

on to the next station, where he turned a key in a box. The box recorded the time: 10:23 P.M. As he moved into the next hall, he had the unsettling impression—as he had so often—that his echoing footfalls were being carefully duplicated by some unseen presence.

He came to the next station and turned the key. The box clicked, and registered 10:34 P.M.

It only took four minutes to get to the next station. That gave him six minutes for a toke.

He ducked into a stairwell, closing and locking the door behind him, and peered down toward the darkened basement, where another door opened to an interior courtyard. His hand went for the light switch at the top of the stairs, but then withdrew. No sense calling attention to himself. He gripped the metal handrail tightly as he crept downward. In the basement, he made his way along the wall until he felt a long horizontal handle. He pushed, and frigid night air streamed in. He wedged open the door and lit up a joint, inhaling the bitter smoke with pleasure as he leaned out into the courtyard. A thin light from the deserted cloister beyond gave a pale illumination to his movements. The faint hum of passing traffic, muffled by so many intervening walls, passages, and parapets, seemed to come from another planet. He felt, with relief, the warm rush of the cannabis—another long night made bearable. Smoke finished, he flicked the roach into the dark, ran his fingers through his crew cut, stretched.

Halfway up the stairs, he heard the door slam shut below. He stopped, feeling a sudden chill. Had he left the door open? No. Shit, what if someone had seen him toke up? But they couldn't have smelt the smoke, and in the dark, it would've looked just like a cigarette.

There was a strange, rotten odor in the air that had nothing to do with weed. But no light flicked on, no footstep sounded on the metal steps. He started up toward the landing above.

Just as he reached it, he sensed a swift movement on

the stairs behind him. He spun around, and a hard jerk on his chest shoved him backward against the wall. The last thing he saw were his shadowy entrails rolling and slipping down the stairs. After a moment, he stopped wondering where all that gore had suddenly come from.

= 13 =

Tuesday

Bill Smithback sat in a heavy chair, watching the sharp, angular figure of Lavinia Rickman behind her birchwood veneer desk, reading his rumpled manuscript. Two bright red fingernails tapped on the glossy finish. Smithback knew that the fingernail ditty did not bode well. A very gray Tuesday morning sat outside the windows.

The room was not a typical Museum office. The untidy stacks of papers, journals, and books that seemed a fixture in other offices were missing. Instead, the shelves and desk were decorated with knickknacks from around the world: a storyteller doll from New Mexico, a brass Buddha from Tibet, several puppets from Indonesia. The walls were painted light institutional green, and the room smelled of pine air freshener.

Additional curios were arranged on both sides of her desk, as formal and symmetrical as shrubs in a French garden: an agate paperweight, a bone letter opener, a Japanese netsuke. And in the center of the motif hovered Rickman herself, bent primly over the manuscript. The swirled stiff orange hair, Smithback thought, didn't go well with the green walls.

The tapping speeded, then slowed as Rickman turned the pages. Finally she flicked over the last page, gathered the loose sheets together, and squared them in the precise center of the desk.

"Well," she said, looking up with a bright smile. "I have a few small suggestions."

"Oh," said Smithback.

"This section on Aztec human sacrifice, for example. It's much too controversial." She licked her finger daintily and found the page. "Here."

"Yes, but in the exhibition—"

"Mr. Smithback, the exhibition deals with the subject *tastefully.* This, on the other hand, is not tasteful. It's far too graphic." She zipped a Magic Marker across his work.

"But it's entirely accurate," Smithback said, wincing inwardly.

"I am concerned with *emphasis,* not accuracy. Something can be *entirely* accurate but have the wrong emphasis, and thus give the wrong impression. Allow me to remind you that we have a large Hispanic population here in New York."

"Yes, but how is this going to offend—"

"Moving on, this section on Gilborg simply must go." She zipped another line across another page.

"But why—?"

She leaned back in her chair. "Mr. Smithback, the Gilborg expedition was a grotesque failure. They were looking for an island that did not exist. One of them, as you are so zealous in pointing out, raped a native woman. We were careful to keep all mention of Gilborg *out* of the exhibition. Now, is it really necessary to document the Museum's failures?"

"But his collections were superb!" Smithback protested feebly.

"Mr. Smithback, I am not convinced that you under-

stand the nature of this assignment." There was a long
silence. The tapping began again. "Do you really think
that the Museum hired you, and is *paying* you, to document failure and controversy?"

"But failure and controversy are part of science, and
who's going to read a book that—"

"There are many corporations that give money to the
Museum, corporations that might very well be disturbed
by some of this," Mrs. Rickman interrupted. "And there
are volatile ethnic groups out there, ready to attack, that
might take *strong* exception."

"But we're talking about things that happened a hundred years ago, while—"

"Mr. Smithback!" Mrs. Rickman had only raised her
voice a little, but the effect was startling. A silence fell.

"Mr. Smithback, I must tell you quite frankly . . ."
She paused, then stood up briskly and walked around
the desk until she was standing directly behind the
writer.

"I must tell you," Mrs. Rickman continued, "that it
seems to be taking you longer than I thought to come
around to our point of view. You are not writing a
book for a commercial publisher. To put it bluntly,
we're looking for the kind of favorable treatment you
gave the Boston Aquarium in your previous—ahem—
assignment." She moved in front of Smithback, perching
stiffly on the edge of the desk. "There are certain things we
expect, and indeed, that we have a *right* to expect. They
are—" she ticked them off on bony fingers.

"One: No controversy.

"Two: Nothing that might offend ethnic groups.

"Three: Nothing that might harm the Museum's reputation.

"Now, is that so unreasonable?" She lowered her
voice and, leaning forward, squeezed Smithback's hand
with her dry one.

"I . . . no." Smithback struggled with an almost overwhelming urge to withdraw his hand.

"Well, then, that's settled." She moved behind the desk, and slid the manuscript over to him.

"Now, there's one small matter we need to discuss." She enunciated very precisely. "There were a few spots in the manuscript where you quoted some interesting comments by people 'close to the exhibition,' but neglected to identify the exact sources. Nothing important, you understand, but I'd like a list of those sources—for my files, nothing more." She smiled expectantly.

Alarms rang in Smithback's head. "Well," he replied carefully, "I'd like to help you out, but the ethics of journalism won't let me." He shrugged his shoulders. "You know how it is."

Mrs. Rickman's smile faded quickly, and she opened her mouth to speak. Just then, to Smithback's relief, the phone rang. He got up to leave, gathering his manuscript together. As he was closing the door, he heard a sharp intake of breath.

"Not *another!*"

The door hissed shut.

= 14 =

D'Agosta just couldn't get used to the Hall of the Great Apes. All those big grinning chimps, stuffed, hanging out of the fake trees, with their hairy arms and hilarious realistic dicks and big human hands with real fingernails. He wondered why it had taken so long for scientists to figure out that man was descended from the apes. Should've been obvious the first time they clapped eyes on a chimp. And he'd heard somewhere that chimps were just like humans, violent, excitable, always beating hell out of each other, even murdering and eating each other. *Jesus,* he thought, *there must be some other way to get around the Museum without going through this hall.*

"This way," said the guard, "down this stairway. It's pretty awful, Lieutenant. I was coming in at—"

"I'll hear that later," said D'Agosta. After the kid, D'Agosta was ready for anything. "You say he's wearing a guard's uniform. You know him?"

"I don't know, sir. It's hard to tell."

The guard pointed down the dim stairs. The stairway

opened onto some kind of courtyard. The body lay at the bottom, in shadow. Everything was streaked and splattered in black—the floor, the walls, the overhead light. D'Agosta knew what the black was.

"You," he said, turning to one of several policemen following him, "get some lights in here. I want the place dusted and swept for fibers pronto. Is the SOC unit on its way? The man's obviously dead, so keep the ambulance people out for a while. I don't want them messing things up."

D'Agosta looked down the stairs again. "Jesus H. Christ," he said, "whose footprints are those? Some jackass walked right through that pool of blood, it looks like. Or maybe our murderer decided to leave us a fat clue."

There was a silence.

"Are those yours?" He turned to the guard. "What's your name?"

"Norris. Eric Norris. As I was saying, I—"

"Yes or no?"

"Yes, but—"

"Shut up. Are those the shoes?"

"Yes. See, I was—"

"Take the shoes off. You're ruining the carpet." *Fucking doorshaker,* D'Agosta thought. "Take them to the forensics lab. Tell them to seal 'em in a crime bag, they'll know what to do. Wait for me there. No, don't wait for me there. I'll call you later. I'll have a few questions for you. No, take the fucking shoes off right here." He didn't want another Prine on his hands. What was it about this Museum, people liked to go around wading in blood? "You'll have to walk over there in your socks."

"Yes, sir."

One of the cops behind D'Agosta snickered.

D'Agosta looked at him. "You think it's funny? He tracked blood all over the place. It's not funny."

D'Agosta moved halfway down the stairwell. The

head was lying in a far corner, face down. He couldn't see it all that well, but he knew that he'd find the top of the skull punched out, the brains floating around somewhere in all that gore. God, what a mess a body could be if it wanted to.

A step sounded on the stairway behind him. "SOC," said a short man, followed by a photographer and several other men in lab coats.

"Finally. I want lights there, there, and there, and wherever else the photographer wants 'em. I want a perimeter set up, I want it set up five minutes *ago,* I want every speck of lint and grain of sand picked up. I want TraceChem used on everything. I want—well, what else do I want? I want every test known to man, and I want that perimeter observed by everyone, got it? No fuckups this time."

D'Agosta turned. "Is the Crime Lab team on the premises? And the coroner's investigator? Or are they out for coffee and croissants?" He patted the breast pocket of his jacket, looking for a cigar. "Put cardboard boxes over those footprints. And you guys, when you're done, squeegee a trail around the body so we can walk without tracking blood everywhere."

"Excellent." D'Agosta heard a low, mellifluous voice behind him.

"Who the hell are you?" he said, turning to see a tall, slender man, wearing a crisp black suit, leaning against the top of the stairwell. Hair so blond it was almost white was brushed straight back above pale blue eyes. "The undertaker?"

"Pendergast," the man said, stepping down and holding out his hand. The photographer, cradling his equipment, pushed past him.

"Well, Pendergast, you better have a good reason to be here, otherwise—"

Pendergast smiled. "Special Agent Pendergast."

"Oh. FBI? Funny, why aren't I surprised? Well, howdo, Pendergast. Why the hell don't you guys phone

ahead? Listen, I got a headless, de-brained stiff down
there. Where're the rest of you, anyway?''

Pendergast withdrew his hand. ''There's just me, I'm
afraid.''

''What? Don't kid me. You guys always travel around
in packs.''

The lights popped on, and the gore around them was
bathed in brilliance. Everything that previously appeared
black was suddenly illuminated, all the various shades
of the body's secret workings made visible. Something
D'Agosta suspected was Norris's breakfast was also visible, lying amidst a wash of body fluids. Involuntarily,
D'Agosta's jaw started working. Then his eye caught a
piece of skull with the dead guard's crew cut still on it,
lying a good five feet from the body.

''Oh Jesus,'' said D'Agosta, stepping back, and then
he lost it. Right in front of the FBI guy, in front of SOC,
in front of the photographer, he blew his own breakfast.
I can't believe it, he thought. *The first time in twenty-
two years, and it's happening at the worst possible moment.*

The coroner's investigator appeared on the stairs, a
young woman in a white coat and plastic apron. ''Who's
the officer in charge?'' she asked, sliding on her gloves.

''I am,'' said D'Agosta, wiping his mouth. He looked
at Pendergast. ''For a few more minutes, anyway. Lieutenant D'Agosta.''

''Dr. Collins,'' the investigator replied briskly.

Followed by an assistant, she walked down to an area
near the body that was being squeegeed free of blood.

''Photographer,'' she said, ''I'm turning the body
over. Full series, please.''

D'Agosta averted his gaze. ''We got work to do, Pendergast,'' he said authoritatively. He pointed at the
vomit. ''Don't clean that up until the SOC has finished
with these stairs. Got it?''

Everyone nodded.

''I wanna know ingress and egress as soon as possible.

See if you can ID the body. If it's a guard, get Ippolito down here. Pendergast, let's go up to the command post, get coordinated, or liaised, or whatever the hell you call it, and then let's return when the team is done for a look-see.''

"Capital," said Pendergast.

Capital? thought D'Agosta. The guy sounded deep South. He'd met types like this before, and they were hopeless in New York City.

Pendergast leaned forward and said quietly, "The blood splattered on the wall is rather interesting."

D'Agosta looked over. "You don't say."

"I'd be interested in the ballistics on that blood."

D'Agosta looked straight into Pendergast's pale eyes. "Good idea," he said finally. "Hey, photographer, get a close-up series of the blood on the wall. And you, you—"

"McHenry, sir."

"I want a ballistic analysis done on that blood. Looks like it was moving fast at a sharp angle. I want the source pinpointed, speed, force, a full report."

"Yes, sir."

"I want it on my desk in thirty minutes."

McHenry looked a little unhappy.

"Okay, Pendergast, any more ideas?"

"No, that was my only one."

"Let's go."

In the temporary command post, everything was in place. D'Agosta always saw to that. Not one piece of paper was loose, not one file was out, not one tape recorder sitting on a desk. It looked good, and now he was glad that it did. Everyone was busy, the phones were lit up, but things were under control.

Pendergast slipped his lean form into a chair. For a formal-looking guy, he moved like a cat. Briefly, D'Agosta gave him an overview of the investigation.

"Okay, Pendergast," he concluded. "What's your jurisdiction here? Did we fuck up? Are we out?"

Pendergast smiled. "No, not at all. As far as I can tell, I would not have done anything differently myself. You see, Lieutenant, we've been in the case from the very beginning, only we didn't realize it."

"How so?"

"I'm from the New Orleans field office. We were working on a series of killings down there, some very odd killings. Not to get into specifics, but the victims had the backs of their skulls removed, and the brains extracted. Same modus operandi."

"No shit. When was this?"

"Several years ago."

"Several *years* ago? That—"

"Yes. They went unsolved. First it was ATF, because they thought drugs might have been involved, then it was FBI when ATF couldn't make any progress. But we couldn't do anything with it, the trail was cold. And then yesterday, I read a wire service report about the double murder here in New York. The MO is too, ah, too peculiar not to make an immediate connection, don't you think? So I flew up last night. I'm not even officially here. Although I will be tomorrow."

D'Agosta relaxed. "So you're from Louisiana. I thought you might be some new boy in the New York office."

"They'll be here," said Pendergast. "When I make my report tonight, they'll be in on it. But I will be in charge of the case."

"You? No way, not in New York City."

Pendergast smiled. "I will be in charge, Lieutenant. I've been pursuing this case for years and I am, frankly, interested in it." The way Pendergast said *interested* sent a strange sensation down D'Agosta's back. "But don't worry, Lieutenant, I am ready and willing to work with you, side by side, in perhaps a different way than the New York office might. If you'll meet me halfway, that is. This isn't my turf and I'm going to need your help. How about it?''

He stood up and held out his hand. *Christ,* D'Agosta thought, *the boys in the New York office will take him apart in two and a half hours and ship the pieces back to New Orleans.*

"Deal," said D'Agosta, grasping his hand. "I'll introduce you around, starting with the security director, Ippolito. Provided you answer one question. You said the MO of the New Orleans killings was the same. What about the bite marks we found in the brain of the older boy? The claw fragment?"

"From what you told me about the autopsy, Lieutenant, the ME was only speculating about the bite marks," Pendergast replied. "I'll be interested to hear the salivase results. Is the claw being tested?"

Later, D'Agosta would remember that his question had been only half answered. Now, he simply replied, "It's being done today."

Pendergast leaned back in his chair and made a tent of his fingers, his eyes looking off into space. "I'll have to pay a visit to Dr. Ziewicz when she examines today's unpleasantness."

"Say, Pendergast? You aren't by any chance related to Andy Warhol, are you?"

"I don't care much for modern art, Lieutenant."

The crime scene was packed but orderly, everyone moving swiftly and speaking in undertones, as if in deference to the dead man. The morgue crew had arrived but was standing out of the way, patiently observing the proceedings. Pendergast stood with D'Agosta and Ippolito, the Museum's Security Director.

"Indulge me if you will," Pendergast was saying to the photographer. "I'd like a shot from here, like this." Pendergast demonstrated briefly. "And I'd like a series from the top of the stairs, and a sequence coming down.

Take your time, get a nice play of line, shadow, and light going.''

The photographer looked carefully at Pendergast, then moved off.

Pendergast turned to Ippolito. ''Here's a question. Why was the guard—what did you say his name was, Mr. Ippolito, Jolley, Fred Jolley?—down here in the first place? This wasn't part of his rounds. Correct?''

''That's right,'' Ippolito said. He was standing in a dry spot near the entrance to the courtyard, his face a poisonous green.

D'Agosta shrugged. ''Who knows?''

''Indeed,'' Pendergast said. He looked out into the courtyard beyond the stairwell, which was small and deep, brick walls rising on three sides. ''And he locked the door behind himself, you say. We have to assume he went outside here, or was headed in that direction. Hmm. The Taurid meteor shower was peaking at about that time last night. Perhaps Jolley here is an aspiring astronomer. But I doubt it.'' He stood still for a minute, looking around. Then he turned back toward them. ''I believe I can tell you why.''

Christ, a real Sherlock Holmes, thought D'Agosta.

''He came down the stairwell to indulge a habit of his. Marijuana. This courtyard is an isolated and well-ventilated spot. A perfect place to, ah, smoke some weed.''

''Marijuana? That's just a guess.''

''I believe I see the roach,'' said Pendergast, pointing into the courtyard. ''Just where the door meets the jamb.''

''I can't see a thing,'' said D'Agosta. ''Hey, Ed. Check out the base of the door. Right there. What is it?''

''A joint,'' said Ed.

''What's the matter with you guys, can't find a fucking joint? I told you to pick up every grain of sand, for Chrissake.''

''We haven't done that grid yet.''

"Right." He looked at Pendergast. *Lucky bastard. Probably wasn't the guard's joint anyway.*

"Mr. Ippolito," Pendergast drawled, "is it common for your staff to use illicit drugs while on duty?"

"Absolutely not, but I'm not convinced it was Fred Jolley that—"

Pendergast shut him up with a wave of the hand. "I assume you can account for all these footprints."

"Those belong to the guard who found the body," said D'Agosta.

Pendergast bent down. "These completely cover any local evidence that may remain," he said, frowning. "Really, Mr. Ippolito," he said, "you should have your men better trained in how to preserve a crime scene."

Ippolito opened his mouth, then closed it again. D'Agosta suppressed a smirk.

Pendergast was walking carefully back underneath the stairwell, where a large metal door stood partially open. "Orient me, Mr. Ippolito. This door under the stairwell goes where?"

"A hallway."

"Leading to—?"

"Well, there's the Secure Area down to the right. But it's not possible the killer went that way, because . . ."

"Excuse me for contradicting you, Mr. Ippolito, but I'm sure the killer *did* go that way," Pendergast replied. "Let me guess. Beyond the Secure Area is the Old Basement, am I right?"

"Right," said Ippolito.

"Where the two children were found."

"Bingo," said D'Agosta.

"This Secure Area sounds interesting, Mr. Ippolito. Shall we take a stroll?"

Beyond the rusty metal door, a row of light bulbs stretched down a long basement corridor. The floor was covered in shabby linoleum, and the walls were hung with murals of Southwestern Pueblo Indians grinding corn, weaving, and stalking deer.

"Lovely," said Pendergast. "A shame they're down here. They look like early Fremont Ellis."

"They used to hang in the Hall of the Southwest," said Ippolito. "It closed in the twenties, I think."

"Ah!" said Pendergast, scrutinizing one of the murals. "It *is* Ellis. My heavens, these are lovely. Look at the light on that adobe facade."

"So," said Ippolito. "How do you know?"

"Why," said Pendergast, "anyone who knows Ellis would recognize these."

"I mean, how do you know the killer came through here?"

"I suppose I was guessing," said Pendergast, examining the next painting. "You see, when someone says 'it's impossible,' I have this very bad habit, I can't help myself, I immediately contradict that person in the most positive terms possible. A very bad habit, but one that I find hard to break. But of course, now we *do* know the killer came through here."

"How?" Ippolito seemed confused.

"Look at this marvelous rendition of old Santa Fe. Have you ever been to Santa Fe?"

There was a momentary silence. "Er, no," said Ippolito.

"There is a mountain range behind the town, called the Sierra de Sangre de Cristo. It means the 'Blood of Christ Mountains' in Spanish."

"So?"

"Well the mountains *do* look quite red in the setting sun, but not, I dare say, *that* red. That's real blood, and it's fresh. A shame, really, it's ruined the painting."

"Holy shit," said D'Agosta. "Look at that."

A broad streak of blood was smeared waist-high across the painting.

"You know, murder is a messy thing. We should find traces of blood all along this corridor. Lieutenant, we'll need the crime lab people in here. I think we have your egress, at any rate." He paused. "Let's finish our little tour, and then call them in. I'd like to go ahead and look for evidence, if you don't mind.''

"Be my guest," said D'Agosta.

"Careful where you walk, Mr. Ippolito, we'll be asking them to check the floors as well as the walls.''

They came to a locked door marked RESTRICTED. "This is the Secure Area," said Ippolito.

"I see," said Pendergast. "And what exactly is the point of this Secure Area, Mr. Ippolito? Is the rest of the Museum insecure?''

"Not at all," the Security Director replied quickly. "The Secure Area is for storing especially rare and valuable objects. This is the best-protected museum in the country. We've recently installed a system of sliding metal doors throughout the Museum. They're all linked to our computer system, and in the event of a burglary we can seal off the Museum in sections, just like the watertight compartments on a—''

"I get the picture, Mr. Ippolito, thank you very much,'' Pendergast said. "Interesting. An old copper-sheathed door," he said, examining it closely.

D'Agosta saw that the copper covering was riddled with shallow dents.

"Fresh dents, by the look of them," Pendergast said. "Now, what do you make of this?'' He pointed downward.

"Jesus H. Christ," breathed D'Agosta, looking at the lower section of the door. The wooden door frame was scored and gouged into a welter of fresh splinters, as if something with claws had been scrabbling at it.

Pendergast stepped back. "I want the entire door analyzed, if you please, Lieutenant. And now to see what's inside. Mr. Ippolito, if you would be so kind as to open the door without getting your hands all over it?''

"I'm not supposed to let anyone in there without clearance.''

D'Agosta looked at him in disbelief. "You mean you want us to get a damn warrant?''

"Oh, no, no, it's just that—"

"He forgot the key," said Pendergast. "We'll wait."

"I'll be right back," said Ippolito, and his hurried footsteps echoed down the corridor. When he was out of hearing D'Agosta turned to Pendergast. "I hate to say it, Pendergast, but I like the way you work. That was pretty slick, the painting, and the way you handled Ippolito. Good luck with the New York boys."

Pendergast looked amused. "Thank you. The feeling is mutual. I'm glad I am working with you, Lieutenant, and not one of these hard-boiled fellows. Judging from what happened back there, you still have a heart. You're still a normal human being."

D'Agosta laughed. "Naw, it wasn't that. It was the fucking scrambled eggs with ham and cheese and ketchup I had for breakfast. And that crew cut. I hate crew cuts."

= 15 =

The herbarium door was shut, as usual, despite the sign that read DO NOT CLOSE THIS DOOR. Margo knocked. *Come on, Smith, I know you're in there.* She knocked again, louder, and heard a querulous voice: "All right, hold your horses! I'm coming!"

The door opened and Bailey Smith, the old Curatorial Assistant of the herbarium, sat back down at his desk with an enormous sigh of irritation and began shuffling through his mail.

Margo stepped forward resolutely. Bailey Smith seemed to consider his job a gross imposition. And when at last he got around to things, it was hard to shut him up. Normally Margo would have merely sent down a requisition slip and avoided the ordeal. But she needed to examine the Kiribitu plant specimens as soon as possible for her next dissertation chapter. Moriarty's write-up was still unfinished, and she'd been hearing rumors of another horrible killing that might shut the Museum down for the rest of the day.

Bailey Smith hummed, ignoring her. Though he was nearly eighty, Margo suspected he only feigned deafness to annoy people.

"Mr. Smith!" she called out. "I need these specimens, please." She pushed a list over the counter top. "Right away, if possible."

Smith grunted, rose from his chair, and slowly picked up the list, scanning it disapprovingly. "May take awhile to locate, you know. How about tomorrow morning?"

"Please, Mr. Smith. I've heard they might close down the Museum at any moment. I really need these specimens."

Scenting the chance to gossip, the old man became friendlier. "Terrible business," he said, shaking his head. "In my forty-two years here I've never seen anything like it. But I can't say I'm surprised," he added, with a significant nod.

Margo didn't want to get Smith going. She said nothing.

"But not the first, from what I hear. And not the last, either." He turned with the list, holding it in front of his nose. "What's this? *Muhlenbergia dunbarii?* We don't have any of that."

Then Margo heard a voice behind her.

"Not the first?"

It was Gregory Kawakita, the young Assistant Curator who had accompanied her to the staff lounge the previous morning. Margo had read the Museum's bio of Kawakita: born to wealthy parents, orphaned young, he had left his native Yokohama and grown up with relatives in England. After studying at Magdalene College, Oxford, he moved to M.I.T. for graduate work, then on to the Museum and an assistant curatorship. He was Frock's most brilliant protégé, which made Margo occasionally resentful. To her, Kawakita didn't seem the kind of scientist who'd wish to be allied with Frock. Kawakita had an instinctual sense for Museum politics, and Frock was controversial, an iconoclast. But despite his self-absorption, Kawakita was undeniably brilliant, and he was working with Frock on a model of genetic mutation that no one but the two of them seemed to fully understand. With Frock's guidance, Kawakita was developing the Extrapolator, a program that could compare and combine genetic codes of different species. When they ran their data through the Museum's powerful computer, the system's throughput was reduced to such a degree that people joked it was in "hand calculator mode."

"Not the first what?" asked Smith, giving Kawakita an unwelcoming stare.

Margo flashed a warning glance at Kawakita, but he continued. "You said something about this murder not being the first."

"Greg, did you *have* to?" Margo groaned sotto voce. "I'll never get my plant specimens now."

"I'm not surprised by any of this," Smith continued. "Now, I'm not a superstitious man," he said, leaning on the counter, "but this isn't the first time some creature has prowled the halls of the Museum. At least that's what people say. Not that I believe a word of it, mind you."

"Creature?" asked Kawakita.

Margo gave Kawakita a light kick in the shins.

"I'm only repeating what everyone's talking about, Dr. Kawakita. I don't believe in starting false rumors."

"Of course not," said Kawakita, winking at Margo.

Smith fixed Kawakita with a stern glare. "They say it's been around a long time. Living down in the basement, eating rats and mice and cockroaches. Have you noticed there aren't any rats or mice loose in the Museum? There *should* be, God knows they're all over the rest of New York. But not here. Curious, don't you think?"

"I hadn't noticed," said Kawakita. "I'll make a special effort to check that out."

"Then there was a researcher here who was breeding

cats for some experiment," Smith continued. "Sloane I think his name was, Doctor Sloane, in the Animal Behavior Department. One day a dozen of his cats escaped. And you know what? They were never seen again. Vanished. Now that's kind of funny. You'd expect one or two at least to show up."

"Maybe they left because there weren't any mice to eat," said Kawakita.

Smith ignored him. "Some say it hatched from one of those crates of dinosaur eggs brought back from Siberia."

"I see," said Kawakita, trying to suppress a grin. "Dinosaurs loose in the Museum."

Smith shrugged. "I only say what I hear. Others think it was something brought back from one of the graves they've robbed over the years. Some artifact with a curse. You know, like the King Tut curse. And if you ask me, those fellows deserve what they get. I don't care what they call it, archaeology, anthropology, or hoodoo-ology, it's just plain old grave robbing to me. You don't see them digging up *their* grandmother's graves, but they sure don't hesitate to dig up somebody else's and take all the goodies. Am I right?"

"Absolutely," said Kawakita. "But what was that you said about these murders not being the first?"

Smith looked at them conspiratorially. "Well, if you tell anybody I told you this I'll deny it, but about five years back, something strange happened." He paused for a minute, as if to gauge the effect his story was having. "There was this curator, Morrissey, or Montana, or something. He was involved with that disastrous Amazon expedition. You know the one I mean, where everyone was killed. Anyway, one day he simply vanished. Nobody ever heard from him again. So people started to whisper about it. Apparently, a guard was overheard saying that his body had been found in the basement, horribly mutilated."

"I see," Kawakita said. "And you think the Museum Beast did it?"

"I don't think anything," Smith responded quickly. "I'm just telling you what I've heard, that's all. I've heard a lot of things from a lot of people, I can tell you."

"So has anyone seen this, ah, creature?" Kawakita asked, unsuccessfully stifling a smile.

"Why, yessir. Couple of people, in fact. You know old Carl Conover in the metal shop? Three years ago now he says he saw it, came in early to get some work done and saw it slouching around a corner in the basement. Saw it right there, plain as day."

"Really?" said Kawakita. "What'd it look like?"

"Well—" Smith began, then stopped. Even he finally noticed Kawakita's amusement. The old man's expression changed. "I expect, Dr. Kawakita, that it looked a bit like Mr. Jim Beam," he said.

Kawakita was puzzled. "Beam? I don't believe I know him—"

Bailey Smith suddenly roared with laughter, and Margo couldn't help grinning herself. "George," she said, "I think he meant that Conover was drunk."

"I see," said Kawakita stiffly. "Of course."

All his good humor had vanished. *Doesn't like having the joke turned on him,* Margo thought. *He can dish it out, but he can't take it.*

"Well, anyway," said Kawakita briskly, "I need some specimens."

"Now, wait just a minute!" Margo protested as Kawakita pushed his own list onto the counter. The old man eyed it and peered at the scientist.

"Week after next okay?" he asked.

= 16 =

Several floors above, Lieutenant D'Agosta sat in a huge leather sofa in the curator's study. He smacked his lips contentedly, propped one chubby leg upon the knee of the other, and looked around. Pendergast, absorbed in a book of lithographs, was reclining in an armchair behind a desk. Above his head, in a gold rococo frame, hung a massive Audubon painting depicting the mating ritual of the snowy egret. Oak paneling with a century's patina ran along the walls above a beadboard wainscot. Delicate gilded lights of hand-blown glass hung just below the pressed tin ceiling. A large fireplace of elaborately carved Dolomite limestone dominated one corner of the room. *Nice place*, D'Agosta thought. *Old money. Old New York. It has class. Not the place to smoke a two-bit cigar.* He lit up.

"It's come and gone two-thirty, Pendergast," he said, exhaling blue smoke. "Where the hell do you think Wright is?"

Pendergast shrugged. "Trying to intimidate us," he said, turning another page.

D'Agosta looked at the FBI agent for a minute.

"You know these Museum big shots, they think they can keep anybody waiting," he said finally, watching for a reaction. "Wright and his cronies have been treating us like second-class citizens since yesterday morning."

Pendergast turned another page. "I had no idea the Museum had a complete collection of Piranesi's Forum sketches," he murmured.

D'Agosta snorted to himself. *This should be interesting,* he thought.

Over lunch, he'd made a few surreptitious calls to some friends in the Bureau. Turned out they'd not only heard of Pendergast, but they'd heard several rumors about him. Graduated with honors from some English university—probably true. A special forces officer who'd been captured in Vietnam and had later walked out of the jungle, the only survivor of a Cambodian death camp—D'Agosta wasn't sure about *that* one. But he was revising his opinion nevertheless.

Now the massive door opened silently and Wright came in, the Security Director at his heels. Abruptly, Wright sat down opposite the FBI agent. "You're Pendergast, I suppose," the Director sighed. "Let's get this over with."

D'Agosta sat back to watch the fun.

There was a long silence while Pendergast turned pages. Wright shifted. "If you're busy," he said irritably, "We can come back another time."

Pendergast's face was invisible behind the large book. "No," he said finally. "Now is a good time." Another page was leisurely turned. Then another.

D'Agosta watched with amusement as the Director reddened.

"The Security Director isn't needed for this meeting," came the voice from behind the book.

"Mr. Ippolito is part of the investigation—"

The agent's eyes suddenly appeared over the spine of the book. "I'm in charge of the investigation, Dr. Wright," Pendergast said quietly. "Now, if Mr. Ippolito would be so kind—?"

Ippolito glanced nervously at Wright, who flicked his hand in dismissal.

"Look, Mr. Pendergast," Wright began as the door closed. "I've got a Museum that needs running, and I don't have much time. I hope this can be brief."

Pendergast laid the open book carefully on the desk in front of him.

"I've often thought," he said slowly, "that this early classicist stuff of Piranesi's was his best. Do you agree?"

Wright looked utterly astonished. "I fail to see," he stammered, "what that has to do with—"

"His later work was interesting, of course, but too fantastical for my taste," Pendergast replied.

"Actually," said the Director in his best lecture voice, "I've always thought—"

The book slammed shut like a shot. "*Actually,* Dr. Wright," Pendergast said tightly, his courtly manner gone, "it's time to forget what you've *always* thought. We're going to play a little game here. I'm going to talk, and y'all are going to listen. Understood?"

Wright sat speechless. Then his face mottled in anger. "Mr. Pendergast, I will not be spoken to in that manner—"

Pendergast cut him off. "In case you haven't read the headlines, Dr. Wright, there have been three grisly murders in this Museum in the last forty-eight hours. *Three.* The press is speculating that some kind of ferocious beast is responsible. Museum attendance is down fifty percent since the weekend. Your staff is *very* upset, to put it mildly. Have you bothered taking a stroll through your Museum today, Dr. Wright? You might find it edifying. The feeling of dread is almost palpable. Most people, if they leave their offices at all, travel in twos and threes. The maintenance staff is finding any reasons it can to avoid the Old Basement. Yet you prefer to act as if nothing is wrong. Believe me, Dr. Wright, something is extremely wrong.''

Pendergast leaned forward, and slowly folded his arms on top of the book. There was something so menacing in his deliberateness, so cold in his pale eyes, that the Director sat back involuntarily. D'Agosta unconsciously held his breath. Then Pendergast continued.

''Now we can handle this one of three ways,'' he said. ''Your way, my way, or the Bureau's way. So far, your way has been far too much in evidence. I understand that the police investigation has been subtly obstructed. Phone calls are returned late, if at all. Staff are busy or not to be found. Those who *are* available—such as Mr. Ippolito—have not proven particularly useful. People are late to appointments. Why, it's enough to make one suspicious. As of now, your way is no longer acceptable.''

Pendergast waited for a response. There was none, and he went on.

''Ordinarily, the Bureau's way would be to close the Museum, suspend operations, cancel exhibitions. Very bad publicity, I assure you. Very expensive, to the taxpayers and to you. But *my* way is a bit more hospitable. All other things being equal, the Museum can remain open. Still, there will be certain conditions. Number one,'' he said, ''I want you to assure complete cooperation of Museum personnel. We will need to speak to you and other senior staff members from time to time, and I want total compliance. I will also need a list of the entire staff. We want to interview everyone who works in, or has had any reason to be in, the vicinity of the murders. There will be no exceptions. I would appreciate your making sure of this personally. We'll be setting up a schedule, and *everyone* is to show up on time.''

"But there are twenty-five hundred employees—" began Wright.

"Number two," Pendergast continued. "Starting tomorrow, we're going to be limiting employee access to the Museum, until such time as this investigation is concluded. The curfew is to be for the safety of the staff. At least, that is what you will tell them."

"But there's vital research going on here that—"

"Number three—" Pendergast casually pointed three fingers, derringer-like, at Wright "—from time to time we may need to close the Museum, either fully or in part. In some instances, only visitors will be denied entry; in others, the Museum will be closed to staff as well. Notice may be short. Your cooperation will be expected."

Wright's fury mounted. "This Museum is closed only three days a year: Christmas, New Year's, and Thanksgiving," he said. "This is unprecedented. It will look terrible." He gave Pendergast a long, appraising look. "Besides, I'm not convinced you have the authority to do that. I think we should—" He stopped. Pendergast had picked up the telephone.

"What's that for?" Wright demanded.

"Dr. Wright, this is growing tiresome. Perhaps we should discuss this with the Attorney General."

Pendergast started to dial.

"Just a moment," said Wright. "Surely we can discuss this without involving other people."

"That's up to you," said Pendergast as he finished dialing.

"For Heaven's sake, put down that phone," Wright said angrily. "Of course, we'll cooperate fully—within reason."

"Very good," Pendergast said. "And if in the future you start to feel that anything is unreasonable, we can always do this again." He replaced the receiver gently.

"If I'm going to cooperate," Wright continued, "I think I've a right to be informed about just what's been done since this latest atrocity. As far as I can see, you've made precious little progress."

"Certainly, Doctor," Pendergast said. He looked at papers on the desk. "According to your time clocks, the most recent victim, Jolley, met his demise shortly after ten-thirty last night," he said. "The autopsy should confirm this. He was, as you know, lacerated in a fashion similar to the previous victims. He was killed while making his rounds, although the stairwell where he was found wasn't part of his normal route. He may have been investigating a suspicious noise or something of that nature. He may have just stopped for some reefer. A recently smoked marijuana cigarette was found near the archway directly outside the stairwell exit. We will, naturally, be testing the body for drug use."

"God, that's all we need," said Wright. "But haven't you found any *useful* clues? What about this wild animal business? You—"

Pendergast held his palm up and waited for silence. "I would prefer not to speculate until we discuss the available evidence with experts. Some of these experts may be from among your own staff. For the record, we've found no signs as yet that any kind of animal had been in the vicinity.

"The body was found lying at the bottom of the stairwell, although it was clear that the attack occurred near the top, as blood and viscera were found along the length of the stairs. He either rolled or was dragged to the bottom. But don't take my word for it, Dr. Wright," Pendergast said, picking up a manila envelope from the desk, "see for yourself." He pulled out a glossy photograph and laid it carefully on the tabletop.

"Oh, my God," Wright said, staring at the photograph. "Heaven help us."

"The right-hand wall of the stairwell was covered with splattered blood," Pendergast said. "Here's a photograph."

He handed it to Wright, who slid it quickly on top of the first.

"It's a simple matter to do a ballistics analysis on splattered blood," Pendergast went on. "In this case, the evidence is consistent with a massive blow directed downward, instantaneously disemboweling the victim."

Pendergast replaced the photographs and checked his watch. "Lieutenant D'Agosta will be checking in with you to make sure that everything is proceeding along the lines we've discussed," he said. "One last question, Doctor. Which of your curators knows the most about the anthropology collections here?"

Dr. Wright seemed not to have heard. Finally he said, "Dr. Frock," in a barely audible voice.

"Very good," said Pendergast. "Oh, and Doctor—I told you earlier that the Museum can remain open, *all other things being equal.* But if anybody else dies inside these walls, the Museum will have to be shut down immediately. The matter will be out of my hands. Understood?"

After a long moment, Wright nodded.

"Excellent," Pendergast replied. "I'm very aware, Doctor, that your *Superstition* exhibition is scheduled to open this coming weekend, and that you have a large preview planned for Friday evening. I'd like to see your opening proceed unvexed, but everything will depend on what we discover in the next twenty-four hours. Prudence may require us to delay the opening party."

Wright's left eyelid began to twitch. "That's quite impossible. Our entire marketing campaign would be derailed. The publicity would be devastating."

"We shall see," Pendergast replied. "Now, unless there's anything else, I don't think we need keep you any longer."

Wright, his face drained of color, stood up and, without a word, walked stiffly out of the room.

D'Agosta grinned as the door closed. "Softened up that bastard nicely," he said.

"What's that again, Lieutenant?" Pendergast asked, leaning back in the leather chair and picking up the book with renewed enthusiasm.

"Come on, Pendergast," D'Agosta said, looking cagily at the FBI agent. "I guess you can drop the genteel act when it suits you."

Pendergast blinked innocently at D'Agosta. "I'm sorry, Lieutenant. I apologize for any unseemly behavior. It's simply that I can't stand pompous, bureaucratic individuals. I'm afraid I can become quite short with them." He raised the book. "It's a bad habit, but very hard to break."

= 17 =

The laboratory looked out over the East River and across to the warehouses and decaying industrial buildings of Long Island City. Lewis Turow stood in the window and watched an enormous barge, piled with garbage and surrounded by countless seagulls, being pushed out to sea. *Probably one minute's worth of New York City garbage,* he thought.

Turow turned away from the window and sighed. He hated New York, but one had to make choices. The choice for him was enduring the city and working in one of the best genetic labs in the country, or working in some half-assed facility in a nice rural spot somewhere. So far he'd chosen the city, but his patience was running out.

He heard a low beeping, then the soft hiss of a mini-printer. The results were coming through. Another soft beep indicated the print job was finished. The three-million-dollar Omega-9 Parallel Processing Computer, which took up a series of large gray boxes along one wall, was now completely silent. Only a few lights indicated that anything was happening. It was a special, hardwired model designed for sequencing DNA and mapping genes. Turow had come to the lab six months before specifically because of this machine.

He fetched the paper out of the bin and scanned it. The first page was a summary of the results, followed by a sequence of nucleic acids found in the sample. Next to those were columns of letters that identified primer sequences and mapped genes from the target group.

The target group, in this case, was unusual: big cats. They had asked for gene matches with Asiatic tiger, jaguar, leopard, bobcat. Turow had thrown in the cheetah, since its genetics were so well known. The outgroup chosen was, as usual, *Homo sapiens*, a control to check that the genetic matching process had been accurate and the sample sound.

He scanned the summary.

Run 3349A5 990
SAMPLE: NYC Crime Lab LA-33
SUMMARY

TARGET GROUP

	% matches	degree of confidence
Panthera leo	5.5	4%
Panthera onca	7.1	5%
Felis lynx	4.0	3%
Felis rufa	5.2	4%
Acinonyx jubatus	6.6	4%

OUTGROUP CONTROL

Homo sapiens	45.2	33%

Well, this is complete bullshit, thought Turow. The sample matched the outgroup a lot more than it matched the target group—the opposite of what should have happened. Only a 4 percent chance that the genetic material was from a big cat, but a 33 percent chance it was from a human being.

Thirty-three percent. Still low, but within the realm of possibility.

So that meant trying GenLab for a match. GenLab was an enormous international DNA database—two hundred gigs and growing—that contained DNA sequences, primers, and mapped genes for thousands of organisms, from the *Escherichia coli* bacterium to *Homo sapiens.* He would run the data against the GenLab database, and see just what this DNA was from. Something close to *Homo sapiens,* it looked like. Not high enough to be an ape, but maybe something like a lemur.

Turow's curiosity was piqued. Till now, he didn't even know that his laboratory did work for the police department. *What the hell made them think this sample came from a big cat?* he wondered.

The results ran to a hefty eighty pages. The DNA sequencer printed out the identified nucleotides in columnar format, indicating species, identified genes, and unidentified sequences. Turow knew that most of the sequences would be unidentified, since the only organism with a complete genetic map was *E. coli.*

C-G	*		G-C	Unidentified
G-C			G-C	*
G-C	*Homo sapiens*		T-A	*
C-G			T-A	*
A-T	A-1 allele		T-A	*
T-A	marker		G-C	*
C-G			C-G	*
A-T	A1		C-G	*
A-T	Polymorphism		C-G	*
A-T	begin		G-C	*
A-T	*		T-A	*

G-C	*		G-C	*
T-A	*		T-A	*
G-C	*		T-A	*
T-A	-		T	
A-T	-			
T-A	-			
G-C	-			
C-G	-			
C-G	A1 Poly end			

Turow glanced over the figures, then carried the paper over to his desk. With a few keystrokes on his SPARC-station 10, Turow could access information from thousands of databases. If the Omega-9 did not have the information he sought, it would automatically dial into the Internet and find a computer that did.

Scanning the printout more closely, Turow frowned. *It must be a degraded sample,* he thought. *Too much unidentified DNA.*

A-T	Unidentified		A-T	*Hemidactylus*
A-T	-		T-A	*turcicus*
A-T	-		C-G	cont'd
A-T	-		T-A	*
A-T	-		C-G	*
A-T	-		T-A	*
T-A	-		G-C	*
G-C	-		G-C	*
G-C	-		G-C	*
A-T	*Hemidactylus*		G-C	*
T-A	*turcicus*		G-C	*
C-G	*		G-C	*
G-C	*		G-C	*

G-C	*	G-C	*
T-A	*	G-C	*
C-G	*	G-C	*
A-T	*	G-C	*

He stopped flipping the pages. Here was something truly odd: the program had identified a large chunk of DNA as belonging to an animal named *Hemidactylus turcicus*.

Now what the hell is that? thought Turow.

The Biological Nomenclature Database told him:

COMMON NAME: TURKISH GECKO

What? thought Turow. He typed, EXPAND.

HEMIDACTYLUS TURCICUS: TURKISH GECKO.
ORIGINAL RANGE: NORTHERN AFRICA
PRESENT BIOLOGICAL RANGE: FLORIDA, BRAZIL, ASIA MINOR, NORTHERN AFRICA.
MEDIUM-SIZE LIZARD OF THE GECKO FAMILY, *GEKKONIDAE,* ARBOREAL, NOCTURAL, LACKING MOVEABLE EYELIDS

Turow flicked out of the database while the information was still scrolling by. It was pure nonsense, obviously. Lizard DNA and human DNA in the same sample? But this wasn't the first time something like this had happened. You couldn't blame the computer, really. It was an inexact procedure, and only the smallest fractions of the DNA sequences of any given organism were known.

He scanned down the printed list. Less than 50 percent of the matches were human—a very low proportion, assuming the subject was human, but not out of the question in a degraded sample. And there was always the possibility of contamination. A stray cell or two could ruin an entire run. This last possibility was looking more and more likely to Turow. *Well, what can you expect from the NYPD?* They couldn't even get rid of the guy who sold crack openly on the corner across from his apartment building.

He continued his scan. *Wait,* he thought, *here's another long sequence:* Tarentola mauritanica. He punched up the database, entered the name. The screen read:

TARENTOLA MAURITANICA: WALL GECKO

Give me a break, Turow thought. *This is some kind of joke.* He glanced at the calendar: April first was Saturday.

He started to laugh. It was a very good joke. A very, very good joke. He didn't think old Buchholtz had it in him. Well, he had a sense of humor, too. He started his report.

Sample LA-33
Summary: Sample conclusively identified as *Homo Gekkopiens,* common name Gecko-man . . .

When he finished the report he sent it upstairs immediately. Then he went out for coffee, still chuckling. He was proud of how he'd handled it. He wondered where in the world Buchholtz got his gecko samples from. *Probably sold them in pet stores.* He could see Buchholtz blending up sample cells from two or three geckos in the ultrablender with a few drops of his own blood. *Let's see what our new man Turow makes of this, he'd probably been thinking.* Turow, returning with the coffee, had to laugh out loud. He found Buchholtz waiting for him in the lab, only Buchholtz wasn't laughing.

= 18 =

Wednesday

Frock sat in his wheelchair, dabbing his forehead with a Gucci handkerchief. "Sit down, please," he said to Margo. "Thank you for coming so promptly. It's dreadful, just dreadful."

"The poor guard," she replied. Nobody in the Museum was talking about anything else.

"Guard?" Frock looked up. "Oh yes, quite a tragedy. No, I mean this." He held up a memorandum.

"All sorts of new rules," said Frock. "Very inconvenient. Effective today, staff are only allowed in the building between ten and five. No working late or on Sundays. There will be guards stationed in each department. You'll be expected to sign in and out of Anthropology each day. They are asking everybody to carry IDs at all times. Nobody will be allowed to enter or leave the Museum without one."

He continued reading. "Let's see, what else . . . ah, yes. Try as much as possible to keep to your assigned section. And I'm supposed to tell you not to go into isolated areas of the Museum alone. If you need to go somewhere, go with someone. The police will be interviewing everyone who works in the Old Basement. Yours is scheduled for early next week. And various sections of the Museum are being posted as off-limits.'' He pushed the memo across the desk.

Margo saw a floor plan attached, the off-limits areas shaded in red. ''Don't worry,'' Frock continued. ''I note your office is just outside the area.''

Lovely, thought Margo. *Just outside where the murderer is probably lurking.* ''This seems like a complicated arrangement, Professor Frock. Why didn't they just close the whole Museum?''

''No doubt they tried, my dear. I'm sure Winston talked them out of it. If *Superstition* doesn't open on schedule, the Museum will be in deep trouble.'' Frock held out his hand for the memo. ''Shall we consider this discussed? There are other things I wish to talk to you about.''

Margo nodded. *The Museum will be in deep trouble.* It seemed to her that it already was. Her office mate, along with half of the Museum staff, had called in sick that morning. Those who did show up were spending most of their time at the coffee machines or photocopiers, trading rumors and staying in groups. If that wasn't bad enough, the Museum's exhibit halls were nearly empty. The vacationing families, school groups, shouting children—the normal visitors—were few and far between. Now the Museum attracted mostly ghoulish rubberneckers.

''I was curious whether you'd obtained any of the plants for your chapter on the Kiribitu yet,'' Frock continued. ''I thought it might be a useful exercise for both of us to run them through the Extrapolator.''

The telephone rang. ''Blast,'' Frock said, picking up the receiver. ''Yes?'' he demanded.

There was a long silence. ''Is this necessary?'' Frock asked. Then he paused. ''If you insist,'' he concluded, dropping the phone into its cradle and heaving a great sigh.

"The authorities want me down in the basement, Heaven knows why. Somebody named Pendergast. Would you mind wheeling me down? We can chat along the way."

In the elevator, Margo continued. "I was able to get a few specimens from the herbarium, though not as many as I'd wanted. But I don't understand. You're suggesting we run them through the G.S.E.?"

"Correct," Frock replied. "Depending on the condition of the plants, of course. Is there printable material?"

G.S.E. stood for Genetic Sequence Extrapolator, the program being developed by Kawakita and Frock for analyzing genetic "prints."

"The plants are in good condition, for the most part," Margo admitted. "But, Dr. Frock, I don't see what use they could be to the Extrapolator." *Am I just jealous of Kawakita?* She wondered to herself. *Is that why I'm resisting?*

"My dear Margo, your situation is tailor-made!" Frock exclaimed, using her first name in his excitement. "You can't replay evolution. But you can *simulate* it with computers. Perhaps these plants are allied genetically, along the same lines as the Kiribitu shamans have developed for their own classification. Wouldn't that make an interesting sidebar for your dissertation?"

"I hadn't thought of that," Margo said.

"We're beta-testing the program now, and this is exactly the kind of scenario we need," Frock continued eagerly. "Why don't you talk to Kawakita about working together?"

Margo nodded. Privately, she thought that Kawakita didn't seem like the type who wanted to share his spotlight—or even his research—with anybody.

The elevator door opened onto a checkpoint manned by two police officers armed with shotguns. "Are you Dr. Frock?" one asked.

"Yes," Frock replied irritably.

"Come with us, please."

Margo wheeled Frock through several intersections, arriving at last at a second checkpoint. Behind the barricade stood two more policemen and a tall, thin man in a somber black suit, blond white hair combed severely back from his forehead. As the policemen moved the barricade, he stepped forward.

"You must be Dr. Frock," he said, extending his hand. "Thank you for coming down. As I told you, I'm expecting another visitor, so I wasn't able to come by your office myself. Had I known you were—" he indicated the wheelchair with a nod,"—I would never have asked. Special Agent Pendergast." He held out his hand. *Interesting accent,* thought Margo. *Alabama? This guy doesn't look anything like an FBI agent.*

"Quite all right," said Frock, mollified by Pendergast's courtesy. "This is my assistant, Miss Green." Pendergast's hand felt cool in Margo's grasp.

"It's an honor to meet such a distinguished scientist as yourself," Pendergast continued. "I hope time will permit me to read your latest book."

"Thank you." Frock nodded.

"In it, do you apply the 'Gambler's Ruin' scenario to your theory of evolution? I always thought that backed up your hypothesis rather well, especially if you assume most genera start out close to the absorbing boundary."

Frock sat up in his wheelchair. "Well, ah, I was planning to make certain references to that in my next book." He seemed at a loss for words.

Pendergast nodded to the officers, who readjusted the barrier. "I need your help, Dr. Frock," he said in a lower tone.

"Certainly," Frock said amiably. Margo was amazed at how quickly Pendergast had won Frock's cooperation.

"I must ask, first of all, that this discussion be kept among ourselves for the time being," said Pendergast. "May I have your assurance? And that of Ms. Green?"

"Of course," said Frock. Margo nodded.

Pendergast motioned to one of the officers, who brought forward a large plastic bag marked EVIDENCE. From it he removed a small, dark object, which he handed to Frock.

"What you're holding," he said, "is the latex cast of a claw found embedded in one of the children that were murdered last weekend."

Margo leaned forward for a closer look. It was about an inch long, perhaps a little less, curved and jagged.

"A claw?" Frock said, bringing the object close to his face and examining it. "Very unusual. But I'd guess it's a fake."

Pendergast smiled. "We haven't been able to identify its source, Doctor. But I'm not sure it's a fake. In the root canal of the claw we found some matter, which is now being sequenced for DNA. The results are still ambiguous, and our tests are continuing."

Frock raised his eyebrows. "Interesting."

"Now this," said Pendergast, reaching into the bag and withdrawing a much larger object, "is a reconstruction of the instrument that raked the same child." He handed it to Frock.

Margo looked at the cast with disgust. At one end, the latex was mottled and uneven, but at the other, details were clear and well-defined. It ended in three hooked claws: a large central claw, and two shorter talons on either side.

"Good heavens!" said Frock. "This looks saurian."

"Saurian?" asked Pendergast dubiously.

"*Dino*-saurian," said Frock. "Typical ornithischian forelimb, I should say, with one difference. Look here. The central digital process is thickened enormously, while the talons themselves are undersized."

Pendergast raised his eyebrows in mild surprise. "Well, sir," he said slowly, "we'd been leaning toward the big cats, or some other mammalian carnivore."

"But *surely* you know, Mr. Pendergast, that all mammalian predators have five digits."

"Of course, Doctor," said Pendergast. "If you would indulge me for a moment, I'd like to describe a scenario to you."

"Certainly," said Frock.

"There is a theory that the murderer is using this—" he hefted the forelimb—"as a weapon to rake his victims. We feel that what I'm holding might be the impression of an *artifact* of some kind, something made by a primitive tribe out of, say, a jaguar or lion forelimb. The DNA appears to be degraded. It may be an old artifact, collected by the Museum a long time ago, then stolen."

Frock's head lowered until his chin was on his chest. The silence stretched out, broken only by the shuffling of the policemen by the barricade. Then Frock spoke.

"The guard who was killed? Did his wounds show evidence of a broken or missing claw?"

"Good question," Pendergast said. "See for yourself." He slid his hand into the plastic bag and removed a heavy plaque of latex, a long rectangle with three jagged ridges down its middle.

"This is a cast of one of the guard's abdominal wounds," Pendergast explained. Margo shuddered. It was a vile-looking thing.

Frock peered at the deep ridges intently. "The penetration must have been remarkable. But the wound shows no indication of a broken claw. Therefore, you are suggesting that *two* such artifacts are in use by the murderer."

Pendergast looked a little uncomfortable, but nodded.

Frock's head sank once more. The silence went on for minutes. "Another thing," he suddenly said, quite loudly. "Do you see how the claw marks *draw together* slightly? How they are farther apart at the top than at the bottom?"

"Yes?" said Pendergast.

"Like a hand clenching into a fist. That would indicate flexibility in the instrument."

"Granted," said Pendergast. "Human flesh, however, is rather soft and easily distorted. We cannot read too much into these casts." He paused. "Dr. Frock, is any artifact capable of doing this missing from the collection?"

"There is no such artifact *in* the collection," said Frock with a faint smile. "You see, this comes from no living animal I've studied. Do you see how this claw has a conical shape, a deep fully enclosed root? See how it tapers to an almost perfect tripyramidal cross section near the top? This appears in only two classes of animal: dinosaur and bird. That is one of the reasons some evolutionary biologists think birds evolved from dinosaurs. I would say it *is* from a bird, except that it is far too large. Thus, dinosaurian."

He placed the latex claw in his lap and looked up again. "Certainly, a clever person familiar with dinosaur morphology could have shaped a claw like this, and used it as a tool for murder. I assume you have tested the original fragment to see if it indeed is composed of a genuine biological material, such as keratin, rather than being cast or carved from some inorganic material?"

"Yes, Doctor. It is real."

"And you are sure that the DNA was real, and not simply blood or flesh from the victim?"

"Yes," Pendergast replied. "As I said, it came from the root canal, not under the cuticle."

"And what, pray tell, *was* the DNA from?"

"The final report isn't in yet."

Frock held up his hand. "Understood. But tell me, why aren't you making use of our own DNA laboratory, here in the Museum? We have facilities equal to that of anybody in the state."

"Equal to anybody in the country, Doctor. But you must understand that our procedures forbid it. Could we be sure of the results if the tests were conducted at the crime scene? With perhaps the murderer himself operating the equipment?'' Pendergast smiled. ''I hope you'll forgive my persistence, Doctor, but would you be willing to *consider* the possibility that this weapon is constructed from relics belonging to the Anthropology collection, and to think about what artifact or artifacts this cast most closely resembles?''

''If you'd like,'' Frock replied.

''Thank you. We can discuss it again in a day or so. Meanwhile, would it be possible to obtain a printed inventory of the Anthropology collection?''

Frock smiled. ''Six million items? You can use the computer catalog, however. Would you like a terminal set up?''

''Perhaps later,'' said Pendergast, replacing the latex plaque in the plastic bag. ''It's kind of you to offer. Our command post is currently in the unused gallery behind reprographics.''

Footsteps sounded behind them. Margo turned to see the tall form of Dr. Ian Cuthbert, Deputy Director of the Museum, followed by the two officers from the elevator.

''Look here, how long is this going to take?'' Cuthbert was complaining. He stopped at the barricade. ''Oh, Frock, so they've got you, too. What a damned nuisance this is.''

Frock nodded imperceptibly.

''Dr. Frock,'' said Pendergast, ''I'm sorry. This is the gentleman I'd been waiting for when we first spoke. You're welcome to remain, if you'd care to.'' Frock nodded again.

''Now, Dr. Cuthbert,'' said Pendergast briskly, turning to the Scotsman. ''I asked you to come down because I'd like some information about this area behind me.'' He indicated a large doorway.

''The Secure Area? What about it? Surely somebody else could—'' Cuthbert began.

''Ah, but my questions are for you,'' Pendergast interrupted, politely but firmly. ''Shall we step inside?''

"If it won't take much time," Cuthbert said. "I've got an exhibition to mount."

"Yes, indeed," said Frock, his tone faintly sardonic. "An *exhibition*." He motioned Margo to wheel him forward.

"Dr. Frock?" Pendergast said politely.

"Yes?"

"I wonder if I might have that cast back."

The copper-sheathed door to the Museum's Secure Area had been removed and a new steel one installed in its place. Across the hall was a small door labelled PACHYDERMAE. Margo wondered how the staff had been able to fit huge elephant bones through it.

Turning away, she wheeled Frock into the narrow walkway beyond the open door to the Secure Area. The Museum kept its most valuable artifacts in small vaults on either side: sapphires and diamonds; ivory and rhinoceros horns heaped on racks like cordwood; bones and skins of extinct animals; Zuñi war gods. Two men in dark suits stood at the far end, talking in low tones. They straightened up when Pendergast entered.

Pendergast stopped at one open vault door, much like the others, sporting a large black combination knob, brass lever, and ornate decorative scrollwork. Inside, a bulb threw a harsh light across the metal walls. The vault was empty except for several crates, all of which were quite large except one. The smaller crate's lid was removed, while one of the larger crates was badly damaged, with excelsior-like stuffing protruding.

Pendergast waited until everybody was inside the vault. "Allow me to provide some background," Pendergast said. "The murder of the guard took place not far from this spot. It appears that afterward, the murderer came down the hallway just outside. The murderer attempted to break down the door that leads to the Secure Area. He may have tried before. The attempts were unsuccessful.

"At first we weren't sure what the killer was after. As you know, there is a lot of valuable material in here." Pendergast motioned to one of the policemen, who came over and handed him a piece of paper. "So we asked around, and found that nothing has come in or out of the Secure Area for six months. Except these crates. They were moved into this vault last week. On your orders, Dr. Cuthbert."

"Mr. Pendergast, allow me to explain—" said Cuthbert.

"One moment, if you please," said Pendergast. "When we inspected the crates, we found something very interesting." He pointed to the damaged crate. "Notice the slats. The two-by-sixes here are deeply scored by claw marks. Our forensic people tell me the marks on the victims were probably made by the same object or instrument."

Pendergast stopped and looked intently at Cuthbert.

"I had no idea—" said Cuthbert. "Nothing had been taken. I merely thought that . . ." His voice trailed away.

"I wonder, Doctor, if you could enlighten us as to the history of these crates?"

"That's easily explained," said Cuthbert. "There's no mystery about it. The crates are from an old expedition."

"I gathered that," Pendergast said. "Which expedition?"

"The Whittlesey expedition," Cuthbert replied.

Pendergast waited.

Finally Cuthbert sighed. "It was a South American expedition that took place over five years ago. It was . . . not entirely successful."

"It was a disaster," Frock said derisively. Oblivious to Cuthbert's angry glance, he continued. "It caused a scandal in the Museum at the time. The expedition broke up early, due to personality conflicts. Some of the expedition members were killed by hostile tribesmen; the rest were killed in a plane crash on the way back to New

York. There were the inevitable rumors of a curse, that kind of thing.''

"That's an exaggeration," Cuthbert snapped. "There was no scandal of any sort."

Pendergast looked at them. "And the crates?" he said mildly.

"They were shipped back separately," Cuthbert said. "But this is all beside the point. There was a very unusual object in one of these crates, a figurine created by an extinct South American tribe. It's to be an important element in the *Superstition* exhibition."

Pendergast nodded. "Go on."

"Last week, when we went to retrieve the figurine, I found that one of the crates had been broken into." He pointed. "So I ordered all of the crates moved temporarily to the Secure Area."

"What was taken?"

"Well, now, that was a little odd," said Cuthbert. "None of the artifacts were missing from the crate. The figurine itself is worth a fortune. It's unique, the only one of its kind in the world. The Kothoga tribe that made it vanished years ago."

"You mean *nothing* was missing?" Pendergast asked.

"Well, nothing important. The only thing that seemed to be missing were the seed pods, or whatever they were. Maxwell, the scientist who packed them, died in the plane crash near Venezuela."

"Seed pods?" asked Pendergast.

"I honestly don't know what they were. None of the documentation survived except for the anthropological material. We had Whittlesey's journal, you see, but that was all. There was a little reconstructive work done when the crates first came back, but since then . . ." he stopped.

"You'd better tell me about this expedition," said Pendergast.

"There's not much to tell. They had originally assembled to search for traces of the Kothoga tribe, and to do a survey and general collection in a very remote area of the rain forest. I think the preliminary work estimated that ninety-five percent of the plant species in the area were unknown to science. Whittlesey, an anthropologist, was the leader. I believe there was also a paleontologist, a mammalogist, a physical anthropologist, perhaps an entomologist, a few assistants. Whittlesey and an assistant named Crocker disappeared and were probably killed by tribesmen. The rest died in the plane crash. The only thing we had any documentation on was the figurine, from Whittlesey's journal. The rest of the stuff is just a mystery, no locality data, nothing.''

''Why did the material sit in these crates for so long? Why wasn't it unpacked and cataloged and put in the collections?''

Cuthbert stirred uncomfortably. ''Well,'' he said defensively, ''ask Frock. He's the chairman of the department.''

''Our collections are enormous,'' said Frock. ''We have dinosaur bones still crated up from the 1930s that have never been touched. It costs a tremendous amount of money and time to curate these things.'' He sighed. ''But in this particular case, it's not a question of mere oversight. As I recall, the Anthropology Department was forbidden to curate these crates upon their return.'' He looked pointedly at Cuthbert.

''That was years ago!'' Cuthbert replied acidly.

''How do you know there are no rare artifacts in the unopened boxes?'' Pendergast asked.

''Whittlesey's journal implied that the figurine in the small crate was the only item of importance.''

''May I see this journal?''

Cuthbert shook his head. ''It's gone missing.''

''Were the crates moved on your own authority?''

''I suggested it to Dr. Wright after I learned the crates had been tampered with,'' Cuthbert said. ''We kept the material together in its original crates until it could be curated. That's one of the Museum's rules.''

"So the crates were moved late last week," Pendergast murmured, almost to himself. "Just prior to the killing of the two boys. What could the killer have been after?" Then he looked back at Cuthbert. "What did you say had been taken from the crates? Seed pods, was it?"

Cuthbert shrugged. "As I said, I'm not sure what they were. They looked like seed pods to me, but I'm no botanist."

"Can you describe them?"

"It's been years, I don't really remember. Big, round, heavy. Rugose on the outside. Light brown color. I've only seen the inside of the crate twice, you understand; once when it first came back, and then last week, looking for Mbwun. That's the figurine."

"Where is the figurine now?" Pendergast asked.

"It's being curated for the show. It should be on display already, we're sealing the exhibition today."

"Did you remove anything else from the box?"

"No. The figurine is the unique piece of the lot."

"I would like to arrange to see it," said Pendergast.

Cuthbert shifted irritably on his feet. "You can see it when the show opens. Frankly, I don't know what you're up to. Why waste time on a broken crate when there's a serial killer loose in the Museum and you chaps can't even find him?"

Frock cleared his throat. "Margo, bring me closer, if you will," he asked.

Margo wheeled him over to the crates. With a grunt he bent forward to scrutinize the broken boards.

Everyone watched.

"Thank you," he said, straightening up. He eyed the group, one at a time.

"Please note that these boards are scored on the *inside* as well as the outside," he said finally. "Mr. Pendergast, are we not making an assumption here?" he finally said.

"I never make assumptions," replied Pendergast, with a smile.

"But you are," Frock persisted. "All of you are making an assumption—that some one, or some thing, broke *into* the crate.''

There was a sudden silence in the vault. Margo could smell the dust in the air, and the faint odor of excelsior.

And then Cuthbert began to laugh raucously, the sound swelling harshly through the chamber.

As they approached Frock's office once again, the curator was unusually animated.

"Did you see that cast?" he said to Margo. "Avian attributes, dinosaurian morphology. This could be the very thing!" He could scarcely contain himself.

"But, Professor Frock, Mr. Pendergast believes it was constructed as a weapon of some sort," Margo said quickly. As she said it, she realized that *she* wanted to believe it, too.

"Stuff!" Frock snorted. "Didn't you get the sense, looking at that cast, of something tantalizingly familiar, yet utterly foreign? We're looking at an evolutionary aberration, the vindication of my theory." Inside the office, Frock immediately produced a notebook from his jacket pocket and started scribbling.

"But, Professor, how could such a creature—?" Margo stopped as she felt Frock's hand close over hers. His grip was extraordinarily strong.

"My dear girl," he said, "there are more things in heaven and earth, as Hamlet pointed out. It isn't always for us to speculate. Sometimes we must simply observe." His voice was low, but he trembled with excitement. "We can't miss this opportunity, do you hear? Damn this steel prison of mine! You must be my eyes and ears, Margo. You must go everywhere, search up and down, be an extension of my fingers. We must *not* let this chance pass us by. Are you willing, Margo?"

He gripped her hand tighter.

$$= 19 =$$

The old freight elevator in Section 28 of the Museum always smelled like something had died in it, Smithback thought. He tried breathing through his mouth.

The elevator was huge, the size of a Manhattan studio, and the operator had decorated it with a table, chair, and pictures cut from the Museum's nature magazine. The pictures focused on a single subject. There were giraffes rubbing necks, insects mating, a baboon displaying its rump, native women with pendulous breasts.

"You like my little art gallery?" the elevator man asked, with a leer. He was about sixty years old and wore an orange toupee.

"It's nice to see someone so interested in natural history," Smithback said sarcastically.

As he stepped out, the smell of rotting flesh hit him with redoubled force; it seemed to fill the air like a Maine fog. "How do you stand it?" he managed to gasp to the elevator man.

"Stand what?" the man said, pausing as he rolled the hoistway doors shut.

A cheerful voice came ringing down the corridor. "Welcome!" An elderly man shouted over the sound of the forced-air ducts as he grasped Smithback's hand. "Nothing but zebra cooking today. You miss the rhinoceros. But come in anyway, come in, please!" Smithback knew his thick accent was Austrian.

Jost Von Oster ran the osteological preparation area, the Museum Laboratory in which animal carcasses were reduced to bones. He was over eighty, but looked so pink, cheerful, and plump that most people thought he was much younger.

Von Oster had started at the Museum in the late twenties, preparing and mounting skeletons for display. His crowning achievement in those days had been a series of horse skeletons, mounted walking, trotting, and galloping. It was said that these skeletons had revolutionized the way animals were exhibited. Von Oster had then turned to creating the lifelike habitat groups popular in the forties, making sure every detail—down to the saliva on an animal's mouth—looked perfectly real.

But the era of the habitat group had passed, and Von Oster had eventually been relegated to the Bug Room. Disdaining all offers of retirement, he cheerfully presided over the osteological lab, where animals—now mostly collected from zoos—were turned into clean white bones for study or mounting. However, his old skills as a master habitat sculptor were still intact, and he had been called in to work on a special shaman life-group for the *Superstition* exhibition. It was the painstaking preparation of this display group that Smithback wanted to include as one chapter in his book.

Following Von Oster's gesture, Smithback stepped into the preparation area. He'd never seen this famous room before. "So glad you could come see my workshop," Von Oster said. "Not many people down here now, what with these dreadful killings. Very glad indeed!''

The workshop looked more like a bizarre industrial kitchen than anything else. Deep stainless-steel tanks lined one wall. On the ceiling near the tanks hung massive pulleys, chains, and grappling hooks for handling the larger carcasses. A drain was drilled into the center of the floor, a small broken bone caught in its grill. In a far corner of the workshop a stainless-steel gurney stood, bearing a large animal. If it hadn't been for the large, hand-lettered sign taped to one leg of the gurney, Smithback wouldn't have guessed that the creature had once been a Sargasso Sea Dugong; it was now almost fully decomposed. Around the corpse lay picks, pliers, tiny knives.

"Thanks for taking time to see me," Smithback managed.

"Not at all!" Von Oster exploded. "I wish we could give tours, but you know this area is off limits to the tourists, the more is the pity. You should have been here for the rhinoceros. *Gott,* she was something!"

Walking briskly across the room, he showed Smithback the maceration tank containing the zebra carcass. Despite a hood drawing the vapors away, the smell was still strong. Von Oster lifted the lid and stood back like a proud cook.

"What you think of *zat!*"

Smithback looked at the soupy brown liquid filling the vat. Under the muddy surface lay the macerating zebra carcass, its flesh and soft tissues slowly liquefying.

"It's a little ripe," Smithback said weakly.

"What you mean, ripe? It just perfect! Under here we got the burner. It keep the water at an even ninety-five degrees. See, first we gut the carcass and drop it in the vat here. Then it rot and in two weeks we pull the plug and drain everything down the sink. What we got left is this big pile of greasy bones. So then we refill the vat and add a little alum and boil those bones. You don't want to boil them too long, they get soft."

Von Oster paused again for air. "You know, just like when they cook the chicken too long. Phhhhtui! Bad! But those bones still greasy, so we wash them *mit* the benzene. That make them pure white."

"Mr. Von Oster—" Smithback began. If he didn't redirect this interview quickly, he would never get out. And he couldn't stand the smell much longer. "I was wondering if you could tell me a little about the shaman group you worked on. I'm writing a book about *Superstition.* You remember our conversation?"

"*Ja, ja!* Of course!" He charged over to a desk and pulled out some drawings. Smithback switched on his microcassette recorder.

"First, you paint the background on a double-curved surface, so you get no corners, see? You want the illusion of depth."

Von Oster began describing the process, his voice pitched with excitement. *This is going to be good,* Smithback thought. *The guy's a writer's dream.*

Von Oster went on for a long time, stabbing the air, making sweeping gestures, taking deep breaths between his heavily accented sentences. When he was finished, he beamed at Smithback. "Now, you want to see the bugs?" he asked.

Smithback couldn't resist. The bugs were famous. It was a process Von Oster himself had invented, but was now in use by all the large natural history museums in the country: the beetles would strip a small carcass of its flesh, leaving behind a cleaned, perfectly articulated skeleton.

The "safe" room that housed the beetles was hot and humid, and little larger than a closet. The beetles, called dermestids, came from Africa and lived in white porcelain tubs with slick sides, roofed with screens. The beetles slowly crawled over rows of dead, skinned animals.

"What are those things?" Smithback asked, peering at the bug-covered carcasses inside the tubs.

"Bats!" said Von Oster. "Bats for Dr. Huysmans. It will take about ten days to clean up those bats." He pronounced it "zose bets."

Between the odors and the bugs, Smithback had had enough. He stood up and extended his hand toward the old scientist. "I gotta go. Thanks for the interview. And those bugs are really something."

"You're most welcome!" Von Oster responded. "Now, wait. Interview, you say. Who you writing this book for?" The idea had suddenly occurred to him that he'd been interviewed.

"For the Museum," said Smithback. "Rickman's in charge of it."

"Rickman?" Von Oster's eyes suddenly narrowed.

"Yes. Why?" Smithback asked.

"You working for Rickman?" Von Oster said.

"Not really. She's just, well, interfering mostly," Smithback said.

Von Oster broke into a pink grin. "*Ach,* she poison that one! Why you working for her?"

"That's just the way it happened," Smithback said, gratified at having found an ally. "You wouldn't believe the kind of crap she's put me through. Oh, God."

Von Oster clapped his hands. "I believe it! I believe it! She making trouble everywhere! This exhibit, she making all kind of trouble!"

Suddenly Smithback was interested. "How so?" he asked.

"She in there every day, saying *zis* not good, *zat* not good. *Gott,* that woman!"

"That sounds like her," Smithback said with a grim smile. "So what wasn't good?"

"That, what you call it, that Kothoga tribe stuff. I was in there just yesterday afternoon and she was carrying on. 'Everybody leave the exhibition! We bring in Kothoga figurine!' Everybody had to drop work and leave."

"The figurine? What figurine? What's so sensitive about it?" It suddenly occurred to Smithback that something so upsetting to Rickman might someday be useful to him.

"That Mbwun figurine, big deal in the exhibition. I not know much about. But she was very upset, I tell you!"

"Why?"

"Like I tell you, that figurine. You not heard? Lots of talk about it, very very bad. I try not to hear."

"What kind of talk would that be, for instance?"

Smithback listened to the old man for quite a while longer. Finally, he backed himself out of the workshop, Von Oster pursuing as far as the elevator.

As the doors rolled shut, the man was still talking. "You unlucky, working for her!" he called after Smithback just before the elevator lurched upward. But Smithback didn't hear him. He was busy thinking.

= 20 =

As the afternoon drew to a close, Margo looked up wearily from her terminal. Stretching, she punched a command to the printer down the hall, then sat back, rubbing her eyes. Moriarty's case write-up was finally done. A little rough around the edges, perhaps; not as comprehensive as she would have liked; but she couldn't afford to spend any more time on it. Secretly, she was rather pleased, and found herself eager to take a printout up to Moriarty's office on the fourth floor of the Butterfield Observatory, where the project team for the *Superstition* exhibition was housed.

She thumbed through her staff directory, looking for Moriarty's extension. Then she reached for her phone and dialed the four-digit number.

"Exhibition central," drawled a voice. There were loud good-byes in the background.

"Is George Moriarty there?" Margo asked.

"I think he's down at the exhibition," the voice responded. "We're locking up here. Any message?"

"No, thanks," Margo replied, hanging up. She looked at her watch: almost five. Curfew time. But the exhibition was being unveiled Friday evening, and she'd promised Moriarty the material.

As she was about to get up, she remembered Frock's suggestion that she call Greg Kawakita. She sighed, picking up the phone again. *Better give him a try.* Chances are he'd be out of the building now, and she could just leave a message on phone-mail.

"Greg Kawakita speaking," came the familiar baritone voice.

"Greg? This is Margo Green." *Stop sounding so apologetic. It's not like he's a department head or anything.*

"Hi, Margo. What's up?" She could hear the clacking of keys coming over the line.

"I have a favor to ask. It's a suggestion of Dr. Frock's, actually. I'm doing an analysis of some plant specimens used by the Kiribitu tribe, and he suggested I run them through your Extrapolator. Perhaps it will find some genetic correspondences in the samples."

There was silence. "Dr. Frock thought it might be a useful test of your program, as well as a help to me," she urged.

Kawakita paused. "Well, you know, Margo, I'd like to help you out, I really would. But the Extrapolator really isn't in shape yet to be used by just anybody. I'm still chasing down bugs, and I couldn't vouch for the results."

Margo's face burned. "Just anybody?"

"Sorry, that was a poor choice of words. You know what I mean. Besides, it's a really busy time for me, and this curfew won't help matters any. Tell you what, why don't you check with me again in a week or two? Okay? Talk to you then."

The line went dead.

Margo stood up, grabbed her jacket and purse, and went down the hall to retrieve her printout. She knew he was planning to postpone her indefinitely. Well, to hell with Kawakita. She'd hunt Moriarty down and give him the copy before she left. If nothing else, it might get her that guided tour of the exhibition, maybe find out what all the fuss was about.

A few minutes later, Margo walked slowly across the deserted Selous Memorial Hall. Two guards were stationed at the entrance, and a single docent stood inside the information center, locking away ledgers and arranging sale items in preparation for the next day's visitors. *Assuming there are any,* thought Margo. Three policemen stood just under the huge bronze statue of Selous, talking among themselves. They didn't notice Margo.

Margo found her thoughts returning to the morning's talk with Frock. If the killer wasn't found, the security measures could get stricter. Maybe her dissertation defense would be delayed. Or the entire Museum could be closed. Margo shook her head. If that happened, she was Massachusetts-bound for sure.

She headed for the Walker Gallery and the rear entrance to *Superstition.* To her dismay, the large iron doors were closed, and a velvet rope was suspended between two brass posts in front of them. A policeman stood beside the sign, motionless.

"Can I help you, Miss?" he said. His nameplate read F. BEAUREGARD.

"I'm going to see George Moriarty," Margo replied. "I think he's in the exhibition galleries. I have to give him something." She brandished the printout in front of the policeman, who looked unimpressed.

"Sorry, Miss," he said. "It's past five. You shouldn't be here. Besides," he said more gently, "the exhibition's been sealed until the opening."

"But—" Margo began to protest, then turned and walked back toward the rotunda with a sigh.

After rounding a corner, she stopped. At the end of the empty hallway she could see the dim vastness of the Hall. Behind her, Officer F. Beauregard was out of sight around the corner. On impulse, she veered sharply left through a small, low passage that opened into another, parallel walkway. Maybe it wasn't too late to find Moriarty, after all.

She moved up a wide flight of stairs, and, looking carefully around before proceeding, walked slowly into a vaulted hall devoted to insects. Then she turned right and entered a gallery that ran around the second level of the Marine Hall. Like everyplace else in the Museum, it felt eerie and deserted.

Margo descended one of the twin sweeping staircases to the granite floor of the main hall. Moving more slowly now, she passed by a life-size walrus habitat group and a meticulously constructed model of an underwater reef. Dioramas such as these, originally fashioned in the thirties and forties, could no longer be made, she knew— they had become much too expensive to produce.

At the far end of the Hall was the entrance to the Weisman Gallery, where the larger temporary exhibitions were held. This was one of the suite of galleries in which the *Superstition* exhibition was being mounted. Black paper covered the inside of the double glass doors, fronted by a large sign that read: GALLERY CLOSED. NEW EXHIBITION IN PROGRESS. THANK YOU FOR YOUR UNDERSTANDING.

The left-hand door was locked. The right one, however, pushed open easily.

As casually as possible, she looked over her shoulder: nobody.

The door hissed shut behind her, and she found herself in a narrow crawl space between the outer walls of the gallery and the back of the exhibition proper. Plywood boards and large nails were strewn around in disarray, and electrical cables snaked across the floor. On her left a huge structure of Sheetrock and boards, hammered clumsily together and supported by wooden buttresses, looked very much like the back side of a Hollywood set.

It was the side of the *Superstition* exhibition that no Museum visitor would ever see.

She moved carefully down the crawl space, scouting for some way to get into the exhibition. The light was poor—metal-shielded light bulbs, spaced about twenty feet apart—and she didn't want to stumble and fall. Soon she came across a small gap between the wooden panels—just big enough, she decided, to squeeze through.

She found herself in a large, six-sided anteroom. Gothic arches in three of the walls framed passages that receded into the gloom. Most of the light came from several backlit photographs of shamans high up on the walls. She looked speculatively at the three exits. She had no idea where she was in the exhibition—where it began, where it ended, or which way she should go to find Moriarty. "George?" she called softly, somehow unable to raise her voice in the silence and gloom.

She took the central passage to another dark hall, longer than the last and crowded with exhibits. At intervals, a brilliant spot illuminated some artifact: a mask, a bone knife, a strange carving covered with nails. The artifacts appeared to float in the velvet darkness. Crazy, dim patterns of light and shadow played across the ceiling.

At the far end of the gallery, the walls narrowed. Margo had the odd feeling that she was walking back into a deep cave. *Pretty manipulative,* she thought. She could see why Frock was upset.

She went deeper into the gloom, hearing nothing but her own footsteps padding on the thick carpet. She couldn't see the exhibits until she was almost on top of them, and she wondered how she'd retrace her steps to the room of the shamans. Perhaps there would be an unlocked exit—a well-lit unlocked exit—someplace else in the exhibit.

Ahead of her, the narrow hall forked. After a moment's hesitation, Margo chose the right-hand passage. As she continued, she noticed small alcoves to either side, each containing a single grotesque artifact. The silence was so intense that she found herself holding her breath.

The hall widened into a chamber, and she stopped in front of a set of Maori tattooed heads. They weren't shrunken—the skulls were clearly still inside, preserved, the label said, by smoking. The eye sockets were stuffed with fibers, and the mahogany-colored skins glistened. The black, shriveled lips were drawn back from the teeth. There were six of them, a crowd grinning hysterically, bobbing in the night. The blue tattoos were breathtakingly complex: intricate spirals that intersected and reintersected, curving in endless patterns around the cheeks and nose and chin. The tattooing had been done in life, the label said, and the heads preserved as a sign of respect.

Just beyond, Margo could see the gallery narrowing to a point. A massive, squat totem pole stood before it, lit from beneath by a pale, orange light. The shadows of giant wolf heads and birds with cruel, hooked beaks thrust upward from the pole and splashed across the ceiling, gray against black. Certain she had reached a dead end, Margo approached the totem pole unwillingly. Then she noticed a small opening, ahead and on the left, leading into an alcove. She continued slowly, walking as quietly as possible. Any thought of calling out again for Moriarty had long since vanished. *Thank God I'm nowhere near the Old Basement,* she thought.

The alcove held a display of fetishes. Some were simple stones carved in the shapes of animals, but the majority were monsters depicting the darker side of human superstition. Another opening brought Margo into a long, narrow room. Thick black felt covered all of the room's surfaces, and a dim blue light filtered from hidden recesses. The ceiling was low above Margo's head. *Smithback would have to go through here on his hands and knees,* she thought.

The room broadened into an octagonal space beneath

a high groined vault. A dappled light filtered down from stained-glass depictions of medieval underworlds set into the vaulted ceiling. Large windows dominated each wall.

She approached the closest window and found herself looking down into a Mayan tomb. A skeleton lay in the center, covered with a thick layer of dust. Artifacts were scattered around the site. A gold breastplate sat on the ribcage, and gold rings encircled bony fingers. Painted pots were arranged in a semicircle around the skull. One of these contained an offering of tiny, dried corncobs.

The next window displayed an Eskimo rock burial, including an Eskimo mummy-bundle wrapped in skins. The next was even more startling: a lidless, rotting European-style coffin, complete with corpse. The corpse was dressed in a much-decayed frock coat, tie, and tails, and was well on its way toward decomposition. Its head was bent stiffly toward Margo as if prepared to tell her a secret, sightless eye sockets bulging, mouth ossified into a rictus of pain. She took a step backward. *Good God,* she thought, *that's somebody's great-grandfather.* The matter-of-fact tone of the label, which tastefully described the rituals associated with a typical nineteenth-century American burial, belied the visual hideousness of the scene. *It's true,* she thought; *the Museum is definitely taking a chance with stuff as strong as this.*

She decided to forego the other windows and proceeded through a low archway in the far side of the octagonal room. Beyond, the passage forked. To her left was a small cul-de-sac; to her right, a long, slender passage led into darkness. She didn't want to go that way; not just yet. She wandered into the dead-end room, and stopped suddenly. Then she moved forward to examine one of the cases more closely.

The gallery dealt with the concept of ultimate evil in its many mythic forms. There were various images of a medieval devil; there was the Eskimo evil spirit, Tornarsuk. But what arrested her was a crude stone altar, placed in the center of the gallery. Sitting on the altar, lit by a yellow spot, was a small figurine, carved in such detail it took Margo's breath away. Covered in scales, it crouched on all fours. Yet there was something—the long forearms, the angle of its head—that was disturbingly human. She shuddered. *What kind of imagination gave rise to a being with both scales and hair?* Her eyes dropped to the label.

MBWUN. This carving is a representation of the mad god Mbwun, possibly carved by the Kothoga tribe of the Upper Amazon basin. This savage god, also known as He Who Walks On All Fours, was much feared by the other indigenous tribes of the area. In local myth, the Kothoga tribe was said to be able to conjure Mbwun at will, and send him on errands of destruction against neighboring tribes. Very few Kothoga artifacts have ever been found, and this is the sole image of Mbwun known to exist. Except for trace references in Amazonian legends, nothing else is known about the Kothoga, or about their mysterious "devil."

Margo felt a chill creep over her. She looked closer, repulsed by the reptilian features, the small, wicked eyes . . . the talons. Three on each forelimb.

Oh, dear God. It couldn't be.

Suddenly, she realized that every instinct she had was telling her to keep absolutely still. A minute passed, then two.

Then it came again—the sound that had galvanized her. An odd rustling, slow, deliberate, maddeningly soft. On the thick carpet, the footsteps had to be close . . . very close. A horrible goatish stench threatened to choke her.

She looked around wildly, fighting down panic, searching for the safest exit. The darkness was complete. As quietly as possible, she moved out of the cul-de-sac and across the fork. Another rustling noise and she was running, running, headlong through the darkness, past the ghoulish displays and leering statues that seemed to leap out of the blackness, down twisting forks and passages, trying always to take the most hidden path.

At last, thoroughly lost and out of breath, she ducked into an alcove containing a display on primitive medicine. Gasping, she crouched behind a case holding a trepanned human skull upon an iron pole. She hid in its shadow, listening.

There was nothing; no noise, no movement. She waited as her breath slowed and reason returned. There was nothing out there. There had never been anything out there, in fact—it was her overzealous imagination, fueled by this nightmarish tour. *I was foolish to sneak in,* she thought. *Now, I don't know if I'll ever want to come back—even on the busiest Saturday.*

Anyway, she had to find a way out. It was late now, and she hoped people were still around to hear her knocking, should she come up against a locked exit. It would be embarrassing, having to explain herself to a guard or policeman. But at least she'd be out.

She peeked over the case lid. Even if it *had* all been her imagination, she didn't care to go back in the same direction. Holding her breath, she stepped quietly out, then listened. Nothing.

She turned left and moved slowly down the corridor, searching for a likely looking route out of the exhibit. At a large fork she stopped, eyes straining in the darkness, debating which of the branching pathways to take. *Shouldn't there be exit signs? Guess they haven't been installed yet. Typical.* But the hall to her left looked promising: the passage seemed to open up into a large foyer, ahead in the blackness where sight failed.

Movement registered in her peripheral vision. Limbs frozen, she glanced hesitatingly to the right. A shadow—black against black—was gliding stealthily toward her, moving with an inky sinuousness over the display cases and grinning artifacts.

With a speed born of horror, she shot down the passage. She felt, more than saw, the walls of the passage roll back and widen about her. Then she saw twin slits of vertical light ahead, outlining a large double doorway. Without slackening her pace, she threw herself against it. The doors flew back, and something on the far side clattered. Dim light rushed in—the subdued red light of a museum at night. Cool air moved across her cheek.

Weeping now, she slammed the doors closed and leaned against them, eyes shut, forehead pressed against the cold metal, sobbing, fighting to catch her breath.

From the crimson gloom behind her came the unmistakable sound of something clearing its throat.

**SUPERSTITION
EXHIBITION**

PART TWO

= 21 =

"What's going on here?" came the stern voice.

Margo whirled around and almost collapsed with relief. "Officer Beauregard, there's—" she began, stopping in mid-sentence.

F. Beauregard, who was righting the brass posts that the swinging door had knocked over, looked up at the sound of his name. "Hey, you're the girl who tried to get in earlier!" The policeman's eyes narrowed. "What's wrong, Miss, can't take no for an answer?"

"Officer, there's a—" Margo tried to start again, then faltered.

The officer stepped back and folded his arms across his chest, waiting. Then a look of surprise crossed his face. "What the hell? Hey, you okay, lady?"

Margo was slumped over, laughing—or crying, she wasn't sure which—and wiping tears from her face.

The policeman freed one folded hand and took her arm. "I think you should come with me."

The implications of that last sentence—sitting in a

room full of policemen, telling her story again and again, maybe having Dr. Frock or even Dr. Wright called in, having to go back into that exhibition—forced Margo to straighten up. *They'll just think I'm crazy.* "Oh no, that's not necessary," she said, snuffling. "I just had a bit of a scare."

Officer Beauregard looked unconvinced. "I still think we should go talk to Lieutenant D'Agosta." With his other hand, he pulled a large, leather-bound notebook out of his back pocket. "What's your name?" he asked. "I'll have to make a report."

It was clear he wouldn't let her go until she gave him the information. "My name's Margo Green," she said finally. "I'm a graduate student working under Dr. Frock. I was doing an assignment for George Moriarty— he's curating this exhibition. But you were right. No-body was in there." She gently freed her arm from the policeman's grip as she spoke. Then she started backing away, toward Selous Memorial Hall, still talking. Officer Beauregard watched her and finally, with a shrug, he flipped open the notebook and started writing.

Back in the Hall, Margo paused. She couldn't go back to her office; it was almost six, and the curfew was sure to be enforced by now. She didn't want to go home— she *couldn't* go home, not just yet.

Then she remembered Moriarty's copy. She pressed one elbow against her side—sure enough, her carryall was still there, hanging unnoticed through the ordeal. She stood still another moment, then walked over to the deserted information kiosk. She picked up the receiver of an internal phone and dialed.

One ring, then: "Moriarty here."

"George?" she said. "It's Margo Green."

"Hi, Margo," Moriarty answered. "What's up?"

"I'm in the Selous Hall," she replied. "I just came from the exhibition."

"My exhibition?" Moriarty said, surprised. "What were you doing there? Who let you in?"

"I was looking for you," she answered. "I wanted to give you the Cameroon copy. *Were you in there?*" She felt panic rising once again to the surface.

"No. The exhibition's supposed to be sealed, in preparation for Friday night's opening," Moriarty said. "Why?"

Margo was breathing deeply, trying to control herself. Her hands were trembling, and the receiver knocked against her ear.

"What did you think of it?" Moriarty asked curiously.

A hysterical giggle escaped Margo. "Scary."

"We brought in some experts to work out the lighting and the placement of the visuals. Dr. Cuthbert even hired the man who designed Fantasyworld's Haunted Mausoleum. That's considered the best in the world, you know."

Margo finally trusted herself to speak again. "George, something was in that exhibition with me." A security guard on the far side of the Hall had spotted her, and was walking in her direction.

"What do you mean, *something?*"

"Exactly that!" Suddenly, she was back in the exhibit, in the dark, beside that horrible figurine. She remembered the bitter taste of terror in her mouth.

"Hey, stop shouting!" Moriarty said. "Look, let's go to The Bones and talk this over. We're both supposed to be out of the Museum, anyway. I hear what you're saying, but I don't understand it."

The Bones, as it was called by everyone in the Museum, was known to other local residents as the Blarney Stone Tavern. Its unimposing facade was nestled between two huge, ornate co-op buildings, directly across Seventy-second Street from the Museum's southern entrance. Unlike typical Upper West Side fern bars, the Blarney Stone did not serve hare pâté or five flavors of mineral water; but you could get homemade meatloaf and a pitcher of Harp for ten dollars.

Museum staffers called it The Bones because Boylan, the owner, had hammered and wired an amazing number of bones into every available flat surface. The walls were lined with countless femurs and tibias, arranged in neat ivory ranks like bamboo matting. Metatarsals, scapulas, and patellas traced bizarre mosaics across the ceiling. Craniums from strange mammals were lodged in every conceivable niche. Where he got the bones was a mystery, but some claimed he raided the Museum at night.

"People bring 'em in," is all Boylan would ever say, shrugging his shoulders. Naturally, the place was a favorite hangout among the Museum staff.

The Bones was doing brisk business, and Moriarty and Margo had to push their way back through the crowd to an empty booth. Looking around, Margo spotted several Museum staffers, including Bill Smithback. The writer was seated at the bar, talking animatedly to a slender blonde woman.

"Okay," Moriarty said, raising his voice over the babble. "Now what were you saying over the phone? I'm not quite sure I caught it."

Margo took a deep breath. "I went down to the exhibition to give you the copy. It was dark. Something was in there. Following me. *Chasing* me."

"There's that word again, *something*. Why do you say that?"

Margo shook her head impatiently. "Don't ask me to explain. There were these sounds, like padded steps. They were so stealthy, so deliberate, I—" she shrugged, at a loss. "And there was this strange smell, too. It was horrible."

"Look, Margo—" Moriarty began, then paused while the waitress took their drink orders. "That exhibition was designed to be creepy. You told me yourself that Frock and others consider it too sensational. I can imagine what it must have been like: being locked in there, alone in the dark . . ."

"In other words, I just imagined it." Margo laughed mirthlessly. "You don't know how much I'd like to believe that."

The drinks arrived: a light beer for Margo, and a pint of Guinness for Moriarty, topped with the requisite half-inch of creamy foam. Moriarty sipped it critically. "These killings, all the rumors that have been going around," he said. "I probably would have reacted the same way."

Margo, calmer now, spoke hesitantly. "George, that Kothoga figurine in the exhibition . . . ?"

"Mbwun? What about it?"

"Its front legs have three claws."

Moriarty was enjoying the Guinness. "I know. It's a marvelous piece of sculpture, one of the highlights of the show. Of course, though I hate to admit it, I suppose its biggest attraction is the curse."

Margo took an exploratory sip from her beer. "George. I want you to tell me, in as much detail as you can, what you know about the Mbwun curse."

A shout came bellowing over the din of conversation. Looking up, Margo saw Smithback appear out of the smoky gloom, carrying an armful of notebooks, his hair backlit and sticking out from his head at a variety of angles. The woman he'd been talking to at the bar was nowhere to be seen.

"A meeting of the shut-outs," he said. "This curfew is a real pain. God save me from policemen and PR directors." Uninvited, he dropped his notebooks on the table and slid in next to Margo.

"I've heard that the police are going to start interviewing those working in the vicinity of the murders," he said. "Guess that means you, Margo."

"Mine's set for next week," Margo replied.

"I haven't heard anything about it," said Moriarty. He didn't look pleased at Smithback's appearance.

"Well, you don't have much to worry about, perched up in that garret of yours," Smithback told Moriarty. "The Museum Beast probably can't climb stairs, anyway."

"You're in a foul mood this evening," Margo said to Smithback. "Did Rickman perform another amputation on your manuscript?"

Smithback was still talking to Moriarty. "Actually, you're just the man I wanted to see. I've got a question for you." The waitress came by again, and Smithback waved his hand. "Macallan, straight up."

"Okay," Smithback went on. "What I wanted to know is, what's the story behind this Mbwun figurine?"

There was a stunned silence.

Smithback looked from Moriarty to Margo. "What'd I say?"

"We were just talking about Mbwun," Margo said uncertainly.

"Yeah?" Smithback said. "Small world. Anyway, that old Austrian in the Bug Room, Von Oster, told me he heard Rickman kicking up a fuss about Mbwun being put on display. Something about sensitive issues. So I did a little digging."

The scotch arrived and Smithback held the glass high in a silent toast, then tossed it off.

"I've obtained a little background so far," he continued. "It seems there was this tribe along the Upper Xingú river in the Amazon, the Kothoga. They'd apparently been a bad lot—supernatural-dabbling, human sacrifice, the whole bit. Since the old boys hadn't left many traces around, anthropologists assumed they died out centuries ago. All that remained was a bunch of myths, circulated by local tribes."

"I know something of this," Moriarty began. "Margo and I were just discussing it. Except not everybody felt—"

"I know, I know. Hold your water."

Moriarty settled back, looking annoyed. He was more used to giving lectures than listening to them.

"Anyway, several years ago, there was this guy named Whittlesey at the Museum. He mounted an expedition to the Upper Xingú, purportedly to search for traces of the Kothoga—artifacts, ancient dwelling sites, whatever." Smithback leaned forward conspiratorially. "But what Whittlesey didn't tell anybody was that he wasn't just going in search of this old tribe's traces. He was going in search of the tribe *itself*. He'd got it into his noggin that the Kothoga still existed, and he was pretty certain he could locate them. He'd developed something he called 'myth triangulation.' "

This time, Moriarty wouldn't be stopped. "That's where you locate all the spots on a map where legends about a certain people or place are heard, identify the areas where the legends are most detailed and consistent, and locate the exact center of this myth region. That's where the source of the myth cycles is most likely to be found."

Smithback looked at Moriarty for a moment. "No kidding," he said. "Anyway, this Whittlesey goes off in 1987 and disappears into the Amazon rain forest, never to be seen again."

"Von Oster told you all this?" Moriarty rolled his eyes. "Tiresome old guy."

"He may be tiresome, but he knows a hell of a lot about this Museum." Smithback examined his empty glass forlornly. "Apparently, there was a big confrontation in the jungle, and most of the expedition team started back early. They'd found something so important they wanted to leave right away, but Whittlesey disagreed. He stayed, along with a fellow named Crocker. Apparently, they both died in the jungle. But when I asked Von Oster for more details about this Mbwun figurine, he suddenly clammed up." Smithback stretched languorously and began looking for the waitress. "Guess

I'll have to hunt down somebody who was part of that expedition."

"Lots of luck," Margo said. "They were all killed in a plane crash coming back."

Smithback peered at her intently. "No shit. And how do you know that?"

Margo hesitated, remembering Pendergast's request for confidentiality. Then she thought of Frock, and how he'd gripped her hand so fiercely that morning. *We can't miss this opportunity. We must not let this chance slip us by.* "I'll tell you what I know," she said slowly. "But you must keep this to yourselves. And you must agree to help me in any way you can."

"Be careful, Margo," Moriarty cautioned.

"Help you? Sure, no problem," said Smithback. "With what, by the way?"

Hesitantly, Margo told them about the meeting with Pendergast in the Secure Room: the casts of the claw and wound, the crates, Cuthbert's story. Then she described the sculpture of Mbwun she'd seen in the exhibition—omitting her panic and flight. She knew Smithback wouldn't believe her any more than Moriarty had.

"So what I was asking George when you came up," she concluded, "is exactly what he knows about this curse of the Kothoga."

Moriarty shrugged. "Not all that much, really. In local legend, the Kothoga tribe was a shadowy group, a witch-doctor cult. They were supposed to be able to control demons. There was a creature—a familiar if you will—they used for vengeance killings. That was Mbwun, He Who Walks On All Fours. Then, Whittlesey came across this figurine, and some other objects, packed them up, and sent them back to the Museum. Of course, such disturbance of sacred objects has been done countless times before. But then when he gets lost in the jungle and never comes out, and the rest of the expedition dies on the return trip . . .'' He shrugged his shoulders. ''The curse.''

''And now, people are dying in the Museum,'' Margo said.

''What are you saying—that the Mbwun curse, the stories of a Museum Beast, and these killings are all linked?'' asked Moriarty. ''Come on, Margo, don't read too much into it.''

She looked at him intently. ''Didn't you tell me that Cuthbert kept the figurine out of the exhibition until the last minute?''

''That's right,'' Moriarty said. ''He handled all work on that relic himself. Not unusual, considering it's such a valuable piece. As for delaying its placement in the exhibition, that was Rickman's idea, I believe. Probably thought it would generate more interest.''

''I doubt it,'' Smithback replied. ''That's not the way her mind works. If anything, she was trying to *avoid* interest. Blow scandal at her, and she shrivels up like a moth in a flame.'' He chuckled.

''Just what's *your* interest in all this, anyway?'' Moriarty demanded.

''You don't think a dusty old artifact would interest me?'' Smithback finally caught the eye of the waitress and ordered another round for the table.

''Well, it's obvious Rickman wouldn't let you write about it,'' Margo said.

Smithback made a face. ''Too true. It might offend all the ethnic Kothoga tribesmen in New York. Actually, it's because Von Oster said that Rickman was bent out of shape about this. So I thought maybe I could dig around, get some dirt. Something that will put me in a better bargaining position when our next *tête-à-tête* comes along. You know, 'This chapter stays, or I'm taking the Whittlesey story to *Smithsonian* magazine,' that sort of thing.''

''Now, wait a minute,'' Margo said. ''I didn't take you into my confidence just so you could make some money off it. Don't you understand? We have to learn more about these crates. Whatever is killing people wants something that's in them. We *have* to find out what it is.''

"What we really need to do is find that journal," Smithback said.

"But Cuthbert says it's been lost," Margo said.

"Have you checked the accession database?" Smithback said. "Maybe there's some information there. I'd do it myself, but my security rating is rock-bottom."

"So is mine," Margo replied. "And it hasn't been my day for computers." She told them about her talk with Kawakita.

"How about Moriarty, here?" Smithback said. "You're a computer whiz, right? Besides, as an Assistant Curator, you have high security access."

"I think you should let the authorities handle this." Moriarty drew back, dignified. "This isn't for us to mess around with."

"Don't you understand?" Margo pleaded. "*Nobody* knows what we're dealing with here. People's lives— perhaps the Museum's future—are at stake."

"I know your motives are good, Margo," Moriarty said. "But I don't trust Bill's."

"My motives are pure as the Pierian spring," Smithback retorted. "Rickman is storming the citadel of journalistic truth. I'm just looking to defend the ramparts."

"Wouldn't it be easier to just do what Rickman wants?" Moriarty asked. "I think your vendetta is a little childish. And you know what? You won't win."

The drinks came, and Smithback tossed his off and exhaled with gusto.

"Someday I'll get that bitch," he said.

= 22 =

Beauregard finished the entry, then stuffed his notebook in a back pocket. He knew he really ought to call the incident in. *Hell with it.* That girl had looked so scared, it was obvious she wasn't up to anything. He'd make his report when he got the chance, and no sooner.

Beauregard was in a bad mood. He didn't like door-shaker duty. Still, it beat directing traffic at a broken light. And it made a good impression down at O'Ryans. *Yeah,* he would say, *I'm assigned to the Museum case. Sorry, can't talk about it.*

For a museum, this place is damn quiet, Beauregard thought. He supposed on a normal day the Museum would be bustling with activity. But the Museum hadn't been normal since Sunday. At least during the day, staff members had come in and out of the new exhibition halls. But then, they'd closed it off for the opening. Except with written permission from Dr. Cuthbert, you couldn't get in unless you were police or security on official business. Thank God his shift ended at six and he could look forward to two days away from this place. A solo fishing trip to the Catskills. He'd been looking forward to it for weeks.

Beauregard ran his hand reassuringly along the holster of his S&W .38 special. Ready for action, as always. And on his other hip, a shot-shell pistol loaded with enough capstun to bring an elephant to its knees.

Behind him, Beauregard heard a muffled pattering sound.

He spun around, heart suddenly racing, to face the closed doors of the exhibition. He located a key, unlocked the doors, and peered in.

"Who's there?"

Only a cool breeze fanned his cheek.

He let the doors close and tested the lock. You could come out, but you couldn't go in. That girl must have gone in through the front entrance. But wasn't that kept locked, too? They never told him anything.

The sound came again.

Well, hell, he thought, *it ain't my job to check inside. Can't let anyone into the exhibition. Never said anything about anyone coming out.*

Beauregard started humming a tune, tapping the beat on his thigh with two fingers. Ten more minutes and he'd be out of this frigging spookhouse.

The sound came again.

Beauregard unlocked the doors a second time, and stuck his head deep inside. He could see some dim shapes: exhibition cases, a gloomy-looking entranceway. "This is a police officer. You in there, please respond."

The cases were dark, the walls vague shadows. No answer.

Withdrawing, Beauregard pulled out his radio. "Beauregard to Ops, do you copy?"

"This is TDN. What's up?"

"Reporting noises at the exhibition's rear exit."

"What kind of noises?"

"Uncertain. Sounds like someone's in there."

There was some talk and a stifled laugh.

"Uh . . . Fred?"

"What?" Beauregard was growing more irritated by the minute. The dispatcher in the situation room was a first-class asshole.

"Better not go in there."

"Why not?"

"It might be the monster, Fred. Might get you."

"Go to hell," Fred muttered under his breath. He wasn't supposed to investigate anything without backup, and the dispatcher knew it.

A scratching noise came from behind the doors, as if something with nails was scrabbling against it. Beauregard felt his breath come hard and fast.

His radio squawked. "Seen the monster yet?" came the voice.

Trying to keep his voice as neutral as possible, Beauregard said: "Repeat, reporting unidentified sounds in the exhibition. Request backup to investigate."

"He wants backup." There was the sound of muffled laughter. "Fred, we don't have any backup. Everyone's busy."

"Listen," said Beauregard, losing his temper. "Who's that with you? Why don't you send him down?"

"McNitt. He's on a coffee break. Right, McNitt?"

Beauregard heard some more laughter.

Beauregard switched off the radio. *Fuck those guys,* he thought. *Some professionalism.* He just hoped the Lieutenant was listening in on that frequency.

He waited in the dark hallway. *Five more minutes and I'm history.*

"TDN calling Beauregard. You read?"

"Ten-four," said Beauregard.

"McNitt there yet?"

"No," said Beauregard. "He finally finish his coffee break?"

"Hey, I was just kidding around," TDN said a little nervously. "I sent him right up."

"Well, he's lost, then," said Beauregard. "And my duty ends in five minutes. I'm off the next forty-eight, and nothing's going to interfere with that. You better radio him."

"He isn't reading," said TDN.

An idea suddenly occurred to Beauregard. "How did McNitt go? Did he take the Section 17 elevator, the one behind the sit room?"

"Yep, that's what I told him. Section 17 elevator. I got this map, same one you have."

"So in order to get here he has to go through the exhibition. That was real smart. You should have sent him up through food services."

"Hey, don't talk to me about smart, Freddy boy. He's the one who's lost. Call me when he arrives."

"One way or another, I'm outta here in five minutes," said Beauregard. "It'll be Effinger's headache then. Over and out."

That was when Beauregard heard a sudden commotion from the exhibition. There was a sound like a muffled thud. *Jesus,* he thought, *McNitt.* He unlocked the doors and went in, unsnapping the holster of his .38.

TDN placed another doughnut in his mouth and chewed, swallowing it with a mouthful of coffee. The radio hissed.

"McNitt to Ops. Come in, TDN."

"Ten-four. Where the hell are you?"

"I'm at the rear entrance. Beauregard ain't here. I can't raise him or anything."

"Lemme try." He punched the transmitter. "TDN calling Beauregard. Fred, come in. TDN calling Beauregard . . . Hey, McNitt, I think he got pissed off and went home. His shift just ended. How did you get up there, anyway?"

"I went the way you said, but when I got to the front

end of the exhibition it was locked, so I had to go around. Didn't have my keys. Got a little lost."

"Stay tight, all right? His relief should arrive any minute. Effinger, it says here. Radio me when he arrives and then come on back."

"Here comes Effinger now. You gonna report Beauregard?" McNitt asked.

"You kidding? I'm no damn baby-sitter."

= 23 =

D'Agosta looked over at Pendergast, reclining in the shabby backseat of the Buick. *Jesus,* he thought, *a guy like Pendergast ought to pull at least a late model Town Car.* Instead, they gave him a four-year-old Buick and a driver who could barely speak English.

Pendergast's eyes were half closed.

"Turn on Eighty-sixth and take the Central Park transverse," shouted D'Agosta.

The driver swerved across two lanes of Central Park West and roared into the transverse.

"Take Fifth to Sixty-fifth and go across," said D'Agosta. "Then go one block north on Third and take a right at Sixty-sixth."

"Fifty-nine faster," said the driver, in a thick Middle Eastern accent.

"Not in the evening rush hour," called D'Agosta. Christ, they couldn't even find a driver who knew his way around the city.

As the car swerved and rattled down the avenue, the driver flew on past Sixty-fifth Street.

"What the hell are you doing?" said D'Agosta. "You just missed Sixty-fifth."

"Apology," said the driver, turning down Sixty-first into a massive traffic jam.

"I can't believe this," D'Agosta said to Pendergast. "You ought to have this joker fired."

Pendergast smiled, his eyes still half closed. "He was, shall we say, a gift of the New York office. But the delay will give us a chance to talk." He settled back into the torn seat.

Pendergast had spent the last half of the afternoon at Jolley's autopsy. D'Agosta had declined the invitation.

"This lab found several kinds of DNA in our sample," Pendergast continued. "One was human, the other, from a gecko."

D'Agosta looked at him. "Gecko? What's a gecko?" he asked.

"A kind of lizard. Harmless enough. They like to sit on walls and bask in the sun. When I was a child, we rented a villa overlooking the Mediterranean one summer, and the walls were covered with them. At any rate, the results were so surprising to the lab technician that he thought it was a joke."

He opened his briefcase. "Here's the autopsy report on Jolley. There's nothing much new, I'm afraid. Same MO, body horrifically mauled, thalamoid region of the brain removed. The coroner's office has estimated that to create such deep lacerations in a single stroke, the required force would exceed—" he consulted a typewritten sheet "—twice what a strong human male can achieve. Needless to say, it's an estimation."

Pendergast turned some pages. "Also, they've now run salivase enzyme tests on brain sections from the older boy and from Jolley."

"And—?"

"Both brains tested positive for the presence of saliva."

"Jesus. You mean the killer's *eating* the fucking brain?"

"Not only eating, Lieutenant, but slobbering over the food as well. Clearly, he, she, or it has no manners. You have the SOC report? May I see it?"

D'Agosta handed it over. "You won't find any surprises there. The blood on the painting was Jolley's. They found traces of blood leading past the Secure Area and down into a stairwell to the subbasement. But last night's rain flushed all traces out of there, of course."

Pendergast scanned the document. "And here's the report on the door to the vault. Someone did quite a lot of pounding and banging, possibly with a blunt instrument. There were also three-pronged scratches consistent with those found on the victims. Once again, the force used was considerable."

Pendergast handed over the files. "It sounds as if we'll need to devote more attention to the subbasement. Basically, Vincent, this DNA business is our best chance for now. If we can trace the origin of that claw fragment, we'll have our first solid lead. That's why I've asked for this meeting."

The car pulled up in front of a warren of ivy-covered redbrick buildings overlooking the East River. A guard ushered them into a side entrance.

Once inside the lab, Pendergast took up a position against a table in the center of the room and chatted with the scientists, Buchholtz and Turow. D'Agosta admired how easily the Southerner could take charge of a scene.

"My colleague and I would like to understand the DNA sequencing process," Pendergast was saying. "We need to know how you arrived at these results, and whether any further analysis might be called for. I'm sure you understand."

"Certainly," said Buchholtz. He was busy and small

and as bald as Mount Monadnock. "My assistant, Dr. Turow here, did the analysis."

Turow stepped forward nervously. "When we were given the sample," he said, "we were asked to identify whether it had come from a large carnivorous mammal. Specifically, a big cat. What we do in such a case is compare the DNA in the sample to the DNA of, say, five or six species that are likely matches. But we would also select an animal that was definitely *not* of the sample, and we call this the outgroup. It's a kind of control. Am I making sense?"

"So far," said Pendergast. "But go easy on me. I'm a child in these matters."

"We usually use human DNA as the outgroup, since we've mapped so much of it. Anyway, we do a PCR— that is, a Polymerase Chain Reaction—on the sample. This causes thousands and thousands of copies of the genes to be made. It gives us a lot to work with, you see."

He pointed to a large machine with long clear strips of Plexiglas attached to its flanks. Behind the strips were dark vertical bands arrayed in complicated patterns. "This is a pulsed-field gel electrophoresis machine. We place the sample in here, and portions of the sample migrate out along these strips through the gel, according to their molecular weights. They show up as these dark bands. By the pattern of bands, and with the aid of our computer, we can figure out what genes are present."

He took a deep breath. "Anyway, we got a negative reading on the big cat genes. A *very* negative reading. It wasn't anywhere close. And to our surprise, we got a *positive* reading on the outgroup, that is, *Homo sapiens*. And, as you know, we identified DNA strands from several species of gecko—or so it appears." He looked a little sheepish. "But even so, most of the genes in the sample were unidentified."

"So that's why you presumed it was contaminated."

"Yes. Contaminated or degraded. A lot of repeated

base pairs in the sample suggested a high level of genetic damage.''

"Genetic damage?" asked Pendergast.

"When DNA is damaged or defective, it often uncontrollably replicates long repeating sequences of the same base pair. Viruses can damage DNA. So can radiation, certain chemicals, even cancer.''

Pendergast had begun to roam around the laboratory, examining his surroundings with an almost catlike curiosity. "These gecko genes interest me a great deal. Just what do they mean exactly?"

"That's the big mystery," said Turow. "These are rare genes. Some genes are very common, like the Cytochrome B gene, which can be found in everything from a periwinkle to man. But these gecko genes—well, we don't know anything about them.''

"What you're really saying is the DNA *didn't* come from an animal, right?" D'Agosta asked.

"Not from any large carnivorous mammal we know of," Buchholtz answered. "We tested all the relevant taxa. There are not nearly enough matches to say it came from a gecko. So, by a process of elimination, I would say it probably came from a human. But it was degraded or contaminated. The results are ambiguous.''

"The sample," said D'Agosta, "was found in the body of a murdered boy.''

"Ah!" said Turow. "That could easily explain how it was contaminated with human genetic material. Really, it would be much easier for us if we knew things like this beforehand.''

Pendergast frowned. "The sample was removed from the root canal of a claw by the forensic pathologist, as I understand it, and every effort was made to prevent contamination.''

"All it can take is one cell," said Turow. "A claw, you say?" He thought a moment. "Let me advance an idea. The claw might be from a lizard that was heavily contaminated by blood from its human victim. Any lizard—not necessarily a gecko." He looked at Buchholtz. "The only reason we identified some of the DNA as gecko is because a fellow in Baton Rouge did some research a few years ago on gecko genetics, and logged his results in GenLab. Otherwise it would have turned up unknown, like most of that sample."

Pendergast looked at Turow. "I'd like further tests done to tell us just what those gecko genes do, if you don't mind."

Turow frowned. "Mr. Pendergast, the chance of a successful analysis is not all that high, and it could take weeks. It seems to me the mystery's already been solved—"

Buchholtz clapped his hand on Turow's back. "Let's not second-guess Agent Pendergast. After all, the police are paying for it, and it is a *very* expensive procedure."

Pendergast smiled more broadly. "I'm glad you mentioned that, Dr. Buchholtz. Just send the bill to Director of Special Operations, FBI." He wrote down the address on his business card. "And please don't worry. Cost is no consideration whatsoever."

D'Agosta had to grin. He knew what Pendergast was doing: getting even for the lousy car. He shook his head. *What a devil.*

= 24 =

Thursday

At eleven-fifteen Thursday morning, a man claiming to be the living incarnation of the Egyptian pharaoh Toth ran amok in the Antiquities wing, knocking over two displays in the Temple of Azar-Nar, breaking a case and pulling a mummy out of its tomb. Three policemen were necessary to restrain him, and several curators worked the rest of the day replacing bandages and collecting ancient dust.

Less than an hour later, a woman ran screaming from the Hall of Great Apes, babbling about something she'd seen crouched in a dark bathroom corner. A television team, waiting on the south steps for a glimpse of Wright, got her entire hysterical exit on film.

Around lunchtime, a group calling itself the Alliance Against Racism had begun picketing outside the Museum, calling for a boycott of the *Superstition* exhibition.

Early that afternoon, Anthony McFarlane, a world-renowned philanthropist and big-game hunter, offered a reward of $500,000 for the capture and safe delivery of the Museum Beast. The Museum immediately disclaimed any connection with McFarlane.

All of these events were duly reported in the press. The following incidents, however, went undisclosed to the world outside the Museum:

By noon, four employees had quit without notice. Thirty-five others had taken unscheduled vacations, nearly three hundred had called in sick.

Shortly after lunch, a junior preparator in the vertebrate paleontology department collapsed at her laboratory table. She was taken to Medical, where she demanded extended leave and worker's compensation, citing severe emotional and physical stress.

By three P.M., security had responded to seven requests for investigations of suspicious noises in various remote sections of the museum. By curfew, police from the Museum command post had responded to four sus pected sightings, all of which remained unverified.

Later, the Museum switchboard would tabulate the number of creature-related calls it received that day: 107, including crank messages, bomb threats, and offers of assistance from exterminators to spiritualists.

= 25 =

Smithback eased open the grimy door and peered inside. This, he thought, had to be one of the more macabre places in the Museum: the storage area of the Physical Anthropology Laboratory, or, in Museum parlance, the Skeleton Room. The Museum had one of the largest collections of skeletons in the country, second only to the Smithsonian—twelve thousand in this room alone. Most were North and South American Indian or African, collected in the nineteenth century, during the heyday of physical anthropology. Tiers of large metal drawers rose in ordered ranks to the ceiling; each drawer contained at least a portion of a human skeleton. Yellowed labels were slotted into the front of each drawer; on these labels were numbers, names of tribes, sometimes a short history. Other, briefer labels carried the chill of anonymity.

Smithback had once spent an afternoon wandering among the boxes, opening them and reading the notes, almost all of which were written in faded, elegant scripts. He had jotted several down in his notebook:

Spec. No. 1880-1770
Walks in Cloud. Yankton Sioux. Killed in Battle of Medicine Bow Creek, 1880.

Spec. No. 1899-1206
Maggie Lost Horse. Northern Cheyenne.

Spec. No. 1933-43469
Anasazi. Canyon del Muerto. Thorpe-Carlson expedition, 1900.

Spec. No. 1912-695
Luo. Lake Victoria. Gift of Maj. Gen. Henry Throckmorton, Bart.

Spec. No. 1872-10
Aleut, provenance unknown.

It was a strange graveyard indeed.

Beyond the storage area lay the warren of rooms housing the Physical Anthropology Lab. In earlier days, physical anthropologists had spent most of their time in this laboratory measuring bones and trying to determine the relationship between the races, where humanity had originated, and similar studies. Now, much more complex biochemical and epidemiological research was being done in the Physical Anthro Lab.

Several years earlier, the Museum—at Frock's insistence—had decided to merge its genetics research and DNA laboratories with the lab. Beyond the dusty bone-storage area lay a spotless assortment of huge centrifuges, hissing autoclaves, electrophoresis apparatus, glowing monitors, elaborate blown-glass distillation columns, and titration setups—one of the most advanced technical facilities of its kind. It was in the no-man's-land between the old and the new that Greg Kawakita had set up shop.

Smithback looked through the tall racks of the storage room toward the lab doors. It was just after ten, and Kawakita was the only one around. Through the open shelves, Smithback could see Kawakita standing one or two rows over, making sharp, jerky overhead movements with his left hand, waving something about. Then, Smithback heard the zing of a line and the whirring of a fly reel. *Well, raise my rent,* Smithback thought. The man was fishing.

"Catch anything?" he called out loudly.

He heard a sharp exclamation and a clatter of a dropped rod.

"Damn you, Smithback," Kawakita said. "You're always sneaking about. This isn't a good time to go around scaring people, you know. I might have been packing a .45 or something."

He walked down his aisle and came around the corner, reeling in his fly rod and scowling good-humoredly at Smithback.

Smithback laughed. "I told you not to work down here with all these skeletons. Now look what's happened: you've gone off the deep end at last."

"Just practicing," Kawakita laughed. "Watch. Third shelf. Buffalo Hump."

He flicked the rod. The line whirred out, and the fly struck, then rebounded off a drawer on the third tier of a shelf at the end of the aisle. Smithback walked over. Sure enough: it contained the bones of someone who had once been Buffalo Hump.

Smithback whistled.

Kawakita drew in some line, loosely holding the loops in his left hand while he gripped the cork butt of the rod in his right. "Fifth shelf, second row. John Mboya," he said.

Again the line arced through the air between the narrow shelves and the tiny fly ticked the correct label.

"Izaak Walton, move over," said Smithback, shaking his head.

Kawakita reeled in the line and started dismantling the bamboo rod. "It's not quite like fishing on a river," he said as he worked, "but it's great practice, especially in this confined space. Helps me relax during breaks. When I don't tangle my line in one of the cases, that is."

When Kawakita was first hired by the Museum, he had declined the sunny fifth-floor office offered him, and instead claimed a much smaller one in the lab, saying he wanted to be closer to the action. Since then, he had already published more papers than some full curators had in their entire careers. His cross-disciplinary studies under Frock had quickly led him to an Assistant Curatorship in evolutionary biology, where he had initially devoted his time to the study of plant evolution. Kawakita skillfully used his mentor's notoriety to advance himself. Lately, he had put aside plant evolution temporarily for the Genetic Sequence Extrapolator program. His only other passion in life, aside from his work, seemed to be fly-fishing; in particular, as he would explain to anyone who listened, his search for the noble and elusive Atlantic salmon.

Kawakita slid the rod into a battered Orvis case and leaned it carefully in a corner. Motioning Smithback to follow, he led the way down long rows of coffined aisles to a large desk and three heavy wooden chairs. The desk, Smithback noticed, was covered with papers, stacks of well-thumbed monographs, and low trays of plastic-covered sand holding various human bones.

"Look at this," Kawakita said, sliding something in Smithback's direction. It was an engraved illustration of a family tree, etched in brown ink on hand-marbled paper. The branches of the tree were labeled with various Latin words.

"Nice," said Smithback, taking a seat.

"That's one word for it, I guess," Kawakita replied.

"A mid-nineteenth century view of human evolution. An artistic masterpiece, but a scientific travesty. I'm working on a little piece for the *Human Evolution Quarterly* about early evolutionary views."

"When will it be published?" Smithback asked with professional interest.

"Oh, early next year. These journals are so slow."

Smithback put the chart down on the desk. "So what does all this have to do with your current work—the GRE, or the SAT, or whatever it is?"

"G.S.E., actually." Kawakita laughed. "Nothing whatsoever. This is just a little idea I had, some after-hours fun. I still enjoy getting my hands dirty from time to time." He replaced the chart carefully in a binder, then turned toward the writer. "So, how's the masterwork coming along?" he asked. "Is Madame Rickman still giving you a hard time?"

Smithback laughed. "Guess my struggles under the tyrant are common knowledge by now. But that's a book in itself. Actually, I came by to talk to you about Margo."

Kawakita took a seat across from Smithback. "Margo Green? What about her?

Smithback started paging aimlessly through one of the monographs scattered about the worktable. "I understand she needs your help on something."

Kawakita's eyes narrowed. "She called last night, asking if she could run some data through the Extrapolation program. I told her it wasn't ready yet." He shrugged. "Technically, that's true. I can't vouch one hundred percent for the accuracy of its correlations. But I'm terribly busy these days, Bill. I just don't have the time to shepherd somebody through the program."

"She's not exactly some scientific illiterate you need to lead around by the nose," Smithback replied. "She's doing some heavy-duty genetics research of her own. You must see her around this lab all the time." He pushed the monographs aside and leaned forward. "It might not hurt to cut the kid a break," he said. "It isn't exactly an easy time for her. Her father died about two weeks ago, you know."

Kawakita looked surprised. "Really? Is that what you were talking about in the staff lounge?"

Smithback nodded. "She hasn't said much, but it's been a struggle. She's considering leaving the Museum."

"That would be a mistake," Kawakita frowned. He started to say something, then stopped abruptly. He leaned back in his chair and gave Smithback a long, appraising look. "This is a mighty altruistic gesture on your part, Bill." He pursed his lips, nodding slowly. "Bill Smithback, the good samaritan. New image for you, eh?"

"That's William Smithback Jr. to you."

"Bill Smithback, the Eagle Scout," Kawakita continued. Then he shook his head. "Nope, it just doesn't ring true. You didn't really come down here to talk about Margo, did you?"

Smithback hesitated. "Well, that was one of my reasons," he admitted.

"I knew it!" Kawakita crowed. "Come on, out with it."

"Oh, all right," Smithback sighed. "Listen: I'm trying to get some information on the Whittlesey expedition."

"The *what?*"

"The South American expedition that brought back the Mbwun figurine. You know, the showpiece for the new exhibition."

Recognition flooded Kawakita's face. "Oh, yes. That's the one old man Smith must have been talking about in the herbarium the other day. What about it?"

"Well, we think there's some kind of link between that expedition and these murders."

"What?" Kawakita said incredulously. "Don't tell

me *you're* starting up with this Museum Beast stuff. And what do you mean, 'we'?"

"I'm not saying I believe anything, okay?" Smithback replied evasively. "But I've been hearing a lot of strange stuff recently. And Rickman's all tense about having the Mbwun figurine in the exhibition. Other things came back from that expedition besides this one relic—several crates, in fact. I want to find out more about them."

"And what, exactly, do I have to do with all of this?" Kawakita asked.

"Nothing. But you're an Assistant Curator. You have high-security access to the Museum computer. You can query the accession database, find out about those crates."

"I doubt they've even been logged," Kawakita said. "But either way, it wouldn't matter."

"Why not?" Smithback asked.

Kawakita laughed. "Wait here a minute." He stood up and headed for the lab. In a few minutes he returned, a piece of paper in one hand.

"You must be psychic," he said, handing over the paper. "Look what I found in my mail this morning."

NEW YORK MUSEUM OF NATURAL HISTORY
INTERNAL MEMORANDUM

To: Curators and Senior Staff
From: Lavinia Rickman
CC: Wright, Lewallen, Cuthbert,
          Lafore

As a result of recent unfortunate events, the Museum is under intense scrutiny by the media and by the public in general. This being the case, I wanted to take the opportunity to review the Museum's policy on external communications.

Any dealings with the press are to be handled through the Museum's public relations office. No comments on Museum matters are to be made, either on or off the record, to journalists or other members of the media. Any statements made or assistance given to individuals who are engaged in preparing interviews, documentaries, books, articles, etc. dealing with the Museum are to be cleared through this office. Failure to follow these guidelines will result in disciplinary action from the Director's Office.

Thank you for your cooperation in this difficult time.

"Christ," muttered Smithback. "Look at this. 'Individuals engaged in preparing books.'"

"She means you, Bill," Kawakita laughed. "So you see? My hands are tied." He extracted a handkerchief from his back pocket and blew his nose. "Allergic to bone dust," he explained.

"I just can't believe this," Smithback said, rereading the memo.

Kawakita clapped an arm around Smithback's shoulder. "Bill, my friend, I know this story would make great copy. And I'd like to help you write the most controversial, outrageous, and salacious book possible. Only I can't. I'll be honest. I've got a career here, and—" he tightened his grip "—I'm coming up for tenure. I can't afford to make those kinds of waves right now. You'll have to go some other route. Okay?"

Smithback nodded with resignation. "Okay."

"You look unconvinced," Kawakita laughed. "But I'm glad you understand, anyway." He gently propelled the writer to his feet. "I'll tell you what. How about a little fishing on Sunday? They're predicting an early hatch on the Connetquot.''

Smithback finally grinned. "Tie me some of your devilish little nymphs," he said. "You're on."

= 26 =

D'Agosta was all the way on the other side of the Museum when yet another call came in. Emergency sighting, Section 18, Computer Room.

He sighed, shoving his radio back into its holster, thinking of his tired feet. Everyone in the damn place was seeing bogeymen.

A dozen people were crowding the hall outside the Computer Room, joking nervously. Two uniformed officers were standing by the closed door. "Okay," said D'Agosta, unwrapping a cigar. "Who saw it?"

A young man edged forward. White lab coat, slope-shouldered, Coke bottle glasses, calculator and pager dangling off the belt. *Cripes,* thought D'Agosta, *where did they get these guys?* He was perfect.

"I didn't actually *see* anything," he said, "but there was this loud thumping noise in the Electrical Systems Room. It sounded like banging, someone trying to get through the door—"

D'Agosta turned to the two cops. "Let's check it out."

He fumbled at the door knob and someone produced a key, explaining, "We locked it. We didn't want anything coming out—"

D'Agosta waved his hand. This was getting ridiculous. Everyone was spooked. How the hell could they be planning a big opening party for the following night? They should have shut the damn place down after the first murders.

The room was large, circular, and spotless. In the center, standing on a large pedestal and bathed in bright neon lights, was a five-foot-tall white cylinder that D'Agosta supposed was the Museum's mainframe. It hummed softly, surrounded by terminals, workstations, tables, and bookcases. Two closed doors were visible on the far walls.

"You guys poke around," he told his men, popping the unlit cigar in his mouth. "I wanna talk to this guy, do the paperwork."

He went back outside. "Name?" he asked.

"Roger Thrumcap. I'm the Shift Supervisor."

"Okay," D'Agosta said wearily, making notations. "You're reporting noises in Data Processing."

"No, sir, Data Processing's upstairs. This is the Computer Room. We monitor the hardware, do systems work."

"The Computer Room, then." He scribbled some more. "You first noticed these noises when?"

"A few minutes after ten. We were just finishing up our journals."

"You were reading the paper when you heard the noises?"

"No, sir. The journal tapes. We were just finishing our daily backup."

"I see. You were just *finishing* at ten o'clock?"

"The backups can't be done during peak hours, sir.

We have special permission to come in at six in the morning.''

"Lucky you. And you heard these noises where?''

"They were coming from the Electrical Room.''

"And that is—?''

"The door to the left of the MP-3. That's the computer, sir.''

"I saw two doors in there." D'Agosta said. "What's behind the other one?''

"Oh, that's just the lights-out room. It's on a carded-entry system, nobody can get in there.''

D'Agosta gave the man a strange look.

"It contains the diskpacks, things like that. You know, the storage devices. It's called a lights-out room because everything's automated, nobody goes in there except for maintenance.'' He nodded proudly. "We're in a zero-operator environment. Compared to us, DP's still in the Stone Age. They still have operators manually mounting tapes, no silos or anything.''

D'Agosta went back inside. "They heard the noises on the other side of that door to the left, there in the back. Let's take a look.'' He turned around. "Keep them out here,'' he said to Thrumcap.

The door to the electrical room swung open, releasing a smell of hot wiring and ozone. D'Agosta fumbled along the wall, found the light and snapped it on.

He did a visual first, by the book. Transformers. Grill-work covering ventilation ducts. Cables. Several large air-conditioning units. A lot of hot air. But nothing else.

"Take a look behind that equipment,'' D'Agosta said.

The officers nosed around thoroughly. One looked back and shrugged.

"All right,'' said D'Agosta, walking out into the computer room. "Looks clean to me. Mr. Thrumcap?''

"Yes?'' He poked his head in.

"You can tell your people to come back in. Looks okay, but we're gonna post a man for the next thirty-six hours.'' He turned to one of the policemen emerging from the electrical room. "Waters, I want you here till the end of your shift. Pro forma, all right? I'll send your relief." *A few more sightings and I'll be fresh out of officers.*

"Right," said Waters.

"That's a good idea," said Thrumcap. "This room is the heart of the Museum, you know. Or rather, the brain. We run the telephones, physical plant, network, mini-printing, electronic mail, security system—"

"Sure," said D'Agosta. He wondered if this was the same security that didn't have an accurate blueprint of the subbasement.

The staff began filing back into the room and taking up their places at the terminals. D'Agosta mopped his brow. *Hot as balls in here.* He turned to leave.

"Rog," he heard a voice behind him. "We got a problem."

D'Agosta hesitated a moment.

"Oh, my God," said Thrumcap, staring at a monitor. "The system's doing a hex dump. What the hell—?"

"Was the master terminal still in backup mode when you left it, Rog?" a short guy with buck teeth was asking. "If it finished and got no response, it might have gone into a low-level dump."

"Maybe you're right," said Roger. "Abort the dump and make sure the regions are all up."

"It's not responding."

"Is the OS down?" Thrumcap asked, bending over bucktooth's CRT. "Lemme see this."

An alarm went off in the room, not loud, but high-pitched and insistent. D'Agosta saw a red light in a ceiling panel above the sleek mainframe. Maybe he'd better stick around.

"Now what?" said Thrumcap.

Jesus, it's hot, D'Agosta thought. *How can these people stand it?*

"What's this code we're getting?"

"I don't know. Look it up."

"Where?"

"In the manual, fool! It's right behind your terminal. Here, I've got it."

Thrumcap started flipping pages. "2291, 2291 ... here it is. It's a heat alarm. Oh, Lord, the machine's overheating! Get maintenance up here right away."

D'Agosta shrugged. The thumping noise they'd heard was probably air-conditioner compressors failing. *It doesn't take a rocket scientist to figure that out. It must be ninety degrees in here.* As he began moving down the hall, he passed two maintenance men hurrying in the opposite direction.

Like most modern supercomputers, the Museum's MP-3 was better able to withstand heat than the "big iron" mainframes of ten or twenty years before. Its silicon brain, unlike the older vacuum tubes and transistors, could function above recommended temperatures for longer periods of time without damage or loss of data. However, the hardwired interface to the Museum's security system had been installed by a third party, outside the operating specifications of the computer manufacturer. When the temperature in the computer room reached ninety-four degrees, the tolerances of the ROM chips governing the Automatic Disaster Control System were exceeded. Failure occurred ninety seconds later.

Waters stood in a corner and glanced around the room. The maintenance men had left over an hour before, and the room was pleasantly chilly. Everything was back to normal, and the only sounds were the hum of the computer and the zombies clicking thousands of keys. He idly glanced at an unoccupied terminal screen and saw a blinking message.

EXTERNAL ARRAY FAILURE AT ROM
ADDRESS 33 B1 4A 0E

It was like Chinese. Whatever it was, why couldn't they just say it in English? He hated computers. He couldn't think of one damn thing computers had done for him except leave the *s* off his last name on bills. He hated those smart-ass computer nerds, too. If there was anything wrong here, let *them* take care of it.

= 27 =

Smithback dumped his notebooks beside one of his favorite library carrels. Sighing heavily, he squeezed himself into the cramped space, placed his laptop on the desk, and turned on the small overhead light. He was only a stone's throw from the oak-panelled reading room, with its red leather chairs and marble fireplace that hadn't seen use in a century. But Smithback preferred the narrow, scuffed carrels. He especially liked the ones that were hidden deep in the stacks, where he could examine documents and manuscripts he'd temporarily liberated—or catch forty winks—in privacy and relative comfort.

The Museum's collection of new, old, and rare books on all aspects of natural history was unrivalled. It had received so many bequests and privately donated collections over the years that its card catalogue was always hopelessly behind. Yet Smithback knew the library better even than most of the librarians. He could find a buried factoid in record time.

Now he pursed his lips, thinking. Moriarty was a stubborn bureaucrat, and Smithback himself had come up empty with Kawakita. He didn't know anyone else who could get him into the accession database. But there was more than one way to approach this puzzle.

At the microfilm card file, he started flipping through the *New York Times* index. He backtracked as far as 1975. Nothing there—or, as he soon discovered, in the relevant natural history and anthropological journals.

He checked the back issues of the Museum's internal periodicals for information on the expedition. Nothing. In the 1985 *Who's Who At NYMNH*, a two-line bio of Whittlesey told him nothing he didn't already know.

He cursed under his breath. *This guy's hidden deeper than the Oak Island treasure.*

Smithback slowly put the volumes back on their racks, looking around. Then, taking some sheets from a notebook, he strolled nonchalantly up to the desk of a reference librarian, first making sure he hadn't seen her before.

"Gotta put these back in the archives," he told the librarian.

She blinked up at him severely. "Are you new around here?"

"I'm from the science library, just got transferred up last week. On rotation, you know." He gave her a smile, hoped it looked bright and genuine.

She frowned at him, uncertain, as the phone on her desk began to ring. She hesitated, then answered it, distractedly handing him a clipboard and a key on a long, blue cord. "Sign in," she said, covering the mouthpiece with her hand.

The library archives lay behind an unmarked gray door in a remote corner of the library stacks. It was a gamble in more ways than one. Smithback had been inside once before, on legitimate business. He knew that the bulk of the Museum's archives were stored elsewhere, and that the library's files were very specific. But something was nagging him. He closed the door and moved forward, scanning the shelves and the stacks of labeled boxes.

He had progressed down one side of the room and was starting up the other when he stopped. Carefully, he reached up and brought down a box labeled CENTRAL RECVG/SHPG: AIR CARGO RECEIPTS. Squatting down, he rustled quickly through the papers.

Once again, he went back as far as 1975. Disappointed, he rustled through them again. Nothing.

As he returned the box to its high perch, his eye caught another label: BILLS OF LADING, 1970–1990. He couldn't risk more than another five minutes, tops.

His finger stopped near the end of the pile. "Gotcha," he whispered, pulling a smudged sheet free of the box. From his pocket, he extracted his microcassette recorder and quietly spoke the pertinent words, dates, and places: Belém; Port of New Orleans; Brooklyn. The *Strella de Venezuela*—Star of Venezuela. *Odd,* he thought. *Awfully long layover in New Orleans.*

"You seem pretty pleased with yourself," the librarian said as she stowed the key back in the desk.

"Have a nice day," Smithback said. He finished the entry on the archives clipboard: Sebastian Melmoth, in 11:10, out 11:25.

Back at the microfilm catalog, Smithback paused. He knew the New Orleans newspaper had a strange name, very antebellum-sounding—*Times-Picayune,* that was it.

He scanned the catalog quickly. There it was: *Times-Picayune,* 1840–present.

He snapped the 1988 reel into the machine. As he neared October, he slowed, then stopped completely. A large, 72-point banner headline stared at him out of the microfilm viewer.

"Oh, God," he breathed.

He now knew, without a shred of doubt, why the Whittlesey crates had spent so long in New Orleans.

= 28 =

"I'm sorry, Miss Green, but his door is still closed. I'll give him your message as soon as possible."

"Thanks," Margo said, hanging up her phone with frustration. How could she be Frock's eyes and ears if she couldn't even talk to him?

When Frock was deeply involved in a project, he often locked himself in his office. His secretary knew better than to disturb him. Margo had tried to reach him twice already that morning, and there was no telling when he'd re-emerge.

Margo glanced at her watch. 11:20 A.M.—the morning was almost gone. She turned to her terminal and tried logging on to the Museum's computer.

HELLO MARGO GREEN@BIOTECH@STF
WELCOME BACK TO MUSENET
DISTRIBUTED NETWORKING SYSTEM,
RELEASE 15-5

COPYRIGHT © 1989–1995 NYMNH AND CERE-
BRAL SYSTEMS INC.
CONNECTING AT 11:20:45 03-30-95
PRINT SERVICE ROUTED TO LJ56

ALL USERS—IMPORTANT NOTICE
DUE TO THIS MORNING'S SYSTEM OUTAGE, A
RESTORE WILL BE PERFORMED AT NOON.
EXPECT DEGRADED PERFORMANCE. REPORT
ANY MISSING OR CORRUPTED FILES TO SYS-
TEMS ADMINISTRATOR ASAP.
ROGER THRUMCAP@ADMIN@SYSTEMS

YOU HAVE 1 MESSAGE(S) WAITING

She brought up the electronic mail menu and read the
waiting message.

MAIL FROM GEORGE MORIARTY@EXHIB@STF
SENT 10:14:07 03-30-95

THANKS FOR THE LABEL COPY—LOOKS PER-
FECT, NO CHANGES NECESSARY. WE'LL PUT IT
IN WITH OTHER FINISHING TOUCHES BEFORE
OPENING TO THE GENERAL PUBLIC.
CARE TO HAVE LUNCH TODAY?
—GEORGE

REPLY, DELETE, FILE (R/D/F)?

Her telephone rang, shattering the silence. "Hello?"
she said.

"Margo? Hi. It's George," came Moriarty's voice.

"Hi," she replied. "Sorry, just got your message now."

"I figured as much," he responded cheerfully. "Thanks again for helping out."

"Glad to," replied Margo.

Moriarty paused. "So ..." he began hesitantly. "How about that lunch?"

"Sorry," Margo said. "I'd like to, but I'm waiting for a call back from Dr. Frock. Could be five minutes, could be next week."

She could tell by the silence that Moriarty was disappointed.

"Tell you what, though," she said. "You could swing by for me on your way to the cafeteria. If Frock's called by then, maybe I'll be free. If he hasn't ... well, perhaps you could hang out for a couple of minutes while I wait, help me with the *Times* crossword or something."

"Sure!" Moriarty replied. "I know every three-letter Australian mammal there is."

Margo hesitated. "And perhaps while you're down here, we can take a peek into the accession database, see about the Whittlesey crates ... ?"

There was a silence. Finally, Moriarty sighed. "Well, if it's that important to you, I guess it couldn't hurt anything. I'll stop by around twelve."

Half an hour later, a knock sounded. "Come in," she called out.

"The damn thing's locked." The voice was not Moriarty's.

She opened the door. "I didn't expect to see *you* here."

"Do you suppose it's luck or fate?" Smithback said, coming in quickly and shutting the door behind him. "Listen, Lotus Blossom, I've been a busy man since last night."

"So have I," she said. "Moriarty will be here any minute to get us into the accession database."

"How did you—"

"Never mind," Margo replied smugly.

The door opened, and Moriarty peered in. "Margo?" he asked. Then he caught sight of Smithback.

"Don't fret, professor, it's safe," the writer said. "I'm not in a biting mood today."

"Don't mind him," Margo said. "He has this annoying habit of popping up unannounced. Come on in."

"Yes, and make yourself comfortable," Smithback said, pointedly gesturing to the chair in front of Margo's terminal.

Moriarty sat down slowly, looking at Smithback, then at Margo, then at Smithback again. "I guess you want me to check the accession records," he said.

"If you wouldn't mind," Margo said quietly. Smithback's presence made the whole thing seem like a setup.

"Okay, Margo." Moriarty put his fingers on the keyboard. "Smithback, turn around. The password, you know."

The Museum's accession database contained information on all the millions of catalogued items in the Museum's collections. Initially, the database had been accessible to all employees. However, someone on the fifth floor had gotten nervous at having the artifacts' detailed descriptions and storage locations available to anyone. Now, access was limited to senior staff—Assistant Curators, such as Moriarty, and above.

Moriarty was sullenly tapping keys. "I could be given a reprimand for this, you know," he said. "Dr. Cuthbert's very strict. Why didn't you just get Frock to do it for you?"

"Like I said, I can't get in to see him," Margo replied.

Moriarty gave the ENTER key a final jab. "Here it is,"

he said. "Take a quick look, I'm not going to bring it up again."

Margo and Smithback crowded around the terminal as the green letters crawled slowly up the screen:

ACCESSION FILE NUMBER 1989-2006
DATE: APRIL 4, 1989
COLLECTOR: JOHN WHITTLESEY, EDWARD MAXWELL, ET AL
CATALOGUER: HUGO C. MONTAGUE
SOURCE: WHITTLESEY/MAXWELL AMAZON BASIN EXPEDITION
LOCATION: BUILDING 2, LEVEL 3, SECTION 6, VAULT 144
NOTE: THE FOLLOWING CATALOGUED ITEMS WERE RECEIVED ON FEBRUARY 1, 1989 IN SEVEN CRATES SENT BACK BY THE WHITTLESEY/MAXWELL EXPEDITION FROM THE UPPER XINGU RIVER SYSTEM. SIX OF THE CRATES WERE PACKAGED BY MAXWELL, ONE BY WHITTLESEY. WHITTLESEY AND THOMAS R. CROCKER JR. DID NOT RETURN FROM THE EXPEDITION AND ARE PRESUMED DEAD. MAXWELL AND THE REST OF THE PARTY PERISHED IN A PLANE CRASH EN ROUTE TO THE UNITED STATES. ONLY WHITTLESEY'S CRATE HAS BEEN PARTIALLY CATALOGUED HERE; THIS NOTE WILL BE SUPERCEDED AS THIS CRATE AND THE MAXWELL CRATES ARE FULLY CATALOGUED. DESCRIPTIONS ARE TAKEN FROM JOURNAL WHEREVER POSSIBLE.
HCM 4/89

"Did you see that?" Smithback said. "I wonder why the cataloguing was never finished."

"Shh!" Margo hissed. "I'm trying to get all this."

NO. 1989-2006.1
BLOW GUN AND DART, NO DATA
STATUS: C.

NO. 1989-2006.2
PERSONAL JOURNAL OF J. WHITTLESEY, JULY
22 [1987] TO SEPTEMBER 17 [1987]
STATUS: T.R.

NO. 1989-2006.3
2 GRASS BUNDLES, TIED WITH PARROT FEATH-
ERS, USED AS SHAMAN'S FETISH, FROM DE-
SERTED HUT
STATUS: C.

NO. 1989-2006.4
FINELY CARVED FIGURINE OF BEAST. SUP-
POSED REPRESENTATION OF "MBWUN" CF.
WHITTLESEY JOURNAL, P. 56–59
STATUS: O.E.

NO. 1989-2006.5
WOODEN PLANT PRESS, ORIGIN UNKNOWN,
FROM VICINITY OF DESERTED HUT.
STATUS: C.

NO. 1989-2006.6
DISK INCISED WITH DESIGNS.
STATUS: C.

NO. 1989-2006.7
SPEAR POINTS, ASSORTED SIZES AND CONDI-
TION.
STATUS: C.

NOTE: ALL CRATES TEMPORARILY MOVED TO
SECURE VAULT, LEVEL 2B, PER IAN CUTHBERT
3/20/95.

D. ALVAREZ, SEC'Y

"What do all those codes mean?" Smithback asked.

"They tell the current status of the artifact," Moriarty
said. "*C* means it's still crated up, hasn't been curated
yet. *O.E.* means 'on exhibit.' *T.R.* means 'temporarily
removed.' There are others—"

"Temporarily removed?" Margo asked. "That's all
you need to put down? No wonder the journal got lost."

"Of course that's not all," Moriarty said. "Whoever
removes an object has to sign it out. The database is
hierarchical. We can see more detail on any entry just
by stepping down a level. Here, I'll show you." He
tapped a few keys.

His expression changed. "That's odd." The message
on the screen read:

INVALID RECORD OR RELATION
PROCESS HALTED

Moriarty frowned. "There's nothing attached to this
record for the Whittlesey journal." He cleared the screen

and started typing again. "Nothing wrong with the others. See? Here's the detail record for the figurine."

Margo examined the screen.

DETAIL LISTING
Item: 1989–2006.4
################################
Removed By:	Cuthbert, I.	40123
Approval:	Cuthbert, I.	40123
Removal Date:	3/17/95	
Removal To:	Superstition Exhibition	
	Case 415, Item 1004	
Reason:	Display	
Return Date:		

################################
Removed By:	Depardieu, B.	72412
Approval:	Cuthbert, I.	40123
Removal Date:	10/1/90	
Removal To:	Anthropology Lab 2	
Reason:	Initial curating	
Return Date:	10/5/90	

################################
END LISTING
=:?

"So what does that mean? We know the journal's lost," Margo said.

"Even if it's lost, there should still be a detail record for it," Moriarty said.

"Is there a restricted flag on the record?"

Moriarty shook his head and hit a few more keys.

"Here's why," he said at length, pointing at the screen. "The detail record's been erased."

"You mean the information about the journal's location has been deleted?'' Smithback asked. "Can they do that?''

Moriarty shrugged. "It takes a high-security ID.''

"More importantly, why should somebody do that?'' Margo asked. "Did the mainframe problem this morning have anything to do with it?''

"No,'' Moriarty said. "This file compare dump I've just done implies the file was deleted sometime before last night's backup. I can't be more specific than that.''

"Deleted, eh?'' Smithback said. "Gone forever. How clean, how neat. How coincidental. I'm beginning to see a pattern here—a nasty one.''

Moriarty switched off the terminal and pushed himself back from the desk. "I'm not interested in your conspiracy theories,'' he said.

"Could it have been an accident? Or a malfunction?'' Margo asked.

"Doubtful. The database has all sorts of referential integrity checks built-in. I'd see an error message.''

"So what, then?'' Smithback pressed.

"I haven't a clue.'' Moriarty shrugged. "But it's a trivial issue, at best.''

"Is that the best you can do?'' Smithback snorted. "Some computer genius.''

Moriarty, offended, pushed his glasses up his nose and stood up. "I really don't need this,'' he said. "I think I'll get some lunch.'' He headed for the door. "Margo, I'll take a rain check on that crossword puzzle.''

"Nice going,'' Margo said as the door closed. "You've got a really subtle touch, you know that, Smithback? George was good enough to get us into the database.''

"Yeah, and what did we learn from it?'' Smithback asked. "Diddly-squat. Only one of the crates was ever accessioned. Whittlesey's journal is still missing.'' He looked at her smugly. "I, on the other hand, have struck oil.''

"Put it in your book," Margo yawned. "I'll read it then. Assuming I can find a copy in the library."

"*Et tu, Brute?*" Smithback grinned and handed her a folded sheet of paper. "Well, take a look at this."

The sheet was a photocopy reproduction of an article from the New Orleans *Times-Picayune* dated October 17, 1988.

GHOST FREIGHTER FOUND BEACHED NEAR NEW ORLEANS

By Antony Anastasia

Special to the *Times-Picayune*

BAYOU GROVE, October 16 (AP)—A small freighter bound for New Orleans ran aground last night near this small coastal town. Details remain sketchy, but preliminary reports indicate that all crew members had been brutally slain while at sea. The Coast Guard first reported the grounding at 11:45 Monday night.

The ship, the *Strella de Venezuela,* was an 18,000-ton freighter, currently of Haitian registry, that plied the waters of the Caribbean and the main trade routes between South America and the United States. Damage was limited, and the vessel's cargo appeared to be intact.

It is not presently known how the crew members met their deaths, or whether any of the crew were able to escape the ship. Henry La Plage, a private helicopter pilot who observed the beached vessel, reported that "corpses were strewn across the foredeck like some wild animal had gotten at them. I seen one guy hanging out a bridge porthole, his head all smashed up. It was like a slaughterhouse, ain't never seen nothing like it."

Local and federal authorities are cooperating

in an attempt to understand the slayings, easily one of the most brutal massacres in recent maritime history. "We are currently looking into several theories, but we've come to no conclusions as of yet," said Nick Lea, a police spokesman. Although there was no official comment, federal sources said that mutiny, vengeance killings by rival Caribbean shippers, and sea piracy were all being considered as possible motives.

"Jesus," Margo breathed. "The wounds described here—"

"—sound just like those on the three bodies found here this week," Smithback nodded grimly.

Margo frowned. "This happened almost seven years ago. It has to be coincidental."

"Does it?" Smithback asked. "I might be forced to agree with you—if it wasn't for the fact that *the Whittlesey crates were on board that ship.*"

"*What?*"

"It's true. I tracked down the bills of lading. The crates were shipped from Brazil in August of 1988—almost a year after the expedition broke up, as I understand it. After this business in New Orleans, the crates sat in customs while the investigation was being conducted. It took them almost a year and a half to reach the Museum."

"The ritualized murders have followed the crates all the way from the Amazon!" Margo said. "But that means—"

"It means," Smithback said grimly, "that I'm going to stop laughing now when I hear talk about a curse on that expedition. And it means you should keep locking this door."

The phone rang, startling them both.

"Margo, my dear." Frock's voice rumbled to her. "What news?"

"Dr. Frock! I wonder if I could come by your office for a few minutes. At your earliest convenience."

"Splendid!" Frock said. "Give me a little time to shuffle some of this paper off my desk and into the wastebasket. Shall we say one o'clock?"

"Thank you," Margo said. "Smithback," she said, turning around, "we've got to—"

But the writer was gone.

At ten minutes to one, another knock sounded.

"Who's there?" Margo said through the locked door.

"It's me, Moriarty. Can I come in, Margo?"

"I just wanted to apologize for walking out earlier," Moriarty said, declining a chair. "It's just that Bill wears on me sometimes. He never seems to let up."

"George, I'm the one who should apologize," Margo said. "I didn't know he was going to appear like that." She thought of telling him about the newspaper article, but decided against it and began to pack up her carryall.

"There's something else I wanted to tell you," Moriarty went on. "While I was eating lunch, I realized there may be some way we can find out more about that deleted database record, after all. The one for Whittlesey's journal."

Margo abruptly put down the carryall and looked at Moriarty, who took a seat in front of her terminal. "Did you see that sign-on message when you logged into the network earlier?" he asked.

"The one about the computer going down? Big surprise. I got locked out twice this morning."

Moriarty nodded. "The message also said they were going to restore from the backup tapes at noon. A full restore takes about thirty minutes. That means they should be done by now."

"So?"

"Well, a backup tape holds about two to three months' worth of archives. If the detail record for the Whittlesey journal was deleted in the last two months—

and if the backup tape is still on the hub up in data processing—I should be able to resurrect it.''

"Really?"

Moriarty nodded.

"Then do it!" Margo urged.

"There's a certain element of risk," Moriarty replied. "If a system operator notices that the tape is being accessed . . . well, he could trace it to your terminal ID.''

"I'll risk it," Margo said. "George," she added, "I know you feel this is all a wild goose chase, and I can't really blame you for that. But I'm convinced those crates from the Whittlesey expedition are connected to these killings. I don't know what the connection is, but maybe the journal could have told us something. And I don't know what we're dealing with—a serial killer, some animal, some creature. And not knowing scares me.'' She gently took Moriarty's hand and gave it a squeeze. "But maybe we're in a position here to be of some help. We have to try.''

When she noticed Moriarty blushing, she withdrew her hand.

Smiling shyly, Moriarty moved to the keyboard.

"Here goes," he said.

Margo paced the room as Moriarty worked. "Any luck?" she asked finally, moving closer to the terminal.

"Don't know yet," said Moriarty, squinting at the screen and typing commands. "I've got the tape, but the protocol's messed up or something, the CRC checks are failing. We may get garbled data, if we get anything. I'm going in the back door, so to speak, hoping to avoid attention. The seek rate is really slow this way.''

Then the keytaps stopped. "Margo," Moriarty said quietly. "I've got it.''

The screen filled.

DETAIL LISTING
Item: 1989–2006.2

\#

Removed By:	Rickman, L.	53210
Approval:	Cuthbert, I.	40123
Removal Date:	3/15/95	
Removal To:	Personal supervision	
Reason:		
Return Date:		

\#

Removed By:	Depardieu, B.	72412
Approval:	Cuthbert, I.	40123

RemLW/@;oval Date: 10/1/90
Remov~DS*-~@2e34 5WIFU
   =++ET2 34 h34!~
   DB ERROR
=:?

"Hell!" Moriarty exclaimed. "I was afraid of that. It's been partially overwritten, corrupted. See that? It just trails off into garbage."

"Yes, but look!" Margo said excitedly.

Moriarty examined the screen. "The journal was removed by Mrs. Rickman two weeks ago, with Dr. Cuthbert's permission. No return date."

Margo snorted. "Cuthbert said the journal had been lost."

"So why was this record deleted? And by whom?" Suddenly his eyes widened. "Oh, Lord, I have to release my lock on the tape before somebody notices us." His fingers danced over the keys.

"George," Margo said. "Do you know what this means? They took the journal out of the crates before the killings started. Around the time Cuthbert had the crates put in the Secure Area. Now they're concealing evidence from the police. Why?''

Moriarty frowned. "You're starting to sound like Smithback," he said. "There could be a thousand explanations."

"Name one," Margo challenged.

"The most obvious would be that somebody else deleted the detail record before Rickman could add a Lost Artifact notation."

Margo shook her head. "I don't believe it. There are just too many coincidences."

"Margo—" Moriarty began. Then he sighed. "Listen," he went on patiently, "this is a trying time for all of us, you especially. I know you're trying to make a tough decision, and then with a crisis like this . . . well . . ."

"These murders weren't committed by some garden-variety maniac," Margo interrupted impatiently. "I'm *not* crazy."

"I'm not saying that," Moriarty continued. "I just think you ought to let the police handle this. It's a very, very dangerous business. And you should be concentrating on your own life right now. Digging into this won't help you make up your mind about your own future." He swallowed. "And it won't bring your father back."

"Is that what you think?" Margo blazed. "You don't—"

She broke off abruptly as her eye fell on the wall clock. "Jesus. I'm late for my meeting with Dr. Frock." She grabbed her carryall and headed for the door. Halfway into the hall, she turned around. "I'll speak to *you* later," she said.

The door slammed.

God, Moriarty thought, sitting at the darkened terminal and resting his chin in his hands. *If a graduate student in plant genetics actually thinks Mbwun might be loose—if even Margo Green starts seeing conspiracies behind every door—what about the rest of the Museum?*

= 29 =

Margo watched Frock spill his sherry down his shirt-front.

"Blast," he said, dabbing with plump hands. He set the glass down on the desk with exaggerated care and looked up at Margo.

"Thank you for coming to me, my dear. It's an extraordinary discovery. I'd say we should go down there this moment and take another look at the figurine, but that Pendergast fellow will be here shortly to make a further nuisance of himself."

Bless you, Agent Pendergast, Margo thought. The last thing she felt like doing was going back down into the exhibition.

Frock sighed. "No matter, we'll know soon enough. Once Pendergast leaves, we'll learn the truth. This Mbwun figurine could be the additional proof I've been searching for. *If,* that is, you are correct about the claws matching the lacerations in the victim."

"But how could such a creature be loose in the Museum?" Margo asked.

"Ah!" Frock exclaimed, eyes shining. "That's the question, is it not? And let me answer a question with a question. What thing, my dear Margo, is *rugose*?"

"I don't know," Margo said. "Rugose, as in bumpy?"

"Yes. It's a regular pattern of ridges, wrinkles, or creases. I'll tell you what's rugose. Reptilian eggs are rugose. As are dinosaur eggs."

A sudden current passed through Margo as she remembered. "That's the word—"

"—that Cuthbert used to describe the seed pods missing from the crate," Frock finished her sentence. "I ask you: were they *really* seed pods? What kind of seed pod would look wrinkled and scaly? But an egg . . ."

Frock drew himself up in his wheelchair. "Next question. *Where have they gone?* Were they stolen? Or did something else happen to them?"

Abruptly, the scientist stopped, sinking back in his wheelchair, shaking his head.

"But if something . . . if something hatched, something broke out of the crates," Margo said, "how does that explain the killings on board the freighter that carried the crates from South America?"

"Margo," Frock said, laughing quietly, "what we have here is a riddle wrapped in a mystery inside an enigma. It is *essential* that we gather more facts without wasting additional time."

There was a soft rapping at the door.

"That must be Pendergast," Frock said, drawing back. Then, louder: "Come in, please!"

The agent walked in, carrying a briefcase, his black suit as ever impeccable, his blond white hair brushed back from his face. To Margo, he looked as collected and placid as before. When Frock gestured to one of the Victorian chairs, Pendergast seated himself.

"A pleasure to see you again, sir," Frock said. "You've

met Miss Green. We were once again in the middle of something just now, so I hope you won't mind if she remains."

Pendergast waved his hand. "Of course. I know you'll both continue to respect my request for confidentiality."

"Of course," said Frock.

"Dr. Frock, I know you're busy and I'll keep this short," Pendergast began. "I was hoping you'd had some success in locating the artifact we spoke about. An artifact that might have been used as a weapon in these murders."

Frock shifted in the wheelchair. "As you requested, I considered the matter further. I ran a search of our accession database, both for single items and for items that could potentially have been broken apart and recombined." He shook his head. "Unfortunately, I found nothing that even remotely resembled the imprint you showed us. There has never been anything like it in the collections."

Pendergast's expression betrayed nothing. Then he smiled. "Officially, we'd never admit this, but the case is—shall we say—a trying one." He indicated his briefcase. "I am awash in false sightings, lab reports, interviews. But we're slow in finding a fit."

Frock smiled. "I believe, Mr. Pendergast, that what you do and what I do are not all that different. I've been in the same predicament myself. And no doubt His Eminence is acting as if nothing out of the ordinary is happening."

Pendergast nodded.

"Wright is very eager that the exhibition go on as scheduled tomorrow night. Why? Because the Museum spent millions it didn't really have to put it together. It's vital that admissions be increased to keep the Museum from slipping into the red. This exhibition is seen as the best way to do that."

"I see," Pendergast said. He picked up a fossil lying on a table next to his chair, turning it over idly in his hand. "Ammonite?" he asked.

"Correct," replied Frock.

"Dr. Frock——" Pendergast began. "Pressure is now being brought to bear from a variety of quarters. As a result, I must be doubly careful to conduct this investigation by the book. I can't share our results with outside entities such as yourself—even when the conventional avenues of investigation are proving fruitless." He put down the fossil carefully and crossed his arms. "That said, do I understand correctly that you are an expert on DNA?"

Frock nodded. "That's partly true. I have devoted some study to how genes affect morphology—the shape of an organism. And I oversee the projects of various graduate students—such as Gregory Kawakita, and Margo here—whose studies involve DNA research."

Pendergast retrieved his briefcase, snapped it open, and withdrew a fat computer printout. "I have a report on DNA from the claw found in one of the first victims. Of course, I can't show it to you. It would be highly irregular. The New York office wouldn't like it."

"I see," said Frock. "And you continue to believe that the claw is your best clue."

"It's our only clue of importance, Dr. Frock. Let me explain my conclusions. I believe we have a madman loose in the Museum. He kills his victims in a ritualistic fashion, removes the back of the skull, and extracts the hypothalamus from the brain."

"For what purpose?" asked Frock.

Pendergast hesitated. "We believe he eats it."

Margo gasped.

"The killer may be hiding in the Museum's subbasement," Pendergast continued. "There are many indications that he has returned there after killing, but so far we've been unable to isolate a specific location or retrieve any evidence. Two dogs were killed during searches. As you probably know, it's a perfect warren of tunnels, galleries, and passages spread over several subterranean levels, the oldest dating back almost 150 years. The Museum has been able to furnish me with maps covering only a small percentage of its total area. I call the killer 'he' because the force used in the killings indicates a male, and a strong one at that. Almost preternaturally strong. As you know, he uses some kind of three-clawed weapon to disembowel his victims, who are apparently chosen at random. We have no motive. Our interviews with selected Museum staff have turned up no leads as yet." He looked at Frock. "You see, Doctor, our best clue remains our only clue—the weapon, the claw. That is why I continue to search for its origin."

Frock nodded slowly. "You mentioned DNA?"

Pendergast waved the computer printout. "The lab results have been inconclusive, to say the least." He paused. "I can see no reason not to tell you that the test on the claw turned up DNA from various species of gecko, in addition to human chromosomes. Hence our assumption that the sample might be degraded."

"Gecko, you say?" Frock murmured in mild surprise. "And it eats the hypothalamus . . . how extraordinary. Tell me, how do you know?"

"We found traces of saliva and teeth marks."

"Human teeth marks?"

"No one knows."

"And the saliva?"

"Indeterminate."

Frock's head sank down on his chest. After a few minutes, he looked up.

"You continue to call the claw a weapon," he said. "I assume, then, that you continue to believe the killer is human?"

Pendergast closed his briefcase. "I simply don't see any other possibility. Do you think, Dr. Frock, an animal could decapitate a body with surgical precision, punch a hole in the skull and locate an internal organ the size of a walnut that only someone trained in human anatomy could recognize? And the killer's ability to elude our searches of the subbasement has been impressive."

Frock's head had sunk on his chest again. As the seconds ticked off into minutes, Pendergast remained motionless, watching.

Frock suddenly raised his head. "Mr. Pendergast," he said, his voice booming. Margo jumped. "I've heard your theory. Would you care to hear mine?"

Pendergast nodded. "Of course."

"Very well," Frock replied. "Are you familiar with the Transvaal Shales?"

"I don't believe so," said Pendergast.

"The Transvaal Shales were discovered in 1945 by Alistair Van Vrouwenhoek, a paleontologist with South Africa's Witwatersrand University. They were Cambrian, about six hundred million years old. And they were full of bizarre life forms the likes of which had never been seen before or since. Asymmetrical life forms, not showing even the bilateral symmetry of virtually all animal life on earth today. They occurred, coincidentally, at the time of the Cambrian mass extinction. Now most people, Mr. Pendergast, believe the Transvaal Shales represent a dead end of evolution: life experimenting with every conceivable form before settling down to the bilaterally symmetric form you see today."

"But you do not hold such a view," Pendergast said.

Frock cleared his throat. "Correct. A certain type of organism predominates in these shales. It had powerful fins and long suction pads and oversized crushing and tearing mouth parts. Those mouth parts could saw through rock, and the fins allowed it to move at twenty miles per hour through the water. No doubt it was a highly successful and quite savage predator. It was, I believe, *too* successful: it hunted its prey into extinction and then quickly became extinct itself. It thus caused the minor mass extinction at the end of the Cambrian era. *It,* not natural selection, killed off all the other forms of life in the Transvaal Shales."

Pendergast blinked. "And?"

"I've run computer simulations of evolution according to the new mathematical theory of fractal turbulence. The result? Every sixty to seventy million years or so, life starts getting very well adapted to its environment. Too well adapted, perhaps. There is a population explosion of the successful life forms. Then, suddenly, a new species appears out of the blue. It is almost always a predatory creature, a killing machine. It tears through the host population, killing, feeding, multiplying. Slowly at first, then ever faster.''

Frock gestured toward the sandstone fossil plaque on his desk. ''Mr. Pendergast, let me show you something.'' The agent stood up and moved forward.

''This is a set of tracks made by a creature that lived during the Upper Cretaceous,'' Frock continued. ''Right on the K-T boundary, to be exact. This is the only such fossil of its kind we've found; there is no other.''

''K-T?'' asked Pendergast.

''Cretaceous-Tertiary. It's the boundary that marks the mass extinction of the dinosaurs.''

Pendergast nodded, but still looked puzzled.

''There is a connection here that has so far gone unnoticed,'' Frock continued. ''The figurine of Mbwun, the claw impressions made by the killer, and these fossil tracks.''

Pendergast looked down. ''Mbwun? The figurine that Dr. Cuthbert removed from the crates and put on display?''

Frock nodded.

''Hmm. How old are these prints?''

''Approximately sixty-five million years old. They came from a formation where the very last of the dinosaurs were found. Before the mass extinction, that is.''

There was another long silence.

''Ah. And the connection? . . .'' asked Pendergast after a moment.

''I said that nothing in the anthropology collections matches the claw marks. But I did not say there were no *representations*, no *sculptures* of such a claw. We've learned that the forelimbs on the figurine of Mbwun have three claws, with a thickened central digit. Now look at these tracks," Frock said, pointing to the fossil. "Think back to the reconstruction of the claw and the claw marks in the victim."

"So you think," Pendergast said, "that the killer might be the same animal that made these tracks? A dinosaur?" Margo thought she detected amusement in Pendergast's voice.

Frock looked at the agent, shaking his head vigorously. "No, Mr. Pendergast, not a dinosaur. Nothing as common as a dinosaur. We're talking about the proof of my theory of aberrant evolution. You know my work. This is the creature I believe *killed off* the dinosaurs."

Pendergast remained silent.

Frock leaned closer to the FBI agent. "I believe," he said, "this creature, this freak of nature, is the cause of the dinosaur's extinction. Not a meteorite, not a change in climate, but some terrible predator—the creature that made the tracks preserved in this fossil. The embodiment of the Callisto Effect. It was not large, but it was extremely powerful and fast. It probably hunted in cooperative packs and was intelligent. But because superpredators are so short lived, they aren't well represented in the fossil record. Except in the Transvaal Shales. And in these tracks here, from the Tzun-je-jin Badlands. Are you following me?"

"Yes."

"We are *in* a population explosion today."

Pendergast remained silent.

"*Human beings,* Mr. Pendergast!" Frock continued, his voice rising. "Five thousand years ago there were only ten million of us on the globe. Today there are six billion! We're the most successful form of life the earth has ever seen!" He tapped the copies of *Fractal Evolution* that lay on his desk. "Yesterday, you asked about my next book. It will constitute an extension of my theory on the Callisto Effect, applying it to *modern* life. My theory predicts that at any moment, some grotesque mutation will come about; some creature that will prey on the *human* population. I'm not saying the killer is the same creature that killed off the dinosaurs. But a *similar* creature . . . well, look at these tracks again. They look like Mbwun! We call it convergent evolution, where two creatures look alike not because they're necessarily related, but because they evolve to do the same thing. A creature that's evolved to kill. There are too many similarities, Mr. Pendergast.''

Pendergast brought his briefcase onto his lap. ''I'm afraid you've lost me, Dr. Frock.''

''Don't you see? *Something came back in that crate from South America.* Unleashed in the Museum. A highly successful predator. That figurine of Mbwun is the proof. The indigenous tribes were aware of this creature, and built a religion around it. Whittlesey inadvertently sent it into civilization.''

''You've seen this figurine yourself?'' Pendergast asked. ''Dr. Cuthbert seemed reluctant to show it to me.''

''No,'' Frock admitted. ''But I have it on the best authority. I plan to make my own observations at the earliest opportunity.''

''Dr. Frock, we looked into the matter of the crates yesterday,'' Pendergast said. ''Dr. Cuthbert assured us there was nothing of value in them, and we have no reason to disbelieve him.'' He stood up, impassive. ''I thank you for your time and help. Your theory is most interesting, and I truly wish I could subscribe to it.'' He shrugged. ''However, my own opinion remains unchanged for the time being. Forgive me for being blunt, but I hope you will be able to separate your conjectures from the cold facts of our investigation, and help us in any way you can.'' He walked toward the door. ''Now, I hope you'll excuse me. If anything comes to mind, please contact me.''

And he left.

Frock sat in his wheelchair, shaking his head. "What a shame," he murmured. "I had high hopes for his co-operation, but it seems he's like all the rest."

Margo glanced at the table next to the chair Pendergast had just vacated. "Look," she said. "He left the DNA printout."

Frock's eyes followed Margo's. Then he chuckled.

"I assume that's what he meant by anything else coming to mind." He paused. "Perhaps he isn't like all the rest, after all. Well, we won't tell on him, Margo, will we?" he said, picking up the phone.

"Dr. Frock to speak with Dr. Cuthbert." A pause. "Hello, Ian? Yes, I'm fine, thank you. No, it's just that I'd like to get into the *Superstition* exhibition right away. What's that? Yes, I know it's been sealed, but . . . No, I'm quite reconciled to the idea of the exhibition, it's just that . . . I see."

Margo noticed Frock's face redden.

"In that case, Ian," Frock continued, "I should like to reexamine the crates from the Whittlesey expedition. Yes, the ones in the Secure Area. I know we saw them yesterday, Ian."

There was a long silence. Margo could hear a faint squawking.

"Now look here, Ian," Frock said. "I'm chairman of this department, and I have a right to . . . Don't you speak to me that way, Ian. Don't you *dare*."

Frock was shaking with rage in a way Margo had never seen before. His voice had dropped almost to a whisper.

"Sir, you have no business in this institution. I shall be making a formal grievance to the Director."

Frock slowly returned the phone to its cradle, his hand trembling. He turned toward Margo, fumbling for his handkerchief. "Please forgive me."

"I'm surprised," said Margo. "I thought that as a Chairman . . ." She couldn't quite complete the sentence.

"I had complete control over the collections?" Frock smiled, his composure returning. "So did I. But this new exhibition, and these killings, have aroused sentiments in people that I hadn't suspected. Technically, Cuthbert outranks me. I'm not sure why he's doing this. It would have to be something profoundly embarrassing, something that would delay or prevent his precious exhibition from opening." He thought for a minute. "Perhaps he's aware of this creature's existence. After all, he was the one who moved the crates. Perhaps he found the hatched eggs, made the connection, hid them. And now he wants to deny me my right to study it!" He sat forward in the wheelchair and balled his fists.

"Dr. Frock, I don't think that's a real possibility," Margo warned. Any thoughts she'd had of telling Frock about Rickman's removal of the Whittlesey journal evaporated.

Frock relaxed. "You're right, of course. This isn't the end of it, though, you can be sure. Still, we don't have time for that now, and I trust your observations of Mbwun. But, Margo, we *must* get in to see those crates."

"How?" said Margo.

Frock slid open a drawer of his desk and fished around for a moment. Then he withdrew a form which Margo immediately recognized: a '10-14,' Request for Access.

"My mistake," he went on, "was in asking." He started to fill out the form longhand.

"But doesn't that need to be signed by Central Processing?" Margo asked.

"Of course," said Frock. "I will send the form to Central Processing via the usual procedure. And I'll take the unsigned copy down to the Secure Area and bully my way in. No doubt the request form will be denied. But by the time that happens, I will have had time to examine the crates. And find the answers."

"But Dr. Frock, you can't do that!" Margo replied in a shocked tone.

"Why not?" Frock smiled wryly. "Frock, a pillar of

the Museum establishment, acting in an unorthodox manner? This is too important for such considerations."

"I didn't mean that," Margo continued. She let her gaze drop to the scientist's wheelchair.

Frock looked down. His face fell. "Ah, yes," he said slowly. "I see what you mean." Crestfallen, he started to return the paper to his desk.

"Dr. Frock," Margo said. "Give me the form. I'll take it down to the Secure Area."

Frock's hand froze. He looked at Margo appraisingly. "I asked you to be my eyes and ears, but I didn't ask you to walk over coals for me," he said. "I'm a tenured curator, a relatively important figure. They wouldn't dare sack me. But you—" he drew a deep breath, raised his eyebrows. "They could make an example of you, expel you from the Ph.D. program. And I'd be powerless to prevent it."

Margo thought for a moment. "I have a friend who's very clever at this kind of thing. I think he could talk his way into or out of any situation."

Frock remained motionless for a moment. Then he tore off the copy and gave it to her. "I'll have the original delivered upstairs. I have to, if we're going to maintain the charade. The guard may call Central Processing to verify receipt. You won't have much time. As soon as it comes in they'll be on the alert. You will have to be gone by then."

From a desk drawer, he withdrew a yellow paper and a key. He showed them to Margo.

"This paper holds the combination to the Secure Area vaults," he said. "And here's the key to the vault itself. All directors have them. With luck, Cuthbert won't have thought to change the combinations." He handed them to Margo. "These will get you through the doors. It's the guards you'll have to deal with." He was talking fast now, his eyes locked on Margo's. "You know what to look for in the crates. Any evidence of eggs, living organisms, even cult objects associated with the creature.

Anything that can prove my theory. Check the smaller crate first, Whittlesey's crate. That's the one that contained the Mbwun figurine. Check the others if you have time, but, for Heaven's sake, expose yourself to as little risk as possible. Go now, my dear, and Godspeed.''

The last thing Margo saw as she left the office was Frock beneath the bow windows, his broad back turned away from her, drumming his fists repeatedly against the arms of his wheelchair. ''Damn this thing!'' he was saying. ''Damn it to hell!''

= 30 =

Five minutes later, in her office several floors below, Margo picked up the phone and dialed. Smithback was in a rare mood. As Margo explained Moriarty's discovery of the deleted accession record and—in somewhat less detail—the events in Frock's office, his mood grew even more cheerful.

She heard him chuckling. "Was I right about Rickman, or what? Concealing evidence. Now I'll make her see the book my way, or—"

"Smithback, don't you *dare*," Margo warned. "This isn't for your personal gratification. We don't know the story behind that journal, and we can't worry about it right now. We *have* to get into those crates, and we only have a few minutes to do it."

"All right, all right," came the answer. "Meet me at the landing outside Entomology. I'm leaving now."

"I never thought Frock could be such a radical," Smithback said. "My respect for the old feller has just gone

up two notches.'' He was making his way down a long
flight of iron stairs. They'd taken a back way in hopes
of avoiding the police checkpoints set up at all elevator
banks.

"You've got the key and the combination, right?" he
asked from the bottom of the stairs. Margo checked her
carryall, then followed him.

She glanced quickly up and down the corridor. "You
know how the hall outside the Secure Area has lighted
alcoves along it? You go ahead, I'll follow a minute
later. Talk to the guard, try to draw him into an alcove
where the light is better, on the pretext of showing him
this form. Get him to turn his back for a couple of
minutes, and then I'll unlock the door and go in. Just
keep him occupied. You're a good talker.''

"That's your plan?" Smithback scoffed. "All right.''
He spun on his heels, continued down the corridor, and
vanished around the corner.

Margo waited, counting to sixty. Then she moved forward, pulling on a pair of latex gloves.

Soon she could hear Smithback's voice, already raised
in righteous protest. "This paper is signed by the Chairman of the department himself! Are you trying to tell
me that . . .''

She poked her head around the corner. About fifty feet
down the hall was an intersection with another hallway
that led to the police barricades. Further down was the
door to the Secure Area itself, and, beyond that, Margo
could see the guard. He had his back to her, and was
holding her form in one hand.

"I'm sorry, sir,'' she could hear him say, "but this
hasn't gone through Processing . . .''

"You're not looking in the right place,'' Smithback
responded. "Take it over here where you can read it,
here in the light.''

They moved down the hall away from Margo, into an
illuminated alcove. As they disappeared from view,
Margo came around the corner and walked briskly down

the hall. At the Secure Area door, she inserted the key and pushed gingerly. The door swung open on oiled hinges. She peered around the edge to make sure she was alone; the darkened room seemed empty, and she eased the door shut behind her.

Her heart was already racing, the blood pounding in her ears. She caught her breath, fumbled for the light switch. The vaults stretched ahead of her in rows to the left and right. When she noticed the third door on the right had a yellow EVIDENCE sheet taped to it, she grasped its dial with one hand and took out Frock's scrap of paper with the other. 56-77-23. She took a deep breath and began, remembering the locker she'd once used to store her oboe in high school music class. *Right, left, right . . .*

There was a loud click. Immediately, she grabbed the lever and pulled downward. The door opened.

Inside, the crates were dim shapes against the far wall. She turned on the light and glanced at her watch. Three minutes had passed.

She had to work very quickly now. She could see the ragged marks where one of the larger crates had been torn and splintered apart. The marks sent shivers down her spine. Kneeling in front of the smaller crate, she removed its top and plunged her hands into the packing material, parting the stiff fibers to expose the artifacts.

Her hand closed around something hard. Pulling it out, Margo saw a small stone, carved with odd designs. *Not very promising.* She exposed a collection of what looked like jade lip plugs, then flint arrowheads, some points, a blow gun tube with a set of darts, long and sharp, the tips blackened with some hardened substance. *Don't want to be pricked by those,* she thought. Still nothing worth taking. She delved deeper. The next layer held a small plant press, screwed shut; a damaged shaman's rattle covered in grotesque designs; and a beautiful manta made of woven cloth and feathers.

On an impulse she stuffed the plant press, covered

with packing fibers, into her bag. The stone disc and rattle followed.

On the bottom layer, she found several jars containing small reptiles. Colorful, but nothing out of the ordinary.

Six minutes had passed. She sat up, listening, expecting any moment to hear the footsteps of the returning guard. But there was nothing.

She hastily stuffed the rest of the artifacts back into the crate and surrounded them with packing material. She picked up the lid, noting its loose inner lining. As she pried the lining away curiously, a brittle, water-damaged envelope slipped out into her lap; hastily, she crammed it into her bag.

Eight minutes. There was no time left.

Back in the central room, she listened, trying to make out the muffled sounds outside. She eased the door open a crack.

"What's your badge number?" Smithback was saying loudly.

Margo couldn't make out the guard's reply. She slipped out and shut the door behind her, quickly peeling off her gloves and stuffing them into her carryall. She straightened up, looked herself up and down, then started walking past the alcove where Smithback and the guard were standing.

"Hey!"

She turned. The guard, flushed, was looking at her.

"Oh, there you are, Bill!" she said, thinking fast, hoping the guard hadn't seen her come out the door. "Am I too late? Have you already been inside?"

"This guy won't let me in!" Smithback complained.

"Listen, you," the guard said, turning back to Smithback. "I've told you a thousand times, and I won't tell you again. That form has to be properly processed before I can give you access. Understand?"

They'd pulled it off.

Margo looked back down the hall. In the distance, she saw a tall, lean figure approaching: Ian Cuthbert.

She grabbed Smithback's arm. "We've got to go. Remember our appointment? We'll have to look at the collections some other time."

"That's right. Of course." Smithback babbled heartily. "I'll get this taken care of later," he said to the guard.

Near the far end of the hall, she pushed Smithback into an alcove.

"Get behind those cabinets," Margo whispered.

They heard Cuthbert's footsteps behind them as they concealed themselves. Then the footsteps stopped, and Cuthbert's voice echoed loudly down the corridor.

"Has anyone tried to gain access to the vaults?" he asked.

"Yes, sir. There was a man trying to get in. They were just here."

"Who?" demanded Cuthbert. "Those people you were just speaking with?"

"Yes, sir. He had a form but it hadn't been properly processed, so I didn't let him in."

"You did *not* let him in?"

"That's right, sir."

"Who issued the form? Frock?"

"Yes, sir. Dr. Frock."

"And you didn't get the name of this person?"

"I think his name was Bill. I don't know about the woman, but—"

"Bill? *Bill?* Oh, that's bloody brilliant. The *first* thing you should do is ask for identification."

"I'm sorry, sir. It was just that he insisted it was—"

But Cuthbert was already striding back angrily. The footfalls faded down the corridor.

At a nod from Smithback, Margo rose gingerly and dusted herself off. They stepped out into the hall.

"Hey, you there!" shouted the guard. "Come here, I need to see your ID! Wait!"

Smithback and Margo took off at a sprint. They raced

around a bend, then ducked into a stairwell and dashed up the wide concrete steps.

"Where are we going?" Margo panted.

"Damned if I know."

They reached the next landing, and Smithback stepped out gingerly into the hallway. He looked up and down the corridor, then wrenched open a door marked MAMMALOGY, PONGIDAE STORAGE.

Inside, they stopped to catch their breath. The room was quiet and cool. As Margo's eyes grew accustomed to the dim light, she noticed stuffed gorillas and chimpanzees standing in ranks like sentinels, and heaping piles of hairy skins on wooden racks. Against one wall were dozens of shelves lined with primate skulls.

Smithback listened intently at the door for a moment. Then he turned to Margo. "Lets see what you found," he said.

"There wasn't much," Margo said, breathing heavily. "I took a couple of unimportant artifacts, that's it. I did find this, though," she said, reaching into her carryall. "It was wedged in the lid of the crate."

The unsealed envelope was addressed simply "H. C. Montague, NYMNH."

The yellowed writing paper was embossed with a curious double-arrow motif. As Smithback peered over her shoulder, Margo held the sheet carefully up to the light and began to read.

Upper Xingú
Sept. 17, 1987

Montague,

I've decided to send Carlos back with the last crate and go on alone in search of Crocker. Carlos is trustworthy, and I can't risk losing the crate should anything happen to me. Take note of the shaman's rattle and other ritual objects. They seem unique. But the figurine I've enclosed, which we found in a deserted hut at this site, is the proof I've been looking for. Note the exaggerated claws, the reptilian attributes, the hints at *bipedalia*. The Kothoga exist, and the Mbwun legend is not mere fabrication.

All my field notes are in this notebook. . . .

= 31 =

Mrs. Lavinia Rickman sat in a wine-colored leather arm-chair in the Director's office. The room was deathly silent. Not even traffic noises from the street three floors below penetrated the thick turret windows. Wright himself sat behind the desk, practically swallowed by the vast length of mahogany. A Reynolds portrait of Ridley A. Davis, the Museum's founder, glared down from behind Wright.

Dr. Ian Cuthbert occupied a sofa along a far wall of the room. He leaned forward, elbows on his knees, his tweed suit loose on his spare frame. He was frowning. Normally humorless and irritable, he looked particularly austere on this afternoon.

Finally, Wright broke the silence.

"He's called twice already this afternoon," the Director snapped at Cuthbert. "I can't avoid him forever. Sooner or later he's going to raise a stink about being denied access to the crates. He may well drag this

Mbwun business into it. There's going to be controversy.''

Cuthbert nodded. ''As long as it's later rather than sooner. When the exhibition is open and running, with forty thousand visitors a day and favorable notices in all the periodicals, let him bloody well raise hell about whatever he likes.''

There was another long silence.

''I hate to play devil's advocate,'' Cuthbert continued at last, ''but when the dust settles from all this, you, Winston, are going to have the necessary increase in attendance. These rumors of a curse may be annoying now, but when things are safe again, everyone's going to want a vicarious shudder and some scandal. Everyone's going to want to go inside the Museum and see for themselves. It's good for business. I'm telling you, Winston, we couldn't have arranged it better ourselves.''

Wright frowned at the Assistant Director. ''Rumors of a curse. Maybe it's true. Look at all the disasters that have followed that ugly little figurine halfway around the world.'' He laughed mirthlessly.

''You're not serious,'' said Cuthbert.

''I'll tell you what I'm serious about,'' Wright snapped. ''I don't want to hear you talking like that again. Frock has important friends. If he starts complaining to them . . . well, you know how stories grow and spread. They'll think you're withholding information. They'll think you're banking on these killings bringing people in to see the exhibition. How's *that* for publicity, eh?''

''Agreed,'' Cuthbert said with a wintry smile. ''But I don't need to remind you that, if this exhibition doesn't open on time, everything becomes academic. Frock must be kept on a short leash. Now, he's sending hired help to do his dirty work. One of them tried to get into the Secure Vault less than an hour ago.''

''Who?'' Wright demanded.

"The security guard made a right hash of it," Cuthbert replied. "But he got the fellow's first name—Bill."

"Bill?" Rickman sat up.

"Yes, I think that was it," Cuthbert said, turning to the public relations director. "Isn't that the name of the journalist who's doing the book on my exhibition? He's your man, isn't he? Is he under control? I hear he's been asking a lot of questions."

"Absolutely," said Rickman, a bright smile on her face. "We've had our ups and downs with him, but he's toeing the line now. Control the sources, and you've controlled the journalist, as I always say."

"Toeing the line, is he?" Wright said. "Then why did you feel it necessary to send that mail message round to half the western world this morning, reminding them not to talk to strangers?"

Mrs. Rickman quickly held up a lacquered hand. "He's been taken care of."

"You'd damned well better make sure of that," Cuthbert said. "You've been in on this little party from the beginning, Lavinia. I'm sure you don't want this journalist of yours digging up any dirty knickers."

There came a hiss of static over the intercom, and a voice said: "Mr. Pendergast to see you."

"Send him in," said Wright. He looked sourly at the others. "This is it."

Pendergast appeared in the doorway, a newspaper tucked under one arm. He paused for a moment.

"My, this *is* a charming tableau," he said. "Dr. Wright, thank you for seeing me again. Dr. Cuthbert, always a pleasure. And you are Lavinia Rickman, ma'am, are you not?"

"Yes," Rickman replied, smiling primly.

"Mr. Pendergast," said Wright, with a small, formal smile. "Please take any seat you wish."

"Thank you, Doctor, but I prefer to stand." Pendergast moved over to the massive fireplace and leaned against the mantle, arms folded.

"Have you come to make a report? No doubt you've asked for this meeting to inform us of an arrest."

"No," said Pendergast. "I'm sorry, no arrests. Frankly, Dr. Wright, we've made very little progress. Despite what Ms. Rickman has been telling the newspapers."

He showed them the newspaper's headline: ARREST NEAR IN "MUSEUM BEAST" MURDERS.

There was a short silence. Pendergast folded the paper and carefully placed it on the mantelpiece.

"What's the problem?" asked Wright. "I don't understand what's taking so long."

"There are many problems, as you are no doubt aware," said Pendergast. "But I'm not really here to brief you on the case. It's enough if I remind you simply that a dangerous serial killer remains loose in the Museum. We have no reason to believe he has stopped killing. As far as we know, all his killings have been nocturnal. In other words, after 5 P.M. As the special agent in charge of this investigation, I'm regretfully informing you that the curfew we've set up must remain in force until such time as the killer is found. There will be no exceptions."

"The opening. . . ." Rickman bleated.

"The opening will have to be postponed. It may be for a week, it may be for a month. I can't make any promises, I'm afraid. I'm very sorry."

Wright stood up, his face livid. "You said the opening could go on as scheduled provided there were no more killings. That was our *agreement*."

"I made no agreement with you, Doctor," Pendergast said mildly. "I'm afraid we are no closer to catching the murderer than we were at the beginning of the week." He gestured toward the newspaper on the mantle. "Headlines like these make people complacent, incautious. The opening would probably be very well attended. Thousands of people, in the Museum after dark . . ." He shook his head. "I have no other choice."

Wright stared at the agent in disbelief. "Because of your incompetence, you expect us to delay the opening, and do the Museum irreparable harm in the process? The answer is no."

Pendergast, unruffled, walked forward into the center of the room. "Forgive me, Dr. Wright, if I didn't make myself clear. I'm not here to ask your permission; I'm merely notifying you of my decision."

"Right," the Director answered, his voice shaking. "I see. You can't do your own job, but you still want to tell me how to do mine. Do you have any idea what delaying the opening would do to our exhibition? Do you know what kind of message it would send to the public? Well, Pendergast, I'm not going to allow it."

Pendergast stared steadily at Wright. "Any unauthorized personnel found on the premises after five o'clock will be arrested and charged with trespassing at a scene of crime. This is a misdemeanor. Second violations will be charged with obstruction of justice, which is a felony, Dr. Wright. I trust I make myself sufficiently clear?"

"The only thing that's clear right now is your path to the door," Wright said, his voice rising. "It's unobstructed. Please take it."

Pendergast nodded. "Gentlemen. Ma'am." Then he turned around and moved silently out of the room.

Closing the door quietly, Pendergast stopped for a moment in the Director's outer office. Then, staring at the door, he quoted,

> So I return rebuk'd to my content,
> And gain by ills thrice more than I have spent.

Wright's executive secretary stopped her gum chewing in mid-snap. "Howzat?" she inquired.

"No, Shakespeare," Pendergast replied, heading for the elevator.

* * *

Inside, Wright fumbled at the telephone with shaking hands.

"What the hell happens now?" exploded Cuthbert. "I'll be damned if a bloody policeman's going to boot us out of our own Museum."

"Cuthbert, be quiet," said Wright. Then he spoke into the handset. "Get me Albany, right away."

There was a silence while he was put on hold. Wright looked over the receiver at Cuthbert and Rickman, controlling his heavy breathing with an effort. "Time to call in some favors," he said. "We'll see who has the final word here: some inbred albino from the Delta, or the Director of the largest natural history museum in the world."

= 32 =

The vegetation here is very unusual. The cycads and ferns look almost primordial. Too bad there isn't time for more careful study. We've used a particularly resilient variety as packing material for the crates; feel free to let Jörgensen take a look, if he's interested.

I fully expect to be with you at the Explorer's Club a month from now, celebrating our success with a brace of dry martinis and a good Macanudo. Until then, I know I can entrust this material and my reputation to you.

Your colleague,

Whittlesey

Smithback looked up from the letter. "We can't stay here. Let's go to my office."

His cubbyhole lay deep in a maze of overflow offices on the Museum's ground level. The honeycomb passages, full of noise and bustle, seemed a refreshing change to Margo after the damp, echoing basement corridors outside the Secure Area. They walked past a large green Dumpster overflowing with back issues of the Museum's magazine. Outside Smithback's office, a large bulletin board was plastered with a variety of irate letters from subscribers, for the amusement of the magazine staff.

Once before, hot on the trail of an issue of *Science* long overdue from the periodical library, Margo had penetrated Smithback's messy lair. It was as she remembered it: his desk a riot of photocopied articles, half-finished letters, Chinese take-out menus, and numerous books and journals the Museum's libraries were no doubt very eager to find.

"Have a seat," Smithback said, pushing a two-foot stack of paper brusquely off a chair. He closed the door, then walked around his desk to an ancient bentwood rocker. Paper crackled beneath his feet.

"Okay," he said in a low tone. "Now, you're sure the journal wasn't there?"

"I told you, the only crate I had a chance to look at was the one Whittlesey packed himself. But it wouldn't have been in the others."

Smithback examined the letter again. "Who's this Montague the thing's addressed to?" he asked.

"Don't know," Margo replied.

"How about Jörgensen?"

"Haven't heard of him, either."

Smithback pulled down the Museum's telephone listing from a shelf. "No Montague here," he murmured, flipping pages. "Aha! Here's Jörgensen. Botany. Says he's retired. How come he still has an office?"

"Not unusual in this place," Margo replied. "Independently wealthy people with little else to fill up their time. Where's his office?"

"Section forty-one, fourth floor," Smithback said,

closing the book and dropping it on his desk. "Near the herbarium." He stood up. "Let's go."

"Wait a minute, Smithback. It's almost four o'clock. I should call Frock and let him know what . . ."

"Later," Smithback said, making for the door. "Come on, Lotus Blossom. My journalist's nose hasn't picked up a decent scent all afternoon."

Jörgensen's office was a small, windowless laboratory with a high ceiling. It held none of the plants or floral specimens Margo expected to see in a botanist's lab. In fact, the room was empty except for a large workbench, a chair, and a coat rack. A drawer of the workbench was open, exposing a variety of worn tools. Jörgensen was bending over the workbench, fiddling with a small motor.

"Dr. Jörgensen?" Smithback asked.

The old man turned and gazed at Smithback. He was almost completely bald, with bushy white eyebrows overhanging intense eyes the color of bleached denim. He was bony and stooped but Margo thought he must be at least six feet four.

"Yes?" he said in a quiet voice.

Before Margo could stop him, Smithback handed Jörgensen the letter.

The man began reading, then started visibly. Without taking his eyes from the letter, he reached around for the battered chair and carefully eased himself into it.

"Where did you get this?" he demanded when he had finished.

Margo and Smithback looked at each other.

"It's genuine," Smithback said.

Jörgensen stared at them. Then he handed the letter back to Smithback. "I don't know anything about this," he said.

There was a silence. "It came from the crate John Whittlesey sent back from the Amazon expedition seven years ago," Smithback prompted hopefully.

Jörgensen continued to stare at them. After a few moments, he returned to his motor.

The two watched him tinker for a moment. "I'm sorry we interrupted your work," Margo said at last. "Perhaps this isn't a good time."

"What work?" asked Jörgensen, without turning around.

"Whatever that is you're doing," Margo replied.

Jörgensen suddenly barked out a laugh. "This?" he said, turning to face them again. "This isn't work. This is just a broken vacuum cleaner. Since my wife died, I've had to do the housework myself. Darn thing blew up on me the other day. I only brought it in here because this is where all my tools are. I don't have much work to do anymore."

"About that letter, sir—" Margo pressed.

Jörgensen shifted in the creaky chair and leaned back, looking at the ceiling. "I hadn't known it existed. The double-arrow motif served as the Whittlesey family crest. And that's Whittlesey's handwriting, all right. It brings back memories."

"What kind?" asked Smithback eagerly.

Jörgensen looked over at him, his brows contracting with irritation. "Nothing that's any of your business," he said tartly. "Or at least, I haven't heard just why it might be your business."

Margo shot Smithback a shut-up look. "Dr. Jörgensen," she began, "I'm a graduate student working with Dr. Frock. My colleague here is a journalist. Dr. Frock believes that the Whittlesey expedition, and the crates that were sent back, have a link to the Museum murders."

"A *curse*?" said Jörgensen, raising his eyebrows theatrically.

"No, not a curse," said Margo.

"I'm glad you haven't bought into that one. There's no curse. Unless you define a curse as a mixture of greed, human folly, and scientific jealousy. You don't need Mbwun to explain . . .''

He stopped. "Why are you so interested?" he asked suspiciously.

"To explain what?" Smithback interjected.

Jörgensen looked at him with distaste. "Young man, if you open your mouth one more time I'm going to ask you to leave."

Smithback narrowed his eyes but remained silent.

Margo wondered if she should go into detail about Frock's theories, the claw marks, the damaged crate, but decided not to. "We're interested because we feel that there's a connection here that no one is paying attention to. Not the police, and not the Museum. You were mentioned in this letter. We hoped you might be able to tell us more about this expedition."

Jörgensen held out a gnarled hand. "May I see that again?"

Reluctantly, Smithback complied.

Jörgensen's eyes passed over the letter again, hungrily, as if sucking in memories. "There was a time," he murmured, "I would have been reluctant to talk about this. Maybe afraid would be a better word. Certain parties might have sought to fire me." He shrugged. "But when you get as old as I am, you don't have much to be afraid of. Except maybe being alone."

He nodded slowly to Margo, clutching the letter. "I would have been on that expedition, if it hadn't been for Maxwell."

"Maxwell? Who's he?" asked Smithback.

Jörgensen shot him a look. "I've knocked down bigger journalists than you," he snapped. "Now I said, be quiet. I'm talking to the lady."

He turned to Margo again.

"Maxwell was one of the leaders of the expedition. Maxwell and Whittlesey. That was the first mistake, letting Maxwell muscle his way in, making the two of them

coleaders. They were at odds right from the beginning.
Neither one had full control. Maxwell's gain was my
loss—he decided they didn't have room for a botanist
on the expedition, and that was it for me. But Whittlesey
was even less happy about it than I. Having Maxwell
along put his hidden agenda at risk."

"What was that?" Margo asked.

"To find the Kothoga tribe. There were rumors of an
undiscovered tribe living on a *tepui,* a vast tableland
above the rain forest. Although the area had not been
scientifically explored, the consensus was that the tribe
was extinct, that only relics remained. Whittlesey didn't
believe this. He wanted to be their discoverer. The only
problem was, the local government denied him a permit
to study on the *tepui.* Said it was reserved for their own
scientists. Yankee go home."

Jörgensen snorted, shook his head.

"Well, what it was really being reserved for was dep-
redation, land rape. Of course, the local government had
heard the same rumors Whittlesey had. If there *were*
Indians up there, the government didn't want them in
the way of timbering and mining. So anyway, the expedition had to approach from the north. A much less
convenient route, but away from the restricted area. And
they were forbidden to ascend the *tepui* itself."

"Did the Kothoga still exist?" Margo asked.

Jörgensen slowly shook his head. "We'll never know.
The government found something on top of that *tepui.*
Maybe gold, platinum, placer deposits. You can detect
lots of things with satellites these days. Anyway, the
tepui was fired from the air in the spring of '88."

"Fired?" Margo asked.

"Burned clear with napalm," Jörgensen said. "Unusual and expensive to do it that way. Apparently, the
fire got out of hand, spread, burned uncontrollably for
months. Then they built a big road in there, coming up
the easy way from the south. They hauled in Japanese
hydraulic mining equipment and literally washed away

huge sections of the mountain. No doubt they leeched the gold and platinum or whatever with cyanic compounds, then just let the poison run into the rivers. There's nothing, I mean *nothing,* left. That's why the Museum never sent a second expedition down to search for the remains of the first." He cleared his throat.

"That's terrible," breathed Margo.

Jörgensen gazed up with his unsettling cerulean eyes. "Yes. It *is* terrible. Of course, you won't read about it in the *Superstition* exhibition."

Smithback held up one hand while slipping out his microcassette recorder with the other. "Excuse me, may I—?"

"No, you may *not* record this. This is not for attribution. Not for quotation. Not for anything. I've received a memo to that effect just this morning, as you probably know. This is for me: I haven't been able to talk about this for years, and I'm going to do it now, just this once. So keep quiet and listen."

There was a silence.

"Where was I?" Jörgensen resumed. "Oh, yes. So Whittlesey had no permit to ascend the *tepui.* And Maxwell was the consummate bureaucrat. He was determined to make Whittlesey play by the rules. Well, when you get out there in the jungle two hundred miles from any kind of government. . . . What rules?" He cackled.

"I doubt if anybody knows exactly what *did* happen out there. I got the story from Montague, and he pieced it together from Maxwell's telegrams. Not exactly an unbiased source."

"Montague?" Smithback interrupted.

"In any case," Jörgensen continued, ignoring Smithback, "it appears Maxwell stumbled upon some unbelievable botany. Around the base of the *tepui,* ninety-nine percent of the plant species were absolutely new to science. They found strange, primitive ferns and monocotyledons that looked like throwbacks to the Mesozoic Era. Even though Maxwell was a physical anthropologist, he went crazy over the strange vegetation. They filled up crate after crate with odd specimens. That was when Maxwell found those seed pods.''

"How important were *they?*''

"They were from a living fossil. Not unlike the discovery of the coelacanth in the 1930s: a species from an entire phylum they thought had become extinct in the Carboniferous. An entire *phylum.*''

"Did these seed pods look like eggs?'' asked Margo.

"I couldn't say. But Montague got a look at them, and he told me they were hard as hell. They'd need to be buried deep in the highly acidic soil of a rain forest in order to germinate. I imagine they're still in those crates.''

"Dr. Frock thought they *were* eggs.''

"Frock should stick to paleontology. He's a brilliant man, but erratic. At any rate, Maxwell and Whittlesey had a falling out. Not unexpected. Maxwell couldn't care less about botany, but he knew a rarity when he saw one. He wanted to get back to the Museum with his seed pods. He learned that Whittlesey intended to scale the *tepui* and look for the Kothoga, and it alarmed him. He was afraid the crates would be seized at dockside and he wouldn't get his precious pods out. They split up. Whittlesey went on deeper into the jungle, up the *tepui,* and was never seen again.

"When Maxwell reached the coast with the rest of the expedition, he sent back a stream of telegrams to the Museum, lambasting Whittlesey and telling his side of the story. Then he and the rest were killed in that plane crash. Luckily, arrangements had been made to ship the crates separately, or maybe it *wasn't* so lucky. Took the Museum a year to untangle the red tape, get the crates back to New York. Nobody seemed in a big hurry to do it.'' He rolled his eyes in disgust.

"You mentioned somebody named Montague?'' Margo asked quietly.

"Montague,'' Jörgensen said, his eyes looking past

Margo. "He was a young Ph.D. candidate at the Museum. Anthropology. Whittlesey's protégé. Needless to say, that didn't exactly put him in the Museum's good graces after Maxwell's telegrams arrived. None of us who'd been friendly with Whittlesey were ever really trusted after that."

"What happened to Montague?"

Jörgensen hesitated. "I don't know," he replied finally. "He just disappeared one day. Never came back."

"And the crates?" Margo pressed.

"Montague had been terribly anxious to see those crates, especially Whittlesey's. But, as I said, he was out of favor, and had been taken off the project. In point of fact, there *was* no project anymore. The whole expedition had been such a disaster that the top brass just wanted to forget anything had happened. When the crates finally arrived, they sat, unopened. Most of the documentation and provenance had burned up in the crash. Supposedly, there was a journal of Whittlesey's, but I never saw it. In any case, Montague complained and pleaded, and in the end they gave him the job of doing the initial curating. And then he just up and left."

"What do you mean, left?" Smithback asked.

Jörgensen looked at him, as if deciding whether or not to answer the question. "He simply walked out of the Museum and never came back. I understand his apartment and all his clothes were abandoned. His family instituted a search and found nothing. But he was a rather strange character. Most people assumed he'd gone off to Nepal or Thailand to find himself."

"But there were rumors," Smithback said. It was a statement, not a question.

Jörgensen laughed. "Of course there were rumors! Aren't there always? Rumors that he embezzled money, rumors that he ran off with a gangster's wife, rumors that he'd been murdered and dumped in the East River. But he was such a nonentity in the Museum that most people forgot about him in a few weeks."

"Rumors that the Museum Beast got him?" Smithback asked.

Jörgensen's smile faded. "Not exactly. But it caused all the rumors of the curse to resurface. Now everyone, they said, who had come in contact with the crates had died. Some of the guards and cafeteria employees—you know those types—said Whittlesey had robbed a temple, that there was something in the crate, a relic with a terrible curse on it. They said the curse followed the relic all the way back to the Museum."

"Didn't you want to study the plants that Maxwell sent back?" Smithback asked. "I mean, you're a botanist, aren't you?"

"Young man, you know nothing of science. There is no such thing as a *botanist* per se. I have no interest in the paleobotany of angiosperms. That whole thing was way out of my field. My specialty is the coevolution of plants and viruses. Or *was*," he said with a certain irony.

"But Whittlesey wanted you to take a look at the plants he sent back as packing material," Smithback continued.

"I have no idea why," Jörgensen said. "This is the first I've heard of it. I never saw this letter before." With a certain reluctance, he handed it back to Margo. "I'd say it's a fake, except for the handwriting and the motif."

There was a silence. "You haven't said what *you* thought about Montague's disappearance," Margo said at last.

Jörgensen rubbed the bridge of his nose and looked at the floor. "It frightened me."

"Why?"

There was a long silence. "I'm not sure," he finally said. "Montague once had a financial emergency and had to borrow money from me. He was very conscientious and went through great difficulties paying it back. It didn't seem in character for him to just disappear like that. The last time I saw him, he was about to do an

inventory of the crates. He was very excited about it.''
He looked up at Margo. "I'm not a superstitious man.
I'm a scientist. Like I said, I don't believe in curses and
that sort of thing . . .'' his voice trailed off.

"But—?'' Smithback prodded.

The old man shot a glance at Smithback. "Very
well,'' he glowered. Then he leaned back in his chair
and looked at the ceiling. "I told you that John Whittlesey was my friend,'' he said. "Before he left, Whittlesey
had collected all the stories he could find about the Kothoga tribe. Mostly from lowland tribes living downstream, Yanomamo and the like. I remember him telling
me one story the day before he left. The Kothoga, according to a Yanomamo informant, had made a deal with
a being called Zilashkee. This was a creature like our
Mephistopheles, but even more extreme: all the evil and
death in the world emanated from this thing, which slith-
ered around on the peak of the *tepui*. Or so the legend
went. Anyway, according to their arrangement, the Kothoga would get the Zilashkee's child for a servant in return for killing and eating all of their own children, and
vowing forevermore to worship him and only him. When
the Kothoga had finished their grisly task, the Zilashkee
sent his child to them. But the beast proceeded to run
rampant through the tribe, murdering and eating people.
When the Kothoga complained, the Zilashkee laughed
and said: *What did you expect? I am evil.* Finally, using
magic or herbal spells or some such thing, the tribe managed to control the beast. It couldn't be killed, you see.
So the Zilashkee child remained under the control of the
Kothoga, and they used it to do their own malignant
bidding. But using it was always a dangerous proposition. The legend says that the Kothoga have been looking for a way to get rid of it ever since.''

Jörgensen looked down at the disassembled motor.
"That was the story Whittlesey told me. When I heard
about the plane crash, the death of Whittlesey, the disappearance of Montague . . . well, I couldn't help but

think the Kothoga had finally managed to unload Zilashkee's child.''

Picking up a piece of the machine, the old botanist turned it over in his hands with a distant expression. ''Whittlesey told me the name of the Zilashkee's child was Mbwun. He Who Walks On All Fours.'' And he dropped the piece with a clank and grinned.

= 33 =

As closing drew near, the visitors began to trickle out toward the Museum exits. The Museum shop—located directly inside the south entrance—did a brisk business.

In the marble hallways leading away from the south entrance, the sounds of conversation and the drumming of feet could be clearly heard. In the Hall of the Heavens near the West entrance, where the opening party for the new exhibition was to be held, the noise was fainter, echoing inside the huge dome like a vaguely remembered dream. And deeper within the Museum, as more laboratories, antique lecture halls, storage vaults, and book-lined offices interposed themselves, the sounds of visitors did not penetrate. The long corridors were dark and silent.

Within the Butterfield Observatory, the noise and bustle could just as well have been on another planet. The staffers, making the most of the curfew, had gone home early. George Moriarty's office, like all six floors of the observatory, was deathly quiet.

Moriarty stood behind his desk, a balled fist pressed tightly against his mouth. "Damn," he mumbled.

Suddenly, one foot lashed out in frustration, the heel slamming against a file cabinet behind him and knocking a pile of papers onto the floor. "Damn!" he howled, this time in pain, as he sank into his chair and began rubbing his ankle.

Slowly, the pain lifted, and with it, his funk. Sighing heavily, he looked around the room. "Jeez, George, you always manage to screw things up, don't you?" he murmured.

He was hopeless socially, he might as well admit it to himself. Everything he did to catch Margo's attention, everything he did to gain her favor, seemed to backfire. What he'd said about her father was about as tactful as a machine gun.

Suddenly, he swiveled toward his terminal and typed in a command. He'd send her an e-mail message, maybe repair some of his damage. He paused a moment, composing, then began to type.

HI, MARGO! JUST CURIOUS TO KNOW IF YOU

Abruptly, Moriarty hit a key, purging the message. He'd probably just mess things up even worse.

He sat for a moment, staring at the blank screen. He knew of only one surefire method to ease his hurt: a treasure hunt.

Many of the *Superstition* exhibition's most prized artifacts were the direct result of his treasure hunts. Moriarty had a deep love for the Museum's vast collections, and he was more familiar with its obscure and secret corners than many longtime staffers. Shy, Moriarty had few friends and often passed his time researching and locating long-forgotten relics from the Museum's storerooms. It gave him a sense of worth and fulfillment that he had been unable to obtain from others.

He turned once again to the keyboard, opening the Museum's accession database and moving casually yet deliberately through its records. He knew his way around the database, knew its shortcuts and back doors, like an experienced riverboat captain knew the contours of a riverbed.

In a few minutes, his fingers slowed. Here was a region of the database he hadn't explored before: a trove of Sumerian artifacts, discovered in the early twenties but never fully researched. Carefully, he targeted first a collection, then a subcollection, then individual artifacts. This looked interesting: a series of clay tablets, early examples of Sumerian writing. The original collector believed they dealt with religious rituals. Moriarty read over the annotated entries, nodding to himself. Maybe they could use these in the exhibition. There was still room for a few more artifacts in one of the smaller miscellaneous galleries.

He checked his sundial watch: almost five. Still, he knew where the tablets were stored. If they looked promising, he could show them to Cuthbert tomorrow morning and get his approval. He could work up the display between the Friday night celebration and the public opening. He quickly jotted a few notes, then flicked off his computer.

The sound of the terminal being snapped into darkness sounded like a pistol shot in the lonely office. Finger still on the power switch, Moriarty paused. Then he stood up, tucked his shirt inside his trousers, and— favoring his bruised heel slightly—left the office, closing the door quietly behind him.

= 34 =

Down in the temporary command post, D'Agosta froze in the act of rapping on Pendergast's window. He peered in to get a better look.

Some tall guy in an ugly suit was moving around Pendergast's office. His face looked sweaty and sunburnt and he swaggered like he owned the place, picking up papers on the desk, laying them down somewhere else, jingling his pocket change.

"Hey, pal," D'Agosta said, opening the door and walking in, "that's FBI property. If you're waiting for Mr. Pendergast, how about doing it outside?"

The man turned. His eyes were small and narrow, and pissed off.

"From now on, ah, *Lieutenant*," he said, staring at the badge hanging from D'Agosta's belt as if trying to read the number, "you'll speak respectfully to the FBI personnel around here. Of which I am now in charge. Special Agent Coffey."

"Well, Special Agent Coffey, as far as I know, and

until someone tells me different, Mr. Pendergast is in charge here, and you're messing with his desk."

Coffey gave him a thin smile, reached into his jacket, and pulled out an envelope.

D'Agosta examined the letter inside. It was from Washington, putting the New York Field Office of the FBI, and one Special Agent Spencer Coffey, in charge of the case. Stapled to the directive were two memos. One, from the Governor's office, formally demanded the change and accepted full responsibility for the transfer of power. The second, with a United States Senate letterhead, D'Agosta folded up without bothering to read.

He handed the envelope back. "So you guys finally snuck in the back door."

"When will Pendergast be back, Lieutenant?" said Coffey, sliding the envelope back into his pocket.

"How would I know?" said D'Agosta. "While you're poking through his desk there, maybe you'd like to check his appointment book."

Before Coffey could respond, Pendergast's voice sounded from outside the office. "Ah, Agent Coffey! How delightful to see you."

Coffey once again reached for the envelope.

"No need," Pendergast said. "I know why you're here." He sat down behind his desk. "Lieutenant D'Agosta, please make yourself comfortable."

D'Agosta, noting only one other chair in the office, sat down with a grin. Watching Pendergast in action was something he'd grown to enjoy.

"A madman is apparently loose in the Museum, Mr. Coffey," Pendergast said. "Therefore, Lieutenant D'Agosta and I have both come to the conclusion that tomorrow night's opening party must not be allowed to proceed. This murderer works at night. He's well overdue for another attack. We cannot be responsible for more people being killed because the Museum is kept open for, shall we say, pecuniary reasons."

"Yeah," said Coffey, "well, you're not responsible

anymore. My orders are that the opening proceeds as planned, and on schedule. We're bolstering the police presence with additional field agents. This place is going to be more secure than the Pentagon lavatory. And I'll tell you something else, Pendergast: once this little party is over and done with and the big shots have gone home, we're gonna wrap this sucker. You're supposed to be hot shit, but you know something? I'm not impressed. You've had four days and all you've caught is your own dick. We're through wasting time."

Pendergast smiled. "Yes, I expected as much. If that's your decision, so be it. You should know, however, that I will be sending a formal memorandum to the Director, stating my own views on the matter."

"Do what you want," Coffey said, "but do it on your own time. Meanwhile, my people will be setting up shop down the hall. I'll expect a briefing from you at curfew."

"My closing report is already prepared," Pendergast said mildly. "Now, Mr. Coffey, is there anything else?"

"Yes," Coffey said. "I expect full cooperation from you, Pendergast."

He left the door open behind him.

D'Agosta watched him walk down the hall. "He looks a lot more pissed off now than before you came in," he said. Then he turned toward Pendergast. "You're not just going to give in to that jerk-off, are you?"

Pendergast smiled. "Vincent, I'm afraid this had grown inevitable. In a sense, I'm surprised it didn't happen sooner. This isn't the first time I've trod on Wright's toes this week. Why should I fight it? This way, at least, no one can accuse us of lack of cooperation."

"But I thought you had pull." D'Agosta tried to keep the disappointment out of his voice.

Pendergast spread his hands. "I have quite a bit of pull, as you put it. But remember, I'm off my turf. Because the killings were similar to those I investigated in New Orleans several years ago, I had good cause to be here—as long as there was no controversy, no call for local involvement. But I knew that Dr. Wright and the Governor had been at Brown together. With the Governor making a formal request for FBI intervention, there's only one possible outcome.''

"But what about the case?" D'Agosta asked. "Coffey's gonna build on all the work you've done, and take the credit himself.''

"You assume there's going to be credit here at all," Pendergast said. "I have a bad feeling about this opening, Lieutenant. A very bad feeling. I've known Coffey for a long time, and he can be relied upon to make a bad situation worse. But you notice, Vincent, that he did *not* send me packing. That he can't do.''

"Don't tell me you're happy to lose the responsibility," said D'Agosta. "*My* main goal in life may be to keep the mower off my ass, but I always figured you different.''

"Vincent, I'm surprised at you," Pendergast said. "It has nothing to do with shirking responsibility. However, this arrangement does allow me a certain degree of freedom. It's true that Coffey has the final say, but his ability to direct *my* actions is limited. The only way I could come up here initially was if I took charge of the case. That tends to make one more circumspect. Now, I'll be able to follow my own instincts." He sat back in his chair, fixing D'Agosta with his pale stare. "I would continue to welcome your help. I may need someone inside the department to help expedite a few things.''

D'Agosta looked thoughtful for a few moments. "There's one thing I could tell about this Coffey right from the get-go," he said.

"What is that?''

"The guy's dipped in green shit.''

"Ah, Vincent," said Pendergast, "you have such a colorful way with words.''

= 35 =

Friday

The office, Smithback noted glumly, looked exactly the same: not a knickknack out of place. He slumped in his chair, feeling a strong sense of déjà vu.

Rickman returned from her secretary's office carrying a slim file, the ubiquitous prim smile frozen on her face. "Tonight's the night!" she said cheerfully. "Planning to attend?"

"Yeah, sure," said Smithback.

She passed him the file. "Read this, Bill," she said, her voice a little less pleasant.

NEW YORK MUSEUM OF NATURAL HISTORY
INTERNAL MEMORANDUM

To: William Smithback Jr.
From: Lavinia Rickman
Re: Untitled work on Superstition Exhibition

Effective immediately, and until further notice, your work at the Museum will be governed by the following provisions:

1. All interviews conducted for the Work in Progress are to be done in my presence.
2. Recording of interviews by you, or the taking of notes during interviews by you, is forbidden. In the interests of timeliness and consistency, I will take on the responsibility of note-taking myself, and pass the edited scripts on to you for inclusion in the Work in Progress.
3. Discussion of Museum matters with employees, or any persons encountered upon the Museum grounds, is prohibited without first obtaining my written approval. Please sign in the space provided below to acknowledge your understanding of and agreement to these provisions.

Smithback read it twice, then looked up.

"Well?" she asked, tilting her head. "What do you think?"

"Let me get this straight," said Smithback. "I'm not even allowed to talk to someone at, say, lunch without your permission?"

"About Museum matters. That is correct," Rickman said, patting the paisley scarf around her neck.

"Why? Wasn't that memo you sent around yesterday a big enough ball and chain?"

"Bill, you know why. You've proven yourself unreliable."

"How so?" Smithback said in a strangled voice.

"I understand you've been running wild all over the Museum, talking to people you have no business with, asking absurd questions about matters that do not pertain to the new exhibition. If you think you can gather in-

formation about the . . . ah . . . recent circumstances that
have occurred, then I must remind you of paragraph seventeen of your contract, which forbids the use of any
information not authorized by myself. Nothing, I repeat,
nothing related to the unfortunate situation will be authorized.''

Smithback sat up. ''Unfortunate situation!'' he exploded. ''Why don't you call it what it is: murder!''

''Please don't raise your voice in my office,'' Rickman said.

''You hired me to write a book, not crank out a three-
hundred-page press release. There's been a string of brutal murders in the week before the Museum's biggest
opening ever. You mean to tell me that's not part of the
story?''

''I and I alone define what will be in this book and
what will not. Understood?''

''No.''

Rickman stood up. ''This is growing tiresome. You
will either sign this document now, or you will be terminated.''

''Terminated? What, do you mean shot or fired?''

''I will not stand for that kind of levity in my office.
Either sign this agreement, or I will accept your resignation immediately.''

''Fine,'' Smithback said. ''I'll simply take my manuscript to a commercial publisher. You need this book
as much as I do. And you and I both know I could get
a huge advance for the inside story on the Museum murders. And, believe me, I know the inside story. All of
it.''

Rickman's face was ghastly, yet still she held her
smile. Her knuckles whitened against her desk.

''That would be a violation of your contract,'' she said
slowly. ''The Museum has the Wall Street law firm of
Daniels, Soller and McCabe on retainer. Undoubtedly
you've heard of them. Should you take such action, you
would instantly be party to a breach of contract lawsuit,

as would your agent and any publisher foolish enough
to sign a contract with you. We'd bring everything we
have to bear on this case, and I wouldn't be surprised
if, after you lose, you never find work in your chosen
field again."

"This is a gross violation of my First Amendment
rights," Smithback managed to croak out.

"Not at all. We would merely be seeking remedy for
breach of contract. Nothing heroic in it for you, and it
wouldn't even make the *Times*. If you are really thinking
of taking this course of action, Bill, I'd consult a good
lawyer first and show him the contract you signed with
us. I'm sure he'll tell you it's as airtight as they come.
Or if you'd prefer, I'll accept your resignation right
now." She opened a desk drawer and extracted a second
piece of paper, leaving the drawer open as she did so.

Her intercom buzzed noisily. "Mrs. Rickman? Dr.
Wright on line one."

Rickman picked up the telephone. "Yes, Winston.
What? The *Post* again? Yes, I'll talk to them. You sent
for Ippolito? Good."

She hung up and went to the office door. "Make sure
Ippolito's on his way to the Director's office," she said
to her secretary. "As for you, Bill, I don't have any more
time to bandy civilities. If you won't sign the agreement,
then pack your things and get out."

Smithback had grown very quiet. All of a sudden, he
smiled. "Mrs. Rickman, I see your point."

She leaned toward him, simpering, eyes bright.
"And—?" she prompted.

"I'll agree to the restrictions," he said.

Rickman moved back behind her desk, triumphant.
"Bill, I'm very glad I won't need to use this." She put
the second sheet of paper back in her drawer and closed
it. "I suppose you're intelligent enough to know you
have no choice."

Meeting her eyes, Smithback reached for the folder.

"You don't mind if I read this over again before I sign, do you?"

Rickman hesitated. "No, I suppose not. Although you'll find it says exactly what it did the first time you read it. There's no room for misinterpretation, so please don't look for gray areas." She looked around the office, swept up her pocketbook, and headed for the door. "Bill, I'm warning you. Don't forget to sign it. Please follow me out, and give the signed document to my secretary. You'll be sent a copy."

Smithback's lips pursed in distaste as he watched her fanny sway under the pleated skirt. He gave a final, furtive glance toward the outer office. Then he quickly slid open the drawer Rickman had just closed and extracted a small object, which he slipped into his jacket pocket. Closing the drawer, he looked around once again and started for the exit.

Then, moving back to the desk, he grabbed the memo and scrawled an illegible signature across the bottom. He handed it to the secretary on the way out. "Save that signature, it'll be valuable someday," he said over his shoulder, letting the door close with a bang.

Margo was hanging up her phone as Smithback walked in. Once again, she had the lab to herself: her office mate, the preparator, had apparently taken a sudden extended vacation.

"I just talked to Frock," she said. "He was pretty disappointed that we didn't find anything more in the crate, and that I didn't get a chance to look for any remaining seed pods. I think he was hoping for evidence of a creature. I wanted to tell him about the letter and Jörgensen, but he said he couldn't talk. I think Cuthbert was in there with him."

"Probably asking about that Request for Access form he sent up," Smithback said. "Doing his Torquemada imitation." He gestured toward the door. "How come this was unlocked?"

Margo looked surprised. "Oh. Guess I forgot again."

"Mind if I lock it, just in case?" He fumbled with the door, then, grinning, he reached into his jacket and slowly withdrew a small, battered book, its leather cover stamped with two overlapping arrowheads. He held it up like a trophy fish for her inspection.

Margo's look of curiosity turned to astonishment. "My God! Is that the journal?"

Smithback nodded proudly.

"How did you get it? *Where* did you get it?"

"Rickman's office," he said. "I had to make a terrible sacrifice for it. I signed a piece of paper forbidding me ever to speak to you again."

"You're joking."

"Only partly. Anyway, at one point in the torture she opened her desk drawer, and I saw this little beat-up book. Looked like a diary. Seemed like a strange thing for Rickman to keep in her desk. Then I remembered your story about how she'd supposedly borrowed the journal." He nodded smugly. "As I always suspected. So I nicked it as I was leaving her office."

He opened the journal. "Now be quiet, Lotus Blossom. Daddy's going to read you a bedtime story."

Margo listened as Smithback began to read; slowly at first, but faster as he got the hang of the sloppy handwriting and frequent abbreviations. Most of the early entries were very short; cursory sentences giving a few details about the day's weather and the expedition's position.

Aug. 31. Rain all night—Canned bacon for breakfast—Something wrong with helicopter this morning, had to waste day doing nothing. Maxwell insufferable. Carlos having more trouble with Hosta Gilbao—demanding additional wages for . . .

"This is boring," said Smithback, interrupting his reading. "Who cares that they ate canned bacon for breakfast?"

"Keep going," urged Margo.

"There really isn't that much here," Smithback said, paging ahead. "Guess Whittlesey was a man of few words. Oh, God. I hope I didn't sign my life away for nothing."

The journal described the expedition's progress deeper and deeper into the rain forest. The first part of the journey was made by Jeep. Then the party was helicoptered two hundred miles to the upper reaches of the Xingú. From there, hired guides rowed the party up the sluggish flow of the river toward the *tepui* of Cerro Gordo. Smithback read on.

Sept. 6. Left dugouts at dropoff site. On foot all the way now. First glimpse of Cerro Gordo this afternoon—rain forest rising into clouds. Cries of tutitl birds, captured several specimens. Guards murmuring among themselves.

Sept. 12. Last of corned beef hash for breakfast. Less humid than yesterday. Continued toward *tepui*—clouds broke free at noon—altitude of plateau possibly eight thousand feet—temperate rain forest—saw five rare candelaria ibex—recovered blow darts and tube, excellent condition—mosquitoes bad—Xingú dried peccary for dinner—not bad, tastes like smoked pork. Maxwell filling crates with useless rubbish.

"Why did Rickman snag this?" Smithback wailed. "There's no dirt in here. What's the big deal?"

Sept. 15. Wind from the S.W. Oatmeal for breakfast. Three portages today owing to brush jams in river—water up to chest—leeches lovely. Around dinner, Maxwell stumbled upon some specimens of flora he is extremely excited about. Indigenous plants indeed quite unique—odd symbiosis, morphology seems very ancient. But more important discoveries lie ahead, I am sure.

Sept. 16. Stayed late in camp this morning, repacking gear. Maxwell now insists on returning with his "find." Idiotic fellow, nuisance is that almost everyone else is returning also. They turned back with all but two of our guides just after lunch. Crocker, Carlos, and I press on. Almost immediately, stopped to repack crate. Specimen jar had broken inside. While I repacked, Crocker wandered off trail, came upon ruined hut . . .

"Now we're getting somewhere," Smithback said.

. . . brought gear down to investigate, reopened crate, retrieved toolbag—before we could investigate hut, old native woman wanders out from brush, staggering—sick or drunk, impossible to tell—points to crate, wailing loudly. Breasts down to her waist—no teeth, nearly bald—great sore on her back, like a boil. Carlos reluctant to translate, but I insist:

Carlos: She says, devil, devil.

Myself: Ask her, what devil?

Carlos translates. Woman goes into hysterics, wailing, clutching chest.

Myself: Carlos, ask her about the Kothoga.

Carlos: She say you come to take devil away.

Myself: What about the Kothoga?

Carlos: She say, Kothoga gone up mountain.

Myself: Up mountain! Where?

More caterwauling from woman. Points at our open crate.

Carlos: She say you take devil.

Myself: What devil?

Carlos: Mbwun. She say you take devil Mbwun in box.

Myself: Ask her more about Mbwun. What is it?

Carlos talks to woman, who calms down a little, and speaks for an extended period of time.

Carlos: She says that Mbwun is son of devil. The foolish Kothoga sorcerer who asked devil Zilashkee for his son to help them defeat their enemies. Devil made them kill and eat all their children—then sent Mbwun as gift. Mbwun helps defeat Kothoga enemies, then turns on Kothoga, starts killing everyone. Kothoga flee to *tepui,* Mbwun follow. Mbwun not ever die. Have to rid Kothoga of Mbwun. Now white man come and take Mbwun away. Beware, Mbwun curse will destroy you! You bring death to your people!

I am flabbergasted, and elated—this tale fits into myth cycles we had only heard secondhand. I tell Carlos to get more details about Mbwun—woman breaks away—great strength for one so old—melts into brush. Carlos follows her, comes back empty-handed—he looks frightened, I don't push matters. Investigate hut. When we return to trail, guides gone.

"She knew they were going to take the figurine back!" Smithback said. "That must have been the curse she was talking about!"

He read on.

Sept. 17. Crocker missing since last night. I fear the worst. Carlos very apprehensive. I will send him back after Maxwell, who must be halfway to the river by now—can't afford to lose this relic, which I believe priceless. I will continue on in search of Crocker. There are trails throughout these woods that must be Kothogan—how civilization

can harness this kind of landscape is beyond me—
perhaps the Kothoga will be saved after all.

That was the end of the journal.

Smithback closed the book with a curse. "I can't believe it! Nothing we didn't already know. And I sold my
soul to Rickman . . . for *this!*"

= 36 =

Behind his desk in the command post, Pendergast was fiddling with an ancient Mandarin puzzle made of brass and knotted silken cord. He seemed totally absorbed. Behind him, the learned sounds of a string quartet emerged from the speakers of a small cassette player. Pendergast did not look up as D'Agosta walked in.

"Beethoven's String Quartet in F Major, Opus 135," he said. "But no doubt you knew that, Lieutenant. It's the fourth movement Allegro, known as *Der schwer gefaßte Entschluß*—the 'Difficult Resolution.' A title that could be bestowed on this case, as well as the movement, perhaps? Amazing, isn't it, how art imitates life."

"It's eleven o'clock," D'Agosta said.

"Ah, of course," Pendergast said, rolling his chair back and standing up. "The Security Director owes us a guided tour. Shall we go?"

The door of Security Command was opened by Ippolito himself. To D'Agosta, the place looked like the control room of a nuclear power plant, all dials and buttons and levers. Across one wall was a vast miniature city of lighted grids, arranged in intricate geometries. Two guards monitored a battery of closed-circuit screens. In the center, D'Agosta recognized the relay box for the repeater stations used to ensure strong signals for the radios the police and Museum guards carried.

"This," said Ippolito, spreading his hands and smiling, "is one of the most sophisticated security systems in any museum in the world. It was designed especially for us. It cost us a pretty penny, I can tell you."

Pendergast looked around. "Impressive," he said.

"It's state of the art," said Ippolito.

"No doubt," Pendergast said. "But what concerns me right now, Mr. Ippolito, is the safety of the five thousand guests who are expected here tonight. Tell me how the system works."

"It was primarily designed to prevent theft," the security director went on. "A large number of the Museum's most valuable objects have small chips attached in inconspicuous places. Each chip transmits a tiny signal to a series of receivers located around the Museum. If the object is moved even one inch, an alarm goes off, pinpointing the location of the object."

"And then what happens?" asked D'Agosta.

Ippolito grinned. At a console, he pressed some buttons. A large screen illuminated floor plans of the Museum.

"The interior of the Museum," Ippolito continued, "is divided into five cells. Each cell includes a number of exhibit halls and storage areas. Most of these run from basement to roof, but, because of the Museum's structural framework, the perimeters in cells two and three are a little more complicated. When I flick a switch on this panel here, thick steel doors drop down from the ceilings to seal off the interior passages between cells. The Museum windows are all barred. Once we've sealed off a certain cell, the burglar is trapped. He can move around within one section of the Museum, but he can't get out. The grid was laid out in such a way that the exits are external to it, making monitoring easy." He moved over to the layouts. "Let's say someone manages to steal an object, and by the time the guards arrive, he's left the room. It won't make any difference. Within a few seconds, the chip will have sent a signal to the computer, instructing it to seal off that entire cell. The whole process is automatic. The burglar is trapped inside."

"What happens if he takes the chip off before he runs?" D'Agosta asked.

"The chips are motion sensitive," Ippolito continued. "That would set off the alarm, too, and the security doors would instantly descend. A burglar couldn't move fast enough to get out."

Pendergast nodded. "How do you reopen the doors once the burglar has been caught?"

"We can open any set of doors from this control room, and each security door has a manual override on it. It's a keypad, actually. Punch in the right code, and the door comes up."

"Very nice," Pendergast murmured. "But the entire system is geared toward preventing someone from getting out. What we're dealing with here is a killer who wants to stay *in*. How will all this help keep tonight's guests safe?"

Ippolito shrugged. "No big deal. We'll just use the system to create a secure perimeter around the reception hall and the exhibition. All the festivities are taking place inside Cell Two." He pointed to the schematic. "The reception is taking place in the Hall of the Heavens, here. That's just outside the entrance to the *Superstition* exhibition, which is itself within Cell Two. All the steel doors for this cell will be closed. We'll be leaving only four doors open: the East Door of the Great Rotunda—which is the gateway to the Hall of the Heavens—and three emergency exits. All will be heavily guarded."

"And what parts of the Museum exactly does Cell Two consist of?" asked Pendergast.

Ippolito pushed some buttons on the console. A large central section of the Museum glowed green on the panels.

"This is Cell Two," Ippolito said. "As you can see, it reaches from the basement to the ceiling, as do all the cells. The Hall of the Heavens is here. The computer lab and the room we're in now, Security Command, are both inside this cell. So is the Secure Area, the central archives, and a variety of other high-security areas. There will be no exit from the Museum except through the four steel doors, which we'll keep open on override. We'll seal the perimeter an hour before the party, drop all the other doors, and set up guards at the access points. I'm telling you, it'll be more secure than a bank vault."

"And the rest of the Museum?"

"We thought about sealing all five cells, but decided against it."

"Good," said Pendergast, eyeing another panel. "In the event of a crisis, we wouldn't want any emergency personnel to be hampered." He pointed at the illuminated panel. "But what about the subbasement? The basement areas of this cell may well connect with it. And that subbasement could lead almost anywhere."

"Nobody would dare try to use that," Ippolito snorted. "It's a maze."

"But we're not talking about an ordinary burglar. We're talking about a killer that's eluded every search you, I, or D'Agosta here have mounted. A killer that seems to call the subbasement home."

"There is only one stairwell connecting the Hall of the Heavens to other floors," Ippolito explained patiently, "and it'll be guarded by my men, just like the emergency exits. I'm telling you, we've got this figured out. The entire perimeter is going to be secure."

Pendergast examined the glowing map for some time

in silence. "How do you know this schematic is accurate?" he asked finally.

Ippolito looked a little flustered. "Of course it's accurate."

"I asked: how do you *know?*"

"The system was designed straight off the architectural drawings from the 1912 reconstruction."

"No changes since then? No doors knocked open here, sealed off there?

"All changes were taken into account."

"Did those architectural drawings cover the Old Basement and subbasement areas?"

"No, those are older areas. But, like I told you, they'll either be sealed or guarded."

There was a long silence while Pendergast continued to look at the panels. Finally, he sighed and turned to face the Security Director.

"Mr. Ippolito, I don't like it."

A throat was cleared behind them. "What doesn't he like now?"

D'Agosta didn't have to turn around. That abrasive Long Island accent could belong only to Special Agent Coffey.

"I'm just reviewing the security procedures with Mr. Pendergast," said Ippolito.

"Well, Ippolito, you're gonna have to review them all over again with me." He turned his narrow eyes on Pendergast. "Remember in the future to invite me to your private parties," he said irritably.

"Mr. Pendergast—" Ippolito began.

"Mr. Pendergast is up here from the Deep South to give us a little help here and there when we need it. I'm running the show now. Got it?"

"Yes, sir," said Ippolito. He reviewed the procedures again while Coffey sat in an operator's chair, twirling a set of earphones around his finger. D'Agosta wandered around the room, looking at the control panels. Pendergast listened carefully to Ippolito, looking for all the world as if he hadn't heard the speech before. When the Security Director finished, Coffey leaned back in his chair.

"Ippolito, you got four holes in this perimeter." He paused for effect. "I want three of them plugged. I want only one way in and one way out."

"Mr. Coffey, fire regulations require—"

Coffey waved his hand. "Let me worry about the fire regulations. You worry about the holes in your security net. The more holes we have, the more trouble we have waiting to happen."

"That, I'm afraid, is precisely the *wrong* way to go," Pendergast said. "If you close these three exits, the guests are going to be locked in. Should something happen, there would be only one way out."

Coffey spread his hands in a gesture of frustration. "Hey, Pendergast, that's just the point. You can't have it both ways. Either you have a secure perimeter or you don't. Anyway, according to Ippolito here, each security door has an emergency override. So what's your problem?"

"That's right," said Ippolito, "the doors can be opened using the keypad in an emergency. All you need is the code."

"May I ask what controls the keypad?" asked Pendergast.

"The central computer. The computer room is right next door."

"And if the computer goes down?"

"We've got backup systems, with redundancies. Those panels on the far wall control the backup system. Each panel has its own alarm."

"That's another problem," said Pendergast quietly.

Coffey exhaled loudly and spoke to the ceiling. "He still doesn't like it."

"I counted eighty-one alarm lights on that bank of controls alone," Pendergast continued, oblivious to Coffey. "In a true emergency, with multiple system failure, most of those alarms would be blinking. No team of operators could deal with that.''

"Pendergast, you're slowing me down," Coffey snapped. "Ippolito and I are going to work out these details, okay? We've got less than eight hours to show-time."

"Has the system been tested?" Pendergast asked.

"We test it every week," said Ippolito.

"What I mean is, has it ever been put to the test in a real situation? An attempted theft, perhaps?"

"No, and I hope it never is."

"I regret to say it," said Pendergast, "but this strikes me as a system designed for failure. I'm a great advocate of progress, Mr. Ippolito, but I'd strongly recommend an old-fashioned approach here. In fact, during the party, I would disable the whole system. Just turn it off. It's too complex, and I wouldn't trust it in an emergency. What we need is a proven approach, something we are all familiar with. Foot patrols, armed guards at every ingress and egress point. I'm sure Lieutenant D'Agosta will provide us with extra men."

"Just say the word," said D'Agosta.

"The word is no." Coffey began to laugh. "Jesus, he wants to *disable* the system right at the moment when it's most needed!"

"I must register my strongest objections to this plan," said Pendergast.

"Well, you can write up your objections, then," said Coffey, "and send them by slow boat to your New Orleans office. Sounds to me like Ippolito here's got things pretty well under control."

"Thank you," Ippolito said, swelling visibly.

"This is a very unusual and dangerous situation," Pendergast continued. "It's not the time to rely on a complex and unproven system."

"Pendergast," said Coffey, "I've heard enough. Why don't you just head down to your office and eat that catfish sandwich your wife put in your lunchbox?"

D'Agosta was startled at the change that came over Pendergast's face. Instinctively, Coffey took a step back. But Pendergast simply turned on his heel and walked out the door. D'Agosta moved to follow him.

"Where're you going?" asked Coffey. "You better stick around while we work out the details."

"I agree with Pendergast," D'Agosta said. "This isn't the time to start messing with video games. You're talking about people's lives here."

"Listen up, D'Agosta. We're the big boys, we're the FBI. We're not interested in the opinions of a traffic cop from Queens."

D'Agosta looked at Coffey's sweaty red face. "You're a disgrace to law enforcement," he said.

Coffey blinked. "Thank you, and I will note that gratuitous insult in my report to my good friend, Chief of Police Horlocker, who will no doubt take appropriate action."

"You can add this one, then: you're a sack of shit."

Coffey threw back his head and laughed. "I love people who slit their own throats and save you the trouble. It's already occurred to me that this case is much too important to have a lieutenant acting as NYPD liaison. You're gonna be pulled off this case in twenty-four hours, D'Agosta. Did you know that? I wasn't going to tell you until after the party—didn't want to spoil your fun—but I guess now's a good time after all. So put your last afternoon on this case to good use. And we'll see you at the four o'clock briefing. Be on time."

D'Agosta said nothing. Somehow, he wasn't surprised.

= 37 =

An explosive sneeze rattled beakers and dislodged dried plant specimens in the Museum's auxiliary botanical lab.

"Sorry," Kawakita apologized, sniffling. "Allergies."

"Here's a tissue," Margo said, reaching into her carryall. She'd been listening to Kawakita's description of his genetic Extrapolator program. *It's brilliant,* she thought. *But I'll bet Frock supplied most of the theory behind it.*

"Anyway," Kawakita said, "you start with gene sequences from two animals or plants. That's the input. What you get is an extrapolation—a guess from the computer of what the evolutionary link is between the two species. The program automatically matches up pieces of DNA, compares like sequences, then figures out what the extrapolated form might be. As an example, I'll do a test run with chimp and human DNA. What we should get is a description of some intermediate form."

"The Missing Link," Margo nodded. "Don't tell me it draws a picture of the animal, too?"

"No!" Kawakita laughed. "I'd get a Nobel Prize if it could do that. What it does instead is give you a list of morphological and behavioral features the animal or plant might possess. Not definite, but probable. And not a complete list, of course. You'll see when we finish this run."

He typed a series of instructions, and data began flowing across the computer screen: a rapid, undulating progression of zeros and ones. "You can turn this off," said Kawakita. "But I like to watch the data download from the gene sequencer. It's as beautiful as watching a river. A trout stream, preferably."

In about five minutes the data stopped and the screen went blank, glowing a soft blue. Then the face of Moe, from the Three Stooges, appeared, saying through the computer's speaker: "I'm thinking, I'm thinking, but nothing's happening!"

"That means the program's running," Kawakita said, chuckling at his joke. "It can take up to an hour, depending on how far apart the two species are."

A message popped on the screen:

ESTIMATED TIME TO COMPLETION: 3.03.40 min.

"Chimps and humans are so close—they share ninety-eight percent of the same genes—that this one should be fairly quick."

A light bulb suddenly popped on the screen over Moe's head.

"Done!" said Kawakita. "Now for the results."

He pressed a key. The computer screen read:

FIRST SPECIES:

Species: *Pan troglodytes*

Genus: *Pan*

Family: *Pongidae*
Order: *Primata*
Class: *Mammalia*
Phylum: *Chordata*
Kingdom: *Animalia*

SECOND SPECIES:
Species: *Homo sapiens*
Genus: *Homo*
Family: *Hominidae*
Order: *Primata*
Class: *Mammalia*
Phylum: *Chordata*
Kingdom: *Animalia*

Overall Genetic Match: 98.4%

"Believe it or not," said Kawakita, "the identification of these two species was made solely on the genes. I didn't tell the computer what these two organisms were. That's a good way to show unbelievers that the Extrapolator isn't just a gimmick or a kludge. Anyway, now we get a description of the intermediate species. In this case, as you said, the Missing Link."

Intermediate form morphological characteristics:
Gracile
Brain capacity: 750cc
Bipedal, erect posture
Opposable thumb
Loss of opposability in toes
Below average sexual dimorphism
Weight, male, full grown: 55 kg

Weight, female, full grown: 45 kg
Gestation period: eight months
Aggressiveness: low to moderate
Estrus cycle in female: suppressed

The list went on and on, growing more and more obscure. Under "osteology," Margo could make out almost nothing.

Atavistic parietal foramina process
Greatly reduced iliac crest
10–12 thoracic vertebrae
Partially rotated greater trochanter
Prominent rim of orbit
Atavistic frontal process with prominent zygomatic process

That must mean beetle browed, thought Margo to herself.

Diurnal
Partially or serially monogamous
Lives in cooperative social groups

"Come on. How can your program tell something like this?" Margo asked, pointing to *monogamous.*

"Hormones," said Kawakita. "There's a gene that codes for a hormone seen in monogamous mammal species, but not in promiscuous species. In humans, this hormone has something to do with pair bonding. It isn't present in chimps, who are notoriously promiscuous animals. And the fact that the female's estrus cycle is suppressed—you also see that only in relatively monogamous species. The program uses a whole arsenal of tools—subtle AI algorithms, fuzzy logic—to interpret the effect of whole suites of genes on the behavior and look of a proposed organism.''

"AI algorithms? Fuzzy logic? You're losing me," Margo said.

"Well, it really doesn't matter. You don't need to know all the secrets, anyway. What it boils down to is making the program think more like a person than a normal computer would. It makes educated guesses, uses intuition. That one trait, 'cooperative,' for example, is extrapolated from the presence or absence of some eighty different genes.''

"That's all?" Margo said jokingly.

"No," Kawakita replied. "You can also use the program to guess at a *single* organism's size, shape, and behavior by entering the DNA for one creature instead of two, and disabling the extrapolation logic. And assuming the funding holds up, I plan to add two other modules for this program. The first will extrapolate back in time from a single species, and the second will extrapolate forward. In other words, we'll be able to learn more about extinct creatures of the past, and guess at beings of the future.'' He grinned. "Not bad, huh?''

"It's amazing," said Margo. She feared her own research project seemed puny by comparison. "How did you develop it?''

Kawakita hesitated, staring at her a little suspiciously. "When I first started working with Frock, he told me he was frustrated by the spottiness of the fossil record. He said he wanted to fill in the gaps, learn what the intermediate forms were. So I wrote this program. He gave me most of the rule tables. We started testing it with various species. Chimps and humans, as well as various bacteria for which we had a lot of genetic data. Then an incredible thing happened. Frock, the old devil, was expecting it, but I wasn't. We compared the domesticated dog with the hyena, and what we got was not a smoothly intermediate species, but a bizarre life form, totally different from either dog or hyena. This happened with a couple of other species pairs, too. You know what Frock said to that?''

Margo shook her head.

''He just smiled and said, 'Now you see the true value of this program.' '' Kawakita shrugged. ''You see, my program vindicated Frock's theory of the Callisto Effect by showing that small changes in DNA can sometimes produce extreme changes in an organism. I was a little miffed, but that's the way Frock works.''

''No wonder Frock was so anxious that I use this program,'' Margo said. ''This can revolutionize the study of evolution.''

''Yeah, except nobody is paying any attention to it,'' said Kawakita bitterly. ''Anything connected with Frock these days is like the kiss of death. It's really frustrating to pour your heart and soul into something, and then just get ignored by the scientific community. You know, Margo, between you and me, I'm thinking of dumping Frock as an adviser and joining Cuthbert's group. I think I'd be able to carry much of my work over with me. You might want to consider it yourself.''

''Thanks, but I'll stick with Frock,'' Margo said, offended. ''I wouldn't have even gone into genetics if it weren't for him. I owe him a lot.''

''Suit yourself,'' said Kawakita. ''But then, you might not even stay at the Museum, right? At least, that's what Bill Smithback tells me. But I've invested everything in this place. My philosophy is, you don't owe anyone but yourself. Look around the Museum: look at Wright, Cuthbert, the whole lot. Are they out for anyone but themselves? We're scientists, you and I. We *know* about survival of the fittest and 'nature red in tooth and claw.' And survival applies to scientists, too.''

Margo looked at Kawakita's glittering eyes. He was right in a way. But at the same time, Margo felt that human beings, having figured out the brutal laws of nature, could perhaps transcend some of them.

She changed the subject. "So the G.S.E. works the same way with plant DNA as with animal DNA?"

"Exactly the same," Kawakita replied, returning to his businesslike manner. "You run the DNA sequencer on two plant species, and then download the data into the Extrapolator. It'll tell you how closely the plants are related, and then describe the intermediate form. Don't be surprised if the program asks questions or makes comments. I added a lot of little bells and whistles here and there while I was developing my artificial intelligence chops."

"I think I've got the idea," said Margo. "Thanks. You've done some amazing work."

Kawakita winked and leaned over. "You owe me one now, kid."

"Anytime," said Margo. *Kid. Owing him one.* She disliked people who talked like that. And when Kawakita said it, he meant it.

Kawakita stretched, sneezed again. "I'm off. Gotta grab some lunch, then go home and pick up my tux for the party tonight. I wonder why I even bothered to come in today—everybody else is home preparing for tonight. I mean, look at this lab. It's deserted."

"Tux, eh?" said Margo. "I brought my dress with me this morning. It's nice, but it's not a Nipon original or anything."

Kawakita leaned toward her. "Dress for success, Margo. The powers that be take a look at some guy wearing a T-shirt, and even though he's a genius they can't *visualize* him as Director of the Museum."

"And you want to be Director?"

"Of course," said Kawakita, surprised. "Don't you?"

"What about just doing good science?"

"Anybody can do good science. But someday I'd like a larger role. As Director, you can do a lot more for science than some researcher fiddling in a dingy lab like this. Today it's just not enough to do outstanding research.'' He patted her on the back. ''Have fun. And don't break anything.''

He left, and the lab settled into silence.

Margo sat for a moment, motionless. Then she opened up the folder with the Kiribitu plant specimens. But she couldn't help thinking there were more important things to be done. When she'd finally reached Frock on the phone, and told him about what little she'd found in the crate, he had grown very quiet. It was as if, suddenly, all the fight had gone out of him. He'd sounded so depressed, she hadn't bothered to tell him about the journal and its lack of new information.

She looked at her watch: after one o'clock. The DNA sequencing of each Kiribitu plant specimen was going to be time-consuming, and she had to complete the sequencing before she could use Kawakita's Extrapolator. But as Frock had reminded her, this was the first attempt to do a systematic study of a primitive plant classification system. With this program, she could confirm that the Kiribitu, with their extraordinary knowledge of plants, had actually classified them biologically. The program would allow her to come up with intermediate plants, hypothetical species whose real counterparts might still be found in the Kiribitu rain forest. At least, that was Frock's intention.

To sequence DNA from a plant, Margo had to remove part of each specimen. After a lengthy exchange of electronic mail that morning, she had finally been given permission to take 0.1 gram from each specimen. It was just barely enough.

She stared at the delicate specimens, smelling faintly of spice and grass. Some of them were powerful hallucinogens, used by the Kiribitu for sacred ceremonies; others were medicinal and quite possibly of great value to modern science.

She picked up the first plant with tweezers, slicing off the top portion of the leaf with an X-Acto knife. In a mortar and pestle, she ground it up with a mild enzyme that would dissolve the cellulose and lyse the cells' nuclei, releasing the DNA. She worked swiftly but meticulously, adding the appropriate enzymes, centrifuging the result and performing a titration, then repeating the process with other plants.

The final centrifuging took ten minutes, and while the centrifuge vibrated in its gray metal case, Margo sat back, her mind wandering. She wondered what Smithback was doing in his new role as Museum pariah. She wondered, with a small thrill of fear, whether Mrs. Rickman had discovered the missing journal. She thought about what Jörgensen had said, and about Whittlesey's own description of his last days on earth. She imagined the old woman pointing a withered finger at the figurine in the box, warning Whittlesey about the curse. She imagined the setting: the ruined hut overgrown by vines, the flies droning in the sunlight. Where had the woman come from? Why had she run off? Then she imagined Whittlesey taking a deep breath, entering that dark hut of mystery for the first time . . .

Wait a minute, she thought. The journal had said they encountered the old woman before entering the deserted hut. And yet, the letter she found wedged in the lid of the crate clearly stated that Whittlesey discovered the figurine *inside* the hut. He didn't enter the hut until after the old woman ran away.

The old woman was *not* looking at the figurine when she cried out that Mbwun was in the crate! *She must have been looking at something else in the crate and calling it Mbwun!* But nobody had realized that, because they hadn't found Whittlesey's letter. They'd only had the journal for evidence, so they'd assumed Mbwun was the figurine.

But they were wrong.

Mbwun, the *real* Mbwun, wasn't the figurine at all. What had the woman said? *Now white man come and take Mbwun away. Beware, Mbwun curse will destroy you! You bring death to your people!*

And that's just what had happened. Death had come to the Museum. But what inside the crate could she have been referring to?

Grabbing the notebook from her carryall, she quickly reconstructed a list of what she had found in Whittlesey's crate the day before:

Plant press with plants
Blow darts with tube
Incised disk (found in the hut)
Lip plugs
Five or six jars with preserved frogs and salamanders (I think?)
Bird skins
Flint arrowheads and spear points
Shaman's rattle
Manta

What else? She rummaged in her handbag. The plant press, disc, and shaman's rattle were still there. She laid them on the table.

The damaged shaman's rattle was interesting, but far from unusual. She'd seen several more exotic specimens in the *Superstition* exhibition.

The disk was obscure. It showed some kind of ceremony, people standing in a shallow lake, bending over, some with plants in their hands, baskets on their backs. Very odd. But it certainly didn't seem to be an object of veneration.

The list wasn't helpful. Nothing inside the crate had looked remotely like a devil, or whatever else could inspire such terror in an old woman.

Margo carefully unscrewed the small, rusty plant press, its screws and plywood holding the blotter paper in place. She eased it open and lifted off the first sheet.

It held a plant stem and several small flowers. Nothing she had ever seen before, but not particularly interesting at first glance.

The next sheets in the press contained flowers and leaves. It was not, Margo thought, a collection made by a professional botanist. Whittlesey was an anthropologist, and he had probably just picked these specimens because they looked showy and unusual. But why would he collect them at all? She went through all the specimens, and in the back found the note she was looking for.

"Selection of plants found in overgrown abandoned garden near hut (Kothoga?) on September 16, 1987. May be cultivated species, some may also be invasive after abandonment." There was a little drawing of the overgrown plot, showing the location of the various plants. *Anthropology,* thought Margo, *not botany.* Still, she respected Whittlesey's interest in the relationship the Kothoga had to their plants.

She continued her inspection. One plant caught her eye: it had a long fibrous stem, with a single round leaf at the top. Margo realized it was some kind of aquatic plant, similar to a lily pad. *Probably lived in an area of floods,* she thought.

Then she realized that the incised disk found in the hut showed the very same plant. She looked at the disk more closely: it depicted people harvesting these very plants from the swamp in a ceremony of sorts. The faces on the figures were twisted, full of sorrow. Very strange. But she felt satisfied to have made the connection; it might make a nice little paper for the *Journal of Ethnobotany.*

Putting the disk aside, she reassembled the press and screwed it down tight. A loud beeping sounded: the centrifuge was finished, the material prepared.

She opened the centrifuge and slid a glass rod into the thin layer of material at the bottom of the test tube. She carefully applied it to the waiting gel, then eased the gel tray into the electrophoresis machine. Her finger moved to the power switch. *Now for another half-hour wait,* she thought.

She paused, her finger still on the switch. Her thoughts kept returning to the old woman and the mystery of Mbwun. Could she have been referring to the seed pods—the ones that resembled eggs? No, Maxwell had taken those back himself. They weren't in Whittlesey's crate. Was it one of the frogs or salamanders in jars, or one of the bird skins? That seemed an unlikely locus for the son of the devil himself. And it couldn't have been the garden plants, because they were hidden in the plant press.

So what was it? Was the crazy old woman ranting about nothing?

With a sigh, Margo switched on the machine and sat back. She replaced the plant press and the incised disk in her carryall, brushing away a few packing fibers clinging to the press, packing fibers from the crate. There were additional traces inside her handbag. Yet another reason to clean the damn thing out.

The packing fibers.

Curious, she picked one up with the tweezers, laid it on a slide, and placed it under the stereozoom. It was long and irregular, like the fibrous vein of a tough-stemmed plant. Perhaps it had been pounded flat by Kothoga women for household uses. Through the microscope, she could see the individual cells gleaming dully, their nuclei brighter than the surrounding ectoplasm.

She thought back to Whittlesey's journal. Hadn't Whittlesey mentioned specimen jars being broken, and his need to repack the crate? So, in the area of the deserted hut, they must have thrown out the old packing material, which had become soaked in formaldehyde, and repacked the crate with material found lying near the abandoned hut. Fibers prepared by the Kothoga, perhaps; probably for weaving into coarse cloth or for the production of rope.

Could the fibers have been what the woman was referring to? It seemed impossible. And yet, Margo couldn't help a little professional curiosity about it. Had the Kothoga actually cultivated the plant?

She plucked out a few fibers and dropped them in another mortar, added a few drops of enzyme, and ground them up. If she sequenced the DNA, she could use Kawakita's program to at least identify the plant's genus or family.

Soon, the centrifuged DNA from the fibers was ready for the electrophoresis machine. She followed her usual procedure, then switched on the current. Slowly, the dark bands began forming along the electrified gel.

A half hour later, the red light on the electrophoresis machine winked out. Margo removed the gel tray and began recording the position of the dots and bands of migrated nucleotides, typing her results into the computer.

She punched in the last position, instructed Kawakita's program to search for matches with known organisms, directed the output to the printer, and waited. Finally, the pages began scrolling out.

At the top of the first sheet, the computer had printed:

Species: Unknown. 10% randomized genetic matches with known species.

Genus: Unknown

Family: Unknown

Order: Unknown

Class: Unknown

Phylum: Unknown

Kingdom: Unknown

Cripes, Margo! What did you put in here? I don't even know if this is an animal or plant. And you won't believe how much CPU time it took to figure that out!

Margo had to smile. So *this* was how Kawakita's sophisticated experiment in artificial intelligence communicated with the outside world. And the results were ridiculous. Kingdom *unknown*? The damn program couldn't even tell if it were a plant or an animal. Margo suddenly felt she knew why Kawakita had been reluctant to show her the program in the first place, why it took a call from Frock to get things in motion. Once you strayed out of its known provinces, the program grew flaky.

She scanned the printout. The computer had identified very few genes from the specimen. There were the usual ones common to almost all life: a few respiration cycle proteins, cytochrome Z, various other universal genes. And there were also some genes linked to cellulose, chlorophylls, and sugars, which Margo knew were specific plant genes.

At the waiting prompt, she typed:

How come you don't even know if it is an animal or plant? I see lots of plant genes in here.

There was a pause.

Didn't you notice the animal genes in there, too? Run the data through GenLab.

Good point, thought Margo. She dialed up GenLab on the modem and soon the familiar blue logo popped up on the screen. She uploaded the DNA data from the fibers and ran it against their botanical sub-bank. Same results: almost nothing. A few matches with common sugars and chlorophylls.

On an impulse she ran the DNA data through the entire databank.

There was a long pause, and then a flood of information filled the screen. Margo quickly hit a series of keys, instructing the terminal to capture the data. There were numerous matches with a variety of genes she had never heard of.

Logging off GenLab, she fed the data she'd captured into Kawakita's program, instructing it to tell her what proteins the genes coded for.

A complicated list of the specific proteins created by each gene started to scroll down the screen.

Glycotetraglycine collagenoid
Suckno's thyrotropic hormone, 2,6 adenosine [gram positive]
1,2,3, oxytocin 4-monoxytocin supressin hormone
2,4 diglyceride diethylglobulin ring-alanine
Gammaglobulin A, x-y, left positive
Hypothalamic corticotropic hormone, left negative
1-1-1 sulphagen (2,3 murine) connective keratinoid, III-IV involution
Hexagonal ambyloid reovirus protein coat
Reverse transcriptase enzyme

The list went on and on. *A lot of these seem to be hormones,* she thought. *But what kind of hormones?*

She located a copy of *Encyclopedia of Biochemistry* that was busily gathering dust on a shelf, dragged it down and looked up *glycotetraglycine collagenoid*:

A protein common to most vertebrate life. It is the protein that bonds muscle tissue to cartilage.

She flipped through to *Suckno's thyrotropic hormone*.

A hypothalamic hormone present in mammals which acts on the pituitary gland.

A terrible thought began to form inside her head. She looked up the next, *1,2,3 oxytocin 4-monoxytocin supressin hormone*:

A hormone secreted by the human hypothalamus gland. Its function is not clearly understood. Recent studies have shown that it might regulate levels of testosterone in the bloodstream during periods of high stress. (Bouchard, 1992; Dennison, 1991).

Margo sat back with a start, the book dropping to the floor with a hollow thud. As she picked up the phone, she glanced at the clock. It was three-thirty.

= 38 =

When the Buick's driver had pulled away, Pendergast mounted the steps to a Museum side entrance, juggling two long cardboard tubes beneath one arm as he showed his identification to the waiting security guard.

At the temporary command post, he shut the door to his office and extracted several yellowed blueprints from the tubes, which he spread across his desk.

For the next hour, he remained nearly motionless, head resting on tented hands, studying. Occasionally he jotted a few words in a notebook, or referred to type-written sheets that lay on one corner of the desk.

Suddenly, he stood up. He took a final look at the curling blueprints, and slowly ran his finger from one point to another, pursing his lips. Then he gathered up most of the sheets, returned them carefully to the card-board tubes, and stowed them in his coat closet. The rest he folded carefully and placed in a two-handled cloth bag that lay open on his desk. Opening a drawer, he removed a double-action Colt .45 Anaconda, narrow and long and evil-looking. The weapon fit snugly into the holster under his left arm: not exactly standard FBI issue, but a comforting companion nonetheless. A handful of ammunition went into his pocket. From the drawer he also removed a large, bulky yellow object, which he placed in the cloth bag. Then, smoothing his black suit and straightening his tie, he slipped his notebook into the breast pocket of his jacket, picked up the cloth bag, and left his office.

New York City had a short memory for violence, and in the vast public spaces of the Museum streams of visitors could be seen once again. Groups of children crowded around exhibits, pressing noses against the glass, pointing and laughing. Parents hovered nearby, maps and cameras in hand. Tour guides walked along, reciting litanies; guards stood warily in doorways. Through it all, Pendergast glided unnoticed.

He walked slowly into the Hall of the Heavens. Potted palms lined two sides of the enormous room, and a small army of workers made last-minute preparations. The speaking platform on the podium was being sound-checked by two technicians, and imitation native fetishes were being placed on a hundred white linen tablecloths. A hum of activity floated up past the Corinthian columns into the vast circular dome.

Pendergast checked his watch: four o'clock precisely. All the agents would be at Coffey's briefing. He walked briskly across the Hall toward the sealed entrance of *Superstition*. A few brief words were exchanged, and a uniformed officer on duty unlocked the door.

Several minutes later, Pendergast emerged from the exhibition. He stood for a moment, thinking. Then he walked back across the Hall and out into the corridors beyond.

Pendergast moved into the quieter backwaters of the Museum, out of the public spaces. Now he was in the storage areas and laboratories where no tourist was permitted. The high ceilings and vast decorative galleries gave way to drab cinder-block corridors lined with cabinets. Steam pipes rumbled and hissed overhead. Pendergast stopped once at the top of a metal staircase, to look around for a moment, consult his notebook, and load his weapon. Then he moved downward into the narrow labyrinths of the Museum's dark heart.

= 39 =

The door to the lab banged open, then eased back slowly. Margo looked up to see Frock backing himself inside, his wheelchair creaking. She quickly stood up and helped wheel him over to the computer terminal. She noticed he was already dressed in his tuxedo. *Probably put it on before he came to work,* she thought. The usual Gucci handkerchief protruded from his breast pocket.

"I can't understand why they put these labs in such out-of-the-way places," he grumbled. "Now what's the great mystery, Margo? And why did I have to come down to hear it? Tonight's foolishness is getting underway shortly, and my presence will be required on the dais. It's a hollow honor, of course—it's only due to my best-selling status. Ian Cuthbert made that abundantly clear in my office this morning." His voice again sounded bitter, resigned.

Quickly, she explained how she had analyzed the fibers from the packing crate. She showed him the incised disk with its harvest scene. She described the discovery and contents of Whittlesey's journal and letter, and the talk with Jörgensen. And she mentioned how the hysterical old woman described in Whittlesey's journal could not have been referring to the figurine when she warned the scientist about Mbwun.

Frock listened, gently turning the stone disk over in his hands. "It's an interesting story," he said. "But why the urgency? Chances are your sample just got contaminated. And for all we know, that old woman was insane, or Whittlesey's recollections just got a bit scrambled."

"That's what I thought originally. But look at this," Margo said, handing Frock the printout.

He scanned it quickly. "Curious," he said. "But I don't think that this . . ."

His voice trailed off as his pudgy fingers ran down the columns of proteins.

"Margo," he said, looking up. "I was far too hasty. It *is* contamination of sorts, but not from a human being."

"What do you mean?" Margo asked.

"See this hexagonal ambyloid reovirus protein? This is the protein from the shell of a virus that infects animals and plants. Look at how much of it there is in here. And you have reverse transcriptase, an enzyme almost always found in association with viruses."

"I'm not sure I understand."

Frock turned to her impatiently. "What you have here is a plant heavily infected with a virus. Your DNA sequencer was mixing them up, coding for both. Many plants carry viruses like this. A bit of DNA or RNA in a protein coat. They infect the plant, take over some of its cells, then they insert their genetic material into the plant's genes. The plant genes start producing more viruses, instead of what they're supposed to produce. The oak-gall virus makes those brown balls you see on oak leaves, but otherwise it's harmless. Burls on maple and pine trees are also caused by viruses. They're just as common in plants as they are in animals."

"I know, Dr. Frock, but—"

"There *is* something in here I don't understand," he said, laying down the printout. "A virus normally codes for other viruses. Why would a virus code for all these human and animal proteins? Look at all these. Most of them are hormones. What good are human hormones in a plant?"

"That's what I wanted to tell you," Margo said. "I looked up some of the hormones. A lot of them seem to be from the human hypothalamus gland."

Frock's head jerked as if he had been slapped. "Hypothalamus?" His eyes were suddenly alive.

"That's right."

"And the creature that's loose in this Museum is *eating* the hypothalamus of its victims! So it must need these hormones—perhaps it's even *addicted* to these hormones," Frock blurted. "Think: there are only two sources: the plants—which, thanks to this unique virus, are probably saturated with the hormones—and the human hypothalamus. When the creature can't get the fibers, it eats the brain!"

"Jesus, how awful," Margo breathed.

"This is stunning. It explains *exactly* what's behind these terrible murders. With this, we can now put the pieces together. We have a creature loose in the Museum, killing people, opening the calvaria, removing the brain, and eating the thalamoid region where the hormones are most concentrated."

He continued to look at her, his hands trembling slightly. "Cuthbert told us that he'd hunted up the crates in order to retrieve the Mbwun figurine, only to find one of the crates broken open and the fibers scattered about. In fact, now that I think of it, one of the larger crates was nearly empty of fibers. So this creature must have been *eating* the fibers for some time. Maxwell obviously used the same fibers to pack his crates. The creature may not need to eat much—the hormonal concentration in the plants must be very high—but it obviously needs to eat regularly.''

Frock leaned back in the wheelchair. ''Ten days ago, the crates were moved into the Secure Area, and then three days later, the two boys are killed. Another day, and a guard is killed. What has happened? Simple: the beast cannot *get* to the fibers anymore, so it kills a human being and eats its hypothalamus, thus satisfying its craving. But the hypothalamus only secretes minute amounts of these hormones, making it a poor substitute for this fiber. Based on the concentrations described in this printout, I'd hazard a guess that it would require fifty human brains to equal the concentration found in half an ounce of these plants.''

''Dr. Frock,'' Margo said, ''I think the Kothoga were *growing* this plant. Whittlesey collected some specimens in his plant press, and the picture on this incised disk is of a plant being harvested. I'm sure these fibers are just the pounded stems from the lily pad in Whittlesey's press—the plant depicted on this disk. And now we know: these *fibers* are what the woman was referring to when she screamed 'Mbwun.' *Mbwun,* son of the devil: That's the name of this plant!''

She quickly brought the strange plant out of the press. It was dark brown and shrivelled, with a web of black veins. The leaf was thick and leathery, and the black stem as hard as a dried root. Gingerly, Margo brought her nose close to it. It smelled musky.

Frock looked at it with a mixture of fear and fascination. ''Margo, that's brilliant,'' he said. ''The Kothoga must have built a whole ceremonial facade around this plant, its harvest and preparation—no doubt to appease the creature. And no doubt that very beast is depicted in the figurine. But how did it get here? Why did it come?''

''I think I can guess,'' Margo said, her thoughts racing. ''Yesterday, the friend who helped me search the crates told me he read of a similar series of murders in

New Orleans several years ago. They'd occurred on a freighter coming in from Belém. My friend located the shipping records of the Museum crates, and he found that the crates were on board that ship."

"So the creature was following the crates," said Frock.

"And that's why the FBI man, Pendergast, came up from Louisiana," Margo replied.

Frock turned, his eyes burning. "Dear God. We've lured some terrible beast into a museum in the heart of New York City. It's the Callisto Effect with a vengeance: a savage predator, bent on *our* destruction this time. Let's pray there's only one."

"But just what kind of creature could it be?" asked Margo.

"I don't know," Frock answered. "Something that lived up on the *tepui,* eating these plants. A bizarre species, perhaps surviving since the time of the dinosaurs in tiny numbers. Or perhaps the product of a freak turn of evolution. The *tepui,* you see, is a highly fragile ecosystem, a biological island of unusual species surrounded by rain forest. In such places, animals and plants can develop strange parallels, strange dependencies on each other. A shared DNA pool—think of it! And then—"

Frock was silent.

"Then!" he said loudly, slapping his hand on the arm of the wheelchair. "Then they discover gold and platinum on that *tepui!* Isn't that what Jörgensen told you? Shortly after the expedition fell apart, they fired the *tepui,* built a road, brought in heavy mining equipment. They destroyed the entire ecosystem of that *tepui,* and the Kothoga tribe with it. They polluted the rivers and swamps with mercury and cyanide."

Margo nodded vigorously. "The fires burned for weeks, out of control. And the plant that sustained this creature became extinct."

"So the creature started on a journey, to follow these crates and the food it so desperately craved."

Frock fell into silence, his head settling on his chest.

"Dr. Frock," Margo finally said quietly. "How did the creature know the crates had gone to Belém?"

Frock looked at her and blinked. "I don't know," he finally said. "That's strange, isn't it?"

Suddenly Frock was gripping the sides of the wheelchair, rising up in his excitement. "Margo!" he said. "We *can* find out exactly what this creature is. We have the means right here. The Extrapolator! We've got the creature's DNA: we'll feed it into the program and get a description."

Margo blinked. "You mean the claw?"

"Exactly!" He wheeled around to the lab's workstation and his fingers began moving over the keys. "I had the printout Pendergast left us scanned into the computer," he said. "I'll load its data into Gregory's program right now. Help me set things up, will you?"

Margo took Frock's place at the keyboard. In a moment, another message flashed:

ESTIMATED TIME TO COMPLETION: 55.30 minutes.

Hey, Margo, this looks like a big job. Why don't you send out for pizza? The best place in town is Antonio's. I recommend the green chili and pepperoni. Shall I fax them your order now?

The time was quarter past five.

= 40 =

D'Agosta watched with amusement as two burly work-men unrolled a red carpet between two lines of palm trees in the Museum's Great Rotunda, out through the bronze doors and down the front steps.

That's gonna get rained on, he thought. It was dusk, and outside D'Agosta could see big thunderheads piling up to the north and west, rising like mountains above the wind-lashed trees along Riverside Drive. A distant roll of thunder rattled the artifacts in the Rotunda's pre-view case, and a few stray drops began to pelt the frosted glass of the bronze doors. It was going to be a monster storm—the satellite picture on the morning news left no doubt. That fancy red carpet was going to get soaked. And a lot of fancy people along with it.

The Museum had closed its doors to the public at five o'clock. The beautiful people wouldn't be arriving until seven. The press was there already: television vans with satellite uplinks, photographers talking loudly to each other, equipment everywhere.

D'Agosta spoke into his police radio, giving orders. He had close to two dozen men stationed strategically around the Hall of the Heavens and in other areas inside and outside the Museum. It was lucky, he thought, that he'd finally figured out his way around much of the place. Already, two of his men had become lost and had to be radioed back out.

D'Agosta wasn't happy. At the four o'clock briefing, he had requested a final sweep through the exhibition. Coffey had vetoed it, as well as heavy weapons for the plainclothes and uniformed men inside the party. Might scare the guests, Coffey had said. D'Agosta glanced over toward the four walk-through metal detectors, equipped with X-ray conveyor belts. *Thank God for those, at least,* he thought.

D'Agosta turned and, once again, looked around for Pendergast. He hadn't been at the briefing. In fact, D'Agosta hadn't seen him since the meeting with Ippolito that morning.

His radio crackled.

"Hey, Lieutenant? This is Henley. I'm here in front of the stuffed elephants, but I can't seem to find the Marine Hall. I thought you said—"

D'Agosta cut him short, watching a crew testing what had to be the biggest bank of lights since *Gone with the Wind.* "Henley? You see the big doorway with the tusks? Okay, just go through that and take two hard rights. Call me when you're in position. Your partner is Wilson."

"Wilson? You know I don't like partnering with a woman, sir—"

"Henley? There's something else."

"What's that?"

"Wilson's gonna be carrying the twelve-gauge."

"Wait a minute, Lieutenant, you're—"

D'Agosta snapped him off.

There was a loud grinding sound behind him, and a

thick steel door began to descend from the ceiling at the north end of the Great Rotunda. They were starting to seal the perimeter. Two FBI men stood in the dimness just beyond the doorway, short-barrel shotguns not quite concealed beneath their loose suit jackets. D'Agosta snorted.

There was a great hollow boom as the steel plate came to rest on the floor. The sound echoed and reechoed through the Hall. Before the echo faded, the boom was duplicated by the descending door at the south end. Only the east door would be left up—where the red carpet ended. *Christ,* thought D'Agosta, *I'd hate to see this place in a fire.*

He heard a loud voice barking at the far end of the Hall and turned to see Coffey, pointing his scurrying men in all directions.

Coffey spotted him. "Hey, D'Agosta!" he shouted, gesturing him over.

D'Agosta ignored him. Now Coffey came swaggering up, his face perspiring. Gizmos and weapons D'Agosta had heard about but had never seen were dangling off Coffey's thick service belt.

"You deaf, D'Agosta? I want you to send two of your men over here for a while and watch this door. Nobody goes in or out."

Jesus, thought D'Agosta. *There are five FBI guys just hanging around in the Great Rotunda, picking their noses.* "My men are tied up, Coffey. Use one of your Rambos over there. I mean, you're deploying most of your men just *outside* the perimeter. I have to station my forces inside to protect the guests, not to mention the traffic duty outside. The rest of the Museum's going to be almost empty, and the party will be underpatrolled. I don't like that."

Coffey hitched up his belt and glared at D'Agosta. "You know what? I don't give a shit what you don't

like. Just do your job. And keep a channel open for me.''
He strode off.

D'Agosta swore. He looked at his watch. Sixty minutes and counting.

= 41 =

The CRT on the computer went blank, and another message came up:

COMPLETED: DO YOU WANT TO PRINT DATA, VIEW DATA, OR BOTH (P/V/B)?

Margo hit the *B* key. As the data marched across the screen, Frock wheeled his chair to a stop and brought his face close to the screen, his ragged breath misting the terminal glass.

SPECIES: Unidentified
GENUS: Unidentified
FAMILY: 12% match to Pongidae; 16% match to Hominidae
ORDER: Possibly primata; 66% common genetic markers lacking; large standard deviation.

CLASS: 25% match to Mammalia; 5% match to Reptilia

PHYLUM: Chordata

KINGDOM: Animalia

Morphological characteristics: Highly robust

Brain capacity: 900–1250cc

Quadrupedal, extreme posterior-anterior dimorphism

Potentially high sexual dimorphism

Weight, male, full grown: 240–260 kg

Weight, female, full grown: 160 kg

Gestation period: Seven to nine months

Aggressiveness: extreme

Estrus cycle in female: enhanced

Locomotor speed: 60–70 kph

Epidermal covering: Anterior pelt with posterior bony plates

Nocturnal

Frock scanned the list, running his finger down.

"Reptilia!" he said. "There are those gecko genes appearing again! It appears that the creature combines reptile and primate genes. And it has posterior scales. They must also be from the gecko genes."

Margo read down the list of characteristics as they became more and more obscure.

Gross enlargement and fusion of metacarpal bones in rear limb

Probable atavistic fusion of forelimb No. 3 & 4 digits

Fusion of proximal and middle phalanx on forelimb

Extreme thickening of calvaria

Probable 90% (?) negative rotation of ischium

Extreme thickening and prismatic cross-sectioning in femur

Nasal cavity enlarged

Three (?) highly involute conchae

Enlarged olfactory nerves and olfactory region of cerebellum

Probable external mucoid nasal glands

Reduced optic chiasm, reduced optic nerve

Frock slowly backed himself away from the monitor.

"Margo," he said, "this describes a killing machine of the highest order. But look how many 'probables' and 'possibles' there are. This is a hypothetical description, at best."

"Even so," said Margo, "it sounds an awful lot like the Mbwun figurine in the exhibition."

"No doubt. Margo, I particularly want to direct your attention to the brain size."

"Nine to twelve hundred and fifty cubic centimeters," Margo said, retrieving the printout. "That's high, isn't it?"

"High? It's unbelievable. The upper limit is within human range. This beast, whatever it is, appears to have the strength of a grizzly bear, the speed of a greyhound, and the intelligence of a human being. I say *appears;* so much of this is conjecture on the part of the program. But look at this cluster of traits."

He stabbed his finger at the list.

"Nocturnal—active at night. External mucoid nasal glands—that means it has a 'wet' nose, possessed by animals with a keen scent. Highly involute conchae— also a trait of animals with enhanced olfactory organs. Reduced optic chiasm—that is the part of the brain that processes eyesight. What we have is a creature with a preternatural sense of smell and very poor eyesight that hunts nocturnally."

Frock thought for a moment, his brows contracted.

"Margo, this frightens me."

"If we're right, the whole *idea* of this creature frightens me," Margo replied. She shuddered at the thought that she'd been working with the fibers herself.

"No, I mean this cluster of olfactory traits. If the program's extrapolation is to be believed, the creature lives by smell, hunts by smell, *thinks* by smell. I've often heard it said that a dog sees an entire landscape of smell, as complex and beautiful as any landscape we see with our eyes. But the olfactory sense is more primitive than sight, and as a result, such animals also have a highly instinctual, primitive reaction to smell. *That* is what frightens me."

"I'm not sure I understand."

"In a few minutes, thousands of people will be arriving in the Museum. They will be congregating together in an enclosed space. The creature will be smelling the concentrated hormonal scent of all these people. That may very well irritate or even anger it."

A silence settled in the lab.

"Dr. Frock," Margo said, "you said that a couple of days elapsed from the locking up of the crates and the first killing. Then, another day to the second killing. It's been three days since then."

"Go on," said Frock.

"It just seems to me the creature may be desperate by now. Whatever effect the thalamoid hormones have on the beast must have worn off—after all, those brain hormones are a poor substitute for the plant. If you're right, the creature must be almost like a drug addict unable to get a fix. All the police activity has kept it lying low. But the question is—how long can it wait?"

"My God," said Frock. "It's seven o'clock. We must warn them. Margo, we *must* stop this opening. Otherwise, we might as well be ringing the dinner bell." He moved toward the door, motioning her to follow.

HE WHO WALKS
ON ALL FOURS

PART THREE

= 42 =

As seven o'clock neared, a tangle of cabs and limousines formed outside the Museum's west entrance. Elegantly dressed occupants emerged gingerly, the men in near-identical dinner jackets, the women in furs. Umbrellas jousted as the guests rushed up the red carpet toward the Museum's awning, trying to avoid the pelting rain that was already turning the sidewalks to streams and the gutters to rushing rivers.

Inside, the Great Rotunda, accustomed to silence at this advanced hour, was resounding with the echoes of a thousand expensive shoes crossing its marble expanse between the rows of palm trees leading to the Hall of the Heavens. The Hall itself held towering stands of bamboo in massive tubs festooned with violet lights. Clusters of drooping orchids had been artfully fixed to the bamboo, recalling tropical hanging gardens.

Somewhere deep inside, an invisible band briskly played "New York, New York." An army of waiters in white tie threaded their way expertly through the crowd, carrying large silver platters crowded with champagne glasses and ranks of hors d'oeuvres. Streams of incoming guests joined the ranks of Museum scientists and staff already grazing on the free food. Spotlights, muted blue, caught the glitter of long sequined evening dresses, strings of diamonds, polished gold cufflinks, and tiaras.

Almost overnight, the opening of the *Superstition* Exhibition had become the preferred event among fashionable New York. Coming-out balls and fund-raising dinners took a backseat to the chance to see, firsthand, what all the fuss was about. Three thousand invitations had gone out and five thousand acceptances had come back.

Smithback, wearing an ill-fitting tuxedo with the twin faux pas of wide, spiked lapels and a frilled shirt, peered into the Hall of the Heavens, scanning for familiar faces. At the far end of the hall, a giant platform had been erected. Along one side was the elaborately decorated entrance to the exhibition, currently locked and guarded. A massive dance floor in the center was quickly filling up with couples. Once inside the hall, Smithback immediately found himself surrounded by innumerable conversations, all conducted at a painfully high volume.

"... that new psychohistorian, Grant? Well, she finally fessed up yesterday, told me what she's been working on all this time. Get this: She's trying to prove that the wanderings of Henry the Fourth after the second crusade were really just a fugue state brought on by acute stress response. It was all I could do to keep from telling her that ..."

"... came up with the ridiculous idea that the Stabian Baths were really just a lot of horse stables! I mean, the man's never even been to Pompeii. He wouldn't know the Villa of the Mysteries from a Pizza Hut. But he's got the gall to call himself a papyrologist ..."

"... that new research assistant of mine? You know, the one with the enormous hooters? Well, yesterday she was standing by the autoclave, see, and she dropped this test tube full of . . .''

Smithback took a deep breath and made the plunge, cutting a path toward the hors d'oeuvres tables. *This is going to be great,* he thought.

Outside the main doors of the Great Rotunda, D'Agosta saw more rapid-fire flashing from the group of photographers, as yet another VIP came through the door, a wimpy handsome guy with an emaciated-looking woman clinging to each arm.

He stood where he could keep an eye on the metal detectors, the people coming in, and the throngs moving through the single door into the Hall of the Heavens. The floor of the Rotunda was slick with rainwater, and the coatcheck counter was stowing umbrellas briskly. In a far corner, the FBI had set up its forward security station: Coffey wanted a ringside seat from which to monitor the evening's events. D'Agosta had to laugh. They had tried to make it inconspicuous, but the network of electrical, telephone, fiber-optic, and ribbon cables snaking out like an octopus from the station made it as easy to ignore as a bad hangover.

There was a rumble of thunder. The tops of the trees along the Hudson River promenade, new leaves still budding, were sawing about wildly in the wind.

D'Agosta's radio hissed.

"Lieutenant, we got another argument over at the metal detector."

D'Agosta could hear a shrill voice in the background. "Surely you know *me.*"

"Pull her aside. We gotta keep this crowd moving. If they won't go through, just pull 'em out of the line. They're holding things up."

As D'Agosta holstered his radio, Coffey walked up with the Museum's Security Director in tow. "Report?" Coffey asked brusquely.

"Everyone's in place," D'Agosta said, removing the

cigar and examining the soggy end. "I've got four plainclothes circulating in the party. Four uniforms patrolling
the perimeter with your men. Five controlling traffic outside, and five supervising the metal detectors and the
entrance. I got uniformed men inside the hall. Two of
them will follow me into the exhibition when the ribbon's cut. I got one man in the computer room, one man
in the Security Control Room . . ."

Coffey squinted. "These uniformed men going into
the exhibition with the crowd. That wasn't part of the
plan."

"It's nothing formal. I just want us to be at or near
the front of the crowd as they go through. You wouldn't
let us do a sweep, remember?"

Coffey sighed. "You can do your thing, but I don't
want a goddamn escort service. Unobtrusive, not blocking the exhibits. Okay?"

D'Agosta nodded.

He turned toward Ippolito. "And you?"

"Well, sir, all my men are in place, too. Exactly
where you wanted them."

"Good. My base of operations will be here in the
Rotunda during the ceremony. Afterward, I'll deploy.
Meanwhile, Ippolito, I want you up front with D'Agosta.
Get up there near the Director and the Mayor. You know
the routine. D'Agosta, I want you to stay in the back-
ground. No glory-boy shit, don't fuck up your last day.
Got it?"

Waters stood in the cool of the computer room, bathed
in neon light, his shoulder aching from the heavy shotgun. This had to be the most boring assignment he'd
ever caught. He glanced at the geek—he had started
thinking of him as that—tapping away at the computer.
Tapping, tapping, for hours the guy had been tapping.
And drinking Diet Cokes. Waters shook his head. First
thing in the morning, maybe he should ask D'Agosta for
a rotation. He was going crazy in here.

The geek scratched the back of his neck and stretched. "Long day," he said to Waters.

"Yeah," said Waters.

"I'm almost done. You won't believe what this program can do."

"You're probably right," said Waters without enthusiasm. He checked his watch. Three more hours until his relief.

"Watch." The geek hit a button. Waters moved a little closer to the screen. He peered at it. Nothing, just a bunch of writing, gibberish that he supposed was the program.

Then, the image of a bug appeared on the screen. At first it was still. Then it stretched its green legs and started walking across the lettering on the screen. Then another animated bug appeared on the screen. The two bugs noticed each other, and moved closer. They started screwing.

Waters looked at the geek. "What *is* this?" he asked.

"Just watch," the geek said.

Soon, four bugs were born, and they started screwing. Pretty soon the screen was full of bugs. Then, the bugs began to eat the letters on the screen. In a couple of minutes, all the words on the screen were gone, and there was nothing left but bugs walking around. Then, the bugs started eating each other. Soon, nothing was left but blackness.

"Pretty cool, huh?" the geek said.

"Yeah," said Waters. He paused. "What does the program do?"

"It's just . . ." the geek looked a little confused. "It's just a cool program, that's all. It's doesn't *do* anything."

"How long did it take you to write that?" asked Waters.

"Two weeks," said the geek proudly, sucking air through his teeth. "On my own time, of course."

The geek turned back to his terminal, and the tapping resumed. Waters relaxed, leaning against the wall nearest the Computer Room door. He could hear the faint sounds of the dance band over his head, the thump of the drums, the low vibration of the basses, the whine of the saxophones. He thought he could even hear the sounds of thousands of footsteps, shuffling and sliding. And here he was, stuck in this psycho ward with nothing but a key-tapping geek for company. The biggest excitement he had was when the geek got up for another Diet Coke.

At that moment, he heard a noise from inside the electrical systems room.

"You hear that?" he asked.

"No," said the geek.

There was another long silence. Then, a definite thump.

"What the hell was that?" said Waters.

"I dunno," said the geek. He stopped typing and looked around. "Maybe you ought to go take a look."

Waters ran his hand over the smooth buttstock of his shotgun and eyed the door leading to the electrical room. *Probably nothing. Last time, with D'Agosta, it had been nothing.* He should just go in there and check things out. Of course, he could always call for backup from Security Command. It was just down the hall. His buddy Garcia was supposed to be in there . . . right?

Perspiration broke across his brow. Instinctively, Waters raised an arm to wipe it off. But he made no move toward the electrical room door.

= 43 =

As Margo rounded the corner into the Great Rotunda, she saw a scene of pandemonium: people shaking off drenched umbrellas, chattering in small and large groups, the racket of their conversations adding to the din from the reception beyond. She pushed Frock up to a velvet rope strung beside the metal detectors, a uniformed policeman standing watchfully next to it. Beyond, the Hall of the Heavens was flooded with yellow light. An enormous chandelier hung from the ceiling, sending flashing rainbows everywhere.

They displayed their Museum IDs to the policeman, who obediently opened the rope and let them through, checking Margo's carryall as he did so. As Margo passed by, the cop gave her a funny glance. Then she looked down, and understood: She was still dressed in jeans and a sweater.

"Hurry," said Frock. "Up front, to the lectern."

The lectern and podium were on the far end of the hall, near the entrance to the exhibition. The hand-carved doors were chained, and the word SUPERSTITION was formed by an arc of crude bone-like letters across the top. On either side were wooden stelae, resembling huge totem poles or the pillars of a pagan temple. Margo could see Wright, Cuthbert, and the Mayor gathered on the platform, talking and joking, while a sound man fiddled with the nearby mikes. Behind them stood Ippolito amid a gaggle of administrators and aides, talking into his radio and gesturing furiously at someone out of sight. The noise was deafening.

"Excuse us!" bellowed Frock. Reluctantly, people moved aside.

"Look at all these people," he yelled back at Margo. "The pheromonal level in this room must be astronomical. It will be irresistible to the beast! We've got to stop this right now." He pointed to one side. "Look—there's Gregory!" He gestured to Kawakita, standing by the edge of the dance floor, drink in hand.

The Assistant Curator worked his way toward them. "There you are, Dr. Frock. They've been looking for you. The ceremony's about to start."

Frock reached out and gripped Kawakita's forearm. "Gregory!" he shouted. "You've got to help us! This event has got to be cancelled, and the Museum cleared at once!"

"What?" said Kawakita. "Is this some kind of joke?" He looked quizzically at Margo, then back at Frock.

"Greg," said Margo over the commotion, "we've discovered what's been killing people. It's not a human being. It's a creature, a beast. It's nothing we've ever come across before. Your Extrapolation program helped us to identify it. It feeds on the packing fibers in the Whittlesey crates. When it can't get those, it needs the human hypothalamus hormones as a substitute. We believe it must have a regular—"

"Whoa! Hold on. Margo, what are you talking about?"

"Dammit, Gregory!" Frock thundered. "We don't have any more time to explain. We've got to get this place cleared *now*."

Kawakita backed up a step. "Dr. Frock, with all due respect . . ."

Frock clutched his arm harder and spoke slowly and deliberately. "Gregory, listen to me. There is a terrible creature loose in this Museum. It needs to kill, and it *will* kill. Tonight. We must get everyone out."

Kawakita backed up another step, looking toward the podium. "I'm sorry," he said over the noise. "I don't know what this is all about, but if you're using my extrapolation program for some kind of joke . . ." He prized his arm free of Frock's gasp. "I really think you should go up to the platform, Dr. Frock. They're waiting for you."

"Greg—" Margo tried to say, but Kawakita had moved away, looking at them speculatively.

"To the podium!" said Frock. "Wright can do it. He can order this place evacuated."

Suddenly they heard a drumroll and a fanfare.

"Winston!" shouted Frock, rolling into the open space in front of the platform. "Winston, listen! We've got to evacuate!"

Frock's final words hung in the air as the fanfare faded away.

"There is a deadly beast loose in the Museum!" Frock shouted into the silence.

A sudden murmur arose in the crowd. Those closest to Frock backed away, looking at each other and muttering in low tones.

Wright glared at Frock while Cuthbert quickly separated himself from the group. "Frock," he hissed. "What in bloody hell are you doing?" He bounded off the platform and came over.

"What is the matter with you, Frock? Have you gone mad?" he said in a vicious whisper.

Frock reached out. "Ian, there is a terrible beast loose

in the Museum. I know we've had our differences, but trust me, *please*. Tell Wright we've got to get these people out. Now."

Cuthbert looked at Frock intently. "I don't know what you're thinking," the Scotsman said, "or what your game is. Perhaps it's some desperate eleventh-hour attempt to derail the exhibition, to turn me into a laughingstock. But I will tell you this, Frock: If you make one more outburst, I will have Mr. Ippolito forcibly remove you from these premises and I will see to it that you never set foot in here again."

"Ian, I beg of you—"

Cuthbert turned and walked back to the podium.

Margo laid a hand on Frock's shoulder. "Don't bother," she said quietly. "They're not going to believe us. I wish George Moriarty were here to help. This is his show, he must be around somewhere. But I haven't seen him."

"What can we do?" Frock asked, trembling with frustration. The conversations around them resumed as the guests near the podium assumed some kind of joke had taken place.

"I guess we should find Pendergast," Margo said. "He's the only one with enough clout to do something about this."

"He won't believe us, either," Frock said, dispiritedly.

"Maybe not right away," Margo said, wheeling him around. "But he'll hear us out. We've got to hurry."

Behind them, Cuthbert signalled for another drumroll and fanfare. Then he walked over to the podium and held up his hands.

"*Ladies and gentlemen!*" he cried out. "*I have the honor to introduce to you the Director of the New York Museum of Natural History, Winston Wright!*"

Margo looked around as Wright took the podium, smiling and waving to the crowd.

"*Welcome!*" he cried out. "*Welcome my friends, fel-*

low New Yorkers, citizens of the world! Welcome to the unveiling of the greatest museum show ever mounted!'' Wright's amplified words echoed through the Hall. A tremendous burst of applause rose to the domed ceiling.

"We'll call security," said Margo. "They'll know where Pendergast is. There's a bank of phones out in the Rotunda."

She began to push Frock toward the entrance. Behind her, she could hear Wright's voice booming through the PA system: *"This is a show about our deepest beliefs, our deepest fears, the brightest and the darkest sides of human nature . . ."*

= 44 =

D'Agosta stood behind the podium, watching Wright's back as he addressed the listening crowd. Then he grabbed his radio. "Bailey?" he said in a low tone. "When they cut that ribbon, I want you and McNitt to get in ahead of the crowd. Just behind Wright and the Mayor, but ahead of everyone else. You got that? Blend in as much as possible, but don't let them push you out of the way."

"Roger, Loo."

"When the human mind evolved to understand the workings of the universe, the first question it asked was: What is life? Next, it asked: What is death? We've learned a lot about life. But, despite all our technology, we've learned very little about death and what lies beyond . . ."

The crowd was rapt, listening.

"We have sealed the exhibition so that you, our honored guests, will be the first inside. You will see many rare and exquisite artifacts, most on display for the first

*time ever. You will see images of beauty and ugliness,
great good and ultimate evil, symbols of man's struggle
to cope with and comprehend the ultimate mystery . . ."*

D'Agosta wondered what that business with the old
curator in the wheelchair had been. Frock, the name was.
He'd shouted something, but then Cuthbert, the honcho
of the event, had sent him off. Museum politics, worse
even than down at One Police Plaza.

*". . . most fervent hope that this exhibition will launch
a new era at our Museum: an era in which technological
innovation and a renaissance in the scientific method
will combine to reinvigorate the interest of the museum-
going public in today's . . ."*

D'Agosta scanned the room, mentally spot-checking
his men. Everyone seemed to be in place. He nodded to
the guard at the exhibition entrance, instructing him to
remove the chain from the heavy wooden doors.

As the speech ended, a roar of applause filled the vast
space once again. Then Cuthbert returned to the podium.

"I want to thank a number of people . . ."

D'Agosta glanced at his watch, wondering where Pendergast was. If he was in the room, D'Agosta would
have known it. Pendergast was a guy that stuck out in a
crowd.

Cuthbert was holding up an enormous pair of scissors,
which he handed to the Mayor. The Mayor grasped one
handle and offered the other to Wright, and the two of
them walked down the platform steps to a huge ribbon
in front of the exhibition entrance. "What are we waiting
for?" said the Mayor facetiously, drawing a laugh. They
snipped the ribbon in half to an explosion of flashbulbs,
and two of the Museum guards slowly pulled open the
doors. The band swung into "The Joint Is Jumpin'."

"Now," said D'Agosta, speaking fast into his radio.
"Get into position."

As the applause and cheers echoed thunderously,
D'Agosta walked briskly forward along the wall, then
ducked past the doors into the empty exhibition. He did

a quick scan inside, then spoke into his radio. "Clear."
Ippolito came up next, scowling at D'Agosta. Arm in
arm, the Mayor and the Director stood in the doorway,
posing for the cameras. Then, beaming, they walked forward into the exhibition.

As D'Agosta moved deeper into the exhibition ahead
of the group, the cheering and applause grew fainter.
Inside, it was cool and smelled of new carpeting and
dust, with a faint unpleasant odor of decay.

Wright and Cuthbert were giving the Mayor a tour.
Behind them, D'Agosta could see his two men, and behind them a vast sea of people, crowding in, craning
their necks, gesturing, talking. From D'Agosta's perspective within the exhibition, it looked like a tidal
wave. *One exit. Shit.*

He spoke into his radio. "Walden, I want you to tell
those Museum guards to slow down the flow. Too many
goddamn people are crowding in here."

"Ten-four, Lieutenant."

"This," said Wright, still holding the Mayor's arm,
"is a very rare sacrificial gurney from Mesoamerica.
That's the Sun God depicted on the front, guarded by
jaguars. The priests would sacrifice the victim on this
table, cut out the beating heart, and hold it up to the sun.
The blood flowed down these channels and collected
here at the bottom."

"Impressive," said the Mayor. "I could use one of
those up in Albany."

Wright and Cuthbert laughed, the sound reverberating
off the still artifacts and display cases.

Coffey stood in the forward security station, legs apart,
hands on hips, his face expressionless. Most of the
guests had arrived, and those who hadn't were probably
not going to venture out. It was raining in earnest now,
sheets of water cascading onto the pavement. Across the
expanse of the Rotunda, through the east door, Coffey
could clearly see the festivities in the Hall of the Heav-

ens. It was a beautiful room, with coruscating stars covering the velvety black dome that floated sixty feet overhead. Swirling galaxies and nebulae glowed softly along the walls. Wright was speaking at the podium, and the cutting ceremony would be starting soon.

"How's it look?" Coffey asked one of his agents.

"Nothing exciting," the agent said, scanning the security board. "No breaches, no alarms. Perimeter's quiet as a tomb."

"The way I like it," Coffey replied.

He glanced back into the Hall of the Heavens in time to see two guards pulling open the huge doors to the *Superstition Exhibition*. He'd missed the ribbon cutting. The crowd was moving forward now, all five thousand at once, it seemed.

"What the hell do you think Pendergast is up to?" Coffey said to another of his agents. He was glad Pendergast was out of his hair for the time being, but he was nervous at the thought of the Southerner wandering around, beholden to no one.

"Haven't seen him," came the response. "Want me to check with Security Command?"

"Naw," Coffey said. "It's nice without him. Nice and peaceful."

D'Agosta's radio hissed. "Walden here. Listen, we need some help. The guards are having a hard time controlling the flow. There's just too many people."

"Where's Spenser? He should be floating around there somewhere. Have him bar the entrance, let people out but not in, while you and the Museum guards set up an orderly line. This crowd has to be controlled."

"Yes, sir."

The exhibition was filling up quickly now. Twenty minutes had gone by and Wright and the Mayor were deep inside the exhibition, near the locked rear exit. They'd moved quickly at first, keeping to the central halls and avoiding the secondary passages. But now,

Wright had stopped at a particular exhibit to explain something to the Mayor, and people were streaming past them into the exhibition's farthest recesses.

"Keep near the front," D'Agosta said to Bailey and McNitt, the two men on advance duty.

He skipped ahead and did a quick visual through two side alcoves. *Spooky exhibition,* he thought. A very sophisticated haunted house, with all the trimmings. The dim lighting, for instance. Not so dim, though, that you couldn't make out nasty little details. Like the Congo power figure, with its bulging eye sockets and torso riddled with sharp nails. Or the nearby mummy, vertical in a freestanding case, that was streaked with dripped blood. *Now that,* thought D'Agosta, *is a little overdone.*

The crowd continued to spread out, and he ducked into the next set of alcoves. All clear.

"Walden, how'd you make out?" D'Agosta radioed.

"Lieutenant, I can't find Spenser. He doesn't seem to be around, and I can't leave the entrance to find him with the crowd the way it is."

"Shit. Okay, I'm calling Drogan and Frazier over to help you."

D'Agosta radioed one of the two plainclothes units patrolling the party. "Drogan, you copy?"

A pause. "Yes, Lieutenant."

"I want you and Frazier to back up Walden at the exhibition entrance, on the double."

"Ten-four."

He looked around. More mummies, but none with blood all over them.

D'Agosta stopped, frozen. *Mummies don't bleed.*

Slowly, he turned around and started pushing past the eager phalanx of gawkers. It was just some curator's sick little idea. Part of the exhibit.

But he had to be sure.

The case was surrounded by people, as were all the others. D'Agosta made his way through the crowd and glanced at the label: "Anasazi burial from Mummy Cave, Canyon del Muerto, Arizona."

The streaks of dried blood on the head and chest of the mummy looked like they had come from above. Trying to remain inconspicuous, he leaned as close to the case as possible and peered up.

Above the mummy's head, the top of the case was open, exposing a ceiling crawling with steam pipes and ductwork. A hand, a watch, and the cuff of a blue shirt protruded over the edge of the case. A small icicle of dried blood hung from the middle finger.

D'Agosta backed into a corner, looked around, and spoke urgently into his radio.

"D'Agosta calling Security Command."

"This is Garcia, Lieutenant."

"Garcia, I've got a dead body in here. We've got to get everybody out. If they see it and panic, we're fucked."

"Jesus," said Garcia.

"Get in touch with the guards and Walden. *Nobody* else is to be allowed into the exhibition. You got that? And I want the Hall of the Heavens cleared in case there's a stampede. Get everyone out, but don't cause any alarm. Now get Coffey for me."

"Roger."

D'Agosta looked around, trying to spot Ippolito. His radio squawked.

"Coffey here. What the hell is it, D'Agosta?"

"We got a dead body in here. It's lying on top of a case. I'm the only one who's spotted it, but that could change at any moment. We've got to get everyone out while there's still time."

As he opened his mouth to speak again, D'Agosta heard, over the noise of the crowd, "That blood looks so *real.*"

"There's a hand up there," D'Agosta heard someone else say.

Two woman were backing away from the case, looking up.

"It's a body!" one said loudly.

"It's not real," the other replied. "It's a gimmick for the opening, it has to be."

D'Agosta held up his hands, moving up to the case. "Please, everyone!"

There was a brief, terrible, listening silence. *"A body!"* someone else screamed.

There was a brief movement of the crowd, followed by a sudden stillness. Then, another scream: *"He's been murdered!"*

The crowd peeled back in two directions, and several people stumbled and fell. A large woman in a cocktail dress toppled backward onto D'Agosta, slamming him up against the case. The air was slowly forced out of his chest as the weight of more bodies pressed against him. Then he felt the case behind him start to give.

"Wait!" he gasped.

From the darkness above, something big slid off the top of the case and flopped onto the tight mass of people, knocking several more down. From his awkward angle, D'Agosta could only tell that it was bloody, and that it had been human. He didn't think it had a head.

Utter pandemonium broke out. The close space filled with screaming and shouting, and people started to run, clawing at each other, stumbling. D'Agosta felt the case topple. Suddenly, the mummy fell to the floor, with D'Agosta on top. As he grabbed the side of the case he felt glass slice into his palm. He tried to stand, but was knocked back into the case by the surging crowd.

He heard the hiss from his radio, found it was still in his right hand, and raised it to his face.

"This is Coffey. What the hell is going on, D'Agosta?"

"We've got a panic on our hands, Coffey. You're going to have to evacuate the Hall immediately, or—

"Shit!" he roared as the radio was knocked from his hand by the surging crowd.

= 45 =

Margo watched dispiritedly as Frock shouted into an internal phone set in the granite walls of the Great Rotunda. Wright's amplified speech poured out of the Hall of the Heavens, preventing Margo from hearing a word Frock said. Finally, Frock reached up, slamming the phone onto its cradle. He wheeled himself around to face her. "This is absurd. Apparently, Pendergast is in the basement somewhere. Or at least, he was. He radioed in about an hour ago. They refuse to contact him without authorization."

"In the basement? Where?" Margo asked.

"Section 29, they said. Why he's down there, or *was* down there, they refuse to say. My guess is they don't know. Section 29 covers a lot of ground." He turned to Margo. "Shall we?"

"Shall we what?"

"Go down to the basement, of course," Frock replied.

"I don't know," Margo said dubiously. "Perhaps we

should get the authorization they need to summon him up."

Frock moved impatiently in his wheelchair. "We don't even know who could give such authorization." He stared at her, becoming aware of her uncertainty. "I don't think you need worry about the creature confronting *us*, my dear," he said. "If I'm right, it will be drawn to the concentration of people here at the exhibition. It's our obligation to do whatever we can to prevent a catastrophe; we took that on when we made these discoveries."

Still Margo hesitated. It was one thing for Frock to speak in grandiose terms. He hadn't been inside that exhibition. He hadn't heard the stealthy padding of feet. He hadn't run blindly in the screaming dark . . .

She took a deep breath. "You're right, of course," she said. "Let's go."

Since Section 29 was inside the Cell Two security perimeter, Margo and Frock had to show their IDs twice on their way to the proper elevator. Apparently, the curfew being suspended for the evening, guards and police officers were more concerned about detaining suspicious or unauthorized characters than restricting the movement of Museum employees.

"Pendergast!" Frock shouted as Margo wheeled him out of the elevator into the dim basement corridor. "This is Doctor Frock. Can you hear me?"

His voice echoed and died.

Margo knew a little of the history behind Section 29. When the Museum's powerplant had been located nearby, the area housed steam pipes, supply tunnels, and the subterranean cubbyholes used by troglodyte workers. After the Museum switched to a more modern power plant in the 1920s, the old works had been removed, leaving a series of ghostly warrens now used for storage.

Margo wheeled Frock down the low-ceilinged hallways. Every so often, Frock would bang on a door or call Pendergast's name. Each time, his shouts were greeted by silence.

"We're getting nowhere," Frock said as Margo stopped for a breather. Frock's white hair was in disarray, and his tuxedo jacket was rumpled.

Margo looked nervously around. She knew approximately where they were: somewhere, at the far end of the confusion of passages, lay the vast, silent space of the old powerhouse: a lightless, subterranean pantheon now used to hold the Museum's collection of whale bones. Despite Frock's predictions of the creature's behavior, the shouting made her nervous.

"This could take hours," Frock said. "He may not be here anymore. Perhaps he never was." He sighed deeply. "Pendergast was our last hope."

"Maybe the noise and confusion will frighten the creature, keep it in hiding, away from the party," Margo said with a hope she didn't feel.

Frock rested his head in his hands. "Not likely. The beast must be driven by smell. It may be intelligent, it may be cunning, but like a human serial killer, when its blood lust is up it cannot control itself."

Frock sat up, his eyes filled with renewed vigor. "Pendergast!" he shouted again. *"Where are you?"*

Waters stood listening, his body tensed. He could feel his heart pounding, and he couldn't seem to gulp enough air into his lungs.

He'd been in plenty of dangerous situations before, been shot at, knifed, even had acid thrown at him once. Every time he'd been cool, almost detached, when he'd had to be. *Now, one little thump and I'm panicking.* He clawed at his collar. *The air's stuffy in this damn room.* He willed himself to breathe slowly and deeply. *I'll just call Garcia. We'll investigate together. And find nothing.*

Then he noticed that the rustling of feet overhead had changed its rhythm. Instead of the scraping and sliding he'd heard before, now he heard a constant drumming, like the sound of running feet. As he listened, he thought he heard a faint screaming. Dread flooded through him.

There was another thump in the electrical room.

Sweet Jesus, something big's happening.

He grabbed his radio. "Garcia? You copy? Requesting backup to investigate suspicious noises in the electrical systems room."

Waters swallowed. Garcia wasn't responding on the regular frequency. As Waters holstered his radio, he noticed that the geek had stood up and was heading for the electrical room.

"What are you doing?" Waters asked.

"I want to see what that noise is," the geek said, opening the door. "I think the air conditioner might have failed again." He put his hand around the doorframe, feeling for a light switch.

"Wait a minute, you," Waters said. "Don't—"

Waters's radio burst into static. "We got a stampede in here!" There was more static. ". . . All units, mobilize for emergency evacuation!" More static. "Can't hold this crowd, we need backup now, *now . . .* "

Jesus. Waters grabbed his radio, punched buttons. In an instant, all bands had been taken. He could hear something terrible happening right over his head. *Shit.*

Waters looked up. The geek was gone, and the door to the electrical room was open, but the light inside was still off. *Why was the light still off?* Without taking his eyes from the open door, he carefully unshouldered his shotgun, pumped a slug into the chamber, and started forward.

Carefully, he moved up to the edge of the door, looked around. Blackness.

"Hey, you," he said. "You in there?" As he moved inside the darkened room, he felt his mouth go dry.

There was a sudden loud thump to his left, and Waters instinctively dropped to his knee and pumped three rounds, each one a flash of light and a deafening blast.

There was a shower of sparks and a gout of flame

licked upward, briefly illuminating the room with lambent orange light. The geek was on his knees, looking up at Waters.

"Don't shoot!" the geek said, his voice breaking. "Please, don't shoot anymore!"

Waters raised himself on trembling legs, ears ringing. "I heard a sound," he cried. "Why didn't you answer me, you stupid shit?"

"It was the air conditioner," the geek said, tears streaming down his face. "It was the air-conditioner pump failing, like before."

Waters backed up, feeling behind him for the wall switch. Gunpowder hung in the air like a blue fog. On the far wall, a large mounted box of metal was smoking from three large, ragged holes in its front casing.

Waters hung his head, sank back against the wall.

With a sudden pop, an electrical arc sliced across the ruined box, followed by a crackling and another shower of sparks. The acrid air grew foul. The lights in the Computer Room flickered, dimmed, brightened. Waters heard one alarm go off, and then another.

"What's happening?" he shouted. The lights dimmed again.

"You destroyed the central switching box," the geek cried, rising to his feet and running past him into the Computer Room.

"Oh, shit," Waters breathed.

The lights went out.

= 46 =

Coffey shouted again into the radio. "D'Agosta, come in!" He waited. *"Shit!"*

He switched to the Security Command channel. "Garcia, what the hell is going on?"

"I don't know, sir," Garcia said nervously. "I think Lieutenant D'Agosta said there was a body in..." There was a pause. "Sir, I'm getting reports of panic in the exhibition. The guards are—"

Coffey cut him off and switched the bands, listening. "We got a stampede in here!" the radio squawked.

The agent switched back to Security Command. "Garcia, get the word out. All units, prepare for emergency evacuation procedures." He turned to look across the Great Rotunda, through the east door into the Hall of the Heavens.

A visible ripple passed through the crowd, and the background chatter began to die away. Over the sounds of the band, Coffey could hear clearly now the sound of muffled screams and the low thunder of running feet.

The movement toward the exhibition entrance faltered. Then the crowd surged backward, rebounding like a pressure wave. There were some angry yells and confused shouts, and Coffey thought he heard crying. Again the crowd was still.

Coffey unbuttoned his jacket, and turned toward the agents in the forward station. "Emergency crowd control procedures. Move out."

Suddenly the crowd surged backward, and a frenzy of shouting and screaming broke from the open door of the Hall. The band faltered, then fell silent. In an instant, everyone was running toward the exit to the Great Rotunda.

"Go, you son of a bitch!" said Coffey, shoving one of his men in the back, holding his radio in his right hand. "D'Agosta, you copy?"

As the crowd began to pour out of the Hall, the agents collided with the surging mass and were forced back. Thrusting himself from the roiling mass of bodies, Coffey backed away slightly, panting and cursing.

"It's like a tidal wave!" one of his men yelled. "We'll never make it in!"

Suddenly the lights dimmed. Coffey's radio crackled again.

"Garcia here. Listen, sir, all the security lights have gone red, the board's lit up like a Christmas tree. The perimeter alarms are all coming on."

Coffey moved forward again, fighting to stand his ground against the crowd streaming past him. He could no longer see the other agents. The lights flickered a second time, and then he felt a low rumble from the direction of the Hall. Coffey looked up and saw the thick edge of the metal security door descending from a slot in the ceiling.

"Garcia!" Coffey shouted into the radio. "The east door is coming down! Shut it off! Get it back up, for Chrissake!"

"Sir, their controls indicate it's still up. But something's happening down here. All the systems are—"

"I don't give a fuck what their controls say. It's coming down!" He was suddenly spun around by the fleeing crowd. The screaming was continuous now, a strange, banshee-like keening noise that raised the hair on a person's neck. Coffey had never seen anything like it, never: smoke, emergency lights blinking, people running over other people, glassy panic in their eyes. The metal detectors had been knocked over and the X-ray machines shattered as people in tuxedos and gowns went running out into the pouring rain, clawing past each other, stumbling and falling across the red carpet and onto the soaked pavement. Coffey saw little flashes on the steps outside the Museum, first a few, and then several.

He yelled into his radio. "Garcia, alert the cops outside. Have them restore order, get the press the hell out of there. And have them get that door up, *now!*"

"They're trying, sir, but all the systems are failing. We're losing power. The emergency doors drop independent of the power grid, and they can't activate the fail-safe controls. Alarms are going off all over the place—"

A man coming through nearly bowled Coffey over as he heard Garcia shout, "Sir! Total system failure!"

"Garcia, where the fuck is the backup system?" He forced a path sideways and found himself pinned against the wall. It was no use, he wasn't going to get inside through the stampede. The door was now halfway down. "Give me the technician! I need the manual override code!"

The lights flickered a third time and went out, plunging the Rotunda into darkness. Over the screams, the rumble of the descending door continued relentlessly.

Pendergast ran his hand over the rough stone wall of the cul-de-sac, rapping a few places lightly with his knuckles. The plaster was cracking and flaking off in pieces, and the light bulb in the ceiling was broken.

Opening the bag, he withdrew the yellow object—a miner's hat—adjusted it carefully on his head and flicked its switch. Tilting his head, he ran the powerful beam of light over the wall in front of him. Then he pulled out the creased blueprints, directing the light onto them. He walked backward, counting his steps. Then, taking a penknife from his pocket, he placed its point into the plaster and gently twisted the blade. A piece of plaster the size of a dinner plate fell away, revealing the faint tracings of an ancient doorway.

Pendergast jotted in his notebook, stepped out of the cul-de-sac, and paced along the hall, counting under his breath. He stopped opposite a stack of crumbling Sheetrock. Then, he pulled it sharply away from the wall. The material fell with a crash and a great billowing of white dust. Pendergast's light exposed an old panel set low in the wall.

He pressed the panel appraisingly. It held fast. When he kicked it savagely, it flew open with a screech. A narrow service tunnel slanted steeply downward, opening onto the ceiling of the subbasement beneath. One floor below him, a thread of water trickled along like an inky ribbon.

Pendergast pulled the panel back into place, made another marking on the blueprint, and continued on.

"Pendergast!" came the faint cry. "This is Doctor Frock. Can you hear me?"

Pendergast stopped, his brows knitted in surprise. He opened his mouth to answer. Suddenly, he froze. There was a peculiar smell in the air. Leaving his bag open on the floor, he ducked into a storage room, locked the door behind him, and reached up, snapping off his light.

The door had a small wired-glass window set into its middle, grimy and cracked. Fishing in a pocket, he drew out a tissue, spat on it, rubbed the window and peered out.

Something big and dark had just entered the lower edge of his field of view. Pendergast could hear a snuffling sound, like a winded horse breathing heavy and fast. The smell grew stronger. In the dim light, Pendergast could see a muscled withers, covered with coarse black hair.

Moving slowly, taking short, choppy breaths through his nose, Pendergast reached inside his suit jacket and drew out the .45. In the darkness, he passed his finger across the cylinder, checking the loaded chambers. Then, steadying the revolver with both hands and levelling it at the door, he began to back up. As he moved away from the window, the shape dropped from view. But he knew beyond any doubt that it was still out there.

There was a faint bump on the door, followed by a low scratching. Pendergast tightened his grip on the revolver as he saw, or thought he saw, the doorknob begin to turn. Locked or not, the rickety door wouldn't stop whatever was outside. There was another muffled thump, then silence.

Pendergast quickly peered out the window. He could see nothing. He held the revolver at twelve-o'clock with one hand and placed his other hand on the door. In the listening silence, he counted to five. Then, quickly, he unlocked the door and swung it open, moving into the center of the passageway and around a corner. At the far end of the hall a dark shape paused at another door. Even in the dim light he could make out the strong, sloping movements of a quadruped. Pendergast was the most rational of men, but he barked a brief laugh of disbelief as he saw the creature claw for the doorknob. The lights in the hallway dimmed, then brightened. Pendergast slowly dropped to one knee, held the gun in combat position, and took aim. The lights dimmed a second time. He saw the creature sit back on its haunches and then rise up, turning toward him. Pendergast centered on the side of the head, let his breath flow out. Then he slowly squeezed the trigger.

There was a roar and a flash as Pendergast relaxed to absorb the kickback. For a split second he saw a white streak move straight up the beast's cranium. Then the creature was gone, around a far corner, and the hallway was empty.

Pendergast knew exactly what had happened. He had seen that streak of white once before, hunting bear: the bullet had ricocheted off the skull, taking a strip of hair and skin while exposing the bone. The perfectly placed shot with a metal-jacketed, chromium-alloy-tipped .45 caliber bullet had bounced off the creature's skull like a spitball. Pendergast slumped forward and let his gun hand sink toward the floor as the lights flickered again and went out.

= 47 =

From where he'd stood next to the hors d'oeuvres tables, Smithback had a great view of Wright standing at the microphone, gesturing, voice booming out from a nearby loudspeaker. Smithback hadn't bothered to listen; he knew, with gloomy certainty, that Rickman would provide him with a hard copy of the speech later. Now, the speech was over, and the crowd had been eagerly piling into the new exhibition for the past half hour. But Smithback remained where he stood, oblivious. He gazed once again down at the table, debating whether to eat a fat gulf prawn or a tiny blini *au caviare*. He took the blini, actually five, and began grazing. The caviar, he noted, was gray and not salty—real sturgeon, not the fake whitefish they tried to pass off at publishing parties and the like.

He snagged a prawn anyway, made it two, followed by a spoonful of *ceviche* and three crackers covered with Scottish smoked cod roe with capers and lemon, a few paper-thin slices of cold red Kobe beef, no steak tartare, thank you very much, but definitely two pieces of that *uni sushi* ... His gaze followed the array of delicacies that went on for fifty feet worth of table. He had never seen anything like it and he wasn't about to let any of it get away.

The band suddenly faltered, and almost simultaneously somebody elbowed him, hard, in the ribs.

"Hey!" Smithback started to say, when, looking up, he almost instantly found himself engulfed in a shoving, grunting, screaming mass of people. He was thrown against the banquet table; he struggled to regain his footing, slipped and fell, then rolled under the table. He crouched, watching the thundering feet go by. There were screams and the horrifying noises of bodies crashing full tilt into one another. He heard a few snatches of shouted phrases: "... dead body!" "... murder!" Had the killer struck again, in the middle of thousands of people? It wasn't possible.

A woman's shoe, black felt with a painfully high spiked heel, bounced under the table and came to rest near his nose. He shoved it away with disgust, noticed he was still clutching a morsel of shrimp in his hand, and bolted it down. Whatever was happening, it was happening fast. It was shocking how quickly panic could sweep a crowd.

The table shuddered and slid, and Smithback saw an enormous platter land just beyond the fringe of the tablecloth. Crackers and Camembert went flying. He grabbed crackers and cheese off his frilled shirt and started eating. Twelve inches from his face, he could see scores of feet stamping and churning a loaf of pâté into mud. Another platter landed with a splat, spraying caviar across the floor in a gray mist.

The lights dimmed. Smithback quickly shoved a wedge of Camembert into his mouth, holding it between his teeth, realizing suddenly that he was eating while the biggest event he'd ever seen was being handed him on a silver platter. He checked his pockets for the micro-cassette recorder as the lights dimmed and brightened.

Smithback talked as fast as he could, mouth close to the microphone, hoping his voice would come through over the deafening roar of humanity. This was an incredible opportunity. The hell with Rickman. Everyone was going to want this story. He hoped that if any other journalists were at the party, they were running like hell to get out.

The lights flickered again.

A hundred thousand for the advance, he wasn't going to take a dime less. He was here, he'd covered the story from the beginning. Nobody could touch his access.

The lights flickered for a third time, then went out.

"Son of a bitch!" yelled Smithback. "Somebody turn on the lights!"

Margo pushed Frock around another corner, then waited while he called again for Pendergast. The sound echoed forlornly.

"This is growing pointless," said Frock in exasperation. "There are several larger storage rooms in this section. Maybe he's inside one and can't hear us. Let's try a few. It's all we have left." He grunted as he fished in a jacket pocket. "Don't leave home without it," he smiled, holding up a curator's master key.

Margo unlocked the first door and peered into the gloom. "Mr. Pendergast?" she called out. Metal shelves stacked with enormous bones rose out of the gloom. A big dinosaur skull, the size of a Volkswagen Beetle, sat near the door on a wooden skid, still partially encased in matrix, black teeth gleaming dully.

"Next!" said Frock.

The lights dimmed.

No answer in the next storage room, either.

"One more try," Frock said. "Over there, across the hall."

Margo stopped at the indicated door, marked PLEIS-

TOCENE—12B, noting as she did so a stairwell door at the far end of the hall. She was pushing open the storage room door as the lights flickered a second time.

"This is—" she began.

Suddenly, a sharp explosion resounded down the narrow hall. Margo looked up, heart pounding, trying to locate the source of the noise. It seemed to have come from around a corner they had not yet explored.

Then the lights went out.

"If we wait a moment," Frock said finally, "the emergency backup system will come on."

Only the faint creaking of the building pierced the silence. The seconds stretched into a minute, two minutes.

Then Margo noticed a strange smell, goatish, fetid, almost rank. With a sob of despair, she remembered where she had smelled it once before: in the darkened exhibition.

"Do you—?" she whispered.

"Yes," hissed Frock. "Get inside and lock the door."

Breathing fast, Margo groped at the doorframe. She called out quietly as the smell grew stronger. "Dr. Frock? Can you follow the sound of my voice?"

"There's no time for that," came his whisper. "Please, forget about me and get inside."

"No," said Margo. "Just come toward me slowly."

She heard his chair rattle. The smell was growing overpowering, the earthy, rotting odor of a swamp, mixed with the sweet smell of warm raw hamburger. Margo heard a wet snuffling.

"I'm right here," she whispered to Frock. "Oh, hurry, please."

The darkness seemed oppressive, a suffocating weight. She cringed against the doorframe, flattening herself to the wall, fighting down an urge to flee.

In the pitch black, wheels rattled and the chair bumped gently against her leg. She grabbed its handles and pulled Frock inside. Turning, she slammed the door closed, locked it, and then sank to the floor, her body rocked by noiseless sobs. Silence filled the room.

There was a scraping on the door, soft at first, then louder and more insistent. Margo shrank away, banging her shoulder against the frame of the wheelchair. In the dark, she felt Frock gently take her hand.

= 48 =

D'Agosta sat up amid the broken glass, grabbed for his radio, and watched the retreating backs of the last guests, their screams and shouts fading.

"Lieutenant?" One of his officers, Bailey, was getting up from underneath another broken case. The Hall was a shambles: artifacts broken and scattered across the floor; broken glass everywhere; shoes, purses, pieces of clothing. Everybody had left the gallery except D'Agosta, Bailey, and the dead man. D'Agosta looked briefly at the headless body, registering the gaping wounds in the chest, the clothing stiffened by dried blood, the man's insides generously exposed like so much stuffing. Dead for some time, apparently. He looked away, then looked back quickly. The man was wearing a policeman's uniform.

"Bailey!" he shouted. "Officer down! Who is this man?"

Bailey came over, his face pale in the dim light.

"Hard to say. But I think Fred Beauregard had a big old Academy ring like that."

"No *shit*," D'Agosta whistled under his breath. He bent closer, got the badge number.

Bailey nodded. "That's Beauregard, Loo."

"Christ!" D'Agosta said, straightening up. "Wasn't he on his forty-eight?"

"That's correct. Last tour was Wednesday afternoon."

"Then he's been in here since—" D'Agosta started. His face hardened into a scowl. "That fucking Coffey, refusing to sweep the exhibition. I'm gonna tear him a new asshole."

Bailey helped him up. "You're hurt."

"I'll bind it up later," D'Agosta said tersely. "Where's McNitt?"

"I don't know. Last I looked, he was caught in the crowd."

Ippolito stepped from around the far corner, talking into his radio. D'Agosta's respect for the Security Director went up a notch. *He may not be the brightest guy, but he's got balls when it comes to the pinch.*

The lights dimmed.

"There's panic in the Hall of the Heavens," said Ippolito, ear at his radio. "They say the security wall is coming down."

"Those idiots! That's the only exit!" He raised his own radio. "Walden! You copy? What's going on?"

"Sir, it's chaos here! McNitt just came out of the exhibition. He got pretty roughed up in there. We're at the exhibition entrance, trying to slow the crowd, but it's no use. There's a lot of people getting trampled, Lieutenant."

The lights dimmed a second time.

"Walden, is the emergency door coming down over the exit to the Rotunda?"

"Just a second." For a moment, the radio buzzed. "Shit, yes! It's halfway down and still dropping! People

are jammed into that door like cattle, it's gonna crush a
dozen or two—''

Suddenly, the exhibition went black. A dull crash of
something heavy toppling to the ground momentarily
overpowered the cries and screams.

D'Agosta pulled out his flashlight. "Ippolito, you can
raise the door with the manual override, right?''

"Right. Anyway, the backup power should come on
in a second—''

"We can't wait around for that, let's get the hell over
there. And, for Chrissake, be careful.''

Gingerly, they picked their way back toward the exhibition entrance, Ippolito leading the way through the
welter of glass, broken wood, and debris. Broken pieces
of once-priceless artifacts lay strewn about. The shouting
and screaming grew louder as they neared the Hall of
the Heavens.

Standing behind Ippolito, D'Agosta could see nothing
in the vast blackness of the Hall. Even the votive candles
had guttered. Ippolito was playing his flashlight around
the entrance. *Why isn't he moving?* D'Agosta wondered
irritably. Suddenly, Ippolito jerked backward, retching.
His flashlight dropped to the ground and rolled away in
the darkness.

"What the hell?'' D'Agosta shouted, running forward
with Bailey. Then he stopped short.

The huge Hall was a shambles. Shining his flashlight
into the gloom, D'Agosta was reminded of earthquake
footage he'd seen on the evening news. The platform
was broken into several pieces, the lectern splintered and
shattered. The bandstand was deserted, chairs toppled
over, crushed instruments lying in heaps. The floor
was a maelstrom of food, clothing, printed programs,
toppled bamboo trees, and trampled orchids, twisted and
smashed into a strange landscape by the thousands of
panicked feet.

D'Agosta brought the flashlight in toward the exhibition entrance itself. The huge wooden stelae surround-

ing the entrance had collapsed in giant pieces. D'Agosta could see limp arms and legs protruding from beneath the intricately carved columns.

Bailey rushed over. "There're at least eight people crushed here, Lieutenant. I don't think any of them are still alive."

"Any of them ours?" D'Agosta asked.

"I'm afraid so. Looks like McNitt and Walden, and one of the plainclothesmen. There are a couple of guard's uniforms here, too, and three civilians, I think."

"All dead? Every one of them?"

"Far as I can tell. I can't budge these columns."

"Shit." D'Agosta looked away, rubbing his forehead. A loud thud resonated from across the Hall.

"That's the security door closing," said Ippolito, wiping his mouth. He knelt at Bailey's side. "Oh, no. Martine . . . Christ, I can't believe it." He turned to D'Agosta. "Martine here was guarding the back stairwell. He must have come over to help control the crowd. He was one of my best men . . ."

D'Agosta threaded his way between the broken columns and moved out into the Hall, dodging the upturned tables and broken chairs. His hand was still bleeding freely. There were several other still forms scattered about, whether dead or alive D'Agosta couldn't tell. When he heard screaming from the far end of the Hall, he shined his light toward the noise. The metal emergency door was fully shut, and a crowd of people were pressed against it, pounding on the metal and shouting. Some of them turned around as D'Agosta's light illuminated them.

D'Agosta ran over to the group, ignoring his squawking radio. "Everybody calm down, and move away! This is Lieutenant D'Agosta of the New York City police."

The crowd quieted a little, and D'Agosta called Ippolito over. Scanning the group, D'Agosta recognized Wright, the Director; Ian Cuthbert, head of this whole farce; some woman named Rickman who seemed pretty important—basically, the first forty or so people who'd entered the exhibition. First in, last out.

"Listen up!" he shouted. "The Security Director's going to raise the emergency door. Everybody, please step back."

The crowd moved aside, and D'Agosta involuntarily groaned. There were several limbs pinned under the heavy metal door. The floor was slick with blood. One of the limbs was moving feebly, and he could hear faint screaming from the far side of the door.

"Dear Jesus," he whispered. "Ippolito, open the son of a bitch."

"Shine your light over here." Ippolito pointed to a small keypad next to the door, then crouched and punched in a series of numbers.

They waited.

Ippolito looked nonplussed. "I can't understand—" He punched in the numbers again, more slowly this time.

"There's no power," said D'Agosta.

"Shouldn't matter," said Ippolito, frantically punching a third time. "The system's got redundant backups."

The crowd started to murmur.

"We're trapped!" one man yelled.

D'Agosta whirled his light onto the crowd. "All of you, just calm down. That body in the exhibition has been dead at least two days. You understand? *Two days.* The murderer's long gone."

"How do you know?" shouted the same man.

"Shut up and listen," said D'Agosta. "We're going to get you out of here. If we can't open the door, they'll do it from the outside. It may take a few minutes. In the meantime, I want you all to get away from the door, stick together, find yourself some chairs that aren't broken, and sit down. Okay? There's nothing you can do here."

Wright stepped forward into the light. "Listen, officer,'' he said, ''We've got to get out of here. Ippolito, for the love of God, open the door!''

''Just a moment!'' said D'Agosta sharply. ''Dr. Wright, please return to the group.'' He looked around at the wide-eyed faces. ''Are there any physicians here?''

There was a silence.

''Nurses? First aid?''

''I know some first aid,'' someone volunteered.

''Great. Mister, ah—''

''Arthur Pound.''

''Pound. Get one or two volunteers to help you. There are several people who look like they got trampled. I need to know number and their condition. I've got a guy back at the exhibition entrance, Bailey, who can help you. He's got a flashlight. We also need a volunteer to help collect some candles.''

A young, lanky fellow in a wrinkled tuxedo came out of the gloom. He finished chewing, swallowed. ''I'll help with that,'' he said.

''Name?''

''Smithback.''

''Okay, Smithback. You got matches?''

''Sure do.''

The Mayor stepped forward. His face was smeared with blood and a large purple welt was emerging beneath one eye. ''Let me help,'' he said.

D'Agosta looked at him with amazement. ''Mayor Harper! Maybe you can take charge of everyone. Keep them calm.''

''Certainly, Lieutenant.''

D'Agosta's radio squawked again, and he grabbed it. ''D'Agosta, this is Coffey. D'Agosta, do you read? What the hell's going on in there? Give me a sit-ref!''

D'Agosta talked fast. ''Listen up, I'm not going to say this twice. We've got at least eight dead, probably more, and an undetermined number of wounded. I guess you know about the people caught under the door. Ippolito can't get the fucking door open. There's about thirty, maybe forty of us here. Including Wright and the Mayor.''

"The Mayor! Shit. Look, D'Agosta, the system's failed totally. The manual override doesn't work on this side, either. I'll get a crew with acetylene to cut you guys out. It may take awhile, this door's built like a bank vault. Is the Mayor okay?''

"He's fine. Where's Pendergast?''

"I don't have a clue.''

"Who else is trapped inside the perimeter?''

"Don't know yet,'' said Coffey. "We're taking reports now. There should be some men in the Computer Room and Security Command, Garcia and a few others. Might be a few on the other floors. We got several plainclothes officers and guards out here. They were pushed out with the crowd, some of them got messed up pretty bad. What the hell happened in the exhibition, D'Agosta?''

"They found the body of one of my men stuffed on top of an exhibit. Gutted, just like the rest.'' He paused, then spoke bitterly. "If you'd let me do the sweep I requested, none of this would have happened.''

The radio squawked again and went silent.

"Pound!'' D'Agosta called. "What's the extent of the injuries?''

"We've got one man alive, but just barely,'' Pound said, looking up from an inert form. "The rest are dead. Trampled. Maybe one or two heart attacks, it's hard to say.''

"Do what you can for the live one,'' D'Agosta said.

His radio buzzed. "Lieutenant D'Agosta?'' said a scratchy voice. "This is Garcia, in Security Command, sir. We got . . .'' The voice trailed out in a burst of static.

"Garcia? Garcia! What is it?'' D'Agosta shouted into the radio.

"Sorry, sir, the batteries on this mobile transmitter

I'm using are weak. We got Pendergast on the honk. I'm patching him over to you.''

"Vincent," came the familiar drawl.

"Pendergast! Where are you?''

"I'm in the basement, Section Twenty-nine. I understand the power is out throughout the Museum, and that we're trapped inside Cell Two. I'm afraid I've got a little more bad news of my own to add. Could you please move to a spot where we can speak privately?''

D'Agosta walked away from the crowd. "What is it?'' he asked in a low tone.

"Vincent, listen to me carefully. There is something down here. I don't know what it is, but it's big, and I don't think it's human.''

"Pendergast, don't play with me. Not now.''

"Vincent, I'm entirely serious. That isn't the bad news. The bad news is, it may be headed your way.''

"What do you mean? What kind of animal is it?''

"You'll know when it's near. The smell is unmistakable. What kind of weapons do you have?''

"Let's see. Three twelve gauges, a couple of service revolvers, two shot pistols loaded with capstun. A few odds and ends, maybe.''

"Forget the capstun. Now, listen, we have to talk fast. Get everyone out of there. This thing went by me just before the lights went out. I saw it through a window in one of the storage rooms down here, and it looked very big. It walks on all fours. I got off two shots at it, then it went into a stairwell at the end of this hall. I've got a set of old blueprints here with me, and I've checked them. You know where that stairwell comes out?''

"No,'' said D'Agosta.

"It only has access to alternate floors. It leads down into the subbasement, too, but we can't assume the thing would go that way. There's an egress on the fourth floor. And there's another one behind the Hall of the Heavens. It's back in the service area behind the platform.''

"Pendergast, I'm having a hard time with this. What the hell exactly do you want us to do?"

"I'd get your men—whoever has the shotguns—and line up at that door. If the creature comes through, let the thing have it. It may have already *come* through, I don't know. Vincent, it took a .45 metal-jacketed slug in the skull at close range, and the bullet grazed right off."

If anyone else had been speaking, D'Agosta would have suspected a joke. Or madness. "Right," he said. "How long ago was this?"

"I saw it a few minutes ago, just before the power went out. I shot at it once, then followed it down the hall after the lights went. I got off another shot, but my light wasn't steady and I missed it. I went down to reconnoiter just now. The hall dead-ends, and the thing has vanished. The only way out is the stairwell leading up to you. It may be hiding in the stairwell, or maybe, if you're lucky, it's gone to a different floor. All I know is that it hasn't come back this way."

D'Agosta swallowed.

"If you can get into the basement safely, do it. Meet up with me here. These blueprints seem to show the way out. We'll talk again once you're in a more secure place. Do you understand?"

"Yes," said D'Agosta.

"Vincent? There's something else."

"What now?"

"This creature can open and close doors."

D'Agosta holstered his radio, licked his lips, and looked back toward the group of people. Most were sitting on the floor, stunned, but a few were trying to help light the armload of candles the lanky guy had scrounged.

D'Agosta spoke to the group as softly as he could. "All of you, move over here and get down against the wall. Put those candles out."

''What is it?'' somebody cried. D'Agosta recognized the voice as Wright's.

''Quiet. Do as I say. You, what's your name, Smith-back, drop that and get over here.''

D'Agosta's radio buzzed into speech as he did a quick visual sweep of the Hall with his flashlight. The remote corners of the hall were so black they seemed to eat the beam of his light. In the center of the hall a few candles were lit next to a still form. Pound and somebody else were bending over it.

''Pound!'' he called out. ''Both of you. Put out those candles and get back over here!''

''But he's still alive—''

''Get back *now!*'' He turned to the crowd that was huddling behind him. ''None of you move or make a sound. Bailey and Ippolito, bring those shotguns and follow me.''

''Did you hear that? Why do they need their guns!'' cried Wright.

Recognizing Coffey's voice on the radio, D'Agosta switched if off with a brusque movement. Moving carefully, flashlights probing the darkness ahead of them, the group crept toward the center of the Hall. D'Agosta played his beam along the wall, found the service area, the dark outlines of the stairwell door. It was closed. He thought he smelled something strange in the air: a peculiar, rotten odor he couldn't place. But the room stunk to begin with. Half the damn guests must have lost control of their plumbing when the lights failed.

He led the way into the service area, then stopped. ''According to Pendergast, there's a creature, an animal, maybe in this stairwell,'' he whispered.

''According to Pendergast,'' said Ippolito sarcastically under his breath.

''Stow that shit, Ippolito. Now listen up. We can't stay here waiting in the dark. We're gonna go in nice and easy. Okay? Do it by the numbers. Safeties off, shells in the chambers. Bailey, you're gonna open the door, then cover us with the light, *fast.* Ippolito, you'll cover the upward staircase and I'll cover the down. If you see a person, demand identification and shoot if you don't get it. If you see anything else, shoot immediately. We move on my signal.''

D'Agosta switched off his flashlight, slipped it in a pocket, and tightened his grip on the shotgun. Then he nodded for Bailey to direct his own light onto the stairwell door. D'Agosta closed his eyes and murmured a brief prayer in the close darkness. Then he gave the signal.

Ippolito moved to the side of the door while Bailey yanked it open. D'Agosta and Ippolito rushed in, Bailey behind them, sweeping the light in a quick semicircle.

A horrible stench awaited them inside the stairwell. D'Agosta took a few steps down into the darkness, sensed a sudden movement *above* him, and heard an unearthly, throaty growl that turned his knees to putty, followed by a dull, slapping sound, like the smacking of a damp towel against the floor. Then wet things were hitting the wall around him and gobs of moisture splattered his face. He spun around and fired at something large and dark. The light was gyrating wildly. ''Shit!'' he heard Bailey wail.

''Bailey! Don't let it go into the Hall!'' He fired into the darkness, again and again, up the stairwell and down, until he was pumping an empty chamber. The acrid smell of gunpowder blended with the nauseating reek as screams resounded in the Hall of the Heavens.

D'Agosta stumbled up the stairs to the landing, almost tripped over something, and moved into the Hall. ''Bailey, where is it?'' he yelled as he jammed shells into his shotgun, temporarily blinded by the muzzle flare.

''I don't know!'' Bailey shouted. ''I can't see!''

''Did it go down or through?'' *Two shells in the shotgun. Three* . . .

''I don't know! I don't know!''

D'Agosta pulled out his flashlight and shone it on Bailey. The officer was soaked in thick clots of blood. Pieces of flesh were in his hair, hanging from his eyebrows. He was wiping his eyes. A hideous smell hung in the air.

"I'm fine," Bailey reassured D'Agosta. "I think. I just got all this shit on my face, I can't see."

D'Agosta swept the light around the room in a fast arc, the shotgun braced against his thigh. The group, huddled together against the wall, blinked in terror. He turned the light back toward the stairwell, and saw Ippolito, or what was left of him, lying partway on the landing, dark blood rapidly spreading from his torn gut.

The thing had been waiting for them just a few steps up from the landing. *But where the fuck was it now?* He shined the light in desperate circles around the Hall. It was gone—the huge space was still.

No. Something *was* moving in the center of the Hall. The light was dim at that distance, but D'Agosta could see a large, dark shape crouched over the injured man on the dance floor, lunging downward with odd, jerking motions. D'Agosta heard the man wail once—then there was a faint crunching noise and silence. D'Agosta propped the flashlight in his armpit, raised his gun, aimed, and squeezed the trigger.

There was a flash and a roar. Screams erupted from the huddled group. Two more shots and the chamber was again empty.

He reached for more shells, came up empty, dropped the shotgun and drew his service revolver. "Bailey!" he yelled. "Get over there fast, get everyone together and prepare to move." He swept the light across the floor of the Hall, but the shape was gone. He moved carefully toward the body. At ten feet, he saw the one thing he'd wanted not to see: the split skull and the brains spread across the floor. A bloody track led into the exhibition. Whatever it was had rushed inside to escape the shotgun blast. It wouldn't stay there long.

D'Agosta leaped up, raced around the columns, and

yanked one of the heavy wooden exhibition doors free. With a grunt, he slammed it to, then raced over to the far side. There was a noise inside the exhibition, a swift heavy tread. He slammed the second door shut and heard the latch fall. Then the doors shuddered as something heavy hit them.

"Bailey!" he yelled. "Get everyone down the stairwell!"

The pounding grew stronger, and D'Agosta backed up involuntarily. The wood of the door began to splinter.

As he aimed his gun toward the door, he heard screams and shouts behind him. They'd seen Ippolito. He heard Bailey's voice raised in argument with Wright. There was a sudden shudder and a great crack opened at the base of the door.

D'Agosta ran across the room. "Down the stairs, now! Don't look back!"

"No," screamed Wright, who was blocking the stairwell. "Look at Ippolito! I'm not going down there!"

"There's a way out!" shouted D'Agosta.

"No there isn't. But through the exhibition, and—"

"There's something *in* the exhibition!" D'Agosta yelled. "Now get going!"

Bailey moved Wright forcibly aside and started pushing people through the door, even as they cried and stumbled across the body of Ippolito. *At least the Mayor seems calm,* D'Agosta thought. *Probably saw worse than this at his last press conference.*

"I'm not going down there!" Wright cried. "Cuthbert, Lavinia, listen to me. That basement's a death trap. I know. We'll go upstairs, we can hide on the fourth floor, come back when the creature's gone."

The people were through the door and staggering down the stairwell. D'Agosta could hear more wood splintering. He paused a moment. There were thirty-odd people below him, only three hesitating on the landing. "This is your last chance to come with us," he said.

"We're going with Doctor Wright," said the Public

Relations Director. In the gleam of the flashlight, Rickman's drawn and fearful face looked like an apparition.

Without a word, D'Agosta turned and followed the group downward. As he ran, he could hear Wright's loud, desperate voice, calling for them to come upstairs.

= 49 =

Coffey stood just inside the tall archway of the Museum's west entrance, watching the rain lash against the elaborate glass-and-bronze doors. He was shouting into his radio but D'Agosta wasn't responding. And what was this shit Pendergast was slinging about a monster? The guy was bent to begin with, he figured, and the blackout sent him over the edge. As usual, everyone had screwed up, and once again it was up to Coffey to clean up the mess. Outside, two large emergency response vehicles were pulling up at the entrance and police in riot gear were pouring out, moving quickly to erect A-frames across Riverside Drive. He could hear the wailing of ambulances frantically trying to nose their way through the steel grid of radio cars, fire engines, and press vans. Crowds of people were scattered around, crying, talking, standing in the rain or lying beneath the Museum's vast awning. Members of the press were trying to slip past the cordon, snaking their microphones and cameras into faces before being pushed back by the police.

Coffey sprinted through the pelting rain to the silver bulk of the Mobile Command Unit. He yanked open the rear door and jumped inside.

Within the MCU, it was cool and dark. Several agents were monitoring terminals, their faces glowing green in the reflected light. Coffey grabbed a headset and sat down. "Regroup!" he shouted on the command channel. "All FBI personnel to the Mobile Command Unit!"

He switched channels. "Security Command. I want an update."

Garcia's voice came on, weary and tense. "We still have total system failure, sir. The backup power hasn't kicked in, they don't know why. All we have are our flashlights and the batteries in this mobile transmitter."

"So? Start it manually."

"It's all computer-driven, sir. Apparently there is no manual start."

"And the security doors?"

"Sir, when we took those power dips the entire security system malfunctioned. They think it's a hardware problem. All the security doors were released."

"Whaddya mean, *all?*"

"The security doors on all five cells closed. It isn't just Cell Two. The whole Museum's shut down tight."

"Garcia, who there knows the most about this security system?"

"That'd be Allen."

"Put him on."

There was a brief pause. "Tom Allen speaking."

"Allen, what about the manual overrides? Why aren't they working?"

"Same hardware problem. The security system was a third-party installation, a Japanese vendor. We're trying to get a representative on the phone now, but it's tough, the phone system is digital and it went out when the computer shut down. We're routing all calls through Garcia's transmitter. Even the T1 lines are out. It's been a chain reaction since the switching box was shot to hell.''

''Who? I didn't know—''

''Some cop—what's his name? Waters?—on duty in the Computer Room, thought he saw something, fired a couple of shotgun rounds into the main electrical switching box.''

''Look, Allen, I want to send a team in to evacuate those people trapped in the Hall of the Heavens. The Mayor's in there, for Chrissake. How can we get in? Should we cut through the east door into the Hall?''

''Those doors are designed to retard cutting. You could do it, but it would take forever.''

''What about the subbasement? I've heard it's like a frigging catacomb down there.''

''There might be ingress points from where you are, but on-line charts are down. And the area isn't fully mapped. It would take time.''

''The walls, then. How about going through the walls?''

''The lower load-bearing walls are extremely thick, three feet in most places, and all the older masonry walls have been heavily reinforced with rebar. Cell Two only has windows on the third and fourth floor, and they're reinforced with steel bars. Most of them are too small to climb through, anyway.''

''Shit. What about the roof?''

''All the cells are closed off, and it would be pretty tough—''

''Goddammit, Allen, I'm *asking* you the *best* way to get some men inside.''

There was a silence.

''The best way to get in would be through the roof,'' came the voice. ''The security doors on the upper floors are not as heavy. Cell Three extends above the Hall of the Heavens. That's the fifth floor. You can't enter there, though—the roof is shielded because of the radiography labs. But you could come in through the roof of Cell

Four. In some of the narrower halls you might be able
to blow a security door to Cell Three with one charge.
Once you were in Cell Three you could go right through
the ceiling of the Hall of the Heavens. There's an access
port for servicing the chandelier in the Hall ceiling. It's
sixty feet to the floor, though.''

"I'll get back to you. Coffey out."

He punched at the radio and shouted, "Ippolito!
Ippolito, you copy?" What the hell was happening in-
side that Hall? He switched to D'Agosta's frequency.
"D'Agosta! This is Coffey. Are you reading me?"

He ran frantically through the bands.

"Waters!"

"Waters here, sir."

"What happened, Waters?"

"There was a loud noise in the electrical room, sir,
and I fired as per regulations, and—"

"Regulations? You fucking turkey, there's no regulation for firing at a noise!"

"Sorry, sir. It was a loud noise, and I heard a
lot of screaming and running in the exhibition and I
thought—"

"For this, Waters, you're dead. I'm gonna have your
ass roasted and sliced up like luncheon meat on a platter.
Think about it."

"Yes, sir."

Outside there was a cough, sputter, and a roar as a
large portable generator started up. The rear door to the
Mobile Command Unit opened and several agents
ducked in, their suits dripping. "The rest are on their
way, sir," one of them said.

"Okay. Tell them we're having a crisis-control meeting here in the MCU in five minutes."

He stepped out into the rain. Emergency services
workers were moving bulky equipment and yellow acetylene tanks up the Museum steps.

Coffey ran back through the rain and up the steps into
the debris-laden Rotunda. Medics clustered at the metal

emergency door blocking the east entrance to the Hall of the Heavens. Coffey could hear the whine of a bone saw.

"Tell me what you've got," Coffey asked the leader of the medical team.

The doctor's eyes looked strained above his blood-flecked mask. "I don't know the full extent of the injuries yet, but we've got several criticals here. We're performing some field amputations. I think a few others might be saved if you can get this door open in the next half hour."

Coffey shook his head. "Doesn't look like that will happen. We're gonna have to cut through it."

An emergency worker spoke up. "We've got some heat-proof blankets we can lay across these people as we work."

Coffey stepped back and raised his radio. "D'Agosta! Ippolito! Come in!"

Silence. Then, he heard a hiss of static.

"D'Agosta here," came the tense voice. "Listen, Coffey—"

"Where have you been? I told you—"

"Shut up and listen, Coffey. You were making too much noise, I had to shut you off. We're on our way to the subbasement. There's a creature loose somewhere in Cell Two. I'm not kidding you, Coffey, it's a fucking *monster*. It killed Ippolito and ran into the Hall. We had to get out."

"A *what?* You're losing it, D'Agosta. Get a grip, you hear me? We're sending men in through the roof."

"Yeah? Well, they'd better have some heavy shit ready if they plan on meeting up with this thing."

"D'Agosta, let me handle it. What's this about Ippolito?"

"He's dead, slashed open, just like all the other stiffs."

"And a monster did this. Okay, sure. Any other police officers with you, D'Agosta?"

"Yeah, there's Bailey."

"I'm relieving you of duty. Put Bailey on."

"Fuck you. Here's Bailey."

"Sergeant," Coffey barked, "You're in charge now. What's the situation?"

"Mr. Coffey, he's right. We had to leave the Hall of the Heavens. We went down the back stairwell near the service area. There's over thirty of us, including the Mayor. No shit, there's really something in here."

"Give me a break, Bailey. Did you see it?"

"I'm not sure what I saw, sir, but D'Agosta saw it, and Jesus, sir, you should see what it did to Ippolito—"

"Listen to me, Bailey. Are you gonna calm down and take over?"

"No sir. As far as I'm concerned, he's in charge."

"I just put *you* in charge!"

Coffey snorted and looked up, enraged. "The son of a bitch just cut me off."

Outside in the rain, Greg Kawakita stood motionless amid a cacophony of yelling, sobbing, and cursing. He remained oblivious to the pelting rain that plastered his black hair to his forehead; the emergency vehicles that passed by, sirens shrieking; the panicky guests that jostled him as they ran past. Again and again he replayed in his mind what Margo and Frock had barked at him. He opened and closed his mouth, moved forward as if to reenter the Museum. Then, slowly, he turned, pulled his sodden tuxedo closer around his narrow shoulders, and walked thoughtfully into the darkness.

= 50 =

Margo jumped as a second gunshot echoed down the hall.

"What's happening?" she cried. In the darkness, she felt Frock's grip tighten.

Outside, they heard running steps. Then the yellow glow of a flashlight streaked by beneath the doorframe.

"That smell is growing fainter," she whispered. "Do you think it's gone?"

"Margo," Frock replied quietly, "you saved my life. You risked your own life to save mine."

There came a soft knocking at the door. "Who is it?" Frock asked in a steady tone.

"Pendergast," a voice said, and Margo rushed to open the door. The FBI agent stood outside, a large revolver in one hand and crumpled blueprints in the other. His crisp well-tailored black suit contrasted with his dirt-streaked face. He shut the door behind him.

"I'm pleased to see you both safe and sound," he said, shining his light first on Margo and then Frock.

"Not half as pleased as we are!" Frock cried. "We came down here searching for you. Were those shots yours?"

"Yes," Pendergast said. "And I assume it was you I heard calling my name?"

"Then you *did* hear me!" Frock said. "That's how you knew to look for us in here."

Pendergast shook his head. "No." He handed Margo a flashlight as he started unfolding his crumpled blueprints. Margo saw they were covered with handwritten notes.

"The New York Historical Society will be very unhappy when they see the liberties I've taken with their property," the agent observed dryly.

"Pendergast," Frock hissed, "Margo and I have discovered exactly what this killer is. You *must* listen. It isn't a human being or any animal we know. Please, let me explain."

Pendergast looked up. "I don't need any convincing, Doctor Frock."

Frock blinked. "You don't? You will? I mean, you will help us stop the opening upstairs, get the people out?"

"It's too late for that," Pendergast said. "I've been talking by police radio to Lieutenant D'Agosta and others. This power failure isn't just affecting the basement, it's affecting the entire Museum. The security system has failed, and all the emergency doors have come down."

"You mean—" Margo began.

"I mean the Museum has been compartmentalized into five isolated cells. We're in Cell Two. Along with the people in the Hall of the Heavens. And the creature."

"What happened?" Frock asked.

"There was a panic even before the power went out and the doors came down. A dead body was discovered inside the exhibition. A police officer. Most of the guests managed to get out, but thirty or forty are trapped inside the Hall of the Heavens." He smiled ruefully. "I was in the exhibition myself, just a few hours before. I wanted to get a look at this Mbwun figurine you mentioned. If I'd gone in by the rear exit instead of the front, perhaps I would have found the body myself, and prevented all this. However, I did get a chance to see the figurine, Doctor Frock. And it's an excellent representation. Take it from somebody who knows.''

Frock stared, his mouth open.

"You've seen it?" Frock managed to whisper.

"Yes. That's what I was shooting at. I was down around the corner from this storeroom when I heard you call my name. Then I noticed an awful smell. I ducked into a room and watched it go by. I came out after it and got off a shot, but it grazed off the thing's scalp. Then the lights went out. I followed it around the corner and saw it grasping at this door, snuffling." Pendergast flicked open the revolver's cylinder, and replaced the two spent cartridges. "*That's* how I knew you were in here."

"My God," Margo said.

Pendergast holstered his gun. "I got off a second shot at it, but I was having trouble aiming my weapon, and I missed. I came down this way to look for it, but the thing had vanished. It must have gone into the stairwell at the end of the corridor. There's no other way out from this cul-de-sac."

"Mr. Pendergast," Frock said urgently. "Tell me, please: *what did it look like?*"

"I saw it only briefly," Pendergast said slowly. "It was low, extremely powerful looking. It walked on all fours, but could rear upright. It was partially covered with hair." He pursed his lips, nodded. "It was dark. But I'd say whoever made that figurine knew what he was doing."

In the glow of Pendergast's light, Margo saw a strange mix of fear, exhilaration, and triumph cross Frock's face.

Then a series of muffled explosions echoed and reechoed above them. There was a brief silence, and then more reports, sharper and louder, boomed nearby.

Pendergast looked upward, listening intently. "D'Agosta!" he said. Drawing his gun and dropping the blueprints, he raced out into the corridor.

Margo ran to the door and shined the flashlight down the hallway. In its thin beam, she could see Pendergast rattling the stairwell door. He knelt to inspect the lock, then, standing, he gave the door a series of savage kicks.

"It's jammed shut," he said when he returned. "Those shotgun blasts we heard sounded like they came from inside the stairwell. Some of the shells must have bent the doorframe and damaged the lock. It won't budge." He holstered the gun and pulled out his radio. "Lieutenant D'Agosta! Vincent, can you hear me?" He waited a moment, then shook his head and replaced the radio in his jacket pocket.

"So we're stuck here?" Margo asked.

Pendergast shook his head. "I don't think so. I've spent the afternoon down in these vaults and tunnels, trying to determine how the beast was able to elude our searches. These blueprints were drafted well before the turn of the century, and they are complicated and contradictory, but they seem to show a route out of the Museum through the subbasement. With everything sealed off, there's no other feasible way out for us. And there are several ways to access the subbasement from this section of the Museum."

"That means we can meet up with the people still upstairs, then escape together!" Margo said.

Pendergast looked grim. "But that also means the beast can find its way back into the subbasement. Personally, I think that while these emergency doors may prevent our own rescue, they won't hamper the beast's movement much. I believe it's been around long enough to find its own secret ways, and that it can move throughout the Museum—or, at least, the lower levels—practically at will."

Margo nodded. "We think it's been living in the Museum for years. And we think we know how and why it came here."

Pendergast looked searchingly at Margo for a long moment. "I need you and Doctor Frock to tell me everything you know about this creature, as quickly as possible," he said.

As they turned to enter the storeroom, Margo heard a distant drumming, like slow thunder. She froze, listening intently. The thunder seemed to have a voice: crying or shouting, she wasn't sure which.

"What was that?" she whispered.

"That," Pendergast said quietly, "is the sound of people in the stairwell, running for their lives."

= 51 =

In the faint light filtering in through the barred laboratory window, Wright could barely make out the old filing cabinet. It was damned lucky, he thought, that the lab was inside the perimeter of Cell Two. Not for the first time, he was glad he'd kept this old laboratory when he'd been promoted to Director. It would provide them with a temporary safe haven, a little breathing room. Cell Two was now completely cut off from the rest of the Museum, and they were effectively prisoners. Everything, all the emergency bars, shutters, and security gates, had come down during the loss of power. At least that's what he'd heard that incompetent police officer, D'Agosta, say.

"Someone is going to pay dearly for this," Wright muttered to himself. Then they all fell quiet. Now that they had stopped running, the enormity of the disaster began to sink in.

Wright moved gingerly forward, pulling out one file-cabinet drawer after another, fishing behind the folders until at last he found what he was looking for.

"Ruger .357 magnum," he said, hefting it in his hands. "Great pistol. Excellent stopping power."

"I'm not sure that's going to stop whatever killed Ippolito," said Cuthbert. He was standing near the laboratory door, a still figure framed in black.

"Don't worry, Ian. One of these speedball bullets would perforate an elephant. I bought this after old Shorter was mugged by a vagrant. Anyway, the creature isn't coming up here. And if he does, this door is solid oak two inches thick."

"What about that one?" Cuthbert pointed toward the rear of the office.

"That goes into the Hall of Cretaceous Dinosaurs. It's just like this one—solid oak." He tucked the Ruger into his belt. "Those fools, going into the basement like so many lemmings. They should have listened to me."

He rummaged in the file drawer again and pulled out a flashlight. "Excellent. Haven't used this in years."

He snapped it on and a feeble beam shot out, wavering as his hand shook a little.

"Not much juice left in that torch, I'd say," Cuthbert murmured.

Wright turned it off. "We'll only use it in an emergency."

"Please!" Rickman spoke suddenly. "Please leave it on. Just for a minute." She was sitting on a stool in the center of the room, clenching and unclenching her hands. "Winston, what are we going to do? We must have a plan."

"First things first," said Wright. "I need a drink, that's Plan A. My nerves are shot." He made his way to the far side of the lab and shone the light in an old cabinet, finally pulling out a bottle. There was a clink of glass.

"Ian?" asked Wright.

"Nothing for me," Cuthbert replied.

"Lavinia?"

"No, no, I couldn't."

Wright came back and sat down at a worktable. He filled the tumbler and drank it off in three gulps. Then he refilled it. Suddenly, the room was full of the warm, peaty scent of single-malt scotch.

"Easy there, Winston," said Cuthbert.

"We can't stay here, in the dark," Rickman said nervously. "There must be an exit somewhere on this floor."

"I'm telling you, everything's sealed off," Wright snapped.

"What about the Dinosaur Hall?" said Rickman, pointing to the rear door.

"Lavinia," said Wright, "the Dinosaur Hall has only one public entrance, and that's been sealed by a security door. We're completely locked in. But you don't need to worry, because whatever killed Ippolito and the others won't be after us. It'll go after the easy kill, the group blundering around in the basement."

There was a swallowing sound, then the loud *snack* of glass hitting the table. "I say we stay here for another half-hour, wait it out. Then, we'll go back down into the exhibition. If they haven't restored power and unsealed the doors by then, I know of another way out. *Through* the exhibition."

"You seem to know all kinds of hiding places," Cuthbert said.

"This used to be my lab. Once in awhile I still like to come down here, get away from the administrative headaches, be near my dinosaurs again." He chuckled and drank.

"I see," said Cuthbert acidly.

"Part of the *Superstition* exhibition is mounted in what used to be the old Trilobite Alcove. I put in a lot of hours down there many years ago. Anyway, there was a passageway to the Broadway corridor behind one of the old trilobite displays. The door was boarded up years ago to make room for another display case. I'm sure that when they were building *Superstition,* they just nailed a piece of plywood over it and painted it. We could kick it in, shoot off the lock with this if necessary.''

"That sounds feasible," said Rickman eagerly.

"I don't recall hearing about any such door in the exhibition," Cuthbert said dubiously. "I'm sure Security would have known about it."

"It was years ago, I tell you," Wright snapped. "It was boarded over and forgotten."

There was a long silence while Wright poured another drink.

"Winston," Cuthbert said, "put that drink down."

The Director took a long swig, then hung his head. His shoulders slumped.

"Ian," he murmured finally. "How could this have happened? We're ruined, you know."

Cuthbert was silent.

"Let's not bury the patient before the diagnosis," said Rickman, in a desperately bright voice. "Good public relations can repair even the worst damage."

"Lavinia, we aren't talking about a few poisoned headache tablets here," Cuthbert said. "There's half a dozen dead people, maybe more, lying two floors below us. The bloody *Mayor* is trapped down there. In a couple of hours, we'll be on every late news show in the country."

"We're ruined," Wright repeated. A small, strangled sob escaped from his throat, and he laid his head down on the table.

"Bloody hell," muttered Cuthbert, reaching over for Wright's bottle and glass and putting them back in the cabinet.

"It's over, isn't it?" Wright moaned without raising his head.

"Yes, Winston, it's over," said Cuthbert. "Frankly, I'll be happy just to get out of here with my life."

"Please, Ian, let's leave here? *Please?*" Rickman pleaded. She stood up and walked over to the door

Wright had closed behind them and swung it open slowly.

"This wasn't locked!" she said sharply.

"Good Lord," Cuthbert said, jumping up. Wright, without lifting his head, fished in his pocket and held out a key.

"Fits both doors," he said in a muffled voice.

Rickman's shaking hand rattled the key loudly in the lock.

"What did we do wrong?" Wright asked plaintively.

"That's clear enough," said Cuthbert. "Five years ago, we had a chance to solve this thing."

"What do you mean?" asked Rickman, coming back toward them.

"You know very well what. I'm talking about Montague's disappearance. We should have taken care of the problem then, instead of pretending it never happened. All that blood in the basement near the Whittlesey crates, Montague gone missing. In hindsight, we now know exactly what happened to him. But we should have gotten to the bottom of it *then*. You remember, Winston? We were sitting in your office when Ippolito came in with the news. You ordered the floor cleaned and the incident forgotten. We washed our hands of it, and hoped whoever or *what*ever killed Montague would disappear."

"There was no proof anyone was killed!" Wright wailed, lifting his head. "And certainly no proof it was Montague! It could have been a stray dog, or something. How could we have known?"

"We didn't know. But we might have found out had you allowed Ippolito to report that monstrous great bloodstain to the police. And you, Lavinia—as I recall, you agreed that we should simply wash that blood away."

"Ian, there was no sense in creating a needless scandal. You know very well that blood could have been from anything," Rickman said. "And Ian, it was you who insisted those crates be moved. You who worried the exhibition would raise questions about the Whittlesey expedition, you who took the journal and then asked me to keep it for you until the exhibition was over. The journal didn't fit in with your theories, did it?''

Cuthbert snorted. ''How little you know. John Whittlesey was my friend. At least, he was once. We had a falling-out over an article he published, and we never patched things up. Anyway, it's rather too late for that now. But I didn't want to see that journal come to light, his theories held up for ridicule.''

He turned and stared at the Public Relations Director. ''What I did, Lavinia, was simply try to protect a colleague who'd gone a bit barmy. *I* didn't cover up a killing. And what about the sightings? Winston, you received several reports a year about people seeing or hearing strange things after hours. You never once did anything about it, did you?''

''How could I have known?'' came the spluttering response. ''Who'd have believed it? They were crank reports, ridiculous . . .''

''Can we change the subject, please?'' cried Rickman. ''I can't wait here, in the dark. Maybe the windows? Perhaps they'll spread a net for us?''

''No,'' said Wright, sighing deeply and rubbing his eyes. ''Those bars are case-hardened steel, several inches thick.'' He peered around the darkened room. ''Where's my drink?''

''You've had enough,'' said Cuthbert.

''You and your damned Anglican moralizing.'' He lurched to his feet and headed for the cabinet with a slightly unsteady gait.

In the stairwell, D'Agosta looked toward the dim figure of Bailey.

''Thanks,'' he said.

''You're in charge, Loo.''

Below them, the large group of guests was waiting,

huddled together on the steps, sniffling and sobbing. D'Agosta turned to face them.

"Okay," he said quietly. "We've got to move fast. The next landing down has a door leading into the basement. We're going to go through it and meet up with some others who know a way out of here. Everybody understand?"

"We understand," came a voice that D'Agosta recognized as the Mayor's.

"Good," D'Agosta nodded. "Okay, let's go. I'll get to the front and lead the way with my light. Bailey, you cover our rear. Let me know if you see anything."

Slowly, the group descended. On the landing, D'Agosta waited until Bailey gave him the all-clear sign. Then he grabbed the door handle.

It didn't budge.

D'Agosta gave it another yank, harder this time. No luck.

"What the—?" He brought his flashlight to bear on the handle. "Shit," he muttered. Then, in a louder tone, he said, "Everybody stay where you are for a moment, be as quiet as possible. I'm going up to talk to my officer at the rear." He retraced his steps.

"Listen, Bailey," he told him softly, "we can't get into the basement. Some of our shells ripped into the door and they've bent the jamb all to hell. There's no way we can get the thing open without a crowbar."

Even in the dark he could see Bailey's eyes widen. "So what are we gonna do?" the sergeant asked. "Go back upstairs?"

"Let me think a minute," D'Agosta said. "How much ammo do you have? I've got six rounds in my service piece."

"I don't know. Fifteen, sixteen rounds, maybe."

"Damn," D'Agosta said, "I don't think—"

He stopped, abruptly shutting off his flashlight and listening to the close darkness. A slight movement of air down the stairwell brought a ripe, goatish smell.

Bailey dropped to one knee, aiming the shotgun up the staircase. D'Agosta quickly turned to the group waiting below him. "Everybody," he hissed, "down to the next landing. Quick!"

There was a series of low murmurs. "We can't go down there!" somebody cried. "We'll be trapped underground!"

D'Agosta's response was drowned by the blast of Bailey's shotgun. "The Museum Beast!" somebody screamed, and the group turned, stumbling and falling down the stairs. "Bailey!" D'Agosta shouted, his ears ringing from the blast. "Bailey, follow me!"

Walking backward down the stairs, one hand holding his handgun, the other feeling its way against the wall, D'Agosta noticed the surface of the stairwell turn to damp stone as he moved below the level of the basement. Farther up the stairwell, he could see the dim form of Bailey following, gasping and cursing under his breath. After what seemed an eternity, D'Agosta's foot hit the subbasement landing. All around him, people held their breaths; then Bailey bumped into him gently.

"Bailey, what the fuck was it?" he whispered.

"I don't know," came the response. "There was that horrible smell, then I thought I saw something. Two red eyes in the dark. I fired."

D'Agosta shone his flashlight up the stairwell. The light showed only shadows and rough-hewn yellow rock, crudely carved. The smell lingered.

He shone the flashlight toward the group, and did a quick head count. Thirty-eight, including himself and Bailey. "Okay," he whispered to the group. "We're in the subbasement. I'm gonna go in first, then you follow at my signal."

He turned and shined his light over the door. *Christ,* he thought, *this thing belongs in the Tower of London.* The blackened metal door was reinforced with horizontal strips of iron. When he pushed it open, cool, damp, moldy air rushed into the stairwell. D'Agosta started forward. At the sound of gurgling water, he stepped back, then played the light downward.

"Listen, everybody," he called. "There's running water down here, about three inches deep. Come forward one at a time, quickly but carefully. There are two steps down on the far side of the door. Bailey, take up the rear. And, for God's sake, close the door behind you."

Pendergast counted the remaining bullets, pocketed them, then looked in Frock's direction. "Truly fascinating. And a clever bit of detection on your part. I'm sorry I doubted you, Professor."

Frock gestured magnanimously. "How were you to know?" he asked. "Besides, it was Margo here who discovered the most important link. If she hadn't tested those packing fibers, we never would have known."

Pendergast nodded at Margo, huddled on top of a large wooden crate. "Brilliant work," he said. "We could use you in the Baton Rouge crime lab."

"Assuming I let her go," Frock said. "And assuming we get out of here alive. Dubious assumptions, at best."

"And assuming I'm willing to leave the Museum," Margo said, surprising even herself.

Pendergast turned to Margo. "I know you understand this creature better than I do. Still, do you truly believe this plan you've described will work?"

Margo took a deep breath, nodded. "If the Extrapolator is correct, this beast hunts by smell rather than sight. And if its need for the plant is as strong as we think it is—" She paused, shrugged. "It's the only way."

Pendergast remained motionless a moment. "If it will save those people below us, we have to try." He pulled out his radio.

"D'Agosta?" he said, adjusting the channel. "D'Agosta, this is Pendergast. Do you read?"

The radio squealed static. Then: "D'Agosta here."

"D'Agosta, what's your status?"

"We met up with that creature of yours," came the response. "It got into the Hall, killed Ippolito and an injured guest. We moved into the stairwell, but the basement door was jammed. We had to go to the subbasement."

"Understood," Pendergast said. "How many of your weapons were you able to take?"

"We only had time to grab one twelve-gauge and a service revolver."

"What's your current position?"

"In the subbasement, maybe fifty yards from the stairwell door."

"Listen closely, Vincent. I've been speaking with Professor Frock. The creature we're dealing with is extremely intelligent. Maybe even as smart as you or I."

"Speak for yourself."

"If you see it again, don't aim for the head. The slugs will just bounce off the skull. Aim for the body."

There was silence for a moment, then D'Agosta's voice returned. "Look, Pendergast, you need to tell Coffey some of this. He's sending some men in, and I don't think he has any idea of what's waiting for him."

"I'll do my best. But first let's talk about getting you out of here. That beast may be hunting you."

"No *shit*."

"I can direct you out of the Museum through the subbasement. It won't be easy. These blueprints are very old, and they may not be completely reliable. There may be water."

"We're standing in half a foot of it now. Look, Pendergast, are you sure about this? I mean, there's a mother of a storm outside."

"It's either face the water, or face the beast. There are forty of you; you're the most obvious target. You've got to move, and move quickly—it's the only way out."

"Can you link up with us?"

"No. We've decided to stay here and lure it away from you. There's no time to explain now. If our plan works, we'll join you further on. Thanks to these blue-prints, I've discovered more than one way to get into the subbasement from Cell Two.''

''Christ, Pendergast, be careful.''

''I intend to. Now, listen carefully. Are you in a long, straight passage?''

''Yes.''

''Very good. Where the hall forks, go right. The hall should fork a second time in another hundred yards or so. When you get to the second fork, radio me. Got it?''

''Got it.''

''Good luck. Pendergast out.''

Pendergast quickly switched frequencies.

''Coffey, this is Pendergast. Do you copy?''

''Coffey here. Goddammit, Pendergast, I've been try-ing to reach you for—''

''No time for that now. Are you sending a rescue team in?''

''Yes. They're preparing to leave now.''

''Then make sure they're armed with heavy-caliber automatic weapons, flak helmets, and bulletproof vests. There's a powerful, murderous creature in here, Coffey. I saw it. It has the run of Cell Two.''

''For Chrissakes, you *and* D'Agosta! Pendergast, if you're trying to—''

Pendergast spoke rapidly into the radio. ''I'll only warn you once more. You're dealing with something monstrous here. Underestimate it at your peril. I'm sign-ing off.''

''No, Pendergast, wait! I order you to—''

Pendergast switched off the radio.

= 52 =

They slogged into the water, dim flashlight beams lick-
ing the low ceiling in front and behind. The flow of air
in the tunnel continued to blow gently into their faces.
D'Agosta was alarmed now. The beast could come up
behind them unannounced, its stench wafted away from
them.

He paused a moment to let Bailey catch up. "Lieutenant," said the Mayor, catching his breath, "are you
certain there's a way out through here?"

"I can only go by what Agent Pendergast said, sir.
He's got the blueprints. But I sure as hell know we don't
want to go back."

D'Agosta and the group started forward again. Dark,
oily drops were falling from a ceiling of arched herringbone bricks. The walls were crusted with lime. Everyone
was silent except for one woman, who was quietly weeping.

"Excuse me, Lieutenant?" said a voice. The young,
lanky guy. Smithback.

"Yes?"

"Would you mind telling me something?"

"Shoot."

"How does it feel to have the lives of forty people, including the Mayor of New York City, in your hands?"

"What?" D'Agosta stopped a moment, glared over his shoulder. "Don't tell me we've got a fucking *journalist* with us!"

"Well, I—" began Smithback.

"Call downtown and make an appointment to see me at headquarters."

D'Agosta played the light ahead and found the fork in the tunnel. He took the right-hand passage, as Pendergast had directed. It had a slight downhill grade, and the water began to move faster, tugging on his pants legs as it rushed past into the blackness beyond. The wound in his hand throbbed. As the group moved around the corner behind him, D'Agosta noted with relief that the breeze was no longer blowing in their faces.

A bloated dead rat came floating past, bumping against people's legs like a lazy, oversized billiard ball. One person groaned and tried to kick it away, but no one complained.

"Bailey!" called D'Agosta behind him.

"Yeah?"

"See anything?"

"You'll be the first to know if I do."

"Gotcha. I'm going to call in upstairs, see if they've made any progress in restoring power."

He grabbed his radio. "Coffey?"

"Reading. Pendergast just shut me off. Where are you?"

"We're in the subbasement. Pendergast has a blueprint. He's leading us out by radio. When are the lights coming on?"

"D'Agosta, don't be an idiot. He'll get you all killed. It doesn't look as if we'll be getting power back any time soon. Go back to the Hall of the Heavens and wait there. We'll be sending the SWAT team in through the roof in a couple of minutes.''

"Then you should know that Wright, Cuthbert, and the Public Relations Director are upstairs somewhere, the fourth floor, probably. That's the only other exit point for that stairwell.''

"What are you talking about? You didn't take them with you?''

"They refused to come along. Wright cut out on his own and the others followed him.''

"Sounds like they had more sense than you did. Is the Mayor all right? Let me talk to the him.''

D'Agosta handed the radio over. "Are you all right, sir?'' Coffey asked urgently.

"We're in capable hands with the Lieutenant.''

"It's my strong opinion, sir, that you should head back to the Hall of the Heavens and wait there for assistance. We're sending in a SWAT team to rescue you.''

"I have every confidence in Lieutenant D'Agosta. As should you.''

"Yes, of course, sir. Rest assured that I'm going to get you safely out of there, sir.''

"Coffey?''

"Sir?''

"There are three dozen people in here besides me. Don't forget that.''

"But I just want you to know, sir, we're being extra—''

"Coffey! I don't think you understood me. Every life down here is worth all the effort you've got.''

"Yes, sir.''

The Mayor handed the radio back to D'Agosta. "Am I wrong, or is that fellow Coffey a horse's ass?'' he muttered.

D'Agosta holstered the radio and proceeded down the passage. Then he stopped, playing his flashlight over an object that loomed out of the blackness in front of them.

It was a steel door, closed. The oily water rushed through a thickly barred grating in its bottom panel. He waded closer. It was similar to the door at the base of the stairwell: thick, double-plated, studded with rusty rivets. An old copper lock, covered with verdigris, was looped through a thick metal D ring along the door's side. D'Agosta grabbed the lock and pulled, but it held fast.

"Pendergast?" said D'Agosta, removing his radio once again.

"Reading."

"We're past the first fork, but we've hit a steel door, and it's locked."

"A locked door? Between the first and second forks?"

"Yes."

"And you took a right at the first fork?"

"Yes."

"One minute." There was a shuffling sound.

"Vincent, go back to the fork and take the left-hand tunnel. Hurry."

D'Agosta wheeled around. "Bailey! We're heading back to that last fork. All of you, let's go. On the double!"

The group turned wearily, murmuring, and started moving back through the inky water.

"Wait!" came the voice of Bailey, from the head of the group. "Christ, Lieutenant, do you smell it?"

"No," said D'Agosta; then "*shit!*" as the fetid stench enveloped him. "Bailey, we're going to have to make a stand! I'm coming up. Fire at the son of a bitch!"

Cuthbert sat on the worktable, absently tapping its scarred surface with a pencil eraser. At the far end of the table, Wright sat motionless, his head in his hands. Rickman stood on her tiptoes by the small window. She was angling the flashlight through the bars in front of the glass, switching it on and off with a manicured finger.

A brief flash of lightning silhouetted her thin form, then a low rumble of thunder filled the room.

"It's pouring out," she said. "I can't see a thing."

"And nobody can see you," said Cuthbert wearily. "All you're doing is wearing out the battery. We may need it later."

With an audible sigh, Rickman switched off the light, plunging the lab once again into darkness.

"I wonder what it did with Montague's body," came the slurred voice of Wright. "Ate him up?" Laughter spluttered out of the gloom.

Cuthbert continued tapping the pencil.

"Ate him up! With a little curry and rice, maybe! Montague pilaf!" Wright chuckled.

Cuthbert stood up, reached over toward the Director, and plucked the .357 from Wright's belt. He checked the bullets, then tucked it into his own belt.

"Return that at once!" Wright demanded.

Cuthbert said nothing.

"You're a bully, Ian. You've always been a bully, a small-minded, jealous bully. First thing Monday morning, I'm going to fire you. In fact, you're fired now." Wright stood up unsteadily. "Fired, you hear me?"

Cuthbert was standing at the front door of the laboratory, listening.

"What is it?" Rickman asked in alarm. Cuthbert held his hand up sharply.

Silence.

At length, Cuthbert turned away from the door. "I thought I heard a noise," he said. He looked toward Rickman. "Lavinia? Could you come here a moment?"

"What is it?" she asked, breathless.

Cuthbert drew her aside. "Hand me the torch," he said. "Now, listen. I don't want to alarm you. But should something happen—"

"What do you mean?" she interrupted, her voice breaking.

"Whatever it was that's been killing people is still loose. I'm not sure we're safe in here."

"But the door! Winston said it was two inches thick—"

"I know. Maybe everything will be fine. But those doors to the exhibition were even thicker than that, and I'd like to take a few precautions. Help me move this table up against the door." He turned toward the Director.

Wright looked up vaguely. "Fired! Clean out your desk by five o'clock Monday."

Cuthbert pulled Wright to his feet, and sat him in a nearby chair. With Rickman's help, Cuthbert positioned the table in front of the oak door of the laboratory.

"That will slow it down, anyway," he said, dusting off his jacket. "Enough for me to get in a few good shots, with luck. At the first sign of trouble, I want you to go through that back door into the Dinosaur Hall and hide. With the security gates down, there's no other way into the Hall. At least that will put two doors between you and whatever's out there." Cuthbert looked around again restlessly. "In the meantime, let's try to break this window. At least then maybe someone will be able to hear us yelling."

Wright laughed. "You can't break the window, you can't, you can't. It's high-impact glass."

Cuthbert hunted around the lab, finally locating a short piece of angle iron. When he swung it vertically through the bars, it bounced off the glass and was knocked out of his hands.

"Bloody hell," he muttered, rubbing his palms together. "We could shoot out the window," he speculated. "Do you have any more bullets hidden away?"

"I'm not talking to you anymore," Wright retorted.

Cuthbert opened the filing cabinet and started fumbling in the dark. "Nothing," he said at last. "We can't waste bullets on that window. I've only got five shots in here."

"Nothing, nothing, nothing. Didn't King Lear say that?"

Cuthbert sighed heavily and sat down. Silence filled the room once again, save only the wind and rain, and the distant roll of thunder.

Pendergast lowered the radio and turned toward Margo. "D'Agosta's in trouble. We've got to move fast."

"Leave me behind," said Frock quietly. "I'm just going to slow you down."

"A gallant gesture," Pendergast told him. "But we need your brains."

He moved slowly out into the hall, sweeping his light in both directions. Then he signaled all clear. They moved down the hall, Margo pushing the wheelchair before her as quickly as possible.

As they threaded their way, Frock would occasionally whisper a few words of direction. Pendergast stopped at every intersection, gun drawn. Frequently, he halted to listen and smell the air. After a few minutes, he took the chair's handlebars from an unprotesting Margo. Then they rounded a corner, and the door of the Secure Area stood before them.

For the hundredth time, Margo prayed silently that her plan would work; that she wasn't simply condemning all of them—including the group trapped in the subbasement—to a horrible death.

"Third on the right!" Frock called as they moved inside the Secure Area. "Margo, do you remember the combination?"

She dialed, pulled the lever, and the door swung open. Pendergast strode over and knelt beside the smaller crate.

"Wait," said Margo.

Pendergast stopped, eyebrows raised quizzically.

"Don't let the smell of it get onto you," she said. "Bundle the fibers in your jacket."

Pendergast hesitated.

"Here," Frock said. "Use my handkerchief to remove them."

Pendergast inspected it. "Well," he said ruefully, "if the Professor here can donate a hundred-dollar handkerchief, I suppose I can donate my jacket." He took the radio and notebook, stuffed them into the waistband of his pants, then removed his suit jacket.

"Since when did FBI agents start wearing hand-tailored Armani suits?" Margo asked jokingly.

"Since when did graduate students in ethnopharmacology start appreciating them?" Pendergast replied, spreading the jacket carefully on the floor. Then, gingerly, he scooped out several fistfuls of fiber and laid them carefully across his open jacket. Finally, he stuffed the handkerchief into one of the sleeves, folded the garment, and tied the sleeves together.

"We'll need a rope to drag it with," said Margo.

"I see some packing cord around the far crate," Frock pointed out.

Pendergast tied the jacket and fashioned a harness, then dragged the bundle across the floor.

"Seems to be snug," he said. "Pity, though, that they haven't dusted these floors in a while." He turned to Margo. "Will this leave enough of a scent for the creature to follow?"

Frock nodded vigorously. "The Extrapolator estimates the creature's sense of smell to be exponentially keener than ours. It was able to trace the crates to this vault, remember."

"And you're sure the—er—meals it's already had this evening won't satiate it?"

"Mr. Pendergast, the human hormone is a poor substitute. We believe the beast *lives* for this plant." Frock nodded again. "If it smells an abundance of fibers, it will track them down."

"Let's get started, then," said Pendergast. He lifted the bundle gingerly. "The alternate access to the sub-basement is several hundred yards from here. If you're right, we're at our most vulnerable from now on. The creature will home in on *us*.''

Pushing the wheelchair, Margo followed the agent into the corridor. He shut the door, then the three moved quickly down the hall, back into the silence of the Old Basement.

= 53 =

D'Agosta moved forward, crouching low in the water, his revolver nosing ahead into the inky darkness. He had turned off his flashlight to avoid betraying his position. The water flowed briskly between his thighs, its smell of algae and lime mixing with the fetid reek of the creature.

"Bailey, you up there?" he whispered into the gloom.

"Yeah," came Bailey's voice. "I'm waiting at the first fork."

"You've got more rounds than I. If we drive off this motherfucker, I want you to stand guard while I go behind and try shooting off the lock."

"Roger."

D'Agosta started toward Bailey, his legs numbing in the frigid water. Suddenly, there was a confusion of sounds in the blackness ahead of him: a soft splash, then another, much closer. Bailey's shotgun went off twice, and several people in the group behind him started whimpering.

"Jesus!" he heard Bailey yell, then there was a low crunching noise and Bailey screamed and D'Agosta felt thrashing in the water ahead of him.

"Bailey!" he cried out, but all he could hear was the gurgle of running water. He pulled out his flashlight and shined it up the tunnel. Nothing.

"Bailey!"

Several people were crying behind him now and somebody was screaming hysterically.

"Shut up!" D'Agosta pleaded. "I have to listen!"

The screams were abruptly muffled. He played the light ahead, off the walls and ceiling, but he could see nothing. Bailey had vanished, and the smell had receded once again. Maybe Bailey had hit the fucker. Or maybe it had just temporarily retreated from the noise of the shotgun. He shone the flashlight downward, and noticed the water flowing red around his legs. A torn shred of NYPD regulation blue cloth floated by.

"I need help up here!" he hissed over his shoulder.

Smithback was suddenly at his side.

"Point this flashlight down the passage," D'Agosta told him.

D'Agosta probed the stone floor with his fingers. The water, he noticed, seemed to be a little higher: as he bent forward, reaching down, it grazed his chest. Something floated by beneath his nose, a piece of Bailey, and he had to turn away for a moment.

There was no shotgun to be found.

"Smithback," he said, "I'm going back to shoot off the lock. We can't backtrack any farther with that thing waiting for us. Feel around in this water for a shotgun. If you see anything, or smell anything, shout."

"You're leaving me here alone?" Smithback asked a little unsteadily.

"You've got the flashlight. It'll just be for a minute. Can you do it?"

"I'll try."

D'Agosta grasped Smithback's shoulder briefly, then started back. For a journalist, the guy had guts.

A hand tugged at him as he waded through the group. "Please tell us what's happening," a feminine voice sobbed.

He gently shook her off. D'Agosta could hear the Mayor talking soothingly to her. Maybe he'd vote for the old bastard next time.

"Everyone get back," he said, and positioned himself in front of the door. He knew he should stand well back from the door to avoid potential ricochets. But it was a thick lock, and he'd have a hard time aiming in the dark.

He moved to within a few feet of the door, placed the barrel of the .38 near the lock, and fired. When the smoke cleared, he found a clean hole in the lock's center. The lock held fast.

"Fuck it," he muttered, placing the muzzle of the revolver directly against the hasp and firing again. Now the lock was gone. He heaved his weight against the door.

"Give me a hand here!" he called out.

Immediately, several people began throwing themselves against it. The rusty hinges gave way with a loud screech, and water gushed through the opening.

"Smithback! Find anything?"

"I got his flashlight!" came the disembodied voice.

"Good boy. Now come on back!"

As D'Agosta moved through the door, he noticed an iron D ring on the other side as well. He stood back and ushered the group through, counting. Thirty-seven. Bailey was gone. Smithback brought up the rear.

"All right, let's shut this thing!" D'Agosta yelled.

Against the heavy flow of the water, the door groaned slowly shut.

"Smithback! Shine one of the lights here. Maybe we can find a way to bar this door."

He looked at it for a second. If they could jam a piece of metal through the D ring, it just might hold. He turned to the group. "I need something, *anything,* made of metal!" he called. "Does anyone have a piece of metal we can use to bar this door?"

The Mayor passed quickly through the group, then came up to D'Agosta, thrusting a small collection of metal items into his hands. As Smithback held the light, D'Agosta inspected the pins, necklaces, combs. "There's nothing here," he muttered.

They heard a sudden splashing on the other side of the door, and a deep grunt. A stench filtered through the low slats in the door. A soft thump and a brief squeal of hinges, and the door was pushed ajar.

"Christ! You there, help me shut this door!"

As before, people flung themselves against the door, forcing it shut. There was a rattle and then a louder boom as the thing met their force, then pushed them back. The door creaked open farther.

At D'Agosta's shout, others joined the effort.

"Keep pushing!"

Another roar; then a tremendous thump heaved everyone back once again. The door groaned under the opposing weights, but continued to open, first six inches, then a foot. The stench became intolerable. Watching the door inch its way from the frame, D'Agosta saw three long talons snake their way around the edge. The shape felt along the door, then swiped forward, the talons alternately sheathing and unsheathing.

"Jesus, Mary, and Joseph," D'Agosta heard the Mayor say, quite matter-of-factly. Somebody else began chanting a prayer in a strange singsong. D'Agosta placed the barrel of the gun near the monstrosity and fired once. There was a terrible roar and the shape vanished into churning water.

"The flashlight!" Smithback cried. "It'll fit perfectly! Shove it into the ring!"

"That'll leave us with just one light," D'Agosta panted.

"Got a better idea?"

"No," D'Agosta said under his breath. Then, louder: "Everybody, *push!*"

With a final heave they slammed the door back into its iron frame, and Smithback shoved the flashlight through the D ring. It slid through easily, its flared end coming to rest against the metal hasp. As D'Agosta caught his breath, they heard another, sudden crash and the door shuddered, but held firm.

"Run, people!" cried D'Agosta. "Run!" They thrashed through the roiling water, falling and sliding. D'Agosta, buffeted from behind, fell face first into the rushing water. He rose and continued forward, trying to ignore the monster's roaring and pounding—he did not think he could hear it and remain sane. He willed himself to think about the flashlight instead. It was a good, heavy police-issue flashlight. It would hold. He hoped to God it would hold. The group stopped at the second fork in the tunnel, crying and shivering. *Time to radio Pendergast and get the fuck out of this maze,* D'Agosta thought. He clapped his hand to his radio holster, and with a shock realized it was empty.

Coffey stood inside the forward security station, staring moodily at a monitor. He was unable to reach either Pendergast or D'Agosta. Inside the perimeter, Garcia in Security Command and Waters in the Computer Room were still responding. Had everybody else been killed? When he thought of the Mayor dead, and the headlines that were sure to follow, a hollow feeling grew in his stomach.

An acetylene torch, flickering near the silver expanse of the metal security door at the east end of the Rotunda, cast ghostly shadows across the tall ceiling. The acrid smell of molten steel filled the air. The Rotunda had grown strangely quiet. Field amputations were still taking place by the security door, but all the other guests had left for home or area hospitals. The journalists had finally been contained behind police barriers. Mobile intensive care units were set up on nearby side streets and medevacs were standing by.

The SWAT team commander came over, buckling an ammo belt over his black fatigues. "We're ready," he said.

Coffey nodded. "Give me a tactical."

The leader pushed a bank of emergency phones aside and unfolded a sheet.

"Our spotter will be leading us by radio. He's got the detailed diagrams from this station. Phase One: We're punching a hole through the roof, here, and dropping to the fifth floor. According to the specs of the security system, this door here will blow with one charge. That gives us access to the next cell. Then we proceed down to this props storage room on the fourth floor. It's right above the Hall of the Heavens. There's a trapdoor in the floor that Maintenance uses for cleaning and servicing the chandelier. We'll lower our men and haul the wounded up in sling chairs. Phase Two: Rescue those in the subbasement, the Mayor and the large group with him. Phase Three: Search for those who may be elsewhere within the perimeter. I understand that people are trapped in the Computer Room and Security Command. The Museum Director, Ian Cuthbert, and a woman as yet unidentified may have gone upstairs. And don't you have agents of your own within the perimeter, sir? The man from the New Orleans field office—"

"Let me worry about him," Coffey snapped. "Who developed these plans?"

"We did, with the assistance of Security Command. That guy Allen has the cell layouts down cold. Anyway, according to the specs of this security system—"

"You did. And who's in charge here?"

"Sir, as you know, in emergency situations the SWAT team commander—"

"I want you to go in there and kill the son of a bitch. Got it?"

"Sir, our first priority is to rescue hostages and save lives. Only then can we deal with—"

"Calling me stupid, Commander? If we kill the thing in there, all our other problems are solved. Right? This is not your typical situation, commander, and it requires creative thinking."

"In a hostage situation, if you take away the killer's hostages, you've removed his base of power—"

"Commander, were you asleep during our crisis-control briefing? We may have an animal in there, not a person."

"But the wounded—"

"Use some of your men to *get* the damn wounded out. But I want the rest of you to go after what's in there and kill it. Then we rescue any stragglers at leisure, in safety and comfort. Those are your direct orders."

"I understand, sir. I would recommend, however—"

"Don't recommend jack shit, Commander. Go in the way you planned, but do the job right. Kill the motherfucker."

The commander looked curiously at Coffey. "You sure about this thing being an animal?"

Coffey hesitated. "Yes," he finally said. "I don't know a hell of a lot about it, but it's already killed several people."

The Commander looked steadily at Coffey for a moment.

"Yeah," he finally said, "well, whatever it is, we've got enough firepower to turn a herd of lions into a fine red mist."

"You're going to need it. Find the thing. Take it out."

Pendergast and Margo looked down the narrow service tunnel into the subbasement. Pendergast's flashlight sent a circle of light onto a sheet of black, oily water roiling past beneath them.

"It's getting deeper," Pendergast said. Then he turned

to Margo. "Are you sure the creature can make it up this shaft?" he asked.

"I'm nearly certain," Margo said. "It's highly agile."

Pendergast stepped back and tried once again to raise D'Agosta on the radio. "Something's happened," he said. "The Lieutenant has been out of contact for fifteen minutes. Ever since they hit that locked door." He glanced down again through the shaft that sloped toward the subbasement below. "How are you planning to lay a scent with all this water?" he asked.

"You estimate they passed beneath here some time ago, right?" Margo asked.

Pendergast nodded. "The last time I spoke to him, D'Agosta told me the group was between the first and second forks," he said. "Assuming they haven't back-tracked, he's well beyond this spot."

"The way I see it," Margo continued, "if we sprinkle some fibers on the water, the flow should carry them to the creature."

"That's assuming the creature's smart enough to re-alize the fibers came floating from upstream. Otherwise, he might just chase them further downstream."

"I think it's smart enough," Frock said. "You mustn't think of this creature as an *animal*. It may be nearly as intelligent as a human being."

Using the handkerchief, Pendergast carefully removed some fibers from the bundle and sprinkled them along the base of the shaft. He dropped another handful into the water below.

"Not too much," Frock warned.

Pendergast looked at Margo. "We'll sprinkle a few more fibers to establish a good upwater trail, then drag the bundle back to the Secure Area and wait. Your trap will be set." After scattering a few more fibers, he se-cured the bundle.

"At the rate this water is moving," he said, "it should take only a few minutes to reach the creature. How fast do you expect the thing to respond?"

"If the extrapolation program is correct," Frock said, "the creature can move at a high rate of speed. Perhaps thirty miles an hour or greater, especially when in need. And its need for the fibers seems overpowering. It won't be able to travel at full speed down these corridors—the residual scent trail we leave will be harder to track—but I doubt the water will slow it much. And the Secure Area is close by."

"I see," Pendergast said. "How unsettling. *'He that has a mind to fight, let him fight, for now is the time.'* "

"Ah," said Frock, nodding. "Alcaeus."

Pendergast shook his head. "Anacreon, Doctor. Shall we go?"

= 54 =

Smithback held the light, but it hardly seemed to penetrate the palpable darkness. D'Agosta, slightly in front, held the gun. The tunnel went on and on, black water rushing past and vanishing into the low-vaulted darkness. Either they were still descending, or the water was getting higher. Smithback could feel it pushing against his thighs.

He glanced at D'Agosta's face, shadowy and grim, his thick features smeared with Bailey's blood.

"I can't go any farther," someone wailed from the rear. Smithback could hear the Mayor's familiar voice— a politician's voice—reassuring, soothing, telling everyone what they wanted to hear. Once again, it seemed to work. Smithback stole a glance backward at the dispirited group. The lean, gowned, bejeweled women; the middle-aged businessmen in their tuxedos; the smattering of yuppies from investment banks and downtown law firms. He knew them all now, had even given them names and occupations in his head. And here they all were, reduced to the lowest common denominator, wallowing around in the dark of a tunnel, covered with slime, pursued by a savage beast.

Smithback was worried, but still rational. Early on, he'd felt a moment of sheer terror when he realized the rumors about a Museum Beast were true. But now, tired and wet, he was more afraid of dying before he wrote his book than he was of dying itself. He wondered if that meant he was brave, or covetous, or just plain stupid. Whatever the case, he knew that what was happening to him down here was going to be worth a fortune. Book party at Le Cirque. *Good Morning America,* the *Today Show, Donahue,* and *Oprah.*

No one could do the story like he could, no one else had his first-person perspective. And he'd been a hero. He, William Smithback, Jr., had held the light against the monster when D'Agosta went back to shoot off the lock. He, Smithback, had thought of using the flashlight to brace the door. He'd been Lieutenant D'Agosta's right-hand man.

"Shine the light up to the left, there." D'Agosta intruded upon his thoughts, and Smithback dutifully complied. Nothing.

"I thought I saw something moving in the darkness," D'Agosta muttered. "Must've been a shadow, I guess."

God, Smithback thought, if only he lived to enjoy his success.

"Is it just my imagination, or is the water getting deeper?" he asked.

"It's getting deeper *and* faster," said D'Agosta. "Pendergast didn't say which way to go from here."

"He didn't?" Smithback felt his guts turn to water.

"I was supposed to radio from the second fork," D'Agosta said. "I lost my radio somewhere back before the door."

Smithback felt another surge against his legs, a strong one. There was a shout and a splash.

"It's all right," the Mayor called out when Smithback

aimed the flashlight to the rear. "Someone fell down. The current's getting stronger."

"We can't tell them we're lost," Smithback muttered to D'Agosta.

Margo swung open the door to the Secure Area, looked quickly inside, and nodded to Pendergast. The agent moved past the door, dragging the bundle.

"Shut it in the vault with the Whittlesey crates," Frock said. "We want to keep the beast in here long enough for us to close the door on it."

Margo unlocked the vault as Pendergast threaded a complex pattern across the floor. They put the bundle inside, then closed and locked the ornate vault door.

"Quick," Margo said. "Across the hall."

Leaving the main door to the Secure Area open, they crossed the hall to the elephant bone storage room. The small window in the door had long ago been broken, and a worn piece of cardboard now covered the opening. Margo unlocked the door with Frock's key, then Pendergast pushed Frock inside. Switching Pendergast's flashlight to its low setting, she balanced it on a ledge above the door, pointing the thin beam in the direction of the Secure Area. Finally, with a pen, she reamed a small hole in the cardboard and, with a last look down the corridor, stepped inside.

The storage room was large, stuffy, and full of elephant bones. Most of the skeletons were disassembled, and the great shadowy bones had been stacked on shelves like oversized cordwood. One mounted skeleton stood in a far corner, a dark cage of bones, two curving tusks gleaming in the pale light.

Pendergast shut the door, then switched off his miner's lamp.

Peering through the hole in the cardboard, Margo had a clear view of the hallway and the open door of the Secure Area.

"Take a look," she said to Pendergast, stepping away from the door.

Pendergast moved forward. "Excellent," he said after a moment. "It's a perfect blind, as long as those flashlight batteries hold out." He stepped back from the door. "How did you happen to remember this room?" he asked curiously.

Margo laughed shyly. "When you took us down here on Wednesday, I remember seeing this door marked PACHYDERMAE and wondering how a person could fit an elephant skull through such a small door." She moved forward. "I'll keep watch through the peephole," she said. "Be ready to rush out and trap the creature in the Secure Area."

In the darkness behind them, Frock cleared his throat. "Mr. Pendergast?"

"Yes?"

"Forgive me for asking, but how experienced *are* you with that weapon?"

"As a matter of fact," the agent replied, "before the death of my wife I spent several weeks each winter big-game hunting in East Africa. My wife was an avid hunter."

"Ah," Frock replied. Margo detected relief in his voice. "This will be a difficult creature to kill, but I don't think it will be impossible. I was never much of a hunter, obviously. But working together we may be able to bring it down."

Pendergast nodded. "Unfortunately, this pistol puts me at a disadvantage. It's a powerful handgun, but nothing like a .375 nitro express rifle. If you could tell me where the creature might be most vulnerable, it would help."

"From the printout," Frock said slowly, "we can assume the creature is heavy boned. As you discovered, you won't kill it with a head shot. And an upper shoulder or chest shot toward the heart would almost certainly be deflected by the massive bones and heavy musculature of the creature's upper body. If you could catch the creature sideways, you might get a shot into the heart from behind the foreleg. But again, the ribs are probably built like a steel cage. Now that I think about it, I don't believe any of the vital parts of the beast are particularly vulnerable. A shot to the gut might kill eventually, but not before it took its revenge."

"Cold comfort," Pendergast said.

Frock moved restlessly in the darkness. "That leaves us in a bit of a quandary."

There was silence for a moment. "There may still be a way." Pendergast said at length.

"Yes?" Frock replied eagerly.

"Once, a few years ago, my wife and I were hunting bushbuck in Tanzania. We preferred to hunt alone, without gun bearers, and the only guns we had were 30-30 rifles. We were in light cover near a river when we were charged by a cape buffalo. It had apparently been wounded a few days earlier by a poacher. Cape buffalo are like mules—they never forget an injury, and one man with a gun looks much like any other."

Sitting in the dim light, waiting for the arrival of a nightmarish creature, listening to Pendergast narrate a hunting story in his typical unhurried manner, Margo felt a sense of unreality begin to creep over her.

"Normally, in hunting buffalo," Pendergast was saying, "one tries for a head shot just below the horn bosses, or for a heart shot. In this case, the 30-30 was an insufficient caliber. My wife, who was a better shot than I, used the only tactic a hunter could use in such a situation. She knelt and fired at the animal in such a way as to break it down."

"Break it down?"

"You don't attempt a kill shot. Instead, you work to stop forward locomotion. You aim for the forelegs, pasterns, knees. You basically shatter as many bones as you can until it can't move forward."

"I see," said Frock.

"There is only one problem with this approach," said Pendergast.

"And that is—?"

"You must be a consummate marksman. Placement is everything. You've got to remain serenely calm and steady, unbreathing, firing between heartbeats—in the face of a charging beast. We each had time for four shots. I made the mistake of aiming for the chest and scored two direct hits before I realized the bullets were just burying themselves in muscle. Then I aimed for the legs. One shot missed and the other grazed but didn't break the bone." He shook his head. "A poor performance, I'm afraid."

"So what happened?" Frock asked.

"My wife scored direct hits on three out of her four shots. She shattered both front cannons and broke the upper foreleg as well. The buffalo tumbled head over heels and came to rest a few yards from where we were kneeling. It was still very much alive but it couldn't move. So I 'paid the insurance,' as a professional hunter would put it."

"I wish your wife was here," Frock said.

Pendergast was quiet. "So do I," he said at length.

Silence returned to the room.

"Very well," Frock said at last. "I understand the problem. The beast has some unusual qualities that you should know about, if you are planning to, ah, break it down. First, the hind quarters are most likely covered in bony plates or scales. I doubt if you could penetrate them effectively with your gun. They armor the upper and lower leg, down to the metatarsal bones, I'd estimate."

"I see."

"You will have to shoot low, aim for the phalanx prima or secunda."

"The lowest bones of the leg," said Pendergast.

"Yes. They would be equivalent to the pasterns on a horse. Aim just below the lower joint. In fact, the joint itself might be vulnerable."

"That's a difficult shot," said Pendergast. "Virtually impossible if the creature is facing me."

There was a short silence. Margo continued her vigil through the peephole, but saw nothing.

"I believe the anterior limbs of the creature are more vulnerable," Frock continued. "The Extrapolator described them as being less robust. The metacarpals and the carpals should both be vulnerable to a direct hit."

"The front knee and the lower leg," Pendergast said, nodding. "The shots you've described already are hardly garden variety. To what extent would the creature have to be broken down to immobilize it?"

"Difficult to say. Both front legs and at least one rear leg, I'm afraid. Even then, it could crawl." Frock coughed. "Can you do it?"

"To have a chance, I'd need at least a hundred and fifty feet of shooting space if the creature were charging. Ideally, I'd get the first shot in before the creature knew what was happening. That would slow it down."

Frock thought for a moment. "The Museum contains several straight, long corridors, three or four hundred feet long. Unfortunately, most of them are now cut in half by these damned security doors. I believe that there's at least one unobstructed corridor within Cell Two, however. On the first floor, in Section Eighteen, around the corner from the Computer Room."

Pendergast nodded. "I'll remember that," he said. "In case this plan fails."

"I hear something!" Margo hissed.

They fell silent. Pendergast moved closer to the door.

"A shadow just passed across the light at the end of the hall," she whispered.

There was another long silence.

"It's here," Margo breathed, "I can see it." Then, even softer: "Oh, my God."

Pendergast murmured in Margo's ear: "Move away from the door!"

She backed up, hardly daring to breathe. "What's it doing?" she whispered.

"It's stopped at the door to the Secure Area," Pendergast replied quietly. "It went in for a moment, and then backed out very fast. It's looking around, smelling the air."

"What does it look like?" Frock asked, an urgency in his voice.

Pendergast hesitated a moment before answering. "I've got a better view of it this time. It's big, it's massive. Wait, it's turning this way ... Good Lord, it's a horrible sight, it's ... Flattened face, small red eyes. Thin fur on the upper body. Just like the figurine. Hold on ... Hold on a minute ... it's coming this way."

Margo suddenly realized she had moved back to the far wall. A snuffling sound came through the door. And then the rank, fetid smell. She slid to the floor in the heavy darkness, the peephole in the cardboard wavering like a star. Pendergast's flashlight shone feebly. *Starlight* ... A small voice in Margo's head was trying to speak.

And then a shadow fell over the peephole and everything went black.

There was a soft muffled thud against the door, and the old wood creaked. The doorknob rattled. There was a long silence, the sound of something heavy moving outside, and a sharp cracking as the creature pressed against the door.

The voice inside Margo's head suddenly became audible.

"Pendergast, turn on your miner's lamp!" she burst out. "Shine it at the beast!"

"What are you talking about!"

"It's nocturnal, remember? It probably hates light."

"That's absolutely correct!" cried Frock.

"Stay back!" Pendergast shouted. Margo heard a small click, then the brilliance of the miner's light blinded her momentarily. As her vision returned, she saw

Pendergast on one knee, his gun leveled at the door, the bright circle of light focused directly on its center.

There was another crunching noise, and Margo could see splinters spray into the room from a widening split in the upper panel. The door bowed inward.

Pendergast stayed steady, sighting along the levelled barrel.

There was another tremendous splintering sound and the door broke inward in pieces, swinging crazily on bent hinges. Margo pressed herself against the wall, forcing herself into it until her spine creaked in protest. She heard Frock shout in amazement, wonder, and fear. The creature squatted in the doorway, a monstrous silhouette in the bright light; then, with a sudden throaty roar, it shook its head and backed out.

"Keep back," Pendergast said. He kicked the broken door aside and moved cautiously out into the hall. Margo heard a sudden shot, then another. Then, silence. After what seemed an eternity, Pendergast returned, motioning them forward. A trail of small red droplets led down the hallway and around the corner.

"Blood!" Frock said, bending forward with a grunt. "So you wounded it!"

Pendergast shrugged. "Perhaps. But I wasn't the first. The droplets originate from the direction of the sub-basement. See? Lieutenant D'Agosta or one of his men must have wounded it earlier but not disabled it. It moved away with amazing speed."

Margo looked at Frock. "Why didn't it take the bait?"

Frock returned her gaze. "We're dealing with a creature possessed of preternatural intelligence."

"What you're saying is that it detected our trap," Pendergast said, a note of disbelief in his voice.

"Let me ask you, Pendergast. Would *you* have fallen for that trap?"

Pendergast was silent. "I suppose not," he said at length.

"Well, then," said Frock. "We underestimated the creature. We *must* stop thinking of it as a dumb animal. It has the intelligence of a human being. Did I understand correctly that the body they found in the exhibition was *hidden?* The beast knew it was being hunted. Obviously, it had learned to conceal its prey. Besides—" he hesitated. "I think we're dealing with more than simply hunger now. Chances are, it's been temporarily sated by this evening's human diet. But it's also been wounded. If your analogy of the cape buffalo is correct, this creature may not only be hungry, but *angry.*"

"So you think it's gone hunting," Pendergast said quietly.

Frock remained motionless. Then he gave a barely perceptible nod.

"So who's it hunting now?" Margo asked.

No one answered.

= 55 =

Cuthbert checked the door again. It was locked and rock solid. He flicked on the flashlight and shined it in the direction of Wright, slumped in his chair and looking morosely at the floor. Cuthbert switched off the flashlight. The room reeked of whisky. There was no noise except for the rain splattering and drumming against the barred window.

"What are we going to do with Wright?" he asked in a low tone.

"Don't worry," Rickman replied, her voice tight and high. "We'll just tell the press he's sick and pack him off to the hospital, then schedule a press conference for tomorrow afternoon—"

"I'm not talking about *after* we get out. I'm talking about *now*. If the beast comes up here."

"Please, Ian, don't talk like that. It scares me. I can't imagine the animal is going to do that. For all we know, it's been in the basement for years. Why would it come up here now?"

"I don't know," said Cuthbert. "That's what worries me." He checked the Ruger once again. Five shots.

He went over to Wright and shook the Director's shoulder. "Winston?"

"Are you still here?" Wright asked, looking up hazily.

"Winston, I want you to take Lavinia and go into the Dinosaur Hall. Come along."

Wright slapped Cuthbert's arm away. "I'm fine just where I am. Maybe I'll take a nap."

"The devil with you, then," said Cuthbert. He sat down in a chair opposite the door.

There was a brief noise—a rattle—at the door, as if the doorknob had been turned, then released.

Cuthbert jumped up, gun in hand. He walked close to the door and listened.

"I hear something," he said quietly. "Get into the Dinosaur Hall, Lavinia."

"I'm afraid," she whispered. "Please don't make me go in there alone."

"Do as I say."

Rickman walked over to the far door and opened it. She hesitated.

"Go on."

"Ian—" Rickman pleaded. Behind her, Cuthbert could see the huge dinosaur skeletons looming out of the darkness. The great black ribs and yawning rows of teeth were suddenly illuminated by a streak of livid lightning.

"Damn you, woman, get in there."

Cuthbert turned back, listening. Something soft was rubbing against the door. He leaned forward, pressing his ear against the smooth wood. Maybe it *was* the wind.

Suddenly he was slammed backward into the room by a tremendous force. Cuthbert could hear Rickman screaming within the Dinosaur Hall.

Wright stood unsteadily. "What was that?" he said.

His head ringing, Cuthbert picked the gun off the floor, scrambled to his feet, and ran to the far corner of the room. "Get into the Dinosaur Hall!" he shouted at Wright.

Wright sagged heavily against the chair. "What's that disgusting smell?" he asked.

There was another savage blow to the door, and the crack of splitting wood sounded like a rifle shot. Cuthbert's finger instinctively tightened on the trigger, and the gun fired unexpectedly, bringing down dust from the ceiling. He lowered the weapon momentarily, his hands shaking. *Stupid, one wasted bullet.* Bloody hell, he wished he knew more about handguns. He raised it again and tried to take aim, but his hands were shaking uncontrollably now. *Got to calm down,* he thought. *Take a few deep breaths. Aim for something vital. Four shots.*

The room gradually returned to silence. Wright was slumped against his chair, as if frozen into place.

"Winston, you idiot!" Cuthbert hissed. "Get into the Hall!"

"If you say so," Wright said, and shuffled toward the door. He seemed finally frightened enough to move.

Then Cuthbert heard that soft sound again, and the wood groaned. The thing was pressing against the door. There was another horrible *cra-ack* and the door split wide open, a piece of wood spinning crazily end over end into the room. The table was thrown to one side. Something appeared in the gloom of the hallway, and a three-tined claw reached through the opening and gripped the broken wood. With a tearing noise the remainder of the door was pulled back into the darkness, and Cuthbert saw a dark shape in the doorway.

Wright lurched into the Dinosaur Hall, almost toppling Rickman, who had appeared in the doorway, choking and sobbing.

"Shoot it, Ian, oh please, *please* kill it!" she screamed.

Cuthbert waited, sighting down the barrel. He held his breath. *Four shots.*

* * *

The commander of the SWAT team moved along the roof, a catlike shape against the dark indigo of the sky, while the spotter on the street below guided his progress. Coffey stood next to the spotter, under a tarp. They both held rubberized waterproof radios.

"Dugout to Red One, move five more feet to the east," the spotter said into his radio, peering upward through his night-vision passive telescope. "You're almost there." He was studying Museum blueprints spread out on a table under a sheet of Plexiglas. The SWAT team's route had been marked in red.

The dark figure moved carefully across the slate roof, the lights of the Upper West Side twinkling around him; below, the Hudson River, the flashing lights of the emergency vehicles on Museum Drive, the high-rise apartment buildings laid out along Riverside Drive like rows of glowing crystals.

"That's it," the spotter said. "You're there, Red One."

Coffey could see the Commander kneel, working swiftly and silently to set the charges. His team waited a hundred yards back, the medics directly behind them. On the street, a siren wailed.

"Set," said the Commander. He stood up and walked carefully backward, unrolling a wire.

"Blow when ready," murmured Coffey.

Coffey watched as everyone on the roof lay down. There was a brief flash of light, and a second later the sharp slap of sound reached Coffey. The Commander waited a moment and then eased forward.

"Red One to Dugout, we've got an opening."

"Proceed," said Coffey.

The SWAT team dropped in through the hole in the roof, followed by the medics.

"We're inside," came the voice of the Commander. "We're in the fifth-floor corridor, proceeding as advised."

Coffey waited impatiently. He looked at his watch: nine-fifteen. They'd been stuck in there, without power, for the longest ninety minutes of his life. An unwelcome vision of the Mayor, dead and gutted, kept plaguing him.

"We're at the Cell Three emergency door, fifth floor, Section Fourteen. Ready to set charges."

"Proceed," said Coffey.

"Setting charges."

D'Agosta and his group hadn't reported in for over half an hour. God, if something happened to the Mayor, no one would care whose fault it really was. Coffey would be the one that caught the blame. That's the way things worked in this town. It had taken him so long to get where he was, and he'd been so careful, and now the bastards were just going to take it away from him. It was all Pendergast's fault. If he hadn't started messing around on other people's turf . . .

"Charges set."

"Blow when ready," Coffey said again. Pendergast had fucked up, not him. He himself had only taken over yesterday. Maybe they wouldn't blame him, after all. Especially if Pendergast wasn't around. That son of a bitch could talk the hind legs off a mule.

There was a long silence. No sound of explosion reached Coffey's ears as he waited outside beneath the sodden tarp.

"Red One to Dugout, we're clean," the Commander said.

"Proceed. Get inside and kill the son of a bitch," said Coffey.

"As discussed, sir, our first priority is to evac the wounded," said the Commander in a flat voice.

"I know! But hurry it up, for God's sake!"

He punched savagely at his transmit button.

The Commander stepped out of the stairwell, looking carefully around before motioning the teams to follow him. One by one, the dark figures emerged, gas masks pushed high on their foreheads, fatigue uniforms blending into the shadows, their M-16s and Bullpups equipped with full-tang bayonets. In the rear, a short, stubby officer was carrying a 40mm six-shot grenade launcher, a big-bellied weapon that looked like a pregnant tommy gun. "We've gained the fourth floor," the Commander radioed the spotter. "Laying down an infrared beacon. Hall of Lesser Apes directly ahead."

The spotter spoke into his radio. "Proceed south seventy feet into the Hall, then west twenty feet to a door."

The Commander took a small black box from his belt and pressed a button. A ruby laser shot out, pencil-thin. He moved the beam around until he had the distance reading he needed. Then he moved forward and repeated the procedure, shining the laser toward the west wall.

"Red One to Dugout. Door in sight."

"Good. Proceed."

The Commander moved ahead to the door, motioning his men to follow.

"The door's locked. Setting charges."

The team quickly moulded two small bars of plastique around the doorknob, then stepped back, unrolling more wire.

"Charges set."

There was a low *whump* as the door flew open.

"The trapdoor should be directly in front of you, in the center of the storage room," the spotter directed.

By moving aside several flats of scenery, the Commander and his men exposed the trapdoor. Undoing the latches, the Commander grasped the iron ring and heaved upward. Stale air rushed up to greet them. The Commander leaned forward. In the Hall of the Heavens below, everything was still.

"We've got an opening," he said into the radio. "Looks good."

"Okay," came Coffey's voice. "Secure the Hall. Send down the medics and evac the injured, fast."

"Red One, roger that, Dugout."

The spotter took over. "Tear out the drywall in the center of the north wall. Behind it you'll find an eight-inch I-beam to anchor your ropes to."

"Will do."

"Careful. It's a sixty-foot drop."

The Commander and his team worked swiftly, punching through the drywall, looping two chains around the I-beam, attaching locking carabiners, a block and tackle. A team member hooked a rope ladder to one of the chains and dropped it through the hole.

The Commander leaned over once again, shining his powerful light down into the gloom of the hall.

"This is Red One. We've got some bodies down here," he said.

"Any sign of the creature?" Coffey asked.

"Negative. Looks like ten, twelve bodies, maybe more. Ladder's in place now."

"What are you waiting for?"

The Commander turned to the medic team. "We'll signal when ready. Start lowering the collapsible stretchers. We'll take 'em out one by one."

He grabbed the rope ladder and started down, swinging over the vast empty space. The men followed, one by one. Two fanned out to provide suppressing fire as necessary, while two others set up tripods with clusters of halogen lamps, hooking them to the portable generators being lowered by ropes. Soon the center of the hall was flooded with light.

"Secure all ingress and egress!" shouted the Commander. "Medic team, descend!"

"Report!" Coffey cried over the radio.

"We've secured the Hall," the Commander said. "No sign of any animal. Medic team deploying now."

"Good. You'll need to find the thing, kill it, and locate the Mayor's party. We believe they went down the stairwell back by the service area."

"Roger, Dugout," said the Commander.

As the Commander's radio buzzed into silence, he heard a sudden report, muffled but unmistakable.

"Red One to Dugout, we just heard a pistol shot. Sounded like it was coming from above."

"Dammit, go after it!" cried Coffey. "Take your men and go after it!"

The Commander turned to his men. "All right. Red Two, Red Three, finish up and secure here. Take the grenade launcher. The rest of you come with me."

= 56 =

The viscous water was now lapping at Smithback's waist. Just keeping his balance was exhausting. His legs had long since gone numb, and he was shivering.

"This water is rising awful damn fast." D'Agosta said.

"I don't think we need to worry about that creature anymore," Smithback said hopefully.

"Maybe not. You know," D'Agosta told him slowly, "You were pretty quick back there, jamming the door with the flashlight like that. I guess you saved all our lives."

"Thanks," said Smithback, liking D'Agosta more and more.

"Don't let it go to your head," D'Agosta said over the rush of the water.

"Everyone okay?" D'Agosta turned back to the Mayor.

The Mayor looked haggard. "It's touch and go. There are a few who are slipping into shock or exhaustion, maybe both. Which way from here?" His eyes searched them.

D'Agosta hesitated. "Ah, I really can't say anything conclusively," he said at last. "Smithback and I will try the right fork first."

The Mayor looked back at the group, then moved closer to D'Agosta. "Look," he said, in a low, pleading tone. "I know you're lost. *You* know you're lost. But if those people back there learn about it, I don't think we'd get them to go any farther. It's very cold standing here, and the water is getting higher. So why don't we all try it together? It's our only chance. Even if we wanted to retrace our steps, half these people would never make it against the current."

D'Agosta looked at the Mayor for a moment. "All right," he said at last. Then he turned to the group. "Listen up now," he shouted. "We're gonna be taking the right tunnel. Everyone join hands, form a line. Hold on tight. Stay against the wall—the current's getting too strong in the center. If anyone slips, give a yell, but don't let go under any circumstances. Everybody got that? Let's go."

The dark shape moved slowly through the broken door, stepping catlike over the splintered wood. Cuthbert felt pins and needles in his legs. He wanted to shoot, but his hands refused to obey.

"Please go away," he said, so calmly he surprised himself.

It stopped suddenly and looked directly at him. Cuthbert could see nothing in the dim light but the huge, powerful silhouette and the small red eyes. They looked, somehow, intelligent.

"Don't hurt me," Cuthbert pleaded.

The creature remained still.

"I've got a gun," Cuthbert whispered. He aimed carefully. "I won't shoot if you go away," he said quietly.

It moved slowly sideways, keeping its head turned

toward Cuthbert. Then there was a sudden movement and it was gone.

Cuthbert backed away in a panic, his flashlight skittering wildly across the floor. He spun around frantically. All was silent. The creature's stench filled the room. Suddenly he found himself stumbling into the Dinosaur Hall, and then he was slamming the door behind him.

"The key!" he cried. "Lavinia, for God's sake!"

He looked wildly around the darkened hall. Before him, a great tyrannosaurus skeleton reared up from the center. In front of it squatted the dark form of a triceratops, its head lowered, the great black horns gleaming in the dull light.

He heard a sobbing, then he felt a key being pressed into his palm. He swiftly locked the door.

"Let's go," he said, guiding her away from the door, past the clawed foot of the tyrannosaur. They moved deeper into darkness. Suddenly, Cuthbert pulled the Public Relations Director to one side, then guided her into a crouch. He peered into the gloom, senses straining. The Hall of Cretaceous Dinosaurs was deathly silent. Not even the sound of the rain penetrated this dark sanctum. The only light came from rows of high clerestory windows.

Surrounding them was a herd of small struthiomimus skeletons, arranged in a defensive U-shaped formation before the monstrous skeleton of a carnivorous dryptosaurus, its head down, jaws open, and huge claws extended. Cuthbert had always relished the scale and drama of this room, but now it frightened him. Now he knew what it was like to be hunted.

Behind them, the entrance to the Hall was blocked by a heavy steel emergency door. "Where's Winston?" Cuthbert whispered, peering through the bones of the dryptosaur.

"I don't know," Rickman moaned, gripping his arm. "Did you kill it?"

"I missed," he whispered. "Please let me go. I need to have a clear shot."

Rickman released him, then crawled backward between two of the struthiomimus skeletons, curling herself into a fetal position with a stifled sob.

"Be silent!" Cuthbert hissed.

The Hall lapsed again into a profound stillness. He looked around, probing the shadows with his eyes. He hoped Wright had found refuge in one of the many dark corners.

"Ian?" came a subdued voice. "Lavinia?"

Cuthbert turned and saw to his horror that Wright was leaning against the tail of a stegosaurus. As he watched, Wright swayed, then recovered.

"Winston!" Cuthbert hissed. "Get under cover!"

But Wright began walking unsteadily toward them. "Is that you, Ian?" Wright said, his voice puzzled. He stopped and leaned for a moment against the corner of a display case. "I feel sick," he said matter-of-factly.

Suddenly an explosive noise rocketed across the hall, echoing crazily in the enormous space. Another crash followed. Dimly, Cuthbert saw that Wright's office door was now a jagged hole. A dark form emerged.

Behind him, Rickman screamed and covered her head.

Through the skeleton of the dryptosaurus, Cuthbert could see the dark shape moving swiftly across the open floor. Straight for him, he thought—but it suddenly veered toward the shadowy figure of Wright. The two shadows merged.

Then Cuthbert heard a wet crunching noise, a scream—and silence.

Cuthbert raised the gun and tried to sight through the ribs of the mounted skeleton.

The silhouette rose up with something in its mouth, shook its head slightly and made a sucking noise. Cuthbert closed his eyes, squeezing the trigger.

The Ruger bucked in his hand, and he heard a blast and a loud clattering. Now Cuthbert saw that the dryptosaurus was missing part of a rib. Behind him, Rickman gasped and moaned.

The dark shape of the creature beyond was gone.

A few moments went by and Cuthbert felt the hinges of his sanity begin to loosen. Then, in a flicker of lightning through the clerestory, Cuthbert clearly saw the beast moving swiftly along the near wall, coming directly toward him, its red eyes fixed on his face.

He swung the barrel and began firing wildly, three quick shots, each white flash illuminating rack upon rack of dark skulls, teeth and claws—the real beast suddenly lost in this wilderness of savage extinct creatures—and then the gun was clicking as the hammer fell harmlessly on the expended chambers.

As if from a half-remembered dream, Cuthbert heard the distant sound of human voices, coming from the direction of Wright's old lab. And suddenly he was running, heedless of obstacles, through the ruined door, through Wright's lab, and into the dark corridor beyond. He heard himself screaming, and then a spotlight was shining in his face and somebody grabbed him and pinned him against a wall.

"Calm down, you're all right! Look, there's blood on him!"

"Get the gun away from him," someone else said.

"Is he the one we're after?"

"No, they said an animal. But don't take any chances."

"Stop struggling!"

Another scream rose in Cuthbert's throat. "It's back there!" he cried. "It'll kill you all! It knows, you can see in its eyes that it knows!"

"Knows what?"

"Don't bother talking to him, he's raving."

Cuthbert suddenly went limp.

The Commander came forward. "Is there anyone else back there?" he asked, shaking Cuthbert's shoulder.

"Yes," Cuthbert finally said. "Wright. Rickman."

The Commander looked up.

"You mean Winston Wright? The Director of the Museum? You must be Dr. Cuthbert, then. Where is Wright?"

"It was eating him," said Cuthbert, "eating the brains. Just eating and eating. It's in the Dinosaur Hall, through the lab there."

"Take him back to the Hall and have the medics evacuate him," said the Commander to two members of his team. "You three, let's go. On the double." He raised his radio. "Red One to Dugout. We've located Cuthbert, and we're sending him out."

"They're in this laboratory, here," said the spotter, pointing at the blueprints. Now that the penetration was complete and the team was deep inside the Museum, the two had moved inside the mobile command unit, away from the hammering rain.

"The lab's clear," the Commander's monotone came over the radio. "Proceeding into the Dinosaur Hall. This other door's been broken down, too."

"Go in and take that thing out!" cried Coffey. "But watch out for Dr. Wright. And keep a clear frequency. I want to be in touch at all times!"

Coffey waited, tensed over the set, hearing the faint hiss and crackle of the static over the open frequency. He heard the clink of a weapon and a few whispers.

"Smell that?" Coffey leaned closer. They were almost there. He gripped the edge of the table.

"Yup," a voice answered.

There was a rattling.

"Kill the light and stay in the shadows. Red Seven, cover the left side of that skeleton. Red Three, go right. Red Four, get your back to the wall, cover the far sector."

There was a long silence. Coffey could hear heavy breathing and faint footfalls.

He heard a sudden explosive whisper. "Red Four, look, there's a body here."

Coffey felt his stomach tighten.

"No head," he heard. "Nice."

"Here's another one," whispered a voice. "See it? Lying in that group of dinosaurs."

More clicking and rattling of weapons, more breathing.

"Red Seven, cover our path of retreat. There's no other way out."

"It may still be here," someone whispered.

"That's far enough, Red Four."

Coffey's knuckles whitened. Why the fuck didn't they get it over with? These guys were a bunch of old women.

More rattling of metal.

"Something's moving! Over there!" The voice was so loud Coffey jumped, and then a burst of automatic weapons fire dissolved immediately into static as the frequency overloaded.

"Shit, shit, shit," Coffey began saying, over and over. Then for an instant he could hear screaming, and then more static; the even cadence of machine-gun fire; then, silence. The tinkling sound of something—what? Shattered dinosaur bones dropping and rolling on the marble floor?

Coffey felt a flood of relief. Whatever it was, it was dead. Nothing could have survived the shitload of firepower just unloaded. The nightmare was finally over. He eased himself down in a chair.

"Red Four! Hoskins! Oh shit!" the voice of the Commander screamed over the frequency. The voice was suddenly buried by the staccato of gunfire, then more static. Or was it a scream?

Coffey surged to his feet and turned to an agent standing behind him. He opened his mouth to speak, but no sound came out. He read his own terror in the agent's eyes.

"Red One!" he yelled into the mike. "Red One! Do you read?"

All he could hear was static.

"Talk to me, Commander! Do you read? Anyone!"

He switched frequencies wildly to the team in the Hall of the Heavens.

"Sir, we're removing the last of the bodies now," came the voice of a medic. "The rear detail of the SWAT team just evacuated Doctor Cuthbert to the roof. We just heard firing from upstairs. Are we going to need more evacuation—?"

"Get the hell out!" Coffey screamed. "Get your asses out! Get the fuck out and pull up the ladder!"

"Sir, what about the rest of the SWAT team? We can't leave those men—"

"They're dead! Understand? That's an order!"

He dropped the radio and leaned back, gazing vaguely out the window. A morgue truck slowly moved up toward the massive bulk of the Museum.

Someone tapped him on the shoulder. "Sir, Agent Pendergast is requesting to speak with you."

Coffey slowly shook his head. "No. I don't want to talk to that fuck, you got that?"

"Sir, he—"

"Don't mention his name to me again."

Another agent opened the rear door and came inside, his suit sodden. "Sir, the dead are coming out now."

"Who? Who are you talking about?"

"The people from the Hall of the Heavens. There were seventeen dead, no survivors."

"Cuthbert? The guy you took out of the lab? Is he out?"

"They've just lowered him to the street."

"I want to talk to him."

Coffey stepped outside and ran down past the ambulance circle, his mind numb. How could a SWAT team buy it, just like that?

Outside, two medics with a stretcher approached. "Are you Cuthbert?" Coffey asked the still form.

The man looked around with unfocused eyes.

The doctor pushed past Coffey, sliced open Cuthbert's shirt, then inspected his face and eyes.

"There's blood here," he said. "Are you hurt?"

"I don't know," said Cuthbert.

"Respiration thirty, pulse one-twenty," said a paramedic.

"You're okay?" the doctor asked. "Is this your blood?"

"I don't know."

The doctor looked swiftly down Cuthbert's legs, felt them, felt his groin, examined his neck.

The doctor turned toward the paramedic. "Take him in for observation." The medics wheeled the stretcher away.

"Cuthbert!" said Coffey, jogging beside him. "Did you see it?"

"See it?" Cuthbert repeated.

"See the fucking creature!"

"It knows," Cuthbert said.

"Knows what?"

"It knows what's going on, it knows exactly what's happening."

"What the hell does that mean?"

"It hates us," said Cuthbert.

As the medics threw open the door of an ambulance, Coffey yelled, "What did it look like?"

"There was sadness in its eyes," said Cuthbert. "Infinite sadness."

"He's a lunatic," said Coffey to no one in particular.

"You won't kill it," Cuthbert added, with calm certainty.

The doors slammed shut.

"The hell I won't!" shouted Coffey at the retreating ambulance. "Fuck you, Cuthbert! *The hell I won't!*"

= 57 =

Pendergast lowered the radio and looked at Margo. "The creature just killed the better part of a SWAT team. Dr. Wright, too, from the sound of it. Coffey withdrew everyone else, and he won't answer my summons. He seems to think everything is my fault."

"He's *got* to listen!" roared Frock. "We know what to do now. All they need to do is come in here with klieg lights!"

"I understand what's happening," said Pendergast. "He's overloaded, looking for scapegoats. We can't rely on his help."

"My God," Margo said. "Dr. Wright . . ." She put a hand to her mouth. "If my plan had worked—if I'd thought everything through—maybe all those people would still be alive."

"And perhaps Lieutenant D'Agosta, and the Mayor, and all those others below us, would be dead," Pendergast said. He looked down the hallway. "I suppose my duty now is to see you two out safely," he said. "Perhaps we should take the route I suggested to D'Agosta. Assuming those blueprints didn't lead him astray, of course."

Then he glanced at Frock. "No, I don't suppose that would work."

"Go ahead!" Frock cried. "Don't stay here on my account!"

Pendergast smiled thinly. "It isn't that, Doctor. It's the inclement weather. You know how the subbasement floods during rainy spells. I heard someone on the police radio saying the rain outside has been approaching monsoon strength for the last hour. When I was sprinkling those fibers into the subbasement, I noticed the water was at least two feet deep and flowing quickly eastward. That would imply drainage from the river. We couldn't get down there now even if we wanted to." Pendergast raised his eyebrows. "If D'Agosta isn't out by now— well, his chances are marginal, at best."

He turned toward Margo. "Perhaps the best thing would be for you two to stay here, inside the Secure Area. We know the creature can't get past this reinforced door. Within a couple of hours, they are sure to restore power. I believe there are several men still trapped in Security Command and the Computer Room. They may be vulnerable. You've taught me a lot about this creature. We know its weaknesses, and we know its strengths. Those areas are near a long, unobstructed hallway. With you two safe in here, I can hunt it for a change."

"No," said Margo. "You can't do it by yourself."

"Perhaps not, Ms. Green, but I plan on making a fairly good imitation of it."

"I'm coming with you," she said resolutely.

"Sorry." Pendergast stood by the open door to the Secure Area expectantly.

"That thing is highly intelligent," she said. I don't think you can go up against it alone. If you think that because I'm a woman—"

Pendergast looked astonished. "Ms. Green, I'm shocked you would have such a low opinion of me. The fact is, you've never been in this kind of situation before. Without a gun, you can't do anything."

Margo looked at him combatively. "I saved your ass back there when I told you to switch on your lamp," she challenged.

He raised an eyebrow.

From the darkness, Frock said, "Pendergast, don't be a Southern gentleman fool. Take her."

Pendergast turned to Frock. "Are you sure you'll be all right on your own, Doctor?" he asked. "We'll need to take both the flashlight and the miner's lamp if we're to have any chance of success."

"Of course!" Frock said with a dismissive wave. "I could use a bit of rest after all this excitement."

Pendergast hesitated a moment longer, then looked bemused. "Very well," he said. "Margo, lock the doctor inside the Secure Area, get his keys and what's left of my suit jacket, and let's go."

Smithback gave the flashlight a savage shake. The light flickered, grew brighter for a moment, then dimmed again.

"If that light goes out," D'Agosta said, "we're fucked. Turn it off; we'll switch it on now and then to check our progress."

They moved through the darkness, the sound of rushing water filling the close air. Smithback led; behind him came D'Agosta, grasping the journalist's hand—which, like the rest of him, had grown almost entirely numb.

Suddenly, Smithback pricked up his ears. In the dark, he gradually became aware of a new sound.

"You hear that?" Smithback asked.

D'Agosta listened. "I hear something," he answered.

"It sounds to me like—" Smithback fell silent.

"A waterfall," D'Agosta said with finality. "But

whatever it is must be a ways off. Sounds carry in this tunnel. Keep it to yourself.''

The group slogged on in silence.

''Light,'' said D'Agosta.

Smithback turned it on, played it down the empty hall in front of them, then switched it off again. The sound was louder now; quite a bit louder, in fact. He felt a surge in the water.

''Shit!'' said D'Agosta.

There was a sudden commotion behind them.

''Help!'' came a feminine voice. ''I've slipped! Don't let go!''

''Grab her, somebody!'' the Mayor shouted.

Smithback snapped on the light and angled it quickly backward. A middle-aged woman was thrashing about in the water, her long evening dress billowing out across the inky surface.

''Stand up!'' the Mayor was shouting. ''Anchor your feet!''

''Help me!'' she screamed.

Smithback shoved the flashlight into his pocket and braced himself against the current. The woman was floating directly toward him. He saw her arm lash out and felt it wrap around his thigh in a viselike grip. He felt himself slipping.

''Wait!'' he cried. ''Stop struggling! I've got you!''

Her legs kicked out and wrapped around his knees. Smithback lost his grip on D'Agosta and staggered forward, marveling at her strength even as he was pulled off balance.

''You're dragging me under!'' he said, toppling to his chest in the water and feeling the current sucking him downward. Out of the corner of his eye he saw D'Agosta wading in his direction. The woman clambered onto him in a blind panic, forcing his head under water. He rose up under her damp gown, and then it was clinging to his nose and chin, disorienting him, suffocating him. A great lassitude began to sweep over him. He went under a second time, a strange, hollow roaring in his ears.

Suddenly he was above the water again, choking and coughing. A dreadful shrieking was coming from the tunnel ahead of them. He was held in a powerful grip. D'Agosta's grip.

"We lost the woman," D'Agosta said. "Come on."

Her shrieks echoed toward them, growing fainter as she was swept farther downstream. Some of the guests were shouting and crying directions to her, others sobbing uncontrollably.

"Quick, everybody!" D'Agosta yelled. "Stay against the wall! Let's move forward, and, whatever you do, don't break the chain." Under his breath, he muttered to Smithback, "Tell me you've still got the flashlight."

"Here it is," Smithback said, testing it.

"We have to keep going, or we'll lose everybody," D'Agosta muttered. Then he laughed a short, mirthless laugh. "Looks like I saved *your* life this time. That makes us even, Smithback."

Smithback said nothing. He was trying to shut out the horrifying, anguished screams, fainter now and distorted by the tunnel. The sound of roaring water grew clearer and more menacing.

The event had demoralized the group. "We'll be all right if we just hold hands!" Smithback heard the Mayor shout. "Keep the chain intact!"

Smithback gripped D'Agosta's hand as hard as he could. They waded downstream in the darkness.

"Light," said D'Agosta.

Smithback switched on the beam. And the bottom dropped out of his world.

A hundred yards ahead, the high ceiling of the tunnel sloped downwards to a narrow semicircular funnel. Beneath it, the roiling water writhed and surged thunderously, then plummeted abruptly into a dark chasm. Heavy mist rose, bearding the mossy throat of the pit with dark spray. Smithback watched, slackjawed, as all his hopes for a best-seller, all his dreams—even his wish to stay alive—disappeared into the whirlpool.

Dimly, he realized that the screaming behind him wasn't screaming, but cheering. He looked back, and saw the bedraggled group staring upward, above his head. At the point where the curved brickwork of the ceiling met the wall of the tunnel, a dark hole yawned, perhaps three feet square. Poking out of it was the end of a rusty iron ladder, bolted to the ancient masonry.

The cheering rapidly died away as the awful truth dawned.

"It's too fucking far to reach," D'Agosta said.

= 58 =

They moved away from the Secure Area and stealthily climbed a stairwell. Pendergast turned to Margo, put a finger to his lips, then pointed to the crimson splashes of blood on the floor. She nodded: the beast had gone this way when it ran from their lights. She remembered that she'd been up this staircase just the day before with Smithback, evading the guard. She followed Pendergast as he flicked off the miner's lamp, cautiously opened the first floor door, and moved out into the darkness beyond, the bundle of fibers clasped over his shoulder.

The agent stopped a moment, inhaling. "I don't smell anything," he whispered. "Which way to Security Command and the Computer Room?"

"I think we go left from here," Margo said. "And then through the Hall of Ancient Mammals. It's not too far. Just around the corner from Security Command is the long hallway Dr. Frock told you about."

Pendergast switched on the flashlight briefly and shone it down the corridor. "No blood spoor," he murmured. "The creature headed straight upstairs from the Secure Area—past this landing and right toward Dr. Wright, I'm afraid." He turned toward Margo. "And how do you propose we lure it here?"

"Use the fibers again," she replied.

"It didn't fall for that trick last time."

"But this time we're not trying to trap it. All we want to do is lure it around the corner. You'll be at the other end of the hallway, ready to shoot. We'll just leave some fibers at one end of the hall. We'll make a—a what do you call it?—at the far end."

"A blind."

"Right, a blind. And we'll be hiding there, in the dark. When it comes, I'll train the miner's light onto it and you can start shooting."

"Indeed. And how will we know when the creature has arrived? If the hallway is as long as Dr. Frock says it is, we may not be able to smell it in time."

Margo was quiet. "That's tough," she finally admitted.

They stood for a moment in silence.

"There's a glass case at the end of the hall," Margo said. "It's meant to display new books written by the Museum staff, but Mrs. Rickman never bothered to have it filled. So it won't be locked. We can put the bundle in there. The creature may be out for blood, but I doubt it'll be able to resist *that*. It'll make some noise prying open the case. When you hear the noise, you shoot."

"Sorry," Pendergast said after a moment, "but I think it's too obvious. We have to ask the question again: If *I* came across a setup like this, would I know it was a trap? In this case, the answer is yes. We need to think of something a little more subtle. Any new trap that uses the fibers as bait is bound to arouse its suspicions."

Margo leaned against the cold marble wall of the corridor. "It has an acute sense of hearing as well as smell," she said.

"Yes?"

"Perhaps the simplest approach is best. We use our-selves as bait. We make some noise. Talk loudly. Sound like easy prey."

Pendergast nodded. "Like the ptarmigan, feigning a broken wing, drawing off the fox. And how will we know it's there?"

"We'll use the flashlight intermittently. Wave it about, shine it down the hall. We'll use the low setting; it may irritate the creature, but it won't rebuff it. But it will allow us to see it. The creature will think we're looking around, trying to find our way. Then, when it comes for us, I switch to the miner's light and you start shooting."

Pendergast thought for a moment. "What about the possibility of the creature coming from the other direc-tion? From behind us?"

"The hall dead-ends in the staff entrance to the Hall of Pacific Peoples," Margo pointed out.

"So we'll be trapped at the end of a cul-de-sac," Pen-dergast protested. "I don't like it."

"Even if we weren't trapped," Margo said, "we wouldn't be able to escape if you miss your shots. Ac-cording to the Extrapolator, the thing can move almost as fast as a greyhound."

Pendergast thought for a moment. "You know, Margo, this plan might work. It's deceptively simple and uncluttered, like a Zurbarán still life or a Bruckner sym-phony. If this creature devastated a SWAT team, it prob-ably feels there isn't much more that human beings can do to it. It wouldn't be as cautious."

"And it's wounded, which may slow it down."

"Yes, it's wounded. I think D'Agosta shot it, and the SWAT team may have gotten one or two additional rounds into it. Maybe I hit it, as well; there's no way to be sure. But, Margo, being wounded makes it infinitely *more* dangerous. I would rather stalk ten healthy lions than one wounded one." He straightened his shoulders and felt for his gun. "Lead on, please. Standing here in the dark with this bundle on my back makes me very uneasy. From now on, we use only the flashlight. Be very careful.''

"Why don't you give me the miner's light, so you'll be free to use the gun?" Margo suggested. "If we meet up with the beast unexpectedly, we'll have to drive it away with the light."

"If it's badly wounded, I doubt anything will drive it away," replied Pendergast. "But here it is."

They moved quietly down the corridor, around a corner, and through a service door leading into the Hall of Ancient Mammals. It seemed to Margo that her stealthy footsteps echoed like gunshots across the polished stone floor. Row upon row of glass cases gleamed dully in the glow of the flashlight: giant elk, saber-toothed cats, dire wolves. Mastodon and wooly mammoth skeletons reared in the center of the gallery. Margo and Pendergast moved cautiously toward the Hall's exit, Pendergast's gun at the ready.

"See that door at the far end, the one marked STAFF ONLY?" Margo whispered. "Beyond that is the corridor housing Security Command, Staff Services, and the Computer Room. Around the corner is the hallway where you can set up your blind." She hesitated. "If the creature is already there . . ."

". . . I'll wish I'd stayed in New Orleans, Ms. Green."

Stepping through the staff entrance into Section 18, they found themselves in a narrow hallway lined with doors. Pendergast swept the area with his flashlight: nothing.

"That's it," said Margo, indicating a door to their left. "Security Command." Margo could briefly hear the murmur of voices as they passed. They passed another door marked CENTRAL COMPUTER.

"They're sitting ducks in there," Margo said. "Should we—?"

"No," came the response. "No time."

They turned the corner and stopped. Pendergast played his light down the hallway.

"What's that doing there?" he asked.

Halfway down the hall, a massive steel security door flashed mockingly at them in the glow of the flashlight.

"The good Doctor was mistaken," Pendergast said. "Cell Two must cut this corridor in half. That's the edge of the perimeter, there."

"What's the distance?" Margo said in a monotone.

Pendergast pursed his lips. "I'd guess a hundred, a hundred and twenty-five feet, at the most."

She turned to the agent. "Is that enough room?"

Pendergast remained motionless. "No. But it'll have to do. Come on, Ms. Green, let's get into position."

The Mobile Command Unit was getting stuffier. Coffey unbuttoned his shirt and loosened his tie with a savage tug. The humidity had to be 110 percent. He hadn't seen rain like this in twenty years. The drains were bubbling like geysers, the tires of the emergency vehicles up to their hubcaps in water.

The rear door swung open, revealing a man wearing SWAT fatigues.

"Sir?"

"What do you want?"

"The men would like to know when we're going back in."

"Going back *in?*" Coffey yelled. "Are you out of your mind? Four of your men were just killed in there, torn apart like frigging hamburger!"

"But sir, there are people still trapped in there. Maybe we could—"

Coffey rounded on the man, eyes blazing, mouth spewing saliva. "Don't you get it? We can't just go busting back in there. We sent men in not knowing what we were up against. We've got to get the power restored, get the systems back on line before we—"

A policeman stuck his head inside the door of the van.

"Sir, we've just had a report of a dead body floating in the Hudson River. It was spotted down at the Boat Basin. Seems like it was flushed out of one of the big storm drains."

"Who the fuck cares about—"

"Sir, it's a woman wearing an evening gown, and it's been tentatively identified as one of the people missing from the party."

"What?" Coffey was confused. It wasn't possible. "Someone from the Mayor's group?"

"One of the people trapped inside. The only women still unaccounted for inside apparently went down into the basement two hours ago."

"You mean, with the *Mayor?*"

"I guess that would be right, sir."

Coffey felt his bladder weakening. It couldn't be true. That fucking Pendergast. Fucking D'Agosta. It was all their fault. They disobeyed him, compromised his plan, sent all those people to their deaths. The Mayor, dead. They were going to have his ass for that.

"Sir?"

"Get out," Coffey whispered. "Both of you, get out." The door closed.

"This is Garcia, over. Does anyone copy?" the radio squawked. Coffey spun around and jabbed the radio with his finger.

"Garcia! What's going on?"

"Nothing, sir, except the power's still out. But I have Tom Allen here. He's been asking to speak with you."

"Put him on, then."

"This is Allen. We're getting a little concerned in here, Mr. Coffey. There's nothing we can do until power's restored. The batteries are failing on Garcia's transmitter, and we've been keeping it off to conserve juice. We'd like you to get us out."

Coffey laughed, suddenly, shrilly. The agents manning the consoles looked uneasily at one another. "You'd like *me* to get *you* out? Listen, Allen, you geniuses created this mess. You swore up and down the system would work, that everything had a backup. So you get your own asses out. The Mayor's dead, and I've already lost more men than I—hello?''

"This is Garcia again. Sir, it's pitch-black in here and we only have two flashlights. What happened to the SWAT team that was being sent in?''

Coffey's laughter stopped abruptly. "Garcia? They got themselves killed. You hear me? *Killed.* Got their guts hung up like birthday ribbons in there. And it's Pendergast's fault, and D'Agosta's fault, and fucking Allen's fault, and *your* fault, too, probably. Now, we've got men on this side working to restore the power. They say it can be done, it just may take a few hours. Okay? I'm gonna take that goddamn thing in there, but in *my* way, in my own sweet time. So you just sit tight. I'm not going to have more men killed to save your sorry asses."

There was a rap on the rear door. "Come in," he barked, switching off the radio.

An agent stepped inside and crouched beside Coffey, the glow of the monitors throwing his face into sharp relief. "Sir, I just got word that the Deputy Mayor is on his way over now. And the Governor's office is on the phone. They want an update."

Coffey closed his eyes.

Smithback looked up at the ladder, its rusty lower rung hanging a good four feet above his head. Maybe if there was no water he could have jumped it, but with the current nearing his chest it was impossible.

"See anything up there?" D'Agosta asked.

"Nope," replied Smithback. "This light's weak. I can't tell how far the thing extends."

"Turn off the light, then," D'Agosta gasped. "Give me a minute to think."

There was a long silence. Smithback felt another surge against his waist. The water was still rising fast. Another foot, and they would all be floating downstream toward—Smithback shook his head, angrily dispelling the thought.

"Where the hell is all this water coming from?" he moaned to no one in particular.

"This subbasement is built below the Hudson River water table," D'Agosta replied. "It leaks whenever there's a heavy rain."

"Leaks, sure—maybe it even floods a foot or two," Smithback panted. "But we're being inundated. They must be building arks out there."

D'Agosta didn't answer.

"The hell with this," a voice said. "Someone get on my shoulders. We'll go up one by one."

"Stow it!" D'Agosta snapped. "It's too damn high for that."

Smithback coughed, cleared his throat. "I've got an idea!" he said.

There was a silence.

"Look, that steel ladder appears to be pretty strong," he urged. "If we can fasten our belts together and loop them over that ladder, we can wait for the water to rise enough so we can grab the lower rung."

"I can't wait that long!" someone cried.

D'Agosta glared. "Smithback, that's the fucking worst idea I ever heard," he growled. "Besides, half the men here are wearing cummerbunds."

"I noticed *you* have a belt on," Smithback retorted.

"So I do," D'Agosta replied defensively. "But what makes you think the water will rise enough for us to reach the rung?"

"Look up there," Smithback said, shining his flashlight along the wall near the bottom of the metal ladder. "See that band of discoloration? It looks like a high-water mark to me. At least once in the past, the water has risen that high. If this is half the storm you think it is, we ought to get fairly close."

D'Agosta shook his head. "Well, I still think it's

crazy," he said, "but I suppose it's better than waiting here to die. You men back there!" he shouted. "Belts! Pass your belts up to me!"

As the belts reached D'Agosta, he knotted them together, buckle to end, starting with the widest buckle. Then he passed them to Smithback, who looped them over his shoulders. Swinging the heavier end, he braced himself against the current, leaned back, and tossed it up toward the lowest rung. The twelve feet of leather fell back into the water, missing by several feet. He tried again, missed again.

"Here, give me that," D'Agosta said. "Let a man do a man's job."

"The hell with that," Smithback said, rearing back dangerously and giving another toss. This time Smithback ducked as the heavy buckle came swinging down; then he slid the far end through and pulled the improvised rope tight around the lower ring.

"Okay, everyone," D'Agosta said. "This is it. I want you all to link arms. Don't let go. As the water rises, it'll carry us toward the ladder. We'll play this back to you in sections as we rise. I hope the son of a bitch holds," he muttered, eyeing the linked belts dubiously.

"And the water rises far enough," said Smithback.

"If it doesn't, you'll hear about it from me, mister."

Smithback turned to respond, but decided to save his breath. The current crept up around his chest, tugging at his armpits, and he felt a slow, inexorable pressure from below as his feet started to lose their hold on the smooth stone floor of the tunnel.

= 59 =

Garcia watched as the pool of light from Allen's flashlight moved slowly across a bank of dead controls, then back again. Nesbitt, the guard on monitoring duty, slouched at the coffee-stained "panic desk" in the middle of Security Command. Next to him sat Waters and the skinny, gawky-looking programmer from the Computer Room. They had knocked on the door of Security Command ten minutes earlier, scaring the three men inside half to death. Now the programmer was sitting quietly in the dark, chewing his cuticles and sniffling. Waters had placed his service revolver on the table and was nervously spinning it.

"What was that?" Waters said suddenly, stopping his pistol in mid-spin.

"What was what?" Garcia asked morosely.

"I thought I heard a noise in the hall just now," Waters said, swallowing hard. "Like feet going by."

"You're always hearing noises, Waters," Garcia said. "That's what got us here in the first place."

There was a brief, uncomfortable silence.

"Are you sure you read Coffey right?" Waters spoke up again. "If that thing destroyed a SWAT team, it could easily get to us."

"Stop thinking about it," said Garcia. "Stop *talking* about it. It happened three floors above us."

"I can't believe Coffey, just leaving us here to rot—"

"Waters? If you don't shut up I'm going to send you back to the Computer Room."

Waters fell silent.

"Radio Coffey again," Allen told Garcia. "We need to get the hell out of here, now."

Garcia slowly shook his head. "It ain't gonna work. Sounded to me like he was about five beers short of a six-pack. Maybe he's bent a bit under the pressure. We're stuck here for the duration."

"Who's his boss?" Allen insisted. "Give me the radio."

"No way. The emergency batteries are almost dead."

Allen started to protest, then stopped abruptly. "I smell something," he said.

Garcia sat up. "So do I." Then he picked up his shotgun, slowly, like a sleeper caught in a bad dream.

"It's the killer beast!" Waters cried loudly. All the men were on their feet in an instant. Chairs were thrown back, smashing against the floor. There was a thump and a curse as somebody struck the side of a desk, then a splintering crash as a monitor fell to the floor. Garcia grabbed the radio.

"Coffey! It's here!"

There was a scratching, then a low rattling at the doorknob. Garcia felt a gush of warmth on his legs and realized his bladder had given way. Suddenly, the door bent inward, wood cracking under a savage blow. In the close, listening darkness, he heard somebody behind him start to pray.

* * *

"Did you hear that?" whispered Pendergast.

Margo played the flashlight down the hall. "I heard something."

From down the hall and around the corner came the sound of splintering wood.

"It's breaking through one of the doors!" said Pendergast. "We need to attract its attention. *Hey!*" he shouted.

Margo grabbed Pendergast's arm. "Don't say anything you wouldn't want it to understand," she hissed.

"Ms. Green, this is no time for jokes," Pendergast snapped. "Surely it doesn't understand English."

"I don't know. We're taking a chance, anyway, just trusting the Extrapolator's data. But the thing has a highly developed brain, and it may well have been in the Museum for years, listening from dark places. It might understand certain words. We can't take the chance."

"As you wish," Pendergast whispered. Then, he said loudly: "Where are you? Can you hear me?"

"Yes!" Margo shouted. "But I'm lost! Help! Can anyone hear us?"

Pendergast lowered his voice. "It must have heard that. Now we can only wait." He dropped to one knee, right hand aiming the .45, left hand bracing right wrist. "Keep playing the light toward the bend in the hallway, move it around as if you're lost. When I see the creature, I'll give you the word. Turn on the miner's light, and keep it aimed on the creature, no matter what. If it's angry—if it's just hunting for revenge now—we have to use any means possible to slow it down. We only have a hundred feet of corridor in which to kill it. If it can run as quickly as you think it can, the beast can cover that distance in a couple of seconds. You can't hesitate, and you can't panic."

"A couple of seconds," Margo said. "I understand."

* * *

Garcia kneeled in front of the monitor bank, the butt of his shotgun snug against his cheek, the barrel pointing into the gloom. Before him, the outline of the door was faintly visible. Behind him stood Waters in a combat stance. "When it comes through, just start firing, and don't stop." Garcia said. "I've only got eight rounds. I'll try to space my shots so you can reload at least once before it reaches us. And turn off that flashlight. You trying to give us away?"

The others in Security Command—Allen, the programmer, and Nesbitt the guard—had retreated to the far wall and were crouched beneath the darkened schematic of the Museum's security grid.

Waters was shaking. "It blew away a SWAT team," he said, his voice breaking.

There was another crash, and the door groaned, its hinges popping. Waters screamed, jumped up and scrambled backward into the dark, his gun lying forgotten on the floor.

"Waters, you prick, get back here!"

Garcia heard the sickening thud of bone against metal as Waters stumbled under the desks toward the far wall, banging his skull. "Don't let it get me!" he screamed.

Garcia forced himself to turn back toward the door. He tried to steady the shotgun. The foul reek of the creature filled his nostrils as the door shuddered under another heavy blow. More than anything, he did not want to see what was about to force its way into the room. He cursed and wiped his forehead with the back of a hand. Except for Waters's sobbing, there was silence.

Margo shined the flashlight down the hall, trying to imitate the random motions of somebody searching for a way out. The light licked across the walls and floor, giving dim illumination to the display cabinets. Her heart was hammering, her breath coming in short gasps.

"Help!" she cried again. "We're lost!" Her voice sounded unnaturally hoarse in her ears.

There were no more sounds from around the corner. The creature was listening.

"Hello?" she called, willing herself to speak again. "Is anybody there?"

The voice echoed and died in the corridor. She waited, staring into the gloom, straining to see any movement.

A dark shape began to resolve itself against the far darkness, at a distance where the flashlight beam failed. The movement stopped. It seemed to have its head up. A strange, liquid snuffling sound came toward them.

"Not yet," Pendergast whispered.

It moved a little farther around the corner. The snuffling noise grew louder, and then the stench, wafting down the hall, violated her nostrils.

The beast took another step.

"Not yet," Pendergast whispered.

Garcia's hand was shaking so violently he could hardly press the transmit button.

"Coffey!" he hissed. "Coffey, for God's sake! Do you copy?"

"This is Agent Slade from the Forward Command Post. Who's speaking, please?"

"This is Security Command," Garcia said, breathing thick and fast. "Where's Coffey? *Where's Coffey?*"

"Special Agent Coffey is temporarily indisposed. As of now, I'm taking command of the operation, pending the arrival of the regional director. What's your status?"

"What's our status?" Garcia laughed raggedly. "Our status is, we're fucked. It's outside the door. It's breaking in. I'm begging you, send a team in."

"Hell!" came the voice of Slade. "Why wasn't I informed?" Garcia heard some muffled talk. "Garcia? Do you have your weapon?"

"What good's a shotgun?" Garcia whispered, almost in tears. "You need to get in here with a fucking bazooka. Help us, *please.*"

"Garcia, we're trying to pick up the pieces here.

Command-and-control is all screwed up. Just hold tight a moment. It can't get through the Security Command door, right? It's metal, isn't it?"

"It's wood, Slade, it's just a goddamn institutional door!" Garcia said, the tears running freely down his face.

"Wood? What kind of place is this? Garcia, listen to me now. Even if we sent someone in, it'd take them twenty minutes to get to you."

"Please . . ."

"You've got to handle it yourself. I don't know what you're up against, Garcia, but get a grip on yourself. We'll be in as soon as we can. Just keep cool and aim—"

Garcia sank to the floor, his finger slipping from the button in despair. It was hopeless, they were all dead men.

= 60 =

Smithback gripped the belt, playing a few more inches back toward the group. If anything, he thought, the water was rising even faster than before; there were surges every few minutes now, and although the current didn't seem to be getting stronger, the roar at the end of the tunnel had grown deafening. The oldest, the weakest, and the poorest swimmers were directly behind Smithback, clutching to the rope of belts; behind them the others were clinging together, treading water desperately. Everyone was silent now; there was no energy left to weep, moan, or even speak. Smithback looked up: two more feet, and he'd be able to grab the ladder.

"Must be a mother of a storm out there," said D'Agosta. He was next to Smithback, supporting an older woman. "Sure rained on the Museum's party," he added with a weak laugh.

Smithback merely looked up, snapping on the light. Eighteen more inches.

"Smithback, quit switching the light on and off, all

right?'' D'Agosta said irritably. ''*I'll* tell you when to check.''

Smithback felt another surge, which buffeted him against the brick walls of the tunnel. There were some gasps among the group but no one cut loose. If the belt rope gave way, they'd all be drowned in thirty seconds. Smithback tried not to think about it.

In a shaky but determined voice, the Mayor started telling a story to the group. It involved several well-known people in City Hall. Smithback, despite scenting a scoop, felt sleepier and sleepier—a sign, he remembered, of hypothermia.

''Okay, Smithback. Check the ladder.'' The gruff voice of D'Agosta jerked him awake.

He shined the light upward, rattling it into life. In the past fifteen minutes the water had risen another foot, bringing the end of the ladder almost within reach. With a croak of delight, Smithback played more of the belts back to the group.

''Here's what we're gonna do,'' said D'Agosta. ''You're gonna go up first. I'll help from down here, then I'll follow last. Okay?''

''Okay,'' Smithback said, shaking himself into consciousness.

D'Agosta pulled the belt taut, then grabbed Smithback by the waistband and heaved him upward. Smithback reached over his head, grabbing the lowest rung with his free hand.

''Give me the light,'' said D'Agosta.

Smithback handed it down, then grabbed the rung with the other hand. He pulled himself up a little, then fell back, the muscles in his arms and back jerking spasmodically. With a deep breath, he pulled himself up again, this time reaching the second rung.

''Now you grab the rung,'' D'Agosta said to someone. Smithback leaned against the rungs, gasping for breath. Then, looking upward again, he grasped the third rung, then the fourth. He felt around lightly with his feet to secure them on the first rung.

"Don't step on anyone's hands!" D'Agosta warned from below.

He felt a hand guide his foot, and he was able to put his weight on the lowest rung. The firmness felt like heaven. He reached down with one hand and helped the elderly woman. Then he turned back, feeling his strength returning, and moved upward.

The ladder ended at the mouth of a large pipe jutting out horizontally where the curved vault of the roof met the tunnel wall. Gingerly, he moved to the pipe and began crawling into the darkness.

Immediately, a putrid odor assaulted his nostrils. *Sewer,* he thought. He stopped involuntarily for a moment, then moved forward again.

The pipe ended, opening into blackness. Gingerly, he brought his feet outward and downward. A hard, firm dirt floor met his shoes a foot or so beneath the mouth of the pipe. He could hardly believe their luck: a chamber of unknown size, hung suspended here between the basement and subbasement. Probably some architectural palimpsest, a long-forgotten by-product of one of the Museum's many reconstructions. He clambered out and moved a few inches forward, then another few inches, sweeping his feet over the blackness of the floor. The stench around him was abominable, but it was not the smell of the beast, and for that he was profoundly grateful. Dry things—twigs?—crunched beneath his feet. Behind him, he could hear grunting, and the sound of others moving down the pipe toward him. The feeble light from D'Agosta's flashlight in the subbasement beyond could not penetrate the blackness.

He turned around, knelt down by the mouth of the pipe, and began helping the bedraggled group out, directing them off to the side, warning them not to stray too far into the dark.

One at a time, people emerged and spread out against

the wall, feeling their way gingerly, collapsing in exhaustion. The room was quiet except for the sound of ragged breathing.

Finally, Smithback heard the voice of D'Agosta coming through the pipe. "Christ, what is that reek?" he muttered to Smithback. "That damned flashlight finally gave out. So I dropped it into the water. Okay, people," he said in a louder voice, standing up, "I want you to count off." The sound of dripping water started Smithback's heart racing until he realized it was simply D'Agosta, wringing out his sodden jacket.

One by one, in tired voices, the group gave their names. "Good," D'Agosta said. "Now to figure out where we are. We may need to look for higher ground, in case the water continues to rise."

"I'd like to look for higher ground anyway," came a voice from the darkness. "It stinks in here something awful."

"It'll be tough without light," Smithback said. "We'll need to go single file."

"I've got a lighter," one voice said. "Shall I see if it still works?"

"Careful," said someone else. "Smells like methane, if you ask me."

Smithback winced as a wavering yellow flame illuminated the chamber.

"Oh, Jesus!" somebody screamed.

The chamber was suddenly plunged into darkness again as the hand holding the lighter involuntarily jerked away—but not before Smithback got a single, devastating image of what lay around him.

Margo strained ahead in the dimness, slowly moving the flashlight around the hall, trying to keep from deliberately spotlighting the beast as it crouched at the corner, observing them.

"Not yet," Pendergast murmured. "Wait until it shows itself fully."

The creature seemed to pause for an eternity, unmoving, as silent and motionless as a stone gargoyle. Margo could see small red eyes watching her in the gloom. Every now and then the eyes disappeared, then reappeared, as the creature blinked.

The creature took another step, then froze again as if making up its mind, its low, powerful frame tensed and ready.

Then it started forward, coming down the hall toward them with a strange, terrifying lope.

"Now!" cried Pendergast.

Margo reached up and fumbled for the miner's helmet, and the hall was suddenly bathed in light. Almost immediately she heard a deafening *WHANG!* as Pendergast's powerful handgun barked next to her. The creature stopped briefly, and Margo could see it squinting, shaking its head against the light. It bent back as if to bite its haunch where the bullet had passed. Margo felt her mind receding from the reality: the low, pale head, horribly elongated, the crease of Pendergast's bullet a white stripe above the eyes; the powerful forequarters, covered with dense fur and ending in long, rending talons; the lower rear haunches, wrinkled skin descending to five-clawed toes. Its fur was matted with crusted blood, and fresh blood shone on the scales of the hindquarters.

WHANG! The creature's right foreleg was yanked behind it, and Margo heard a terrible roar of rage. It spun back to face them and sprang forward, ropes of saliva swinging madly from its jaws.

WHANG! went the gun—*a miss*—and the creature kept coming, accelerating with horrible deliberation.

WHANG!

She saw, as if in slow motion, the left hind leg jerk back, and the creature falter slightly. But it recovered, and, with a renewed howl, coarse hair bristling high on its haunches, it came for them again.

WHANG! went the gun, but the creature did not slow, and at that point Margo realized with great clarity that

their plan had failed, that there was time for only one
more shot and that the creature's charge could not be
stopped. "Pendergast!" she cried, stumbling backward,
her miner's light tilting crazily upward, scrambling away
from the red eyes that stared straight into her own with
a terrifyingly comprehensible blend of rage, lust, and
triumph.

Garcia sat on the floor, ears straining, wondering if the
voice he'd heard was real—if there was somebody else
out there, trapped in this nightmare—or whether it had
just been a trick of his overheated brain.

Suddenly, a very different sound boomed outside the
door; then there was another, and another.

He scrambled to his feet. *It couldn't be true.* He fumbled with the radio.

"Do you hear that?" a voice behind him said.

Then the sound came again, twice; then, a short silence; then again.

"I swear to God, somebody's shooting in the hall!"
Garcia cried.

There was a long, dreadful silence. "It's stopped,"
said Garcia in a whisper.

"Did they get it? Did they get it?" Waters whim-
pered.

The silence stretched on. Garcia clutched the shotgun,
its pump and trigger guard slick from sweat. Five or six
shots, that's all he'd heard. And the creature had killed
a heavily armed SWAT team.

"Did they get it?" Waters asked again.

Garcia listened intently, but could hear nothing from
the hall. This was the worst of all: the brief raising, then
sudden dashing, of his hopes. He waited.

There was a rattling at the door.

"No," whispered Garcia. "It's back."

= 61 =

"Hand me that lighter!" D'Agosta barked. Smithback, falling blindly backward, saw the sudden spark of the flint and instinctively covered his eyes.

"Oh, Christ—" he heard D'Agosta groan. Then Smithback jerked as he felt something clutch his shoulder and drag him to his feet.

"Listen, Smithback," the voice of D'Agosta hissed in his ear, "you can't crap out on me now. I need you to help me keep these people together."

Smithback gagged as he forced his eyes open. The dirt floor ahead of him was awash in bones: small, large, some broken and brittle, others with gristle still clinging to their knobby ends.

"Not twigs," Smithback said, over and over again under his breath. "No, no, not twigs." The light flicked out again, D'Agosta conserving its flame.

Another yellow flash, and Smithback looked wildly around. What he had kicked aside was the remains of a dog—a terrier, by the looks of it—glassy, staring eyes, light fur, small brown teats descending in ordered rows to the torn-out belly. Scattered around the floor were other carcasses: cats, rats, other creatures too thoroughly mauled or too long dead to be recognizable. Behind him, someone was screaming relentlessly.

The light went out, then reappeared, farther ahead now as D'Agosta moved forward. "Smithback, come with me," came his voice. "Everybody, stare straight ahead. Let's go." As Smithback slowly placed one foot in front of the other, looking down just enough to avoid stepping on the loathesomeness beneath, something registered in his peripheral vision. He turned his head toward the wall to his right.

A pipe or duct had once run along the wall at shoulder height, but it had long since collapsed, its remains lying broken on the floor, half buried in offal. The heavy metal supports for the ductwork remained bolted to the wall, projecting outward like tines. Hung on the supports were a variety of human corpses, their forms seeming to waver in the dull glow of the flame. Smithback saw, but did not immediately comprehend, that all of the corpses had been decapitated. Scattered on the floor along the wall beneath were small ruined objects that he knew must be heads.

The bodies farthest from him had hung there the longest; they seemed more skeleton than flesh. He turned away, but not before his brain processed the final horror: on the meaty wrist of the nearest corpse was an unusual watch in the shape of a sundial. Moriarty's watch.

"Oh, my God . . . oh, my God," Smithback repeated over and over. "Poor George."

"You knew that guy?" D'Agosta said grimly. "Shit, this thing gets hot!"

The lighter flicked out again and Smithback immediately stopped moving.

"What kind of a place is this?" somebody behind them cried.

"I haven't the faintest," D'Agosta muttered.

"I do," Smithback said woodenly. "It's a *larder*."

The light came back on and he started forward again, more quickly now. Behind him, Smithback could hear the Mayor urging the people to keep moving in a dead, mechanical voice.

Suddenly, the light flicked out again, and the journalist froze in position. "We're at the far wall," he heard D'Agosta say in the darkness. "One of the passages here slopes down, the other slopes up. We're taking the high road."

D'Agosta flicked on the lighter again and continued forward, Smithback following. After several moments, the smell began to dissipate. The ground grew damp and soft beneath his feet. Smithback felt, or imagined he felt, the faintest hint of a cool breeze on his cheek.

D'Agosta laughed. "Christ, that feels fine."

The tunnel grew damp underfoot, then ended abruptly in another ladder. D'Agosta stepped towards it, reaching up with the lighter. Smithback moved forward eagerly, sniffing the freshening breeze. There was a sudden rushing sound and then a thud-*thud!* above, and a bright light passed quickly above them, followed by a splash of viscous water.

"A manhole!" D'Agosta cried. "We made it, I can't believe it, we fucking made it!"

He scrambled up the ladder and heaved against the round plate.

"It's fastened down," he grunted. "Twenty men couldn't lift this. *Help!*" he started calling, clambering up the ladder and placing his mouth close to one of the pry-holes, *"Somebody help us, for Chrissake!"* And then he started to laugh, sinking against the metal ladder and dropping the lighter, and Smithback also collapsed to the floor of the passage, laughing, crying, unable to control himself.

"We made it," D'Agosta said through his laughter. "Smithback! We made it! Kiss me, Smithback—you fucking journalist, I love you and I hope you make a million on this.''

Smithback heard a voice above them from the street. ''You hear somebody yelling?''

''Hey, you up there!'' D'Agosta cried out. ''Want to earn a reward?''

''Hear that? There *is* somebody down there. Yo!''

''Did you hear me? Get us out of here!''

''How much?'' another voice asked.

''Twenty bucks! Call the fire department, get us out!''

''Fifty bucks, man, or we walk.''

D'Agosta couldn't stop laughing. ''Fifty dollars then! Now get us the hell out of here!''

He turned around and spread his arms. ''Smithback, move everybody forward. Folks, Mayor Harper, welcome back to New York City!''

The door rattled once more. Garcia pressed the buttstock tight against his cheek, crying quietly. It was trying to get in again. He took a deep breath and tried to steady the shotgun.

Then he realized that the rattling had resolved itself into a knock.

It sounded again, louder, and Garcia heard a muffled voice.

''Is anyone in there?''

''Who is it?'' Garcia answered thickly.

''Special Agent Pendergast, FBI.''

Garcia could hardly believe it. As he opened the door he saw a tall, thin man looking placidly back at him, his pale hair and eyes ghostly in the dim hallway. He held a flashlight in one hand and a large pistol in the other. Blood trailed down one side of his face, and his shirt was soaked in crazy Rorschach patterns. A shortish young woman with mousy brown hair stood beside him, a yellow miner's lamp dwarfing her head, her face, hair, and sweater covered with more dark, wet stains.

Pendergast finally broke into a grin. "We did it," he said simply.

Only Pendergast's grin made Garcia realize that the blood covering the two was not their own. "How—?" he faltered.

They pushed their way past him as the others, lined up under the dark Museum schematic, stared, frozen by fear and disbelief.

Pendergast indicated a chair with the flashlight. "Have a seat, Ms. Green," he said.

"Thank you," said Margo, the miner's light on her forehead bobbing upward. "Such a gentleman."

Pendergast seated himself. "Does anyone have a handkerchief?" he asked.

Allen came forward, pulling one from his pocket.

Pendergast handed it to Margo, who wiped the blood from her face and handed it back. Pendergast carefully wiped his face and hands. "Much obliged, Mr.—?"

"Allen. Tom Allen."

"Mr. Allen." Pendergast handed the blood-soaked handkerchief to Allen, who started to return it to his pocket, froze, then dropped it quickly. He stared at Pendergast. "Is it dead?"

"Yes, Mr. Allen. It's quite dead."

"You killed it?"

"We killed it. Rather, Ms. Green here killed it."

"Call me Margo. And it was Mr. Pendergast who fired the shot."

"Ah, but Margo, you told me where to place the shot. I never would have thought of it. All big game—lion, water buffalo, elephant—have eyes on the *sides* of their head. If they're charging, you'd never consider the eye. It's just not a viable shot."

"But the creature," Margo explained to Allen, "had a primate's face. Eyes rotated to the front for stereoscopic vision. A direct path to the brain. And with that incredibly thick skull, once you put a bullet inside the brain, it would simply bounce around until it was spent.''

''You killed the creature with a shot through the eye?'' Garcia asked, incredulously.

''I'd hit it several times,'' Pendergast said, ''but it was simply too strong and too angry. I haven't had a good look at the creature—I think I'll leave that until much later—but it's safe to say that no other shot could have stopped it in time.''

Pendergast adjusted his tie knot with two slender fingers—unusually fastidious, Margo thought, considering the blood and bits of gray matter covering his white shirt. She would never forget the sight of the creature's brain exploding out of the ruined eye socket, at once a horrifying and beautiful sight. In fact, it was the eyes—the horrible, angry eyes—that had given her a sudden, desperate flash of an idea, even as she'd scrambled backward, away from the rotting stench and slaughterhouse breath.

Suddenly, she was clutching her sides, shivering.

In a moment, Pendergast had motioned to Garcia to give up his uniform jacket. He draped it over her shoulders. ''Calm down, Margo,'' he said, kneeling at her side. ''It's all over.''

''We have to get Dr. Frock,'' she stammered through blue lips.

''In a minute, in a minute,'' Pendergast said soothingly.

''Shall we make a report?'' Garcia asked. ''This radio has just about enough juice left for one more broadcast.''

''Yes, and we have to send a relief party for Lieutenant D'Agosta,'' Pendergast said. Then he frowned. ''I suppose this means talking to Coffey.''

''I don't think so,'' Garcia said. ''Apparently, there's been a change of command.''

Pendergast's eyebrows raised. ''Indeed?''

''Indeed.'' Garcia handed the radio to Pendergast.

"An agent named Slade is claiming to be in charge. Why don't you do the honors?"

"If you wish," Pendergast said. "I'm glad it's not Special Agent Coffey. Had it been, I'm afraid I would have taken him to task. I respond sharply to insults." He shook his head. "It's a very bad habit, but one I find hard to break."

= 62 =

Four Weeks Later

When Margo arrived, Pendergast and D'Agosta were already in Frock's office. Pendergast was examining something on a low table while Frock talked animatedly next to him. D'Agosta was walking restlessly around the office, looking bored, picking things up and putting them down again. The latex cast of the claw sat in the middle of Frock's desk like a nightmare paperweight. A large cake, purchased by Frock in celebration of Pendergast's imminent departure, sat in the middle of the warm sunlit room, the white icing already beginning to droop.

"Last time I was there, I had a crayfish gumbo that was truly magnificent," Frock was saying, gripping Pendergast's elbow. "Ah, Margo," he said, wheeling around. "Come in and take a look."

Margo crossed the room. Spring had finally taken hold of the city, and through the great bow windows she could see the blue expanse of the Hudson River flowing southward, sparkling in the sunlight. On the promenade below, joggers filed past in steady ranks.

A large re-creation of the creature's feet lay on the low table, next to the Cretaceous plaque of fossil footprints. Frock traced the tracks lovingly. "If not the same family, certainly the same order," he said. "And the creature did indeed have five toes on the hind feet. Yet another link to the Mbwun figurine."

Margo, looking closely, thought the two didn't seem all that similar.

"Fractal evolution?" she suggested.

Frock looked at her. "It's possible. But it would take extensive cladistic analysis to know for sure." He grimaced. "Of course, that won't be possible, now that the government has whisked the remains away for God only knows what purpose."

In the month since the opening night disaster, public sentiment had gone from shock and incredulity, to fascination, to ultimate acceptance. For the first two weeks, the press had been abuzz with stories of the beast, but the conflicting accounts of the survivors created confusion and uncertainty. The only item that could settle the controversy—the corpse—was immediately removed from the scene in a large white van with government plates, never to be seen again. Even Pendergast claimed to be ignorant of its whereabouts. Publicity soon turned to the human cost of the disaster, and to the lawsuits that threatened the manufacturers of the security system and, to a lesser degree, the police department and the Museum itself. *Time* magazine had run a lead story entitled "How Safe Are Our National Institutions?" Now, weeks later, people had begun to view the creature as a one-of-a-kind phenomenon: a freak throwback, like the dinosaur fishes that occasionally showed up in the nets of deep-sea fishermen. Interest had started to wane: the opening-night survivors were no longer interviewed on talk shows, the projected Saturday morning cartoon series had been cancelled, and "Museum Beast" action figures were going unsold in toy stores.

Frock glanced around. "Forgive my lack of hospitality. Sherry, anyone?"

There were murmurs of "No, thanks."

"Not unless you've got a 7-Up chaser," D'Agosta said. Pendergast blanched and looked in his direction.

D'Agosta took the latex cast of the claw from Frock's desk and held it up. "Nasty," he said.

"Exceptionally nasty," Frock agreed. "It truly was part reptile, part primate. I won't go into the technical details—I'll leave that to Gregory Kawakita, who I've put to work analyzing what data we do have—but it appears that the reptilian genes are what gave the creature its strength, speed, and muscle mass. The primate genes contributed the intelligence and possibly made it endothermic. Warm-blooded. A formidable combination."

"Yeah, sure," D'Agosta said, laying the cast down. "But what the hell *was* it?"

Frock chuckled. "My dear fellow, we simply don't have enough data yet to say *exactly* what it was. And since it appears to have been the last of its kind, we may never know. We've just received an official survey of the *tepui* this creature came from. The devastation there has been complete. The plant this creature lived on, which by the way we have posthumously named *Liliceae mbwunensis*, appears to be totally extinct. Mining has poisoned the entire swamp surrounding the *tepui*. Not to mention the fact that the entire area was initially torched with napalm, to help clear the area for mining. There were no traces of any other similar creatures wandering about the forest anywhere. While I am normally horrified by such environmental destruction, in this case it appears to have rid the earth of a terrible menace." He sighed. "As a safety precaution—and against my advice, I might add—the FBI has destroyed all the packing fibers and plant specimens here in the Museum. So the plant, too, is truly extinct."

"How do we know it was the last of its kind?" Margo asked. "Couldn't there be another somewhere?"

"Not likely," said Frock. "That *tepui* was an ecological island—by all accounts, a unique place in which animals and plants had developed a singular interdependence over literally millions of years."

"And there certainly aren't any more creatures in the Museum," Pendergast said, coming forward. "With those ancient blueprints I found at the Historical Society, we were able to section off the subbasement and comb every square inch. We found many things of interest to urban archaeologists, but no further sign of the creature."

"It looked so sad in death," Margo said. "So lonely. I almost feel sorry for it."

"It *was* lonely," said Frock, "lonely and lost. Traveling four thousand miles from its jungle home, following the trail of the last remaining specimens of the precious plants that kept it alive and free from pain. But it was very evil, and very fierce. I saw at least twelve bullet holes in the carcass before they took it away."

The door opened and Smithback walked in, theatrically waving a manila envelope in one hand and a magnum of champagne in the other. He whipped a sheaf of papers out of the envelope, holding them skyward with one long arm.

"A book contract, folks!" he said, grinning.

D'Agosta scowled and turned away, picking up the claw again.

"I got everything I wanted, and made my agent rich," Smithback crowed.

"And yourself rich, too," said D'Agosta, looking as if he'd like to use the claw on the writer.

Smithback cleared his throat dramatically. "I've decided to donate half the royalties to a fund set up in memory of Officer John Bailey. To benefit his family."

D'Agosta turned toward Smithback. "Get lost," he said.

"No, really," said Smithback. "Half the royalties. After the advance has earned out, of course," he added hastily.

D'Agosta started to step toward Smithback, then stopped abruptly. "You got my cooperation," he said in a low voice, his jaw working stiffly.

"Thanks, Lieutenant. I think I'll need it."

"That's Captain, as of yesterday," said Pendergast.

"Captain D'Agosta?" Margo asked. "You've been promoted?"

D'Agosta nodded. "Couldn't happen to a nicer guy, the Chief tells me." He pointed a finger at Smithback. "I get to read what you say about me *before* it goes to press, Smithback."

"Now wait a minute," Smithback said, "there are certain ethics that journalists have to follow—"

"Balls!" D'Agosta exploded.

Margo turned to Pendergast. "I can see this will be an exciting collaboration," she whispered. Pendergast nodded.

There was a light rapping, and the head of Greg Kawakita appeared from around the door to the outer office. "Oh, I'm sorry, Doctor Frock," he said, "your secretary didn't tell me you were busy. We can go over the results later."

"Nonsense!" cried Frock. "Come in, Gregory. Mr. Pendergast, Captain D'Agosta, this is Gregory Kawakita. He's the author of the G.S.E., the extrapolation program that allowed us to come up with such an accurate profile of the creature."

"You have my gratitude," Pendergast said. "Without that program, none of us would have been here today."

"Thanks very much, but the program was really Dr. Frock's brainchild," Kawakita said, eyeing the cake. "I just put the pieces together. Besides, there were a lot of things the Extrapolator *didn't* tell you. The forward placement of the eyes, for instance."

"Why, Greg, success has made you humble," Smithback said. "In any case," he continued, turning to Pendergast, "I've got a few questions for *you*. This vintage champagne doesn't come free, you know." He fixed the FBI agent with an expectant gaze. "Whose bodies did we discover in the lair, anyway?"

Pendergast raised his shoulders in a slight shrug. "I guess there's no harm in telling you—although this is not for publication until you receive official word. As it happens, five of the eight remains have been identified. Two were those of homeless street persons, who crept into the Old Basement, presumably looking for warmth on a winter's night. Another was that of a foreign tourist we found on Interpol's missing persons list. Another, as you know, was George Moriarty, the Assistant Curator under Ian Cuthbert."

"Poor George," Margo whispered. For weeks, she had avoided thinking about Moriarty's last moments, his final struggle with the beast. To die that way, then to be hung up like a side of beef . . .

Pendergast waited a moment before continuing. "The fifth body has been tentatively identified from dental records as a man named Montague, an employee of the Museum who vanished several years ago."

"Montague!" Frock said. "So the story was true."

"Yes," said Pendergast. "It seems that certain members of the Museum administration—Wright, Rickman, Cuthbert, and perhaps Ippolito—suspected there was something prowling the Museum. When a vast quantity of blood was found in the Old Basement, they had it washed away without notifying the police. When Montague's disappearance coincided with that discovery, the group did nothing to shed any light on the event. They also had reason to believe that the creature was somehow connected to the Whittlesey expedition. Those suspicions may have been behind the moving of the crates. In retrospect, it was a terribly unwise move: It was what precipitated the killings."

"You're right, of course," Frock said, wheeling himself back toward his desk. "We know the creature was highly intelligent. It realized it would be in danger if its existence in the Museum was discovered. I think it must have curbed its normally fierce nature as a means of self-preservation. When it first reached the Museum, it was desperate, perhaps feral, and it killed Montague when it saw him with the artifacts and the plants. But after that, it grew quickly cautious. It knew where the crates were, and it had a supply of the plant—or, at least, it would until the packing material gave out. It was parsimonious in its consumption. Of course, the hormones in the plant were highly concentrated. And the beast supplemented its diet occasionally, in stealthy ways. Rats living in the subbasement, cats escaped from the Animal Behavior department . . . once or twice, even luckless human beings that wandered too deep into the Museum's secret places. But it was always careful to conceal its kills, and several years passed in which it remained—for the most part—undetected." He shifted slightly, the wheelchair creaking.

"Then it happened. The crates were removed, put under lock and key in the Secure Area. The beast grew first hungry, then desperate. Perhaps it grew murderous with rage at the beings who had deprived it of the plants— beings who themselves could be a substitute, though poor, for that which they'd taken away. The frenzy grew, and the beast killed, then killed again."

Frock withdrew his handkerchief and wiped his forehead. "But it didn't lose *all* rationality," he continued. "Remember how it hid the body of the policeman in the exhibition? Even though its blood lust had been aroused, even though it was mad with desire for the plants, it had the presence of mind to realize that the killings were attracting unwanted attention to itself. Perhaps it had planned on bringing the body of Beauregard back down to its lair. Chances are, it was unable to do so—the exhibition was far beyond its usual haunts—so it hid the body instead. After all, the hypothalamus was its primary objective; the rest was just meat.''

Margo shuddered.

''I've wondered more than once just why the beast went into that exhibition,'' Pendergast said.

Frock raised his index finger. ''So have I. And I think I know the reason. Remember, Mr. Pendergast, what *else* was in the exhibition.''

Pendergast nodded slowly. ''Of course. The figurine of Mbwun.''

''Exactly,'' said Frock. ''The figurine depicting the beast itself. The creature's one link with its home, the home that it had lost utterly.''

''You seem to have it all figured out,'' Smithback said. ''But if Wright and Cuthbert were aware of this thing, how did they know it was connected with the Whittlesey expedition?''

''I believe I can answer that,'' Pendergast said. ''They knew, of course, why the ship carrying the crates from Belém to New Orleans was delayed so long—much the way you learned, I expect, Mr. Smithback.''

Smithback suddenly looked nervous. ''Well,'' he began, ''I—''

''They also read Whittlesey's journal. And they knew the legends as well as anybody. Then, when Montague— the person assigned to curating the crates—disappeared, and a pool of blood was discovered near the location of the crates, it didn't take a savant to put everything together. And besides,'' he said, his expression clouding, ''Cuthbert more or less confirmed it for me. As well as he was able, of course.''

Frock nodded. ''They paid a terrible price. Winston and Lavinia dead, Ian Cuthbert institutionalized . . . it's distressing beyond words.''

''True,'' Kawakita said, ''but it's no secret that it's made you top contender for the next Director of the Museum.''

He would think of that, Margo thought.

Frock shook his head. "I doubt if it will be offered me, Gregory. Once the dust settles, rational heads will prevail. I'm too controversial. Besides, the Directorship doesn't interest me. I have too much new material here for me to delay my next book any longer."

"One thing that Dr. Wright and the rest didn't know," Pendergast went on—"in fact, something that nobody here knows—is that the killings didn't start in New Orleans. There was a very similar murder in Belém, in the warehouse where the crates had been housed while awaiting shipping. I learned about it when I was investigating the shipboard killings."

"That must have been the creature's first stop on the way to New York," Smithback said. "I guess it brings the story full circle." He guided Pendergast to the sofa. "Now, Mr. Pendergast, I suppose this also solves the mystery of what happened to Whittlesey."

"The creature killed him, that seems fairly certain," said Pendergast. "Say, you don't mind if I get a piece of that cake—"

Smithback placed a restraining hand on his arm. "How do you know?"

"That it killed Whittlesey? We found a souvenir in its lair."

"You did?" Smithback whipped out his microcassette recorder.

"Put that back in your pocket, if you please, Mr. Smithback. Yes, it was something Whittlesey wore around his neck, apparently. A medallion in the shape of a double arrow."

"That was embossed on his journal!" Smithback said.

"And on the letterhead of the note he sent Montague!" Margo chimed in.

"Apparently it was Whittlesey's family crest. We found it in the lair; a piece of it, anyway. Why the beast carried it from the Amazon we'll never know, but there it is."

"We found other artifacts in there, too," said D'Agosta, through a mouthful of cake. "Along with a pile of Maxwell's seed pods. The thing was a regular collector."

"Like what?" Margo asked, walking toward one of the bow windows and gazing out at the landscape beyond.

"Things you wouldn't expect. A set of car keys, a lot of coins and subway tokens, even a beautiful gold pocket watch. We looked up the guy whose name was inscribed inside the watch, and he told us he'd lost it three years ago. He'd visited the Museum, and been pickpocketed." D'Agosta shrugged. "Maybe that pickpocket is one of the unidentified bodies. Or maybe we'll never find him."

"The creature kept it hung by its chain from a nail in the wall of its lair," Pendergast said. "It liked beautiful things. Another sign of intelligence, I suppose."

"Was everything picked up from inside the Museum?" asked Smithback.

"As far as we can tell," Pendergast said. "There's no evidence the creature could—or wanted to—obtain egress from the Museum."

"No?" Smithback said. "Then what about the exit you were leading D'Agosta toward?"

"He found it," Pendergast said simply. "You were all very lucky."

Smithback turned to ask D'Agosta another question, and Pendergast took the opportunity to get up and head for the cake. "It was awfully nice of you to throw me this party, Dr. Frock," he said as he returned.

"You saved our lives," Frock said. "I thought a little cake might be in order as our way of wishing you bon voyage."

"I'm afraid, then," Pendergast continued, "that I may be at this party under false pretenses."

"Why is that?" Frock asked.

"I may not be leaving New York permanently. The directorship of the New York office is up for reassignment, you see."

"You mean it's not going to Coffey?" Smithback smirked.

Pendergast shook his head. "Poor Mr. Coffey," he said. "I hope he enjoys his position in the Waco field office. In any case, the Mayor, who has become a great fan of Captain D'Agosta here, seems to think I have a good shot at it."

"Congratulations!" cried Frock.

"It isn't certain yet," Pendergast said. "Nor am I certain I care to remain up here. Although the place does have its charms."

He got up and walked to the bow window, where Margo was standing, staring out at the Hudson River and the green hills of the Palisades beyond.

"What are your plans, Margo?" he asked.

She turned to face him. "I've decided to stay at the Museum until I've finished my dissertation."

Frock laughed. "The truth is, I refused to let her go," he said.

Margo smiled. "Actually, I've received an offer from Columbia. Tenure-track Assistant Professorship, starting next year. Columbia was my father's alma mater. So I've *got* to finish it, you see."

"Great news!" said Smithback. "We'll have to celebrate over dinner tonight."

"Dinner? Tonight?"

"Café des Artistes, seven o'clock," he said. "Listen, you've got to come. I'm a world-famous author, or about to become one. This champagne's getting warm," he continued, reaching for the bottle.

Everyone crowded round as Frock brought out glasses. Smithback angled the bottle toward the ceiling and fired off the cork with a satisfying *pop*.

"What'll we drink to?" asked D'Agosta, as the glasses were filled.

"To my book," said Smithback.

"To Special Agent Pendergast, and a safe journey home," Frock said.

"To the memory of George Moriarty," Margo said quietly.

"To George Moriarty."

There was a silence.

"God bless us, everyone," Smithback intoned. Margo punched him playfully.

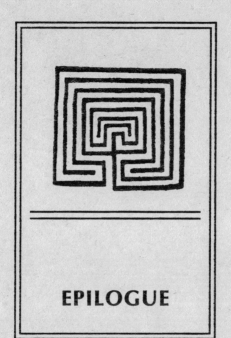

EPILOGUE

= 63 =

Long Island City, Six Months Later

The rabbit jerked as the needle sank into its haunch. Kawakita watched as the dark blood filled up the syringe.

He placed the rabbit carefully back in its hutch, then transferred the blood to three centrifugal test tubes. He opened the nearby centrifuge, slotted the tubes into the drum, and shut the lid. Flicking the switch, he listened to the hum slowly build to a whine as the force of the rotation separated the blood into its components.

He sat back in the wooden chair and let his eyes roam around the surroundings. The office was dusty and the lighting dim, but Kawakita preferred it that way. No sense in drawing attention to oneself.

It had been very difficult in the beginning: finding the right place, assembling the equipment, even paying the rent. It was unbelievable how much they wanted for run-down warehouses in Queens. The computer had been the hardest item to come by. Instead of buying one, he had finally managed to hack his way over the telephone long

lines into a large mainframe at the Solokov College of Medicine. It was a relatively secure site from which to run his Genetic Extrapolation Program.

He peered through the dingy window to the shop floor below. The large space was dark and relatively vacant, the only light coming from aquariums sitting on metal racks along the far wall. He could hear the faint bubbling of the filtration systems. The lights from the tanks cast a dim greenish glow across the floor. Two dozen, give or take a few. Soon, he'd need more. But money was becoming less and less of a problem.

It was amazing, thought Kawakita, how the most elegant solutions were the simplest ones. Once you saw it, the answer was obvious. But it was *seeing* that answer for the first time that separated the timeless scientist from the merely great.

The Mbwun riddle was like that. He, Kawakita, had been the only one to suspect it, to see it, and—now—to prove it.

The whine of the centrifuge began to decrease in pitch, and soon the COMPLETED light began blinking a slow, monotonous red. Kawakita got up, opened the lid, and removed the tubes. The rabbit blood had been divided into its three constituents: clear serum on top, a thin layer of white blood cells in the middle, and a heavy layer of red blood cells at the bottom. He carefully suctioned off the serum, then placed drops of the cells into a series of watchglasses. Finally, he added various reagents and enzymes.

One of the watchglasses turned purple.

Kawakita smiled. It had been so simple.

After Frock and Margo had blundered up to him at the party, his initial skepticism had quickly changed to fascination. He had been on the periphery before, not really paying attention. But practically from the minute he'd hit Riverside Drive that evening—carried along in the stream of countless other hysterical guests who'd rushed from the opening—he began thinking. Then, in

the aftermath, he began asking questions. When later he'd heard Frock pronounce the mystery solved, Kawakita's curiosity had only increased. Perhaps, to be fair, he'd had a little more objective distance than those who'd been inside the Museum that night, fighting the beast in the dark. But whatever the reason, there seemed to be small defects with the solution: little problems, minor contradictions that everyone had missed.

Everyone except Kawakita.

He'd always been a very cautious researcher; cautious, yet full of insatiable curiosity. It had helped him in the past: at Oxford, and in his early days at the Museum. And now, it helped him again. His caution had made him build a keystroke capture routine into the Extrapolator. For security reasons, of course—but also to learn what others might use his program for.

So it was only natural that he'd go back and examine what Frock and Margo had done.

All he'd had to do was press a few keys, and the program reeled off every question Frock and Margo had asked, every bit of data they had entered, and every result they had obtained.

That data had pointed him toward the *real* solution to the Mbwun mystery. It had been there under their noses the whole time, had they known what questions to ask. Kawakita learned to ask the right questions. And along with the answer came a stunning discovery.

A soft knock sounded at the warehouse door. Kawakita walked down the stairs to the main floor of the warehouse, moving without sound or hesitation through the gloom.

"Who is it?" he whispered, his voice hoarse.

"Tony," said the voice.

Kawakita effortlessly slid back the iron bar from the door and pulled it open. A figure stepped through.

"It's dark in here," the man said. He was small and wiry, and walked with a distinct roll to his shoulders. He looked around nervously.

"Keep the lights off," said Kawakita sharply. "Follow me."

They walked to the far end of the warehouse. There, a long table had been set up under dull infrared lamps. The table was covered with drying fibers. At the end of the table was a scale. Kawakita scooped up a small handful of fibers and weighed them, removing several, then dropping a few back on. Then he slid the fibers into a Ziploc bag.

He looked at his visitor expectantly. The man dug his hand into his pants pocket and extended a wad of crumpled bills. Kawakita counted them: five twenties. He nodded and handed over the small bag. The man grabbed it eagerly, and began to tear open the seam.

"Not here!" said Kawakita.

"Sorry," the man said. He moved toward the door as quickly as the dim light would allow.

"Try larger amounts," Kawakita suggested. "Steep it in boiling water, that increases the concentration. I think you'll find the results very gratifying."

The man nodded. "Gratifying," he said slowly, as if tasting the word.

"I will have more for you on Tuesday," Kawakita said.

"Thank you," the man whispered, and left.

Kawakita closed the door and slid the bolt back in place. It had been a long day, and he felt bone tired, but he was looking forward to nightfall, when the sounds of the city would subside and darkness would cover the land. Night was rapidly becoming his favorite time of the day.

Once he reconstructed what Frock and Margo had done with his program, everything else fell into place. All he'd needed was to find one of the fibers. But that proved a difficult task. The Secure Area had been painstakingly cleaned, and the crates had been emptied of their artifacts and burned, along with the packing material. The lab where Margo had done the initial work

was now spotless, the plant press destroyed. But nobody had remembered to clean out Margo's handbag, which was notorious throughout the Anthropology Department for its untidiness. Margo herself had thrown it in the Museum incinerator several days after the disaster, as a precaution. But not before Kawakita had found the fiber he needed.

Despite his other trials, the supreme challenge had been growing the plant from a single fiber. It had taxed all his abilities, his knowledge of botany and genetics. But he was channeling all his ferocious energies into one thing now—thoughts of tenure vanished, a leave of absence taken from the Museum. And he had finally achieved it, not five weeks earlier. He remembered the surge of triumph he felt when the little green node appeared on an agar-covered petri dish. And now he had a large and steady supply growing in the tanks, fully inoculated with the reovirus. The strange reovirus that dated back sixty-five million years.

It had proven to be a perversely attractive type of lily pad, blooming almost continuously, big deep-purple blossoms with venous appendages and bright yellow stamens. The virus was concentrated in the tough, fibrous stem. He was harvesting two pounds a week, and poised to increase his yield exponentially.

The Kothoga knew all about this plant, thought Kawakita. What appeared to be a blessing turned out for them to be a curse. They had tried to control its power, but failed. The legend told it best: the devil failed to keep his bargain, and the child of the devil, the Mbwun, had run wild. It had turned on its masters. It could not be controlled.

But Kawakita would not fail. The rabbit serum tests proved that he would succeed.

The final piece of the puzzle fell into place when he remembered what that cop, D'Agosta, had mentioned at the going-away party for the FBI agent: that they had found a double-arrow pendant belonging to John Whit-

tlesey in the creature's lair. Proof, they said, that the monster had killed Whittlesey. Proof. What a joke.

Proof, rather, that the monster **was** *Whittlesey.*

Kawakita remembered clearly the day everything came together for him. It was an apotheosis, a revelation. It explained everything. The creature, the Museum Beast, He Who Walks On All Fours, *was* Whittlesey. And the proof lay within his grasp: his extrapolation program. Kawakita had placed human DNA on one side and the reovirus DNA on the other. And then he had asked for the intermediate form.

The computer gave the creature: He Who Walks On All Fours.

The reovirus in the plant was astonishing. Chances are, it had existed relatively unchanged since the Mesozoic era. In sufficient quantities, it had the power to induce morphological change of an astonishing nature. Everyone knew that the darkest, most isolated areas of rain forest held undiscovered plants of almost inconceivable importance to science. But Kawakita had already discovered his miracle. By eating the fibers and becoming infected with the reovirus, Whittlesey had turned into Mbwun.

Mbwun—the word the Kothoga used for the wonderful, terrible plant, *and for the creatures those who ate it became.* Kawakita could now visualize parts of the Kothoga's secret religion. The plants were a curse that was simultaneously hated and needed. The creatures kept the enemies of the Kothoga at bay—yet they themselves were a constant threat to their masters. Chances are, the Kothoga only kept one of the creatures around at a time—more than that would be too dangerous. The cult would have centered around the plant itself, its cultivation and harvesting. The climax of their ceremonials was undoubtedly the induction of a new creature—the force-feeding of the plant to the unwilling human victim. Initially, large quantities of the plant would be needed to ensure sufficient reovirus to effect the bodily change.

Once the transformation was complete, the plant need be consumed only in small quantities, supplemented of course by other proteins. But it was critical that the dose be maintained. Otherwise, intense pain, even madness, would result as the body tried to revert. Of course, death would intervene before that happened. And the desperate creature would, if at all possible, find a substitute for the plant—the human hypothalamus being by far the most satisfactory.

In the close, comforting darkness, listening to the tranquil humming of the aquaria, Kawakita could guess at the drama that had played itself out in the jungle. The Kothoga, laying eyes on a white man for the first time. Whittlesey's accomplice, Crocker, had no doubt been found first. Perhaps the creature had been old, or enfeebled. Perhaps Crocker had killed the creature with the expedition's gun as the creature disembowelled him. Or perhaps not. But when the Kothoga found Whittlesey, Kawakita knew there was only one possible outcome.

He wondered what Whittlesey must have felt: bound, perhaps ceremonially, being force-fed the reovirus from the strange plant he himself had collected just days earlier. Perhaps they brewed him a liquor from the plant's leaves, or perhaps they simply forced him to eat the dried fibers. They must have attempted to do with this white man what they had failed to do with their own kind: create a monster they could *control*. A monster that would keep out the road builders and the prospectors and the miners that were poised to invade the *tepui* from the south and destroy them. A monster that would terrorize the surrounding tribes *without* terrorizing its masters; that would ensure the security and isolation of the Kothoga forever.

But then civilization came anyway, with all its terrors. Kawakita imagined the day it happened: the Whittlesey-thing, crouched in the jungle, seeing the fire come falling from the sky, burning the *tepui,* the Kothoga, the precious plants. He alone escaped. And he alone knew

where the life-giving fibers could still be found after the jungle was destroyed: He knew, because he had sent them there.

Or perhaps Whittlesey was already gone when the *tepui* was burned. Perhaps the Kothoga had been unable to control, once again, the creature they had created. Maybe Whittlesey, in his pitiful, terrible condition, had set his own agenda, which hadn't included sticking around as the Kothoga's avenging angel. Perhaps he'd simply wanted to go home. So he had abandoned the Kothoga, and the Kothoga had been destroyed by progress.

But, for the most part, Kawakita was indifferent to the anthropological details. He was interested in the power inherent in the plant, and the harnessing of such power.

You needed to control the source before you could control the creature.

And that, thought Kawakita, *is exactly why I'm going to succeed where the Kothoga failed.* He was controlling the source. Only he knew how to grow this difficult and delicate swamp lily from the depths of the Amazon jungle. Only he knew the proper pH of the water, the right temperature, the proper light, the correct mix of nutrients. Only he knew how to inoculate the plant with the reovirus.

They would be dependent on him. And, with the genetic splicing he had done through the rabbit serum, he'd been able to purify the essential strength of the virus, engineering it to be cleaner while diminishing some of the more unpleasant side effects.

At least, he was fairly sure he had.

These were revolutionary discoveries. Everyone knew that viruses inserted their own DNA into the cells of their victim. Normally, that DNA would simply instruct the victim's cells to make more viruses. That's what happened in every virus known to man: from the flu to AIDS.

This virus was different. It inserted a whole array of

genes into its victim: *reptile* genes. Ancient reptile genes; sixty-five-million-year-old genes. Found today in the lowly gecko and a few other species. And it had apparently borrowed primate genes—no doubt human genes—over time, as well. A virus that stole genes from its host, and incorporated those genes into its victims.

Those genes, instead of making more viruses, remade the *victim*. Reshaped the victim, bit by bit, into a monster. The viruses instructed the body's own machinery to change the bone structure, the endocrine system, the limbs and skin and hair and internal organs. It changed the behavior, the weight, speed, and cunning of the victim. Gave the victim uncanny senses of smell and hearing, but diminished its eyesight and voice. Gave it immense power, and bulk, and speed, while leaving its wonderful hominid brain relatively intact. In short, the drug—the *virus*—turned a human victim into a terrible killing machine. No, the word *victim* did not fairly describe one infected with the virus. A better word might be *symbiont*. Because it was a privilege to receive the virus. A gift. A gift from Greg Kawakita.

It was beautiful. In fact, it was sublime.

The possibilities for genetic engineering were endless. And already, Kawakita had ideas for improvements. New genes the reovirus could insert into its host. Human genes as well as animal genes. He controlled what genes the reovirus would insert into its host. He controlled what the host would become. Unlike the primitive, superstitious Kothoga, he was in control—through science.

An interesting side effect of the plant was its narcotic effect: a wonderful, "clean" rush, without the unpleasant down of so many other drugs. Perhaps that was how the plant had originally ensured its own ingestion and, thus, its propagation. But for Kawakita, this side effect had provided cash from which to finance his research. He hadn't wanted to sell the drug originally, but the financial pressures he'd experienced had made it inevitable. He smiled as he thought of how easy it had been.

The drug had already been given a name by the select coterie of eager users: *glaze.* The market was avid, and Kawakita could sell as much as he could make. Too bad it seemed to go so quickly.

Night had fallen. Kawakita removed his dark glasses and inhaled the rich fragrance of the warehouse, the subtle odor of the fibers, the smell of water and dust and internal combustion from the ambient air, mingled with mold and sulphur dioxide and a multitude of other smells. His chronic allergies had all but vanished. *Must be the clean Long Island air,* he thought wryly. He removed his tight shoes and curled his toes with pleasure.

He had made the most stunning advancement in genetics since the discovery of the double helix. It would have won him a Nobel Prize, he thought with an ironic smile.

Had he chosen that route.

But who needed a Nobel Prize, when the whole world was suddenly there for the plucking?

There came another knock at the door.

Some call it the greatest scientific discovery
of all time . . .

Others call it . . .

BLASPHEMY

DOUGLAS PRESTON

Science and religion go head-to-head in the latest science-
based thriller from the *New York Times* bestselling author of
Tyrannosaur Canyon and coauthor of *The Wheel of Darkness*.

Available from Forge in Hardcover in January 2008.

July

Ken Dolby stood before his workstation, his smooth, polished fingers caressing the controls of Isabella. He
waited, savoring the moment, and then he unlocked a
cage on the panel and pulled down a small red bar.

There was no hum, no sound, nothing to indicate that
the most expensive scientific instrument on earth had
been turned on. Except that, two hundred miles away, the
lights of Las Vegas dimmed ever so slightly.

As Isabella warmed up, Dolby began to feel the fine vibration of her through the floor. He thought of the machine as a woman, and in his more imaginative moments
he even had imagined what she looked like—tall and
slender, with a muscular back, black as the desert night,

beaded with sweat. Isabella. He had shared these feelings
with no one—no point in attracting ridicule. To the rest of
the scientists on the project, Isabella was an "it," a dead
machine built for a specific purpose. But Dolby had always felt a deep affection for the machines he created—
from when he was ten years old and constructed his first
radio from a kit. Fred. That was the radio's name. And
when he thought of Fred, he saw a fat carroty-haired
white man. The first computer he had built was Betty—
who looked in his head like a brisk and efficient secretary.
He couldn't explain why his machines took on the per-
sonalities they did—it just happened.

And now this, the world's most powerful particle ac-
celerator . . . Isabella.

"How's it look?" asked Hazelius, the team leader, coming over and placing an affectionate hand on his shoulder.

"Purring like a cat," said Dolby.

"Good." Hazelius straightened up and spoke to the
team. "Gather round, I have an announcement to make."

Silence fell as the team members straightened up from
their workstations and waited. Hazelius strode across the
small room and positioned himself in front of the biggest
of the plasma screens. Small, slight, as sleek and restless
as a caged mink, he paced in front of the screen for a moment before turning to them with a brilliant smile. It
never ceased to amaze Dolby what a charismatic presence the man had.

"My dear friends," he began, scanning the group with
turquoise eyes. "It's 1492. We're at the bow of the *Santa
Maria,* gazing at the sea horizon, moments before the
coastline of the New World comes into view. Today is the
day we sail over that unknown horizon and land upon the
shores of our very own New World."

He reached down into the Chapman bag he always carried and pulled out a bottle of Veuve Clicquot. He held it
up like a trophy, his eyes sparkling, and then thumped it
down on the table. "This is for later tonight, when we set

foot on the beach. Because tonight, we bring Isabella to one hundred percent full power."

Silence greeted the announcement. Finally Kate Mercer, the assistant director of the project, spoke. "What happened to the plan to do three runs at ninety-five percent?"

Hazelius returned her look with a smile. "I'm impatient. Aren't you?"

Mercer brushed back her glossy black hair. "What if we hit an unknown resonance or generate a miniature black hole?"

"Your own calculations show a one in quadrillion chance of that particular downside."

"My calculations might be wrong."

"Your calculations are never wrong." Hazelius smiled and turned to Dolby. "What do you think? Is she ready?"

"You're damn right she's ready."

Hazelius spread his hands. "Well?"

Everyone looked at each other. Should they risk it? Volkonsky, the Russian programmer, suddenly broke the ice. "Yes, we go for it!" He high-fived a startled Hazelius, and then everyone began slapping each other on the back, shaking hands, and hugging, like a basketball team before a game.

Five hours and as many bad coffees later, Dolby stood before the huge flat-panel screen. It was still dark—the matter–antimatter proton beams had not been brought into contact. It took forever to power up the machine, increasing it by increments of 5 percent, focusing and collimating the beams, checking the superconducting magnets, running various test programs, before going up to the next 5 percent.

"Power at ninety percent," Dolby intoned.

"Christ damn," said Volkonsky somewhere behind him, giving the Sunbeam coffeemaker a blow that made it rattle like the Tin Man. "Empty already!"

Dolby repressed a smile. During the two weeks they'd been up on the mesa, Volkonsky had revealed himself as a

wiseass, a slouching, mangy specimen of Eurotrash with long greasy hair, ripped T-shirts, and a pubic clump of beard clinging to his chin. He looked more like a drug addict than a brilliant software engineer. But then, a lot of them were like that.

Another measured ticking of the clock.

"Beams aligned and focused," said Rae Chen. "Luminosity fourteen TeV."

"Isabella work fine," said Volkonsky.

"My systems are all green," said Checchini, the particle physicist.

"Security, Mr. Wardlaw?"

The senior intelligence officer, Wardlaw, spoke from his security station. "Just cactus and coyotes, sir."

"All right," said Hazelius. "It's time." He paused dramatically. "Ken? Bring the beams into collision."

Dolby felt a quickening of his heart. He touched the dials with his spiderlike fingers, adjusting them with a pianist's lightness of touch. He followed with a series of commands rapped into the keyboard.

"Contact."

The huge flat-panel screens all around suddenly woke up. A sudden singing noise seemed to float in the air, coming from everywhere and nowhere at once.

"What's that?" Mercer asked, alarmed.

"A trillion particles blowing through the detectors," said Dolby. "Sets up a high vibration."

"Jesus, it sounds like the monolith in *2001*."

Volkonsky hooted like an ape. Everyone ignored him.

An image appeared on the central panel, the Visualizer. Dolby stared at it, entranced. It was like an enormous flower—flickering jets of color radiating from a single point, twisting and writhing as if trying to tear free of the screen. He stood in awe at the intense beauty of it.

"Contact successful," said Rae Chen. "Beams are focused collimated. God, it's a perfect alignment!"

Cheers and some ragged clapping.

"Ladies and gentlemen," said Hazelius, "welcome to

the shores of the New World." He gestured to the Visualizer. "You're looking at an energy density not seen in the universe since the Big Bang." He turned to Dolby. "Ken, please increase power in increments of tenths to ninety-nine."